medical microbiology

review
of
medical
microbiology

12th
EDITION

ERNEST JAWETZ, PhD, MD

Professor of Microbiology and Chairman
Department of Microbiology
Professor of Medicine, Lecturer in Pediatrics
University of California School of Medicine
San Francisco

JOSEPH L. MELNICK, PhD

Distinguished Service Professor of Virology and Epidemiology
Baylor College of Medicine
Houston

EDWARD A. ADELBERG, PhD

Professor of Human Genetics
Yale University School of Medicine
New Haven

Los Altos, California 94022

LANGE Medical Publications

A Concise Medical Library for Practitioner and Student

Review of Medical Microbiology, 12th ed. **$10.00**

Table of Contents

Preface

The authors' intention in preparing this *Review* has been to make available a reasonably comprehensive, accurate, up-to-date presentation of those aspects of medical microbiology which are of particular significance in the fields of clinical infections and chemotherapy. The book is directed primarily at the medical student, house officer, and practicing physician. However, because the necessity for a clear understanding of microbiologic principles has increased in recent years as a result of important developments in biochemistry, genetics, immunology, virology, chemotherapy, and other fields of direct medical significance, a considerable portion of this *Review* has been devoted to a discussion of the relevant basic science aspects. It is to be expected that the inclusion of these sections will extend the book's usefulness to students in introductory microbiology courses as well. In general, details of technic and procedure have been excluded.

With the appearance of the Twelfth Edition the authors are pleased to report that Spanish, German, French, Italian, Portuguese, Turkish, Serbo-Croatian, Japanese, and Polish translations have proved successful.

The authors wish to reaffirm their gratitude to everyone who assisted them with the preparation of this edition and to all those whose comments and criticisms have helped to keep the biennial revisions of this *Review* accurate and up to date. We are especially grateful to the following for their help: Janet S. Butel, Stephen N. Cohen, John Conte, Margaret Ann Fraher, Moses Grossman, Lavelle Hanna, F. Blaine Hollinger, C. Alan Phillips, Carol F. Phillips, Kenneth Powell, and Dorothy Purifoy.

Ernest Jawetz
Joseph L. Melnick
Edward A. Adelberg

San Francisco
June, 1976

SI Units of Measurement in the Biologic Range

Prefix	Abbreviation	Magnitude
kilo-	k	10^3
deci-	d	10^{-1}
centi-	c	10^{-2}
milli-	m	10^{-3}
micro-	μ	10^{-6}
nano-	n	10^{-9}
pico-	p	10^{-12}

These prefixes are applied to metric and other units. For example, a micrometer (μm) is 10^{-6} meter (formerly micron, μ); a nanogram (ng) is 10^{-9} gram (formerly millimicrogram, mμg); and a picogram (pg) is 10^{-2} gram (formerly micromicrogram, $\mu\mu$g). Any of these prefixes may also be applied to seconds, units, mols, equivalents, osmols, etc. The Angstrom (A, 10^{-7}) is now expressed in nanometers (eg, 40 A = 4 nm).

1...
The Microbial World

Before the discovery of microorganisms, all known living things were believed to be either plant or animal; no transitional types were thought to exist. During the 19th century, however, it became clear that the microorganisms combine plant and animal properties in all possible combinations. It is now generally accepted that they have evolved, with relatively little change, from the common ancestors of plants and animals.

The compulsion of biologists to categorize all organisms in one of the 2 "kingdoms," plant or animal, resulted in a number of absurdities. The fungi, for example, were classified as plants because they are largely nonmotile, although they have few other plant-like properties and show strong phylogenic affinities with the protozoa.

In order to avoid the arbitrary assignment of transitional groups to one or the other kingdom, Haeckel proposed in 1866 that microorganisms be placed in a separate kingdom, the **Protista**. Members of the kingdom Protista are distinguished from true plants and animals by their simple organization: They are unicellular, or, if multicellular, their tissues show little differentiation. The Protista can be subdivided as follows, based on their fundamental type of cell structure, **eukaryotic** or **prokaryotic**. The eukaryotic type of cell structure, which is the more advanced, is shared with the cells of plants and animals; the prokaryotic type of cell structure is the more primitive. The 2 types of cell structure are described in Chapter 2.

    I. **Higher protists:** (Eukaryotic).
        A. Algae (except blue-green)
        B. Protozoa
        C. Fungi
        D. Slime molds
    II. **Lower protists:** (Prokaryotic).
        A. Bacteria
        B. Blue-green algae*

*In the latest edition of *Bergey's Manual of Determinative Bacteriology* (8th ed. Williams & Wilkins, 1974), the blue-green algae are renamed the **Cyanobacteria** and are placed with the other bacteria in a new kingdom, **Procaryotae**. This kingdom corresponds to the group which we call here the "lower protists."

The bacteria include 2 groups, the **chlamydiae (bedsoniae)** and the **rickettsiae,** which differ from other bacteria only in being somewhat smaller (0.2–0.5 μm in diameter) and in being obligate intracellular parasites. They were formerly thought to represent transitional groups between the bacteria and the viruses. It is now clear, however, that **viruses** are sharply differentiated from all cellular organisms. A viral particle consists of a nucleic acid molecule, either DNA or RNA, enclosed in a protein coat or **capsid**. The capsid serves only to protect the nucleic acid and to facilitate attachment and penetration of the virus into the host cell. Viral nucleic acid is the infectious principle; inside the host cell it behaves like host genetic material in that it is replicated by the host's enzymatic machinery and also governs the formation of specific (viral) proteins. Maturation consists of assemblage of newly synthesized nucleic acid and protein subunits into mature viral particles; these are liberated into the extracellular environment.

The general properties of animal viruses pathogenic for man are described in Chapter 27. Bacterial viruses are described in Chapter 9.

Higher Protists

The higher protists share with true plants and animals the type of cell construction called eukaryotic ("possessing a true nucleus"). In such cells the nucleus contains a set of chromosomes which are separated, following replication, by an elaborate mitotic apparatus. The nuclear membrane is continuous with the ramifying endoplasmic reticulum. The cytoplasm of the cell contains self-replicating organelles (mitochondria and, in photosynthetic cells, chloroplasts), as well as microtubular elements. Motility organelles (cilia or flagella) are complex multistranded elements.

A. Algae: The term "algae" refers in general to chlorophyll-containing higher protists. The algae are divided into 6 phylogenetic groups, for descriptions of which the reader is referred to Smith GM: *Cryptogamic Botany*, 2nd ed. Vol 1: *Algae and Fungi*. McGraw-Hill, 1955.

B. Protozoa: In Smith's classification of algae, several types of photosynthetic, flagellated, unicellular forms are included which many textbooks class with the protozoa. These include members of Volvocales in

Chlorophyta, members of Euglenophyta, the dinoflagellates in Pyrrophyta, and some of the golden browns in Chrysophyta. These have not been classified as algae arbitrarily but because definite phylogenetic series are recognized which link them to typical algal forms.

On the other hand, these photosynthetic flagellates probably represent transitional forms between algae and protozoa; according to this view, the protozoa have evolved from various algae by loss of chlorophyll. They thus have a polyphyletic origin (ancestors in many different groups). Indeed, mutations of flagellates from green to colorless have been observed in the laboratory. The resulting forms are indistinguishable from certain protozoa.

The most primitive protozoa are thus the flagellated forms. "Protozoa" are unicellular, nonphotosynthetic higher protists. From the flagellated forms appear to have evolved the ameboid and the ciliated types; intermediate types are known which have flagella at one stage in the life cycle and pseudopodia (characteristic of the ameba) at another stage. The simplest classification of protozoa would be the following:

Phylum: Protozoa
> **Class I**: Mastigophora. The flagellate protozoa.
> **Class II**: Rhizopoda. The ameboid protozoa. (Some also form flagella.)
> **Class III**: Sporozoa. Parasites with complex life cycles which include a resting or spore stage.
> **Class IV**: Ciliata. The ciliate protozoa. High degree of internal organization.

C. Fungi: Those who argue that fungi have evolved from the algae point to similarities between the most primitive fungi (the phycomycetes) and members of the Chlorophyceae (in the Chlorophyta). However, the latter always store starch as their food reserve, and their motile cells are always multiflagellate; the most primitive fungi generally store glycogen (never starch), and the motile cells in the aquatic forms are usually uniflagellate. It thus appears more reasonable to trace their origin from the protozoa. (*Note:* The fungi show no evolutionary link with the mycelial bacteria called "actinomycetes.")

The fungi are nonphotosynthetic microorganisms growing as a mass of branching, interlacing filaments ("hyphae") known as a mycelium. Although the hyphae exhibit cross-walls, the cross-walls are perforated and allow the free passage of nuclei and cytoplasm. The entire organism is thus a coenocyte (a multinucleate mass of continuous cytoplasm) confined within a series of branching tubes. These tubes, made of polysaccharides such as chitin, are homologous with cell walls. The mycelial forms are called molds; a few types, yeasts, do not form a mycelium but are easily recognized as fungi by the nature of their sexual reproductive processes and by the presence of transitional forms. The fungi differ from bacteria, including the

filamentous actinomycetes, in being eukaryotic. They are subdivided as follows:

> **Class I**: Phycomycetae. Mycelium usually nonseptate, asexual spores produced in indefinite numbers within a structure called a sporangium. Sexual fusion results in formation of a resting, thick-walled cell termed a zygote. *Example:* The black mold *Rhizopus nigricans.*
> **Class II**: Ascomycetae. Sexual fusion results in formation of a sac or ascus containing the meiotic products as 4 or 8 spores (ascospores). Asexual spores (conidia) are borne externally at the tips of hyphae. *Examples:* Trichophyton, Microsporum, Blastomyces.
> **Class III**: Basidiomycetae. Sexual fusion results in formation of a club-shaped organ called a basidium, on the surface of which are borne the 4 meiotic products (basidiospores). Asexual spores (conidia) are borne externally at the tips of hyphae. *Example:* *Psalliota campestris (Agaricus campestris),* the common mushroom.
> **Class IV**: Fungi imperfecti. This is not a true phylogenetic group but merely a "taxonomic dumpheap" onto which are thrown all forms in which the sexual process has not yet been observed. Most of them resemble ascomycetes morphologically. *Pathogens:* Epidermophyton, Sporotrichum, Cryptococcus, Candida.

The evolution of the ascomycetes from the phycomycetes is seen in the transitional Protoascomycetae, members of which form a zygote but then transform this directly into an ascus. The basidiomycetes are believed to have evolved in turn from the ascomycetes.

While the fungi are classified on the basis of their sexual processes, the sexual stages are difficult to induce and are rarely observed. Descriptions of species thus deal principally with various asexual structures, including the following: (See Figs 25–1 to 25–6 for drawings of some of these structures.)

1. Sporangiospores—Asexual spores borne internally inside a sac known as a sporangium. The sporangium is borne at the tip of a filament called a sporangiophore. These structures are characteristic of the phycomycetes.

2. Conidia—Asexual spores borne externally (not enclosed in a sac). The hyphae which bear them are called conidiophores. Conidia are formed by abstriction of the conidiophore; some species of fungi produce 2 types of conidia of differing size, in which case they are designated microconidia and macroconidia.

3. Thallospores—This term denotes actively reproducing cells which are formed by segmentation of the mycelium. Once formed, thallospores may reproduce by fission, by budding, or by growth into a new mycelium. There are 2 types: (1) arthrospores (oidia), produced by disarticulation of a filament of a septate mycelium into separate cells, and (2) blastospores, produced by budding from the ends or sides of the mycelial filaments. Blastospores are also known as "yeast-like cells."

4. Chlamydospores—Thick-walled, enlarged, resting spores formed (like thallospores) by segmentation of the mycelium. The chlamydospores remain as part of the mycelium, surviving after the remainder of the mycelium has died and disintegrated.

D. Slime Molds: These organisms are characterized by the presence, as a stage in the life cycle, of an ameboid multinucleate mass of cytoplasm called a plasmodium. The creeping plasmodium, which reaches macroscopic size, gives rise to walled spores which germinate to produce naked uniflagellate swarm spores or, in some cases, naked nonflagellated amebas ("myxamoebae"). These usually undergo sexual fusion before growing into typical plasmodia again.

The plasmodium of a slime mold is analogous to the mycelium of a true fungus. Both are coenocytes; but in the latter, cytoplasmic flow is confined to the branching network of chitinous tubes, whereas in the former the cytoplasm can flow (creep) in all directions.

Lower Protists (Bacteria & Blue-Green Algae)

The bacteria form a heterogeneous group of microorganisms distinguished from higher protists by the following criteria: size range ($0.2-2$ μm for the smallest diameter); prokaryotic cell construction; and a unique system of genetic transfer (see Chapter 4).

The blue-green algae include a variety of prokaryotic forms which overlap bacteria and eukaryotic algae in their range of cellular sizes. They are photosynthetic, possessing the same chlorophylls as the eukaryotic algae and oxidizing H_2O to gaseous oxygen in their photosynthesis (see Chapter 5). By these properties they differ from the photosynthetic bacteria, which have specialized chlorophylls and do not produce gaseous oxygen.

Both the blue-green algae and the photosynthetic bacteria contain their photosynthetic pigments in a series of lamellae just under the cell membrane. In some photosynthetic bacteria, these lamellae differentiate under certain environmental conditions into ovoid or spherical bodies called chromatophores. In contrast, the eukaryotic algae always contain their photosynthetic pigments in autonomous cytoplasmic organelles (chloroplasts). There is strong evidence to support the hypothesis that the chloroplasts of eukaryotic algae and plants evolved from endosymbiotic blue-green algae.

The blue-green algae exhibit a type of motility called "gliding" or "creeping," the mechanism of which is unknown. Many nonphotosynthetic bacteria also possess gliding motility; some of these resemble certain blue-green algae so closely that they are believed to be "colorless blue-greens" which have lost their photosynthetic pigments in the course of evolution.

No further generalizations can be made about the lower protists. The reader is referred instead to the descriptions of the various bacterial groups in Chapter 3.

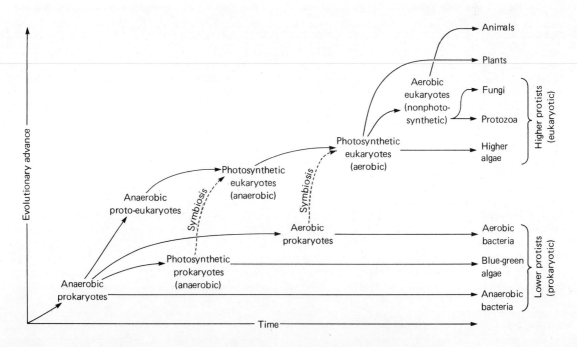

Figure 1–1. Evolutionary relationships of the major groups of microorganisms.

Summary

The concepts presented above are summarized in Fig 1−1. Listed at the right are the major groups of present-day microorganisms; the horizontal scale indicates time, and the vertical scale indicates relative evolutionary advance. Thus, the earliest cell type to emerge on earth was presumably anaerobic and prokaryotic. From this ancestral type, 3 parallel lines of evolution diverged, leading to (1) photosynthesis; (2) aerobic respiration; and (3) such eukaryotic structural features as microtubular systems and nuclear complexity ("proto-eukaryotes").

The contemporary eukaryotes are pictured as arising by a sequence of further events: (1) establishment of endosymbiosis between a blue-green alga and an anaerobic proto-eukaryotic cell, the chloroplast evolving from the endosymbiont; and (2) establishment of a second endosymbiont, an aerobic prokaryote, leading to the evolution of the mitochondrion. These 2 events would have produced an aerobic photosynthetic eukaryote, comparable to present-day higher algae. Loss of the chloroplast would account for the appearance of protozoa and ultimately of fungi and slime molds.

Present-day bacteria and blue-green algae, according to this line of reasoning, represent forms which have evolved with relatively little change from the earliest prokaryotic groups.

•   •   •

General References

Books

Ainsworth GG, Sneath PHA (editors): *Microbial Classification: 12th Symposium of the Society for General Microbiology.* Cambridge Univ Press, 1962.

Brock TD (editor): *Milestones in Microbiology.* Prentice-Hall, 1961.

Burnett JH: *Fundamentals of Mycology.* St. Martin's Press, 1968.

Fenner F & others: *The Biology of Animal Viruses,* 2nd ed. Academic Press, 1974.

Lewin R (editor): *Physiology and Biochemistry of Algae.* Academic Press, 1962.

Moulder JW: *The Psittacosis Group as Bacteria.* Wiley, 1964.

Sleigh M: *The Biology of Protozoa.* Elsevier, 1973.

Smith GM: *Cryptogamic Botany,* 2nd ed. Vol 1. McGraw-Hill, 1955.

Stent GS: *Molecular Biology of Bacterial Viruses.* Freeman, 1963.

Articles & Reviews

Barghoorn EW: The oldest fossils. Sci Am 224:30, May 1971.

Cohen SS: Are/were mitochondria and chloroplasts microorganisms? Am Sci 58:281, 1974.

Knoll AH, Barghoorn ES: Precambrian eukaryotic organisms: A reassessment of the evidence. Science 190:52, 1975.

Lwoff A: The concept of virus. J Gen Microbiol 17:239, 1957.

Raff RA, Mahler HR: The nonsymbiotic origin of mitochondria. Science 177:575, 1972.

Van Niel CB: Natural selection in the microbial world. J Gen Microbiol 13:201, 1955.

2...
Cell Structure

OPTICAL METHODS

The Light Microscope

The resolving power of the light microscope under ideal conditions is about half the wavelength of the light being used. (Resolving power is the distance that must separate 2 point sources of light if they are to be seen as 2 distinct images.) With yellow light of a wavelength of 0.4 μm, the smallest separable diameters are thus about 0.2 μm. The **useful magnification** of a microscope is that magnification that makes visible the smallest resolvable particles. Microscopes used in bacteriology generally employ a 90-power objective lens with a 10-power ocular lens, thus magnifying the specimen 900 times. Particles 0.2 μm in diameter are therefore magnified to about 0.2 mm and so become clearly visible. Further magnification would give no greater resolution of detail and would reduce the visible area (field).

Further improvement in resolving power can be accomplished only by the use of light of shorter wavelengths. The **ultraviolet microscope** uses wavelengths of about 0.2 μm, thus allowing resolution of particles with diameters of 0.1 μm. Such microscopes, employing quartz lenses and photographic systems, are too expensive and complicated for general use.

The Electron Microscope

Using a beam of electrons focused by magnets, the electron microscope can resolve particles 0.001 μm apart. Viruses, with diameters of 0.01–0.2 μm, can be easily resolved.

An important advance in electron microscopy is the technic of "shadowing." This involves depositing a thin layer of metal (such as platinum) on the object by placing it in the path of a beam of metal ions in a vacuum. The beam is directed obliquely, so that the object acquires a "shadow" in the form of an uncoated area on the other side. When an electron beam is then passed through the coated preparation in the electron microscope and a positive print made from the "negative" image, a 3-dimensional effect is achieved (eg, Figs 2–24, 2–25, and 2–26).

Other important advances in electron microscopy include the use of ultrathin secretions of embedded material and the method of freeze-drying specimens which prevents the distortion caused by conventional drying procedures. An important recent advance has been negative staining with an electron-dense material such as phosphotungstic acid (eg, Fig 27–34).

Darkfield Illumination

By arranging the condenser lens system so that no light reaches the eye unless reflected from an object on the microscope stage, structures which provide insufficient contrast with the surrounding medium can be made visible. This technic is particularly valuable for observing organisms such as the spirochetes, which are difficult to observe by transmitted light.

Phase Microscopy

The phase microscope takes advantage of the fact that light waves passing through transparent objects, such as cells, emerge in different phases depending on the properties of the materials through which they pass. A special optical system converts difference in phase into difference in intensity, so that some structures appear darker than others. An important feature is that internal structures are thus differentiated in living cells; with ordinary microscopes, killed and stained preparations must be used.

Autoradiography

If cells which have incorporated radioactive atoms are fixed on a slide, covered with a photographic emulsion, and stored in the dark for a suitable period of time, tracks appear in the developed film emanating from the sites of radioactive disintegration. If the cells are labeled with a weak emitter such as tritium, the tracks are sufficiently short to reveal the position in the cell of the radioactive label. This procedure, called autoradiography, has been particularly useful in following the replication of DNA, using tritium-labeled thymidine as a specific tracer (Fig 4–1).

EUKARYOTIC CELL STRUCTURE

The principal features of the eukaryotic cell are shown in the electron micrograph in Fig 2–1. Note the following structures.

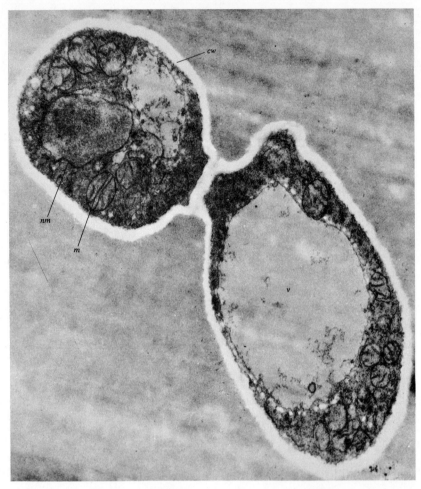

Figure 2—1. Thin section of a eukaryotic cell. A dividing cell of the unicellular yeast Lipomyces (17,500 ✕). *n* = nucleus; *nm* = nuclear membrane; *v* = vacuole; *m* = mitochondrion; *cw* = cell wall. Electron micrograph taken by Dr CF Robinow. (From Stanier RY, Doudoroff M, Adelberg EA: *The Microbial World,* 2nd ed. Copyright © 1963. By permission of Prentice-Hall, Inc, Englewood Cliffs, NJ.)

Nucleus

The nucleus is bounded by a membrane (**nm**) which is continuous with the endoplasmic reticulum. The chromosomes, embedded in the nuclear matrix, are not distinguishable. The mitotic apparatus is not present at this stage in the division cycle.

Cytoplasmic Structures

The cytoplasm of eukaryotic cells is characterized by the presence of an **endoplasmic reticulum, vacuoles,** and self-reproducing **plastids**. The plastids include the **mitochondria,** which contain the electron transport system of oxidative phosphorylation, and the **chloroplasts** (in photosynthetic organisms), which contain the chlorophylls and other photosynthetic components. The plastids contain their own DNA and multiply by binary fission.

Surface Layers

The cytoplasm is enclosed within a lipoprotein cell membrane. Most animal cells have no other surface layers; many eukaryotic microorganisms, however, have an outer **cell wall** which may be composed of a polysaccharide such as cellulose or chitin, or may be inorganic, as in the silica wall of diatoms.

Motility Organelles

Many eukaryotic cells propel themselves through water by means of protein appendages called **cilia** or **flagella** (cilia are short; flagella are long). In every case the organelle consists of a bundle of 9 fibrils surrounding 2 central fibrils (Figs 2—2 and 2—3). The fibrils are assembled from small units called microtubules.

PROKARYOTIC CELL STRUCTURE

The prokaryotic cell is simpler than the eukaryotic cell at every level, with one exception: The cell

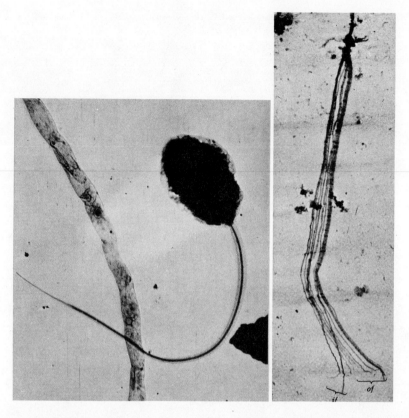

Figure 2–2. Eukaryotic flagella (3000 ✕). *Left:* A zoospore of the fungus Allomyces, with a single flagellum. *Right:* A partially disintegrated flagellum of Allomyces, showing the 2 inner fibrils *(if)* and 9 outer fibrils *(of)*. (Courtesy of Manton I & others: J Exp Bot 3:204, 1952.)

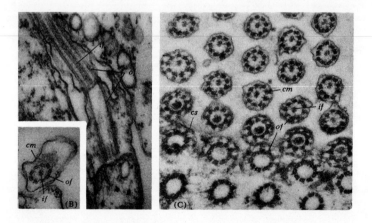

Figure 2–3. Fine structure of eukaryotic flagella and cilia (31,500 ✕). *(A)* Longitudinal section of a flagellum of Bodo, a protozoon, showing kinetoplast *(k)* from which extend the outer fibrils *(of)*. Note the origin of the inner fibrils *(if)* at the cell surface. *(B)* Cross-section of same flagellum near the surface of the cell, showing outer fibrils *(of)*, inner fibrils *(if)*, and extension of cell membrane *(cm)*. *(C)* Cross-section through surface layer of the ciliate protozoon Glaucoma, which cuts across a field of cilia just within the cell membrane (lower half) as well as outside the cell membrane (upper half). *cs* = cell surface. Electron micrographs taken by Dr D Pitelka. (From Stanier RY, Doudoroff M, Adelberg EA: *The Microbial World,* 2nd ed. Copyright © 1963. By permission of Prentice-Hall, Inc, Englewood Cliffs, NJ.)

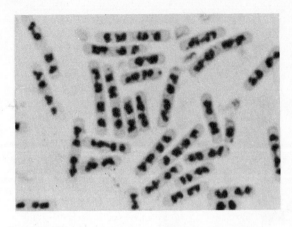

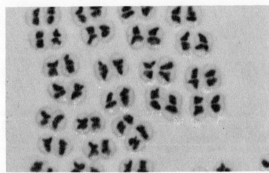

Figure 2–4. Nuclei of *Bacillus cereus* (2500 ×). (Courtesy of Robinow C: Bacteriol Rev 20:207, 1956.)

Figure 2–5. Nuclei of a tetrad-forming coccus; cells hydrolyzed with acid before staining (2500 ×). (Courtesy of Robinow C.)

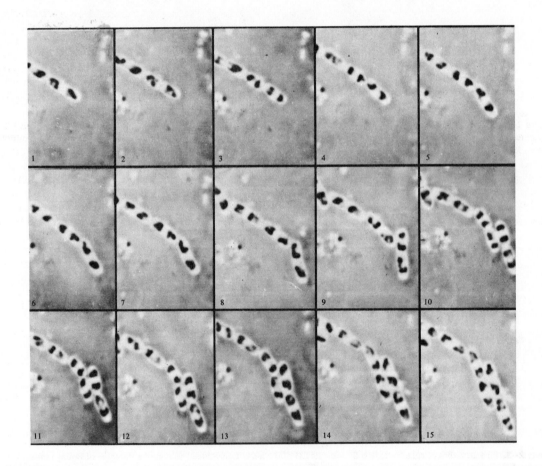

Figure 2–6. Growth and nuclear division in a bacterium (1750 ×). Successive photomicrographs of a group of cells of *Escherichia coli*, suspended in a concentrated protein solution to enhance the contrast between nuclei and cytoplasm. Sequence represents 78 minutes, or 2.5 generations. Phase contrast photomicrographs taken by Dr DJ Mason & Dr D Powelson. (Courtesy of Stanier RY, Doudoroff M, Adelberg EA: *The Microbial World*, 3rd ed. Copyright © 1970. By permission of Prentice-Hall, Inc, Englewood Cliffs, NJ.)

wall may be more complex. The following information has been obtained mostly from work on bacteria, but it is assumed to apply to blue-green algae also.

Nucleus

The prokaryotic nucleus can be seen with the light microscope in stained material (Figs 2–4 and 2–5) or by phase contrast microscopy of cells suspended in a medium of appropriate refractive index (Fig 2–6). It is Feulgen positive, indicating the presence of DNA. The negatively charged DNA is neutralized by small polyamines rather than by basic proteins.

Electron micrographs such as Fig 2–7 reveal the absence of a nuclear membrane and of a mitotic apparatus. The nuclear region is filled with DNA fibrils; the DNA of the bacterial nucleus can be extracted as a single continuous molecule with a molecular weight of

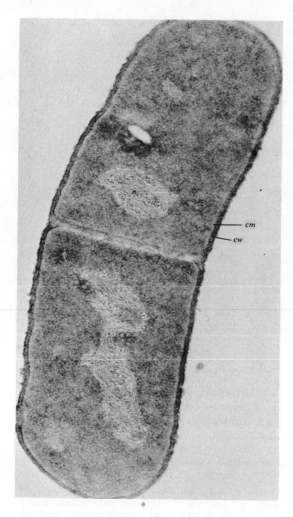

Figure 2–7. Thin section of a prokaryotic cell (42,000 ×). A dividing cell of the unicellular bacterium *Bacillus subtilis. n* = nucleus; *cm* = cytoplasmic membrane; *cw* = cell wall. Electron micrograph taken by Dr C Robinow. (From Stanier RY, Doudoroff M, Adelberg EA: *The Microbial World,* 3rd ed. Copyright © 1970. By permission of Prentice-Hall, Inc, Englewood Cliffs, NJ.)

approximately 3×10^9 (see Chromosome Structure, Chapter 4). It may thus be considered to be a single chromosome, approximately 1 mm long in the unfolded state.

The nucleus can be isolated by gentle lysis of lysozyme-treated bacteria, followed by centrifugation. The structures thus isolated consist of DNA associated with smaller amounts of RNA, RNA polymerase, and possibly other proteins. The DNA appears to be looped around an RNA core, which serves to hold the DNA in its compact form.

The electron microscopy of serial thin sections through bacterial cells shows that the DNA is attached at one point to an invagination of the cell membrane. This attachment plays a key role in the segregation of the 2 sister chromosomes following chromosomal replication (see Cell Division). The genetics and chemistry of the bacterial chromosome are presented in Chapter 4.

Cytoplasmic Structures

Prokaryotic cells lack autonomous plastids, such as mitochondria and chloroplasts. The cytochrome enzymes are localized instead in the cell membrane; in photosynthetic organisms, the photosynthetic pigments are localized in **lamellae** underlying the cell membrane (Fig 2–8). In some photosynthetic bacteria, the lamellae may become convoluted and pinch off into discrete particles called **chromatophores** (Fig 2–9).

Bacteria often store reserve materials in the form of insoluble cytoplasmic **granules,** which are deposited as osmotically inert, neutral polymers. In the absence of a nitrogen source, carbon source material is converted by some bacteria to the polymer **poly-β-hydroxybutyric acid,** and by other bacteria to various glycogen-like polymers of glucose collectively called **granulose** (Fig 2–10). The granules are used as carbon source when protein and nucleic acid synthesis is resumed. Similarly, certain sulfur-oxidizing bacteria convert excess H_2S from the environment into intracellular granules of elemental **sulfur.** Finally, many bacteria accumulate reserves of inorganic phosphate as granules of polymerized metaphosphate, called **volutin.**

Cell Membrane

A. Structure: The bacterial cell membrane is visible in light micrographs of plasmolysed, stained preparations (Fig 2–11) and in electron micrographs of thin sections (Fig 2–12). It is a typical "unit membrane," composed of phospholipids and proteins; Fig 2–13 illustrates a currently favored model of membrane organization. The membranes of prokaryotes are distinguished from those of eukaryotic cells by the absence of sterols, the only exception being mycoplasmas, which incorporate them into their membranes when growing in sterol-containing media.

Convoluted invaginations of the cell membrane form specialized structures called **mesosomes** (Fig 2–14). There are 2 types: septal mesosomes, which function in the formation of cross-walls during cell

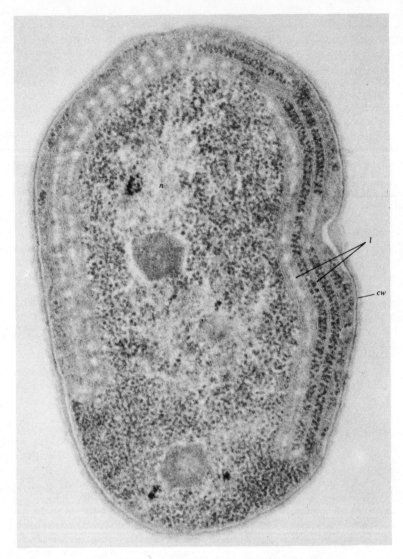

Figure 2—8. Thin section of a prokaryotic alga (80,500 ×). The blue-green alga Anacystis. *l* = lamellae bearing photosynthetic pigments; *cw* = cell wall; *n* = nuclear region. (Reprinted by permission of the Rockefeller Institute Press, from Ris H, Singh RN: J Biophys Biochem Cytol 9:63, 1961.)

division; and lateral mesosomes. The bacterial chromosome (DNA) is attached to a septal mesosome (see Cell Division, below). More extensive modifications of the cell membrane into the cytoplasm are found in bacteria with exceptionally active electron transport systems (eg, photosynthetic and nitrogen-fixing bacteria).

B. Function: The major functions of the cell membrane are: (1) selective permeability and transport of solutes into the cell; (2) electron transport and oxidative phosphorylation, in aerobic species; (3) the excretion of hydrolytic exoenzymes; and (4) serving as the site of enzymes and carrier molecules which function in the biosynthesis of DNA, cell wall polymers, and membrane lipids.

1. Permeability and transport—The membrane is both an osmotic barrier (charged molecules do not

penetrate passively) and an osmotic link: specific proteins ("permeases") are present which either catalyze energy-dependent active transport against a gradient or facilitate diffusion.

There are 2 types of active transport. In one, small molecules such as amino acids and sugars, as well as certain inorganic ions, are pumped into the cell to provide internal free concentrations which may be 100—1000 times higher than the external concentrations. For many such solutes, the membrane has been found to contain specific binding proteins, which have considerable mobility of diffusion within the phospholipid matrix. A current model for active transport assumes that the binding ("carrier") protein has a much lower affinity for its substrate when facing inward than when facing outward, the result of an

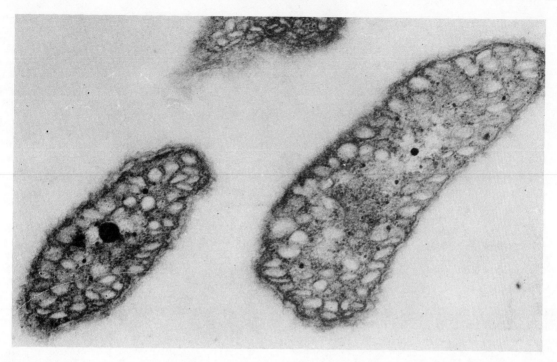

Figure 2—9. Ultrathin section of *Rhodospirillum rubrum,* showing nuclear area and chromatophores. (Courtesy of Vatter A, Wolfe R: J Bacteriol 75:840, 1958.)

energy-dependent conformational change in tertiary structure. Free rotation of the carrier within the membrane thus leads to net inward transport; rotation of the discharged carrier to the outward-facing position is accompanied by a return to the high-affinity conformation.

In the second system, which leads to the uptake of certain sugars (eg, glucose, mannose), the substrate becomes phosphorylated during the transfer process (Fig 2—15). The carrier protein (HPr in Fig 2—15) is first phosphorylated in the cytoplasm at the expense of phosphoenolpyruvate; the phosphorylated carrier binds the free sugar at the exterior membrane face and transports it into the cytoplasm, releasing it as sugar-phosphate.

2. Electron transport and oxidative phosphorylation—The cytochromes and other enzymes of the respiratory chain, including certain dehydrogenases, are located in the cell membrane, most or all being concentrated in the mesosomes. The bacterial cell membrane is thus a functional analogue of the mitochondrial inner membrane—a relationship which has been taken by many biologists to support the theory that mitochondria have evolved from symbiotic bacteria.

3. Excretion of hydrolytic exoenzymes—All organisms which rely on macromolecular organic polymers as a source of nutrients (eg, proteins, polysaccharides, lipids) excrete hydrolytic enzymes which degrade the polymers to subunits small enough to penetrate the cell membrane. Higher animals excrete such enzymes into the lumen of the digestive tract; bacteria excrete them directly into the external medium (in the

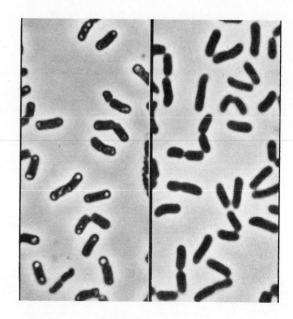

Figure 2—10. Poly-β-hydroxybutyric acid granules (1900 X). Formation and utilization of the polymer by *Bacillus megaterium.* **Left:** Cells grown on glucose plus acetate, showing granules (light areas). **Right:** Cells from the same culture after 24 hours' further incubation in the presence of a nitrogen source but without an exogenous carbon source. The polymer has been completely metabolized. Phase contrast photomicrograph taken by Dr JF Wilkinson. (From Stanier RY, Doudoroff M, Adelberg EA: *The Microbial World,* 2nd ed. Copyright © 1963. By permission of Prentice-Hall, Inc, Englewood Cliffs, NJ.)

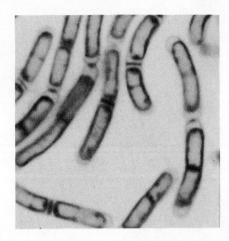

Figure 2–11. Cell wall and membrane in *Bacillus megaterium* (3600 ×). (See text for explanation.) (Courtesy of Robinow C.)

case of gram-positive cells), or into the space between the peptidoglycan layer and the outer membrane of the cell wall in the case of gram-negative bacteria (see Cell Wall, below). The mechanism of excretion of proteins through the cell membrane is obscure, although in one case (penicillinase excretion by Bacillus) the enzyme is associated with periplasmic membrane vesicles which are released at the site of lateral mesosomes.

4. Biosynthetic functions—The cell membrane is the site of the carrier lipids on which the subunits of the cell wall are assembled (see Synthesis of Cell Wall, Chapter 5), as well as of the enzymes of cell wall biosynthesis. The enzymes of phospholipid synthesis are also localized in the cell membrane. Finally, the proteins of the DNA replicating complex are present at discrete sites in the membrane, presumably in the septal mesosomes to which the DNA is attached.

C. Antibacterial Agents Affecting the Cell Membrane: Detergents, which contain lipophilic and hydrophilic groups, disrupt cell membranes and kill the cell (see Chapter 7). One class of antibiotic, the polymyxins, consists of detergent-like cyclic peptides which selectively damage membranes containing phosphatidyl ethanolamine, a major component of bacterial membranes. A number of antibiotics specifically interfere with biosynthetic functions of the cell membranes—eg, nalidixic acid, phenethyl alcohol, and novobiocin inhibit DNA synthesis, and novobiocin also inhibits teichoic acid synthesis.

Cell Wall

The internal osmotic pressure of most bacteria ranges from 5–20 atmospheres as a result of solute concentration via active transport. In most environments, this pressure would be sufficient to burst the cell were it not for the presence of a high-tensile-strength cell wall (Fig 2–16). The bacterial cell wall owes its strength to a layer composed of a substance variously referred to as murein, mucopeptide, or **peptidoglycan** (all are synonyms). The structure of peptidoglycan will be discussed below.

Bacteria are classified as gram-positive or gram-negative according to their response to the Gram staining procedure. This procedure, named for its inventor, was developed in an attempt to selectively stain bacteria in infected tissues. The cells are first stained with crystal violet and iodine and then washed with acetone or alcohol. The latter step decolorizes gram-negative bacteria but not gram-positive bacteria.

The difference between gram-positive and gram-negative bacteria has been shown to reside in the cell wall: gram-positive cells can be decolorized with acetone or alcohol if the cell wall is removed after the staining step but before the washing step. Although the chemical composition of gram-positive and gram-nega-

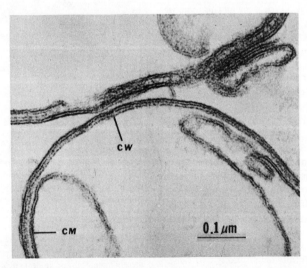

Figure 2–12. The cell membrane. Fragments of the cell membrane (CM) are seen attached to the cell wall (CW) in preparations made from *Escherichia coli*. (From Schnaitman CA: Solubilization of the cytoplasmic membrane of *Escherichia coli* by Triton X-100. J Bacteriol 108:545, 1971.)

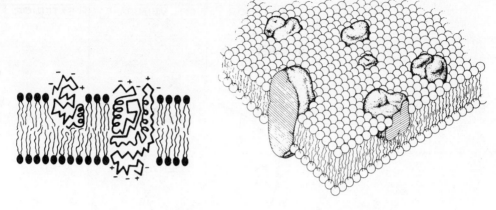

Figure 2—13. A model of membrane structure. Folded polypeptide molecules are visualized as embedded in a phospholipid bilayer, with their hydrophilic regions protruding into the intracellular space, extracellular space, or both. (From Singer SJ, Nicolson AL: The fluid mosaic model of the structure of cell membranes. Science 175:720, 1972. Copyright © 1972 by the American Association for the Advancement of Science.)

tive walls is now fairly well known (see below), the reason gram-positive walls block the dye-extraction step is still unclear.

In addition to osmotic protection, the cell wall plays an essential role in cell division as well as serving as a primer for its own biosynthesis. Various layers of the wall are the sites of major antigenic determinants of the cell surface, and one layer—the lipopolysaccharide of gram-negative cell walls—is responsible for the nonspecific endotoxin activity of gram-negative bacteria. The cell wall is, in general, nonselectively permeable; one layer of the gram-negative wall, however—the outer membrane—hinders the passage of relatively large molecules.

The biosynthesis of the cell wall and the antibiotics which interfere with this process will be discussed in Chapter 5.

A. The Peptidoglycan Layer: Peptidoglycan is a complex polymer consisting, for the purposes of description, of 3 parts: a backbone, composed of alternating N-acetylglucosamine and N-acetylmuramic acid; a set of identical tetrapeptide side chains attached to N-acetylmuramic acid; and a set of identical peptide cross-bridges (Fig 2—17). The backbone is the same in all bacterial species; the tetrapeptide side chains and the peptide cross-bridges vary from species to species, those of *Staphylococcus aureus* being illustrated in Fig 2—17.

The tetrapeptide side chains of all species, however, have certain important features in common. Most have L-alanine at position 1 (attached to N-acetylmuramic acid); D-glutamate, or substituted D-glutamate, at position 2; and D-alanine at position 4. Position 3 is the most variable one: most gram-negative bacteria carry diaminopimelic acid (DAP) at this position, to which is linked the lipoprotein cell wall component discussed below. Gram-positive bacteria may carry DAP, L-lysine, or any of several other L-amino acids at position 3.

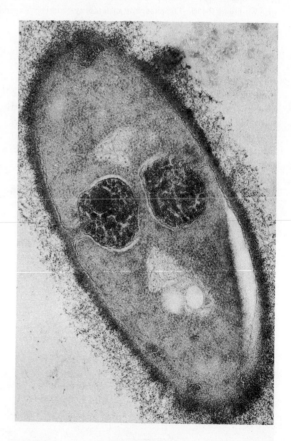

Figure 2—14. Septal mesosomes. A septal mesosome, formed as a concentric fold of the plasma membrane, grows inward. The new transverse septum is seen forming at the base of the concentric mesosome. Cell division will occur by fusion of the membrane layers surrounding the mesosome. (From Ellar DJ, Lundgren D, Slepecky RA: Fine structure of *Bacillus megaterium* during synchronous growth. J Bacteriol 94:1189, 1967.)

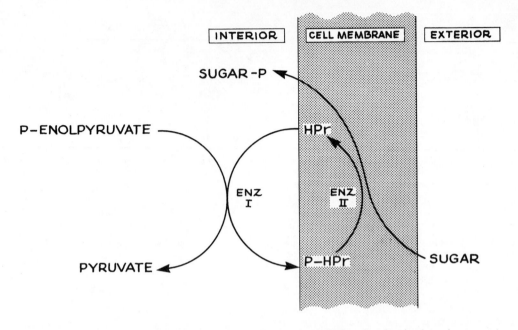

Figure 2–15. The phosphotransferase system. HPr = membrane protein; P-HPr = phosphorylated membrane protein.

DAP is a unique element of prokaryotic cell walls and is the immediate precursor of lysine in the bacterial biosynthesis of that amino acid (Fig 5–1). Bacterial mutants which are blocked prior to DAP in the biosynthetic pathway grow normally when provided with DAP in the medium; when given L-lysine alone, however, they lyse, since they continue to grow but are specifically unable to make new cell wall peptidoglycan.

The cross-bridges vary greatly in composition from species to species. The fact that all peptidoglycan chains are cross-linked means that the entire peptidoglycan layer of the bacterial cell is a single, giant mole-

Figure 2–16. Cell walls of *Streptococcus faecalis,* removed from protoplasts by mechanical disintegration and differential centrifugation (11,000 ✕). (Courtesy of Salton M, Horne R: Biochim Biophys Acta 7:177, 1951.)

cule. In gram-positive bacteria, it consists of concentric sheets cross-linked in 3 dimensions; in gram-negative bacteria it forms a 2-dimensional monolayer.

B. Special Components of Gram-Positive Cell Walls: Most gram-positive cell walls contain considerable amounts of **teichoic acids**, which may form up to 50% of the dry weight of the wall and 10% of the dry weight of the total cell. In addition, some gram-positive walls may contain polysaccharide molecules.

1. Teichoic acids—These are water-soluble polymers, containing ribitol or glycerol residues joined through phosphodiester linkages (Fig 2–18B). Their exact location in the cell envelope is not certain; most of the teichoic acid remains associated with cell wall material during cell fractionation, and covalent linkage to muramic acid has been demonstrated. However, a small percentage (consisting entirely of glycerol teichoic acids) remains associated with the cell membrane. This material, called membrane teichoic acid or lipoteichoic acid, has been found to be covalently linked to membrane glycolipid and is concentrated in the mesosomes.

The teichoic acids constitute major surface antigens of those gram-positive species which possess them, and their accessibility to antibodies has been taken as evidence that they lie on the outside surface of the peptidoglycan layer. Their activity is often increased, however, by partial digestion of the peptidoglycan; thus, much of it may lie between the cell membrane and the peptidoglycan layer, possibly extending upward through pores in the latter (Fig 2–18A).

The repeat units of some teichoic acids are shown in Fig 2–18B. The repeat units may be glycerol, joined by 1,3- or 1,2- linkages; ribitol, joined by 1,5- linkages; or more complex units in which glycerol or ribitol is

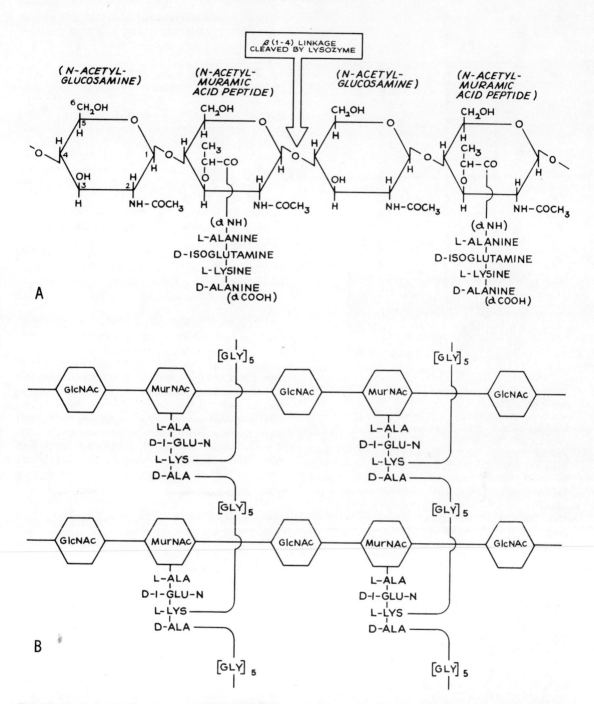

Figure 2—17. *A:* A segment of the peptidoglycan of *Staphylococcus aureus*. The backbone of the polymer consists of alternating subunits of N-acetylglucosamine and N-acetylmuramic acid connected by $\beta(1-4)$ linkages. The muramic acid residues are linked to short peptides, the composition of which varies from one bacterial species to another. In some species the L-lysine residues are replaced by diaminopimelic acid, an amino acid which is found in nature only in prokaryotic cell walls. Note the D-amino acids, which are also characteristic constituents of prokaryotic cell walls. The peptide chains of the peptidoglycan are cross-linked between parallel polysaccharide backbones, as shown in Fig 2—17B. *B:* Schematic representation of the peptidoglycan lattice which is formed by cross-linking. Bridges composed of pentaglycine peptide chains connect the a-carboxyl of the terminal D-alanine residue of one chain with the ε-amino group of the L-lysine residue of the next chain. The nature of the cross-linking bridge varies among different species.

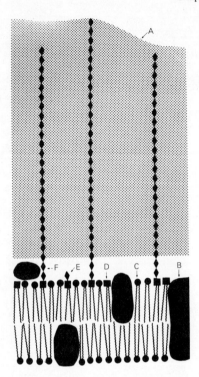

Figure 2—18A. Lipoteichoic acids. A model of the cell wall and membrane of a gram-positive bacterium, showing lipoteichoic acid molecules extending through the cell wall. The wall teichoic acids, covalently linked to muramic acid residues of the peptidoglycan layer, are not shown. *A:* cell wall, *B:* protein, *C:* phospholipid, *D:* glycolipid, *E:* phosphatidyl glycolipid, *F:* lipoteichoic acid. (From Van Driel D & others: Cellular location of the lipoteichoic acids of *Lactobacillus fermenti* NCTC 6991 and *Lactobacillus casei* NCTC 6375. J Ultrastruct Res 43:483, 1971.)

joined to a sugar residue such as glucose, galactose, or N-acetylglucosamine. The chains may be 30 or more repeat units in length, although chain lengths of 10 or less are common.

Most teichoic acids contain large amounts of D-alanine, usually attached to position 2 or 3 of glycerol, or position 3 or 4 of ribitol. In some of the more complex teichoic acids, however, D-alanine is attached to one of the sugar residues. In addition to D-alanine, other substituents may be attached to the free hydroxyl groups of glycerol and ribitol: eg, glucose, galactose, N-acetylglucosamine, N-acetylgalactosamine, or succinate. A given species may have more than one type of sugar substituent in addition to D-alanine; in such cases it is not certain whether the different sugars occur on the same or on separate teichoic acid molecules.

The function of the teichoic acids is unknown, but they do provide a high density of regularly oriented charges to the cell envelope, and these must certainly affect the passage of ions through the outer surface layers.

2. Polysaccharides—The hydrolysis of gram-positive walls has yielded, from certain species, neutral sugars such as mannose, arabinose, galactose, rhamnose, and glucosamine and acidic sugars such as glucuronic acid and mannuronic acid. It has been proposed that these sugars exist as subunits of polysaccharides in the cell wall; the discovery, however, that teichoic acids may contain a variety of sugars (see Fig 2—18B) leaves the true origin of these sugars uncertain.

C. Special Components of Gram-Negative Cell Walls: Gram-negative cell walls contain 3 polymers which lie outside of the peptidoglycan layer: lipoprotein, outer membrane, and lipopolysaccharide (Fig 2—19).

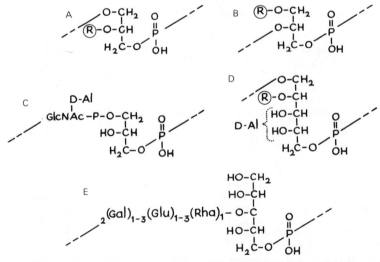

Figure 2—18B. Repeat units of some teichoic acids. *A:* Glycerol teichoic acid of *Lactobacillus casei* 7469 (R = D-alanine). *B:* Glycerol teichoic acid of *Actinomyces antibioticus* (R = D-alanine). *C:* Glycerol teichoic acid of *Staphylococcus lactis* I3. D-Alanine occurs on the 6 position of N-acetylglucosamine. *D:* Ribitol teichoic acids of *Bacillus subtilis* (R = glucose) and *Actinomyces streptomycini* (R = succinate). (The D-alanine is attached to position 3 or 4 of ribitol.) *E:* Ribitol teichoic acid of the type 6 pneumococcal capsule.

1. Lipoprotein– Molecules of an unusual lipoprotein serve to cross-link the outer membrane and peptidoglycan layers. The protein component contains 57 amino acids, representing repeats of a 15-amino-acid sequence; it is peptide linked to diaminopimelic acid residues of the peptidoglycan tetrapeptide side chains. The lipid component is noncovalently linked to the outer membrane (Fig 2–19).

2. Outer membrane–The outer membrane of the gram-negative wall presents something of an enigma: although it exhibits a typical phospholipid bilayer, it is relatively permeable to small molecules, charged and uncharged alike. It does, however, hinder the penetration of larger molecules–hence the relative resistance of gram-negative bacteria to a number of antibiotics (eg, actinomycin). It also blocks the escape of excreted hydrolytic enzymes, which accumulate between the peptidoglycan layer and the outer membrane.

3. Lipopolysaccharide (LPS)–The lipopolysaccharide of gram-negative cell walls consists of a complex lipid, called lipid A, to which is attached a polysaccharide made up of a core and a terminal series of repeat units (Fig 2–20A).

Lipid A consists of a chain of glucosamine disaccharide units connected by pyrophosphate bridges, to which are attached a number of long chain fatty acids (Fig 2–20B). β-Hydroxymyristic acid, a C_{14} fatty acid, is always present and is unique to this lipid; the other fatty acids vary according to the bacterial species.

The polysaccharide core, shown in Fig 2–20C, is constant in all gram-negative species. Each species, however, contains a unique repeat unit, that of *Salmonella newington* being shown in Fig 2–20D. The repeat units are usually linear trisaccharides or branched tetra- or pentasaccharides.

LPS, which is extremely toxic to animals, has been called the endotoxin of gram-negative bacteria because it is firmly bound to the cell surface and is released only when the cells are lysed. When LPS is split into lipid A and polysaccharide, all of the toxicity is associated with the former. The polysaccharide, on the other hand, represents a major surface antigen of the bacterial cell–the so-called **O antigen**. Antigenic specificity is conferred by the terminal repeat units, which form a sort of molecular fur on the cell surface. The number of possible antigenic types is very great: over 1000 have been recognized in Salmonella alone.

LPS is attached to the outer membrane by hydrophobic bonds. It is synthesized on the inner membrane and transported to its final exterior position. Its function is unknown; although mutants lacking various parts of the polysaccharide grow normally in culture, mutants lacking lipid A have never been observed. An essential role for lipid A is thus postulated.

D. Enzymes Which Attack Cell Walls: The β1,4-linkage of the peptidoglycan backbone is hydrolyzed by the enzyme **lysozyme**, which is found in animal secretions (tears, saliva, nasal secretions) as well as in egg white. Gram-positive bacteria treated with lysozyme in low-osmotic-strength media lyse; if the osmotic strength of the medium is raised to balance the internal osmotic pressure of the cell, free protoplasts are liberated (Fig 2–21). The outer membrane of the gram-negative cell wall prevents access of lysozyme unless disrupted by an agent such as EDTA*; in osmotically protected media, cells treated with EDTA-lysozyme form spheroplasts which still possess remnants of the complex gram-negative wall.

Bacteria themselves possess a number of **autolysins**: hydrolytic enzymes which attack peptidoglycan, including glycosidases, amidases, and peptidases. These enzymes presumably play essential functions in cell growth and division, but their activity is most apparent during the dissolution of dead cells (autolysis).

Enzymes which degrade bacterial cell walls are also found in cells which digest whole bacteria, eg, protozoa and the phagocytic cells of higher animals.

*Ethylenediaminetetraacetic acid, a chelating agent.

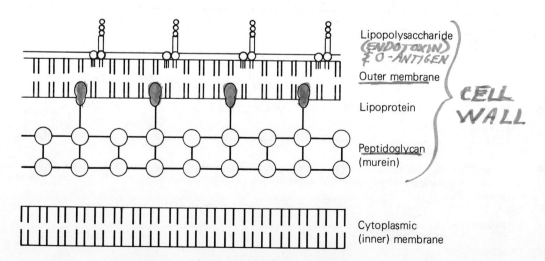

Figure 2–19. A model of the gram-negative cell envelope.

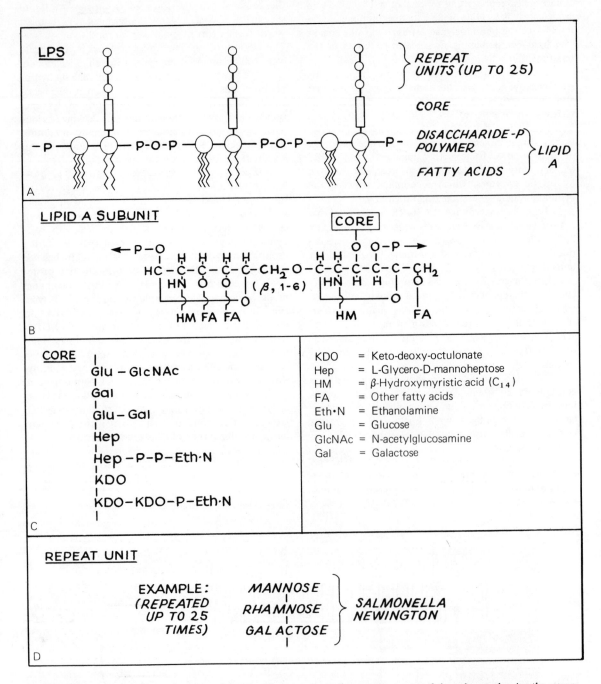

Figure 2—20. The lipopolysaccharide LPS of the gram-negative cell envelope. *A:* A segment of the polymer, showing the arrangements of the major constituents. *B:* The structure of lipid A. *C:* The polysaccharide core. *D:* A typical repeat unit *(Salmonella newington).*

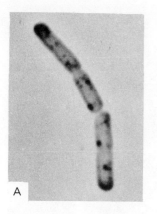 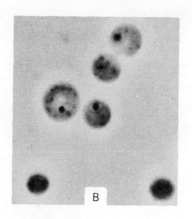 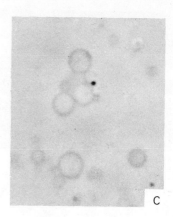

Figure 2—21. *Bacillus megaterium* phase contrast photomicrographs (3000 ×). *A:* Before treatment. *B:* After treatment with lysozyme and sucrose (protoplasts). *C:* After treatment with lysozyme alone; the empty structures are cytoplasmic membranes. (Courtesy of Weibull C: J Bacteriol 66:688, 1963.)

E. Cell Wall Growth: As the protoplast increases in mass, the cell wall is elongated by the deposition of new material in an equatorial region. A cross-septum forms in this region which eventually splits in the process of cell division. The elongation process can be followed by labeling cells with fluorescent antibody and allowing further growth to occur in the absence of antibody (Fig 2—22).

F. Protoplasts, Spheroplasts, and L Forms: Removal of the bacterial cell wall may be accomplished by hydrolysis with lysozyme or by blocking peptidoglycan biosynthesis with an antibiotic such as penicillin. In osmotically protective media, such treatments liberate protoplasts from gram-positive cells and spheroplasts from gram-negative cells (see above).

If such cells are able to grow and divide, they are called **L forms.** L forms are difficult to cultivate and usually require a medium that is solidified with agar as well as having the right osmotic strength. L forms are produced more readily with penicillin than with lysozyme, suggesting the need for residual peptidoglycan.

Some L forms are capable of reverting to the normal bacillary form upon removal of the inducing stimulus. Thus, they are able to resume normal cell wall synthesis. Other L forms, however, are stable and never revert. The factor which determines their capacity to revert may again be the presence of residual peptidoglycan, which normally acts as a primer in its own biosynthesis.

Some bacterial species produce L forms spontaneously. The spontaneous or antibiotic-induced formation of L forms in the host may produce chronic infections, the organisms persisting by becoming sequestered in protective regions of the body. Since L form infections are relatively resistant to antibiotic treatment, they present special problems in chemotherapy. Their reversion to the bacillary form can produce relapses of the overt infection.

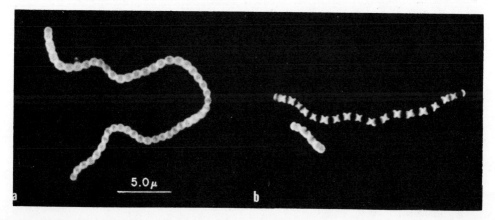

Figure 2—22. Growth of the bacterial cell wall. *(a)* Chain of streptococci, stained with fluorescent antibody directed against cell wall antigens. *(b)* After 15 minutes' growth in the absence of antibody. New cell wall material, unstained by antibody, has been deposited in the equatorial region of each cell. (From Cole RM, Hahn JJ: Cell wall replication in *Streptococcus pyogenes.* Science 135:722, 1962. Copyright © 1962 by the American Association for the Advancement of Science.)

Figure 2–23. *Bacillus megaterium,* stained by a combination of positive and negative staining (1400 X). (See section on staining, above.) (Courtesy of Welshimer H: J Bacteriol 66:112, 1953.)

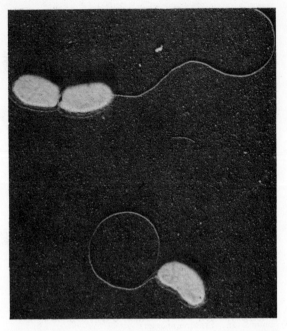

Figure 2–24. *Vibrio metchnikovii,* a monotrichous bacterium (7500 X). (Courtesy of van Iterson W: Biochim Biophys Acta 1:527, 1947.)

Capsule

The capsule consists of excreted slime, usually polysaccharide, although in one case *(Bacillus anthracis)* it consists of a polypeptide of D-glutamic acid. Fig 2–23 shows encapsulated cells. The chemical composition of some bacterial capsules is shown in Table 2–1.

Mutations affecting capsule production are easily demonstrated, since encapsulated cells form "smooth" or "mucoid" colonies while nonencapsulated cells produce "rough" colonies. Nongenetic variation is also easily demonstrated, since most capsule formers do so only under special environmental conditions such as the presence of high sugar concentrations, blood serum, or growth in a living host organism.

The only known function of the capsule is to protect the cell from phagocytosis and from viruses which must attach to the cell wall.

Flagella

Bacterial flagella are threadlike appendages composed entirely of protein, 12–30 nm in diameter. They are the organs of locomotion for the forms that possess them. Three types of arrangement are known: **mono-**

trichous (single polar flagellum), **lophotrichous** (tuft of polar flagella), or **peritrichous** (flagella distributed over the entire cell). The 3 types are illustrated in Figs 2–24, 2–25, and 2–26.

Experiments in which the cell wall has been dissolved by lysozyme, leaving flagellated protoplasts (Fig 2–27), have proved that flagella originate in the protoplast and not in the cell wall. A basal structure at the point of insertion is visible in electron micrographs like that shown in Fig 2–26. An electron micrograph of the basal structure is shown in Fig 2–28. The basal

Table 2–1. Chemical composition of the capsule in certain bacteria.*

Organism	Nature of Capsule	Chemical Subunits
Bacillus anthracis	Polypeptide	D-Glutamic acid
Leuconostoc mesenteroides	Dextran	Glucose
Streptococcus pneumoniae (pneumococcus)	Complex polysaccharides (many types), eg,	
	Type II	Rhamnose, glucose, glucuronic acid
	Type III	Glucose, glucuronic acid
	Type VI	Galactose, glucose, rhamnose
	Type XIV	Galactose, glucose, N-acetylglucosamine
	Type XVIII	Rhamnose, glucose
Streptococcus spp	Hyaluronic acid	N-Acetylglucosamine, glucuronic acid
Streptococcus salivarius	Levan	Fructose
Acetobacter xylinum	Cellulose	Glucose
Enterobacter aerogenes	Complex polysaccharide	Glucose, fucose, glucuronic acid

*From Stanier RY, Doudoroff M, Adelberg EA: *The Microbial World,* 3rd ed. Copyright 1970. By permission of Prentice-Hall, Inc, Englewood Cliffs, NJ.

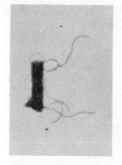

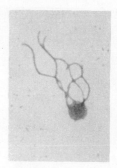

Figure 2—27. *Bacillus megaterium* stained with flagella stain (2000 X). *Left:* Untreated cell. *Right:* Protoplast freed from cell wall by treatment with lysozyme and sucrose. (Courtesy of Weibull C: J Bacteriol 66:688, 1953.)

Figure 2—25. Electron micrograph of *Spirillum serpens,* showing lophotrichous flagellation (9000 X). (Courtesy of van Iterson W: Biochim Biophys Acta 1:527, 1947.)

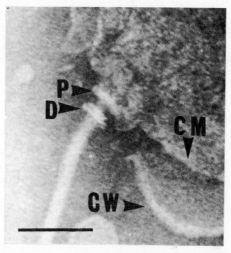

Figure 2—28. Negatively stained autolysing *Vibrio metchnikovii* showing structures seen at the base of the flagellum. The proximal disk (P) appears to be continuous with the cytoplasmic membrane (CM); the cell wall (CW) is separated from the distal disk (D), which is a composite of 2 thinner disks. (The bar denotes 100 nm.) (Courtesy of Vaituzis Z, Doetsch RN: J Bacteriol 100:512, 1969.)

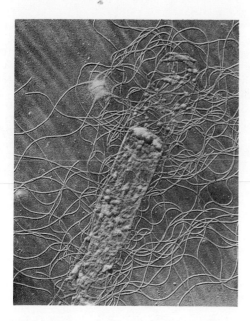

Figure 2—26. Electron micrograph of *Proteus vulgaris,* showing peritrichous flagellation (9000 X). Note basal granules. (Courtesy of Houwink A, van Iterson W: Biochim Biophys Acta 5:10, 1950.)

structure imparts to the flagellum an active rotatory movement, by an unknown mechanism, which propels the cell through the liquid medium.

Flagella have been removed from bacterial cells by rapid shaking and purified by differential centrifugation. Chemical analysis and x-ray diffraction studies on suspensions of purified flagella show them to be elastic proteins similar to hair and muscle fibers.

A bacterial flagellum is made up of a single kind of subunit, called flagellin; the flagellum is formed by the aggregation of subunits to form a hollow cylindric structure. If flagella are removed by mechanically agitating a suspension of bacteria, new flagella are rapidly formed by the synthesis, aggregation, and extrusion of flagellin subunits; motility is restored within 3—6 minutes. The flagellins of different bacterial species presumably differ from one another in primary structure.

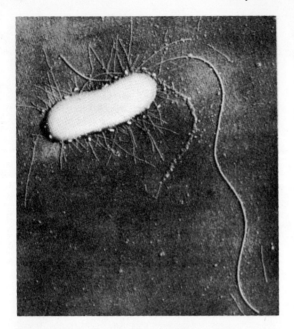

Figure 2—29. Surface appendages of bacteria. Electron micrograph of a cell of *Escherichia coli* possessing 3 types of appendages: ordinary pili (short, straight bristles); a sex pilus (longer, flexible, with phage particles attached); and several flagella (longest, thickest). Diameters: Ordinary pili: 7 nm; sex pili: 8.5 nm; flagella: 25 nm. (Courtesy of Dr Judith Carnahan and Dr Charles Brinton.)

Pili (Fimbriae)

Many gram-negative bacteria possess rigid surface appendages called pili (Latin "hairs") or fimbriae (Latin "fringes"). They are shorter and finer than flagella; like flagella, they are composed of protein subunits. Their function is unknown, although in one case (sex pili) they play an essential role in the attachment of conjugating cells to each other. Pili are illustrated in Fig 2—29 in which the sex pili have been coated with phage particles for which they serve as specific receptors.

Endospores

Members of 3 bacterial genera are capable of forming endospores (Fig 2—30). The 2 most common are gram-positive rods: the obligately aerobic genus Bacillus and the obligately anaerobic genus Clostridium. The third is a gram-positive coccus, Sporosarcina. These organisms undergo a cycle of differentiation in response to environmental conditions: under conditions of nutritional depletion, each cell forms a single internal spore which is liberated when the mother cell undergoes autolysis. The spore is a resting cell, highly resistant to dessication, heat, and chemical agents; when returned to favorable nutritional conditions and activated (see below), the spore germinates to produce a single vegetative cell.

A. Sporulation: The sporulation process begins when nutritional conditions become unfavorable, depletion of the nitrogen or carbon source (or both) being the most significant factor. Sporulation occurs massively in cultures which have terminated exponential growth as a result of such depletion.

Sporulation involves the production of many new structures, enzymes, and metabolites along with the

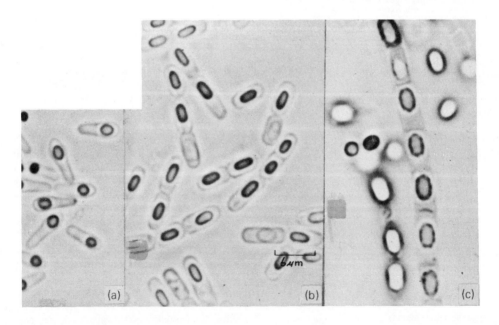

Figure 2—30. Sporulating cells of Bacillus species. *A:* Unidentified bacillus from soil. *B: B cereus. C: B megaterium.* (From Robinow CF, in: *The Bacteria.* Vol 1. Gunsalus IC, Stanier RY [editors] . Academic Press, 1960.)

disappearance of many vegetative cell components. These changes represent a true process of **differentiation**: a series of genes whose products determine the formation and final composition of the spore are activated, while another series of genes involved in vegetative cell function are inactivated.

Morphologically, sporulation begins with the isolation of a terminal nucleus by the inward growth of the cell membrane (Fig 2–31). The growth process involves an infolding of the membrane so as to produce a double membrane structure whose facing surfaces correspond to the cell wall synthesizing surface of the cell envelope. The growing points move progressively toward the pole of the cell so as to engulf the developing spore.

The 2 spore membranes now engage in the active synthesis of special layers which will form the cell envelope: the **spore wall** and **cortex**, lying between the facing membranes; and the **coat** and **exosporium**, lying outside of the facing membranes. In the newly isolated cytoplasm, or **core**, many vegetative cell enzymes are degraded and are replaced by a set of unique spore constituents. A thin section of a sporulating cell is shown in Fig 2–32.

B. Properties of Endospores:

1. Core—The core is the spore protoplast. It contains a complete nucleus (chromosome), all of the components of the protein-synthesizing apparatus, and an energy-generating system based on glycolysis. Cytochromes are lacking even in aerobic species, the spores of which rely on a shortened electron transport pathway involving flavoproteins. A number of vegetative cell enzymes are increased in amount (eg, alanine racemase), and a number of unique enzymes are formed (eg, dipicolinic acid synthetase). The energy for germination is stored as 3-phosphoglycerate rather than as ATP.

The heat resistance of spores is due in part to their dehydrated state and in part to the presence of large amounts (5–15% of the spore dry weight) of calcium dipicolinate, which is formed from an intermediate of the lysine biosynthetic pathway (Fig 2–33). In some way not yet understood, these properties result in the stabilization of the spore enzymes, most of which exhibit normal heat lability when isolated in soluble form.

2. Spore wall—The innermost layer surrounding the inner spore membrane is called the spore wall. It contains normal peptidoglycan and becomes the cell wall of the germinating vegetative cell.

3. Cortex—The cortex is the thickest layer of the spore envelope. It contains an unusual type of peptidoglycan, with many fewer cross-links than are found in cell wall peptidoglycan. Cortex peptidoglycan is extremely sensitive to lysozyme, and its autolysis plays a key role in spore germination.

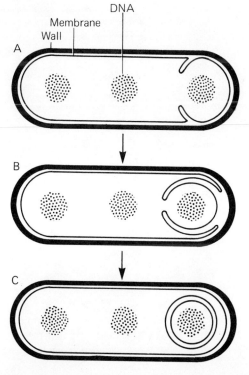

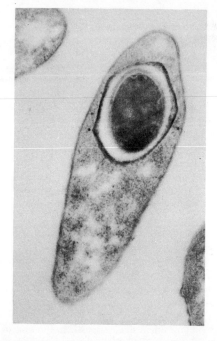

Figure 2–31. The sporulation process. *A:* Inward growth of an invagination of the cell membrane. *B:* Membrane growing points move toward the pole of the cell. *C:* Fusion of membranes completes the isolation of the spore protoplast.

Figure 2–32. Thin section through a sporulating cell of a bacillus (33,000 ×). Electron micrograph taken by Dr CL Hannay. (From Stanier RY, Doudoroff M, Adelberg EA: *The Microbial World,* 2nd ed. Copyright © 1963. By permission of Prentice-Hall, Inc, Englewood Cliffs, NJ.)

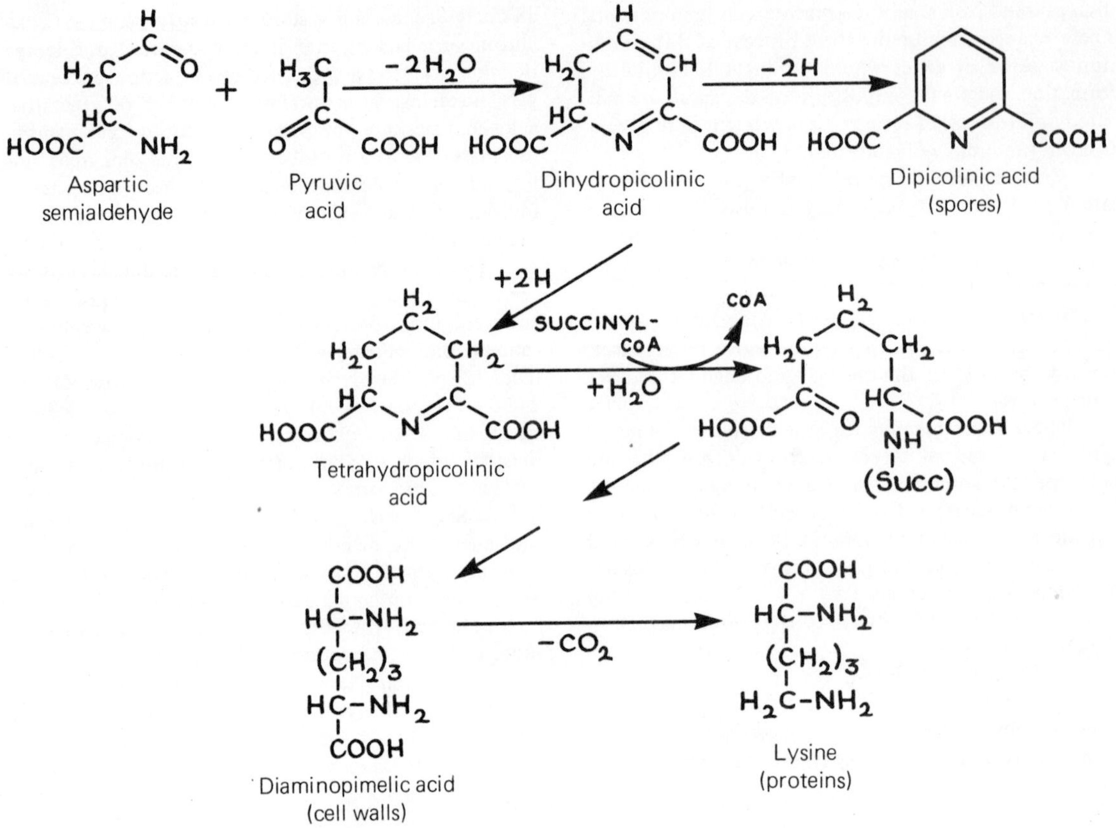

**Aspartic
semialdehyde**   **Pyruvic
acid**   **Dihydropicolinic
acid**   **Dipicolinic acid
(spores)**

$-2H_2O$ $-2H$

**Tetrahydropicolinic
acid** $+2H$ **SUCCINYL-
CoA**   CoA   **(Succ)**

$+H_2O$

**Diaminopimelic acid
(cell walls)** $-CO_2$ **Lysine
(proteins)**

Figure 2–33. The biosynthesis of dipicolinic acid, diaminopimelic acid, and lysine.

4. Coat—The coat is composed of a keratin-like protein, containing many intramolecular disulfide bonds. The impermeability of this layer confers on spores their relative resistance to antibacterial chemical agents.

5. Exosporium—The exosporium is a lipoprotein membrane containing some carbohydrate.

C. Germination: The germination process occurs in 3 stages: activation, initiation, and outgrowth.

1. Activation—Even when placed in an environment which favors germination (eg, a nutritionally rich medium), bacterial spores will not germinate unless first activated by one or another agent which damages the spore coat. Among the agents which can overcome spore dormancy are heat, abrasion, acidity, and compounds containing free sulfhydryl groups.

2. Initiation—Once activated, a spore will initiate germination if the environmental conditions are favorable. Different species have evolved receptors which recognize different effectors as signalling a rich medium: thus, initiation is triggered by L-alanine in one species and by adenosine in another. Binding of the effector activates an autolysin which rapidly degrades the cortex peptidoglycan. Water is taken up, calcium dipicolinate is released, and a variety of spore constituents are degraded by hydrolytic enzymes.

3. Outgrowth—Degradation of the cortex and

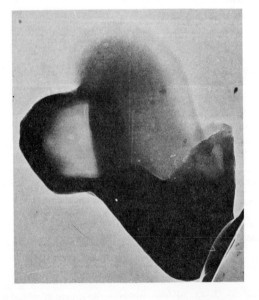

Figure 2–34. Electron micrograph of germinating spore of *Bacillus mycoides*. (Courtesy of Knaysi G, Baker R, Hillier J: J Bacteriol 53:525, 1947.)

outer layers results in the emergence of a new vegetative cell consisting of the spore protoplast with its surrounding wall (Fig 2–34). A period of active biosynthesis follows; this period, which terminates in cell division, is called outgrowth. Outgrowth requires a supply of all nutrients essential for cell growth.

STAINING

Stains combine chemically with the bacterial protoplasm; if the cell is not already dead, the staining process itself will kill it. The process is thus a drastic one and may produce artifacts.

The commonly used stains are salts. **Basic** stains consist of a colored cation with a colorless anion (eg, methylene blue$^+$ chloride$^-$); **acidic** stains are the reverse (eg, sodium$^+$ eosinate$^-$). Bacterial cells are rich in nucleic acid, bearing negative charges as phosphate groups. These combine with the positively charged basic dyes. Acidic dyes do not stain bacterial cells and hence can be used to stain background material a contrasting color (see Negative Staining, below).

The basic dyes stain bacterial cells uniformly unless the cytoplasmic RNA is destroyed first. Special staining technics can be used, however, to differentiate flagella, capsules, cell walls, cell membranes, granules, nuclei, and spores.

Gram's Stain

An important taxonomic characteristic of bacteria is their response to Gram's stain. The Gram staining property appears to be a fundamental one, since the Gram reaction is correlated with many other morphologic properties in phylogenetically related forms (see Chapter 3). An organism which is potentially gram-positive may appear so only under a particular set of environmental conditions and in a young culture.

The Gram staining procedure (see Chapter 26 for details) begins with the application of a basic dye, crystal violet. A solution of iodine is then applied; all bacteria will be stained blue at this point in the procedure. The cells are then treated with alcohol. "Gram-positive" cells retain the crystal violet-iodine complex, remaining blue; "gram-negative" cells are completely decolorized by alcohol. As a last step, a counterstain (such as the red dye safranin) is applied, so that the decolorized gram-negative cells will take on a contrasting color.

The basis of the differential Gram reaction is the structure of the cell wall, as discussed earlier in this chapter.

The Acid-Fast Stain

Acid-fast bacteria are those that retain carbolfuchsin (basic fuchsin dissolved in a phenol-alcohol-water mixture) even when decolorized with hydrochloric acid in alcohol. A smear of cells on a slide is flooded with carbolfuchsin and heated on a steam bath. Following this, the decolorization with acid-alcohol is carried out, and finally a contrasting (blue or green) counterstain is applied. Acid-fast bacteria (Mycobacterium species and some of the related actinomycetes) appear red; others take on the color of the counterstain.

Negative Staining

This procedure involves staining the background with an acidic dye, leaving the cells contrastingly colorless. The black dye nigrosin is commonly used. This method is used for those cells or structures difficult to stain directly (Fig 2–23).

The Flagella Stain

Flagella are too fine (12–30 nm in diameter) to be visible in the light microscope. However, their presence and arrangement can be demonstrated by treating the cells with an unstable colloidal suspension of tannic acid salts, causing a heavy precipitate to form on the cell walls and flagella. In this manner the apparent diameter of the flagella is increased to such an extent that subsequent staining with basic fuchsin makes the flagella visible in the light microscope. Fig 2–35 shows cells stained by this method.

In some bacteria the flagella form into bundles during movement, and such bundles may be thick enough to be observed on living cells by darkfield or phase contrast microscopy.

The Capsule Stain

Capsules are usually demonstrated by the negative staining procedure or a modification of it (Fig 2–23). One such "capsule stain" (Welch method) involves treatment with hot crystal violet solution followed by a rinsing with copper sulfate solution. The latter is used to remove excess stain because the conventional washing with water would dissolve the capsule. The copper salt also gives color to the background, with the

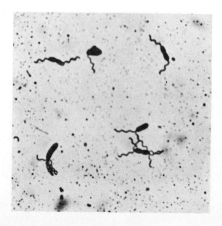

Figure 2–35. Flagella stain of Pseudomonas species. (Courtesy of Leifson E: J Bacteriol 62:377, 1951.)

result that the cell and background appear dark blue and the capsule a much paler blue.

Staining the Cell Wall & the Cytoplasmic Membrane

Fig 2–11 shows the result of staining plasmolyzed cells with Victoria blue, which is specific for the cell wall and cell membrane. The Victoria blue dyes are water-soluble basic dyes belonging to the phenol-methane series; the reason for their specific reaction with the cell wall and membrane is not understood.

Staining of Nuclei

Nuclei are stainable with the Feulgen stain, which is specific for DNA.

The Spore Stain

Spores are most simply observed as intracellular refractile bodies in unstained cell suspensions or as colorless areas in cells stained by conventional methods. The spore wall is relatively impermeable, but dyes can be made to penetrate it by heating the preparation. The same impermeability then serves to prevent decolorization of the spore by a period of alcohol treatment sufficient to decolorize vegetative cells. The latter can finally be counterstained. Spores are commonly stained with malachite green or carbolfuchsin.

MORPHOLOGIC CHANGES DURING GROWTH

Cell Division

In general, bacteria reproduce by binary fission. Following elongation of the cell, a transverse cell membrane is formed, and subsequently a new cell wall. In bacteria, the new transverse membrane and wall grow inward from the outer layers (Fig 2–14). The nuclei, which have doubled in number preceding the division, are distributed equally to the 2 daughter cells.

Although bacteria lack a mitotic spindle, the transverse membrane is formed in such a way as to separate the 2 sister chromosomes formed by chromosomal replication. This is accomplished by the attachment of the chromosome to the cell membrane. The completion of a cycle of DNA replication apparently triggers active membrane synthesis between the sites of attachment of the 2 sister chromosomes, which are pushed apart by the inward growth of the transverse membrane (Fig 4–4). The deposition of new cell wall material follows, resulting in the elongation and eventual doubling of the cell envelope.

Cell Groupings

If the cells remain temporarily attached following division, certain characteristic groupings result. Depending on the plane of division and the number of divisions through which the cells remain attached, the following arrangement may occur in the coccal forms: chains (streptococci), pairs (diplococci), cubical bundles (sarcinae), or flat plates. Rods may form pairs or chains.

Following fission of some bacteria, characteristic postfission movements occur. For example, a "whipping" motion can bring the cells into parallel positions; repeated division and whipping results in the "palisade" arrangement characteristic of diphtheria bacilli.

Life Cycle Changes

As bacteria progress from the dormant to the actively growing state, certain changes usually take place. The cells tend to become larger, granules disappear, and the protoplasm stains more deeply with basic dyes. When growth slows down again, a gradual change in the reverse direction takes place. Finally, in very old cultures there appear morphologically unusual cells called involution forms. These include filaments, buds, and branched cells, many of which are nonviable.

●   ●   ●

General References

Books

Archibald AR: Teichoic acids. Pages 162–172 in: *Methods in Carbohydrate Chemistry.* Vol 6. Whistler RL (editor). Academic Press, 1972.

Gould GW, Hurst A (editors): *The Bacterial Spore.* Academic Press, 1969.

Leive L (editor): *Membranes and Walls of Bacteria.* Dekker, 1973.

Mandelstam J, McQuillen K: *Biochemistry of Bacterial Growth,* 2nd ed. Wiley, 1973.

Murray RGE: Fine structure and taxonomy of bacteria. Pages 119–144 in: *Microbial Classification.* Ainsworth GC, Sneath PHA (editors). Cambridge Univ Press, 1962.

Rogers HJ, Perkins HR: *Cell Walls and Membranes.* E & FN Spon, Ltd, 1968.

Tipper DJ, Gauthier TT: Structure of the bacterial endospore. Page 3 in: *Spores.* Vol 5. Halvorson HO, Hanson R, Campbell LL (editors). American Society for Microbiology, 1972.

Articles & Reviews

Archibald AR, Baddiley J, Blumson NL: The teichoic acids. Adv Enzymol 30:223, 1967.

Baddiley J: Teichoic acids in cell walls and membranes of bacteria. Essays Biochem 8:35, 1972.

Berg H: Chemotaxis in bacteria. Annu Rev Biophys Bioeng 4:119, 1975.

Berg H: How bacteria swim. Sci Am 233:36, Aug 1975.

Cairns J: The chromosome of *Escherichia coli.* Cold Spring Harbor Symp Quant Biol 28:43, 1963.

Clasener H: Pathogenicity of the L-phase of bacteria. Annu Rev Microbiol 26:55, 1972.

Costerton JW, Ingram JM, Cheng KJ: Structure and function of the cell envelope of gram-negative bacteria. Bacteriol Rev 38:87, 1974.

Doetsch RN, Hageage GJ: Motility in procaryotic organisms. Biol Rev 43:317, 1968.

Hanson RS, Peterson JA, Yousten AA: Unique biochemical events in bacterial sporulation. Annu Rev Microbiol 24:53, 1970.

Keynan A: The transformation of bacterial endospores into vegetative cells. Symp Soc Gen Microbiol 23:85, 1973.

Knox KW, Wicken AJ: Immunological properties of teichoic acids. Bacteriol Rev 37:215, 1973.

Machtigen NA, Fox CF: Biochemistry of bacterial membranes. Annu Rev Biochem 42:575, 1973.

Murrell W: The biochemistry of the bacterial endospore. Adv Microb Physiol 1:133, 1967.

Osborn MJ: Structure and biosynthesis of the bacterial cell wall. Annu Rev Microbiol 38:501, 1969.

Ryter A: Association of the nucleus and the membrane of bacteria: A morphological study. Bacteriol Rev 32:39, 1968.

Salton MRJ: Structure and function of bacterial cell membranes. Annu Rev Microbiol 21:417, 1967.

Schleifer KH, Kandler O: Peptidoglycan types of bacterial cell walls and their taxonomic implications. Bacteriol Rev 36:407, 1972.

3 . . .
The Major Groups of Bacteria

PRINCIPLES OF CLASSIFICATION

Although it may be said of the higher organisms that no 2 individuals are exactly alike, it is nevertheless true that such individuals tend to form clusters of highly similar types. Furthermore, between any 2 clusters there is generally a sharp discontinuity. It is common practice to speak of each cluster as a **species**.

For hundreds of years, biologists have been naming and describing species of plants, animals, and microorganisms. Having at hand a large number of such names and accompanying descriptions, the next step was to compile this information in some orderly and systematic manner, ie, to classify it. In order to understand the problems and limitations of bacterial classification, it is necessary first to discuss 2 fundamental issues: the meaning of the term "species," and the types and purposes of classification.

"Species" Defined

A "species" is a stage in the evolution of a population of organisms. To understand this it is necessary to consider how species originate in higher plants and animals with obligatory sexual life-cycles.

A. Evolution in Higher Organisms: Imagine an island inhabited by a large, interbreeding population of a given species of plant. For the purposes of illustration, we will oversimplify and characterize the species as "broad-leaved plants." As generation follows generation, any mutant genes which arise will be thoroughly distributed throughout the population by interbreeding; in this way the population always remains homogeneous. The entire population may gradually change, as an adaptive response to a changing environment, but it cannot, as long as all individuals are free to interbreed at random, undergo divergent evolution into 2 or more different species. This can only occur if a segment of the population becomes isolated.

1. Geographic isolation—Isolation must at first be geographic, ie, 2 segments of an interbreeding population must become physically separated from each other. This can occur in many ways. For example, seeds may be transmitted by animals over a usually impassable mountain range, or seeds may be waterborne to a neighboring island. In any case, the result is that interbreeding between individuals on either side of the barrier is prevented. Within each segment, however, homogeneity is maintained by continued interbreed-

ing; 2 independent populations are thus established.

Each population continues to evolve. The probability is high, however, that evolution—owing either to different selective forces in their environments or to pure chance—will follow different courses in the 2 populations. We may thus picture the plants in the 2 populations as becoming more and more dissimilar. Up to a certain point the possibility remains that the 2 populations, upon removal of the geographic barrier, will mingle and finally "homogenize" as free interbreeding is once again established. But eventually, if they remain isolated, a point in their divergent evolution is reached where differences have accumulated to such an extent as to make interbreeding between the 2 populations impossible. They are then said to have become physiologically isolated.

2. Physiologic isolation—Two temporarily separated populations may become physiologically isolated in a variety of ways: For example, they may evolve different flowering seasons, or factors which cause hybrid progeny to be sterile. In any case, physiologic isolation represents a "point of no return"; removal of the geographic barrier now will permit intermingling but not interbreeding, with the result that the 2 populations are destined to remain different. Furthermore, the discontinuity will be a fairly large one, since many genetic differences will usually have accumulated before physiologic isolation occurs.

The point in evolution at which physiologic isolation occurs is thus a highly significant one and is therefore chosen as the point at which new species are said to have arisen. A "species" may thus be defined as follows: "A given stage of evolution at which actually or potentially interbreeding arrays of forms become segregated into two or more separate arrays which are physiologically incapable of interbreeding."*

Coming back to the oversimplified illustration, let us assume that the population of broad-leaved plants becomes split into two geographically isolated segments. On one side of the barrier, the population gradually evolves so as to possess short stems, serrated leaves, and a flowering season in the spring; whereas on the other side the population evolves long stems, smooth-edged leaves, and a fall flowering season. At this point, should the geographic barrier disappear (for

*Dobzhansky T: *Genetics and the Origin of Species.* Columbia Univ Press, 1957.

example, by geologic change), the 2 types will spread and intermingle; but due to their different flowering seasons they will be physiologically isolated. A taxonomist visiting the island would then find 2 "species" of plants. He would probably classify them as follows:

Genus I: Broad-leaved plants.
 Species 1: Short stems, serrated leaves, spring-flowering.
 Species 2: Long stems, smooth-edged leaves, fall-flowering.

Note that what was originally a description of a species (possession of broad leaves) is now the description of a genus, illustrating that a "species" is really a stage in evolution.

3. Repetition of the process—All the individuals of "species 1" are freely interbreeding, as are the individuals of "species 2." Assume that a segment of the "species 1" population again becomes geographically isolated; further evolution will lead to physiologic isolation, and again new species will emerge. For example, in the cut-off segment of the "species 1" population, evolution may lead to the acquisition of the deciduous habit, while the other segment continues to retain its leaves all year. Let us assume also that the 2 types evolve different pollination systems. The taxonomist will probably then set up the following classification:

Family I: Broad-leaved plants.
 Genus I: Short stems, serrated leaves, spring-flowering.
  Species 1: Deciduous; wind-pollinated.
  Species 2: Nondeciduous; insect-pollinated.
 Genus II (one species): Long stems, smooth-edged leaves, fall-flowering.

Note that the original species has now become a family which includes 2 genera and 3 species. Thus, as the processes of geographic and physiologic isolation have repeated themselves over millions of years, organisms with obligate sexual life-cycles have evolved along more and more divergent lines, until the present-day array of species has been reached.

B. Evolution in Bacteria: Unlike higher plants and animals, bacteria (and many other microorganisms) multiply almost entirely vegetatively. There is thus no mechanism by which discontinuous "species" can arise; instead, mutations accumulate so as to produce gradients of related types. As bacteria evolve to occupy their niches more and more efficiently, divergent lines of evolution will occur to the extent that the niches differ; groups of related ecologic types can thus often be recognized, but within each group there may be few real discontinuities. The term "species" thus has no real meaning when applied to bacteria; it cannot even be defined, as it can for sexually reproducing organisms. Bacterial taxonomists must be purely arbitrary in deciding to what extent 2 types must differ before being classed as different "species."

In recent years, the technics of molecular genetics have introduced new criteria for determining the degree of evolutionary relatedness between different bacteria. The DNA is extracted from pure cultures of the types in question and their relative base compositions determined. The parameter most often used is the mols percent of guanine (G) plus cytosine (C) in the total DNA; the G + C content may be directly measured or indirectly calculated from buoyant density or melting point determinations. For 2 organisms to be considered closely related, their G + C contents must be closely similar (although such similarity is not proof of relatedness).

Within a well defined, closely-knit group such as the aerobic sporeforming bacilli, much higher degrees of relatedness can be recognized by the relative abilities of heat-denatured DNAs from different strains to reanneal with each other during slow cooling. Such reannealing reflects the existence in the 2 types of DNA of identical nucleotide sequences.

Types & Purposes of Classification

While many sorts of systematic compilations are conceivable, only 2 are generally used in taxonomy: keys, or "artificial classifications"; and phylogenetic (or "natural") classifications.

A. Keys: In a "key," descriptive properties are arranged in such a way that an organism on hand may be readily identified. Organisms which are grouped together in a "key" are not necessarily related in the phylogenetic sense; they are listed together because they share some easily recognizable property. It would be perfectly reasonable, for example, for a key to bacteria to include a group such as "bacteria forming red pigments," even though this would include such unrelated forms as *Serratia marcescens* and purple sulfur bacteria. The point is that such a grouping would be useful; the investigator having a red-pigmented culture to identify would immediately narrow his search to a relatively few types.

B. Phylogenetic Classification: A phylogenetic classification groups together types that are **related**, ie, those that share a common ancestor. Species which have arisen through divergent evolution from a common ancestor are grouped together in a single genus; genera with a common origin are grouped in a single family, etc. Recognition of phylogenetic relationships in higher organisms is greatly aided by the existence of fossil remnants of common ancestors and by the multitude of morphologic features which can be studied. Bacteria, on the other hand, have not been preserved as recognizable fossils and exhibit relatively few morphologic properties for study. Evolutionary trends are thus difficult to determine or even to guess at, and a phylogenetic classification of bacteria is certainly a long way from being realized.

Bergey's Manual of Determinative Bacteriology

There is no universally accepted natural classification of bacteria since there is no mechanism for the evolution of discrete bacterial species and we are almost totally ignorant of bacterial evolution. A few groups, such as the photosynthetic bacteria, have been thoroughly classified by studies with enrichment cultures, but we do not know how such major groups are related to each other. The few evolutionary lines which are discernible will be presented later in this chapter.

In spite of these objections, however, an attempt at a phylogenetic classification of bacteria has been published in the USA as *Bergey's Manual of Determinative Bacteriology.** First published in 1923, it has now reached its 8th edition. The 6th edition, in 1948, grouped the bacteria in 6 orders containing 36 families. The 7th edition, in 1957, rearranged the genera into 10 orders and 47 families. The 8th edition, in 1974, groups the bacteria into 19 "parts" (eg, spirochetes, spiral and curved bacteria, gram-negative aerobic rods and cocci) each of which contains numerous genera. In some parts, the genera are grouped into families and orders; in others, they are not.

In view of the divergent views that exist regarding bacterial classification, it is probable that the *Manual* will undergo further major changes with each edition. We will therefore not follow Bergey's classification in this chapter but instead will describe the major groups of bacteria, using common names. We will also refer to the medically important genera, about which there is good agreement among bacteriologists.

Bergey's Manual does serve several useful purposes, however, if we ignore its attempt to represent a phylogeny. First, it represents an exhaustive compilation of names and descriptions; second, the latest edition includes a completely practical although artificial key to the genera, as an aid to identification of newly isolated types. The *Manual* has a companion volume, called *Index Bergeyana,* containing the literature index, the host and habitat index, and descriptions of organisms which the editors consider inadequately described or whose taxonomic positions are uncertain.

A key to the genera of bacteria has also been published separately in Skerman VBD: *A Guide to the Identification of the Genera of Bacteria,* 2nd ed. Williams & Wilkins, 1967.

An informal classification is presented on the following pages and in Table 3—1.

Computer Taxonomy of Bacteria

Taxonomy by computer has been developed for groups of bacteria in which a large number of strains exist which can be described in terms of 100 or more clear-cut taxonomic properties (eg, presence or absence of certain enzymes, presence or absence of certain pigments, presence or absence of certain morphologic structures). Punch cards are prepared for each strain; the computer then compares the cards and prints out a list of the strains in such an order that each strain is followed in the list by the strain with which it shares

*Buchanan RE, Gibbons NE (editors): *Bergey's Manual of Determinative Bacteriology,* 8th ed. Williams & Wilkins, 1974.

the most characteristics. When this is done, the list often reveals several broad subgroups of strains, each subgroup characterized by a large number of shared common characteristics. The median strain within each subgroup can then be arbitrarily considered as a type species.

Table 3—1. Key to the principal groups of bacteria (listing the genera which include species pathogenic for man).

	Genera
I. Flexible, thin-walled cells, motility conferred by gliding mechanism: Myxobacteria	
II. Flexible, thin-walled cells, motility conferred by axial filament: Spirochetes	Treponema Borrelia Leptospira
III. Rigid, thick-walled cells, immotile or motility conferred by flagella: Eubacteria A. Mycelial (actinomycetes)	Mycobacterium Actinomyces Nocardia Streptomyces
B. Simple unicellular 1. Lacking cell walls	Mycoplasma
2. Possessing cell walls a. Obligate intracellular parasites	Rickettsia Coxiella Chlamydia
b. Free-living (1) Gram-positive (a) Cocci	Streptococcus Diplococcus Staphylococcus
(b) Nonsporulating rods	Corynebacterium Listeria Erysipelothrix
(c) Sporulating rods Obligate aerobes Obligate anaerobes	Bacillus Clostridium
(2) Gram-negative (a) Cocci	Neisseria
(b) Nonenteric rods Spiral forms Straight, very small rods	Spirillum Pasteurella Brucella Yersinia Francisella Haemophilus Bordetella
(c) Enteric rods	Escherichia (and related coliform bacteria) Salmonella Shigella Klebsiella Proteus Vibrio Pseudomonas

DESCRIPTIONS OF THE PRINCIPAL GROUPS OF BACTERIA

A key to the principal groups of bacteria is presented in Table 3–1. Three major groups can be recognized on the basis of the mechanism of movement and the character of the cell wall: myxobacteria, spirochetes, and eubacteria.

Myxobacteria

The myxobacteria are thin-walled, flexible, rod-shaped organisms. They propel themselves along solid surfaces by an unknown gliding mechanism: no motil-

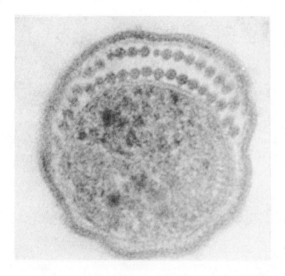

Figure 3–1. Cross section of a large spirochete, showing the location of the fibrils of the axial filament between the cell membrane and the cell wall (X 258,000). (Reproduced, with permission, from Listgarten MA, Socransky SS: Electron microscopy of axial fibrils, outer envelope and cell division of certain oval spirochetes. J Bacteriol 88:1087, 1964.)

ity organelles are detectable. There are no human pathogens in this group.

Spirochetes

The spirochetes are thin-walled, flexible, helical rods. They propel themselves by undulation of an axial filament which is wound about the cell body. The axial filament is formed from 2 tufts of polar flagella lying between the cell membrane and cell wall (Fig 3–1); it can be freed by enzymatic digestion of the outer envelope (Fig 3–2). Three genera contain important pathogens for man: Treponema, Borrelia, and Leptospira (see Chapter 20).

Eubacteria

The eubacteria include stalked, budding, and mycelial organisms as well as simple unicellular forms. Since there are no pathogens among the stalked and budding forms, they will not be considered further here.

A. Mycelial Forms (Actinomycetes): The mycelial (branching filamentous) growth of these gram-positive organisms confers on them a superficial resemblance to the fungi, strengthened by the presence—in higher forms—of external asexual spores or conidia. The resemblance ends there, however. The actinomycetes are prokaryotic organisms, whereas the fungi are eukaryotic, and in the lower actinomycetes (eg, mycobacteria; Fig 3–3) the mycelium breaks up into typical unicellular bacteria. In one group, the Actinoplanes, sporangia are formed which rupture to release flagellated bacilli. The bacilli ultimately lose their flagella and initiate new mycelial growth.

1. Mycobacteria—Members of the genus Mycobacterium, which includes the agents of tuberculosis, are acid-fast organisms: they are relatively impermeable to dyes, but once stained they resist decolorization with acidified organic solvents. Their acid-fastness, along with their tendency to form a pellicle at the surface of aqueous media, is due to their high content of lipids: lipids may account for up to 40% of the dry weight of

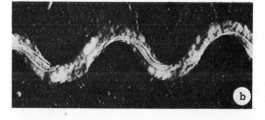

Figure 3–2. *Treponema pallidum.* Electron micrographs showing axial filament. *(a)* Without digestion. *(b)* After 20 minutes of tryptic digestion. *(c)* After 10 minutes of peptic digestion. (Courtesy of Swain RHA: J Pathol Bacteriol 69:117, 1955.)

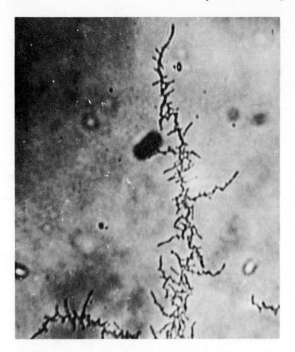

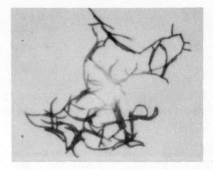

Figure 3—4. Early growth, a species of Nocardia (× 490). (Courtesy of Ordal EJ: *The Biology of Bacteria,* 3rd ed. Heath, 1948.)

Figure 3—3. The surface growth on agar of *Mycobacterium fortuitum* (× 600). Photomicrograph by Gordon R and Lechevalier H. (From Stanier RY, Doudoroff M, Adelberg EA: *The Microbial World,* 3rd ed. Copyright © 1970. By permission of Prentice-Hall, Inc, Englewood Cliffs, NJ.)

the cell and up to 60% of the dry weight of the cell wall. They include true waxes along with glycolipids. The only other bacteria containing lipids of these types are corynebacteria and certain nocardiae, which also tend to be acid-fast. The mycobacteria are characterized further in Chapter 17.

2. Nocardia and Actinomyces—These 2 genera form much more advanced mycelia than do the myco-

bacteria, but they too tend to break up in older cultures to form irregularly shaped cells. A typical young mycelium of Nocardia is shown in Fig 3—4.

Actinomyces species are anaerobes; Nocardia species are aerobes, and many are acid-fast. Both groups include pathogens for man.

3. Higher actinomycetes—Several genera (eg, Streptomyces, Micromonospora) remain fully mycelial, reproducing by externally borne asexual spores, or conidia (Fig 3—5). Although their normal habitat is the soil, some Streptomyces species may contaminate wounds or scratches and initiate abscesses similar to those caused by nocardiae.

B. Unicellular Forms:

1. Forms lacking cell walls (mycoplasmas)—The mycoplasmas (Fig 3—6) are highly pleomorphic organisms, resembling the L forms which are induced in ordinary bacteria by removal of the cell wall. Unlike L forms, however, mycoplasmas never produce walled cells, and there are no antigenic relationships between mycoplasmas and the L forms derived from ordinary

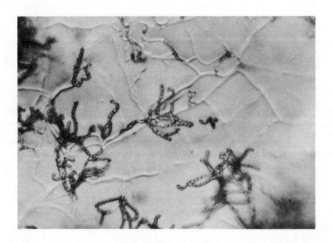

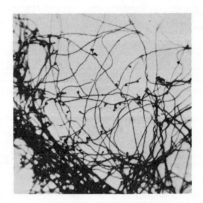

Figure 3—5. Streptomycetaceae. *Left:* Streptomyces, showing chains of aerial conidia (× 780). *Right:* Micromonospora, showing single conidia on short lateral branches. (From Stanier RY, Doudoroff M, Adelberg EA: *The Microbial World,* 2nd ed. Copyright © 1963. By permission of Prentice-Hall, Inc, Englewood Cliffs, NJ.)

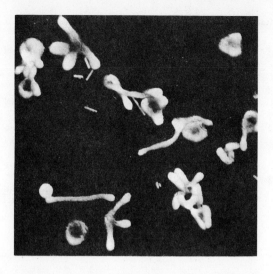

Figure 3—6. Electron micrograph of cells of a member of the Mycoplasma group, the agent of bronchopneumonia in the rat (X 1960). (Reproduced, with permission, from Klieneberger-Nobel E, Cuckow FW: A study of organisms of the pleuropneumonia group by electron microscopy. J Gen Microbiol 12:99, 1955.)

bacteria. The mycoplasmas, which include 2 species pathogenic for man, are described in Chapter 23.

2. Forms possessing cell walls—These bacteria include spheres (cocci), straight rods (bacilli), and helical forms (spirilla), as illustrated in Fig 3—7.

a. Obligate intracellular parasites—Two groups—the rickettsiae (genera Rickettsia and Coxiella) and the smaller chlamydiae (genus Chlamydia)—are obligate intracellular parasites and include pathogens for man. They are gram-negative. The basis of their obligate parasitism is unknown, although the chlamydiae appear to be unable to generate ATP by their own metabolism and may depend on the host for energy-rich compounds. They are described more fully in Chapters 21 and 22.

b. Free-living forms—The majority of the bacteria pathogenic for man fall into this group. The medically important genera are grouped in Table 3—1 according to their gram-staining properties, their morphology, and (in the case of the gram-negative rods) whether or not they normally inhabit the intestinal tract of man and other mammals. They are discussed in detail in Chapters 14—19.

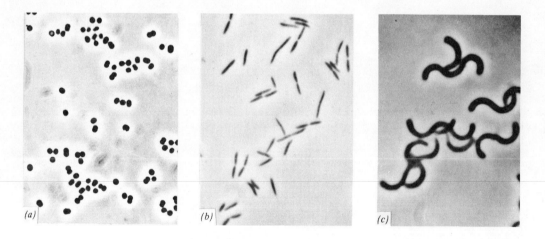

(a) *(b)* *(c)*

Figure 3—7. The cell shapes that occur among unicellular true bacteria. *(a)* Coccus. *(b)* Rod. *(c)* Spiral. (Phase contrast, X 1500.) (From Stanier RY, Doudoroff M, Adelberg EA: *The Microbial World,* 3rd ed. Copyright © 1970. By permission of Prentice-Hall, Inc, Englewood Cliffs, NJ.)

General References

Books

Ainsworth GC, Sneath PHA (editors): *Microbial Classification: Twelfth Symposium of the Society for General Microbiology.* Cambridge Univ Press, 1962.

Alexander M: *Microbial Ecology.* Wiley, 1971.

Buchanan RE, Gibbons NE (editors): *Bergey's Manual of Determinative Bacteriology,* 8th ed. Williams & Wilkins, 1974.

Skerman BVD: *A Guide to the Identification of the Genera of Bacteria,* 2nd ed. Williams & Wilkins, 1967.

Sneath PHA, Sokal RR: *The Principles and Practice of Numerical Classification.* Freeman, 1973.

Stanier RY, Ingraham JL, Adelberg EA: *The Microbial World,* 4th ed. Prentice-Hall, 1976.

Articles & Reviews

Jones D, Sneath PHA: Genetic transfer and bacterial taxonomy. Bacteriol Rev 34:40, 1970.

Mandel M: New approaches to bacterial taxonomy: Perspectives and prospects. Annu Rev Microbiol 23:239, 1969.

Ormsbee RA: Rickettsiae (as organisms). Annu Rev Microbiol 23:275, 1969.

Razin S: Structure and function in mycoplasmas. Annu Rev Microbiol 23:317, 1969.

4...
Microbial Genetics

THE PHYSICAL BASIS OF HEREDITY

In formulating a general concept of the mechanism of inheritance, 2 basic biologic phenomena must be accounted for: **heredity**, or stability of type (eg, the progeny formed by the division of a unicellular organism are identical with the parent cell); and the rare occurrence of **heritable variations**. Genetic and cytologic analyses of plant and animal cells have established that the physical basis for both of these phenomena is the **gene** (the genetic determinant controlling the properties of organisms). The genes are located along the thread-like **chromosomes** in the cell nucleus. The chromosomes undergo duplication (replication) prior to cell division; when the cell divides, each cell receives an identical set of chromosomes and therefore an identical set of genes.

This duplication is usually an exact process, which accounts for heredity; any given gene, however, has a low probability of **mutation**, and mutation accounts for variation. Mutated genes are usually stable and are replicated in the new form in subsequent generations. A gene mutation thus causes a heritable change in one or more properties of the organism.

In eukaryotic and prokaryotic cells (see Chapter 1), the chemical substance of the chromosome which is responsible for both gene replication and gene function is deoxyribonucleic acid (DNA). In viruses, it can be either DNA or RNA (ribonucleic acid). One of the basic problems of genetics is thus to explain gene replication and function in terms of nucleic acid structure. In the following sections this problem will be discussed with particular reference to the **prokaryotic** chromosome of the bacterium *Escherichia coli*. In general, however, the material to be presented applies equally to the **eukaryotic** microorganisms: protozoa, fungi, slime molds, and algae. The exceptions are as follows:

(1) Every eukaryotic cell contains several different chromosomes in its nucleus. Following chromosomal replication, nuclear division takes place by **mitosis**, such that each daughter nucleus receives a copy of each chromosome.

(2) Sexuality in eukaryotic organisms involves **cell fusion**, followed by the fusion of 2 haploid nuclei. (A haploid nucleus contains one set of chromosomes.) Nuclear fusion produces a diploid nucleus containing 2 identical set of chromosomes.

(3) A diploid nucleus may undergo **meiosis**, in which a reductive division first produces 2 haploid nuclei and a mitotic division then produces 4 haploid nuclei. At the start of meiosis, the homologous chromosomes of the diploid nucleus pair and exchange segments. This process of "crossing over," together with the random distribution of homologues to the daughter nuclei, is the basis of **genetic recombination** in eukaryotic organisms. All plants, animals, and higher protists exhibit classical mendelian inheritance as a result of the meiotic process.

(4) A eukaryotic microorganism may go through meiosis immediately after nuclear fusion, so that the organism remains haploid throughout most of its life cycle. In some eukaryotic organisms, however, meiosis may be postponed for many cell generations, so that the organism is diploid throughout a major part of its life cycle. Many fungi, for example, are capable of such alteration between haploid and diploid phases of growth.

THE PROKARYOTIC CHROMOSOME

Chromosome Structure

The electron micrograph in Fig 2–7 shows the bacterial nucleus to be a packed mass of DNA fibers when seen in cross section. When bacterial DNA is extracted and purified by ordinary chemical methods, a preparation is obtained having an average molecular weight of about 5×10^6. In the intact cell, however, the bacterial nucleus consists of a single continuous DNA molecule with a molecular weight of about 3×10^9 which is sheared into several hundred fragments by the extraction procedure. Using gentler methods, Cairns has been able to extract the unbroken chromosome of *E coli* (Fig 4–1). Cairns's pictures show the bacterial chromosome to be a continuous DNA structure approximately 1 mm long. The structure of the DNA molecule is now well known through the work of Watson and Crick; it consists of a double helix made up of 2 complementary polynucleotide strands in each of which purine and pyrimidine bases are arranged along a backbone made of alternating deoxyribose and

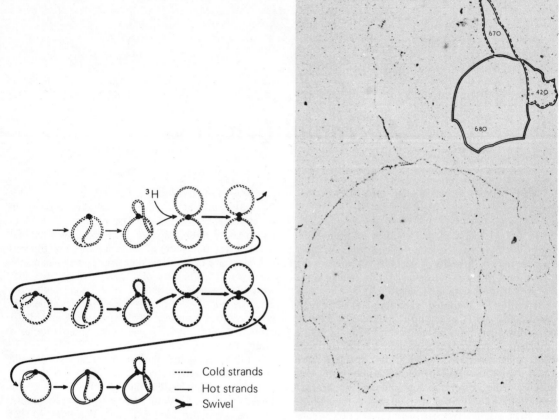

Figure 4—1. Replication of the circular chromosome of *E coli*. **Left:** Diagram showing that introduction of radioactive tritium (^{3}H) toward the end of a replication cycle would lead, 2 cycles later, to a chromosome labeled as found experimentally. Replication begins at the "swivel" and proceeds counterclockwise along the 2 complementary strands of the DNA double helix. **Right:** Autoradiograph of a chromosome extracted from an Hfr cell of *E coli* 2 generations after addition of ^{3}H. Grain counts per unit length in the regions indicated by solid lines are double those in the regions indicated by dashed lines. The numbers in the insert are the lengths (in micrometers) between the 2 forks. (Courtesy of Cairns J: Cold Spring Harbor Symp Quant Biol 28:43, 1963.)

phosphate groups (Fig 4—2). The 2 strands are held together by hydrogen bonds between neighboring bases; the stereochemistry is such that hydrogen bonds can be formed only between adenine and thymine (A-T pair) and between guanine and cytosine (G-C pair) (Fig 4—3). Thus, a sequence of bases along one strand such as G-C-C-A-C-T-C-A must be matched on the opposite strand by the complementary sequence of C-G-G-T-G-A-G-T.

The chromosome of *E coli,* with a molecular weight of 3×10^9, contains about 5×10^6 base pairs. It has been shown both by genetic analysis and by Cairns's photographs to be a circular structure.

Chromosome Replication

In viruses, prokaryotic cells, and eukaryotic cells, DNA has been shown to replicate according to the semiconservative mechanism first proposed by Watson and Crick. The complementary strands separate, each then acting as a **template** on which is assembled a complementary strand by the enzymatic polymerization of nucleotide subunits. The sequence of bases in the new

strand is rigidly dictated by the hydrogen bonding possibilities described above, ie, wherever the template carries adenine the new strand will acquire a thymine, etc. Replication thus leads to the formation of 2 new double helices, each identical with the original double helix.

The bacterial chromosome replicates sequentially along the entire structure, starting at a particular site called the **replicator**. In order for chromosomal replication to keep in step with cell division, some type of regulatory system must exist. It has been postulated that a gene elsewhere on the chromosome produces a regulator substance, or "initiator." Replication would then start when a molecule of initiator combines with a replicator. Control of replication, according to this model, would involve activation or inhibition of initiator formation or action (or both).

According to a model proposed by Jacob and Brenner, for which considerable evidence has accumulated, the enzymes of replication form a complex which is fixed at a specific site in the cell membrane. The replication cycle begins with the attachment of

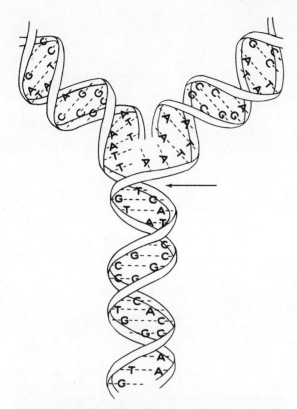

Figure 4—2. Structure and replication of DNA according to the Watson and Crick model. The vertical double strand is unwinding at the point indicated by the arrow, and the 2 arms have acted as templates for the synthesis of complementary strands. Synthesis is proceeding downward along the vertical double strand.

the replicator to the complex; the chromosome then moves past the complex, unwinding and replicating as it goes (Fig 4—4). Separation of the 2 daughter chromosomes is accomplished by localized membrane synthesis; later, a transverse cell wall will form between the DNA attachment sites.

In Figs 4—1, 4—2, and 4—4, replication is shown to proceed in one direction along the duplex molecule of DNA. Such unidirectional replication has indeed been verified for some circular DNA viruses and is consistent with observations of DNA transfer between conjugating bacteria (Figs 4—11 and 4—12). It has recently been shown, however, that vegetative chromosomal replication in several species of bacteria, including *E coli,* is **bidirectional**: 2 replicating forks may move away simultaneously from the replicator site, meeting approximately halfway around the chromosome. It is not yet clear how to reconcile these newer findings with Cairns's autoradiographs. Perhaps the cell is capable of both types of replication (unidirectional and bidirectional) according to the growth conditions or the genetic state of the cell.

In a bacterial cell, several different genetic (DNA) structures may be present and replicating independently at the same time; eg, chromosome, sex factor,

and bacteriophage particles. The term **replicon** has been coined to describe an independent unit of replication.

Chromosome Function

The chromosome, consisting of about 5×10^6 nucleotide pairs, is subdivided into segments, each of which determines the amino acid sequence and hence the structure of a discrete protein. These proteins, as enzymes and as components of membranes and other cell structures, determine all the properties of the organism. A segment of chromosomal DNA which determines the structure of a discrete protein is called a unit of genetic function or a **gene**. The mechanism by which the sequence of nucleotides in a gene determines the sequence of amino acids in a protein is as follows:

(1) An RNA polymerase forms a single polyribonucleotide strand, called "messenger RNA" (mRNA), using DNA as a template. The mRNA has a nucleotide sequence complementary to one of the strands in the DNA double helix.

(2) Amino acids are enzymatically activated and transferred to specific adaptor molecules of RNA, called "transfer RNA" (tRNA). Each adaptor molecule has at one end a triplet of bases complementary to a triplet of bases on mRNA, and at the other end its specific acid.

(3) mRNA and tRNA come together on the surface of the ribosome. As each tRNA finds its complementary nucleotide triplet on mRNA, the amino acid which it carries is put into peptide linkage with the amino acid of the preceding (neighboring) tRNA molecule. The ribosome moves along the mRNA, the polypeptide growing sequentially until the entire mRNA molecule has been translated into a corresponding sequence of amino acids. This concept is diagrammed in Fig 4—5.

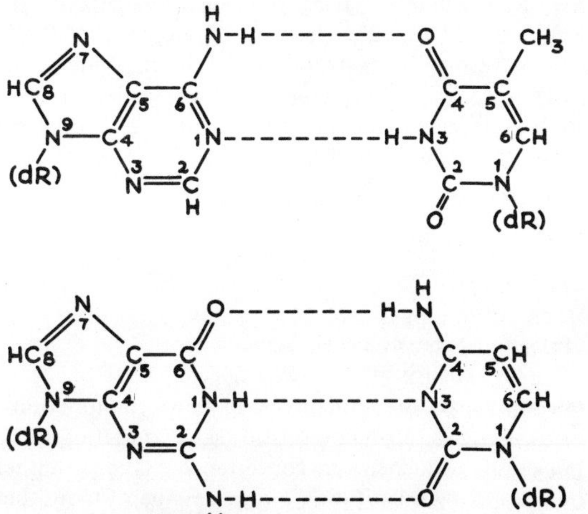

Figure 4—3. Normal base-pairing in DNA. Hydrogen bonds are indicated by dotted lines. (dR = deoxyribose of the sugar-phosphate backbone of DNA.)

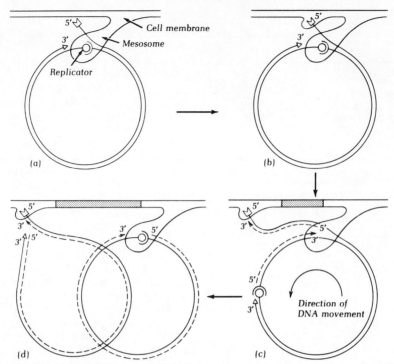

Figure 4—4. Replication of the bacterial chromosome, according to the model of Jacob and Brenner. *(a)* The chromosome is attached to a mesosome at the replicator site, which serves as a swivel. One of the strands is broken. *(b)* The 5′ end of the broken strand attaches to a new site in the membrane. *(c)* The chromosome rotates counterclockwise past the mesosomal attachment site, at which is fixed the replicating enzyme system. Newly synthesized strands are shown as dashed lines. The attachment sites are separated by localized membrane synthesis (shown by shaded area). *(d)* The cycle of replication has been completed. The final step will be the joining of the free ends of one strand of the new chromosome (solid line). (From Stanier RY, Doudoroff M, Adelberg EA: *The Microbial World,* 3rd ed. Copyright © 1970. By permission of Prentice-Hall, Inc, Englewood Cliffs, NJ.)

Thus, the nucleotide sequence of the DNA gene represents a code which determines, through the mediation of mRNA, the structure of a specific protein. In many cases such proteins act as subunits which polymerize to form active enzymes; many high molecular weight enzymes are now known to be made up of identical subunits having molecular weights in the range of 10^4 to 10^5. The triplet code requires that a gene governing the formation of a protein of molecular weight 30,000 should contain on the order of 1000 nucleotide pairs; the chromosome of *E coli* thus has sufficient DNA for 5000 such genes.

MUTATION

Mutation at the Molecular Level

Any change in the nucleotide sequence of a gene which changes the structure—and hence the function—of a specific protein constitutes a mutation. The nucleotide sequence can conceivably change in either of 2 ways: by substitution of one base-pair for another as the result of an error during replication; or by breakages of the sugar-phosphate backbone of DNA with subsequent deletion or inversion of the segment between the breaks, or insertion of a new segment.

A. Sequence Changes Due to Base-Pair Substitution: Many mutations are capable of reversion; ie, the original base sequence can be restored. There is ample evidence that most revertible mutations involve only a single base-pair change, resulting from a replication error. The position of such "point mutations" can be accurately mapped within the structural gene by crossing 2 mutants and measuring the frequency with which they recombine to produce a nonmutant ("wild type") sequence. (See Recombination, below, and pertinent sections in Chapter 9.) When this is done, all point mutations are found to recombine with each other and to occupy positions along a one-dimensional genetic map.

1. Spontaneous mutation—As pointed out by Watson and Crick in their first paper on the structure of DNA, the most likely basis of spontaneous point mutations is a rare tautomeric shift of electrons in a purine or pyrimidine base. For example, thymine normally exists in the keto state, in which state it forms a hydrogen bond with adenine. If, however, thymine exists in the rare enol state at the moment that it is acting as template during DNA replication, it will form a hydrogen bond with guanine instead (Fig 4—6). The new strand will then carry a guanine in place of adenine, and in all future replications a guanine and cytosine (G-C) pair will be formed where the original

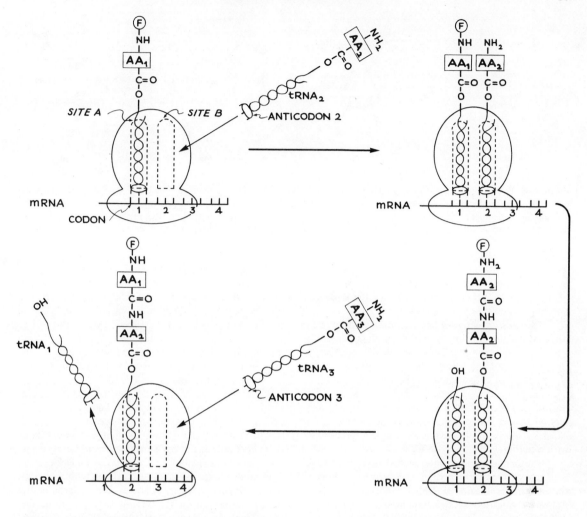

Figure 4–5. Four stages in the lengthening of a polypeptide chain on the surface of a 70S ribosome. ***Top left:*** A tRNA molecule, bearing the anticodon complementary to codon 1 at one end and AA_1 at the other, binds to site A. AA_1 is attached to the tRNA through its carboxyl group; its amino nitrogen bears a formyl group (F). ***Top right:*** A tRNA molecule, bearing AA_2, binds to site B; its anticodon is complementary to codon 2. ***Bottom right:*** An enzyme complex catalyses the transfer of AA_1 to the amino group of AA_2, forming a peptide bond. (Note that transfer in the opposite direction is blocked by the prior formylation of the amino group of AA_1.) ***Bottom left:*** The ribosome moves to the right, so that sites A and B are now opposite codons 2 and 3; in the process, tRNA$_1$ is displaced and tRNA$_2$ moves to site A. Site B is again vacant and is ready to accept tRNA$_3$ bearing AA_3. (When the polypeptide is completed and released, the formyl group is enzymatically removed.) (Redrawn and reproduced by permission of Stanier RY, Doudoroff M, Adelberg EA: *The Microbial World,* 3rd ed. Copyright © 1970. Prentice-Hall, Inc, Englewood Cliffs, NJ.)

DNA carried an adenine and thymine (A-T) pair.

Any of the 4 bases is capable of tautomerization at a rate compatible with the observed rates of spontaneous mutation, and it is possible that many spontaneous mutations have occurred by this mechanism. The evidence comes from experiments in which spontaneous mutations have been reversed by mutagenic agents of the types discussed below.

2. Induced mutation—Several types of mutagenic agents apparently act by greatly increasing the rate of tautomerization of the bases, or by otherwise permitting hydrogen bond formation with a "wrong" base during replication. For example, 5-bromouracil is mutagenic because it is incorporated into DNA in place of thymine and tautomerizes to the enol form more frequently than thymine. 2-Aminopurine acts similarly, being incorporated in place of adenine. It is capable of forming hydrogen bonds with cytosine in either of its tautomeric forms, and thus can cause G-C pairs to replace A-T pairs.

Certain mutagens act by chemically altering the bases in DNA in such a way as to promote a replication error. Nitrous acid, for example, deaminates adenine, guanine, or cytosine. The deaminated product of adenine (hypoxanthine) forms hydrogen bonds with cytosine instead of thymine, causing an A-T to be replaced by G-C at a later replication; the deaminated product of cytosine (uracil) forms hydrogen bonds

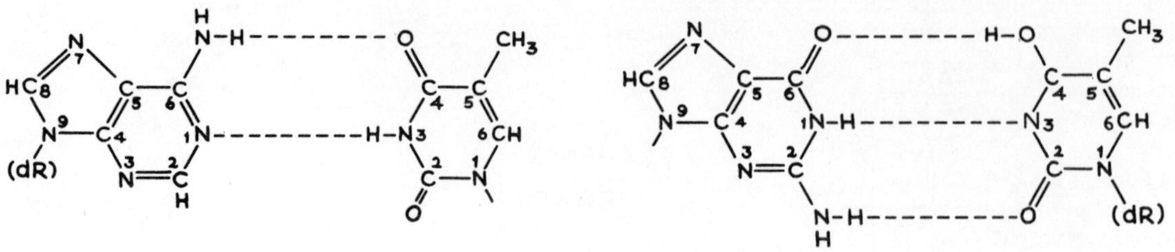

Adenine | Thymine (keto form)

Guanine | Thymine (enol form)

Figure 4—6. Base pairing in DNA. *Left:* Thymine in its normal (keto) state forms 2 hydrogen bonds with adenine. *Right:* Thymine may exist in the enol state as the result of a rare tautomeric shift of electrons. In this state, thymine forms 3 hydrogen bonds with guanine. If the tautomeric shift occurred during replication, guanine would be incorporated into DNA in place of adenine, and a G-C pair would ultimately replace an A-T pair in the nucleotide sequence. (dR = deoxyribose of the sugar-phosphate backbone of DNA.)

with adenine instead of guanine, causing a G-C pair to be replaced by A-T at a later replication. (Deamination of guanine to xanthine does not change the hydrogen bonding possibilities.)

The most effective chemical mutagens known are certain alkylating agents, of which ethylmethanesulfonate is a good example. These agents alkylate the purine and pyrimidine bases at several positions: eg, the N-3 position of cytosine and the O-6 and N-7 positions of guanine. Although guanine alkylated at the N-7 position pairs normally, N^3-methylcytosine and O^6-methylguanine mispair in a nonspecific manner, and N-3 alkylation of cytosine has been shown to correlate with mutation in a virus system.

The mutagen proflavine (and other acridine dyes) acts in a different way. Proflavine intercalates between the stacked base-pairs of DNA in such a way as to cause the **insertion** or **deletion** of a single base-pair during replication. This shifts the "reading frame" of the coded message from that point on, forming an entirely new set of triplets. For example, if a portion of the correct message reads --/AGG/CTC/CAA/GCC/GAT/TCG/--, deletion of the fourth base changes the message to --AGG/TCC/AAG/CCG/ATT/CG--. This mechanism of mutation has been proved by showing that a second proflavine-induced mutation near the first one can reverse the effect of the first by restoring the reading frame. In the above hypothetical case, imagine that a second proflavine treatment causes insertion of a G between the seventh and eighth bases. The new sequence is now --AGG/TCC/AGA/GCC/GAT/TCG/--. Note that the final message differs from the wildtype sequence only in the second and third triplets; if these code for amino acids that are not critical to the functioning of the protein produced by this gene, wildtype activity will have been restored. Either of the proflavine-induced mutations alone, however, produces a reading frame shift leading to "missense triplets" throughout the remainder of the gene and thus to the mutant state.

A mutation which restores the function of a gene inactivated by a previous mutation is called a **suppressor mutation**. The above situation is an example of an **intragenic** suppressor mutation. Suppressor mutations can also occur at other places on the chromosome (**extragenic** suppressors). The extragenic suppressor loci are genes which code for components of the translation system, such as tRNA; by mutation, they alter one or another component so as to compensate for the original coding error in the DNA. For example, one such suppressor mutation has been shown to act by altering the anticodon in serine tRNA.

Radiations (x-rays, ultraviolet light, etc) are commonly used to induce mutations. The mechanism of radiation-induced mutation is not well understood. It has been established, however, that ultraviolet light (UV) acts principally by causing covalent bond formation between neighboring pyrimidines in DNA. Such "pyrimidine dimers," if not excised or hydrolyzed by repair enzyme systems, cause gaps to appear in the complementary strands produced by replication. The newly replicated duplexes thus contain a dimer opposite a gap at each site of original UV damage and must be repaired in order to function correctly. Such repair is accomplished by recombination between sister duplexes whose UV-induced lesions are at different positions; an undamaged chromosome is produced by recombining good segments of the damaged ones. It is during this recombinational repair process that the mutations attributable to UV apparently occur.

The second most frequent products of the action of UV on DNA are hydrated pyrimidines, in which a molecule of water has been added across the 4–5 double bond. Polynucleotides containing hydrated pyrimidines have been directly shown to cause copying errors in replication experiments in vitro.

B. Sequence Change Due to Breakage of Sugar-Phosphate Linkages: When a large number of spontaneous or induced mutations are studied, many are found which never revert. When a nonreverting mutation is mapped, it is usually found to overlap (fail to recombine with) a series of point-mutation sites. The mutation has thus affected a sequence of bases rather than a single base-pair, suggesting that **deletion** of a segment of DNA has occurred. In many cases, deletions can be directly visualized by allowing "heteroduplexes" to form between single-stranded DNA molecules prepared from the wildtype strain and the deletion mutant: in the electron microscope, a single-stranded loop of wildtype DNA is seen at the site of the deletion.

Mutation at the Cellular Level

The set of genetic determinants carried by a cell is called its **genotype.** The observable properties of the cell are called its **phenotype.** A gene mutation can only be recognized if it brings about an observable phenotypic change; such changes may be described in terms of gross morphology or physiology, but in most cases it is now possible to define the phenotypic change in terms of the loss or gain of a particular protein or its function (eg, a specific enzyme or its activity). For convenience, we will discuss phenotypic change in terms of enzyme activity only.

A. Phenotypic Expression in Uninucleate Cells:

1. Gain mutations—When a mutation confers on the cell the ability to synthesize an active enzyme, there is no detectable lag between the time of mutation and the beginning of enzyme synthesis.

2. Loss mutations—Most cell proteins are stable. In *E coli,* for example, there is no protein turnover in actively growing cells, and a turnover of only about 5% per hour in resting cells. Thus, when a mutation causes the synthesis of an enzyme to stop, the cell remains enzymatically active. If the cell continues to grow, however, the amount of preexisting enzyme per cell is halved at each generation. After 6 generations, the progeny of the original mutant will each have less than 1% of the wildtype enzyme level.

This **phenotypic lag** has certain practical consequences. For example, the sensitivity of bacteria to attack by viruses (bacteriophages, or "phages") depends upon the presence in the cell wall of specific receptor sites. The mutation to phage resistance reflects the loss of synthesis of phage receptor. If such mutations are induced, the phage resistance phenotype will not be detected until a sufficient number of generations has taken place to dilute out the original receptors. In other words, there is a **delay in phenotypic expression.**

B. Phenotypic Expression in Multinucleate Cells:

1. Gain mutations—Many microbial cells are multinucleate. *E coli,* for example, has an average of about 4 nuclei per cell during exponential growth. When a gain mutation occurs in a multinucleate cell, the mutant nucleus synthesizes the new active enzyme and phenotypic expression is immediate. A gain mutation is thus **dominant**; the active form ("allele") of the gene is expressed, and the inactive allele is not.

2. Loss mutations—When, in a multinucleate cell, a loss mutation occurs, only the mutant nucleus ceases to make active enzyme while the other nuclei continue. The loss mutation is thus **recessive** and is not expressed in the original cell. After several generations, however, the mutant nucleus will have segregated into a separate cell (Fig 4–7), and this segregant cell will be genetically pure for the mutant state. Phenotypic

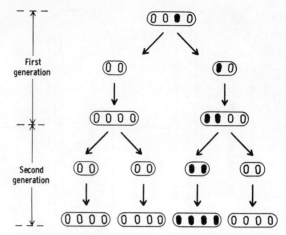

Figure 4–7. Segregation of a mutant nucleus. The nucleus containing the mutation is shown in black. If the mutation occurs in a cell with 4 nuclei, 2 generations are required before a pure mutant cell is produced.

expression of a loss mutation must thus await both phenotypic lag and nuclear segregation.

Mutation at the Population Level

A. Mutant Frequency and Mutation Rate:

1. Relation between frequency and rate—The proportion of mutants in a cell population is the **mutant frequency.** Frequencies ranging from 1×10^{-5} to 1×10^{-10} are commonly observed when individual phenotypes are considered. The frequency of mutants in a given culture reflects 3 independent parameters: (1) The probability that a cell will mutate during a given interval, such as a generation. This is the **mutation rate.** (2) The distribution in time of mutational events over the growth period of the culture. For example, exceptionally early mutations will produce extremely large **clones** of mutant progeny. (A clone constitutes the total progeny of a single cell.) (3) The growth rates of the mutant cells relative to the parental type.

2. Measurement of mutation rate—The mutation rate can be related to average mutant frequencies by a complex equation which takes into account all of the above parameters. However, there are methods which permit a **direct estimation** of the number of mutations which have occurred in a culture (as opposed to the number of mutant cells in the culture) and thus permit a simple estimation of the mutation rate.

The mutation rate is commonly expressed in units of "mutations per cell per generation"; in other words, the probability that a mutation will occur during the event of a single cell doubling in size and dividing to become 2 cells. When one cell goes through 2 successive generations to become 4 cells, for example, 3 such "cell-doubling events" occur (Fig 4–7). In general terms, when N_0 cells increase to form N_1 cells, the number of doubling events is equal to $N_1 - N_0$. The mutation rate **(a)** is thus expressed by the simple formula,

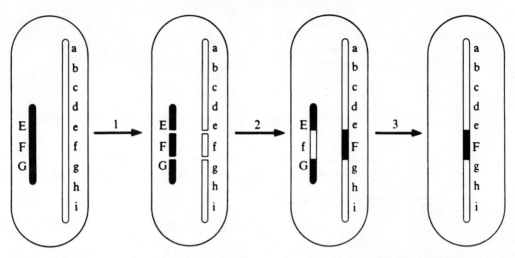

Figure 4—8. The model of genetic recombination by breakage and reunion. (From Stanier RY, Doudoroff M, Adelberg EA: *The Microbial World,* 2nd ed. Copyright © 1963. By permission of Prentice-Hall, Inc, Englewood Cliffs, NJ.)

$$a = \frac{M}{N_1 - N_0}$$

where M = the number of mutations occurring during the growth of N_0 cells to form N_1 cells.

B. Selection:

1. Relative selection—Although any given type of mutant may be present in a culture at very low frequency (eg, 10^{-6}), small differences between the mutant and parent in either growth rate or death rate can lead to tremendous population shifts. For example, consider a culture containing 10^7 penicillin-sensitive (pen-s) cells and 10 penicillin-resistant (pen-r) cells. If the pen-s cells have a generation (doubling) time of 60 minutes and the pen-r cells a generation time of 50 minutes, then after 3 transfers of the culture, permitting 30 generations of the pen-s cells, the frequency of pen-r cells will have changed from 1×10^{-6} to 1×10^{-4} — a 100-fold increase. After 3 more transfers, 1% of the culture will be penicillin-resistant.

2. Absolute selection—In medical or microbiologic practice, microbial populations are commonly subjected to absolute selection, either consciously or unconsciously. For example, growth of the above-described culture in the presence of penicillin will lead to the death of all pen-s cells, so that the final culture will be 100% pen-r after one transfer. Since most mutants occur in cultures at very low frequencies, absolute selection is generally employed for their detection. The usual practice is to plate the culture on an agar medium which will permit only the sought-for mutant type to form colonies.

INTERCELLULAR TRANSFER & GENETIC RECOMBINATION IN BACTERIA

The Formation of Bacterial Zygotes

In eukaryotic organisms, the diploid cell formed by the fusion of 2 haploid sexual cells (gametes) is called the **zygote**. Zygotes may also be formed in bacteria, but true cell fusion does not take place; instead, part of the genetic material of a donor cell is transferred to a recipient cell, and the recipient thus becomes diploid for only a part of its genetic complement. In the partial zygote, the genetic fragment from the donor is called the **exogenote** and the genetic complement of the recipient is called the **endogenote**. Exogenote and endogenote usually pair and recombine immediately after transfer. This recombinational step occurs by breakage and reunion of the paired genotes (Fig 4–8).

During succeeding nuclear and cell divisions, the **recombinant chromosome** is segregated into a single haploid cell. This cell can be experimentally detected by plating the partial zygotes on a selective medium on which only recombinants can grow.

The 3 processes by which recombination occurs in bacteria differ from each other primarily in the mechanism of the transfer process. These processes—transformation, transduction, and plasmid-mediated conjugation—are briefly summarized in the following sections.

Restriction & Modification

Bacterial cells of many species contain 2 enzymes with complementary functions. One enzyme **modifies** all the DNA in the cell by methylating bases at a few specific sites on the DNA. The other enzyme degrades all DNA which is not so modified; this process is called **restriction.**

The degrading enzymes are called **restriction endonucleases**; the DNA site recognized by a particular restriction endonuclease is a specific sequence of 6–8 base pairs, which is a palindrome: that is, the sequence reads the same in both directions, starting from the $3'$ end of each strand. For example, the sequence recognized by the restriction endonuclease of *E coli* called EcoR1 recognizes the sequence

```
  ↓    *
- - G A A T T C - -
- - C T T A A G - -
         *   ↑
```

cutting it at the symmetric sites indicated by the arrows. The asterisks represent the sites which are methylated by the modifying enzyme of *E coli,* thus protecting the sequence from endonuclease attack.

When a zygote is formed by the transfer of DNA between bacterial strains with different specificities of restriction and modification, the DNA which penetrates the recipient will be rapidly degraded in most of the cells. In a few cells, however (10^{-7} to 10^{-2} of the zygotes), the exogenote may escape restriction and recombination can take place.

For example, a conjugation between *E coli* strain B and *E coli* strain K12 yields recombinants at an extremely low frequency. From such crosses, however, a few recombinants have been isolated which are K12 strains carrying strain B's genes for modification and restriction. Such recombinants show high frequencies of recombination with *E coli* strain B.

Restriction and modification also affect the transfer of phages from one strain of bacterium to another (see p 104).

TRANSFORMATION

In transformation, the recipient cell takes up soluble DNA released from the donor cell. In some cases, transforming DNA is released spontaneously; eg, it is found in the extracellular slime of certain Neisseria species. Usually, however, it is necessary to extract the DNA from donor cells by chemical procedures and to protect it from degradation by DNases.

Transformation occurs only in bacteria which are capable of taking up high molecular weight DNA from the medium. Originally discovered in the pneumococcus, it was subsequently discovered to occur in a number of other bacterial species, both gram-positive and gram-negative. Most studies have been carried out on the pneumococcus, Haemophilus, and Bacillus; more recently, transformation has been found to occur in *E coli* in the presence of high concentrations of calcium ion. In some species, transformable cells are capable of taking up DNA from any source, although they form genetic recombinants only if the donor is a closely related organism. This specificity presumably reflects the requirement of endogenote and exogenote to **pair** before exchanges can take place: pairing of DNA molecules demands close homology of nucleotide sequences.

Little is known about the mechanism of DNA uptake. The ability to take up DNA is called **competence**; the state of competence appears only at certain stages in the division cycle or in the culture, and only a fraction of the population is usually competent at any one time. Competent cells do not take up DNA molecules of molecular weight less than about 4×10^5; double-stranded DNA is taken up much more efficiently than single-stranded DNA.

During penetration, one strand of the donor DNA is integrated with recipient DNA and the other strand is degraded. The recombinant chromosome thus formed consists of double-stranded DNA of the recipient in which a short region of one of the 2 strands has been replaced by a strand of donor DNA.

TRANSDUCTION BY BACTERIOPHAGE

In transduction, a fragment of donor chromosome is carried to the recipient by a temperate bacteriophage which has been produced in the donor cell. (A temperate phage is one capable of becoming prophage; see Chapter 9.) As in transformation, only a small fragment of the donor's chromosome is transferred to the recipient. Transduction occurs in many bacterial genera. First discovered in Salmonella, it has since been shown to occur in the gram-negative organisms Escherichia, Shigella, Pseudomonas, Vibrio, and Proteus as well as in the gram-positive organisms Staphylococcus and Bacillus. Transduction may be generalized or restricted: in **generalized transduction,** the phage has a roughly equal chance of carrying any segment of the donor's chromosome; in **restricted transduction,** the transducing particles carry only those segments which are immediately adjacent to the site of prophage attachment.

Restricted Transduction

The mechanism of prophage attachment is shown in Fig 9–7, for phage λ (lambda). When λ is induced, λDNA is detached from the chromosome by the reversal of the steps shown in Fig 9–7; detachment is followed by phage replication, maturation, and host cell lysis. As a rare event (about 10^{-6} to 10^{-5} of the cells), the cross-over event occurs at a different position, generating a circle of DNA in which part of the λ genome has been replaced by a segment of host chromosome (Fig 4–9). The recombinant circles, lacking certain essential phage genes, are defective; they cannot replicate or mature unless the cell is simultaneously infected with a normal phage that supplies the missing phage gene products. When this occurs the cell lyses and liberates both normal phage particles and "transducing particles"; when a transducing particle is adsorbed by a recipient cell, it injects its DNA in the normal fashion; the recipient thus receives a segment of the donor's chromosome.

Generalized Transduction

Although generalized transducing phages may occasionally incorporate host DNA by the mechanism described above, the great majority of their transducing particles contain mostly host DNA; it thus appears

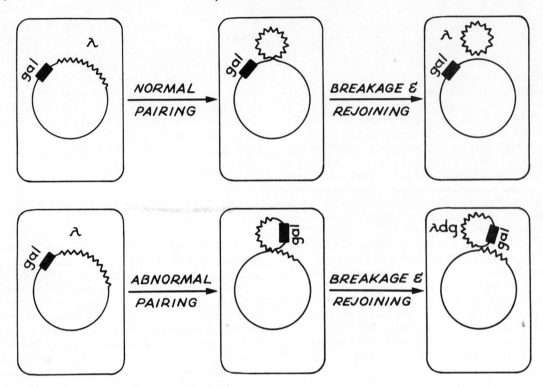

Figure 4–9. *Upper Row:* Detachment of λ prophage to form a normal λ vegetative DNA. *Lower Row:* Detachment of λ prophage to form λ dg DNA, which will mature as a transducing particle. ("λ dg" is an abbreviation for "lambda defective carrying gal genes.")

that phage heads can be assembled around condensed segments of host DNA as well as around condensed phage genomes. The mechanism by which this assembly takes place is not known. It is only known that the products of certain phage genes are essential for normal head assembly; presumably these "morphopoietic factors" complex with phage DNA and provide a matrix for assembly of the head subunits. Transducing phage particles may thus arise when morphopoietic factors complex with fragments of host DNA of the right size. As in restricted transduction, only about one particle in 10^5 or 10^6 is a transducing particle.

It has been found that phage P1, a typical generalized transducing phage, does not form a prophage which is integrated into the host chromosome. Instead, the prophage occupies an independent site in the cell. This difference is compatible with the different mechanisms of formation of transducing particles.

High-Frequency Transduction

In restricted transduction, the transducing particle contains part of a phage genome linked to a segment of host DNA. When this is injected into the recipient, the entire DNA structure becomes integrated into the bacterial chromosome. The transduced recipient then produces a clone of cells every one of which carries the defective prophage plus the extra segment of donor DNA. If these cells also carry a normal prophage (as a result of simultaneous infection of the original recipient by a normal particle and a transducing par-

ticle), then, on induction, a lysate is produced in which half of the particles are transducing particles. This is the phenomenon of "high-frequency transduction."

Abortive Transduction

In many generalized transductions, failure of the exogenote to be integrated may lead to persistence without replication. Thus, when the zygote divides, only one of the daughter cells receives the exogenote. In further cell generations, the exogenote is again transmitted without replicating, so that only one cell in the clone at any given time is a partial diploid. This situation is called "abortive transduction."

In abortive transduction, the genes of the exogenote function normally. Thus, if a gal⁺/gal⁻ cell is produced by an abortive transduction, the cell in which the nonreplicating gal⁺ gene resides will produce the galactose-fermenting enzyme. During further generations the clone of cells arising from each gal⁻ segregant will produce no more enzyme, and the enzyme will be diluted out by the cell division process. If a gal⁺/gal⁻ abortive transductant is plated on a medium in which galactose is the sole source of carbon and energy, it will produce a minute colony (containing about 10^6 cells) after 4 days of growth as a result of the limited production of the galactose-fermenting enzyme. (A normal gal⁺ cell would produce a very large colony, containing over 10^9 cells, in 2 days of growth.) The production of a minute colony as the result of abortive transduction is shown in Fig 4–10.

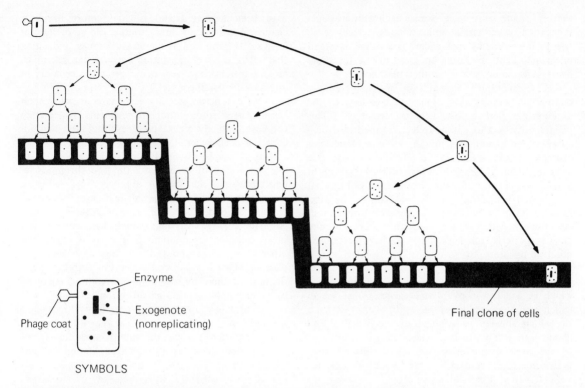

SYMBOLS

Enzyme

Exogenote
(nonreplicating)

Phage coat

Final clone of cells

Figure 4–10. Abortive transduction. At each division only one of the daughter cells receives the active gene. The other cell goes through a few cell divisions, until the active gene product (eg, enzyme) is diluted out. Plating an abortive transductant produces a minute colony, in which only one cell is capable of further growth and division. (From Stanier RY, Doudoroff M, Adelberg EA: *The Microbial World,* 3rd ed. Copyright © 1970. By permission of Prentice-Hall, Inc, Englewood Cliffs, NJ.)

PLASMID-MEDIATED CONJUGATION

Plasmids

Bacteria are hosts to small, extrachromosomal genetic elements called plasmids. Plasmids are dispensable to the cell under ordinary conditions of growth. Their presence is detectable when the genes they carry confer new properties on the host, and they are generally named for these properties. The best-known plasmids are:

(1) **The sex factors**—These mediate chromosome transfer by the mechanism described below. The most widely studied is F, the sex factor found in *E coli* K12.

(2) **The Col factors**—These carry genes which cause their hosts to produce **colicins**, proteins which are lethal toxins for coliform bacteria.

(3) **The resistance (R) factors**—These carry genes conferring on the host cell resistance to various antimicrobial agents, such as antibiotics. A single plasmid, for example, may carry separate genes for resistance to streptomycin, chloramphenicol, tetracyclines, and sulfonamides. In some cases it has been possible to dissociate the plasmid into several smaller ones: an element, called resistance transfer factor (RTF), carrying the genes governing the intercellular transfer process; and separate elements, called R determinants, carrying the resistance genes. In other cases, the various elements remain tightly linked, and the entire plasmid is then referred to as an R factor.

(4) **The penicillinase plasmids of staphylococci**—These plasmids carry a gene which causes the cell to produce a potent penicillinase, thus rendering it resistant to penicillin. They differ from the R factors in that they are not capable of transfer by conjugation. They can be carried from cell to cell, however, by phage-mediated transduction.

As will be discussed below, plasmids share many properties with bacterial viruses (phages). They are of major clinical significance, not only because they may carry genes for resistance to therapeutic drugs but also because some of them mediate bacterial recombination—a process which leads to the emergence of strains with new combinations of antigenic and virulence factors.

A. Physical Properties: All plasmids discovered to date are circular, double-stranded DNA molecules. Their molecular weights range from 3×10^6 to 1×10^8, which is sufficient to code for 5–160 average polypeptides.

B. Replication: Plasmids are replicons; their replication appears to occur by the mechanism previously described for the bacterial chromosome. The DNA is attached to a specific membrane site, and the 2 replicas are segregated into different daughter cells at cell division. In most cases, plasmid replication is so regulated that it occurs only once during each chromosomal replication cycle. Plasmid replication is unusually sensitive to inhibition by such agents as acridine dyes and ultraviolet light; by using these agents at threshold doses, cells can be "cured" of their plasmids.

C. Compatibility: Plasmids can be classified into a number of compatibility groups; 2 members of the same group cannot coexist in the same cell. This phenomenon is thought to reflect competition for a specific attachment site in the cell membrane. For example, *E coli* K12 may be inferred to carry one attachment site for F; one for each of several groups of R factors; and additional sites for different Col factors.

D. Self-Transfer: Some, but not all, of the plasmids found in gram-negative bacteria can bring about their own transfer by the conjugation process. Grampositive bacteria, on the other hand, have never been observed to conjugate.

Plasmid transfer occurs as follows. The cell extrudes a special protein thread, called a **sex pilus**, which is coded for by plasmid genes. This thread, which may be several times the length of the cell, has a tip which adheres to gram-negative cell walls. Any gram-negative cell which touches it becomes tethered to the plasmid-containing cell; the 2 cells are then drawn into direct contact by a mechanism which is not yet understood (Fig 4–11).

The plasmid then undergoes a special type of replication called "transfer replication," one parental strand passing into the recipient and the other remaining in the donor cell (Fig 4–12). Complementary strands are synthesized in the donor and recipient simultaneously with transfer. The daughter molecules are circularized by ligase action immediately after transfer replication is complete.

With the use of a micromanipulator, tethered cells have been separated and isolated before having a chance to come into direct contact. Some of the isolated cells produced recombinant clones, indicating that DNA can be transferred through the sex pilus. Most transfers, however, occur after the cells are in direct, wall-to-wall contact.

No cytoplasm, or any cell material other than DNA, passes from donor to recipient. The mating couples eventually break apart, resulting in 2 plasmid-containing cells where there had been one before.

E. Recombination: Plasmids undergo crossing over with each other and with the host chromosome, depending on the extent of their base sequence homologies. Since both plasmids and chromosome are circular, an odd number of cross-overs serves to integrate the 2 DNA structures, which then replicate as a single unit. An even number of cross-overs, on the other hand, brings about an exchange of segments. A plasmid which is capable of integrating with the bacterial chromosome (by recombination within a region of base-pair homology) is called an **episome**.

F. Mobilization: If a gram-negative cell harbors 2 plasmids, one self-transferable and the other not, the former may bring about the simultaneous transfer of the latter–ie, the latter is "mobilized." Mobilization is brought about when the 2 plasmids are either permanently or transiently integrated by a cross-over; mobilization can also occur without integration if the nontransferable plasmid simply lacks one or more gene functions (eg, pilus formation) that the self-transferable plasmid can provide.

The bacterial chromosomes may also be mobilized by integration with a self-transferable plasmid. If the integration is relatively stable, the cell in which it has occurred may give rise to a clone every cell in which is capable of chromosome transfer. The strain

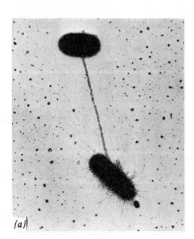 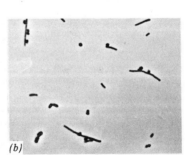 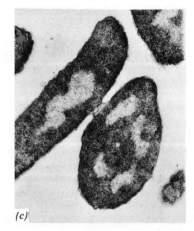

Figure 4–11. *(a)* A male and a female cell joined by an F pilus. The F pilus has been "stained" with male-specific RNA phage particles. The male cell also possesses ordinary pili, which do not adsorb male-specific phages and which are not involved in mating. *(b)* Mating pairs of *E coli* cells. Hfr cells are elongated. *(c)* Electron micrograph of a thin section of a mating pair. The cell walls of the mating partners are in intimate contact in the "bridge" area. (Electron micrograph [a] by Carnahan J and Brinton C. From Stanier RY, Doudoroff M, Adelberg EA: *The Microbial World,* 3rd ed. Copyright 1970. By permission of Prentice-Hall, Inc, Englewood Cliffs, NJ. Photographs [b] and [c] from Gross JD, Caro LG: DNA transfer in bacterial conjugation. J Mol Biol 16:269, 1966.)

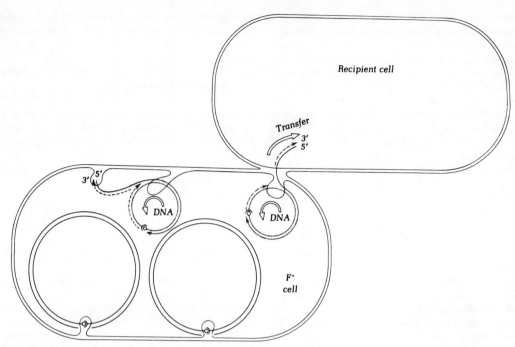

Figure 4–12. An F⁺ cell, containing 2 autonomous F replicons and 2 chromosomes, is shown conjugating with a recipient cell. Replication of F is proceeding according to the mechanism outlined in Fig 4—4. The F at the left is replicating within the host cell; the F at the right is being driven into the recipient by replication. (From Stanier RY, Doudoroff M, Adelberg EA: *The Microbial World,* 3rd ed. Copyright © 1970. By permission of Prentice-Hall, Inc, Englewood Cliffs, NJ.)

obtained by isolation of such a clone is called **Hfr,** for "high-frequency recombination"; chromosome transfer by Hfr strains is described below.

Some chromosome-mobilizing plasmids are found among the R and Col factors; others have no other detectable effect on the host and are known simply as "sex factors."

G. Population Dynamics: Plasmids are occasionally irreversibly lost by their host cells, and hence would ultimately disappear from bacterial populations in nature if their loss were not compensated by cell-to-cell transfer and replication. As discussed above, such transfer may occur either by conjugation or by phage transduction. The rates of loss and transfer are such as to maintain each type of plasmid in a small percentage of the natural host population at any given time. When selection is applied, however, as in the case of R factor selection by antibiotics, a majority of host cells may harbor a given type of plasmid (see below).

The transmission frequency of plasmids is limited mainly by the efficiency of pilus formation, which in most host strains is repressed to a level of 10^{-5} per cell, and by species specificity. For example, F (the sex factor of *E coli* K12), which is totally nonrepressed, is transferred from one *E coli* strain to another with a frequency of 1.0, but from *E coli* to *Proteus mirabilis* at a frequency of 1×10^{-5} or less.

H. Cell Properties Determined by Plasmid Genes:

1. Drug resistance—In gram-negative bacteria, genes governing resistance to such drugs as neomycin, kanamycin, streptomycin, chloramphenicol, tetracy-clines, penicillins, and sulfonamides are found on one or another plasmid in various combinations. In the gram-positive staphylococci, genes governing resistance to such agents as penicillin, erythromycin, and heavy metals (eg, Hg^{++} and Co^{++}) are found on plasmids. Genes conferring resistance to the same agents may also be found on the chromosome, but in such cases they do so by different mechanisms. Most plasmid-governed resistance is mediated by enzymatic inactivation of the drug (eg, by acetylation or phosphorylation), whereas chromosome-mediated resistance usually reflects a lowered affinity of its target molecule for the drug. These findings are compatible with the fact that plasmids are (by definition) dispensable to the cell: only chromosomal genes can confer resistance by structurally altering the binding site for the drug since the genes determining the structures of indispensable cell components must themselves be indispensable.

2. Toxins—Enteropathogenic strains of *E coli* of porcine origin produce an enterotoxin and an *a*-hemolysin; the genes for these toxins are usually present on transmissible plasmids. (Similarly, the toxin of *Corynebacterium diphtheriae* and the erythrogenic toxin of Streptococcus are determined by genes of temperate phages, which are closely related to plasmids as discussed below.)

I. Relation to Viruses: Bacterial viruses possess all of the properties described above for plasmids; a Pseudomonas phage has even been found to promote conjugation. The major difference thus appears to be the ability of phages to form a mature, protein-coated virion which can be liberated and passed to other cells through the medium. Their many similarities suggest a close evolutionary relationship between phages and plasmids—an inference which is supported by the ability of some plasmids and phages to recombine with each other.

J. Clinical Significance: The ease with which plasmids can transfer from cell to cell, and the strong selection which chemotherapy has exerted for drug resistance, have combined to produce striking results. In Japan, for example, the frequency of R-governed multiple-resistant Shigella strains rose from 10–20% in 1955 to 80% in 1968. In England, multi-resistant *Salmonella typhimurium* first appeared in 1961 and rose to 21% of all *S typhimurium* isolates by 1964.

In general, 60–90% of resistance markers in the gram-negative pathogens are carried on transferable plasmids. Although the experimentally determined rate of transfer of resistance in vivo is very low, epidemiologic evidence indicates that such transfer accounts for the rapid rise in incidence of drug-resistant strains of gram-negative pathogens.

The use of antibiotics as feed supplements for domestic animals has led to a large increase (by selection) in R factors among the normal gram-negative flora of such animals, and such R factors are transmissible to man. For example, one study carried out in England showed a much higher incidence of bacteria carrying multiple-resistance R factors in the fecal contents of farm workers who were in contact with antibiotic-fed pigs than in a control group who were in contact only with normal pigs.

RTFs (plasmids carrying the genes for self-transfer but not for drug resistance) have also been discovered to be extremely common in the bacterial flora of man and animals. For example, 20 out of 60 *E coli* strains isolated from healthy humans and animals were found in one study to carry RTFs, as did 15 out of 21 enteropathogenic strains isolated from patients. (RTFs are detected in the following way: Strain A, which is being screened for the presence of an RTF, is mated with strain B, which carries only a nontransferable R determinant. Strain B is then mated with a third strain—strain C—which is plasmid-free. The transfer of the R determinant from strain B to strain C reveals the presence of an RTF acquired from strain A.)

K. The Use of Plasmids for Cloning Segments of Eukaryotic DNA: A given plasmid, such as an R factor, can be isolated in the form of circular DNA, and a segment of DNA taken from a eukaryotic cell can be inserted into the circle by the following procedure (Fig 4–13). (1) The plasmid is cleaved at one specific site

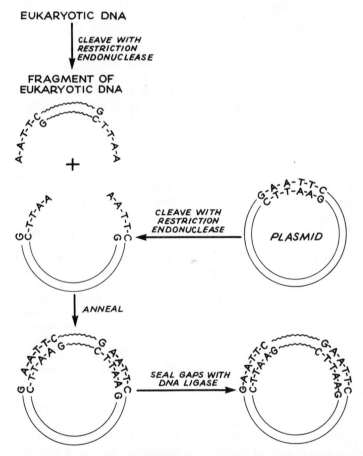

Figure 4–13. The insertion of a fragment of eukaryotic DNA into a bacterial plasmid by in vitro procedures. See text.

by a restriction endonuclease. As shown on p 42, this type of enzyme makes staggered cuts in the DNA duplex, converting the circle into a linear molecule with short single-stranded ends. (2) Fragments of eukaryotic DNA are prepared by cleavage with the same restriction endonuclease. (3) The linear plasmid molecules and eukaryotic DNA fragments are mixed and their overlapping single-stranded ends are allowed to "anneal" with each other. (4) The molecules are covalently joined at the overlap regions by treatment with DNA ligase.

The plasmid DNA containing the inserted segment is then introduced into a transformable bacterium, where it reestablishes itself as an independent replicon. The "infected" cell gives rise to a clone, every cell of which contains a plasmid carrying an inserted fragment of eukaryotic DNA. The clone can be expanded by large-scale mass culture, the cells harvested, and the plasmid DNA reextracted. The inserted fragment of eukaryotic DNA can then be cleaved out by restriction endonuclease action and purified on any desired scale.

Such methods have already been used to clone large amounts of Xenopus (frog) ribosomal RNA genes (rDNA), sea urchin histone genes, and selected genes of Drosophilia. The method holds great promise for the isolation of mammalian and plant genes whose products are important in medicine or in agriculture.

Chromosome Transfer

A. The F⁻, F⁺, and Hfr States: Cells of *E coli* K12 which carry F are called F⁺; those which have lost it are called F⁻. F⁺ cells will transfer replicas of their sex factors to F⁻ cells by the process described above.

In a population of F⁺ cells, the integration of F and chromosome by crossing over occurs about once per 10^5 cells at each generation; the cells in which this occurs, and the clones which arise from them, are called Hfr (see above). Integration does not always occur at the same site on the bacterial chromosome. There are 8 or 10 preferred sites, presumed to represent base-pair regions homologous with regions on F. Fig 4–14 illustrates the integration at one of these sites as a random event.

The integration process is reversible; in a population of Hfr cells, detachment by a second cross-over occurs about once per 10^5 cells at each generation. Thus, every F⁺ population contains a few Hfr cells, and every Hfr population contains a few F⁺ cells.

B. DNA Transfer by Hfr Donors: When a suspension of Hfr cells is mixed with an excess of F⁻ cells, every Hfr cell will attach to an F⁻ cell and initiate replicative transfer. Since F and the chromosome have merged to form a single replicon, chromosomal DNA as well as F DNA passes into the recipient (Fig 4–15).

The order in which chromosome markers move into the recipient depends on the chromosomal site at which F has become integrated, as illustrated in Fig 4–16.

DNA transfer proceeds at a constant rate in each mating pair: approximately 5×10^4 base-pairs per

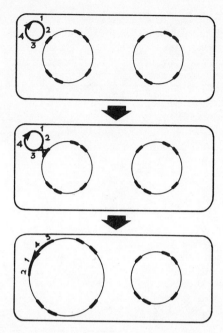

Figure 4–14. The attachment of F to chromosome. The sex factor (F) is shown as a smaller circle, not drawn to scale. The dark segments along the chromosome (larger circle) represent sites having base-pair homology with F DNA. The numbers represent regions of F DNA; the arrowhead represents the site at which the circle breaks at the time of conjugal transfer.

minute at 37° C. Transfer is interrupted by spontaneous breakage of the DNA molecule at random times; thus, the chance of a given marker's being transferred decreases exponentially with its distance from the transfer origin. A marker close to the origin will be transferred with a probability of 1.0, while the terminal marker will be transferred with a probability of less than 0.01.

C. Formation and Transfer of F-Genotes: As a very rare event (10^{-8} – 10^{-6} per cell per generation), an Hfr cell will undergo F detachment by a cross-over in an abnormal region (Fig 4–17). The F that is formed includes within its circular structure a segment of chromosomal DNA; it is called an **F-genote**, and the cell that carries it is called F′ (F-prime), rather than F⁺.

The cell in which the F-genote arose is called a primary F′ cell; its chromosome has a deletion corresponding to the segment on the F-genote. Transfer of the F-genote to a normal F⁻ cell gives rise to a secondary F′ strain, in which part of the chromosome is present in the diploid state. Crossing over occurs at a high rate in such cells, so that the F-genote undergoes alternate integration and detachment from the chromosome.

When a culture of a secondary F′ strain is mated with an F⁻, 2 types of transfer take place: some cells (those in which F is at that moment detached) transfer only the F-genote; others (those in which F is integrated) transfer both F-genote DNA and contiguous chromosomal DNA.

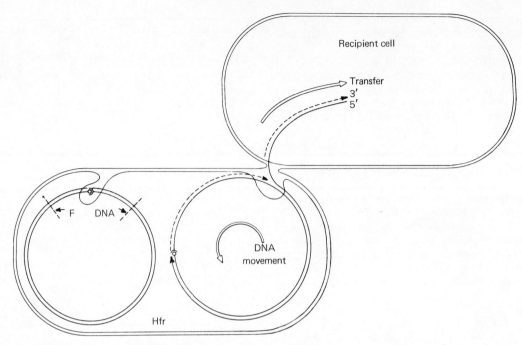

Figure 4–15. DNA transfer by an Hfr cell. Since F and chromosome are integrated, F replicative transfer causes the sequential transfer of chromosomal DNA. (From Stanier RY, Doudoroff M, Adelberg EA: *The Microbial World,* 3rd ed. Copyright © 1970. By permission of Prentice-Hall, Inc, Englewood Cliffs, NJ.)

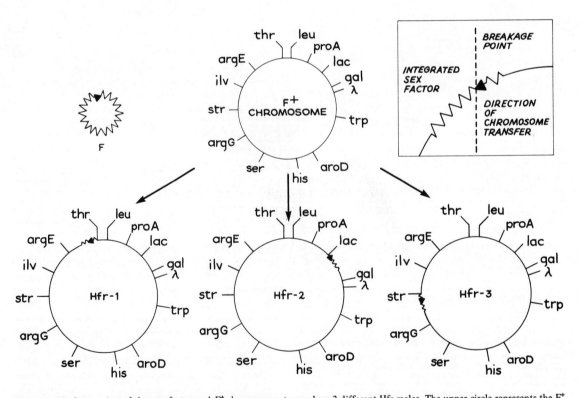

Figure 4–16. Integration of the sex factor and F⁺ chromosome to produce 3 different Hfr males. The upper circle represents the F⁺ chromosome; only a few of the known genetic loci, or "markers," are shown. The lower circles represent cases in which the sex factor (F) has integrated with the chromosome between met and thr, between lac and gal, and between str and ser, respectively. (The 3- and 4-letter symbols represent genes governing biochemical activities of the cell, eg, "lac," the set of loci governing the utilization of β-galactosides; "his," the set of loci governing the biosynthesis of histidine, etc). See Fig 4–12 for mechanism of integration.

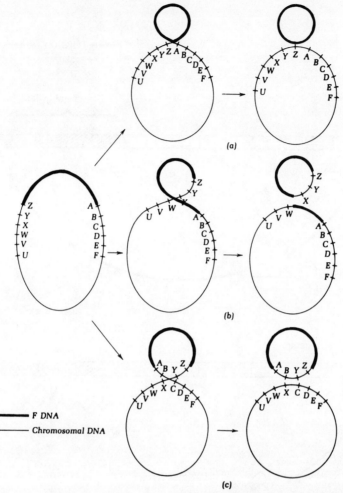

Figure 4–17. The generation of F genotes, in primary F' cells. At the left is an Hfr chromosome, with the integrated F DNA at the top. Letters A–F and U–Z represent chromosomal markers. *(a)* Crossing over within the original region of pairing between F and chromosome regenerates a normal F. *(b)* Pairing in an exceptional region, followed by crossing over, generates an F genote carrying the chromosomal markers XYZ. The chromosome of the primary F' contains a segment of F DNA and has a deletion of the XYZ segment. *(c)* Exceptional pairing in a different region has generated an F genote containing a full complement of F DNA, plus chromosomal genes from both sides of the former attachment site. (From Stanier RY, Doudoroff M, Adelberg EA: *The Microbial World,* 3rd ed. Copyright © 1970. By permission of Prentice-Hall, Inc, Englewood Cliffs, NJ.)

GENES OF STRUCTURE & GENES OF REGULATION

A gene which determines the structure of a particular protein (eg, an enzyme) is called a **structural gene.** The activity of a structural gene, in terms of production of messenger RNA for enzyme synthesis, is strictly regulated in the cell. It has been shown that many structural genes lie adjacent to specific sites concerned with the regulation of structural gene activity. Such a site is called an **operator.** Under certain conditions, the cell produces cytoplasmic substances called **repressors;** when an operator gene binds its specific repressor substance, the structural gene adjacent to it is prevented from producing mRNA and is thus inactivated. In many cases, a series of structural genes determining a series of coordinated enzymes (eg, the enzymes of a particular metabolic pathway) form a continuous segment of DNA under the control of a single adjacent operator gene. A gene sequence under the coordinated control of a single operator is called an **operon.**

Each specific type of repressor molecule of the cell must, of course, be formed by its own structural gene. A gene concerned with the production of a repressor substance is called a **regulator gene.** Both operator genes and regulator genes can be detected when they occur in mutant form. For example, the operator can mutate to a state in which it is unable to bind repressor. The operon now functions under all conditions and is said to be "derepressed."

Mutations of the regulator gene produce phenotypes similar to those produced by mutations of the

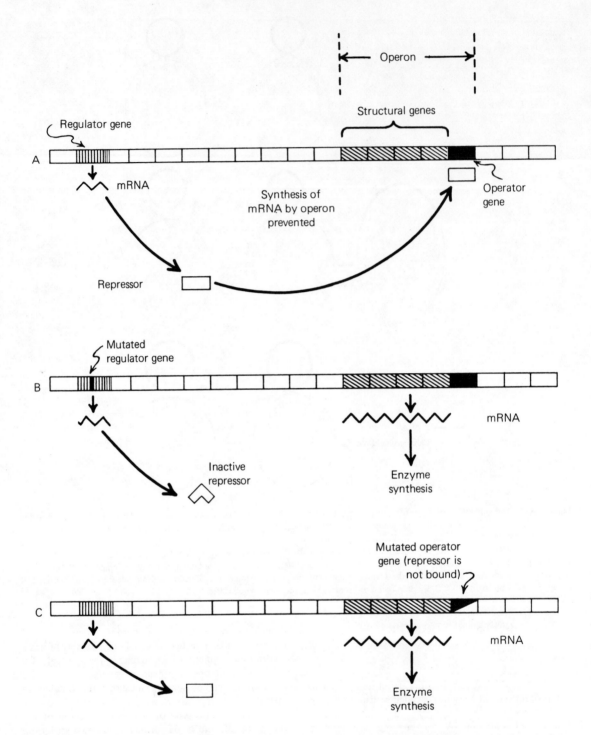

Figure 4–18. Genetic regulation of enzyme synthesis. The product of the regulator gene, the repressor, prevents the functioning of the operon which it controls by binding to the operator site. Mutations at either the regulator gene or the operator gene can interfere with repression, thus permitting enzyme synthesis. (**Note:** Enzyme inducers generally act by inactivating repressors. In feedback repression of biosynthetic enzymes, however, the repressor is normally inactive and must be activated by the biosynthetic end product. See p 68.)

corresponding operator gene. For example, a mutated regulator gene may fail to make repressor, giving rise to the derepressed phenotype (Fig 4–18). Regulator genes can be distinguished from operator genes, however, by the behavior of diploid cells carrying one normal gene and one mutated gene. In such diploids the derepressed state is **dominant** if the mutation has altered the operator gene but **recessive** if the mutation has inactivated the regulator gene.

The biochemical basis of enzyme regulation will be discussed in Chapter 5.

GENETICS OF DRUG RESISTANCE

Bacteria can become resistant to drugs by any one of 3 genetic mechanisms: mutation, recombination, or the acquisition of a plasmid carrying drug resistance genes.

Mutation to Drug Resistance

Mutations occurring in genes on the bacterial chromosome may confer drug resistance on the cell. Such mutations are of ordinary kinds described on pp 38–42, occurring at rates of 10^{-9} to 10^{-5} per cell per generation. They are discussed further in Chapter 10.

Recombination

Once a mutation to drug resistance has arisen in a population of bacterial cells, it can be transferred to other cells by any of the 3 mechanisms described earlier in this chapter—transformation, transduction, or conjugation—depending on which mechanism the species in question is capable of performing. Recombination between 2 cells, each resistant to a different drug, can produce a cell resistant to both. The transfer of mutant chromosomal genes, including genes for drug resistance, occurs at a very low rate in nature, 10^{-5} per cell per generation being a rough average for the transfer of any particular chromosomal gene by transduction or by conjugation. The rate at which transformation occurs in nature is not known, but is probably much lower.

Acquisition of Plasmids

A. Gram-Negative Bacteria: As discussed above, 60–90% of resistance genes in the gram-negative pathogens are carried on plasmids. Since many of these are self-transferable and can mobilize others which are not, drug resistance can spread through a population of sensitive bacteria in epidemic fashion. R factors recombine with each other frequently, producing new combinations of resistance determinants.

B. Gram-Positive Bacteria: Resistance to penicillin, erythromycin, and other antimicrobial agents has been found in the virulent staphylococci to be plasmid-determined. Although the plasmids of gram-positive bacteria cannot undergo conjugal transfer, they can be carried from cell to cell by transducing phages. The majority of hospital strains of staphylococci now carry penicillinase plasmids.

•   •   •

General References

Books

Adelberg E (editor): *Papers on Bacterial Genetics,* 2nd ed. Little, Brown, 1966.

Beckwith JR, Zipser D (editors): *The Lactose Operon.* Cold Spring Harbor Laboratory, 1970.

Braun W: *Bacterial Genetics,* 2nd ed. Saunders, 1965.

Campbell AM: *Episomes.* Harper, 1969.

Cold Spring Harbor Symposia on Quantitative Biology: Vol 31: *The Genetic Code.* Cold Spring Harbor, New York, 1966.

Cold Spring Harbor Symposia on Quantitative Biology: Vol 38: *Chromosome Structure and Function.* Cold Spring Harbor, New York, 1973.

Drake JW: *The Molecular Basis of Mutation.* Holden-Day, 1970.

Fincham JRS, Day PR: *Fungal Genetics,* 3rd ed. Davis, 1971.

Freese E: Molecular mechanisms of mutation. Pages 1–56 in: *Chemical Mutagens: Principles and Methods for Their Detection.* Vol 1. Hollaender A (editor). Plenum Press, 1971.

Goodenough U, Levine RP: *Genetics.* Holt, Rinehart, & Winston, 1974.

Hartman P, Suskind S: *Gene Action,* 2nd ed. Prentice-Hall, 1969.

Hayes W: *The Genetics of Bacteria and Their Viruses,* 2nd ed. Blackwell, 1968.

Jacob F, Wollman E: *Sexuality and the Genetics of Bacteria.* Academic Press, 1961.

King RC: *A Dictionary of Genetics,* 2nd ed. Oxford Univ Press, 1972.

Lewin BM: *The Molecular Basis of Gene Expression.* Wiley, 1970.

Meynell GG: *Bacterial Plasmids.* MIT Press, 1973.

Sager R: *Cytoplasmic Genes and Organelles.* Academic Press, 1972.

Stent G: *Molecular Genetics.* Freeman, 1971.

Woese CR: *The Genetic Code: The Molecular Basis for Genetic Expression.* Harper & Row, 1967.

Wolstenholme A, O'Connor M (editors): *Bacterial Episomes and Plasmids.* A Ciba Foundation Symposium. Little, Brown, 1969.

Articles & Reviews

Auerbach C, Kilben BJ: Mutation in eukaryotes. Annu Rev Genet 5:163, 1971.

Bachman BJ & others: Recalibrated linkage map of *Escherichia coli* K-12. Bacteriol Rev 40:116, 1976.

Beckwith J, Rossow P: Analysis of genetic regulatory mechanisms. Annu Rev Genet 8:1, 1974.

Beneveniste R, Davies J: Mechanisms of antibiotic resistance in bacteria. Annu Rev Biochem 42:471, 1973.

Boyer HW: DNA restriction and modification mechanisms in bacteria. Annu Rev Microbiol 25:153, 1971.

Clowes RC: Molecular structure of bacterial plasmids. Bacteriol Rev 36:361, 1972.

Curtiss R: Bacterial conjugation. Annu Rev Microbiol 23:69, 1969.

Gillham NW: Genetic analysis of the chloroplast and mitochondrial genomes. Annu Rev Genet 8:347, 1974.

Gots JS, Benson CE: Biochemical genetics of bacteria. Annu Rev Genet 8:77, 1974.

Hartman PE, Roth JR: Mechanisms of suppression. Adv Genet 17:1, 1973.

Helinski DR: Plasmid determined resistance to antibiotics: Molecular properties of R factors. Annu Rev Microbiol 27:437, 1973.

Helling RB: Eukaryotic genes in prokaryotic cells. Stadler Symposium 7:15, 1975.

Hotchkiss RD, Gabor M: Bacterial transformation. Annu Rev Genet 4:193, 1970.

Howard-Flanders P: DNA repair and recombination. Br Med Bull 29:226, 1973.

Levinthal M: Bacterial genetics excluding *E coli*. Annu Rev Microbiol 28:219, 1974.

Low KB: *Escherichia coli* K-12 F-prime factors, old and new. Bacteriol Rev 36:587, 1972.

Meselson MS, Radding CM: A general model for genetic recombination. Proc Natl Acad Sci USA 72:358, 1975.

Meynell E, Meynell GG, Datta N: Phylogenetic relationships of drug-resistance factors and other transmissible bacterial plasmids. Bacteriol Rev 32:55, 1968.

Morrow JF & others: Replication and transcription of eukaryotic DNA in *E coli*. Proc Natl Acad Sci USA 71:1743, 1974.

Novick R: Extrachromosomal inheritance in bacteria. Bacteriol Rev 33:210, 1969.

Orgel L: The chemical basis of mutation. Adv Enzymol 27:289, 1965.

Polisky B & others: Specificity of substrate recognition by the *Eco*RI restriction endonuclease. Proc Natl Acad Sci USA 72:3310, 1975.

Radding CM: Molecular mechanisms in genetic recombination. Annu Rev Genet 7:87, 1973.

Roth JR: Frameshift mutations. Annu Rev Genet 8:319, 1974.

Sanderson KE: Linkage map of *Salmonella typhimurium*, edition IV. Bacteriol Rev 36:558, 1972.

Willets N: The genetics of transmissible plasmids. Annu Rev Genet 6:257, 1972.

Witkin EM: Ultraviolet-induced mutation and DNA repair. Annu Rev Microbiol 23:487, 1969.

5...
Microbial Metabolism

THE ROLE OF METABOLISM IN BIOSYNTHESIS & GROWTH

Major Functions Served by Metabolism

The major function of any microbial cell is growth. Other functions, such as motility, luminescence, and synthesis of capsular substances, also exist but are often dispensable. Growth is defined as the orderly increase in mass or number of all components of the cell; cell multiplication is a common but not an essential consequence of growth. In some microorganisms, such as certain slime molds, growth is accompanied by repeated nuclear division but not by cell division. The result is the formation of a greatly enlarged, multinucleate cell or "coenocyte."

Since the major cell components (chromosomes, protein-synthesizing systems, enzymes, membranes, walls, flagella) are made up of macromolecules, the major function served by the metabolism of a microbial cell can be more precisely stated in terms of the **synthesis of macromolecules**. These macromolecules are assembled from their respective subunits: proteins from amino acids; nucleic acids from nucleotides; polysaccharides from simple sugars; and lipids from glycerol or other alcohols, fatty acids, and (in phospholipids) special subunits such as choline.

In every case, the condensation of subunits to form a macromolecule requires that the subunit be **activated**—ie, coupled by means of a suitable energy-rich bond to a substituent group such as phosphate (P), pyrophosphate (PP), adenosine monophosphate (AMP), or coenzyme A (CoA). The energy of the activating group's linkage then provides the energy needed for the condensation, and the activating group is split off in the process. In general, the ultimate source of such activating groups is adenosine triphosphate (ATP).

The arrangement (sequence) of subunits in the ultimate macromolecule is determined in one of 2 ways. In nucleic acids and in proteins, it is **template-directed**: DNA serves as template for its own synthesis and for the synthesis of the various types of RNA; messenger RNA serves as template for the synthesis of proteins. In carbohydrate and lipids, on the other hand, the arrangement of subunits is determined entirely by enzyme specificities.

Given these systems for the orderly and directed condensation of subunits, the principal functions of metabolism are seen to be 3-fold: (1) to generate the subunits themselves from intermediates of metabolism, (2) to generate ATP from adenosine diphosphate (ADP) and inorganic phosphate, and (3) to generate reducing power (as $NADP.H_2$) for those instances in which the substrates taken from the medium are more oxidized than the overall products of biosynthesis.

The Generation of the Subunits of Macromolecules

The subunits of macromolecules include fatty acids, monosaccharides, amino acids, purines, and pyrimidines. All of these may be furnished by the medium; however, many microorganisms can synthesize the entire complement from suitable sources of carbon (eg, glucose), nitrogen (eg, ammonia), and sulfur (eg, sulfate). All biosynthetic pathways are under negative end product regulation, including both repression of enzyme synthesis and inhibition of enzyme action, so that subunits are not synthesized if they are available in the medium (see below). The availability of such compounds is greatly increased by the action of specific transport systems in the bacterial cell membrane that produce internal concentrations of subunits 100- or 1000-fold over the external concentrations.

When a subunit is unavailable, the microbial cell synthesizes it by a biosynthetic pathway. All biosynthetic pathways originate from a relatively small number of metabolic intermediates. All of the aliphatic amino acids, for example, derive from just 4 intermediates: pyruvate, 3-phosphoglycerate, oxalacetate, and a-ketoglutarate. The aromatic ring of phenylalanine, tyrosine, and tryptophan derives from a condensation of D-erythrose-4-phosphate and p-enolpyruvate; and most of the carbon skeleton of histidine comes from pentose phosphate. These relationships are shown schematically in Fig 5—1.

The pyrimidine ring is formed by the addition of a carbamyl group to aspartic acid, followed by ring closure; the purine ring is built up by condensations involving glycine, formate, CO_2, and amido or amino groups from glutamine and aspartic acid. The fatty acids are all synthesized primarily from acetate as a building block, while the simple sugars are formed by a series of transformations starting with hexose phosphate.

All of these biosynthetic pathways are outlined in other sources. (See, for example, Harper HA: *Review of Physiological Chemistry*, 15th ed. Lange, 1975.) They are essentially the same in all organisms which

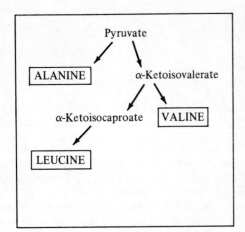

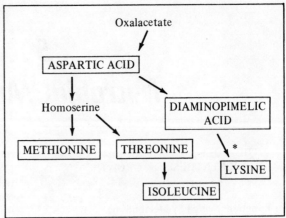

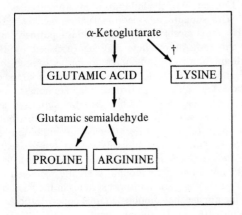

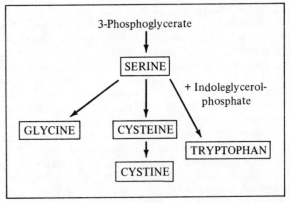

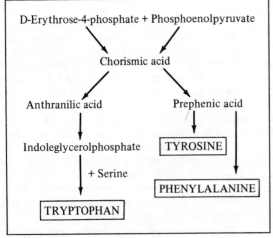

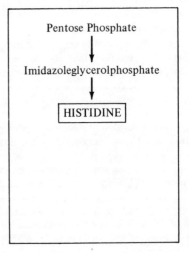

*In bacteria.
†In fungi.

Figure 5—1. Biosynthetic families of amino acids. (In many cases, the arrow represents 2 or more sequential reactions.)

Table 5–1. Pathways of carbohydrate metabolism.

Pathway	Key Intermediates for Biosynthesis
Embden-Meyerhof pathway	Glucose-1-phosphate 3-Phosphoglyceraldehyde *p*-Enolpyruvate Pyruvate
Direct oxidative pathway	Pentosephosphates D-Erythrose-4-phosphate
Tricarboxylic acid (TCA) cycle	Acetyl-CoA Oxalacetate *a*-Ketoglutarate CO_2

possess them. Different organisms lack one or another biosynthetic enzyme system, however, and in such cases the macromolecular subunits must be furnished by the environment. Man, for example, requires 8 amino acids in his diet.

The subunits, then, are either supplied by the environment or are derived through biosynthetic pathways from a number of **key intermediates** of metabolism. As shown in Table 5–1, these intermediates are in turn generated by relatively few metabolic pathways that are common to most organisms.

The Generation of ATP

There are 2 general mechanisms for the generation of ATP by nonphotosynthetic organisms: substrate phosphorylation and oxidative phosphorylation. In both cases, bond energy from a metabolic intermediate is used to create a molecule of ATP from ADP and inorganic phosphate (Pi).

A. Substrate Phosphorylation: This term is used to describe the 2 steps in the Embden-Meyerhof pathway at which an energy-rich phosphate bond is created: (1) The oxidation of 3-phosphoglyceraldehyde by NAD in the presence of Pi produces 1,3-diphosphoglyceric acid, and the new phosphate group is then transferred to ADP. (2) The dehydration of 2-phosphoglyceric acid redistributes the bond energy of the molecule so that the phosphate bond of the product, *p*-enolpyruvate, is energy-rich and transferable to ADP also.

An analogous process occurs when *a*-ketoglutarate is oxidized to succinic acid in the TCA cycle. One of the intermediates in this process is succinyl-CoA; the energy of the CoA bond can then be used to form ATP from ADP plus Pi.

B. Oxidative Phosphorylation: In respiration, a pair of electrons is passed from reduced NAD to oxygen through a series of catalytic intermediates—principally the flavoproteins and cytochromes. At 3 of the steps involved in this process, the transfer of electrons is coupled with the phosphorylation of ADP.

The Generation of Reducing Power

Many of the oxidative steps of catabolism, in which ATP is generated, are coupled with the reduction of NAD or NADP. If the compound being used as

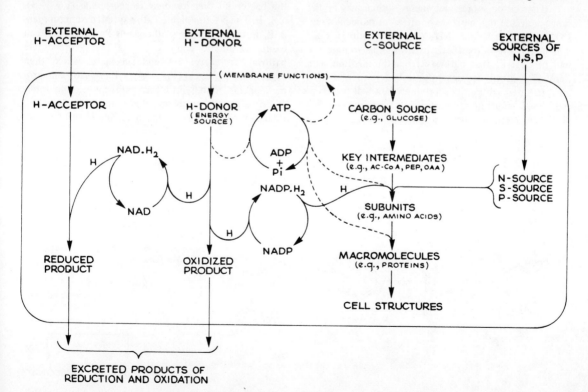

Figure 5–2. Relationships between nutrition, metabolism, and growth.

Glucose-6-phosphate ⟶ 6-Phospho-gluconate ⟶ 2-Keto-3-deoxy-6-phosphogluconate ⟶ Pyruvate + Glyceraldehyde-3-phosphate

Figure 5–3. The Entner-Doudoroff pathway.

carbon source is as reduced as or more reduced than the overall products of biosynthesis, its oxidation will generate the required reducing power. If the carbon source is more oxidized than the overall products of biosynthesis, however, net reducing power is achieved by the oxidation of additional carbon source molecules to CO_2.

Summary: Nutrition in Relation to Metabolism

The relationships outlined above are summarized in Fig 5–2. Bacterial cells must take in from the medium, as a minimal set of requirements, a carbon source, an energy source, and sources of elements (N, S, P, etc). Metabolism of the carbon source provides key intermediates from which the cell can synthesize the subunits of the macromolecules. Oxidation of the energy source provides both ATP and reducing power to drive these biosyntheses, as well as ATP for the activation of the subunits. The activated subunits are polymerized to form the macromolecules, which self-assemble to form cell structures. The net result is cell growth; it is usually, but not always, accompanied by cell division.

The carbon source and energy source may be the same molecule (eg, glucose) or different molecules (eg, CO_2 as carbon source, NH_3 as energy source). Cells which lack any biosynthetic pathway must obtain the end product of that pathway from the medium, as a "growth factor." If biosynthetically competent cells are presented with an end product they will preferentially use it, shutting off endogenous synthesis.

The medium must also furnish the cell with a terminal H acceptor in order for oxidations to occur. For aerobes, this is O_2; for anaerobes, it may be an organic compound, or an organic by-product of the catabolism of the carbon source. Thus, many bacteria can grow fermentatively using glucose as the source of carbon, as the source of energy, and (through its catabolism) as the H acceptor.

METABOLIC PATHWAYS UNIQUE TO MICROORGANISMS

Pathways of Catabolism

Table 5–1 lists the principal pathways, common to all groups of organisms, by which the key intermediates for biosynthesis are formed. In certain microorganisms these have been supplemented by several unique pathways, including the following:

A. The Entner-Doudoroff Pathway: In addition to the Embden-Meyerhof and the direct oxidative pathways, many microorganisms break down hexose via the Entner-Doudoroff pathway, first discovered in the bacterium *Pseudomonas saccharophila* (Fig 5–3).

B. The β-Ketoadipate Pathway: Many microorganisms, notably bacteria of the genus Pseudomonas, can oxidize aromatic compounds via the β-ketoadipate pathway to acetyl-CoA and succinate, which then enter the TCA cycle (Fig 5–4). Other oxidizable aromatic acids funnel into this pathway via the intermediates shown, eg, benzene is oxidized to catechol, toluene is oxidized to benzoic acid, and so on.

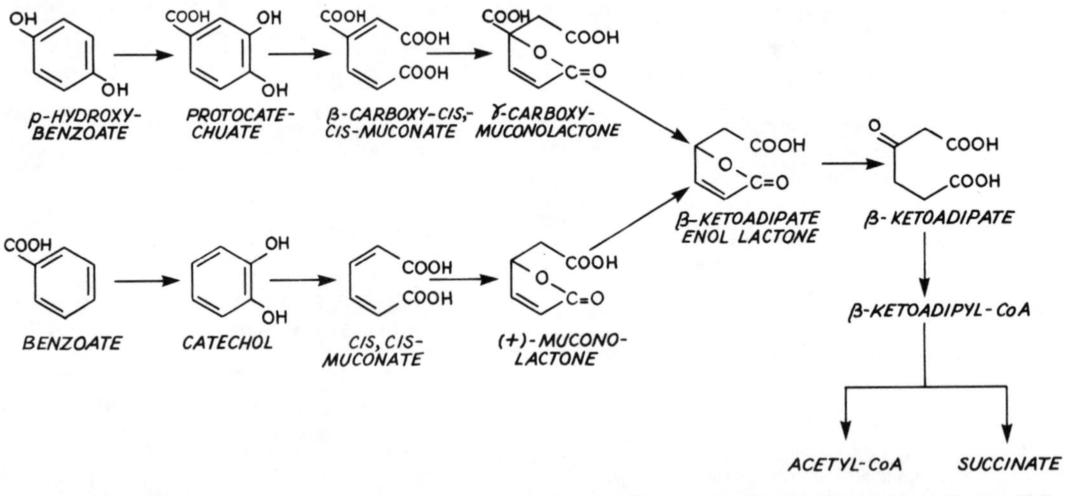

p-HYDROXY-BENZOATE — PROTOCATE-CHUATE — β-CARBOXY-CIS,CIS-MUCONATE — γ-CARBOXY-MUCONOLACTONE

BENZOATE — CATECHOL — CIS,CIS-MUCONATE — (+)-MUCONO-LACTONE

β-KETOADIPATE ENOL LACTONE — β-KETOADIPATE — β-KETOADIPYL-CoA — ACETYL-CoA   SUCCINATE

Figure 5–4. The β-ketoadipate pathway. (After Stanier RY, Adelberg EA, Ingraham JL: *The Microbial World,* 4th ed. Prentice-Hall, 1976.)

Pathways of Biosynthesis

A. The Glyoxylate Cycle: A special problem of biosynthesis arises in the case of microorganisms that are furnished acetate as the sole source of carbon for growth under aerobic conditions. Since, under aerobic conditions, acetate is completely oxidized to CO_2 in the TCA cycle, this pathway cannot provide a net synthesis of C_4 compounds necessary for many biosynthetic pathways. Instead, acetate is metabolized by the set of reactions shown in Fig 5–5.

Note that with each turn of the cycle, 2 molecules of acetate (activated as acetyl-CoA) are converted to one molecule of succinate. Note also that several enzymes of this pathway are also those of the TCA cycle; indeed, the glyoxylate cycle and the TCA cycle go on simultaneously when acetate is the sole carbon source. Under these conditions, the 2 unique enzymes of the glyoxylate cycle (isocitritase and malate synthetase) are induced.

B. Nitrogen Fixation: Certain bacteria are capable of fixing atmospheric nitrogen (N_2) and reducing it to NH_3 inside the cell; the reduction is catalysed by nitrogenase. The electrons for the reduction are transferred from a suitable donor to enzyme-bound N_2 through an electron transport chain consisting of ferredoxin, azoferredoxin, and molybdoferredoxin; the reduction also requires ATP. The isolated enzyme system is quite sensitive to inhibition by molecular oxygen.

The principal nitrogen-fixing bacteria are symbiotic forms of the genus Rhizobium and free-living forms of Azobacter and Clostridia as well as certain blue-green algae. One group of enteric bacteria, in the genus Enterobacter, also fixes nitrogen.

The symbiotic rhizobia inhabit the root tissues of leguminous plants (peas, beans, alfalfa, etc), causing formation of root nodules. In the nodule, true hemoglobin is formed; its role may be to lower the redox potential within the nodule and thus protect the bacterial nitrogenase system from inhibition by oxygen.

The role of nitrogen fixation in the nitrogen cycle of the biosphere is discussed on p 93.

C. The Synthesis of Carbohydrates From CO_2: A special mechanism is found in organisms that use CO_2 as the sole source of carbon for the production of intermediates. This occurs in photosynthetic organisms and in bacteria which obtain their energy by the oxidation of inorganic substances. In such organisms, CO_2 is converted to carbohydrate according to the general scheme shown in Fig 5–6. Note the requirement for 12 molecules of $NADPH_2$ for each molecule of hexose produced. These are furnished by noncyclic photophosphorylation or (in the case of autotrophic bacteria) by the oxidation of reduced inorganic substances from the environment. The key step in this cycle is the fixation of CO_2 by ribulose diphosphate to form 3-phosphoglyceric acid (Fig 5–7).

The conversion of 3-phosphoglyceric acid to hexose and ribulose diphosphate via 3-phosphoglyceraldehyde is a complex process involving 12 separate enzymatic reactions. (For further details, see Elsden SR: Photosynthetic and lithotrophic carbon dioxide fixation. In: *The Bacteria.* Vol 3: *Biosynthesis.* Gunsalus IC, Stanier RY [editors]. Academic Press, 1962.)

D. Synthesis of Cell Wall Peptidoglycan (Murein): The structure of peptidoglycan is shown in Fig 2–17; the pathway by which it is synthesized is shown in simplified form in Fig 5–8. The major precursors of peptidoglycan are UDP-linked acetylglucosamine (UDP-GlcNAc) and UDP-linked muramic acid pentapeptide (UDP-MA-pentapeptide). The pentapeptide, in the case of *Staphylococcus aureus,* is the tetrapeptide shown in Fig 2–17 plus one additional (terminal) D-alanine residue.

The synthesis of peptidoglycan begins with the

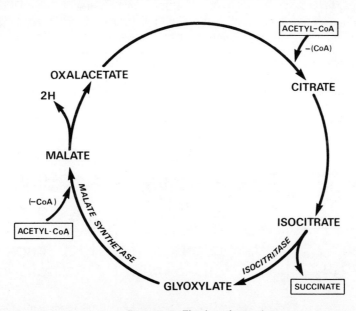

Figure 5–5. The glyoxylate cycle.

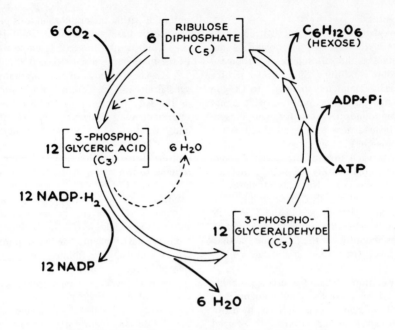

Figure 5—6. Path of carbon in photosynthesis and autotrophy.

stepwise synthesis in the cytoplasm of UDP-MA-penta-peptide. Acetylglucosamine is first attached to UDP and then converted to UDP-muramic acid by condensation with *p*-enolpyruvate and reduction. The amino acids of the pentapeptide are sequentially added, each addition catalyzed by a different enzyme and each involving the split of ATP to ADP + Pi.

The UDP-MA-pentapeptide is attached to a lipid of the cell membrane and receives a molecule of GlcNAc from UDP. The pentaglycine derivative is next formed in a series of reactions, using glycyl-tRNA as the donor; the completed disaccharide is then transferred to the growing end of a glycopeptide polymer in the cell wall. Finally, cross-linking is accomplished by a transpeptidation reaction, in which the free amino group of a pentaglycine residue displaces the terminal D-alanine residue of a neighboring pentapeptide.

This biosynthetic pathway is of particular importance in medicine, as it provides a basis for the selective antibacterial action of several chemotherapeutic agents. Unlike their host cells, bacteria are not isotonic

with the body fluids. Their contents are under high osmotic pressure, and their viability depends on the integrity of the peptidoglycan lattice in the cell wall being maintained throughout the growth cycle. Any compound that inhibits any step in the biosynthesis of peptidoglycan causes the wall of the growing bacterial cell to be weakened and the cell to lyse. The sites of action of several antibiotics are shown in Fig 5—8.

E. Synthesis of Cell Wall Lipopolysaccharide: The general structure of the antigenic lipopolysaccharide of gram-negative cell walls is shown in Fig 2—20. The biosynthesis of the repeating end-group, which gives the cell wall its antigenic specificity, is shown in Fig 5—9. Note the resemblance to peptidoglycan synthesis: in both cases, a series of subunits is assembled on a lipid carrier in the membrane and then transferred to open ends of the growing polymer fabric of the cell wall.

F. Synthesis of Extracellular Capsular Polymers: The capsular polymers, a few examples of which are listed in Table 2—1, are enzymatically synthesized

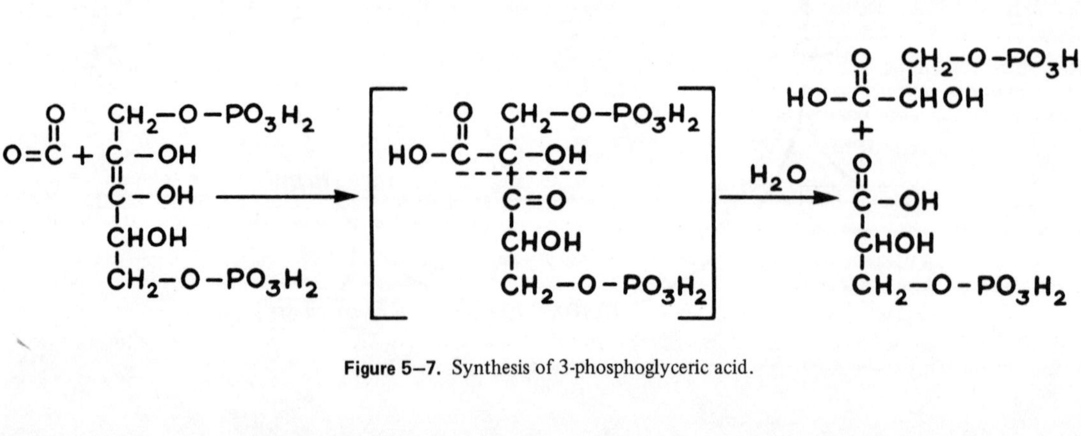

Figure 5—7. Synthesis of 3-phosphoglyceric acid.

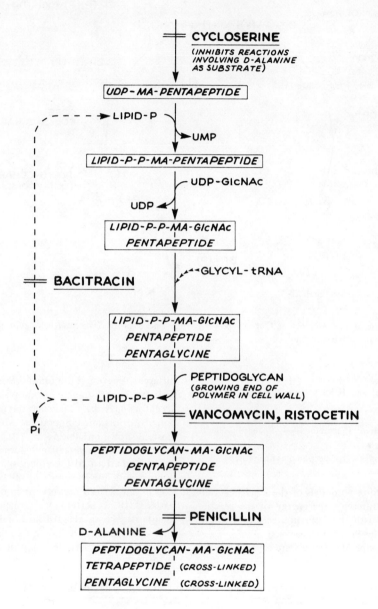

Figure 5—8. The biosynthesis of cell wall peptidoglycan, showing the sites of action of 5 antibiotics which inhibit cell wall synthesis.

from activated subunits. No membrane-bound lipid carriers have been implicated in this process. The presence of a capsule is often environmentally determined: dextrans and levans, for example, can only be synthesized using the disaccharide sucrose (fructose-glucose) as the source of the appropriate subunit, and their synthesis thus depends on the presence of sucrose in the medium.

G. **Synthesis of Reserve Food Granules:** When nutrients are present in excess of the requirements for growth, bacteria convert certain of them to intracellular reserve food granules. The principal ones are starch, glycogen, poly-β-hydroxybutyrate (PBHB), and volutin, which consists mainly of inorganic polyphos-

phate. The type of granule formed is species-specific. The granules are degraded when exogenous nutrients are depleted.

PATTERNS OF MICROBIAL ENERGY-YIELDING METABOLISM

In the nonphotosynthetic bacteria, ATP is generated by oxidation-reduction reactions which may be treated as coupled half-reactions of the following general types:

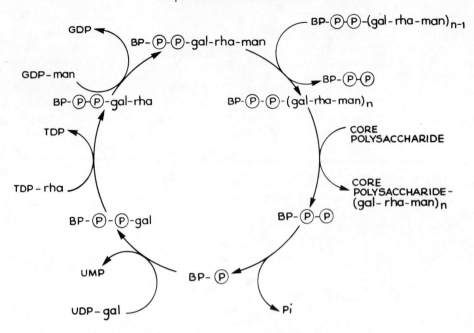

Figure 5–9. Synthesis of the repeating unit of the polysaccharide side chain of *Salmonella newington* and its transfer to the lipopolysaccharide core. BP = bactoprenol.

Oxidation half-reaction: H donor $\xrightarrow{-2H}$ Oxidized product

Reduction half-reaction: H acceptor $\xrightarrow{+2H}$ Reduced product

(where H stands for one electron plus one proton)

When the redox potentials of the 2 half-reactions are sufficiently different, the energy of the reaction may be coupled with the formation of a molecule of ATP from ADP plus Pi.

Different groups of microbes are capable of using different types of H donors and H acceptors. H donors may be either organic or inorganic compounds; H acceptors may be molecular oxygen, inorganic compounds, or organic compounds. Altogether, 5 patterns exist, as shown in Table 5–2.

Note that mammalian tissues obtain ATP exclusively by pattern III (aerobic respiration of organic H donors) with the exception of the lactic acid fermentation in muscle. All parasitic microorganisms use either pattern III or pattern V (fermentation); many are facultative, being able to grow fermentatively under anaerobic conditions but switching preferentially to respiration under aerobic conditions.

Table 5–2. Patterns of energy-yielding oxidation-reduction reactions used by microorganisms.

H DONOR	H ACCEPTOR		
	O_2 (Aerobic Respiration)	NO_3^-, $SO_4^=$, CO_2 (Anaerobic Respiration)	Organic Compounds (Fermentation)
Inorganic substances	I. Aerobic respiration of inorganic substances Example: (Nitrosomonas) $NH_3 \to NO_2^-$ $O_2 \to H_2O$	II. Anaerobic respiration of inorganic substances Example: *(Thiobacillus denitrificans)* $S \to SO_4^=$ $NO_3^- \to N_2$	(None)
Organic substances	III. Aerobic respiration of organic substances Example: (Many organisms) Glucose $\to CO_2$ $O_2 \to H_2O$	IV. Anaerobic respiration of organic substances Example: (Desulfovibrio) Lactic acid $\to CO_2$ $SO_4^= \to H_2S$	V. Fermentation of organic substances Example: (Streptococcus) Glucose $\xrightarrow{-4H}$ 2 pyruvate $\downarrow$ +4H 2 lactic acid

Pattern III: The Aerobic Respiration of Organic H Donors

For every naturally occurring organic compound, a microorganism exists which is capable of catabolizing it. Some bacteria can oxidize only one or a few H donors (eg, a limited number of carbohydrates); others, such as certain pseudomonads, can oxidize at least 100—the limit has not yet been found.

Pattern V: Fermentation

Fermentations are metabolic processes in which both H donor and H acceptor are organic compounds. We will consider them in 3 groups.

A. Fermentations Based on the Embden-Meyerhof Pathway: Almost all of the fermentations carried out by clinically significant bacteria fall into this group. They are characterized by the oxidation of carbohydrate to pyruvate via the Embden-Meyerhof pathway, generating (per molecule of glucose, for example) 2 net molecules of ATP and 2 molecules of $NADH_2$. NAD is regenerated from $NADH_2$ by the reduction of pyruvate—either directly, as in lactic acid homofermentation, or indirectly, as in the others.

The different fermentations of this group are thus characterized by the reduction products formed from pyruvate, reflecting the enzymatic constitutions of different species. The major products of fermentation, listed in Table 5–3, form the basis for many diagnostic laboratory tests.

The details of the enzymatic pathways are presented in Figs 5–10 to 5–15.

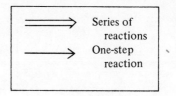

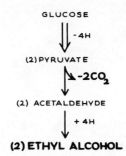

Figure 5–10. Ethyl alcohol fermentation.

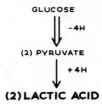

Figure 5–11. Lactic acid homofermentation.

Table 5–3. Microbial fermentations based on the Embden-Meyerhof pathway.

Fermentation	Organisms	Products
Ethyl alcohol (Fig 5–10)	Some fungi (notably some yeasts)	Ethyl alcohol, CO_2.
Lactic acid (homofermentation) (Fig 5–11)	Streptococcus Some species of Lactobacillus	Lactic acid (accounting for at least 90% of the energy source carbon).
Butylene glycol (Fig 5–12)	Enterobacter Aeromonas *Bacillus polymyxa*	Ethyl alcohol, acetoin, 2,3-butylene glycol, CO_2, lactic acid, acetic acid, formic acid. (Total acids = 21 mols.*)
Propionic acid (Fig 5–13)	*Clostridium propionicum* Propionibacterium *Corynebacterium diphtheriae* Some species of: Neisseria Veillonella Micromonospora	Propionic acid, acetic acid, succinic acid, CO_2.
Mixed acid (Fig 5–14)	Escherichia Salmonella Shigella Proteus	Lactic acid, acetic acid, formic acid, succinic acid, H_2, CO_2, ethyl alcohol. (Total acids = 159 mols.*)
Butyl alcohol-butyric acid (Fig 5–15)	Butyribacterium *Zymosarcina maxima* Some species of: Clostridium Neisseria	Butyl alcohol, butyric acid, acetone, isopropanol, acetic acid, ethyl alcohol, H_2, CO_2.

*Per 100 mols of glucose fermented.

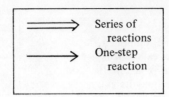

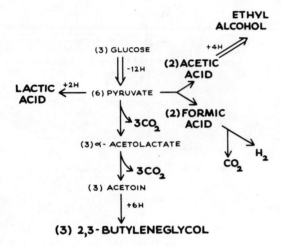

Figure 5-12. Butylene glycol fermentation.

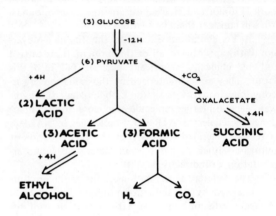

Figure 5-14. Mixed acid fermentation.

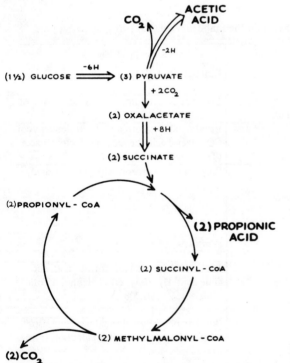

Figure 5-13. Propionic acid fermentation.

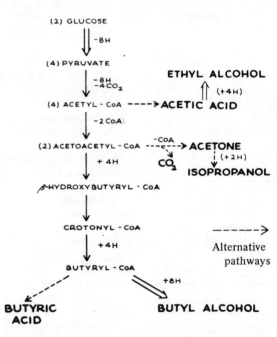

Figure 5-15. Butyl alcohol-butyric acid fermentation.

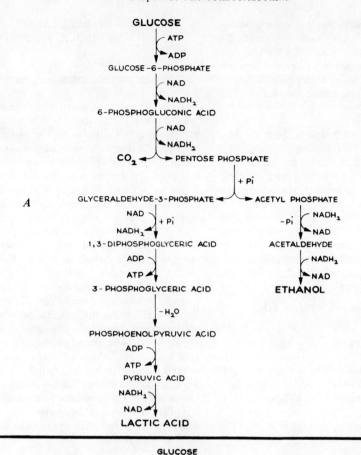

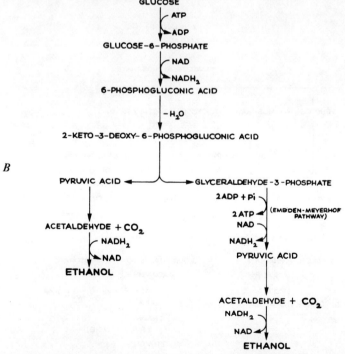

Figure 5–16. *A:* The bacterial heterolactic fermentation of glucose. *B:* Mechanism of the alcoholic fermentation of glucose by the bacterium *Zymomonas lindneri.* (From Stanier RY, Doudoroff M, Adelberg EA: *The Microbial World,* 3rd ed. Copyright © 1970. By permission of Prentice-Hall, Inc, Englewood Cliffs, NJ.)

B. Fermentations Based on the Hexose Monophosphate Shunt: Two fermentations begin with the formation of 6-phosphogluconate from glucose: heterolactic fermentation, carried out by certain harmless lactic acid bacteria; and bacterial alcoholic fermentation, carried out by the nonparasitic species *Zymomonas lindneri*. Their mechanisms are outlined in Fig 5–16.

C. Miscellaneous Special Pathways: Several unique pathways exist, including the following:

1. Bifidobacterium—This unusual bacterium is the predominant organism in the intestinal tract of breast-fed infants; it disappears upon weaning. Its fermentation is outlined in Fig 5–17.

2. Clostridia—A number of clostridia, including the agents of tetanus and botulism, carry out fermentations in which the H donor and H acceptor are amino acids taken from the medium. For example, *Cl tetani* is capable of the following pair of oxidation-reductions:

$$\text{Alanine} \xrightarrow{-4H} \text{Acetic acid} + NH_3 + CO_2$$

$$2 \text{ glycine} \xrightarrow{+4H} 2 \text{ acetic acid} + 2 NH_3$$

3. Methane fermentation—Certain strict anaerobes, called "methane bacteria," carry out the following reaction; how it is coupled with ATP generation is not clear:

$$\overset{*}{C}H_3COOH \longrightarrow \overset{*}{C}H_4 + CO_2$$

THE REGULATION OF METABOLIC PATHWAYS

In their normal environment, microbial cells regulate their metabolic pathways so efficiently that no intermediate or subunit is made in excess. Each metabolic reaction is regulated not only with respect to all others in the cell but also with respect to the concentrations of nutrients in the environment. Thus, when a sporadically available carbon source suddenly becomes abundant, the enzymes required for its catabolism increase in both amount and activity; conversely, when a subunit (such as an amino acid) suddenly becomes abundant, the enzymes required for its biosynthesis decrease in both amount and activity.

The regulation of enzyme activity as well as enzyme synthesis provides both fine control and coarse control of metabolic pathways. For example, the inhibition of enzyme activity by the end product of a pathway constitutes a mechanism of fine control since the flow of carbon through that pathway is instantly and precisely regulated. The inhibition of enzyme synthesis by the same end product, on the other hand, constitues a mechanism of coarse control. The pre-existing enzyme molecules continue to function until they are diluted out by further cell growth, although unnecessary protein synthesis ceases immediately.

The mechanisms by which the cell regulates enzyme activity and enzyme synthesis are discussed in the following sections.

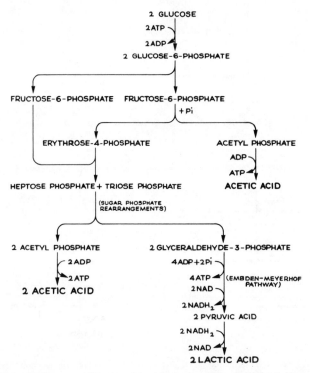

Figure 5–17. The pathway of glucose fermentation by Bifidobacterium. (From Stanier RY, Doudoroff M, Adelberg EA: *The Microbial World,* 3rd ed. Copyright © 1970. By permission of Prentice-Hall, Inc, Englewood Cliffs, NJ.)

The Regulation of Enzyme Activity

A. Enzymes as Allosteric Proteins: In many cases, the activity of an enzyme catalyzing an early step in a metabolic pathway is inhibited by the end product of that pathway. Such inhibition cannot depend on competition for the enzyme's substrate binding site, however, because the structures of the end product and the early intermediate (substrate) are usually quite different. Instead, such inhibition depends on the fact that regulated enzymes are **allosteric**: each enzyme possesses not only a catalytic site, which binds substrate, but also one or more other sites which bind small regulatory molecules, or **effectors**. The binding of an effector to its site causes a conformational change in the enzyme such that the affinity of the catalytic site for the substrate is reduced (allosteric inhibition) or increased (allosteric activation).

Allosteric proteins are usually polymeric. In some cases the subunits are identical, each subunit possessing both a catalytic site and an effector site; in other cases, the subunits are different, one type possessing only a catalytic site and the other only an effector site.

B. Feedback Inhibition: The general mechanism which has evolved in microorganisms for regulating the flow of carbon through biosynthetic pathways is the most efficient that one can imagine. The end product in each case allosterically inhibits the activity of the first—and only the first—enzyme in the pathway. For example, the first step in the biosynthesis of isoleucine not involving any other pathway is the conversion of L-threonine to a-ketobutyric acid, catalyzed by threonine deaminase. Threonine deaminase is allosterically and specifically inhibited by L-isoleucine and by no other compound (Fig 5–18); the other 4 enzymes of the pathway are not affected (although their synthesis is repressed, as discussed below).

C. Allosteric Activation: In some cases it is advantageous to the cell for an end product or an intermediate to activate rather than inhibit a particular enzyme. In the breakdown of glucose by *E coli*, for example, overproduction of the intermediates glucose-6-phosphate and phosphoenolpyruvate signals the diversion of some glucose to the pathway of glycogen synthesis; this is accomplished by the allosteric activation of the enzyme converting glucose-1-phosphate to ADP-glucose (Fig 5–19).

D. Cooperativity: Many polymeric enzymes, possessing more than one substrate binding site, show cooperative interactions of substrate molecules. The binding of substrate by one catalytic site increases the affinity of the other sites for additional substrate molecules. The net effect of this interaction is to produce an exponential increase in catalytic activity in response to an arithmetic increase in substrate concentration.

The Regulation of Enzyme Synthesis

A. Regulatory Proteins: As discussed in Chapter 4, enzyme synthesis is controlled by regulatory proteins, each produced by a specific regulator gene (Fig 4–18). The regulatory proteins are allosteric: one site

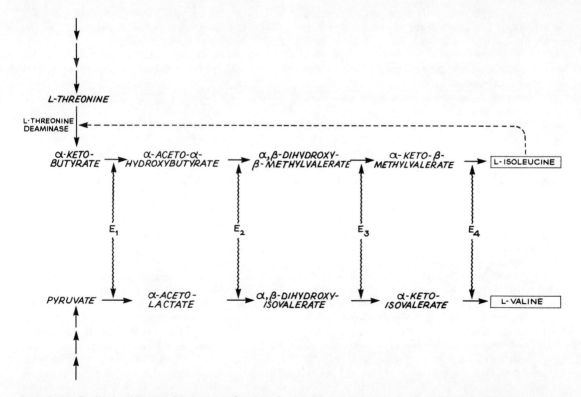

Figure 5–18. Feedback inhibition of L-threonine deaminase by L-isoleucine (dashed line). The pathways for the biosynthesis of isoleucine and valine are mediated by a common set of 4 enzymes, as shown.

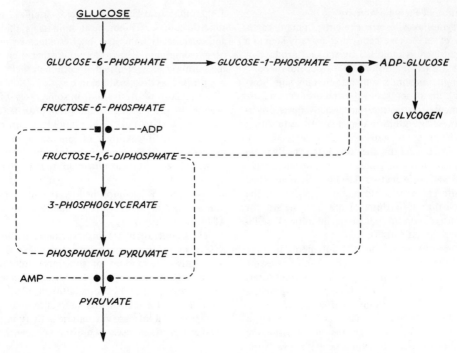

Figure 5–19. Regulation of glucose utilization by a combination of allosteric activation (--•) and allosteric inhibition (--■). (After Stanier RY, Adelberg EA, Ingraham JL: *The Microbial World,* 4th ed. Prentice-Hall, 1976.)

binds to an operator region of DNA, either potentiating transcription of an adjacent region or blocking it; the other site binds an effector molecule, which alters the affinity of the DNA binding site. Regulatory proteins which potentiate gene transcription—and thus enzyme synthesis—are called **activators**; those that block enzyme synthesis by interfering with transcription are called **repressors**.

B. Enzyme Induction: In microorganisms, many of which have evolved the ability to use a variety of sporadically occurring carbon sources, the enzymes for the catabolism of these carbon sources are **inducible**: they are synthesized only when the carbon source is present in the medium. Most such enzymes are under "negative control," ie, their synthesis is normally blocked by specific repressors. Induction of enzyme synthesis occurs when an inducer molecule (usually the substrate of the catabolic pathway) enters the cell and binds to the effector site of the repressor; such binding alters the repressor so that it can no longer bind to its cognate site on DNA, and enzyme synthesis begins.

In a few cases, inducible enzymes have been found to be under "positive control," ie, transcription requires the binding to DNA of an activator protein, which is in turn activated by the binding (at an effector site) of the inducer molecule.

C. End Product Repression: The regulation of biosynthetic pathways demands a response opposite to that found in catabolic pathways: Instead of enzyme synthesis being induced when the substrate of the pathway becomes available, enzyme synthesis is repressed when the end product of the pathway is made

in excess or becomes available as a nutrient. Thus, the repressor of a biosynthetic enzyme is normally unable to bind to the operator site on DNA and gains this ability only when it has bound its specific effector, ie, the end product of the pathway.

Feedback repression, as we may call this phenomenon, differs from feedback inhibition of enzyme activity in that the synthesis of every enzyme in the pathway is repressed. In some cases (notably in bacteria), this is accomplished by the action of a repressor on an **operon** (see Chapter 4), blocking transcription of a polycistronic messenger RNA. In other cases, the repressor acts on scattered genes, each with its own (but identical) operator site.

D. Catabolite Expression: Many of the enzymes of catabolic pathways are subject to a regulation process called **catabolite repression**. If the cell is provided with a rapidly metabolizable energy source, such as glucose, the enzymes which degrade alternative sources of energy cease to be synthesized. For example, β-galactosidase, which hydrolyzes lactose, is not synthesized by cells when glucose is present.

The synthesis of all enzymes subject to catabolite repression is under the positive control of a protein called CAP (catabolite activator protein). CAP binds to DNA at sites adjacent to each gene governing a catabolite repressible enzyme and activates the gene's transcription; CAP, in turn, is activated by 3',5'-cyclic AMP. When a rapidly metabolizable substrate such as glucose binds to the cell membrane, the internal concentration of cyclic AMP falls and synthesis of the catabolite repressible enzymes ceases.

Patterns of Regulation in Branched Biosynthetic Pathways

Many biosynthetic pathways are branched, each branch leading to a different, indispensable end product. Aspartic acid, for example, is the starting point for a pathway which branches out to form lysine, methionine, threonine, and isoleucine (Fig 5–20). It would clearly be fatal if the presence in excess of any one of these end products were to shut off the entire pathway starting at aspartate, yet to be efficient the cell must regulate the early steps in the pathway as well as the late ones.

A number of different solutions to this problem have evolved:

A. Isofunctional Enzymes: The first step in the pathway is catalyzed by 2 or more different enzymes with the same catalytic activity. For example, there are 3 aspartokinases in *E coli*, labeled (a), (b), and (c) in Fig 5–20. Enzymes (a) and (c) also catalyze the third step in the pathway, reducing aspartic semialdehyde to homoserine. Enzyme (a) is both inhibited and repressed by threonine; enzyme (b) is repressed by methionine; and enzyme (c) is both inhibited and repressed by lysine. Thus, if one of the 3 end products of the branched pathway is present in excess, the flow of carbon through the common pathway is proportionately reduced. (Note in Fig 5–20 that the final branches of the pathway are separately controlled by their respective end products.)

B. Sequential Feedback Inhibition: Fig 5–21 illustrates a second solution to the problem of regulating the early steps of a branched pathway. The 2 end products inhibit the first steps in their own branches, causing the accumulation of a common intermediate. The latter compound then serves as the feedback inhibitor of the first step in the common pathway.

C. Concerted and Cumulative Feedback Inhibition: In still other cases, the enzyme catalyzing the first step of a branched pathway possesses 2 or more

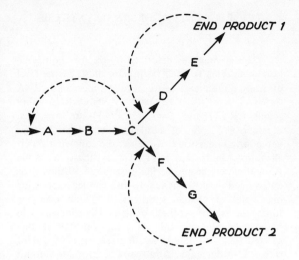

Figure 5–21. Regulation of a branched biosynthetic pathway by sequential feedback inhibition (dashed lines).

effector sites, each binding a different end product. In **concerted feedback inhibition**, all effector sites must be occupied for the enzyme to be inhibited. In **cumulative feedback inhibition**, each end product causes partial inhibition; the effects of binding more than one end product are additive. The latter is the more efficient of the 2 mechanisms.

D. The Diversity of Microbial Regulatory Systems: Different groups of microorganisms have evolved different mechanisms for regulating the same pathway. In the aspartate pathway shown in Fig 5–20, for example, aspartokinase is regulated by the use of separately inhibited isofunctional enzymes in the enteric bacteria but by concerted feedback inhibition in Pseudomonas. Thus, regulatory systems appear to have developed late in the evolution of the different microbial groups.

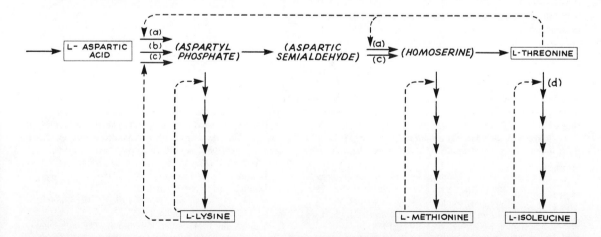

Figure 5–20. Regulation of a branched pathway by feedback inhibition (dashed lines). (a), (b), and (c) are isofunctional aspartokinases; (a) and (c) also catalyze the third step in the pathway. (d) is L-threonine deaminase. Feedback repression of enzyme synthesis is not shown. (After Stanier RY, Adelberg EA, Ingraham, JL: *The Microbial World*, 4th ed. Prentice-Hall, 1976.)

THE REGULATION OF RNA SYNTHESIS

The mechanisms described above for the regulation of enzyme (protein) synthesis all act at the level of transcription and hence regulate messenger RNA (mRNA) as well. The 2 classes of stable RNA—ribosomal (rRNA) and transfer (tRNA)—are regulated together by a different set of mechanisms which are as yet poorly understood. However, the following generalizations can be made: (1) The synthesis of stable RNA is closely geared to the growth rate of the cell as determined by nutrient supply. In rich media, allowing high rates of protein synthesis and short doubling times, the rate of synthesis of stable RNA increases; in poor media, allowing only low rates of protein synthesis and long doubling times, the rate of synthesis of stable RNA decreases. At all growth rates, the amount of stable RNA made by the cell is precisely that which is sufficient to support the permitted level of protein synthesis. (2) Regulation of stable RNA synthesis is not effected by varying the concentration of RNA precursors (nucleotide triphosphates) but by varying the number of RNA polymerase molecules actively engaged in transcribing the rRNA and tRNA genes.

One mechanism by which stable RNA synthesis is coupled to protein synthesis has been partially elucidated. When protein synthesis is arrested—eg, by depriving the cell of an essential amino acid—2 regulatory molecules are rapidly synthesized on the ribosomes, ppGpp and ppGppp.* These molecules, in turn, effect the repression of stable RNA synthesis. In E coli, a mutation in the gene called **rel** (for "relaxed synthesis of RNA") abolishes the production of the 2 guanosine polyphosphates, and stable RNA synthesis continues in the absence of protein synthesis.

Additional mechanisms must exist for the regulation of stable RNA synthesis, however, since the modulation of such synthesis as a function of growth rate is normal in the **rel** mutants.

*ppGpp: guanosine-3′,5′-di(diphosphate); ppGppp: guanosine-3′-diphosphate-5′-triphosphate.

THE REGULATION OF DNA SYNTHESIS & CELL DIVISION

In bacteria, the rate of DNA polymerization is a constant at a given temperature. In E coli cells growing at 37° C, for example, chromosome replication takes 40 minutes. In rich media, however, cells may double in as few as 20 minutes; this increase, which requires a corresponding increase in the rate of DNA synthesis, does not reflect a change in the rate of polymerization but rather an increase in the number of replication forks. In other words, a new round of replication begins before the previous round has been completed.

There is a precise relationship between the timing of DNA replication and cell division. For example, in E coli at 37° C, cell division occurs 20 minutes after completion of chromosomal replication. Since both (R), the replication period, and (D), the period between replication and division, are constant, totaling 60 minutes, the following situations may occur: (1) At doubling times of less than 60 minutes, a second round of replication begins during D and each daughter cell receives a chromosome containing a replication fork. (2) At a doubling time of 60 minutes or longer, each daughter cell receives a chromosome without a replication fork.

Thus, the E coli cell is so regulated that (1) 2 rounds of DNA replication are initiated at intervals equal to the doubling time of the culture, and (2) a cell division event occurs at a precise interval (eg, 60 minutes at 37° C) after each initiation event. If DNA synthesis is selectively inhibited, cell elongation continues but cell division is prevented.

The regulation of DNA replication and cell division appears to be achieved through the synthesis of specific proteins; if protein synthesis is blocked, ongoing rounds of DNA replication are completed, but the initiation of new rounds of replication is blocked, as is cell division.

•   •   •

General References

Books

Barker HA: *Bacterial Fermentations.* Wiley, 1957.

Cohen GN: *Biosynthesis of Small Molecules.* Harper, 1967.

Cold Spring Harbor Symposia on Quantitative Biology: Vol 26: *Cellular Regulatory Mechanisms.* Vol 28: *Synthesis and Structure of Macromolecules.* Vol 33: *Replication of DNA in Microorganisms.* Cold Spring Harbor, New York, 1961, 1963, 1968.

Doelle HW: *Bacterial Metabolism.* Academic Press, 1969.

Gunsalus IC, Stanier RY (editors): *The Bacteria.* Vol 2: *Metabolism.* Vol 3: *Biosynthesis.* Academic Press, 1961, 1962.

Haynes R, Hanawalt P (editors): *The Molecular Basis of Life—An Introduction to Molecular Biology: Readings from Scientific American.* Freeman, 1968.

Kornberg A: *DNA Synthesis.* Freeman, 1974.

Lehninger AL: *Biochemistry.* Worth, 1970.

Lehninger AL: *Bioenergetics.* Benjamin, 1965.

Maaløe O, Kjeldgaard N: *Control of Macromolecular Synthesis.* Benjamin, 1965.

Mandelstam J, McQuillen K (editors): *The Biochemistry of Bacterial Growth,* 2nd ed. Wiley, 1973.

Smith L: The respiratory chain system of bacteria. Pages 55—122 in: *Biological Oxidations.* Singer TP (editor). Interscience, 1968.

Sokatch JR: *Bacterial Physiology and Metabolism.* Academic Press, 1969.

Watson JD: *Molecular Biology of the Gene,* 2nd ed. Benjamin, 1970.

Articles & Reviews

Dalton H, Mortenson LE: Dinitrogen (N_2) fixation (with a biochemical emphasis). Bacteriol Rev 36:231, 1972.

Fraenkel DA, Vinopal RT: Carbohydrate metabolism in bacteria. Annu Rev Microbiol 27:69, 1973.

Horecker BL: Biosynthesis of bacterial polysaccharides. Annu Rev Microbiol 20:253, 1966.

Jones NC, Donachie WD: Protein synthesis and the release of the replicated chromosome from the cell membrane. Nature 251:252, 1974.

Kornberg A: Active center of DNA polymerase. Science 163:1410, 1969.

Monod J, Changeux J, Jacob F: Allosteric proteins and cellular control systems. J Mol Biol 6:306, 1963.

6 . . .

Cultivation of Microorganisms

Cultivation is the process of propagating organisms by providing the proper environmental conditions: nutrients, pH, temperature, and aeration. Other factors which must be controlled include the salt concentration and osmotic pressure of the medium and such special factors as light for photosynthetic organisms.

NUTRITION

The provision of nutrients for the growth of an organism is called nutrition. In the following discussion, the nutrients are classified according to their role in metabolism.

Hydrogen Donors

All chemosynthetic organisms require an energy source in the form of H donors (ie, oxidizable substrates). In addition, photosynthetic organisms require H donors in order to carry on photosynthesis. Types of compounds which can serve as H donors are discussed in Chapter 5.

Hydrogen Acceptors

H acceptors are required in energy-yielding oxidation-reduction reactions. For aerobes, gaseous oxygen (O_2) is required. Anaerobes require either inorganic compounds (sulfate, nitrate, carbonate) or organic compounds. In the latter case (called "fermentation"), either the carbon source or a fragment derived from it by catabolism usually serves; in a few instances, however, there is a requirement for a unique H acceptor which must be present in the medium.

Carbon Source

All organisms require a source of carbon for synthesis of the numerous organic compounds which comprise protoplasm. For photosynthetic and lithotrophic organisms, CO_2 is the sole source. Other organisms use the organic energy source as carbon source also; in addition, they require small amounts of CO_2 for such purposes as the carboxylation of phosphoenolpyruvate to form 4-carbon biosynthetic intermediates, the formation of carbamyl phosphate as a precursor of arginine and pyrimidines, and the biosynthesis of the purine ring. In most cases, sufficient CO_2 is produced in catabolism to satisfy this requirement;

however, growth frequently cannot be initiated unless CO_2 is present in the environment.

Nitrogen Source

Many cell constituents, principally the proteins, contain nitrogen; in bacteria, nitrogen accounts for approximately 10% of the cellular dry weight.

The form in which nitrogen is required depends on the organism's enzymatic reducing abilities; although in protoplasm nitrogen is organically combined $(R-NH_2)$, a given microbial species may obtain it from the environment in one or more of the forms shown in Table 6–1.

Table 6–1. Sources of nitrogen in microbial nutrition.

Compound	Valence of N
NO_3^-	+5
NO_2^-	+3
N_2	0
NH_3	−3
$R-NH_2$	−3

When the nitrogen source is $R-NH_2$ (R = organic radical), the organism uses it by deamination to NH_3, which is then incorporated into nitrogenous compounds, or by direct transfer of the amino group to suitable acceptors (transamination), or both:

$$\underset{\substack{\text{Amino} \\ \text{donor}}}{R-\underset{\underset{NH_2}{|}}{CH}-COOH} + \underset{\substack{\text{Amino} \\ \text{acceptor}}}{R_1-\underset{\underset{O}{\|}}{C}-COOH} \xrightarrow{\substack{\text{TRANS-} \\ \text{AMINATION}}}$$

$$\underset{\substack{\text{Deaminated} \\ \text{donor}}}{R-\underset{\underset{O}{\|}}{C}-COOH} + \underset{\substack{\text{Aminated} \\ \text{acceptor}}}{R_1-\underset{\underset{NH_2}{|}}{CH}-COOH}$$

Most microorganisms can use NH_3 as the sole nitrogen source. The principal reaction by which NH_3 is introduced into organic molecules is the reaction catalyzed by glutamic dehydrogenase:

$$HOOC-\overset{\overset{O}{\|}}{C}-CH_2-CH_2-\overset{\overset{O}{\|}}{C}-COOH \xrightarrow[\substack{+2H \\ from \\ NADPH_2}]{+NH_3}$$

a-Ketoglutaric acid

$$HOOC-\overset{\overset{O}{\|}}{C}-CH_2-CH_2-\underset{\underset{NH_2}{|}}{CH}-COOH + H_2O$$

Glutamic acid

Distribution of the nitrogen into other compounds can then be effected by transamination between glutamic acid and various keto acids and by modification of the new amino acids thus formed.

A limited number of microorganisms can fix atmospheric nitrogen (N_2) by converting it to NH_3 in the cell. Some bacteria can use nitrate as nitrogen source, reducing it to the level of NH_3 in the cell.

Minerals

In addition to carbon and nitrogen, living cells require a number of other minerals for growth:

A. Sulfur: Like nitrogen, sulfur is a component of many organic cell substances; the bulk of it occurs as sulfhydryl (−SH) groups in proteins. Some organisms require organic sulfur (R−SH) or H_2S, but most species can reduce sulfate ($SO_4^=$) to the organic form.

B. Phosphorus: Phosphate ($PO_4^=$) is required as a component of ATP, of nucleic acids, and of such coenzymes as NAD, NADP, and flavins. Phosphate is always assimilated as free inorganic phosphate.

C. Enzyme Activators: Numerous minerals are needed as enzyme activators. Magnesium ion (Mg^{++}) and ferrous ion are also found in porphyrins: magnesium in the chlorophyll molecule and iron as a part of the coenzymes of the cytochromes and peroxidases. Mg^{++} and K^+ are both essential for the function and integrity of ribosomes. Ca^{++} is required as a constituent of gram-positive cell walls, although it is dispensable for gram-negative bacteria. In formulating a medium for the cultivation of most microorganisms, it is necessary to provide sources of potassium, magnesium, calcium, and iron, usually as their ions (K^+, Mg^{++}, Ca^{++}, and Fe^{++}). Many other minerals are required but are adequately provided as contaminants of tap water and of other medium ingredients.

The uptake of iron, which forms insoluble hydroxides at neutral pH, is facilitated in many bacteria and fungi by their production of **siderochromes**— compounds which chelate iron and promote its transport as a soluble complex. They include hydroxamic acids (−$CONH_2OH$), called sideramines, and derivatives of catechol (eg, 2,3-dihydroxybenzoylserine).

Growth Factors

A growth factor is an organic compound which a cell must contain in order to grow but which it is unable to synthesize. Many microorganisms, when provided with the nutrients listed above, are able to synthesize all of the organic constituents of their protoplasm, including amino acids (the subunits of proteins), vitamins (for coenzymes), purines and pyrimidines (components of nucleic acids), fatty acids (components of fats and lipids), and other compounds.

Each of these essential compounds is synthesized by a discrete sequence of enzymatic reactions; each enzyme is produced under the control of a specific gene. When an organism undergoes a gene mutation resulting in failure of one of these enzymes to function, the chain is broken and the end product is no longer produced. The organism must then obtain that compound from the environment: the compound has become a **growth factor** for the organism.

Different microbial species vary widely in their growth factor requirements. The compounds involved are found in and are essential to all organisms; the differences in requirement reflect differences in synthetic abilities. Some species require no growth factors, while others (like some of the lactobacilli) have lost, by mutation, the ability to synthesize as many as 30–40 essential compounds and hence require them in the medium. This type of mutation can be readily induced in the laboratory.

ENVIRONMENTAL FACTORS AFFECTING GROWTH

A suitable growth medium must contain all the nutrients required by the organism to be cultivated, and such factors as pH, temperature, and aeration must be carefully controlled. A liquid medium is used; the medium can be gelled for special purposes by adding agar or silica gel. Agar, a polysaccharide extract of a marine alga, is uniquely suitable for microbial cultivation because it is resistant to microbial action and because it dissolves at 100° C but does not gel until cooled below 45° C; cells can be suspended in the medium at 45° C and the medium quickly cooled to a gel without harming them.

Nutrients

On the previous pages the function of each type of nutrient is described and a list of suitable substances presented. In general, the following must be provided: (1) Hydrogen donors and acceptors: about 2 gm/liter. (2) Carbon source: about 1 gm/liter. (3) Nitrogen source: about 1 gm/liter. (4) Minerals: sulfur and phosphorus, about 50 mg/liter of each; trace elements, 0.1−1 mg/liter of each. (5) Growth factors: amino acids, purines, pyrimidines, about 50 mg/liter of each; vitamins, 0.1−1 mg/liter of each.

For studies of microbial metabolism it is usually necessary to prepare a completely synthetic medium in which the characteristics and concentration of every ingredient are exactly known. Otherwise it is much cheaper and simpler to use natural materials such as yeast extract, protein digest, or similar substances.

Most free-living microbes will grow well on yeast extract; parasitic forms may require special substances found only in blood or in extracts of animal tissues.

For many organisms, a single compound (such as an amino acid) may serve as energy source, carbon source, and nitrogen source; others require a separate compound for each. If natural materials for non-synthetic media are deficient in any particular nutrient, they must be supplemented.

Hydrogen Ion Concentration (pH)

Most organisms have a fairly narrow optimal pH range. The optimal pH must be empirically determined for each species. Most organisms grow best at a pH of 6.0–8.0, although some forms have optima as low as pH 2.0 *(Thiobacillus thiooxidans)* and others have optima of pH 8.5 *(Alcaligenes faecalis).*

Temperature

Different microbial species vary widely in their optimal temperature ranges for growth: Psychrophilic forms grow best at low temperatures (15–20° C); mesophilic forms grow best at 30–37° C; and thermophilic forms grow best at 50–60° C. Most organisms are mesophilic; 30° C is optimal for many free-living forms and the body temperature of the host for symbionts of warm-blooded animals. The upper end of the temperature range tolerated by any given species correlates well with the general thermal stability of that species' proteins as measured in cell extracts.

Aeration

The role of oxygen as hydrogen acceptor is discussed in Chapter 5. Many organisms are obligate aerobes, specifically requiring oxygen as hydrogen acceptor; some are facultative, able to live aerobically or anaerobically; and others are obligate anaerobes, requiring a substance other than oxygen as hydrogen acceptor and being sensitive to oxygen inhibition.

The toxicity of O_2 results from its reduction by enzymes in the cell (such as flavoproteins) to hydrogen peroxide (H_2O_2) and the even more toxic free radical, superoxide (O_2^-). Aerobes and aerotolerant anaerobes are protected from these products by the presence of superoxide dismutase, an enzyme which catalyses the reaction

$$2O_2^- + 2H^+ \rightarrow O_2 + H_2O_2$$

and by the presence of catalase, an enzyme which catalyses the reaction

$$2H_2O_2 \rightarrow 2H_2O + O_2$$

One exception to this rule is the lactic acid bacteria, aerotolerant anaerobes which do not contain catalase. This group relies instead on peroxidases, which reduce H_2O_2 to $2H_2O$ at the expense of oxidizable organic substrates. All strict anaerobes lack both superoxide dismutase and catalase; the former enzyme is indispensable for survival in the presence of O_2.

The supply of air to cultures of aerobes is a major technical problem. Vessels are usually shaken mechanically to introduce oxygen into the medium, or air is forced through the medium by pressure or suction. The diffusion of oxygen often becomes the limiting factor in growing aerobic bacteria; when a cell concentration of $4–5 \times 10^9$ per ml is reached, the rate of diffusion of oxygen to the cells sharply limits the rate of further growth.

Obligate anaerobes, on the other hand, present the problem of oxygen exclusion. Many methods are available for this: Reducing agents such as sodium thioglycollate can be added to liquid cultures; tubes of agar can be sealed with a layer of petrolatum and paraffin; or the culture vessel can be placed in a container from which the oxygen is removed by evacuation or by chemical means.

Ionic Strength & Osmotic Pressure

To a lesser extent, such factors as osmotic pressure and salt concentration may have to be controlled. For most organisms the properties of ordinary media are satisfactory; but for marine forms and organisms adapted to growth in strong sugar solutions, for example, these factors must be considered. Organisms requiring high salt concentrations are called **halophilic**; those requiring high osmotic pressures are called **osmophilic.**

Most bacteria are able to tolerate a wide range of external osmotic pressures and ionic strengths because of their ability to regulate internal osmolality and ion concentration. Osmolality appears to be regulated by the active transport of K^+ ions into the cell; internal ionic strength is kept constant by a compensating excretion of the positively charged organic polyamine putrescine. Since putrescine carries several positive charges per molecule, a large drop in ionic strength is effected at only a small cost in osmotic strength.

CULTIVATION METHODS

Two problems will be considered: the choice of a suitable medium, and the isolation of a bacterial organism in pure culture.

The Medium

The technic used and the type of medium selected depend upon the nature of the investigation. In general, 3 situations may be encountered: (1) One may need to raise a crop of cells of a particular species which is on hand; (2) one may need to determine the numbers and types of organisms present in a given material; or (3) one may wish to isolate a particular type of microorganism from a natural source.

A. Growing Cells of a Given Species: Microorganisms observed microscopically to be growing in a natural environment may prove exceedingly difficult to grow in pure culture in an artificial medium. Certain parasitic forms, for example, have never been cultivated outside the host. In general, however, a suitable medium can be devised by carefully reproducing the conditions found in the organism's natural environment. The pH, temperature, and aeration are simple to duplicate; the nutrients present the major problem. The contribution made by the living environment is important and difficult to analyze; a parasite may require an extract of the host tissue, and a free-living form may require a substance excreted by a microorganism with which it is associated in nature. Considerable experimentation may be necessary in order to determine the requirements of the organism, and success depends upon providing a suitable source of each category of nutrient listed at the beginning of this chapter. The cultivation of obligate parasites, such as rickettsiae, is a special problem and is discussed in Chapter 28.

B. Microbiologic Examination of Natural Materials: A given natural material may contain many different micro-environments, each providing a niche for a different species. Plating a sample of the materials under one set of conditions will allow a selected group of forms to produce colonies but will cause many other types to be overlooked. For this reason it is customary to plate out samples of the material using as many different media and conditions of incubation as is practicable. Six to 8 different culture conditions are not an unreasonable number if most of the forms present are to be discovered.

Since every type of organism present must have a chance to grow, solid media are used and crowding of colonies is avoided. Otherwise, competition will prevent some types from forming colonies.

C. Isolation of a Particular Type of Microorganism: A small sample of soil, if handled properly, will yield a different type of organism for every micro-environment present. For fertile soil (moist, aerated, rich in minerals and organic matter) this means that hundreds or even thousands of types can be isolated. This is done by selecting for the desired type. One gm of soil, for example, is inoculated into a flask of liquid medium which has been made up for the purpose of favoring one type of organism, eg, aerobic nitrogen fixers (Azotobacter). In this case the medium contains no combined nitrogen and is incubated aerobically. If cells of Azotobacter are present in the soil, they will grow well in this medium; forms unable to fix nitrogen will grow only to the extent that the soil has introduced contaminating fixed nitrogen into the medium. When the culture is fully grown, therefore, the percentage of Azotobacter in the total population will have increased greatly; the method is thus called "enrichment culture." Transfer of a sample of this culture to fresh medium will result in further enrichment of Azotobacter; after several serial transfers, the culture can be plated out on a solidified enrichment medium and colonies of Azotobacter isolated.

Liquid medium is used to permit competition and hence optimal selection, even when the desired type is represented in the soil as only a few cells in a population of millions. Advantage can be taken of "natural enrichment." For example, in looking for kerosene oxidizers, oil-laden soil is chosen since such soil is already an enrichment environment for such forms.

Enrichment culture, then, is a procedure whereby the medium is prepared so as to duplicate the natural environment ("niche") of the desired microorganism, thereby selecting for it. An important principle involved in such selection is the following: The organism selected for will be the type whose nutritional requirements are barely satisfied. Azotobacter, for example, grows best in a medium containing organic nitrogen, but its minimum requirement is the presence of N_2; hence it is selected for in a medium containing N_2 as the sole nitrogen source. If organic nitrogen is added to the medium, the conditions no longer select for Azotobacter but rather for a form for which organic nitrogen is the minimum requirement.

When searching for a particular type of organism in a natural material, it is advantageous to plate the organisms obtained on a differential medium if available. A differential medium is one which will cause the colonies of a particular type of organism to have a distinctive appearance. For example, colonies of *Escherichia coli* have a characteristic iridescent sheen on agar containing the dyes eosin and methylene blue (EMB agar). EMB agar containing a high concentration of one sugar will also cause organisms which ferment that sugar to form reddish colonies. Differential media are used for such purposes as recognizing the presence of enteric bacteria in water or milk and the presence of certain pathogens in clinical specimens from patients.

Table 6–2 presents some examples of enrichment culture conditions and the types of bacteria which they will select.

Isolation of Microorganisms in Pure Culture

In order to study the properties of a given organism, it is necessary to handle it in pure culture free of all other types of organisms. To do this, a single cell must be isolated from all other cells and cultivated in such a manner that its collective progeny also remain isolated. Several methods are available:

A. Plating: Unlike cells in a liquid medium, cells in or on a gelled medium are immobilized. Therefore, if few enough cells are placed in or on a gelled medium, each cell will grow into an isolated colony. The ideal gelling agent for most microbiologic media is **agar**, an acidic polysaccharide extracted from certain red algae. A 1.5–2% suspension in water dissolves at 100° C, forming a clear solution which gels at 45° C. Thus, a sterile agar solution can be cooled to 50° C, bacteria or other microbial cells added, and then quickly cooled below 45° C to form a gel. (Although most microbial cells are killed at 50° C, the time-course of the killing process is sufficiently slow at this temperature to permit this procedure. See Fig 7–3.) Once gelled, agar will not again liquefy until it is heated above 80° C, so that any temperature suitable for the incubation of a microbial culture can subsequently be used. In the pour-plate method, a suspension of cells is mixed with melted agar at 50° C and poured into a Petri dish. When the agar solidifies, the cells are immobilized in the agar and grow into colonies. If the

Table 6–2. Some enrichment cultures.

Constituents of all media: $MgSO_4$, K_2HPO_4, $FeCl_3$, $CaCl_2$, $CaCO_3$, trace elements.

Nitrogen Source	Carbon Source	Atmosphere	Illumination	Predominant Organism Initially Enriched
N_2	CO_2	Aerobic or anaerobic	Dark	None
			Light	Blue-green algae
	Alcohol, fatty acids, etc	Anaerobic	Dark	None
		Air	Dark	Azotobacter
	Glucose	Anaerobic	Dark	*Clostridium pasteurianum*
		Air	Dark	Azotobacter
$NaNO_3$	CO_2	Aerobic or anaerobic	Dark	None
			Light	Green and blue-green algae
	Alcohol, fatty acids, etc	Anaerobic	Dark	Denitrifiers
		Air	Dark	Aerobes
	Glucose	Anaerobic	Dark	Fermenters
		Air	Dark	Aerobes
NH_4Cl	CO_2	Anaerobic	Dark	None
		Aerobic	Dark	Nitrosomonas
		Aerobic or anaerobic	Light	Green and blue-green algae
	Alcohol, fatty acids, etc	Anaerobic	Dark	Sulfate or carbonate reducers
		Aerobic	Dark	Aerobes
	Glucose	Anaerobic	Dark	Fermenters
		Aerobic	Dark	Aerobes

cell suspension was sufficiently dilute, the colonies will be well separated, so that each has a high probability of being derived from a single cell. To make certain of this, however, it is necessary to pick a colony of the desired type, suspend it in water, and replate. Repeating this procedure several times ensures that a pure culture will be obtained.

Alternatively, the original suspension can be streaked on an agar plate with a wire loop. As the streaking continues, fewer and fewer cells are left on the loop, and finally the loop may deposit single cells on the agar. The plate is incubated and any well-isolated colony is then removed, resuspended in water, and again streaked on agar. If a suspension is streaked (and not just a bit of growth from a colony or slant), this method is just as reliable and much faster than the pour-plate method.

B. Dilution: A much less reliable method is that of extinction dilution. The suspension is serially diluted and samples of each dilution are plated. If only a few samples of a particular dilution exhibit growth, it is presumed that some of these cultures started from single cells. This method is not used unless plating is for some reason impossible. An undesirable feature of this method is that it can only be used to isolate the predominant type of organism in a mixed population.

●   ●   ●

General References

Books

Alexander M: *Microbial Ecology.* Wiley, 1971.

Guirard BM, Snell EE: Nutritional requirements of microorganisms. Pages 33–93 in: *The Bacteria.* Vol 4: *Physiology of Growth.* Gunsalus IC, Stanier RY (editors). Academic Press, 1962.

Luria SE: The bacterial protoplasm: Composition and organization. Page 1 in: *The Bacteria.* Vol 1: *Structure.* Gunsalus IC, Stanier RY (editors). Academic Press, 1960.

Meynell GG, Meynell E: *Theory and Practice in Experimental Bacteriology.* Cambridge Univ Press, 1965.

Precht H (editor): *Temperature and Life.* Springer, 1973.

Schlegel HG (editor): *Anreicherungskultur und Mutantenauslese. [Enrichment Culture and Mutant Selection.]* Fischer (Stuttgart), 1965. [The only systematic description of enrichment methods. Many of the articles are in English.]

Articles & Reviews

Brown AD: Aspects of bacterial response to the ionic environment. Bacteriol Rev 28:296, 1964.

Hutner SH: Inorganic nutrition. Annu Rev Microbiol 26:313, 1972.

Morris JG: The physiology of obligate anaerobiosis. Adv Microb Physiol 12:169, 1975.

Nielands JB: Hydroxamic acids in nature. Science 156:1443, 1967.

Wang CC, Newton A: Iron transport in *Escherichia coli:* Roles of energy-dependent uptake and 2,3-dihydroxybenzoylserine. J Bacteriol 98:1142, 1969.

7...
The Growth & Death of Microorganisms

DEFINITION & MEASUREMENT OF GROWTH

The Meaning of Growth

Growth is the orderly increase in all of the components of an organism. Thus, the increase in size which results when a cell takes up water or deposits lipid is not true growth. Cell multiplication is a consequence of growth; in unicellular organisms, multiplication leads to an increase in the number of individuals making up a population or a culture.

The Measurement of Growth

Microbial growth can be measured in terms of cell concentration (the number of cells per unit volume of culture) or of cell density (dry weight of cells per unit volume of culture). These 2 parameters are not always equivalent because the average dry weight of the cell varies at different stages in the history of the culture. Nor are they of equal significance: In studies on microbial biochemistry or nutrition, cell density is the significant quantity; in studies on microbial inactivation, cell concentration is the significant quantity.

A. Cell Concentration: The viable cell count (Table 8−1) is usually considered the measure of cell concentration. However, the general practice is to measure the light absorption or light scattering of a culture by photoelectric means and to relate viable counts to optical measurements in the form of a standard curve. By means of the standard curve, all further optical readings can be converted to cell concentration. However, it is essential that a separate standard curve be determined for each stage in the growth of the culture so that differences in average cell size can be taken into account.

B. Cell Density: Since it is technically difficult to perform a large number of dry weight measurements, and since such measurements are accurate only with relatively large amounts of cells, various indirect methods are used. These include photoelectric measurements, nitrogen determination, and centrifugation in special vessels. In each case it is necessary to construct a standard curve equating the measurement values with known dry weights.

EXPONENTIAL GROWTH

The Growth Constant

Since the 2 new cells produced by the growth and division of a single cell are each capable of growing at the same rate as the parent cell, the number of cells in a culture increases with time as a geometric progression—ie, exponentially.

The rate of growth of a culture at a given moment is directly proportionate to the number of cells present at that moment. This relationship is given by the following equation:

$$\frac{dN}{dt} = kN \qquad \ldots\,(1)$$

Integration of the above expression gives:

$$N = N_0 e^{kt} \qquad \ldots\,(2)$$

where N_0 is the number of cells at time zero and N is the number of cells at any later time t.

In equation (2) above, k is the growth constant. Solving the equation for k gives:

$$k = \frac{\ln(N/N_0)}{t} \qquad \ldots\,(3)$$

Thus, k represents the rate at which the natural logarithm of cell number increases with time and can be determined graphically as shown in Fig 7−1.

The Generation

In practice it is customary to express the growth rate of a microbial culture in terms of generations per hour. For organisms which reproduce by binary fission, a generation is defined as a doubling of cell number. Thus, the number of cells (N) increases with generations (g) as follows:

g	N
0	1
1	2
2	4
3	8
4	16
5	32

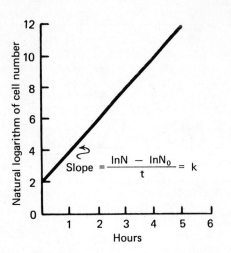

Figure 7—1. The rate at which the natural logarithm of cell number increases with time.

This relationship can be expressed as follows:

$$N = N_0 2^g \qquad \dots (4)$$

Combining equations (2) and (4), we find

$$N_0 e^{kt} = N_0 2^g \qquad \dots (5)$$

Equation (5) can be rearranged to give:

$$\frac{g}{t} = \frac{k}{\ln 2} \qquad \dots (6)$$

Equation (6) thus relates g/t (generations per hour) with k, the growth constant.

The number of generations per hour is usually determined by plotting cell number against time on a semilogarithmic scale and reading off directly the time required for the number to double. For example, if such a plot shows the doubling time ("generation time") to be 40 minutes, the growth rate of the culture is said to be 1.5 generations per hour.

Alternatively, the generation time can be calculated directly from equation (4), which can be solved for g (the number of generations) as follows:

$$g = \frac{\log N - \log N_0}{\log 2} \qquad \dots (7)$$

Thus, for example, if an inoculum of 10^3 cells grows exponentially to 1×10^9 cells,

$$g = \frac{\log(10^9) - \log(10^3)}{\log 2} = \frac{9 - 3}{0.3} = 20 \text{ generations}$$

If, for example, this growth required 13.3 hours, the growth rate was 20/13.3, or 1.5 generations per hour.

THE GROWTH CURVE

If a liquid medium is inoculated with microbial cells taken from a culture which has previously been grown to saturation and the number of viable cells per ml determined periodically and plotted, a curve of the type shown in Fig 7—2 is usually obtained. The curve may be discussed in terms of 6 phases, represented by the letters A—F (Table 7—1).

The Lag Phase (A)

The lag phase represents a period during which the cells, depleted of metabolites and enzymes as the result of the unfavorable conditions which obtained at the end of their previous culture history, adapt to their new environment. Enzymes and intermediates are formed and accumulate until they are present in concentrations which permit growth to resume.

If the cells are taken from an entirely different medium, it often happens that they are genetically incapable of growth in the new medium. In such cases, the lag represents the period necessary for a few mutants in the inoculum to multiply sufficiently for a net increase in cell number to be apparent.

The Exponential Phase (C)

During the exponential phase, the mathematics of which has already been discussed, the cells are in steady state. New cell material is being synthesized at a constant rate, but the new material is itself catalytic and the mass increases in an exponential manner. This continues until one of 2 things happens: Either one or more nutrients in the medium becomes exhausted, or toxic metabolic products accumulate and inhibit growth. For aerobic organisms, the nutrient which becomes limiting is usually oxygen: When the cell concentration exceeds about 1×10^7/ml (in the case of bacteria), the growth rate will decrease unless oxygen is forced into the medium by agitation or by bubbling in air. When the cell concentration reaches $4-5 \times 10^9$/ml, the rate of oxygen diffusion cannot meet the

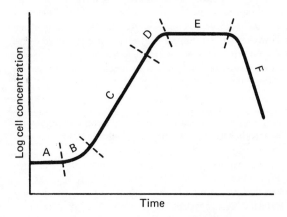

Figure 7—2. Cell concentration curve.

Table 7–1.

Section of Curve	Phase	Growth Rate
A	Lag	Zero
B	Acceleration	Increasing
C	Exponential	Constant
D	Retardation	Decreasing
E	Maximum stationary	Zero
F	Decline	Negative (death)

demand even in an aerated medium, and growth is progressively slowed.

The Maximum Stationary Phase (E)

Eventually, the exhaustion of nutrients or the accumulation of toxic products causes growth to cease completely. In most cases, however, cell turnover takes place in the stationary phase: There is a slow loss of cells through death, which is just balanced by the formation of new cells through growth and division. When this occurs, the total cell count slowly increases although the viable count stays constant.

The Phase of Decline (the Death Phase, F)

After a period of time in stationary phase, which varies with the organism and with the culture conditions, the death rate increases until it reaches a steady level. The mathematics of steady-state death are discussed below. Frequently, after the majority of cells have died, the death rate decreases drastically, so that a small number of survivors may persist for months or even years in the culture. This persistence may in some cases reflect cell turnover, a few cells growing at the expense of nutrients released from cells which die and lyse.

THE MAINTENANCE OF CELLS IN EXPONENTIAL PHASE

Cells can be maintained in exponential phase by transferring them repeatedly into fresh medium of identical composition while they are still growing exponentially. Two devices have been invented for carrying out this process automatically: the chemostat and the turbidostat.

The Chemostat

This device consists of a culture vessel equipped with an overflow siphon and a mechanism for dripping in fresh medium from a reservoir at a regulated rate. The medium in the culture vessel is stirred by a stream of sterile air; each drop of fresh medium that enters causes a drop of culture to siphon out.

The medium is prepared so that one nutrient

limits growth yield. The vessel is inoculated, and the cells grow until the limiting nutrient is exhausted; fresh medium from the reservoir is then allowed to flow in, at such a rate that the cells use up the limiting nutrient as fast as it is supplied. Under these conditions, the cell concentration remains constant and the growth rate is directly proportionate to the flow rate of the medium.

The chemostat thus provides a steady-state culture of exponentially growing cells and permits the growth rate to be regulated. It has the disadvantage, however, that the growing cells are always in a state of semi-starvation for one nutrient and must be grown at less than maximal rate if good regulation is to be achieved. These disadvantages are not present in the turbidostat.

The Turbidostat

This device resembles the chemostat except that the flow of medium is controlled by a photoelectric mechanism which measures the turbidity of the culture. When the turbidity exceeds the chosen level, fresh medium is allowed to flow in. Thus, the cells can grow at maximum rate at a constant cell concentration. The growth rate can be controlled in the turbidostat only by varying the nature of the medium or the culture conditions (eg, temperature).

SYNCHRONOUS GROWTH

In ordinary cultures the cells are growing nonsynchronously: At any moment, cells are present in every possible stage of the division cycle. In order to study the sequence of events that takes place in a single cell during the division cycle, the culture must be synchronized.

Synchrony has been achieved for a variety of microorganisms by several technics. Some microorganisms, for example, go through one or 2 synchronous divisions when diluted from a stationary phase culture into fresh medium. In many cases, however, it is necessary to bring the cells into synchrony by a more involved process. Pneumococci, for example, will divide synchronously after several alternating periods of incubation at high and low temperature. *Escherichia coli* has been synchronized by 2 different methods: In one, a thymine-requiring mutant is starved for thymine until viability begins to drop. Replacing thymine in the culture then causes the surviving cells to undergo several synchronous divisions. In the other method, a heavy cell suspension is deposited in a filter paper pile. As the adsorbed cells divide, the newly formed daughter cells are released from the filter paper; they can be recovered as a synchronously dividing population by washing the paper briefly with warm medium.

In all cases, synchrony only persists for 1–4 cycles. After that time the cells become more and more out of phase until their division times become completely random.

GROWTH PARAMETERS

Physiologic studies may be carried out by introducing controlled variations in individual environmental factors and then quantitatively determining the effect of such variations on bacterial growth. To be most useful, experiments of this type should involve determination of meaningful growth parameters. Growth parameters which may be determined include total growth and exponential growth rate.

Total Growth

A culture eventually stops growing when one of 3 things occurs: (1) when one or more nutrients are exhausted; (2) when toxic products accumulate; or (3) when an unfavorable ion equilibrium develops (eg, unfavorable pH).

If total growth (G) is limited by exhaustion of a nutrient, then

$$G = KC \qquad \ldots (8)$$

where K is a constant and C is the initial concentration of the limiting nutrient. Such an equation implies a straight line relationship between C and G.

Exponential Growth Rates

If some nutrient is initially present at a sufficiently low concentration, metabolic intermediates will be formed at a limited rate and the overall growth rate will be a function of the concentration of the limiting nutrient. Experiments show that a hyperbolic curve results, in accordance with the following general equation:

$$R = R_K \frac{C}{C_1 + C} \qquad \ldots (9)$$

where R = Growth rate
R_K = Maximum rate reached with increasing concentration of nutrient
C = Concentration of the limiting nutrient
C_1 = Value of C at which $R = \frac{1}{2} R_K$

Total growth is a useful parameter in many microbial assays; for example, in the assay of a vitamin or a carbon source in some natural material. For most physiologic studies, however, growth rate is the most meaningful parameter. One method, for example, is to compare concentrations of nutrients or inhibitors which give half-maximal growth rates.

DEFINITION & MEASUREMENT OF DEATH

The Meaning of Death

For a microbial cell, death means the irreversible loss of the ability to reproduce (grow and divide). The empiric test of death is the culture of cells on solid media: A cell is considered dead if it fails to give rise to a colony on any medium. Obviously, then, the reliability of the test depends upon choice of medium and conditions: A culture in which 99% of the cells appear "dead" in terms of ability to form colonies on one medium may prove to be 100% viable if tested on another medium. Furthermore, the detection of a few viable cells in a large clinical specimen may not be possible by directly plating a sample, as the sample fluid itself may be inhibitory to microbial growth. In such cases, the sample may have to be diluted first into liquid medium, permitting the outgrowth of viable cells before plating.

The conditions of incubation in the first hour following treatment are also critical in the determination of "killing." For example, if bacterial cells are irradiated with ultraviolet light and plated immediately on any medium, it may appear that 99.99% of the cells have been killed. If such irradiated cells are first incubated in a suitable buffer for 20 minutes, however, plating will indicate only 10% killing. In other words, irradiation determines that a cell will "die" if plated immediately, but will live if allowed to repair irradiation damage before plating.

A microbial cell that is not physically disrupted is thus "dead" only in terms of the conditions used to test viability.

The Measurement of Death

When dealing with microorganisms, one does not customarily measure the death of an individual cell but the death of a population. This is a statistical problem: Under any condition which may lead to cell death, the probability of a given cell's dying is constant per unit time. For example, if a condition is employed which causes 90% of the cells to die in the first 10 minutes, the probability of any one cell dying in a 10-minute interval is 0.9. Thus, it may be expected that 90% of the surviving cells will die in each succeeding 10-minute interval, and a death curve similar to that shown in Fig 7–3 will be obtained.

The number of cells dying in each time interval is thus a function of the number of survivors present, so that death of a population proceeds as an exponential process according to the general formula:

$$S = S_0 e^{-kt} \qquad \ldots (10)$$

where S_0 is the number of survivors at time zero, and S is the number of survivors at any later time t. As in the case of exponential growth, $-k$ represents the rate of exponential death when the fraction $ln\ (S/S_0)$ is plotted against time.

The one-hit curve shown in Fig 7–3A is typical of the kinetics of inactivation observed with many antimicrobial agents. The fact that it is a straight line from time zero (dose zero)—rather than exhibiting an initial shoulder—means that a single "hit" by the inactivating agent is sufficient to kill the cell, ie, only a single target must be damaged in order for the entire cell to be inactivated. Such a target might be the chromosome of a uninucleate bacterium or the cell membrane; conversely, it could not be an enzyme or other cell constituent which is present in multiple copies.

A cell which contains several copies of the target to be inactivated exhibits a multi-hit curve of the type shown in Fig 7–3B. Extrapolation of the straight-line portion of the curve to the ordinate permits an estimate of the number of targets (eg, 4 in Fig 7–3B).

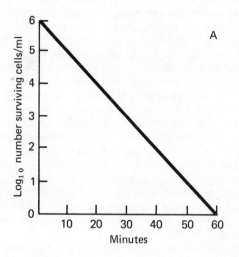

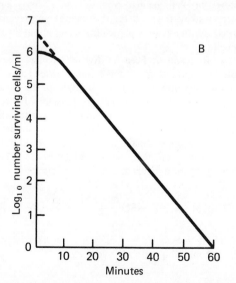

Figure 7–3. Death curve of microorganisms. *A:* Single-hit curve. *B:* Multi-hit curve. The straight-line portion extrapolates to 6.5, corresponding to 4×10^6 cells. The number of **targets** is thus 4×10^6, or 4 per cell.

Sterilization

In practice, we speak of "sterilization" as the process of killing all of the organisms in a preparation. From the above considerations, however, we see that no set of conditions is guaranteed to sterilize a preparation. Consider Fig 7–3, for example. At 60 minutes, there is one organism (10^0) left per ml. At 70 minutes there would be 10^{-1}, at 80 minutes 10^{-2}, etc. By 10^{-2} organisms per ml we mean that in a total volume of 100 ml, one organism would survive. How long, then, does it take to "sterilize" the culture? All we can say is that after any given time of treatment, the probability of having any surviving organisms in 1 ml is that given by the curve. After 2 hours, in the above example, the probability is 1×10^{-6}. This would usually be considered a safe sterilization time, but a thousand-liter lot might still contain one viable organism.

Note that such calculations depend upon the curve's remaining unchanged in slope over the entire time range. Unfortunately, it is very common for the curve to bend upward after a certain period, as a result of the population being heterogeneous with respect to sensitivity to the inactivation agent. Extrapolations are thus dangerous and can lead to such errors as those which were encountered in early preparations of sterile poliovaccine.

The Effect of Drug Concentration

When antimicrobial substances (drugs) are used to inactivate microbial cells, it is commonly observed that the concentration of drug employed is related to the time required to kill a given fraction of the population, as shown in the following expression:

$$C^n t = K \qquad \ldots . (11)$$

where C is the drug concentration, t is the time required to kill a given fraction of the cells, and n and K are constants.

This expression says that, for example, if $n = 5$ (as it is for phenol), then doubling the concentration of the drug will reduce the time required to achieve the same extent of inactivation 32-fold. That the effectiveness of a drug varies with the fifth power of the concentration suggests that 5 molecules of the drug are required to inactivate a cell, although there is no direct chemical evidence for this conclusion.

In order to determine the value of n for any drug, inactivation curves are obtained for each of several concentrations, and the time required at each concentration to inactivate a fixed fraction of the population is determined. For example, let the first concentration used be C_1 and the time required to inactivate 99% of the cells be t_1. Similarly, let C_2 and t_2 be the second concentration and time required to inactivate 99% of the cells. From equation (11), we see that

$$C_1{}^n t_1 = C_2{}^n t_2 \qquad \ldots . (12)$$

Solving for n gives:

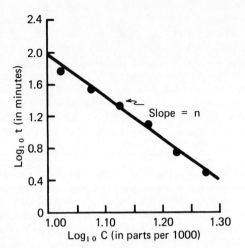

Figure 7–4. Relationship between drug concentration and time required to kill a given fraction of a cell population.

$$n = \frac{\log t_2 - \log t_1}{\log C_1 - \log C_2}$$

Thus, n can be determined by measuring the slope of the line which results when $\log t$ is plotted against $\log C$ (Fig 7–4). If n is experimentally determined in this manner, K can be determined by substituting observed values for C, t, and n in equation (11).

ANTIMICROBIAL AGENTS

Definitions

The following terms are commonly employed in connection with antimicrobial agents and their uses.

A. Bacteriostatic: Having the property of inhibiting bacterial multiplication; multiplication resumes upon removal of the agent.

B. Bactericidal: Having the property of killing bacteria. Bactericidal action differs from bacteriostasis only in being irreversible; ie, the "killed" organism can no longer reproduce, even after being removed from contact with the agent. In some cases the agent causes lysis (dissolving) of the cells; in other cases the cells remain intact and may even continue to be metabolically active.

C. Sterile: Free of life of every kind. Sterilization may be accomplished by filtration (in the case of liquids or air) or by treatment with microbicidal agents. Since the criterion of death for microorganisms is the inability to reproduce, sterile material may contain intact, metabolizing microbial cells.

D. Disinfectant: A chemical substance used to kill microorganisms on surfaces, but too toxic to be applied directly to tissues.

E. Septic: Characterized by the presence of pathogenic microbes in living tissue.

F. Aseptic: Characterized by absence of pathogenic microbes.

Possible Modes of Action

Antibacterial agents may affect cells in a variety of ways, many of which are poorly understood. Some broad generalizations can be made, however. At high concentrations many agents are so destructive that, among other things, the cell proteins precipitate from the colloidal state ("coagulate"). Under certain conditions, some agents may specifically disrupt the cell membrane. Many of the cell's essential enzymes possess sulfhydryl (–SH) groups and can only function if these remain free and reduced; hence agents which oxidize or combine with sulfhydryl groups are strongly inhibitory. Finally, many agents may act by interfering with one or a few specific enzymatic reactions (chemical antagonism).

A. Protein Denaturation: Proteins exist in a folded, 3-dimensional state, determined by intramolecular covalent disulfide linkages and a number of noncovalent linkages such as ionic, hydrophobic, and hydrogen bonds. This state is called the **tertiary structure** of the protein; it is readily disrupted by a number of physical or chemical agents, causing the protein to become nonfunctional. The disruption of the tertiary structure of a protein is called protein denaturation.

B. Disruption of Cell Membrane or Wall: The cell membrane acts as a selective barrier, allowing some solutes to pass through and excluding others. Indeed, some compounds are actively transported through the membrane, becoming concentrated within the cell. The membrane is also the site of many enzymes involved in the biosynthesis of components of the cell envelope. Substances which concentrate at the cell surface may alter the physical and chemical properties of the membrane, preventing its normal function and therefore killing or inhibiting the cell.

The cell wall acts as a corseting structure, protecting the cell against osmotic lysis. Thus, agents which destroy the wall (eg, lysozyme) or prevent its normal synthesis (eg, penicillin) bring about lysis of the cell.

C. Removal of Free Sulfhydryl Groups: Enzyme proteins containing cysteine have side-chains terminating in sulfhydryl groups. In addition to these, at least one key enzyme (coenzyme A, required for acyl group transfer) contains a free sulfhydryl group. Such enzymes and coenzymes cannot function unless the sulfhydryl groups remain free and reduced. Oxidizing agents thus interfere with metabolism by tying neighboring sulfhydryls in disulfide linkages:

$$R-SH + HS-R \xrightarrow{-2H} R-S-S-R$$

Many metals such as mercuric ion likewise interfere by combining with sulfhydryls:

$$\begin{matrix} R-SH \\ R-SH \end{matrix} + \underset{Cl}{\overset{Cl}{Hg}} \longrightarrow \begin{matrix} R-S \\ R-S \end{matrix}{>}Hg + 2HCl$$

There are many sulfhydryl enzymes in the cell; therefore, oxidizing agents and heavy metals do widespread damage. The exact reason for the requirement of free sulfhydryl groups is not certain, although in many cases (eg, coenzyme A) they probably represent the normal site of substrate attachment.

D. Chemical Antagonism: The interference by a chemical agent with the normal reaction between a specific enzyme and its substrate is known as "chemical antagonism." The antagonist acts by combining with some part of the holoenzyme (either the protein apoenzyme, the mineral activator, or the coenzyme), thereby preventing attachment of the normal substrate. ("Substrate" is here used in the broad sense to include cases in which the inhibitor combines with the apoenzyme, thereby preventing attachment to it of coenzyme.)

An antagonist combines with an enzyme because of its chemical affinity for an essential site on that enzyme. Enzymes perform their catalytic function by virtue of their affinity for their natural substrates; hence any compound structurally resembling a substrate in essential aspects may also have an affinity for the enzyme. If this affinity is great enough, the "analogue" will displace the normal substrate from the enzyme and prevent the proper reaction from taking place.

Many holoenzymes include a mineral ion either as a bridge between enzyme and coenzyme or between enzyme and substrate. Chemicals which combine readily with these minerals will again prevent attachment of coenzyme or substrate; for example, carbon monoxide and cyanide ($-C\equiv N$) combine with the iron atom in the porphyrin enzymes and prevent their function in respiration.

Chemical antagonists can be conveniently discussed under 2 headings: antagonists of energy-yielding processes, and antagonists of biosynthetic processes. The former include poisons of respiratory enzymes (carbon monoxide, cyanide) and of oxidative phosphorylation (dinitrophenol); the latter include analogues of the building-blocks of proteins (amino acids) and of nucleic acids (nucleotides). In some cases the analogue simply prevents incorporation of the normal metabolite (eg, 5-methyltryptophan prevents incorporation of tryptophan into protein), and in other cases the analogue replaces the normal metabolite in the macromolecule, causing it to be nonfunctional. The incorporation of *p*-fluorophenylalanine in place of phenylalanine in proteins is an example of the latter type of antagonism.

Reversal of Antibacterial Action

In the section on definitions, the point was made that bacteriostatic action is, by definition, reversible. Reversal can be brought about in several ways:

A. Removal of Agent: When cells which are inhibited by the presence of a bacteriostatic agent are removed by centrifugation, washed thoroughly in the centrifuge, and resuspended in fresh growth medium, they will resume normal multiplication.

B. Reversal by Substrate: When a chemical antagonist of the analogue type forms a dissociating complex with the enzyme, it is possible to displace it by adding a high concentration of the normal substrate. Such cases are termed "competitive inhibition." The ratio of inhibitor concentration to concentration of substrate reversing the inhibition is called the **antibacterial index**; it is usually very high (100–10,000), indicating a much greater affinity of enzyme for its normal substrate.

C. Inactivation of Agent: Agents can often be inactivated by adding to the medium a substance which combines with it, preventing its combination with cellular constituents. For example, mercuric ion can be inactivated by addition to the medium of sulfhydryl compounds such as thioglycollic acid.

D. Protection Against Lysis: Osmotic lysis can be prevented by making the medium isotonic for naked bacterial protoplasts. Concentrations of 10–20% sucrose are required. Under such conditions penicillin-induced protoplasts remain viable and continue to grow as L forms.

Resistance to Antibacterial Agents

The ability of bacteria to become resistant to antibacterial agents is an important factor in their control. The mechanisms by which resistance is acquired are discussed on p 108.

Physical Agents

A. Heat: Application of heat is the simplest means of sterilizing materials, providing the material is itself resistant to heat damage. A temperature of 100° C will kill all but spore forms of bacteria within 2–3 minutes; a temperature of 121° C for 15 minutes is utilized to kill spores. Steam is generally used, both because bacteria are more quickly killed when moist and because steam provides a means for distributing heat to all parts of the sterilizing vessel. Steam must be kept at a pressure of 15 lb/square inch above atmospheric pressure to obtain a temperature of 121° C; autoclaves or pressure cookers are used for this purpose. For sterilizing materials which must remain dry, circulating hot air electric ovens are available; since heat is less effective on dry material, it is customary to apply a temperature of 160–170° C for 1 hour or more.

Under the conditions described above (ie, excessive temperatures applied for long periods of time), heat undoubtedly acts by denaturing cell proteins and by disrupting cell membranes.

B. Radiation: Ultraviolet light is sometimes used as a sterilizing agent. Its action is due in part to the production of peroxides ($R-O-O-R$) in the medium, which in turn act as oxidizing agents. Some of the more penetrating radiations, such as x-rays, ionize (and hence inactivate) the cell constituents through which they pass. However, some of the effect of x-ray irradiation can be traced again to peroxide formation, since cells can be partially protected by the exclusion of oxygen during irradiation.

Much of the killing action of radiation, however, is due to a direct effect on the nucleic acids of the cell. The major effect of ultraviolet absorption by DNA is the production of cross-links between neighboring pyrimidine residues (production of pyrimidine dimers).

Bacteria contain several enzymatic systems for the repair of DNA which contains pyrimidine dimers. One system, called **photoreactivation**, consists of an enzyme which cleaves the pyrimidine dimers. This enzyme is activated by visible light; hence, cells which have been "killed" by ultraviolet light can be reactivated by exposure to intense light of wavelength 400 nm. A second system is called the **dark repair** system. It requires the action of 4 enzymes operating in succession: (1) a specific endonuclease which makes single-strand cuts on either side of the dimer, excising it from the DNA; (2) a 3′ exonuclease, which widens the gap in the DNA strand by sequential digestion; (3) DNA polymerase, which fills in the gap by lengthening the 3′ end using the opposite strand as template; and (4) polynucleotide ligase, which rejoins the free ends. A third system consists of **replication followed by recombination** between sister DNA duplexes: replication produces 2 duplexes, each with a single-strand gap opposite a dimer; recombination produces a normal duplex, free of dimer-opposite-gap lesions.

The relative resistance of different bacterial strains to radiation and other agents which directly damage DNA is due to the relative effectiveness of their repair enzyme systems.

Chemical Agents

Because antibacterial agents must be safe for the host organism under the conditions employed (selective toxicity), the number of commonly used antibacterial agents is much lower than the number of cell poisons and inhibitors available. Thus cyanide, arsenic, and other poisons are not included below because of the limitations on their practical usefulness.

A. Alcohols: Compounds with the structure $R-CH_2OH$ (where R means "alkyl group") are toxic to cells at relatively high concentrations. Ethyl alcohol (CH_3CH_2OH) and isopropyl alcohol ($[CH_3]_2CHOH$) are commonly used. At the concentrations generally employed (70% aqueous solutions) they act as protein denaturants.

B. Phenol: Phenol and many phenolic compounds are strong antibacterial agents. At the high concentrations generally employed (1–2% aqueous solutions) they denature proteins.

C. Heavy Metal Ions: Mercury, copper, and silver salts are all protein denaturants at high concentrations but are too injurious to human tissues to be used in this manner. They are commonly used at very low concentrations, under which conditions they act by combining with sulfhydryl groups. Mercury can be made safer for external use by combining it with organic compounds (eg, Mercurochrome, Merthiolate). Except when used on clean skin surfaces these organic mercurials are of doubtful practical value, since they are readily inactivated by extraneous organic matter.

D. Oxidizing Agents: Strong oxidizing agents inactivate cells by oxidizing free sulfhydryl groups. Useful agents include hydrogen peroxide, iodine, hypochlorite, chlorine, and compounds slowly liberating chlorine (chloride of lime).

E. Alkylating Agents: A number of agents react with compounds in the cell to substitute alkyl groups for labile hydrogen atoms. The two agents of this type which are commonly used for disinfection purposes are formaldehyde (sold as the 37% aqueous solution **formalin**) and **ethylene oxide**. Ethylene oxide gas, rendered inexplosive by mixture with 90% CO_2 or a fluorocarbon, is the most reliable disinfectant available for dry surfaces. It is extensively used for the disinfection of surgical instruments and materials, which must be placed in special vacuum chambers for the purpose.

F. Detergents: Compounds which have the property of concentrating at interfaces are called "surface-active agents" or "detergents." The interface between the lipid-containing membrane of a bacterial cell and the surrounding aqueous medium attracts a particular class of surface-active compounds, namely, those possessing both a fat-soluble group and a water-soluble group. Long-chain hydrocarbons are very fat-soluble, while charged ions are very water-soluble; a compound possessing both structures will thus concentrate at the surface of the bacterial cell:

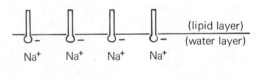

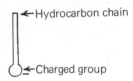

Two general types of such surface-active agents or detergents are known: anionic and cationic.

1. Anionic detergents—Detergents in which the long-chain hydrocarbon has a negative charge are called "anionic." These include soaps (sodium salts of long-chain carboxylic acids); synthetic products resembling soaps except that the carboxyl group is replaced by a sulfonic acid group; and bile salts, in which the fat-soluble portion has a steroid structure. Some examples are shown in Figs 7–6, 7–7, and 7–8.

The synthetic detergents have advantages in solubility and cost over the natural soaps (obtained by saponification of animal fat). Bile salts are notable in that they completely dissolve pneumococcus cells, thus providing an aid in identification.

2. Cationic detergents—The fat-soluble moiety can be made to have a positive charge by combining it with a quaternary (valence = +5) nitrogen atom (Fig 7–5).

Since the detergents concentrate at the cell membrane, and since the latter is a delicate, essential cell

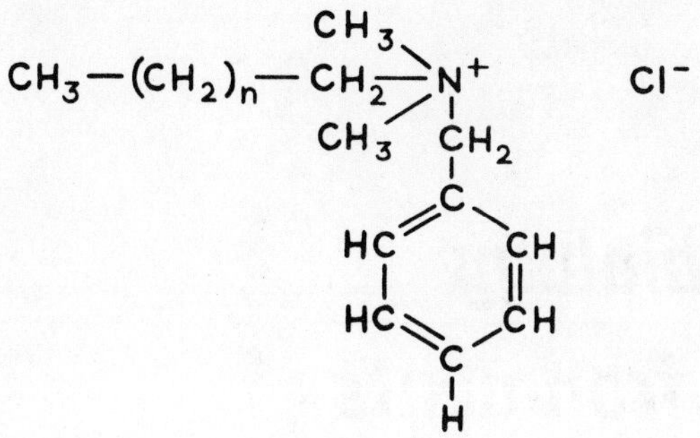

Figure 7–5. Alkyl-dimethyl-benzyl-ammonium chloride (Roccal).

component, the inference is drawn that detergents act by disrupting the normal function of the cell membrane. Support for this view comes from experiments showing that cells exposed to detergents leak soluble nitrogen and phosphorus compounds into the medium.

Chemotherapeutic Agents

To be a useful chemotherapeutic agent, a compound must be either bacteriostatic or bactericidal in vivo (action not reversed by substances in host tissues or fluids), and at the same time remain noninjurious to the host. These requirements for in vivo effectiveness and selective toxicity narrow the list of important chemotherapeutic agents to a very few compounds, principally the sulfonamides, the antibiotics, and the antituberculosis agents.

The natures and modes of action of these drugs are discussed in Chapter 10.

$$CH_3CH_2CH_2CH_2CH_2CH_2CH_2CH_2CH_2CH_2CH_2CH_2CH_2CH_2CH_2\overset{O}{\overset{/\!/}{C}}-O^-Na^+$$

Figure 7–6. Sodium salt of palmitic acid (a soap).

$$CH_3CH_2CH_2CH_2CH_2CH_2CH_2CH_2CH_2CH_2CH_2CH_2-O-\overset{O}{\underset{O}{\overset{\|}{\underset{\|}{S}}}}-O^-Na^+$$

Figure 7–7. Sodium lauryl sulfate (a synthetic anionic detergent, Duponol WA).

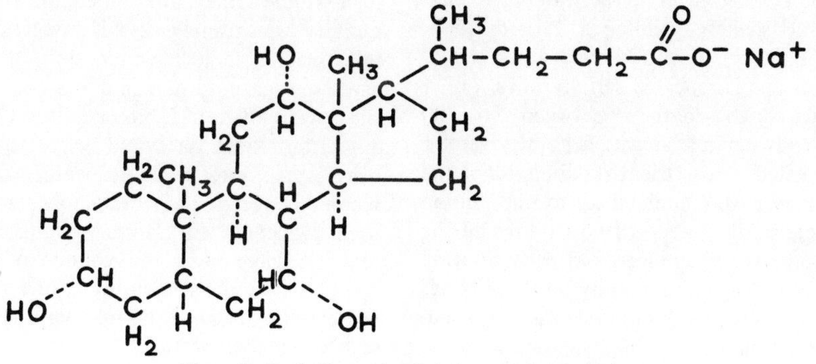

Figure 7–8. Sodium salt of cholic acid (a bile salt).

• • •

General References

Books

Gunsalus IC, Stanier RY (editors): *The Bacteria.* Vol 4: *Physiology of Growth.* Academic Press, 1962.

Hugo WB (editor): *Inhibition and Destruction of the Microbial Cell.* Academic Press, 1971.

Lawrence CA, Block SS (editors): *Disinfection, Sterilization, and Preservation.* Lea & Febiger, 1968.

Mandelstam J, McQuillen K (editors): *The Biochemistry of Bacterial Growth,* 2nd ed. Wiley, 1973.

Meynell GG, Meynell E: *Theory and Practice in Experimental Bacteriology.* Cambridge Univ Press, 1965.

Articles & Reviews

Novick A: Growth of bacteria. Annu Rev Microbiol 9:97, 1955.

Scherbaum OH: Synchronous division of microorganisms. Annu Rev Microbiol 14:283, 1960.

Senez JC: Some considerations on the energetics of bacterial growth. Bacteriol Rev 26:95, 1962.

8 . . .
The Microbiology
of Special Environments

WATER

Methods of Study

A. Quantitative Analysis: Bacteria cannot be accurately counted by microscopic examination unless there are at least 100 million (10^8) cells per ml. Natural bodies of water, however, rarely contain more than 10^5 cells per ml. The method employed is therefore the plate count: a measured volume of water is serially diluted (see below), following which 1 ml from each dilution tube is plated in nutrient agar and the resulting colonies counted. Since only those cells which are able to form colonies are counted, the method is also known as the "viable count."

A typical example of serial dilution would be the following: One ml of the water sample is aseptically transferred by pipet to 9 ml of sterile water. The mixture is thoroughly shaken, yielding a 1:10 dilution. (For obvious reasons, this is also known as the "10^{-1}" dilution.) The process is repeated serially until a dilution is reached which contains between 30–300 colony-forming cells per ml, at which point several 1 ml samples are plated in a nutrient medium. Since the original sample may have contained up to one million (10^6) viable bacteria, it is necessary to dilute all the way to 10^{-5}, plate 1 ml samples from each dilution tube, and then count the colonies only on those plates containing 30–300 colonies. The reasons for these numerical limits are that over 300 the plate becomes too crowded to permit each cell to form a visible colony, whereas below 30 the percent counting error becomes too great. (The statistical error of sampling can be calculated as follows: The standard deviation of

the count equals the square root of N, where N equals the average of many samples. Ninety-five percent of all samples will give counts within 2 standard deviations of the average. For example, if the average count is 36, then 95% of all samples will lie between 24 and 48 (36 ± 12). (In other words, within 95% confidence limits a sample count of 36 has an error of plus or minus 33%.) Assume that the above procedure has been carried out with the results shown in Table 8–1. The 10^{-3} dilution has a suitable number of colonies, the others being either too high or too low for accuracy. The original water sample is calculated to have contained 72,000 (72×10^3) viable cells per ml.

B. Qualitative Analysis: The methods of plating and enrichment culture (see Chapter 6) are used to obtain a picture of the aquatic bacterial population. While such methods are satisfactory for general biologic studies, they are inadequate for the purpose of sanitary water analysis; this involves the detection of intestinal bacteria in water, since their presence indicates sewage pollution and the consequent danger of the spread of enteric diseases (see Chapter 18). Since any enteric bacteria would be greatly outnumbered by other types present in the water samples, a selective technic is necessary in order to detect them. A widely used procedure for sanitary water analysis is as follows: A large measured volume of water is filtered through a sterilized membrane of a type which retains bacteria on its surface while permitting the rapid passage of smaller particles and water. The membrane is then transferred to the surface of an Endo agar plate. (Endo's medium is a selective, differential medium for coliform bacteria.) Upon incubation, coliform bacteria give rise to typical colonies on the surface of the membrane. The advantages of this method are speed (the complete test takes less than 24 hours) and quantitation, the number of coliform cells being determined for a given volume of water.

Control of Bacteria in Water

Bacteria are controlled in water only in connection with sanitation measures. Two problems are encountered: the sanitation of drinking water and the purification of sewage.

A. Sanitation of Drinking Water: Since drinking water supplies may at any time become contaminated with sewage and cause an epidemic of enteric disease,

Table 8–1. Example of a viable count.

Dilution	Plate Count*
Undiluted	⎱ Too crowded
10^{-1}	⎰ to count
10^{-2}	510
10^{-3}	72
10^{-4}	6
10^{-5}	1

*Each count is the average of 3 replicate plates.

water supplies for large cities are usually filtered and chlorinated. The presence of only 2 parts per million of chlorine will rid the water of the most dangerous contaminant, the typhoid organism. Before chlorination, however, the majority of the bacteria are removed by filtration through beds of sand. In "slow sand filters" removal of bacteria is actually accomplished by their adsorption on the gelatinous film of slime-forming microbes which build up in the sand layers. In "rapid sand filters" chemicals are first added to coagulate organic matter and bacteria; after the precipitate is settled out or is removed mechanically, a rapid filtration through clean sand completes the purification.

B. Sewage Purification: In modern cities, domestic sewage is pumped through a disposal plant which accomplishes the following general objectives:

1. Screening—Bulky, nondecomposable material is screened and removed (bottles, paper, boxes, gravel, etc).

2. Sludge formation—The screened sewage is allowed to settle in large tanks. The sediment, containing much of the organic matter and microorganisms, is called **sludge**. It is drained off at the bottom of the tank and separated from the supernatant, which still contains large amounts of putrescible organic matter. The sludge and supernatant are then treated separately as described below.

The amount of organic matter in the supernatant can be greatly reduced if, instead of simply allowing sludge to form by settling, an activated sludge is caused to form by aeration of the sewage. As air is forced through the sewage, a floc or precipitate is formed, the particles of which teem with actively oxidizing microbes. After a period of time, during which the organic matter is oxidized to a very great extent, the sludge is allowed to settle. The supernatant and part of the sludge are removed for treatment as described below, and part of the sludge is returned to the tank to activate fresh sewage.

3. Sludge digestion—The sludge obtained by either process described above consists of organic matter rich in bacteria and other microbes. It is then pumped to anaerobic tanks where fermentation is allowed to go on for weeks or months. Much of the organic matter is converted to gases (CO_2, CH_4, NH_3, H_2, and H_2S). The methane content of the gas may be as high as 75%, and the collected gas may consequently be burned with the production of useful heat. When fermentation is complete, the sludge is removed and disposed of in one of several ways: It may be dried and discarded, or dried and sold as fertilizer (nitrogen may have to be added), or it may be pumped into a large body of water.

4. Disposal of supernatant—The supernatant, after chlorination, may be pumped into a large body of water. When none is nearby, however, the supernatant must be treated to remove remaining putrescible material as well as enteric bacteria. This is accomplished by aerating and filtering the fluid: It is sprayed over a bed of sand or broken stone, which then filters it as in the process described earlier for drinking water purification. The aeration is necessary to ensure formation of an oxidizing microbial film on the filter-bed particles.

In some cases, the untreated supernatant is used directly for subsurface irrigation of crop land. Some authorities feel, however, that this introduces the danger of spreading enteric disease.

MILK

Methods of Study

A. Quantitative Analysis: Bacteria in milk are counted either directly under the microscope or by plate count. The direct procedure has been rigidly standardized and is known as the "Breed count." The plate count method employs a medium containing skimmed milk in addition to other ingredients, ensuring maximal development of colonies of milk-inhabiting organisms.

Most procedures connected with the bacteriologic analysis of milk have been devised as tests of the safety of the product for human consumption. In addition to the counting procedures, a rough index of bacterial activity in milk is provided by the reductase test. Bacteria contain many enzymes which reduce various substrates. Various dyes are available which are susceptible to bacterial reduction ("reductase activity") and change color when reduced. These dyes thus serve as indicators; in a typical test, a standard amount of a dye such as methylene blue is added to a measured volume of milk, and the time necessary for it to change from blue to colorless is determined. Grade A raw milk which is to be pasteurized, for example, should show a reduction time under standard conditions of 6 hours or more.

B. Qualitative Analysis: The types of organisms present in milk are determined by the procedures described above for water bacteriology. Milk, like water, is subject to fecal contamination and is thus also analyzed for the presence of coliform organisms.

Nature of the Environment & of the Bacterial Population

A. The Environment: Milk constitutes an ideal bacterial habitat, consisting of emulsified fat droplets and dissolved, physiologic concentrations of salts, sugars, and proteins in water. Milk also contains enzymes originating in the animal. Sugar is present in the form of lactose, a disaccharide in which glucose is linked to one of its stereoisomers, galactose. The pH of fresh milk is about 6.8, which is within the optimal range for most bacteria. As normally handled (in filled containers), milk tends to be anaerobic.

B. The Bacterial Population: Because bacteria invade milk usually as dust-borne contaminants, almost any type may be present. Milk constitutes a typical enrichment culture medium, however, and so only the most suited types will predominate. The first organism to flourish in milk is usually *Streptococcus lactis,* which ferments the lactose principally to lactic acid. As the pH drops, other species, such as *Lactobacillus casei* and *L acidophilus,* may replace *S lactis* as the predominant type. If the milk is kept at body temperature, *Enterobacter (Aerobacter) aerogenes* and *Escherichia coli* may be favored.

Other organisms which may develop in milk under special conditions include anaerobic sporeformers (clostridia), *Streptococcus faecalis* and related enterococci, *Pseudomonas aeruginosa* (producing blue pigment), and lactose-fermenting yeasts.

Ecology

A. Effect of the Environment on Bacteria: As discussed above, the environmental factors which most affect the bacterial population are the degree of anaerobiosis, the temperature, the presence of lactose as the principal sugar, and the pH (which drops as fermentation ensues). The selective effect of these factors has been described above.

B. Effect of Bacteria on Milk:

1. Souring—Milk, whether raw or pasteurized (see below), will sour on standing, mainly as a result of the production of lactic acid by *S lactis* or by the lactobacilli. Many dairy products are purposely allowed to sour in this way, as in the manufacture of "buttermilk," butter, sour cream, yoghurt, and cheese. When *E coli* or *E aerogenes* propagate, mixed acid or butylene glycol fermentations take place; these produce less acidity than lactic acid bacteria but cause the production of gas and unpleasant flavors.

2. "Abnormal fermentations"—All changes due to microbial activity other than souring are referred to as "abnormal fermentations," although many of the processes involved are not fermentative. Included are gas formation by yeasts or bacteria; "ropiness," due to gum secretion by bacteria; "sweet curdling," due to secretion by bacteria of the protein coagulating enzyme rennin; various color productions due to pigment-forming bacteria; and digestion of milk proteins and fats by bacterial enzymes (proteolytic and lipolytic).

Control of Bacteria in Milk

It has not yet proved economically feasible to sterilize milk completely except by drastic heating, and this destroys the flavor of fresh milk. (Heat sterilization is used in the production of canned evaporated milk.) However, because contaminated milk is a method of transmission of many diseases, rigid control is necessary.

A. Diseases Transmitted by Milk: Two general classes of disease may be transmitted by milk: those which are transmitted from the animal, the causative microbe being able to infect both animals and men; and those transmitted from other contaminating sources, which are ultimately derived from infected persons.

1. Transmission from the animal—Tuberculosis and undulant fever are the most important of these

diseases. Both are transmissible from animal to animal or from animal to man. The route from the animal's tissues to the milk is not known for certain, but it is possible that Brucella organisms, which cause undulant fever, may be secreted directly from the bloodstream into the udder. Some authorities also list streptococcal infections in this category, since the streptococci pathogenic for man (Lancefield group A) can be transmitted to cows from infected dairy workers, causing udder infections. One rickettsial disease, Q fever, is also transmitted in the milk of infected animals.

2. Transmission from infected persons—Milk which is not handled under scrupulously clean conditions may at any time become contaminated by dust or droplets bearing pathogenic microorganisms. Still more likely is direct infection from diseased milk-handlers and dairy workers. The diseases most commonly transmitted by contaminated milk are typhoid fever, dysentery, tuberculosis, and streptococcal infections.

B. Control of Pathogenic Bacteria in Milk: Since many diseases transmitted by milk are the result of milk contamination, an obvious control measure is to insist on sanitary procedures in milk production and bottling. Communities which enforce the provisions of their own Medical Milk Commission with regard to "Certified Raw Milk" or of the USPHS with regard to "Grade A Raw Milk" supervise the production of milk under sanitary conditions. However, even the most sanitary handling procedures cannot prevent the transmission of tuberculosis or undulant fever from infected animals, and the only safe milk is therefore that which has been pasteurized. In the USA, it is becoming the practice to check all dairy cattle by the tuberculin test; an agglutinin test is used to detect infection with Brucella.

Pasteurization may be carried out by maintaining the milk at 62° C for 30 minutes and then rapidly cooling it; this will kill all pathogenic bacteria which may be present, although many harmless forms (eg, *S lactis*) survive. Alternatively, pasteurization can be accomplished by heating an extremely thin layer of milk for 3—5 seconds at 74° C. Pasteurization is the only procedure which renders milk absolutely safe without destroying its favor and palatability.

C. Safety Standards: A very sensitive, practical method used to determine whether milk has been properly pasteurized is known as the phosphatase test, which consists of quantitatively determining the activity of the enzyme phosphatase in a sample of the milk. Because this enzyme is more resistant than any pathogenic bacterium to pasteurization, its destruction indicates that the milk is safe. Phosphatase activity indicates improper pasteurization or adulteration with raw milk.

A satisfactory phosphatase test, however, does not guarantee that the milk has not become contaminated by handlers after pasteurization. To determine this, milk is analyzed for the presence of coliform organisms by the procedures described in the section on water bacteriology above. Even a negative coliform test does not eliminate the possibility that diphtheria or streptococcal organisms may have been introduced. The best protection against this danger is the insistence on sanitary procedures of dairies and medical examination of milk handlers.

FOODS

Methods of Study

The plate count and enrichment culture methods are also used for the examination of foods. Solid food samples must be ground and suspended in liquid for dilution and plating; care must be taken to avoid introducing bacteria from other sources during preparation of the sample. Coliform analysis is carried out on food samples as well as on water and milk to determine whether fecal contamination has occurred.

Nature of the Environment & of the Bacterial Population

A. Meat: The interior of intact meat is usually sterile or nearly so unless taken from an infected animal. The surface, however, becomes contaminated from dust or from handling immediately upon dismemberment of the animal. Any organotrophic bacterium may be found, including those from soil, dung, or human handlers.

B. Ground Meat: The grinding process introduces the surface contaminants into the interior of the meat and may also warm the meat enough to encourage considerable bacterial multiplication. The interior of the meat is somewhat anaerobic, and fermentative organisms are enriched for. The number of bacteria in ground meat is so high that a count of 10 million per gram is considered a safe maximum. (Since such counts are made on aerobic plates, the many obligate anaerobes present are not included in this figure.)

C. Fish: The general picture is similar to that for unground meat, but the bacterial population will include many marine halophilic and psychrophilic forms. The "phosphorescence" of spoiling fish is due to the growth of luminescent marine bacteria (such as Achromobacter) on the surface.

D. Shellfish: These become contaminated during handling, but they also bear organisms acquired from their marine environment. Shellfish gathered near a sewage outlet will contain numbers of sewage bacteria, including both pathogenic enterobacteria and viruses. Outbreaks of infectious hepatitis have been traced to oysters contaminated with the viral agent of this disease. Oysters are often "planted" near sewage outlets because they fatten rapidly on sewage. In recent years it has become mandatory that such oysters be transported to fresh water and left there long enough so that they will have cleansed themselves of sewage organisms before they are marketed.

E. Fruits and Vegetables: Most vegetables have a considerable surface contamination of soil organisms.

Fruits acquire a surface flora through dust contamination and handling. Fruits and vegetables with tough skins are fairly proof to penetration by bacteria unless bruised; soft fruits and vegetables will spoil much more readily. Acid fruits offer a selective environment for yeasts and molds; otherwise, a typical array of soil microorganisms is found.

The number of microbial cells contaminating the surfaces of fruits and vegetables varies over a wide range. For example, on the unwashed surfaces of leafy vegetables, the count may be as high as 2×10^6/gm. On the unwashed surfaces of tomatoes, counts as high as 5×10^3/sq cm have been recorded; on washed tomatoes, the counts vary between 4 and 7×10^2/sq cm.

F. Eggs: Bacteria may be incorporated into eggs from infected ovaries or oviducts; otherwise the interiors of eggs are usually sterile. The surface becomes contaminated immediately after laying, but penetration of the egg by bacteria is normally prevented by a dry, mucilaginous coating on the surface. This coating is easily removed, however, by washing or overhandling, in which case the interior of the egg becomes contaminated. Bacteria on eggs comes from soil and from the feces of the birds. A mixed flora is common, but fermenters predominate inside the egg. Egg products, like ground meat, show the result of mixing surface contaminants throughout the material; counts are similar to those of ground meat.

G. Bread: The flour from which bread is made contains polysaccharide carbohydrates and protein; fats are added in the form of "shortening." Hydrolysis of the polysaccharides by the yeast or bacteria added to make the bread rise, and partial hydrolysis of the protein by enzymes in the flour, yield a mixture which is ideal for bacterial growth. Baking kills most microorganisms, but spores of bacilli, clostridia, and of fungi persist and will germinate to produce a new flora unless preservatives are added.

Ecology

A. Effect of Environment on Bacterial Population: When organisms begin to grow in food products, selection will determine the predominant type (eg, fermentative organisms are selected for in the anerobic interior of ground meat). Variables which most affect bacterial growth are moisture, factors permitting penetration (bruising of fruits, washing of eggs, etc), and autolysis ("self-dissolving"); as cells die, enzymes are released which dissolve cell walls and protoplasts to a variable extent depending upon the tissue and the environmental conditions. The "ripening" or "tenderizing" of meat, for example, is a result of autolysis. Autolysis results in digestion of polysaccharides, proteins, and fats, rendering the product much more susceptible to bacterial growth.

B. Effect of Bacteria on Food: The interest in food bacteriology is focused on spoilage and disease transmission. Since pathogens affect the consumer rather than the food, only spoilage need be considered here. Disease transmission is discussed below.

Spoilage is the result of microbial growth in or on food. The metabolic activity associated with growth causes both a breakdown of the food substance and the release of the products of fermentation, digestion, and other processes. Spoilage may be defined as the process by which food is rendered aesthetically unfit for human consumption. Only rarely is spoilage accompanied by actual poisoning of the food. (The term food poisoning is restricted to infection by enteric pathogens contaminating food, or ingestion of food containing exotoxins produced by staphylococci or *Clostridium botulinum.*)

Spoilage usually involves alterations in flavor, odor, and color, the production of sliminess, etc. Many types of spoiled food can be eaten with safety; there is no reason, for example, to throw away moldy bread, bacon, or other foods if the taste and odor have not become unpleasant. Other types of spoiled food might, if eaten, cause a mild indigestion.

Unpleasant odors and tastes are produced by "putrefactive" organisms, ie, those which digest proteins and produce H_2S, sulfhydryl compounds, or amines. These compounds, while not poisonous in the concentrations involved, have vile smells. Molds produce a "musty" odor and taste, and some bacteria produce great quantities of slime (as in "ropy bread"). Eggs have a high sulfur content, and their spoilage results in H_2S production, rendering them completely unpalatable. Canned oysters may become covered with a layer of red yeast, in which case they are considered "spoiled" although unchanged in odor, taste, and safety.

Many fungi produce poisonous substances, called **mycotoxins**, which cause serious—sometimes fatal—diseases if ingested. They also produce a variety of **hallucinogens**, such as lysergic acid. The mycotoxins of importance to man include the toxins of the poisonous mushrooms, the toxins of *Claviceps purpurea* (ergot, a parasite of rye), and the **aflatoxins**.

The aflatoxins are produced by the fungus *Aspergillus flavus;* they are highly toxic (as well as carcinogenic) for animals. Aflatoxins have caused serious damage to livestock when their feed has become contaminated with *A flavus*. The risk to humans is unknown; there is strong circumstantial evidence, however, based on epidemiologic data, that aflatoxins may cause cirrhosis and cancer of the liver in parts of the world where human foodstuffs are subject to aflatoxin contamination (eg, India and Africa). Aflatoxins have been found in the food and in the urine of children in India who exhibited cirrhosis of the liver.

Control of Bacteria in Food

A. Prevention of Spoilage: For some foods, such as meats, much can be accomplished along the lines of preventing contamination through the use of sanitary procedures. Some foods, however, already have a rich surface flora from their natural environment (fruits, vegetables, etc), and contamination during handling plays a relatively minor role. In the case of meat, fruit, eggs, and vegetables, it is important to prevent penetration of the food by bacteria (see above). Most effort, however, is directed toward preservative measures; the following measures are used either singly or in combination.

1. Irradiation—Ultraviolet light is used to reduce surface contamination of food materials and equipment in many types of food processing but is relatively ineffective. Irradiation with high-penetrating gamma rays has proved to be much more effective and is used to extend the "shelf life" of packaged nonsterilized food products, including those which are preserved by chilling, freezing, drying, heating, or by the addition of chemical preservatives.

2. Low temperature—Bacterial activity is markedly slowed at refrigeration temperatures and virtually negligible at temperatures below freezing. Refrigeration and freezing are well known methods of food preservation and need no further discussion here.

3. Drying—Foods which are kept completely dry will stay preserved indefinitely, since moisture is essential to microbial activity. Examples of dried foods are hay, raisins, "cured" meat, powdered eggs, and powdered milk. All of these contain dormant microorganisms and will spoil if exposed to humidity.

4. Heat—A temperature of 121° C for 15 minutes is utilized to kill heat-resistant bacterial spores. Such conditions are obtainable with steam at a pressure of 15 lb/square inch above atmospheric pressure. Industrial autoclaves and home pressure cookers are used for heat sterilization of canned foods.

5. Salt—Most bacteria are unable to grow at high salt concentrations. Meat and fish are often "salt-cured" by immersion in brine or by rubbing salt into the surface.

6. Sugar—High sugar concentrations produce osmotic pressures which are too high for most bacteria, although permitting the growth of molds. Many fruits are packed in syrup, and meat is sometimes rubbed with sugar instead of, or mixed with, salt ("sugar-cured" ham).

7. Smoking—Smoke contains volatile bactericidal substances which are gradually absorbed by the meat or fish being smoked. The smoking process is slow, however, and the food is often salt-treated first to prevent spoilage early in the process.

8. Chemical preservatives—Only a few chemicals are useful preservatives at concentrations harmless to humans. Calcium propionate, for example, is used to prevent growth of molds in bread; sodium benzoate is used in cider and some vegetable products; and sulfite is used to preserve some fruits. Nitrites, used in the curing of meats, are bacteriostatic. Sorbic acid, a 6-carbon unsaturated fatty acid, and sorbates are used as fungistatic agents in various foods, particularly cheeses.

9. Acids—Many foods which are soured for the purpose of flavor are thereby preserved, since few bacteria can tolerate the pH values produced by the lactic acid or acetic acid bacteria. Examples are buttermilk, pickles, sauerkraut, and vinegar.

B. Prevention of Disease Transmission: Since few

of the preservative measures listed above are bactericidal, it is essential that pathogenic organisms be prevented from contaminating food. The infectious diseases transmissible by food are Shigella and Salmonella infections, dysentery, and streptococcal infection. Salmonellae other than *S typhi* are widespread contaminants of poultry and eggs in the USA.

The principal bacterial toxins which may be produced in food and cause poisoning are those of staphylococci, *Clostridium perfringens,* and *C botulinum. C botulinum* is an obligate anaerobe; it is usually found in improperly sterilized canned foods. Since the canning industry now observes rigid standards of sterilization, most cases of botulism arise from home-canned foods, although outbreaks of botulism from ingestion of commercially canned foods have occurred as recently as 1971. Correct pressure-cooking technics can eliminate most incidents of botulism; food suspected of contamination with botulinus toxin can be rendered completely safe by boiling for 10–20 minutes.

Staphylococci grow well in meats and dairy products, where they produce a potent exotoxin. This can usually be prevented by careful refrigeration and sanitary measures to prevent their introduction into foods.

Typhoid fever, Salmonella infections, and dysentery are enteric diseases transmitted by fecal contamination of food. They are preventable only by rigid sanitation control and medical examination of food handlers. Salmonella infection may also be acquired by the ingestion of meat or eggs from infected animals.

AIR

The air does not constitute a bacterial habitat; bacteria exist in the air only as accidental contaminants. However, many pathogens are transmitted through the air on dust particles or on the dry residues of saliva droplets, and control measures are attempted for this reason.

Types of Infectious Particles

Pathogenic microorganisms occur in the air associated with 2 types of particles: the residues of evaporated exhalation droplets (**droplet nuclei**), and the much larger **dust particles.** These 2 types of particles are very different with respect to their source, their settling behavior, their significance in disease, and the methods which must be used to assess them and to control them. Some of these differences are summarized in Table 8–2.

Viability of Airborne Organisms

Both dust-borne and droplet-nuclei-borne organisms lose viability in air, and the kinetics of survival are similar to those shown in Fig 7–3. Usually the curve changes slope sharply, revealing the presence of a more resistant fraction, even in experiments dealing with a single type of organism. The presence of 2 populations with different death rates probably reflects differences in the microenvironments of the particles rather than genetic differences in the organisms. The death rates are markedly affected by the humidity and temperature of the air, and there are great differences in death rates among different species

Table 8–2. Characteristics of and control measures for airborne infections.

	Droplet Nuclei	Dust Particles
Source of particles in air	Evaporation of droplets expelled from the respiratory tract by sneezing, coughing, and talking (in decreasing order of effectiveness).	Movements which cause the shedding of particles from skin and clothing; air turbulence sufficient to redistribute previously settled dust.
Settling behavior	Remain suspended indefinitely as a result of minor air turbulence (average settling velocity in still air, 0.04 feet/minute).	Settle rapidly to the ground (average settling velocity, 1.5 feet/minute). Redistributed by major air turbulence.
Organisms per particle	Rarely more than one.	Usually many.
Access to susceptible tissues and significance in disease	Deposited in lungs; probably responsible for most pulmonary infections.	Deposited on external surfaces and in upper respiratory tract.
Epidemiologic characteristics	Propagated epidemics (disease transmitted serially from person to person).	Epidemics associated with specific places as reservoirs of infection.
Control measures	Ventilation; ultraviolet irradiation of the air; evaporation of glycols.	Prevention of accumulation of infectious material (eg, by sterilization of clothing and bedding); prevention of dispersal (eg, by oiling of floors and bedding, and by proper design of ventilation system).

of organisms. In general, organisms which are normally airborne (eg, *M tuberculosis*) are more resistant to inactivation than organisms which are normally water-borne (eg, *E coli*).

Epidemiology of Droplet-Nuclei-Borne Infections

In propagated epidemics, succeeding crops of cases, or "generations," occur as a result of the incubation period which intervenes between successive cases. At each generation, the relationship between the number of new cases (C), the number of infectors (I), and the number of susceptibles (S) is given by the equation*

$$C = KIS \qquad \ldots . (1)$$

where K is a constant representing the effective contact rate.

For droplet-nuclei-borne infections, K is related to the volume of air (s) breathed by a susceptible, the number of infectious doses (i) liberated by an infector, and the volume of air (V) which passes through the space in which contact occurs, all measured over the same interval of time, by the equation

$$K = si/V \qquad \ldots . (2)$$

For an epidemic to occur, C/I must exceed 1; the greater the ratio C/I, the more severe the epidemic. Since equation [1] can be rearranged as

$$C/I = KS \qquad \ldots . (3)$$

it is seen that the severity of an epidemic is directly proportionate to K, the effective contact rate, and to S, the number of susceptibles.

These simple equations have been used to make some illuminating calculations. For example, in a measles epidemic occurring in a school where contact took place only in a well defined classroom area, K was estimated by equation [1] to be 0.1. Since both s and V were known, i could be calculated from equation [2]; it was found to be 270. Thus each infector liberated enough measles virus to infect 270 persons. This represented about 1 infectious dose per 3000 cubic feet of air, which was the volume breathed by 10 children during the time interval used for the calculation. Thus, under such conditions, one child in 10 could be expected to be infected. (Since, however, the distribution of particles in air is random, there is about one chance in 3 under such conditions that no child would be infected. Chance thus may play a significant part in deciding whether an epidemic will occur.)

Control of Epidemics of Airborne Infections

Some control measures for dust-borne infections are indicated in Table 8–2. The accumulation of infectious organisms on fabrics can be minimized by a bac-

*The equations in this section are from Riley R, O'Grady F: *Airborne Infection*. Macmillan, 1961.

tericidal rinse at the end of the laundering process, or by heat sterilization when feasible. The dispersal of dust can be minimized by the oiling or other wetting of blankets and floors; however, the design of the ventilation system often limits what can be accomplished by such measures.

The control measures for droplet-nuclei-borne infections include the following:

A. Sanitary Ventilation: If equations [2] and [3] above are combined, it is found that

$$C/I = si/V_S \qquad \ldots . (4)$$

where V_S is the volume of air per susceptible. Thus, the severity of an epidemic as well as its probability of being initiated (which are proportionate to C/I) are inversely proportionate to V_S. In order to achieve a value of C/I less than 1, the corresponding V_S may require **1 air change per minute** under ordinary circumstances of room size and occupancy. This is more than 5 times that supplied by ordinary air-conditioning installations.

B. Ultraviolet Irradiation: The use of ultraviolet light can accomplish the equivalent of 1 air change per minute by the killing of air-borne organisms. This can be done either by installing high-intensity ultraviolet lamps in the air supply ducts, or by irradiating the air in the upper levels of the room by indirect lamps. The latter method requires good mixing of upper and lower air, but this condition does obtain in many situations. Ultraviolet barriers or "curtains" can also be set up at room entrances so that personnel can pass through quickly and avoid radiation injury.

C. Chemical Disinfection: Propylene glycol and some related compounds are effective germicides in the vapor phase. They presumably act by condensing on droplet nuclei and dehydrating the nuclei-borne organisms. This method is only successful within a narrow range of relative humidities, and is therefore not always reliable.

D. Evaluation: Control measures against dust-borne and droplet-nuclei-borne infections must be separately evaluated by methods which assay only the appropriate particles. The best criterion of success is the lowering of the incidence of disease; in practice, however, it is almost impossible to design valid controls for comparison. For this reason, there are very few data which permit a valid evaluation of the efficacies of the methods listed above.

When the data indicate that a control measure has failed, it can mean that the transmission route which is being controlled is not significant in the spread of the disease being studied, or the exposure to the disease is taking place outside of the controlled area.

SOIL

The earth is covered with green plants which rapidly convert nitrate, sulfate, and CO_2 into organic matter. The plants die—or are eaten by animals which in turn die—and so return the elements to the soil in organic form. The nitrogen and sulfur are then present principally as the amino (–NH$_2$) and sulfhydryl (–SH) groups of proteins; the carbon is present principally in the form of the reduced "carbon skeletons" of carbohydrates, proteins, fats, and nucleic acids.

Without a mechanism for the "mineralization" of these elements, the surface of the earth would long ago have been depleted of the nitrate, sulfate, and CO$_2$ needed for plant growth, and life on the earth would have ceased. But, as we have seen in the previous sections on metabolism, such a mechanism does exist, in the form of microbial metabolic activities. Thus nitrogen, sulfur, and carbon are constantly undergoing cycles of transformations, from the oxidized, inorganic state to the reduced, organic state and back again. These cycles, and hence all life on the earth, are completely dependent on microbial action, as illustrated in the following paragraphs.

One other major element, phosphorus (as phosphate), is converted to organic form during plant growth, being incorporated chiefly into nucleic acids. On return to the soil, nucleic acids are hydrolyzed by microbial enzymes, again liberating free phosphate. No oxidation or reduction is involved.

The Nitrogen Cycle (See Fig 8–1.)

A. Decomposition: The proteins of organic mat-

ter are digested by many microorganisms to free amino acids, from which ammonia (NH$_3$) is then liberated by deamination. Urea, the principal form in which higher animals excrete nitrogen, is hydrolyzed to NH$_3$ and CO$_2$ by various urea-decomposing bacteria.

B. Oxidation of Ammonia: Soil rich in ammonia from decomposing organic matter is abundantly occupied by cells of Nitrosomonas, which obtain their energy for growth by oxidizing NH$_3$ to nitrite (NO$_2^-$). As nitrite is formed, the Nitrobacter cells which are present multiply and convert the nitrite to nitrate (NO$_3^-$).

C. Nitrate Reduction and Denitrification: Nitrate serves as the final hydrogen acceptor for various anaerobic bacteria, being reduced by some to NH$_3$ and by others to gaseous N$_2$. In the former case no nitrogen is lost from the soil, since the ammonia usually stays in solution as ammonium ion (NH$_4^+$); N$_2$ escapes, however, and the latter process is hence termed "denitrification."

D. Conversion of Nitrate to Organic Nitrogen: Green plants, as well as many microorganisms, convert nitrate to organic nitrogen and reduce it once again to amino groups, thus completing the cycle.

E. Nitrogen Fixation: One other important source of nitrogen is the atmosphere. Atmospheric nitrogen is reduced to organic nitrogen by nitrogen-fixing bacteria and certain algae, balancing the losses due to denitrification. This process, although a reduction, is not a

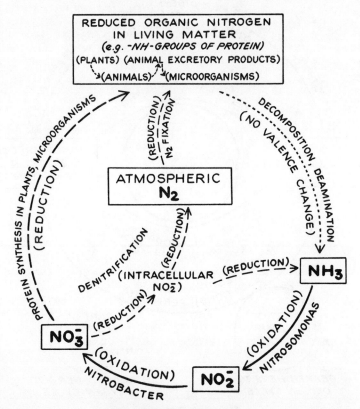

Figure 8–1. The nitrogen cycle.

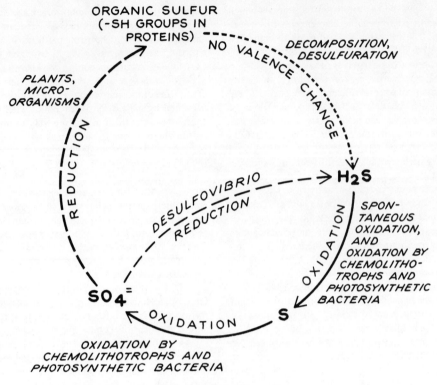

Figure 8—2. The sulfur cycle.

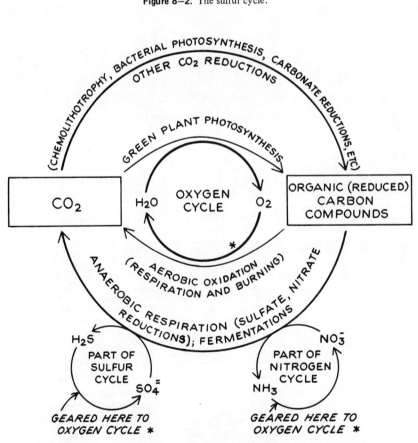

Figure 8—3. The carbon cycle.

mechanism for anerobic respiration but rather a means of obtaining nitrogen. Many nitrogen fixers, in fact, are aerobes. Two types of fixation are distinguished: symbiotic and nonsymbiotic (see p 59).

The Sulfur Cycle (See Fig 8—2.)

A. Decomposition: Following digestion, the sulfur-containing amino acids are broken down by many microorganisms and in the process H_2S is released.

B. Oxidation of H_2S to Free Sulfur: H_2S spontaneously oxidizes to S in the presence of oxygen; in addition, it is oxidized as an energy source by certain chemolithotrophs and as a hydrogen donor by some photosynthetic bacteria.

C. Oxidation of S to $SO_4^=$: Certain chemolithotrophs and photosynthetic bacteria oxidize sulfur to sulfate.

D. Conversion of Sulfate to Organic Sulfur: This process is analogous to the conversion of nitrate to organic nitrogen in the nitrogen cycle.

E. Sulfate Reduction: Desulfovibrio uses $SO_4^=$ as the final hydrogen acceptor in anaerobic respiration.

The Carbon Cycle (See Fig 8—3.)

The valence changes of carbon are frequently associated with valence changes of oxygen; hence the inclusion of an "oxygen cycle." Since anaerobic respiration of organic matter may involve electron transfer from carbon to sulfate or nitrate, the sulfur and nitrogen cycles are also "geared" to the carbon cycle. By "gearing" we mean that the organic carbon oxidation is coupled with a reduction of nitrate or sulfate by electron transfer.

A. Green Plant Photosynthesis and Aerobic Oxidation: For each molecule of CO_2 reduced in photosynthesis, one molecule of O_2 is produced from H_2O. This process just balances the reduction of O_2 to H_2O in aerobic oxidations, so that the oxygen content of the atmosphere remains remarkably constant at about 20%.

B. Other CO_2 Reductions: A relatively small amount of CO_2 is reduced to organic carbon by processes which do not result in the formation of oxygen. These include chemolithotrophic reduction, bacterial photosynthesis, carbonate reduction in anaerobic respiration, and CO_2 fixations in chemo-organotrophic nutrition.

C. Anaerobic Respiration: Anaerobic organotrophs oxidize carbon compounds to CO_2 with nitrate, sulfate, or organic molecules as electron acceptors. When nitrate or sulfate is reduced, their respective cycles are affected; reoxidation of the nitrogen and sulfur is usually accomplished aerobically, causing a half-turn of the oxygen cycle.

●   ●   ●

General References

Books

Alexander M: *Microbial Ecology.* Wiley, 1971.

Frazier WC: *Food Microbiology,* 2nd ed. McGraw-Hill, 1967.

Gregory PH, Monteith JL (editors): *Airborne Microbes.* Cambridge Univ Press, 1967.

Hers JF, Winkler KC (editors): *Airborne Transmission and Airborne Infection.* Wiley, 1973.

Hugo WB (editor): *Inhibition and Destruction of the Microbial Cell.* Academic Press, 1971.

Lawrence CA, Block SS (editors): *Disinfection, Sterilization, and Preservation.* Lea & Febiger, 1968.

Riley R, O'Grady F: *Airborne Infection.* Macmillan, 1961.

Stanier RY, Ingraham JL, Adelberg EA: *The Microbial World,* 4th ed. Prentice-Hall, 1976.

Articles & Reviews

Diet and aflatoxin toxicity. Nutr Rev 29:181, 1971.

Nakamura M, Schulze JA: *Clostridium perfringens* food poisoning. Annu Rev Microbiol 24:359, 1970.

Wogan GN: Aflatoxin risks and control measures. Fed Proc 27:932, 1968.

9 . . .
Bacteriophage

Bacteria are host to a special group of viruses called bacteriophage, or "phage." Although any given phage is highly host-specific, it is probable that every known type of bacterium serves as host to one or more phages. Phages have not been successfully used in therapy. They are important, however, because they furnish ideal materials for studying host-parasite relationships and virus multiplication.

LIFE CYCLES OF PHAGE & HOST

Fig 9–1 summarizes our concepts of phage-host life cycles. The following sections of this chapter are devoted to a detailed account of these cycles and to the experimental evidence for their existence.

Fig 9–1 shows the following:

(1) Life cycle of uninfected bacterium: An uninfected bacterium may reproduce by binary fission, showing no involvement with phage.

(2) Adsorption of free phage: When an uninfected bacterium is exposed to free phage, infection will take place if the cell is sensitive. Bacteria may also be genetically resistant to phage infection; such cells lack the necessary receptors on their surface. (Contrast this with "immunity" due to the presence of prophage. See p 102.)

When infection takes place, the phage is adsorbed onto the cell surface and the nucleic acid of the phage

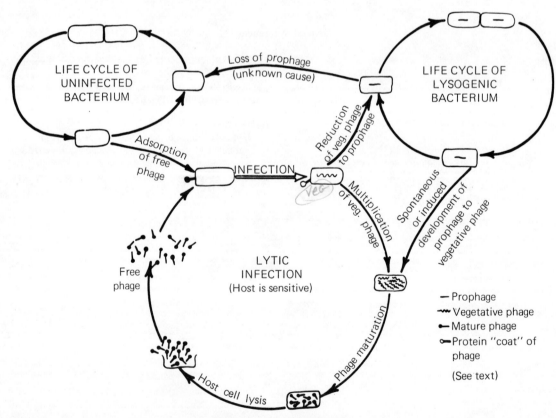

Figure 9–1. Phage-host life cycles.

penetrates the cell. In this state, the phage nucleic acid is called "vegetative phage."

(3) Lytic infection: The injected vegetative phage material may be reproduced, forming many replicas. These mature by acquisition of protein coats, following which the host cell lyses and free phage is liberated.

(4) Reduction of vegetative phage to prophage: Many phages, termed "temperate," are capable of reduction to prophage as an alternative to producing a lytic infection. The bacterium is now lysogenic (see pp 102–104); after an indeterminate number of cell divisions, one of its progeny may lyse and liberate infective phage.

(5) Loss of prophage: Occasionally a lysogenic bacterium may lose its prophage, remaining viable as an uninfected cell. The cause of this spontaneous loss is unknown.

METHODS OF STUDY

Assay

Since phages (like all viruses) multiply only within living cells, and since their size precludes direct observation except with the electron microscope, it is necessary to follow their activities by indirect means. For this purpose, advantage is taken of the fact that one phage particle introduced into a crowded layer of dividing bacteria on a nutrient agar plate will produce a more or less clear zone of lysis in the opaque film of bacterial growth. This zone of lysis is called a "plaque"; it results from the fact that the initially infected host cell bursts (lyses) and liberates dozens of new phage particles, which then infect neighboring cells. This process is repeated cyclically until bacterial growth on the plate ceases as a result of exhaustion of nutrients and accumulation of toxic products. When handled properly, each phage particle produces one plaque; any material containing phage can thus be titrated by making suitable dilutions and plating measured samples with an excess of sensitive bacteria. The plaque count is analogous to the colony count for bacterial titration.

Isolation & Purification

In order to study the physical and chemical properties of phage, it is necessary to prepare a large batch of purified virus as free as possible of host cell material. For this purpose, a liquid culture of the host bacterium is inoculated with phage and incubated until the culture is completely lysed. The now clear culture fluid, or lysate, contains in suspension only viral particles and bacterial debris. These materials are easily separated from each other by differential centrifugation. The centrifuged pellet of phage material can be resuspended and washed in the centrifuge as often as needed and may then be used for chemical and physical analysis in the laboratory or for electron microscopy.

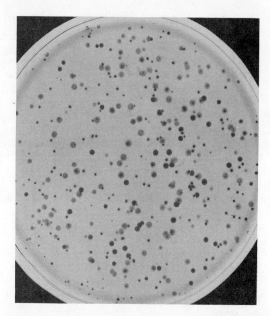

Figure 9–2. Different phage plaque types. (Courtesy of Stent GS.)

PROPERTIES OF PHAGE

One group of phages has been studied more extensively than any other: certain phages which attack *Escherichia coli* strain B (coliphages). Of the numerous coliphages, 7 have been selected for intensive study. Unless otherwise noted, the information given below applies to this group, which has been numbered T1 through T7.

Morphology

A typical phage particle consists of a "head" and a "tail." The head represents a tightly packed core of nucleic acid, surrounded by a protein coat or capsid. The protein capsid of the head is made up of identical subunits, packed to form a prismatic structure, usually hexagonal in cross-section. The smallest known phage has a head diameter of 25 nm; others range from 55 × 40 nm up to 100 × 70 nm.

The phage tail varies tremendously in its complexity from one phage to another. The most complex tail is found in phage T2 and in a number of other coli and typhoid phages. In these phages, the tail consists of at least 3 parts: a hollow core, ranging from 6–10 nm in width; a contractile sheath, ranging from 15–25 nm in width; and a terminal base-plate, hexagonal in shape, to which may be attached prongs, tail fibers, or both. Electron micrographs of phage preparations embedded in electron-dense material such as phosphotungstate show the phages to exist in 2 states: in one, the head contrasts highly with the medium, the sheath is expanded, and the base-plate appears to have a series of prongs. In the second state, the head is of low contrast, the sheath is contracted, and the base-

plate is now revealed to have 6 fibers attached to it.
The former state presumably represents active phage,
containing nucleic acid; the latter state presumably
represents phage which has ejected its nucleic acid (eg,
into a host cell). These 2 states are diagrammed in Fig
9–3.

A number of other tail morphologies have been
reported. In some of these, sheaths are visible but the
contracted state has not been observed; and in one case
no sheath can be seen. The phages also vary with
respect to the terminal structure of the tail: Some have
base-plates, some have "knobs," and some appear to
lack specific terminal structures.

The phage tail is the adsorption organ for those
phages which possess them. Some phages lack tails
altogether; in the RNA phages, for example, the capsid
is a simple icosahedron.

Although most phages have the head-and-tail
structure described above, some **filamentous phages**
have been discovered which possess a very different
morphology. One of these, called "fd," has been characterized in some detail. It is a rod-shaped structure
measuring 6 nm in diameter and 800 nm in length. It
contains DNA and protein, which are complexed in a
manner which is not completely understood. The DNA
may be intertwined with the protein, rather than
forming a core.

Chemistry

Phage particles contain only protein and one kind
of nucleic acid. Most phages contain only DNA; however, a group of phages which specifically attack male
strains of *E coli* contain only RNA. The nucleic acid
makes up about 50% of the dry weight and (in the
T-even phages) consists of a single molecule (called the
phage chromosome) with a molecular weight of 1.3×10^8. In phages T2, T4, and T6, a unique base (hydroxymethylcytosine) is present to which are attached
short chains of glucose units. This pyrimidine has never
been found in the nucleic acid of the bacterial host.

The proteins which make up the head, the core,
the sheath, and the tail fibers are distinct from each
other; in each case, the structure appears to be made of
repeating subunits.

PHAGE REPRODUCTION

Adsorption

The kinetics of phage adsorption have been thoroughly analyzed, and the process has been shown to be
a first-order reaction; the rate of adsorption is proportionate to the concentration both of the phage and of
the bacterium. Under optimal conditions, the observed
rates are compatible with the assumption that almost
every collision between phage and host cell results in
adsorption. If the bacteria are mixed with an excess of
phage, adsorption will continue until as many as 300
particles are adsorbed per cell. For the T-phages, this
represents a coating of most or all of the cell surface.

Before the phage can be adsorbed onto the host
cell, the phage surface must be modified by attachment of positively charged cations (the nature and
number of cations varying from one phage to another)
and, in some cases, of the amino acid tryptophan.
Each phage is quite specific with regard to the cofactors required for adsorption.

The bacterial surface, ie, the cell wall, is complex
and heterogeneous. In gram-negative bacteria, there
appear to be 3 distinct layers: an inner layer composed
of peptidoglycan (see Chapter 2) and 2 outer layers of
lipoprotein and lipopolysaccharide. Different bacterial
strains are highly specific with regard to the phages
which they will adsorb. For example, a strain able to
adsorb phages T2, T4, and T6 can give rise to mutants
unable to combine with one or another of these
viruses. This specificity has been found to reside in the
cell wall; when cell walls are isolated and purified, they
exhibit the same adsorption patterns as the cells from
which they are prepared. The factors in the cell wall
responsible for adsorption appear to be discrete, localized "receptors"; the receptors for phages T3, T4, and
T7 reside in the lipopolysaccharide layer, whereas the
receptors for phages T2 and T6 reside in the lipoprotein layer. Ability to adsorb phage is obviously a
factor in the determination of bacterial sensitivity to
infection.

In certain phages (eg, phages T2, T4, T6), the
attachment of phage particles (or of empty phage
capsids) causes a profound change in the cell membrane: at low phage multiplicities, the membrane

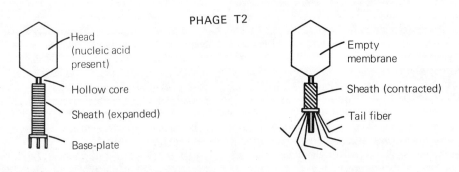

PHAGE T2

Head
(nucleic acid
present)

Hollow core

Sheath (expanded)

Base-plate

Empty
membrane

Sheath (contracted)

Tail fiber

Figure 9–3. Diagrams of phage T2 based on electron micrographic observation.

becomes permeable to small molecules; and at high multiplicities the cell lyses ("lysis from without"). Even a single phage or ghost particle will affect the membrane, causing not only a permeability change but also the inhibition of host DNA and protein synthesis.

Penetration

Experiments in which the phage nucleic acid was labeled with ^{32}P and the phage protein with ^{35}S have shown that the nucleic acid enters the host cell, whereas the protein coat of the invading virus remains outside. The protein can be removed by mechanical agitation after infection without interfering with reproduction of the phage within. Phages with contractile tails, such as T2 (Fig 9–3), behave as hypodermic syringes, injecting the phage DNA into the periplasmic space between the cell wall and cell membrane. In other phages, the mechanism of wall penetration is unknown. The DNA is then taken into the cell through the membrane by a process which may require host cell energy.

The filamentous DNA phages penetrate the host cell by a different mechanism. The entire phage structure penetrates the cell wall; the major protein of the phage coat is then deposited on the cell membrane, which is penetrated by the phage DNA. A minor coat protein enters the cytoplasm along with the DNA.

Intracellular Development of DNA Phages

Some phages always lyse their host cells shortly after infection, generally in a matter of minutes and usually before the host cell can divide again. (See "lytic infection" cycle in Fig 9–1.) Once such a phage injects its contents into the host cell, ensuing events can be only indirectly ascertained. The most informative data have come from experiments with isotopically labeled phage and labeled metabolites, and from experiments involving premature lysis of infected cells by artificial means.

The process of intracellular development is probably as follows:

(1) For several minutes following infection (eclipse period), active phage is not detectable by artificially induced premature lysis (eg, by sonic oscillation). However, chemical analysis and isotopic tracer studies show that during this period the host cell stops synthesizing bacterial DNA and shifts to production of viral DNA. This involves not only a new arrangement of nucleic acid "building blocks" (purines, pyrimidines, deoxyribose, phosphate) but also, at least in the case of T2, T4, and T6, production of a new type of pyrimidine, hydroxymethylcytosine. The invading phage thus directs the synthesis of new enzymes in the host.

(2) Immediately after penetration of the host cell by phage DNA, a number of new proteins ("early proteins") are synthesized. These include certain enzymes necessary for the synthesis of phage DNA: a new DNA polymerase, new kinases for the formation of nucleoside triphosphates, and a new thymidylate synthetase. The T-even phages (T2, T4, T6), which

incorporate hydroxymethylcytosine instead of cytosine into their DNA, also cause the appearance of a series of enzymes needed for the synthesis of hydroxymethylcytosine, as well as an enzyme that destroys the deoxycytidine triphosphate of the host. Later on in the eclipse period, "late proteins" appear, which include the subunits of the phage head and tail as well as a lysozyme which degrades the peptidoglycan layer of the host cell wall. All of these enzymes and phage proteins are synthesized by the host cell using the genetic information provided by the phage DNA.

(3) During the eclipse period, up to several hundred new phage chromosomes are produced; as fast as they are formed, they undergo random exchanges of genetic material (see below). The newly formed phage DNA is built with building block compounds which come partly from the medium and partly from degraded host DNA.

(4) The protein subunits of the phage head and tail aggregate spontaneously (self-assemble) to form the complete capsid. In the case of a complex capsid such as that of phage T4, capsid formation results from the coming together of 3 independent subassembly lines: one each for the head, the tail, and the tail fibers. Each subassembly proceeds in a defined sequence of protein additions.

(5) Maturation consists of irreversible combination of phage nucleic acid with a protein coat. The mature particle is a morphologically typical infectious virus and no longer reproduces in the cell in which it was formed. If the cells are artificially lysed late in the eclipse period, immature phage particles are found in which the DNA and protein are not yet irreversibly attached, so that the DNA is easily removed.

Lysis & Liberation of New Phage

Phage synthesis continues until the cell disintegrates, liberating infectious phage. The cell bursts as a result of osmotic pressure after the cell wall has been weakened by the phage lysozyme. (The exceptions are the filamentous DNA phages, in which the mature virus particles are extruded through the cell wall without killing the host.)

REPLICATION OF RNA PHAGES

When a molecule of viral RNA enters the cytoplasm of the host cell, it is immediately recognized as messenger RNA by the ribosomes, which bind to it and initiate its translation into viral proteins. One such viral protein is a complex enzyme, RNA polymerase. This enzyme brings about the replication of the viral RNA: It polymerizes the ribonucleoside triphosphates of adenine, guanine, cytosine, and uracil, using viral RNA as template.

The first step in the process of RNA replication is the formation of double-stranded intermediates, in which the entering viral RNA strand (called the "plus" strand) is hydrogen-bound to the complementary "minus" strand synthesized by the polymerase. The polymerase now uses the double-stranded molecule as a template for the repeated synthesis of new plus strands, each new plus strand displacing the previous one from the double-stranded intermediate.

As the newly synthesized plus strands are released from the replicative intermediate, they are either used by the polymerase to form a new double-stranded intermediate or are assembled into mature virions by the attachment of coat protein subunits.

The complete nucleotide sequence of one RNA phage, MS2, has been determined. It is a single molecule, 3566 nucleotides in length, and contains 3 functional genes coding respectively for the RNA polymerase, the coat protein, and a second protein called the "A protein." The single-stranded RNA molecule is capable of folding back on itself and forming double-stranded regions by base pairing; the secondary structure which results appears to play a major role in the regulation of viral RNA replication and translation.

PHAGE GENETICS

Phage particles exhibit the same 2 fundamental genetic properties that are characteristic of organized cells: general stability of type and a low rate of heritable variation (see Chapter 4).

Phage Mutation

All phage properties are controlled by phage genes and are subject to change through gene mutation. The mechanisms of gene mutation described in Chapter 4 apply equally well to phages; indeed, most of our knowledge concerning the chemical basis of mutation comes from studies on phage genetics.

The DNA of phage T2 has a molecular weight of 1.2×10^8; this is sufficient to code for about 200 different proteins of molecular weight 30,000.

Phage Recombination

If a bacterium simultaneously adsorbs 2 related but slightly different DNA phage particles, both can infect and reproduce; on lysis, the cell releases both types. When this occurs, many of the progeny are observed to be recombinants. For example, one can prepare a double mutant of T2 which differs from wild type in the type of plaque it forms (large plaques, due to rapid lysis of the host) and in its host range (ability to lyse E coli B/2, a mutant strain resistant to lysis by T2). The mutant is designated T2hr ("h" for "host range"; "r" for "rapid lysis"). The wild type is designated T2++. When a cell of E coli B is simultaneously infected with both types and allowed to lyse, the following 4 types of progeny are found:

Parental Types	Recombinant Types
T2++	T2+r
T2hr	T2h+

The "r" mutation occurs very frequently; when a large number of "r" mutants of independent origin were isolated and crossed with each other 2 at a time, it was found that most of them were nonallelic and produced wild type recombinants. Recombination between phage genomes occurs by the breakage and rejoining of DNA molecules (Fig 9–4).

The closer together 2 markers lie on the same strand, the lower will be the probability of a "crossover" between them. The different pairs of r mutants were found to give widely different recombination frequencies, and these data permitted construction of a linkage map of phage T2, part of which is diagrammed in Fig 9–5.

$$h \quad r_{13} \qquad\qquad\qquad\qquad r_2 \; r_8 \; r_3 \; r_9$$

Figure 9–5. Linkage map of phage T2.

Proof of linkage was obtained by showing that map distances were additive: eg, the distance between h and r_2 equaled the sum of the distance $h-r_{13}$ and $r_{13}-r_2$.

Simultaneous infection of a cell by 3 parental phage types can yield 3-way recombinants, ie, a single progeny may have genes from all 3 parents. Evidence so far obtained supports the concept that "mating" of vegetative phage takes place in pairs but that it is repeated many times between different particles before maturation. When a particle matures, it is removed from the "mating pool."

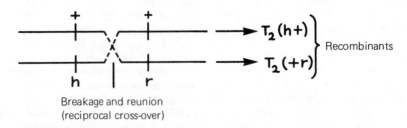

Figure 9–4. Recombination between phage genomes by breakage and reciprocal reunion.

Genetic Fine Structure

Phage T2 forms plaques when plated on *E coli* strain K12; r mutants, however, do not. This discovery made possible the detection of extremely low frequencies of recombination between different r mutants: a culture of *E coli* B is infected with the 2 r mutants, and the lysate plated on K12. Since 10^8 phage particles can easily be plated, and since only wildtype recombinants can form plaques, a recombination frequency lower than 10^{-6} can be accurately measured.

In a great many such crosses, the lowest frequency observed has been 10^{-4}, or 0.01%. The total genetic map of T2 is estimated to be about 800 cross-over units long (1 unit = the distance separating 2 markers which give 1% recombinant progeny). The minimum recombinational unit is thus 0.01/800, or 1.2×10^{-5} of the total map. It has also been estimated that the total DNA of the phage genome contains about 2×10^5 nucleotide pairs, in terms of the Watson and Crick structure (Fig 4–2). Thus, recombination can separate 2 mutant loci which are only 1 or 2 nucleotide pairs apart.

The Genetic Map of Phage T4 (See Fig 9–6.)

Two special classes of phage mutants have greatly extended our knowledge of the phage chromosome:

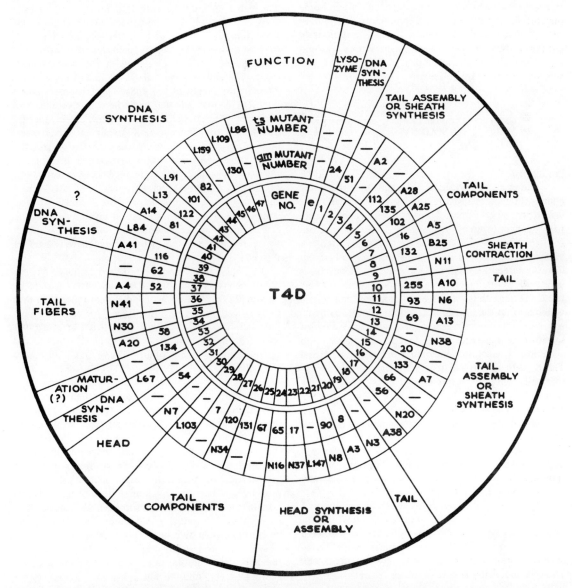

Figure 9–6. The genetic map of bacteriophage T4D. The inner circle shows the division of the map into 48 functional units. Each unit has been shown to be functionally distinct from the others by complementation test. The size shown for each unit is arbitrary. The next 2 circles show the location of the am and ts mutations which have been used to reconstruct the map. The outer circle describes the functions controlled by each unit, as determined by studies on the defects exhibited by the various mutants. (After Epstein & others: Cold Spring Harbor Symp Quant Biol 28:375, 1963.)

temperature sensitive (ts) mutants and a certain group of host range mutants. The latter, which have been given the scientifically meaningless name of "amber" (am) mutants, are unable to grow on *E coli* strain B (the normal host of T4) but are able to grow on certain strains of *E coli* strain K12. The ts mutants are able to form plaques on *E coli* B at 25° C but not at 42° C, in contrast with wild type T4, which forms plaques at both temperatures.

By infecting bacterial cells with ts and am mutants and examining the infected cells and their lysates by serology, electron microscopy, and biochemical tests, it has been shown that a variety of different classes are represented: Some mutations have affected DNA replication, some the head protein, some the tail fibers, and so on. Recombination tests have allowed the mapping of the ts and am mutations in relation to the classical markers such as the r loci and the h loci; the results are shown in Fig 9–6. As in *E coli,* the genetic map is circular.

LYSOGENY

Prophage

Earlier in this chapter it was mentioned that some phages ("temperate phages") fail to lyse the cells they infect, and then appear to reproduce synchronously with the host for many generations. Their presence can be demonstrated, however, because every so often one of the progeny of the infected bacterium will lyse and liberate infectious phage. To detect this event it is necessary to use a sensitive indicator strain of bacterium, ie, one that is lysed by the phage. The bacteria which liberate the phage are called "lysogenic"; when a few lysogenic bacteria are plated with an excess of sensitive bacteria, each lysogenic bacterium grows into a colony in which are liberated a few phage particles. These particles immediately infect neighboring sensitive cells, with the result that plaques appear in the film of bacterial growth; in the center of each plaque is a colony of the lysogenic bacterium.

A culture of lysogenic bacteria can also be centrifuged, removing the cells and leaving the temperate phage particles in the supernatant. Their number can be measured by plating suitable dilutions of the supernatant on a sensitive bacterial indicator strain and counting typical plaques.

The release of infectious phage in a culture of lysogenic bacteria is restricted to a very few cells of any given generation. For example, in one bacterial type about 1 in 200 lyse and liberate phage during each generation; in another type it may be 1 in 50,000. The remainder of the cells, however, retain the potentiality to produce active phage and transmit this potentiality to their offspring for an indefinite number of generations.

With the rare exceptions mentioned, lysogenic bacteria contain no detectable phage, either as morphologic, serologic, or infectious entities. However, the fact that they carry the potentiality to produce, generations later, phage with a predetermined set of characteristics means that each cell must contain one or more specific noninfectious structures endowed with genetic continuity. This structure is termed "prophage." Prophage has the following properties: (1) From studies on the life cycle of virulent phage, genetic continuity is known to imply persistence of phage nucleic acid; serologic studies fail to detect the presence of phage protein. (2) Since all the cells in the clone are lysogenic, prophage must be reproduced regularly along with the host.

The Nature of Prophage Integration

Two entirely different mechanisms of prophage formation are found in different phages. In one mechanism, discovered in phage λ, the prophage consists of a molecule of DNA integrated with the host chromosome. The chromosomes of *E coli* and of phage λ are circular; the length of the phage chromosome is about one-fiftieth that of the bacterial chromosome. The phage and bacterial chromosomes each carry a specific **attachment site**. The bacterial attachment site is immediately adjacent to the *gal* locus (see Fig 4–16); the phage attachment site is similarly located at a specific point on the phage genetic map. When λ infects a cell of *E coli,* recombination between the 2 attachment sites occurs, with the result that the 2 circles are integrated (Fig 9–7). This integration process requires the action of a phage gene product: phage mutants defective in this gene (the *int* locus) are unable to lysogenize the cell.

In the other system, discovered in phage P1, the phage chromosome circularizes and enters a state of "quiescent" replication which is synchronous with that of the host; no phage proteins are formed. The prophage in the "P1 type" of system is not integrated with the chromosome; it is probably attached to the cell membrane, as are other autonomous replicons in the cell.

Further Properties of the Lysogenic System

A. Immunity: Lysogenic bacteria are immune to infection by phage of the type already carried in the cell as prophage. When nonlysogenic cells are exposed to temperate phage, many permit phage multiplication and are lysed, while other cells are lysogenized. Once a cell carries prophage, however, neither it nor its progeny can be lysed by homologous phage. Adsorption takes place, but the adsorbed phage simply persists without reproducing and is quickly "diluted out" by continued cell division.

It has been shown that temperate phages cause the appearance in the cytoplasm of a repressor substance which inhibits multiplication of vegetative phage. Repressor also blocks the detachment of prophage (which otherwise would occur by the reversal of the integration process described above) as well as the expression of other phage genes (eg, formation of phage proteins). The establishment of the lysogenic

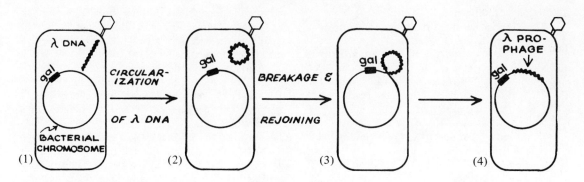

Figure 9–7. The integration of prophage and host chromosome. *(1)* The phage DNA is injected into the host. *(2)* The ends of the phage DNA are covalently joined to form a circular element. *(3)* Pairing occurs between a sequence of bases adjacent to the gal locus and a homologous sequence on the phage DNA. *(4)* Breakage and reciprocal rejoining ("crossing over") within the region of pairing integrates the 2 circular DNA structures. The integrated phage DNA is called prophage. The length of λ DNA has been exaggerated for diagrammatic purposes. It is actually 1–2% of the chromosomal length.

state is thus dependent on the production and action of repressor. The λ repressor has been isolated and characterized as a protein which specifically binds to λ DNA.

The immunity of a lysogenic cell to homologous phage is clearly different from the phenomenon of "resistance" to virulent phage, which is exhibited by certain bacteria. In the latter case, resistance is caused by failure to adsorb the phage.

B. Induction: "Vegetative phage" is defined as rapidly reproducing phage on its way to mature infective phage, whereas "prophage" reproduces synchronously with the host cell. On rare occasions prophage "spontaneously" develops into vegetative (and later into mature) phage. This accounts for the sporadic cell lysis and liberation of infectious particles in a lysogenic culture. However, the prophage of practically every cell of certain lysogenic cultures can be induced by various treatments to form and liberate infectious phage. For example, ultraviolet light will induce phage formation and liberation by most of the cells in a lysogenic culture at a dose which would kill very few nonlysogenic bacteria.

Induction requires the inactivation or destruction of repressor molecules present in the cell. Phage mutants have been obtained which produce thermolabile repressors: These phages can be induced simply by raising the temperature to 44° C. Agents such as UV, which damage host DNA, induce prophage development because the phage repressor has a strong affinity for the sites of damage (eg, single-strand breaks). The binding of repressor by these sites effectively prevents the repressor from acting on the phage DNA.

C. Mutation to Virulence: When virulent phage is mixed with bacterial cells, all of the infected cells lyse. When temperate phage is mixed with nonlysogenic bacteria, some of the cells reproduce the phage and are lysed, while others are lysogenized.

The outcome of the infection of any given cell appears to be determined by a race between phage replication and the formation of repressor: If the former proceeds far enough before repressor appears, the cell will lyse; if repressor is formed early, the cell will survive and become lysogenic.

Temperate phage can mutate to the virulent state. Virulent mutants can then be used in multiple infection experiments with temperate phage and recombinants obtained, showing that virulence is genetically determined like other properties of phage.

Two types of virulent mutants have been found. In one type, the mutation has made the phage resistant to the repressor, so that it can multiply even in lysogenic cells which are otherwise immune; in the other type, the phage has lost the ability to produce repressor. Virulent mutants of temperate phages are quite different from the naturally virulent phages such as T2. The latter cause the appearance of enzymes which degrade host DNA and stop the synthesis of ribosomal RNA, whereas the former do not interfere with the normal metabolism of the host in this manner.

D. Effect on Genotype of Host: When a lysogenic phage, grown on host "A," infects and lysogenizes host "B" of a different genotype, some of the cells of host "B" may acquire one or more closely linked genes from host "A." For example, if the phage is grown in a lactose-nonfermenting host, about 1 in every million cells infected becomes lactose-fermenting. The transferred property is heritable. This phenomenon, called "transduction," is described in more detail in Chapter 4.

In other instances, phage genes may themselves determine new host properties. For example, cells of *Corynebacterium diphtheriae* become toxigenic when lysogenized by a certain phage, with 100% efficiency. In Salmonella, phage infection confers a new antigenic surface structure on the host cell. The acquisition of new cell properties as the result of phage infection is called "phage conversion." Phage conversion differs from transduction in that the genes controlling the new properties are found only in the phage genome, and are never found in the chromosome of the host bacterium.

Restriction & Modification

The phenomena of restriction and modification, as described in Chapter 4, were discovered as a result of their effects on phage multiplication. It was observed that if phage λ is grown in *E coli* strain K12, only about 1 in 10^4 particles can multiply in strain B. The few that succeed, however, liberate progeny which infect B with an efficiency of 1.0, but infect strain K12 with an efficiency of 10^{-4}.

It was shown that the DNA of particles formed in K12 is modified by a K12 enzyme so as to be immune to degradation in K12. In strain B, however, the DNA of such particles is rapidly degraded by the restricting enzyme of the host. The few particles which escape restriction are modified by the specific modification enzyme of strain B; the progeny formed are now susceptible to degradation in K12, but not in B. The modifying enzymes have been shown to act by methylating bases at specific sites in the DNA.

Certain temperate phages carry genes which govern the formation of new modification and restriction enzymes in the host. Thus, *E coli* cells carrying P1 prophage will degrade all DNA not modified in a P1-containing cell.

As discussed in Chapter 4, a given restricting enzyme recognizes a particular site on DNA and causes cleavage at that site unless the site has already been protected by the homologous modifying enzyme. Restriction appears to be a mechanism by which a cell protects itself against invasion by foreign DNA.

•   •   •

General References

Books

Hayes W: *The Genetics of Bacteria and Their Viruses,* 2nd ed. Blackwell, 1968.

Hershey AD (editor): *The Bacteriophage Lambda.* Cold Spring Harbor Laboratory, 1971.

Stent G: *The Molecular Biology of Bacterial Viruses.* Freeman, 1963.

Stent G: *Molecular Genetics.* Freeman, 1971.

Stent G (editor): *Papers on Bacterial Viruses,* 2nd ed. Little, Brown, 1965.

Articles & Reviews

Boyer HW: DNA restriction and modification mechanisms in bacteria. Annu Rev Microbiol 25:153, 1971.

Calendar R: The regulation of phage development. Annu Rev Microbiol 24:241, 1970.

Echols H: Developmental pathways for the temperate phage: Lysis vs lysogeny. Annu Rev Genet 6:157, 1972.

Fiers W & others: Complete nucleotide sequence of bacteriophage MS2 RNA: Primary and secondary structure of the replicase gene. Nature 260:500, 1976.

Herskowitz I: Control of gene expression in bacteriophage lambda. Annu Rev Genet 7:289, 1973.

Horne RW, Wildy P: Symmetry in virus structure. Virology 15:348, 1961.

Lindberg AA: Bacteriophage receptors. Annu Rev Microbiol 27:205, 1973.

Lwoff A: The concept of virus. J Gen Microbiol 17:239, 1957.

Lwoff A, Horne R, Tournier P: A system of viruses. Cold Spring Harbor Symp Quant Biol 27:51, 1962.

Marvin DA, Wachtel E: Structure and assembly of filamentous bacterial viruses. Nature 253:19, 1975.

Valentine R, Ward R, Strand M: The replication cycle of RNA bacteriophages. Adv Virus Res 15:1, 1969.

10 . . .
Antimicrobial Chemotherapy

Although various chemicals have been used for the treatment of infectious diseases since the 17th century (eg, quinine for malaria and emetine for amebiasis), chemotherapy as a science begins with Paul Ehrlich. He was the first to formulate the principles of selective toxicity and to recognize the specific chemical relationships between parasites and drugs, the development of drug-fastness in parasites, and the role of combined therapy in combating this development. Ehrlich's experiments in the first decade of the 20th century led to the arsphenamines, the first major triumph of planned chemotherapy.

The current era of rapid development in antimicrobial chemotherapy began in 1935, with the discovery of the sulfonamides by Domagk. In 1940, Chain and Florey demonstrated that penicillin, which had been observed in 1929 by Fleming, could be made into an effective chemotherapeutic substance. During the past 25 years, chemotherapeutic research has largely centered around antimicrobial substances of microbial origin called antibiotics. The isolation, concentration, purification, and mass production of penicillin was followed by the development of streptomycin, tetracyclines, chloramphenicol, and many other agents. Although these substances were all originally isolated from filtrates of media in which their respective molds, or streptomyces, had grown, several have subsequently been synthesized. In recent years chemical modification of molecules by biosynthesis has been a prominent method of new drug development. Brief summaries of antimicrobial agents commonly employed in medical treatment are presented at the end of this section.

SELECTIVE TOXICITY

The fundamental principle of chemotherapy is the principle of selective toxicity, which may be stated as follows: In order to be useful for systemic treatment of infectious disease, a substance must be harmful to parasites but relatively innocuous to host cells. This is the main difference between useful systemic antimicrobial drugs and disinfectants, which are highly active against the parasite in vitro but are not sufficiently well tolerated by the host to permit systemic administration. "Selective toxicity" must be based on certain unique features of structure or of function of the parasite which set it apart from host cells. Explanations of a few known instances of selective toxicity are presented below.

For each antimicrobial drug found safe for therapeutic use, hundreds have been discarded because they proved toxic not only to the parasite but also to the host.

MECHANISM OF ACTION OF ANTIMICROBIAL DRUGS

Competitive antagonism is rare among antimicrobial drugs. Most effective antimicrobial substances act by interfering with the synthesis, assembly, or function of the macromolecular components of microbial cells. A brief summary of the probable mechanisms of action of certain antimicrobial drugs is given below.

Inhibition of Growth by Analogues of Essential Metabolites
(*Example:* Sulfonamides.)

An enzyme usually catalyzes a single reaction. The substrate attaches to the enzyme's active center where it is activated, metabolized, and released. A competitor is a chemical compound similar to (but not identical with) the substrate which can combine with the enzyme's active center but cannot be metabolized. It remains attached to the active center and prevents combination of the active center with the true substrate.

For many microorganisms, para-aminobenzoic acid (PABA) is an essential metabolite in the synthesis of folic acid, which serves as an important step in the eventual synthesis of purines. The specific mode of action of PABA probably involves an ATP-dependent condensation of a pteridine with PABA to yield dihydropteroic acid, which is subsequently converted to folic acid. Sulfonamides are structural analogues of PABA.

Sulfonamides can enter into the reaction in place of PABA and compete for the active center of the

p-Aminobenzoic
acid (PABA)

Basic ring
structure
of sulfonamides

enzyme. As a result, nonfunctional analogues of folic acid are formed, preventing further growth of the bacterial cell.

Animal cells cannot synthesize folic acid and depend on an exogenous source. Some bacteria likewise do not synthesize folic acid, but require it for growth. These bacteria, like animal cells, are not inhibited by sulfonamides. Many other bacteria cannot use the form of folic acid that occurs in most tissues but synthesize folic acid by the reaction described above, and consequently are susceptible to sulfonamide action. The inhibiting action of sulfonamides on bacterial growth can be counteracted by an excess of PABA in the environment.

Tubercle bacilli are not inhibited markedly by sulfonamides, but their growth is inhibited by aminosalicylic acid (para-aminosalicylic acid, PAS). Conversely, most sulfonamide-susceptible bacteria are resistant to PAS. This suggests that the enzyme catalytic site for PABA differs in different types of organisms.

Trimethoprim (a diaminotrimethoxybenzylpyrimidine) inhibits the dihydrofolic acid reductase of bacteria and protozoa much more efficiently than the same enzymes of mammalian cells. These enzymes convert dihydro- to tetrahydrofolic acid, a stage in the sequence leading to the synthesis of purines and DNA. Sulfonamides and trimethoprim produce sequential blocking, resulting in marked enhancement of activity.

Such mixtures of sulfonamide (5 parts) and trimethoprim (1 part) (co-trimoxazole) have been used in urinary tract infections, enteric fevers, and some other bacterial and parasitic (malarial) infections. Pyrimethamine plus sulfonamide is currently used in the treatment of toxoplasmosis.

Inhibition of Cell Wall Synthesis
(*Example:* Penicillins.)

In contrast to animal cells, bacteria possess a rigid outer layer, the cell wall. It maintains the shape of microorganisms and "corsets" the bacterial cell, which has a high internal osmotic pressure. The internal pressure is 3−5 times greater in gram-positive than in gram-negative bacteria. Injury to the cell wall (eg, by lysozyme) or inhibition of its formation may lead to lysis of the cell. In a hypertonic environment (eg, 20% sucrose), damaged cell wall formation leads to forma-

tion of spherical bacterial "protoplasts" limited by the fragile cytoplasmic membrane. If such "protoplasts" are placed in an environment of ordinary tonicity, they may explode.

The cell wall contains a chemically distinct complex polymer "mucopeptide," peptidoglycan, consisting of polysaccharides and a highly cross-linked polypeptide. The polysaccharides regularly contain the amino sugars N-acetylglucosamine and acetylmuramic acid. The latter is found only in bacteria. To the amino sugars are attached pentapeptide chains. The final rigidity of the cell wall is imparted by cross-linking of the peptide chains (eg, through pentaglycine bonds) as a result of transpeptidation reactions carried out by at least 2 enzymes (an endopeptidase and a glycosidase). The peptidoglycan layer is much thicker in the cell wall of gram-positive bacteria than in the cell wall of gram-negative bacteria.

All penicillins and all cephalosporins are selective inhibitors of bacterial cell wall synthesis through inhibition of the terminal cross-linking of the linear glycopeptides—the "transpeptidation" reaction. Penicillins and cephalosporins inhibit the activity of the "transpeptidase" enzymes. Low concentrations of these drugs which inhibit the glycosidase inhibit the formation of dividing cross-walls in bacteria and result in the formation of greatly elongated, threadlike, bizarre forms. Higher concentrations, which inhibit endopeptidase activity completely, arrest cell wall formation. As a result, cells may lyse (aided by lytic enzymes in the cell wall) or, if the surrounding medium is hypertonic (eg, 20% sucrose), change to protoplasts. In penicillin-inhibited cells, nucleotides accumulate which are cell wall precursors. However, the synthesis of proteins and nucleic acids continues for some time.

The inhibition of the "transpeptidation" enzymes (see above) by penicillins and cephalosporins may be due to a structural similarity of these drugs to acyl-D-alanyl-D-alanine. The transpeptidation reaction involves loss of a D-alanine from the pentapeptide.

The remarkable lack of toxicity of penicillins to mammalian cells must be attributed to the absence of a bacterial type cell wall, with its peptidoglycan, in animal cells. The difference in susceptibility of gram-positive and gram-negative bacteria to various penicillins or cephalosporins probably depends on structural differences in their cell walls (eg, amount of peptidoglycan, presence of lipids, nature of cross-linking, activity of autolytic enzymes) which determine penetration, binding, and activity of the drugs.

The susceptibility to penicillins is, in part, determined by the organism's production of penicillin-destroying enzymes (β-lactamases). Certain penicillins (eg, methicillin, cloxacillin) have a high affinity for the β-lactamase produced by some gram-negative bacteria, eg, pseudomonas. They bind the enzyme, are not hydrolyzed by it, and thus protect simultaneously present hydrolyzable penicillins (eg, ampicillin) from destruction. This is a form of "synergism" of known mechanism.

Several other drugs, including bacitracin, vanco-mycin, ristocetin, and novobiocin, inhibit early steps in the biosynthesis of the peptidoglycan. Since the early stages of synthesis take place inside the cytoplasmic membrane, these drugs must penetrate the membrane to be effective. For these drugs, inhibition of peptidoglycan synthesis is not the sole mode of antibacterial action.

Cycloserine, an analogue of D-alanine, interferes also with peptidoglycan synthesis. This drug blocks the action of alanine racemase, an essential enzyme in the incorporation of D-alanine in the pentapeptide of peptidoglycan.

Inhibition of Cell Membrane Function
(*Example:* Polymyxins.)

The cytoplasm of all living cells is bounded by the cytoplasmic membrane, which serves as a selective permeability barrier and thus controls the internal composition of the cell. If the functional integrity of the cytoplasmic membrane is disrupted, purine and pyrimidine nucleotides and proteins escape from the cell and cell damage or death ensues. The cytoplasmic membrane of certain bacteria and fungi can be more readily disrupted by certain agents than the membranes of animal cells. Consequently, selective chemotherapeutic activity is possible.

The outstanding examples of this mechanism are the polymyxins acting on gram-negative bacteria and the polyene antibiotics acting on fungi. Polymyxins act selectively on membranes rich in phosphatidyl ethanolamine. However, polymyxins are inactive against fungi and polyenes are inactive against bacteria. This is because sterols are present in the fungal cell membrane and absent in the bacterial cell membrane. Polyenes must interact with a sterol in the fungal cell membrane prior to exerting their effect. Bacterial cell membranes do not contain that sterol and consequently are resistant to polyene action—a good example of cell individuality and of selective toxicity.

Inhibition of Protein Synthesis
(*Examples:* Chloramphenicol, Aminoglycosides.)

It is established that chloramphenicol, tetracyclines, aminoglycosides, erythromycins, and lincomycins can inhibit protein synthesis in bacteria. Puromycin is an effective inhibitor of protein synthesis in animal and other cells. The concepts of protein synthesis are undergoing rapid change, and the precise mechanism of action is not fully established for these drugs. Bacteria have 70S ribosomes, whereas mammalian cells have 80S ribosomes. The subunits of each type of ribosome and their functional specificities are sufficiently different to explain why antimicrobial drugs can inhibit protein synthesis in bacterial ribosomes without having a major effect on mammalian ribosomes.

Chloramphenicol attaches to the 50S subunit of bacterial ribosomes and interferes greatly with the binding of amino acids to nascent peptide chains. This effect is partly or completely attributable to the inhibition of peptidyl transferase by chloramphenicol.

Chloramphenicol is bacteriostatic for many bacteria, and its action is readily reversible upon withdrawal of the drug.

Bacterial resistance to chloramphenicol is often associated with the production of an enzyme (chloramphenicol acetyltransferase) which destroys the drug. The production of this enzyme is under control of extrachromosomal genes in a bacterial plasmid. The latter may be transmitted either by conjugation or by transduction.

The tetracyclines bind to the 30S subunit of bacterial ribosomes. They inhibit protein synthesis by blocking the binding of charged aminoacyl-transfer RNA (tRNA) to the 30S subunit. Tetracyclines are bacteriostatic for many bacteria and chlamydiae, and their action is reversible upon withdrawal of the drug. Tetracycline-susceptible microorganisms actually concentrate drug from the surrounding environment. Tetracycline-resistant microorganisms have "impaired permeability" to the drug, or fail to concentrate drug from the environment. Tetracycline resistance is sometimes under genetic control of a plasmid transmissible by conjugation, sometimes under chromosomal control.

Macrolides (erythromycins, oleandomycins) bind to the 50S subunit of bacterial ribosomes, perhaps competing with amino acids for ribosomal binding sites. A major effect of macrolide inhibition of protein synthesis appears to be an inhibition of aminoacyl translocation reactions. Erythromycin-resistant microorganisms have altered proteins that are under chromosomal control on the 50S ribosomal subunit.

Lincomycins bind to the 50S subunit of bacterial ribosomes, the attachment site being similar to or the same as that for macrolides. The mode of action may be similar to that of macrolides and seems to affect peptide chain initiation. Lincomycin-resistant microorganisms probably have a modified protein on the 50S ribosomal subunit.

All aminoglycosides (streptomycin, kanamycin, neomycin, gentamicin, tobramycin, etc) effectively inhibit protein synthesis of bacteria by several mechanisms. They cause progressive breakdown of polysomes. Each aminoglycoside binds to a surface protein on the 30S subunit of the bacterial ribosome. There the aminoglycoside distorts the "recognition region" of the ribosome and causes a misreading of the mRNA message. This results in the insertion of improper amino acids in the peptide chain and the synthesis of nonfunctional proteins. In aminoglycoside-dependent cells, misreading of the genetic message is a requirement for growth.

Aminoglycoside resistance of some microorganisms is due to the production of adenylating, phosphorylating, or acetylating enzymes which destroy the drug. The genetic control of these enzymes resides in a transmissible plasmid. Other microorganisms are resistant because of an altered or missing protein on the 30S subunit of the ribosome which does not permit the drug to attach. The receptor protein is under chromosomal control.

Inhibition of Nucleic Acid Synthesis

Drugs such as the actinomycins are effective inhibitors of DNA synthesis. Actually they form complexes with DNA by binding to the deoxyguanosine residues. The DNA-actinomycin complex inhibits the DNA-dependent RNA polymerase and blocks mRNA formation. Actinomycin also inhibits DNA virus replication. Actinomycins inhibit animal as well as bacterial cells and are not sufficiently selective to be employed in antibacterial chemotherapy. Rifampin inhibits the DNA-dependent RNA-polymerase of bacteria.

The halogenated pyrimidines (eg, 5-iodo-2'-deoxyuridine, idoxuridine, IDU) can block the synthesis of functionally intact DNA and thus interfere with the replication of infective DNA viruses. IDU can interfere with the incorporation of thymidine into viral DNA, and IDU itself is incorporated into DNA to form nonfunctional DNA. The systemic administration of IDU is difficult because of its severe toxicity, but local application to DNA virus-producing cells (especially in herpes simplex keratitis) can result in significant suppression of viral replication in vivo. Cytarabine inhibits replication of DNA viruses but is too toxic for systemic use. Adenine arabinoside may have some clinical usefulness in blocking DNA virus replication in systemic herpesvirus infections.

Nalidixic acid, used mostly as a urinary antiseptic, is a potent inhibitor of DNA synthesis, but it is not known whether its antibacterial action depends on this effect. Resistance to nalidixic acid is common and is chromosomally determined. Oxolinic acid is a related urinary antiseptic.

RESISTANCE TO ANTIMICROBIAL DRUGS

There are many different mechanisms by which microorganisms might exhibit resistance to drugs. The following are fairly well supported by evidence:

(1) Microorganisms produce enzymes which destroy the active drug. *Examples:* Staphylococci resistant to penicillin G produce a beta-lactamase which destroys the drug. Other beta-lactamases are produced by gram-negative rods. Gram-negative bacteria resistant to aminoglycosides (by virtue of a plasmid) produce adenylating, phosphorylating, or acetylating enzymes that destroy the drug. Gram-negative bacteria may be resistant to chloramphenicol if they produce a chloramphenicol acetyltransferase.

(2) Microorganisms change their permeability to the drug. *Examples:* Tetracyclines accumulate in susceptible bacteria but not in resistant bacteria. Resistance to polymyxins is probably associated with a change in permeability to the drugs.

(3) Microorganisms develop an altered structural target for the drug (see also ¶5, below). *Examples:* Chromosomal resistance to aminoglycosides is associated with the loss or alteration of a specific protein on the 30S subunit of the bacterial ribosome which serves as a binding site in susceptible organisms. Erythromycin-resistant organisms have an altered protein on the 50S subunit of the bacterial ribosome.

(4) Microorganisms develop an altered metabolic pathway that bypasses the reaction inhibited by the drug. *Example:* Some sulfonamide-resistant bacteria do not require extracellular PABA but, like mammalian cells, can utilize preformed folic acid.

(5) Microorganisms develop an altered enzyme which can still perform its metabolic function but is much less affected by the drug than the enzyme in the susceptible organism. *Example:* In some sulfonamide-susceptible bacteria, the tetrahydropteroic acid synthetase has a much higher affinity for sulfonamide than for PABA. In sulfonamide-resistant mutants the opposite is the case.

ORIGIN OF DRUG RESISTANCE

The origin of drug resistance may be genetic or nongenetic.

Nongenetic Origin

Active replication of bacteria is usually required for most antibacterial drug actions. Consequently, microorganisms which are metabolically inactive (nonmultiplying) may be phenotypically resistant to drugs. However, their offspring are fully susceptible. *Example:* Mycobacteria often survive in tissues for many years after infection yet are restrained by the host's defenses and do not multiply. Such "persisting" organisms are resistant to treatment and cannot be eradicated by drugs. Yet if they start to multiply (eg, following corticosteroid treatment of the patient), they are fully susceptible to the same drugs.

Microorganisms may lose the specific target structure for a drug for several generations and thus be resistant. *Example:* Penicillin-susceptible organisms may change to L forms during penicillin administration. Lacking most cell wall, they are then resistant to cell wall inhibitor drugs (penicillins, cephalosporins) and may remain so for several generations as "persisters." When these organisms revert to their bacterial parent forms by resuming cell wall production, they are again fully penicillin-susceptible.

Genetic Origin

The vast majority of drug-resistant microbes have emerged as a result of genetic changes and subsequent selection processes. Genetic changes may be chromosomal or extrachromosomal.

A. Chromosomal Resistance: In all microbial populations, mutants arise spontaneously which exhibit a change at a chromosomal locus which, by one of the mechanisms outlined above, controls susceptibility or resistance to a given drug. Although these mutants arise spontaneously, the presence of the drug serves to select them out. Thus the "selection pressure" of the antimicrobial drug plays an important part in favoring the survival and proliferation of drug-resistant mutants in a single host (patient) or in an environment (eg, hospital).

B. Extrachromosomal Resistance: Genetic loci controlling drug resistance often occur on extrachromosomal pieces of microbial DNA (plasmids, episomes). Such plasmids may remain separate from the chromosome and divide in the process of microbial division, or they may become integrated into the chromosome at times and again separated from it. Plasmids carrying drug resistance may be transmitted from a resistant organism to a susceptible organism of the same species by transduction, ie, by being carried by a specific bacteriophage. *Example:* The plasmid carrying the gene for beta-lactamase production can be transferred from a resistant staphylococcus to a susceptible staphylococcus if carried by a suitable bacteriophage.

In gram-negative bacteria, plasmids may carry genes for one or a series of drug resistance factors. Such "resistance transfer factor" (RTF) plasmids may pass from a gram-negative bacterium of one species by conjugation to a gram-negative bacterium of the same or a different species. Such RTF plasmids often transfer multiple drug resistance, since the genes controlling resistance to sulfonamides, trimethoprim, streptomycin, tetracycline, chloramphenicol, etc may be at adjoining genetic loci. *Example:* Shigellae resistant to tetracycline, chloramphenicol, streptomycin, and ampicillin may conjugate with *E coli* susceptible to these drugs and transfer resistance to them.

Cross-Resistance

Microorganisms resistant to a certain drug may also be resistant to other drugs which share a mechanism of action. Such relationships exist mainly between agents that are closely related chemically (eg, polymyxin B-colistin; erythromycin-oleandomycin; neomycin-kanamycin), but they may also exist between unrelated chemicals (erythromycin-lincomycin). In certain classes of drugs, the active nucleus of the chemical is so similar among many congeners (eg, tetracyclines) that full cross-resistance is to be expected.

Emergence of drug resistance in infections may be minimized in the following ways: (1) maintain sufficiently high levels of the drug in the tissues to inhibit both the original population and first step mutants; (2) simultaneously administer 2 drugs which do not give cross-resistance, each of which delays the emergence of mutants resistant to the other drug (eg, ethambutol and isoniazid in the treatment of tuberculosis); and (3) avoid exposure of microorganisms to a particularly valuable drug by restricting its use, especially in hospitals.

Clinical Implications of Drug Resistance

In 1936, when sulfonamides were first employed for the treatment of gonorrhea, practically all strains of gonococci were susceptible and most cases were cured by these drugs. Six years later, the majority of strains were resistant and most cases failed to respond to sulfonamide therapy but were still highly susceptible to penicillin. At present, the resistance of gonococci to penicillin is increasing markedly. Until 1962, meningococci were regularly susceptible to sulfonamides. Subsequently, sulfonamide-resistant meningococci spread widely in some military populations. Sulfonamides have now lost their usefulness in the prevention and treatment of meningococcal infections. A similar increase in resistance has taken place with staphylococci. In 1944, the vast majority of strains of staphylococci isolated from hospitalized patients or members of hospital staffs were found to be sensitive to penicillin. By 1948, 65–85% of staphylococci in hospitals were resistant to penicillin. This change has been attributed to the fact that large-scale use of penicillin in hospitals has resulted in elimination of penicillin-sensitive staphylococci and their replacement by resistant variants producing penicillinase. The widespread use of tetracyclines also resulted in elimination of tetracycline-sensitive staphylococci and their replacement by tetracycline-resistant ones. Thus, a majority of "hospital staphylococci" are both penicillin-resistant and tetracycline-resistant. These strains present both a clinical problem in the individual patient and an epidemiologic one with respect to the entire hospital population and the community. Recently, tetracycline-resistant strains of pneumococci and group A streptococci have also appeared.

A similar situation has developed with respect to gram-negative enteric organisms, especially in hospitals. The excessive use of drugs leads to suppression of drug-susceptible microorganisms and favors the survival of drug-resistant ones. This "selection pressure" of drugs in the hospital environment gradually brings about prevalence of drug-resistant microbial species, eg, enterobacter, proteus, pseudomonas, serratia, and fungi.

To a limited extent, drug-resistant mutants have arisen in tuberculosis. They may complicate the treatment of individual patients in whom they arise and may be transmitted to contacts, giving rise to primary drug-resistant infections.

In closed environments—eg, hospitals or military establishments—the intensive exchange of drug-resistant organisms between persons and their spread by fomites greatly contribute to the problem. The possibility also exists that certain drug-resistant organisms may exhibit enhanced virulence or ability to disseminate.

DRUG DEPENDENCE

Certain organisms not only are resistant to a drug but even require it for growth. This has been best demonstrated for streptomycin. When streptomycin-dependent meningococci are injected into mice, progressive fatal disease results only if the animals are treated simultaneously with streptomycin. In the absence of streptomycin, the microorganisms cannot proliferate and the animals remain well. This phenomenon probably plays no role in human infection. Drug-dependent bacteria have been used in live vaccines.

ANTIMICROBIAL ACTIVITY IN VITRO

Antimicrobial activity is measured in vitro in order to determine (1) the potency of an antibacterial agent in solution, (2) its concentration in body fluids or tissues, and (3) the sensitivity of a given microorganism to known concentrations of the drug.

Measurement of Antimicrobial Activity

Determination of these quantities may be undertaken by one of 2 principal methods: dilution or diffusion.

Using an appropriate standard test organism and a known sample of drug for comparison, these methods can be employed to estimate either the potency of antibiotic in the sample or the "sensitivity" of the microorganism.

A. Dilution Tests: These are carried out by incorporating antimicrobial substances in graded amounts into liquid or solid bacteriologic media. The media are subsequently inoculated with test bacteria and incubated. The end point is taken as that amount of antimicrobial substance required to inhibit the growth of, or to kill, the test bacteria.

B. Diffusion Method: A filter paper disk, a porous cup, or a bottomless cylinder containing measured quantities of drug is placed on a solid medium which has been heavily seeded with the test organisms. After incubation, the diameter of the clear zone of inhibition surrounding the deposit of drug is taken as a measure of the inhibitory power of the drug against the particular test organism. Obviously, this method is subject to many physical and chemical factors in addition to the simple interaction of drug and organisms (eg, nature of medium, diffusibility and molecular size of drug, stability of drug). Nevertheless, standardization of conditions permits quantitative assay of drug potency or sensitivity of the organism.

When determining bacterial sensitivity by the diffusion method, most laboratories use disks of antibiotic-impregnated filter paper. A concentration gradient of antibiotic is produced in the medium by diffusion from the disk. As the diffusion is a continuous process, the concentration gradient is never stable for long; but some stabilization can be achieved by allowing diffusion to start before bacterial growth begins. The greatest difficulties arise from the varying growth rates of different microorganisms and must be corrected by varying the density of the inoculum.

Since it is not feasible to state directly the antibiotic concentration in the medium at any given distance from the diffusion center, interpretation of the results of diffusion tests must be based on comparisons between dilution and diffusion methods. Such comparisons have been made, and, under the sponsorship of WHO, international reference standards have been established. Linear regression lines can express the relationship between log of minimum inhibitory concentration in dilution tests and diameter of inhibition zones in diffusion tests.

Use of a single disk for each antibiotic with careful standardization of the test conditions permits the evaluation of "susceptibility" for a microorganism by comparing the size of the inhibition zone against a standard of the same drug (Kirby-Bauer method).

It is fundamentally wrong to regard inhibition around a disk containing a certain amount of antibiotic as implying sensitivity to the same concentration of the antibiotic per milliliter of medium, blood, or urine.

Factors Affecting Antimicrobial Activity

Among the many factors which affect antimicrobial activity in vitro, the following must be considered because they significantly influence the results of tests.

A. pH of Environment: Some drugs are more active at acid pH (eg, nitrofurantoin); others at alkaline pH (eg, aminoglycosides, sulfonamides).

B. Components of Medium: Salts may strikingly inhibit aminoglycosides. PABA in tissue extracts antagonizes sulfonamides. Serum proteins bind penicillins in varying degrees, ranging from 40% for methicillin to 98% for dicloxacillin.

C. Stability of Drug: At incubator temperature, several antimicrobial agents lose their activity. Chlortetracycline is inactivated rapidly and penicillins more slowly, whereas aminoglycosides, chloramphenicol, and polymyxin B are quite stable for long periods.

D. Size of Inoculum: In general, the larger the bacterial inoculum, the lower the apparent "sensitivity" of the organism. Large bacterial populations are less promptly and completely inhibited than small ones. In addition, the likelihood of the emergence of a resistant mutant is much greater in large populations.

E. Length of Incubation: In many instances, microorganisms are not killed but only inhibited upon short exposure to antimicrobial agents. The longer incubation continues, the greater the chance for resistant mutants to emerge or for the least susceptible members of the microbial population to begin multiplying as the drug deteriorates.

F. Metabolic Activity of Microorganisms: In general, actively and rapidly growing organisms are more susceptible to drug action than those in the resting phase. "Persisters" are metabolically inactive organisms which survive long exposure to a drug but whose offspring are fully susceptible to the same drug. A specialized form of "persisters" might be L forms of bacteria. Under treatment with drugs which inhibit cell wall formation, cell wall deficient forms may develop in certain tissues possessing suitable osmotic properties. These protoplasts could persist in tissues while the drug (eg, penicillin) was administered and might later revert to intact bacterial forms, causing relapse of disease.

ANTIMICROBIAL ACTIVITY IN VIVO

The problem of the activity of antimicrobial agents in vivo is much more complex than in vitro. It involves not only drug and parasite but also a third factor, the host. The interrelationships of host, drug, and parasite are diagrammed in Fig 10–1. Drug-parasite and host-parasite relationships are discussed in the following paragraphs. Host-drug relationships (absorption, excretion, distribution, metabolism, and toxicity) are dealt with mainly in pharmacology texts.

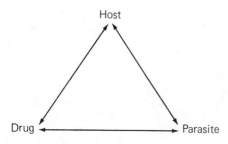

Figure 10–1. Interrelationships of host, drug, and parasite.

DRUG-PARASITE RELATIONSHIPS

Several important interactions between drug and parasite have been discussed in the preceding pages. The following are additional important in vivo factors.

Environment

The environment in the test tube is constant for all members of a microbial population. In the host, however, varying environmental influences are brought to bear on microorganisms located in different tissues and in different parts of the body. Therefore, the response of the microbial population is much less uniform within the host than in the test tube.

A. State of Metabolic Activity: In the test tube, the state of metabolic activity is relatively uniform for the majority of microorganisms. In the body it is diverse; undoubtedly, many organisms are at a low level of biosynthetic activity and are thus relatively insusceptible to drug action. These "dormant" microorganisms or "persisters" often survive exposure to high concentrations of drugs and subsequently may produce a clinical relapse of the infection. Alternatively, "persisters" may be cell wall deficient forms insusceptible to drugs which inhibit cell wall formation.

B. Distribution of Agent: In the test tube, all microorganisms are equally exposed to the drug. In the body the antimicrobial agent is unequally distributed in tissues and fluids. The concentration in urine is often much greater than the concentration in blood or tissue. The lesion induced by the microorganism may

protect it from the drug. The walls of abscesses, for example, are avascular and may delay passage of the drug. Necrotic tissue or pus may adsorb the drug and thus prevent its contact with bacteria.

C. Location of Organisms: In the test tube, the microorganisms come into direct contact with the drug. In the body they may often be located within tissue cells. Drugs enter tissue cells at different rates. Some (eg, tetracyclines) reach about the same concentration inside monocytes as in the extracellular fluid. With others (eg, streptomycin) the intracellular concentration is only a small fraction (perhaps 5–10%) of the extracellular concentration.

D. Interfering Substances: In the test tube, drug activity may be impaired by binding of the drug to protein or to lipids or by interaction with salts. The biochemical environment of microorganisms in the body is very complex and results in significant interference with drug action. The drug may be bound by blood and tissue proteins or phospholipids; it may also react with nucleic acids in pus and may be physically adsorbed onto exudates, cells, and necrotic debris. In necrotic tissue the pH may be highly acid and thus unfavorable for drug action (eg, aminoglycosides).

Concentration

In the test tube, microorganisms are exposed to an essentially constant concentration of drug. In the body this is not so.

A. Absorption: The absorption of drugs from the intestinal tract (if taken by mouth) or from tissues (if injected) is irregular. There is also a continuous excretion as well as inactivation of the drug. Consequently, the available levels of drug in the body fluctuate continuously, and the microorganisms are exposed to varying concentrations of the antimicrobial agent.

B. Distribution: The distribution of drugs varies greatly with different tissues. Some drugs penetrate poorly into certain tissues (eg, CNS) or body cavities (eg, pleural space). Drug concentrations following systemic administration may therefore be inadequate for effective treatment. In such situations the drug may be administered locally (eg, injection of drugs into the pleural space in empyema). On surface wounds or mucous membranes, local (topical) application of poorly absorbed drugs permits highly effective local concentrations without toxic side-effects. Drug concentrations in urine are often much higher than in blood.

C. Variability of Concentration: The critical consideration in antimicrobial therapy is the necessity of maintaining an effective concentration of the drug in contact with microorganisms at their site of proliferation or establishment in the tissues for a sufficient length of time to cause eradication of infecting organism. Because the drug is administered intermittently and is absorbed and excreted irregularly, the levels constantly fluctuate at the site of infection. In order to maintain sufficient drug concentrations for a sufficient time, the time-dose relationship has to be considered. The larger each individual drug dose, the longer the permissible interval between doses. The smaller the individual dose, the shorter the interval which will ensure adequate drug levels. A good general rule in antimicrobial therapy is as follows: Give a sufficiently large amount of an effective drug as early as possible, and continue treatment long enough to ensure eradication of infection; but give an antimicrobial drug only when it is indicated by rational choice.

HOST-PARASITE RELATIONSHIPS

Host-parasite relationships may be altered by antimicrobial drugs in several ways.

Alteration of Tissue Response

The inflammatory response of the tissues to infections may be altered if the drug suppresses the multiplication of microorganisms but does not eliminate them from the body, and an acute process may in this way be transformed into a chronic one. Conversely, the suppression of inflammatory reactions in tissues by corticosteroids may reduce the effectiveness of bacteriostatic drugs. The administration of antineoplastic drugs depresses inflammatory reactions and immune responses and consequently leads to enhanced susceptibility to infection and diminished response to antimicrobial drugs.

Alteration of Immune Response

If an infection is modified by an antimicrobial drug, the immune response of the host may also be altered. An example will suffice to illustrate this phenomenon:

Infection with beta-hemolytic group A streptococci is followed frequently by the development of antistreptococcal antibodies and occasionally by the development of rheumatic fever. If the infective process can be interrupted early and completely with antimicrobial drugs, the development of an immune response and of rheumatic fever can be prevented (presumably by rapid elimination of the antigen). Drugs and doses which rapidly eradicate the infecting streptococci (eg, penicillin) are more effective in preventing rheumatic fever than those that merely suppress the microorganisms temporarily (eg, tetracycline).

Alteration of Microbial Flora

Antimicrobial drugs affect not only the infecting microorganisms but also susceptible members of the normal microbial flora of the body. An imbalance is thus created which in itself may lead to disease. A few examples will serve:

(1) In hospitalized patients who receive antimicrobials, the normal microbial flora is suppressed. This creates a partial void which is filled by the organisms most prevalent in the environment, particularly drug-resistant "hospital" staphylococci, pseudomonas, fungi, etc. Such superinfecting organisms subsequently may produce serious drug-resistant infections.

(2) In women taking tetracycline antibiotics by mouth, the normal vaginal flora may be suppressed, permitting marked overgrowth of candida. This leads to unpleasant local inflammation (vaginitis) and itching which is difficult to control.

(3) In the presence of urinary tract obstruction, the tendency to bladder infection is great. When such urinary tract infection due to a sensitive microorganism (eg, *E coli*) is treated with an appropriate chemotherapeutic drug, the organism may be eradicated. However, very often a "superinfection" due to drug-resistant proteus, pseudomonas, or enterobacter occurs after the drug-sensitive microorganisms are eliminated. A similar process accounts for respiratory tract superinfections in patients being treated for chronic bronchitis or bronchiectasis.

(4) In persons receiving antimicrobial drugs by mouth, the normal intestinal flora may be suppressed. Drug-resistant staphylococci may establish themselves in the bowel in great numbers and may cause serious enterocolitis.

CLINICAL USE OF ANTIBIOTICS

Selection of Antibiotics

The rational selection of antimicrobial drugs depends upon the following:

A. Diagnosis: A specific etiologic diagnosis must be formulated. This can often be done on the basis of a clinical impression. Thus in typical streptococcal sore throat, gonorrhea, or lobar pneumonia, the relationship between clinical picture and etiologic agent is sufficiently constant to permit selection of the antibiotic of choice on the basis of clinical impression alone. Even in these cases, however, as a safeguard against diagnostic error, it is preferable to obtain a representative specimen for bacteriologic study before giving antimicrobial drugs.

In most infections the relationship between etiologic agent and clinical picture is not constant. It is therefore important to obtain proper specimens for bacteriologic identification of the etiologic agent. As soon as such specimens have been secured, chemotherapy can be started on the basis of the "best guess." Once the etiologic agent has been identified by laboratory procedures, chemotherapy can be modified as necessary.

The "best guess" of an etiologic organism is based, among others, on the following considerations: (1) the site of infection (eg, pneumonia, urinary tract infection); (2) the age of the patient (eg, meningitis; neonatal, young child, adult); (3) where the infection was acquired (hospital, community); (4) mechanical predisposing factors (intravenous drip, urinary catheter, respirator, exposure to vector); and (5) predisposing host factors (immunodeficiency, corticosteroids, transplant, cancer chemotherapy, etc).

When the etiologic agent of a clinical infection is known, the drug of choice can often be selected on the basis of current clinical experience. At other times, laboratory tests for antibiotic sensitivity (see below) are necessary to determine the drug of choice.

B. Sensitivity Tests: Laboratory tests for antibiotic sensitivity are indicated in the following circumstances: (1) When the microorganism recovered is of a type which is often resistant to antimicrobial drugs (eg, gram-negative enteric bacteria). (2) When an infectious process is likely to be fatal unless treated specifically (eg, meningitis, septicemia). (3) In certain infections where eradication of the infectious organisms requires the use of drugs which are rapidly bactericidal, not merely bacteriostatic (eg, bacterial endocarditis, acute osteomyelitis). The laboratory aspects of antibiotic sensitivity testing are discussed in Chapter 26.

C. Serum Assay of Bactericidal Activity: This test determines directly whether adequate amounts of the correct drugs are being administered to the patient from whom an etiologic organism has been isolated. Serum is obtained during therapy, diluted, inoculated with the previously isolated organism, and incubated. Subcultures at intervals must indicate bactericidal activity in significant serum dilutions (depending upon inoculum size and time after drug administration, usually at least 1:5) to suggest adequate therapy.

Dangers of Indiscriminate Use

(1) Widespread sensitization of the population, with resulting hypersensitivity, anaphylaxis, rashes, fever, blood disorders, cholestatic hepatitis, and perhaps connective tissue diseases.

(2) Changes in the normal flora of the body, with disease resulting from "superinfection" due to overgrowth of drug-resistant organisms.

(3) Masking serious infection without eradicating it. For example, the clinical manifestations of an abscess may be suppressed while the infectious process continues.

(4) Direct drug toxicity, particularly with prolonged use of certain agents. Important examples are aplastic anemia due to inappropriate use of chloramphenicol; renal damage or auditory nerve damage due to aminoglycoside antibiotics.

(5) Development of drug resistance in microbial populations, chiefly through the elimination of drug-sensitive microorganisms from antibiotic-saturated environments (eg, hospitals) and their replacement by drug-resistant microorganisms.

COMBINED ANTIBIOTIC ACTION

Indications

Combinations of antimicrobial agents may rationally be used (1) to prevent or delay the emergence of resistant mutants, especially in chronic infections such as tuberculosis; (2) to achieve additive or synergistic effects against a homogeneous population of resistant organisms; (3) for emergency treatment of serious infections before laboratory studies are completed (eg,

suspected gram-negative bacterial sepsis); or (4) rarely, in mixed infections.

Mechanisms

When 2 antimicrobial agents act simultaneously on a homogeneous microbial population, the effect may be one of the following: (1) Indifference, ie, the combined action is no greater than that of the more effective agent when used alone. (2) Addition, ie, the combined action is equivalent to the sum of the actions of each drug when used alone. (3) Synergism, ie, the combined action is significantly greater than the sum of both effects. (4) Antagonism, ie, the combined action is less than that of the more effective agent when used alone.

All these effects may be observed both in vitro (particularly in terms of bactericidal rate) and in vivo. Antagonism is sharply limited by time-dose relationships and is therefore a rare event in clinical antimicrobial therapy. An example of antagonism is the increased rate of treatment failure resulting from the addition of chloramphenicol or tetracycline to penicillin in pneumococcal meningitis. Indifference and simple addition are most common with drug combinations. Synergism is the most desirable form of combined drug action in the treatment of infections, but it is rare. An example is the simultaneous action of a penicillin and an aminoglycoside on enterococci. While neither of these drugs is capable of bactericidal action, the cell wall inhibitor (penicillin) facilitates the entry of the protein synthesis inhibitor (aminoglycoside) into the cell and often results in bactericidal action and therapeutic success in enterococcal endocarditis.

Another example is the simultaneous block of a metabolic pathway by the components of co-trimoxazole. The sulfonamide interferes with PABA uptake and the trimethoprim inhibits the dihydrofolate reductase (see p 106).

The effects which can be achieved with combinations of antimicrobial drugs vary with different combinations and are specific for each strain of microorganism. Thus no combination is uniformly synergistic. Combined effects cannot be predicted from the behavior of the microorganism toward single drugs.

Combined therapy should not be used indiscriminately; every effort should be made to employ the single antibiotic of choice. In resistant infections, detailed laboratory study can at times define synergistic drug combinations which may be essential to eradicate the microorganisms.

CHEMOPROPHYLAXIS

Anti-infective chemoprophylaxis implies the administration of drugs to prevent the establishment of pathogenic microorganisms in the body. The term may also include the administration of drugs soon after exposure to pathogens but before the development of symptoms and disease.

It is not possible to remove—or prevent the establishment of—all possible microorganisms with one or even with several antimicrobial drugs. **The useful effect of chemoprophylaxis is limited to the action of a specific drug against a specific microorganism.** Any effort to prevent the establishment of any or all microorganisms usually selects the most drug-resistant ones as the cause of subsequent infection. In all forms of chemoprophylaxis, the risk of a possible infection in a given individual must be weighed against the toxicity, cost, efficacy, and inconvenience of the proposed chemoprophylaxis.

Antibacterial chemoprophylaxis is an accepted clinical procedure for the prevention of group A streptococcus, meningococcus, and plague infections. Prophylactic drugs have also been used against rickettsial and poxvirus infections. The prevention of bacterial endocarditis, of postcoital cystitis, and of exacerbations in chronic bronchitis in persons at high risk at a particular time has also been recommended.

The reduction of lower bowel flora prior to elective bowel surgery has found wide application, but its efficacy as "chemoprophylaxis" is not proved. Specific bactericidal drugs aimed at the pathogens most likely to complicate cardiac surgical procedures may be helpful at times. In the large majority of elective "clean" surgical procedures, however, there is little evidence that "chemoprophylactic drugs" affect the incidence or severity of postoperative infections.

"Prophylactic" antimicrobials in surgery might be considered only if the risk of postoperative infection is greater than 5%. The drug (eg, a cephalosporin) should then be given just prior to the procedure and for not more than 48 hours afterward to limit the disadvantages of toxicity and selection pressure favoring superinfection.

Table 10–1. Practical chemical disinfectants.

Disinfection of inanimate environment

Table tops, instruments	5% Lysol or other phenolic compound
	1–10% formaldehyde
	0.1% mercury bichloride
	Quaternary ammonium compounds (0.1%)
Excreta, bandages, bedpans	1% sodium hypochlorite
	5% Lysol or other phenolic compound
Air	Propylene glycol mist or aerosol
	Formaldehyde vapor
Heat-sensitive instruments	Ethylene oxide gas

Disinfection of skin or wounds

	Washing with soap and water
	Soaps or detergents containing 2% hexachlorophene or 1.5% trichlorocarbanilide
	2% tincture of iodine
	70% ethyl alcohol; 70–90% isopropyl alcohol
	Polyvinylpyrrolidone-bound iodine (water soluble)
	Nitrofurazone, 0.2% jelly or solution

Topical application of drugs to skin

In candidiasis	Gentian violet, 1:2000
	Nystatin cream, 100,000 units/gm
	Candicidin ointment, 0.6 mg/gm
	Miconazole, 2% cream
In burns	Silver nitrate, 0.5%
	Mafenide acetate cream
	Silver sulfadiazine
In dermatophytosis	Undecylenic acid powder or 5–10% cream
	Tolnaftate cream, 1%
In pyoderma	Ammoniated mercury, 2–5% ointment
	Bacitracin-neomycin-polymyxin ointment
	Potassium permanganate, 0.01%

Topical application of drugs to eyes

For gonorrhea prophylaxis	1% silver nitrate
For bacterial conjunctivitis	Sulfacetamide ointment
	Chloramphenicol ointment

DISINFECTANTS

Disinfectants and antiseptics differ from systemically active antimicrobials in that they possess little selective toxicity: they are toxic not only for microbial parasites but for host cells as well. Therefore, they can be used only to inactivate microorganisms in the inanimate environment or, to a limited extent, on skin surfaces, but they cannot be administered systemically and are not active in tissues.

The antimicrobial action of disinfectants is determined by concentration, time, and temperature, and the evaluation of their effect may be complex. The known modes of action of several classes of chemical disinfectants are described in Chapter 7. A few examples of disinfectants which are employed in medicine or public health are listed in Table 10–1.

ANTIMICROBIAL DRUGS FOR SYSTEMIC ADMINISTRATION

PENICILLINS

The penicillins are derived from molds of the genus Penicillium (eg, *P notatum*) and obtained by extraction of submerged cultures grown in special media. The most widely used natural penicillin at present is penicillin G. From fermentation brews of penicillium, 6-aminopenicillanic acid has been isolated on a large scale. This makes it possible to synthesize an almost unlimited variety of penicillin-like compounds by coupling the free amino group of the penicillanic acid to free carboxyl groups of different radicals.

All penicillins share the same basic structure. A thiazolidine ring (a) is attached to a beta-lactam ring (b) which carries a free amino group (c). The acidic radicals attached to the amino group can be split off by bacterial and other amidases. The structural integrity of the 6-aminopenicillanic acid nucleus is essential to the biologic activity of the compounds. If the beta-lactam ring is enzymatically cleaved by beta-lactamases (penicillinases), the resulting product, penicilloic acid, is devoid of antibacterial activity. However, it carries an antigenic determinant of the penicillins and acts as a sensitizing hapten when attached to serum proteins.

The different radicals (R) attached to the aminopenicillanic acid determine the essential pharmacologic properties of the resulting drugs. The clinically important penicillins of 1976 fall into 3 main groups: (1) highest activity against gram-positive bacteria, inactivated by penicillinases (eg, penicillin G, penicillin V, benzathine penicillin); (2) somewhat lower activity against gram-positive bacteria but resistant to penicillinases (eg, methicillin, nafcillin, oxacillin, dicloxacillin); (3) broad spectrum activity against both gram-negative and gram-positive bacteria, inactivated by penicillinase (eg, ampicillin, carbenicillin). Some representatives are shown in Fig 10–2. Most penicillins are dispensed as sodium or potassium salts of the free acid. Potassium penicillin G contains about 1.7 mEq of K^+ per million units (2.8 mEq/gm). Procaine salts and benzathine salts of penicillin provide repository forms for intramuscular injection. In dry form, penicillins are stable, but solutions rapidly lose their activity and must be prepared fresh for administration.

Antimicrobial Activity

All penicillins have the same mode of action: They inhibit the synthesis of bacterial cell walls by blocking the terminal cross-linking of linear glycopeptides ("transpeptidation") into the complex peptidoglycan. Since active cell wall synthesis is a requirement for susceptibility to penicillins, metabolically inactive cells, or L forms, are unaffected. Most penicillins are much more active against gram-positive than gram-negative bacteria, probably because of differences in cell wall composition, but ampicillin and carbenicillin have similar activity against both kinds of bacteria.

Penicillin G and penicillin V are often measured in units (1 million units = 0.6 gm), but the semisynthetic penicillins are measured in grams. Whereas 0.002–1 μg/ml of penicillin G is lethal for a majority of susceptible gram-positive organisms, 10–100 times more is required to kill gram-negative bacteria (except neisseriae). The activity of penicillins also varies with their protein binding, which ranges from 40% to more than 95% for different drugs.

Resistance

Certain organisms (eg, many staphylococci, coliforms, pseudomonas) produce beta-lactamases (penicillinases), which inactivate some penicillins. Penicillinase-producing staphylococci are susceptible to methicillin, other beta-lactamase-resistant penicillins, and the cephalosporins. The genetic control of this enzyme in staphylococci resides in a plasmid which is transmissible to other staphylococci by transduction.

Certain organisms (eg, coliforms) produce an enzyme, amidase, which splits off the R side chain from 6-aminopenicillanic acid and inactivates the drug. The relative importance of this mechanism is in doubt.

Certain bacteria are genetically resistant to penicillins but do not destroy the drug. Their resistance must reside in the nature of the mucopeptide structure and synthesis. Such mutants arise infrequently in susceptible populations, and the resistance is of small magnitude. Among penicillinase-producing staphylococci, mutants arise infrequently which are insusceptible to the penicillinase-resistant penicillins (eg, methicillin) and cephalosporins.

Metabolically inactive cells are not susceptible to penicillin, but the offspring of these "persisters" are fully susceptible. Cell wall deficient forms are resistant to penicillins and cephalosporins.

Absorption, Distribution, & Excretion

After intramuscular or intravenous administration, absorption of most penicillins is rapid and complete. After oral administration, only 5–35% of the dose is absorbed, depending on acid stability, binding to foods, presence of buffers, etc. After absorption, penicillins are widely distributed in tissues and body fluids. Protein binding is 40–60% for penicillin G, ampicillin, and methicillin; 90% for nafcillin; and 95–98% for oxacillin and dicloxacillin. For most rapidly absorbed penicillins, a parenteral dose of 3–6 gm/24 hours yields serum levels of approximately 1–6 μg/ml.

Special dosage forms have been designed for delayed absorption to yield drug levels for long periods. After a single IM dose of benzathine penicillin, 1.5 gm (2.4 million units), serum levels of 0.03 unit/ml are maintained for 10 days and levels of 0.005 unit/ml for 3 weeks. Procaine penicillin given intramuscularly yields levels for 24 hours.

In many tissues, penicillin concentrations are similar to those in serum. Lower levels occur in joints, eyes, and CNS. However, in meningitis, penetration is enhanced and levels of 0.2 μg/ml occur in the CSF with a daily parenteral dose of 12 gm.

Most of the absorbed penicillin is rapidly excreted by the kidneys. About 10% of renal excretion is by glomerular filtration and 90% by tubular secretion. The latter can be partially blocked by probenecid to achieve higher systemic and CSF levels. In the newborn and in persons with renal failure, penicillin excretion is reduced and systemic levels remain elevated longer.

Clinical Uses

Penicillins are the most widely used antibiotics,

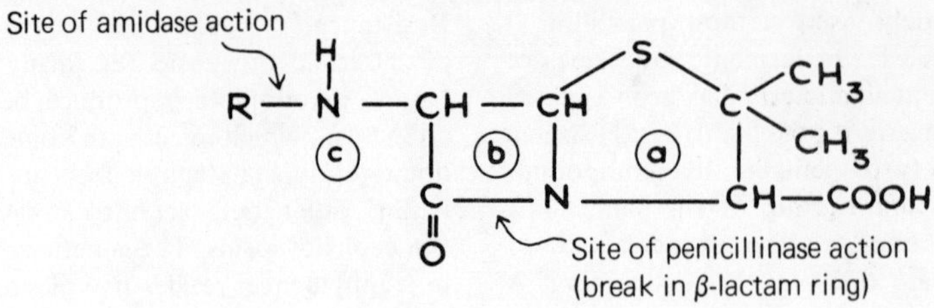

6-Aminopenicillanic acid

The following 8 structures can each be substituted at the R to produce a new penicillin.

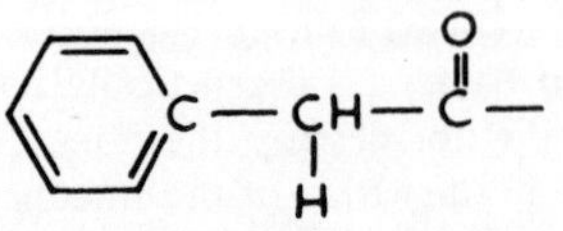

Penicillin G (benzylpenicillin):
High activity against gram-positive bacteria. Low activity against gram-negative bacteria. Acid-labile. Destroyed by β-lactamase; 60% protein-bound.

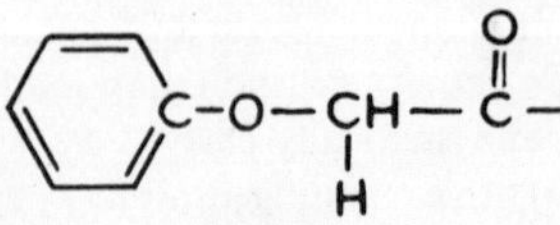

Penicillin V (phenoxymethyl penicillin):
Similar to peniclllin G, but relatively acid-resistant.

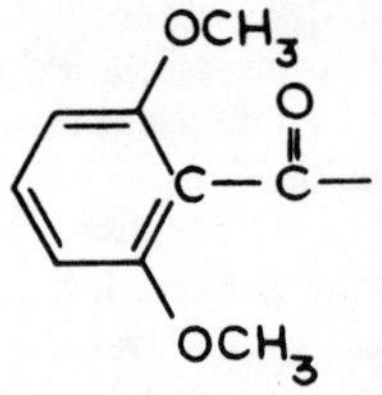

Methicillin (dimethoxyphenylpenicillin):
Lower activity than penicillin G but resistant to penicillinase. Acid-labile. 40% protein-bound.

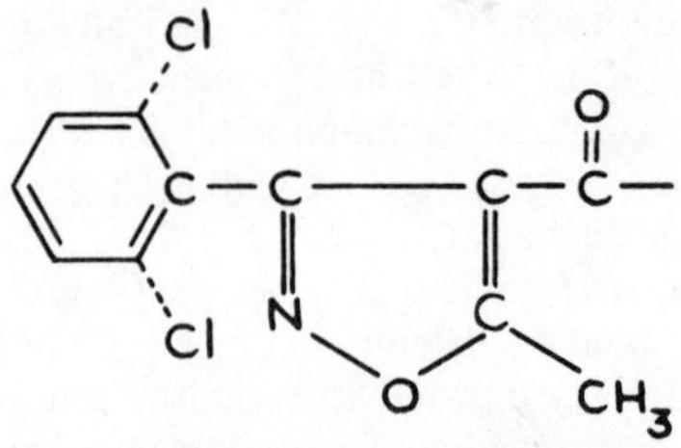

Oxacillin; cloxacillin (one Cl in structure); dicloxacillin (2 Cls in structure); flucloxacillin (one Cl and one F in structure) (isoxazolyl penicillins): Similar to methicillin in penicillinase resistance, but acid-stable. Highly protein-bound (95–98%).

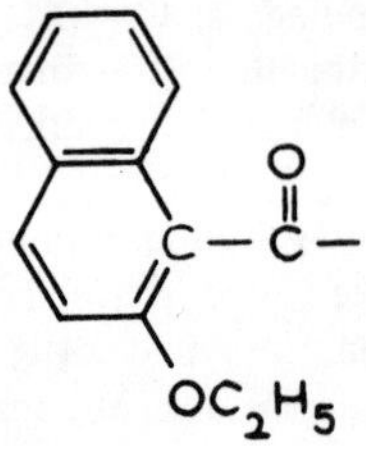

Nafcillin (ethoxynaphthamidopenicillin):
Similar to isoxazolyl penicillins; less strongly protein-bound (90%).

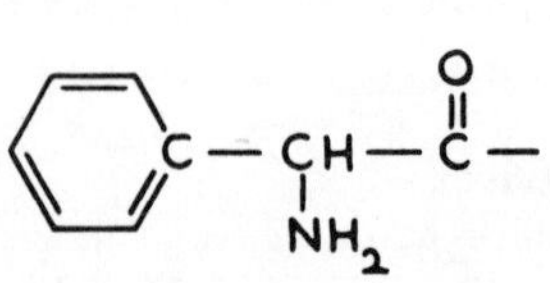

Ampicillin (alpha-aminobenzylpenicillin):
Similar to penicillin G (destroyed by β-lactamase), but acid-stable and more active against gram-negative bacteria. Carbenicillin has –COONa instead of –NH$_2$ group.

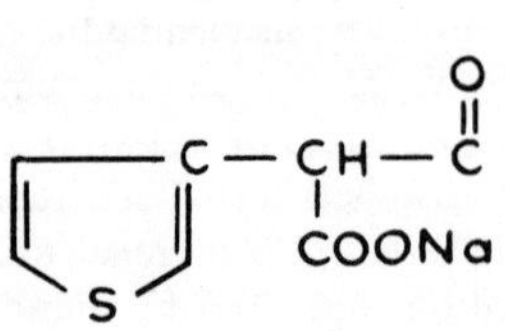

Ticarcillin:
Similar to carbenicillin.

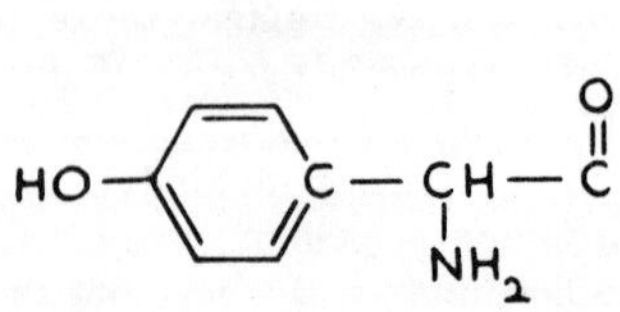

Amoxicillin:
Similar to ampicillin but better absorbed; gives higher blood levels.

Figure 10–2. Structures of the penicillins.

Table 10—2. Drug selections, 1975–1976.

Suspected or Proved Etiologic Agent	Drug(s) of First Choice	Alternative Drug(s)
Gram-negative cocci		
Gonococcus	Penicillin[1], ampicillin	Tetracycline[2], spectinomycin
Meningococcus	Penicillin[1]	Chloramphenicol, tetracycline
Gram-positive cocci		
Pneumococcus	Penicillin[1]	Erythromycin[3]
Streptococcus, hemolytic groups A,B,C	Penicillin[1]	Erythromycin[3]
Streptococcus viridans	Penicillin[1]	Cephalosporin[4], vancomycin
Staphylococcus, nonpenicillinase-producing	Penicillin[1]	Cephalosporin, vancomycin, lincomycin
Staphylococcus, penicillinase-producing	Penicillinase-resistant penicillin[5]	Cephalosporin, vancomycin, lincomycin
Streptococcus faecalis (enterococcus)	Ampicillin plus aminoglycoside	Penicillin plus gentamicin
Gram-negative rods		
Enterobacter (Aerobacter)	Gentamicin or kanamycin	Chloramphenicol
Bacteroides (except *B fragilis*)	Penicillin or chloramphenicol	Clindamycin
B fragilis	Clindamycin	Chloramphenicol or penicillin
Brucella	Tetracycline plus streptomycin	Streptomycin plus sulfonamide[6]
Escherichia		
E coli sepsis	Kanamycin, gentamicin	Cephalothin, ampicillin
E coli urinary tract infection (first attack)	Sulfonamide[7] or co-trimoxazole[8]	Ampicillin, cephalexin
Haemophilus (meningitis, respiratory infections)	Ampicillin	Chloramphenicol
Klebsiella	Cephalosporin or kanamycin	Gentamicin, chloramphenicol
Mima-Herellea	Kanamycin	Tetracycline, gentamicin
Pasteurella (plague, tularemia)	Streptomycin plus tetracycline	Sulfonamide[6]
Proteus		
P mirabilis	Penicillin or ampicillin	Kanamycin, gentamicin
P vulgaris and other species	Kanamycin or carbenicillin	Chloramphenicol, gentamicin
Pseudomonas		
Ps aeruginosa	Gentamicin or polymyxin	Carbenicillin plus gentamicin
Ps pseudomallei (melioidosis)	Tetracycline plus sulfonamide	Chloramphenicol
Ps mallei (glanders)	Streptomycin plus tetracycline	
Salmonella	Chloramphenicol or ampicillin	Co-trimoxazole[8]
Serratia	Gentamicin	Co-trimoxazole[8]
Shigella	Ampicillin or chloramphenicol	Tetracycline, kanamycin
Vibrio (cholera)	Tetracycline	Chloramphenicol
Gram-positive rods		
Actinomyces	Penicillin[1]	Tetracycline, sulfonamide
Bacillus (eg, anthrax)	Penicillin[1]	Erythromycin
Clostridium (eg, gas gangrene, tetanus)	Penicillin[1]	Tetracycline, erythromycin
Corynebacterium	Erythromycin	Penicillin, cephalosporin
Listeria	Ampicillin plus aminoglycoside	Tetracycline
Acid-fast rods		
Mycobacterium tuberculosis	INH plus rifampin or ethambutol[9]	Other antituberculosis drugs
Mycobacterium leprae	Dapsone or sulfoxone	Other sulfones, amithiazone
Mycobacteria, atypical	INH plus ethambutol plus rifampin	Other antimycobacterial drugs
Nocardia	Sulfonamide[6]	Tetracycline, cycloserine
Spirochetes		
Borrelia (relapsing fever)	Tetracycline	Penicillin
Leptospira	Penicillin	Tetracycline
Treponema (syphilis, yaws)	Penicillin	Erythromycin, tetracycline
Mycoplasma	Tetracycline	Erythromycin
Psittacosis-lymphogranuloma-trachoma agents (chlamydiae)	Tetracycline, sulfonamide[6]	Erythromycin, chloramphenicol
Rickettsiae	Tetracycline	Chloramphenicol

[1] Penicillin G is preferred for parenteral injection; penicillin G (buffered) or penicillin V for oral administration. Only highly sensitive microorganisms should be treated with oral penicillin.

[2] All tetracyclines have the same activity against microorganisms and all have comparable therapeutic activity and toxicity. Dosage is determined by the rates of absorption and excretion of different preparations.

[3] Erythromycin estolate and troleandomycin are the best absorbed oral forms.

[4] Cephalothin and cephaloridine are the best accepted cephalosporins at present.

[5] Parenteral methicillin, nafcillin, or oxacillin. Oral dicloxacillin or other isoxazolylpenicillin.

[6] Trisulfapyrimidines have the advantage of greater solubility in urine over sulfadiazine for oral administration; sodium sulfadiazine is suitable for intravenous injection in severely ill persons.

[7] For previously untreated urinary tract infection, a highly soluble sulfonamide such as sulfisoxazole or trisulfapyrimidines is the first choice.

[8] Co-trimoxazole is a mixture of 1 part (80 mg) trimethoprim plus 5 parts (400 mg) sulfamethoxazole.

[9] Either or both.

particularly in the following areas:

Penicillin G is the drug of choice in infections caused by streptococci, pneumococci, meningococci, nonpenicillinase-producing staphylococci, gonococci, spirochetes, clostridia, aerobic gram-positive rods, and some others (eg, *Bacteroides melaninogenicus*). Most of these infections respond to daily doses of penicillin G, 0.4–4 gm. Intermittent intramuscular injection is the usual method of administration. Much larger amounts (6–120 gm daily) can be given by intravenous infusion in serious infections. Oral administration of buffered penicillin G or penicillin V is indicated in minor infections in daily doses of 1–4 gm. Oral administration is subject to so many variables that it should not be relied upon in seriously ill patients unless serum levels are monitored.

Penicillin G is inhibitory for enterococci (*Streptococcus faecalis*), but for bactericidal effects (eg, in enterococcal endocarditis) an aminoglycoside must be added. Penicillin G in ordinary doses is excreted in sufficiently high concentrations into the urine to inhibit some gram-negative organisms in urinary tract infections, particularly *Proteus mirabilis.* However, this treatment fails in the presence of large numbers of beta-lactamase-producing bacteria in urine.

Benzathine penicillin G is a salt of very low solubility given intramuscularly for low but prolonged drug levels. A single injection of 2.4 million units (1.5 gm) is satisfactory treatment for group A streptococcal pharyngitis and, if given once a week for 2–3 weeks, is satisfactory treatment for syphilis. The same injection once every 3–4 weeks is satisfactory prophylaxis against group A streptococcal reinfection in rheumatics.

Infection with beta-lactamase-producing staphylococci is the only indication for the use of lactamase-resistant penicillins, eg, methicillin, nafcillin, or oxacillin (8–16 gm IV for adults, 50–100 mg/kg/day IV for children); oxacillin, dicloxacillin, or nafcillin, 2–6 gm/day by mouth, can be given for milder staphylococcal infections.

Ampicillin, 2–3 gm/day, can be given orally for treatment of some urinary tract infections with coliforms. In larger doses, ampicillin suppresses salmonella infections. For bacterial meningitis in small children, ampicillin, 200 mg/kg/day IV, is the present choice, but ampicillin-resistant haemophilus strains are on the increase. Amoxicillin is better absorbed and gives higher levels than ampicillin. Carbenicillin resembles ampicillin but is more active against pseudomonas and proteus. Up to 30 gm IV are given daily. Resistance emerges rapidly.

Side-Effects

Penicillins possess less direct toxicity than any of the other antimicrobial drugs. Most serious side-effects are due to hypersensitivity.

A. Toxicity: Very high doses (more than 30 gm/day IV) may produce CNS concentrations which are irritating. In patients with renal failure, smaller doses may produce encephalopathy, delirium, and convulsions. With such doses, direct cation toxicity (K^+) may also occur. Lactamase-resistant penicillins occasionally cause granulopenia. Oral penicillins can cause diarrhea. Carbenicillin may cause a bleeding tendency.

B. Allergy: All penicillins are cross-sensitizing and cross-reacting. Any material (including milk, cosmetics) containing penicillin may induce sensitization. The responsible antigens are degradation products, eg, penicilloic acid, bound to host protein. Skin tests with penicilloyl-polylysine, with alkaline hydrolysis products, and with undegraded penicillin identify many hypersensitive persons. Among positive reactors to skin tests, the incidence of subsequent allergic reactions is high. Antibodies to penicillin (IgG) are not correlated with allergic reactions except rare hemolytic anemia. While a history of a penicillin reaction in the past is not reliable, the drug must be administered with caution to such persons.

Allergic reactions may occur as typical anaphylactic shock, typical serum sickness-type reactions (urticaria, joint swelling, angioneurotic edema, pruritus, respiratory embarrassment within 7–12 days of penicillin dosage), and a variety of skin rashes, fever, nephritis, eosinophilia, vasculitis, etc. The incidence of hypersensitivity to penicillin is negligible in children but may be 1–5% among adults in the USA. Acute anaphylactic life-threatening reactions are very rare (0.05%). Corticosteroids can sometimes suppress allergic manifestations to penicillins.

CEPHALOSPORINS

In 1945, Brotzu isolated a cephalosporium mold which yielded several antibiotics, called cephalosporins, which resembled penicillins but resisted the action of penicillinase and were active against both gram-positive and gram-negative bacteria. The nucleus of the cephalosporins, 7-aminocephalosporanic acid, bears a close resemblance to the nucleus of penicillin, 6-aminopenicillanic acid.

Although the intrinsic activity of the natural cephalosporins is low, modification of the nucleus by attachment of various R groups has yielded several compounds of high therapeutic activity and low toxicity. The cephalosporins have molecular weights of about 420; they are freely soluble in water and relatively stable. Cephalothin, cefazolin, and cephaloridine must be injected parenterally since they are not well absorbed from the gastrointestinal tract. Serum levels of 10–20 µg/ml are reached with cephalothin, 8–12 gm/day IV and 20–40 µg/ml with cefazolin, 4 gm/day IM. The drugs are distributed widely in tissues but penetrate poorly into the CNS. Cephalosporins should not be used in meningitis. Cephalexin and cephradine are sufficiently well absorbed from the gut to be excreted in significant amounts into the urine. Urinary tract infections can be treated, but these oral drugs are rarely suitable for treatment of major systemic infections.

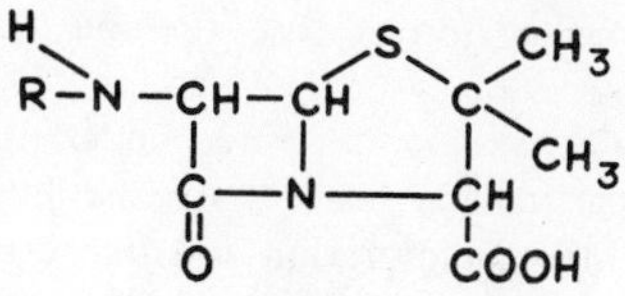

6-Aminopenicillanic acid

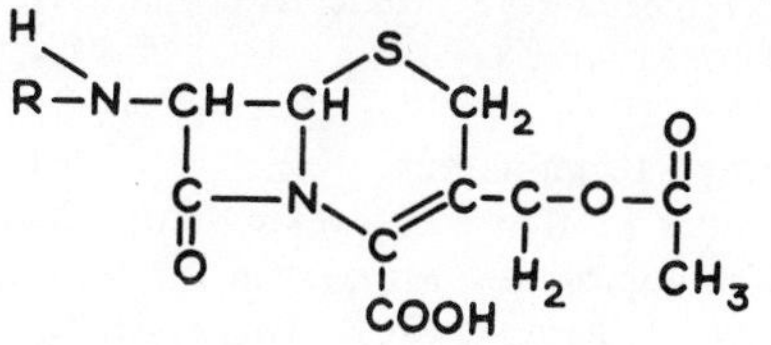

7-Aminocephalosporanic acid

Activity

The cephalosporins are active in concentrations of 10 μg/ml or less against gram-positive organisms, including penicillinase-producing staphylococci, and against many gram-negative bacteria. Typically, enterobacter are resistant, whereas klebsiellae are susceptible. The antistaphylococcal activity of the cephalosporins is comparable to that of penicillinase-resistant penicillins. Most enterococci, herellea, serratia, pseudomonas, proteus, and some strains of coliforms are resistant to 10 μg/ml but may be inhibited by the levels reached in urine (300–500 μg/ml). The cephalosporins are bactericidal because they interfere with cell wall synthesis (like penicillins) and are moderately resistant to penicillinase. A cephalosporinase (β-lactamase) can be produced by some bacteria.

Side-Effects

A. Allergy: Cephalosporins can be sensitizing, and specific hypersensitivity reactions, including anaphylaxis, can occur. Because of the chemical difference in drug nucleus structure, the antigenicity of cephalosporins differs from that of penicillins. Consequently, most individuals who are hypersensitive to penicillins can tolerate cephalosporins. The degree of cross-allergenicity between penicillins and cephalosporins remains controversial (6–16%). Some cross-antigenicity can be demonstrated in vitro.

B. Toxicity: Pain on injection, thrombophlebitis, rashes, and granulocytopenia. There is occasional renal toxicity, particularly with cephaloridine, which is therefore being abandoned.

SPECTINOMYCIN

Spectinomycin is an aminocyclitol antibiotic for intramuscular administration, proposed as an alternative to penicillin for the treatment of gonorrhea. Injection of 2 gm into each buttock (once) produces blood levels of 100 μg/ml. About 10% of gonococci are prob-

ably resistant, but cure rates of 85% or more are claimed. Adverse reactions include pain at the injection site, fever, and nausea.

Spectinomycin (Trobicin) is available in vials containing 2 and 4 gm for reconstitution to 400 mg/ml.

THE TETRACYCLINE DRUGS

The tetracyclines have the basic structure shown below. The following radicals occur in the different chemical forms:

	R	R_1	R_2	Renal Clearance (ml/min)
Tetracycline	–H	–CH$_3$	–H	65
Chlortetracycline	–Cl	–CH$_3$	–H	35
Oxytetracycline	–H	–CH$_3$	–OH	90
Demeclocycline	–Cl	–H	–H	35
Methacycline	–H	=CH$_2$*	–OH	31
Doxycycline	–H	–CH$_3$	–OH	16
Minocycline	–N(CH$_3$)$_2$	–H	–H	< 10

*No hydroxyl at C6.

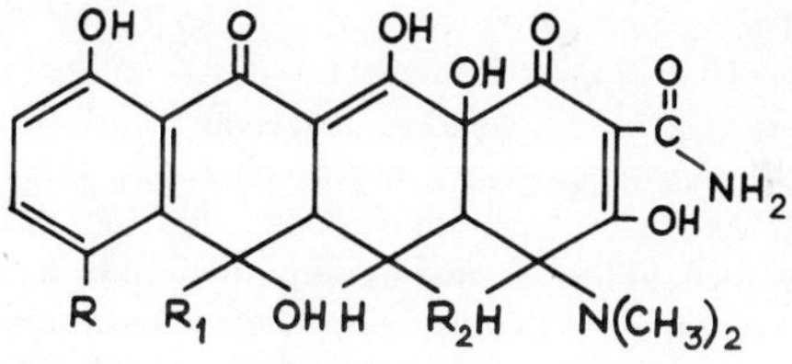

Tetracyclines

The tetracyclines are available as hydrochlorides. They have virtually identical antimicrobial properties and give complete cross-resistance. However, they differ in physical and pharmacologic characteristics. Chlortetracycline is much less stable than the others. All tetracyclines are readily absorbed from the intestinal tract and distributed widely in tissues; they penetrate poorly, however, into the CSF. Some can also be administered intramuscularly or intravenously. They are excreted in stool and into bile and urine at varying rates. With doses of tetracycline hydrochloride of 2 gm daily orally, blood levels reach 6–8 μg/ml. Demeclocycline, methacycline, minocycline, and doxycycline are excreted more slowly; similar blood levels are achieved by daily doses of 0.6, 0.3, 0.2, and 0.1 gm, respectively.

Activity

Tetracyclines are concentrated by susceptible bac-

Table 10—3. Some blood levels of antibiotics.

	Route	Daily Dose	Expected Concentration per ml Blood or per gm Tissue
Penicillin	IM	0.6–1 million units	1 unit
	Oral	0.6 million units	0.2 unit
Methicillin, nafcillin	IV	6–12 gm	5–30 µg
Cloxacillin, dicloxacillin	Oral	2–4 gm	3–12 µg
Ampicillin	Oral	2–3 gm	3–4 µg
	IV	4–6 gm	10–40 µg
Cephalothin	IV	8–12 gm	10–20 µg
Cefazolin	IM	2–4 gm	8–40 µg
Tetracyclines	Oral	2 gm	6–8 µg
Chloramphenicol	Oral	2 gm	8–10 µg
Erythromycin	Oral	2 gm	0.5–2 µg
Streptomycin	IM	1 gm	10–20 µg
Kanamycin	IM	1 gm	10–15 µg
Gentamicin	IM	0.3 gm	3–6 µg
Vancomycin	IV	2 gm	10–20 µg
Clindamycin	IM	2.4 gm	3–6 µg
Polymyxin B	IV	0.15 gm	1–3 µg
Colistin	IM	0.3 gm	2–5 µg

teria and inhibit protein synthesis by inhibiting the binding of amino-acyl tRNA to the 30S unit of bacterial ribosomes. Resistant bacteria are relatively nonpermeable to the drugs.

The tetracyclines are principally bacteriostatic agents. They inhibit the growth of susceptible gram-positive and gram-negative bacteria (inhibited by 0.1–10 µg/ml) and are drugs of choice in infections caused by rickettsiae, chlamydiae, and *Mycoplasma pneumoniae.* They do not inhibit fungi and may even stimulate the growth of yeasts. They temporarily suppress parts of the normal bowel flora. Their therapeutic usefulness is limited by the occurrence of "superinfections": while one microorganism is suppressed, another is permitted to multiply freely and produce pathogenic effects. This has occurred particularly with tetracycline-resistant pseudomonas, proteus, staphylococci, and yeasts.

The tetracyclines are sometimes employed in combination with streptomycin in the treatment of brucella and pasteurella infections. Minocycline can eradicate the meningococcal carrier states.

Side-Effects

The tetracyclines produce varying degrees of gastrointestinal upset (nausea, vomiting, diarrhea), skin rashes, mucous membrane lesions, and fever in many patients, particularly when administration is prolonged and dosage high. It is not definitely known what part is played by allergy and what part by direct toxicity. Replacement of bacterial flora (see above) occurs commonly. Overgrowth of yeasts on anal and vaginal mucous membranes during tetracycline administration is troublesome. Overgrowth of staphylococci in the

intestines during tetracycline therapy may lead to enterocolitis.

Tetracyclines are deposited in bony structures and teeth, particularly in the fetus and during the first 6 years of life. Discoloration and fluorescence of the teeth occur in newborns if tetracyclines are taken for prolonged periods by pregnant women. In pregnancy, hepatic damage may occur. Outdated tetracycline can produce renal damage. Minocycline can cause marked vestibular reactions.

Bacteriologic Examination

Because of its instability in vitro, chlortetracycline often appears less active than the other members of the group. Antimicrobial efficacy of the tetracyclines is virtually identical, so that only one stable tetracycline need be included in antibiotic sensitivity tests. Cross-resistance of microorganisms to tetracyclines is virtually complete; an organism resistant to one of the drugs may be assumed to be resistant to the others also.

CHLORAMPHENICOL

Chloramphenicol is a substance produced originally from cultures of *Streptomyces venezuelae* but now manufactured synthetically.

$$O_2N-\text{(ring)}-\underset{\underset{H}{|}}{\overset{\overset{OH}{|}}{C}}-\underset{\underset{H}{|}}{\overset{\overset{CH_2OH}{|}}{C}}-\underset{\underset{H}{|}}{\overset{\overset{O}{\|}}{N}}-\overset{\overset{O}{\|}}{C}-CHCl_2$$

Chloramphenicol

Crystalline chloramphenicol is a stable compound which is rapidly absorbed from the gastrointestinal tract, widely distributed into tissues and body fluids, including the CSF, and penetrates well into cells. Most of the drug is inactivated in the liver by conjugation with glucuronic acid or by reduction to inactive arylamines. Excretion is mainly in the urine, 90% in inactive form. Although chloramphenicol is usually administered orally (2 gm daily give blood levels up to 10 µg/ml), the succinate can be injected intramuscularly or intravenously in similar dosage.

Activity

Chloramphenicol is a potent inhibitor of protein synthesis in microorganisms. It blocks the attachment of amino acids to the nascent peptide chain on the 50 S unit of ribosomes by interfering with the action of peptidyl transferase. Chloramphenicol is principally bacteriostatic, and its spectrum is similar to that of the tetracyclines. Dosage and blood levels are also similar to those of the tetracyclines. Chloramphenicol is a drug of possible first choice in (1) meningococcal infection in patients hypersensitive to penicillin; (2) typhoid fever; (3) *Haemophilus influenzae* infections not responding to ampicillin; and (4) bacteroides and other anaerobic infections.

Chloramphenicol resistance is due to destruction of the drug by an enzyme which is under plasmid control.

Side-Effects

Chloramphenicol infrequently causes gastrointestinal upsets. However, prolonged administration of more than 3 gm daily to adults regularly results in abnormalities of early forms of red blood cells, elevation of serum iron, and anemia. These changes are reversible upon discontinuance of the drug. Very rare individuals exhibit an apparent idiosyncrasy to chloramphenicol and develop severe or fatal depression of bone marrow function. The mechanism of this aplastic anemia is not understood, but it is distinct from the dose-related reversible effect described above. For these reasons the use of chloramphenicol is generally restricted to those infections where it is clearly the most effective drug by laboratory test or experience.

In premature and newborn infants, chloramphenicol can induce collapse ("gray syndrome") because the normal mechanism of detoxification (glucuronide conjugation in the liver) is not yet developed.

Bacteriologic Examination

Chloramphenicol is very stable and diffuses well in agar media. For these reasons, it tends to give larger zones of growth inhibition by the "disk test" than the tetracyclines, even when tube dilution tests show identical effectiveness.

ERYTHROMYCINS
(Macrolides)

Erythromycin is obtained from *Streptomyces erythreus* and has the chemical formula $C_{37}H_{67}NO_{13}$. Drugs related to erythromycin are spiramycin, oleandomycin, and others. These drugs give complete cross-resistance but are less effective than erythromycin.

Erythromycins inhibit protein synthesis of bacteria, probably by blocking the amino-acyl translocation reaction on the 50S ribosomal unit.

The activity of erythromycins is enhanced at alkaline pH.

The erythromycins inhibit gram-positive organisms. They are less effective than penicillin in most penicillin-sensitive infections but are useful alternate drugs in cases of penicillin allergy. Erythromycin estolate and troleandomycin are the most readily absorbed forms and yield the highest levels. The base and the stearate are less well absorbed. The oral dose of either drug is 2 gm daily. Special forms (erythromycin gluceptate or lactobionate) are given IV in a dose of 0.5 gm every 8–12 hours (40 mg/kg/day).

Most erythromycin-sensitive microbial strains produce significant numbers of erythromycin-resistant mutants. In clinical infections, these mutants emerge and become dominant if the infection is not controlled within a few days. Resistance may be under control of plasmids and may be associated with absence of a receptor protein on the 50S ribosome unit.

Undesirable side-effects are drug fever, mild gastrointestinal upsets, and cholestatic hepatitis as a hypersensitivity reaction to the esters.

Because of the great frequency of resistant mutants, the "disk test" may suggest sensitivity and the tube dilution test may indicate resistance of large microbial populations.

LINCOMYCINS

Lincomycin (derived from *Streptomyces lincolnensis*) and clindamycin (a chlorine-substituted derivative) resemble erythromcyins in mode of action and antibacterial spectrum but are chemically distinct. Clindamycin is very active against bacteroides.

The drugs are acid-stable and can be given by mouth or by injection of 600 mg IV 3–4 times daily (10–20 mg/kg/day). Serum levels reach 3–6 µg/ml, and the drugs are widely distributed in tissues, except the CNS. Excretion is mainly through liver, bile, and urine.

Probably the most important indication for intravenous clindamycin is the treatment of severe anaerobic infections, including those caused by bacteroides. Lincomycins have also been suggested for treatment of gram-positive coccal infections in persons hypersensitive to penicillins, but erythromycins may be preferable. Successful treatment of staphylococcal infections of bone with lincomycins has been recorded. Lincomycins should not be used in meningitis. Clindamycin sometimes causes severe diarrhea and enterocolitis, which may be fatal.

VANCOMYCIN

Vancomycin is an amphoteric material produced by *Streptomyces orientalis*, dispensed as the hydrochloride. It has a high molecular weight (3300) and is poorly absorbed by the intestine.

Vancomycin is markedly bactericidal for staphylococci and enterococci. The drug inhibits early stages in cell wall mucopeptide synthesis. Drug-resistant strains do not emerge rapidly. The dosage is 0.5 gm every 6–12 hours IV (injected in a 30-minute period) for serious systemic staphylococcal or enterococcal infections; orally for staphylococcal enterocolitis.

Undesirable side-effects are thrombophlebitis, skin rashes, nerve deafness, and kidney damage.

BACITRACIN

Bacitracin is a polypeptide obtained from a strain of *Bacillus subtilis*. It is stable and poorly absorbed from the intestinal tract or from wounds. Its best use is for topical application to skin, wounds, or mucous membranes.

Bacitracin is mainly bactericidal for gram-positive bacteria, including penicillin-resistant organisms. For topical use, concentrations of 500–2000 units per milliliter of solution or gram of ointment are used. In combination with polymyxin B or neomycin, bacitracin is useful for the suppression of mixed bacterial flora in surface lesions. It has no place in systemic therapy.

Bacitracin is toxic for the kidney, causing proteinuria, hematuria, and nitrogen retention. For this reason, systemic administration is undesirable. Bacitracin is said not to induce hypersensitivity readily.

NOVOBIOCIN

Novobiocin is an acidic material produced by *Streptomyces niveus,* dispensed as the sodium or calcium salt. It is readily absorbed from the intestinal tract, distributed widely, and excreted in the urine. High levels of the drug appear in blood and body fluids, but much is bound to proteins and not available for antimicrobial action. Novobiocin is predominantly bacteriostatic. Novobiocin inhibits the synthesis of DNA and teichoic acid at the cell membrane.

Novobiocin is active against gram-positive cocci, including penicillin-resistant staphylococci, and some strains of proteus and other gram-negative bacilli. Resistant variants occur in most bacterial strains and emerge very promptly. Therefore, novobiocin has been used only in combination with a second antimicrobial drug in serious staphylococcal infections. The dosage is 0.5 gm every 6–8 hours orally. A special form may be given intravenously.

Frequent undesirable side-effects include fever, skin rashes, nausea, vomiting, eosinophilia, granulocytopenia, jaundice, and impaired renal function. At present there is no clear-cut indication for the use of this drug.

POLYMYXINS

Polymyxin B and polymyxin E (colistin) are basic polypeptides, poorly absorbed from the intestinal tract but readily absorbed after injection. They are not widely distributed in tissues and body fluids. Unless locally introduced, they do not reach the spinal fluid or pleural space. Colistin is dispensed as a methanesulfonate complex and produces less intense local and systemic side-effects than polymyxin B sulfate.

Activity

The polymyxins are strongly bactericidal against gram-negative bacilli, including pseudomonas that are resistant to other antibiotics. Polymyxins coat the bacterial cell membrane and destroy its osmotic function as a selective permeability barrier.

In tissues, polymyxins are strongly bound to membranes rich in phosphatidyl ethanolamine and are inhibited by pus. This limits their availability for antibacterial action.

Polymyxin B sulfate can be injected IM or IV (2.5 mg/kg/day) in serious gram-negative infections, including pseudomonas sepsis. It can be given intrathecally (up to 5 mg/day) for pseudomonas meningitis. Colistin methanesulfonate (3–5 mg/kg/day) IM for urinary tract infections contains a local anesthetic and causes less pain than polymyxin B given intramuscularly. It should not be given intravenously or intrathecally.

Side-Effects

The polymyxins produce reversible CNS side-effects, including drowsiness, abnormal sensations, and ataxia. Pain at the site of intramuscular injection necessitates simultaneous administration of a local anesthetic. In doses exceeding 2.5 mg/kg/day, damage to the kidney may occur, particularly if renal function is impaired.

Bacteriologic Examination

The polymyxins are large molecules and diffuse poorly through agar. Consequently, inhibition zones in "disk tests" are always very small, even when the organism is highly sensitive by the tube dilution test. Organisms highly sensitive in vitro (inhibited by 0.1–1 μg/ml) may not respond in vivo if parenchymatous organs are involved in the infection. In susceptible strains of bacteria, resistance to polymyxin develops infrequently.

AMINOGLYCOSIDES

Aminoglycosides are drugs which share chemical, antimicrobial, pharmacologic, and toxic characteristics. The group includes streptomycin, kanamycin, neomycin, gentamicin, tobramycin, sisomycin, amikacin, and others. All of these drugs inhibit bacterial protein synthesis by several mechanisms. They cause breakdown of polysomes, attach to the 30S unit of the bacterial ribosome, distort the recognition region, and result in a misreading of the genetic message. Clinically important bacterial resistance to aminoglycosides is mediated by transmissible plasmids and results in enzymatic inactivation of the drug. Mutants with chromosomal resistance lack a protein on the ribosome which serves as receptor site. All aminoglycosides are much more active at alkaline than at acid pH; all are nephrotoxic and can induce nitrogen retention; and all are ototoxic and can induce deafness. All are stable in neutral solutions for weeks.

Aminoglycosides are often synergistic with penicillins against streptococci, particularly enterococci. The penicillins enhance entry of the aminoglycoside into the cell.

NEOMYCIN & KANAMYCIN

Kanamycin is a close relative of neomycin with similar activity and complete cross-resistance. Paromomycin is also closely related and gives cross-resistance. These drugs are stable, poorly absorbed from the intestinal tract, readily absorbed and distributed after intramuscular injection, and slowly excreted in the urine. Kanamycin is less toxic than neomycin, and only kanamycin is used systemically now.

Activity

Kanamycin is bactericidal for many gram-negative bacilli, including some strains of proteus, but ineffective against pseudomonas and serratia. There is some activity against *M tuberculosis* and against staphylococci. Kanamycin, 1 gm IM daily (15 mg/kg/day), is administered in serious infections due to gram-negative organisms which are resistant to other drugs. Oral doses of 4–6 gm daily are used for reduction of intestinal flora preoperatively but are ineffective in most bacterial diarrheas except those caused by enteropathogenic *E coli.*

Because of its greater systemic toxicity, neomycin is limited to topical application to skin or wounds.

Neomycin and kanamycin may cause renal damage. They may also cause nerve deafness without warning signs and are therefore limited in use. Intraperitoneal administration of 3–5 gm has induced respiratory paralysis, which can be overcome by neostigmine.

GENTAMICIN

In concentrations of 0.5–5 µg/ml, gentamicin is bactericidal for many gram-positive and gram-negative bacteria, including many strains of proteus, serratia, and pseudomonas. Gentamicin is ineffective against streptococci and bacteroides.

After IM injection of 3–5 mg/kg/day, serum levels reach 3–6 µg/ml and the drug is widely distributed. Gentamicin is indicated in serious infections caused by gram-negative bacteria insusceptible to other drugs, when up to 7 mg/kg/day have been used. Gentamicin may precipitate with carbenicillin in vitro, but enhancement of bactericidal action against pseudomonas occurs sometimes in vivo.

Gentamicin is nephrotoxic and ototoxic, particularly in impaired renal function, which predisposes to cumulation and toxic effects. Gentamicin sulfate, 0.1%, has been used topically in creams or solutions for infected burns or skin lesions.

STREPTOMYCINS

Streptomycin is an aminoglycoside derived from *Streptomyces griseus,* available as the sulfate. It is bactericidal against both gram-positive and gram-negative bacteria and mycobacteria. Dihydrostreptomycin is similar to streptomycin in antibacterial properties but is not used clinically because of its ototoxicity.

After intramuscular injection, streptomycin is rapidly absorbed and distributed in tissues and body fluids; it is excreted through the kidneys. It diffuses poorly into the synovial spaces or into the CSF. Only 5% of the extracellular concentration reaches the interior of cells. After oral administration, it is poorly absorbed from the gastrointestinal tract; most of it is excreted in the feces.

Activity

Like other aminoglycosides, streptomycin inhibits protein synthesis.

The streptomycins are predominantly bactericidal against susceptible microorganisms (inhibited in vitro by 0.1–20 µg/ml). The therapeutic effectiveness of streptomycin is limited by its toxicity and by the rapid emergence of resistant mutants. In tuberculosis, 1 gm is injected IM twice weekly (or daily), together with one or 2 other antituberculosis drugs (INH, rifampin).

Streptomycin may be given in a dosage of 1–2 gm/day IM with a penicillin in enterococcal endocarditis to enhance bactericidal action. In tularemia and plague, it is given with tetracyclines.

Resistance

All microbial strains produce streptomycin-resistant chromosomal mutants with relatively great frequency. Chromosomal mutants characteristically have low resistance, whereas plasmid-mediated resistance is high as a result of enzymatic destruction of the drug. In tuberculosis, combinations with isoniazid or other antituberculosis drugs are commonly employed. In this fashion, the period of useful streptomycin treatment is significantly prolonged.

Side-Effects

A. Allergy: Fever, skin rashes, and other allergic manifestations may result from hypersensitivity to streptomycin. This occurs most frequently upon prolonged contact with the drug, in patients receiving a protracted course of treatment (eg, tuberculosis), or in medical personnel preparing and handling the drug. (Nurses preparing solutions should wear gloves.)

B. Toxicity: Streptomycin is markedly toxic for

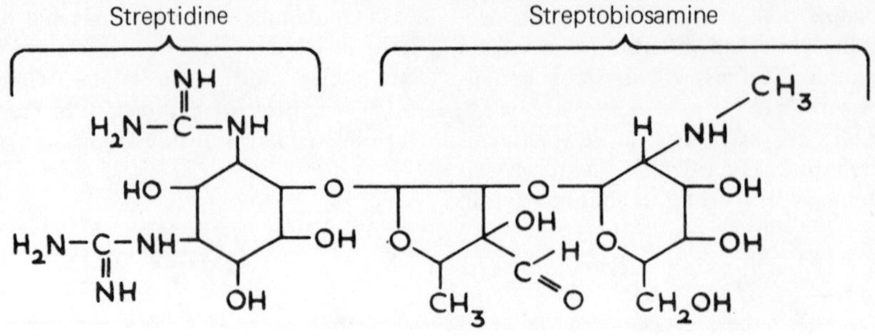

Streptidine   Streptobiosamine

Streptomycin

the vestibular portion of the eighth cranial nerve, causing tinnitus, vertigo, and ataxia, which are often irreversible. Dihydrostreptomycin (now abandoned) has less vestibular toxicity but is more toxic for the auditory portion of the eighth nerve, causing deafness. Both drugs have some toxic effects on the kidney.

Bacteriologic Examination

When sensitivity determinations with streptomycin are carried out in liquid media, a single resistant organism in the inoculum may grow out rapidly, although the bulk of the population is streptomycin-sensitive. Conversely, testing on solid media may fail to reveal the presence of resistant mutants in the population unless a very large inoculum is employed.

ISONIAZID
(Isonicotinic Acid Hydrazide, INH)

Isoniazid has little effect on most bacteria but is strikingly active against mycobacteria, especially *M tuberculosis.* Most tubercle bacilli are inhibited by

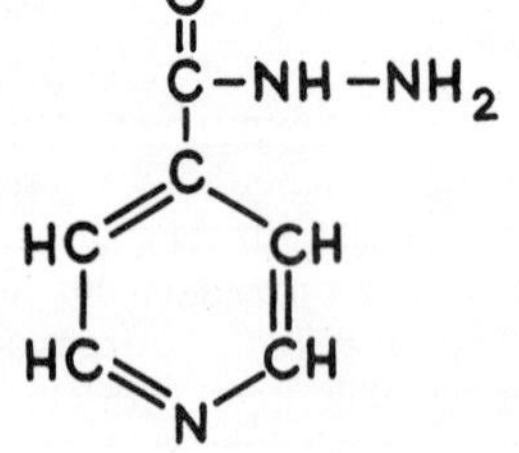

Isoniazid

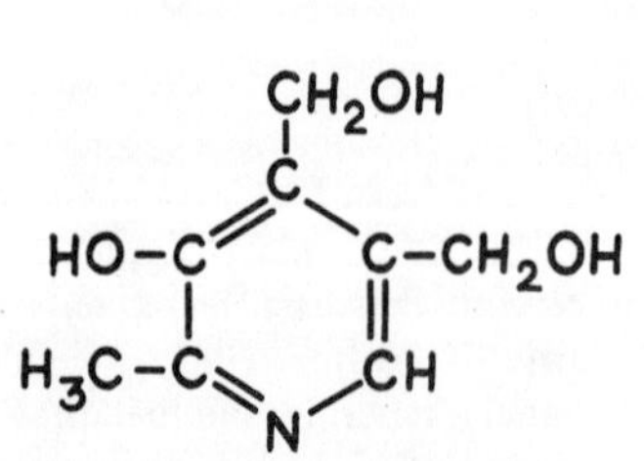

Pyridoxine

$0.1-1$ µg/ml of isoniazid in vitro, but large populations of tubercle bacilli usually contain some isoniazid-resistant organisms. For this reason, the drug is best employed in combination with other antimycobacterial agents (especially rifampin or ethambutol) to reduce the emergence of resistant tubercle bacilli. Isoniazid has been shown to exert competitive antagonism against pyridoxine-catalyzed reactions in *E coli,* but the antituberculosis mechanism is uncertain. Isoniazid and pyridoxine are structural analogues. Patients receiving isoniazid excrete pyridoxine in excess amounts, which results in peripheral neuritis. This can be prevented by the administration of pyridoxine, $0.3-0.5$ gm daily, which does not interfere with the antituberculosis action of isoniazid.

Isoniazid is rapidly and completely absorbed from the gastrointestinal tract and is in part acetylated and in part excreted in the urine. In the ordinary systemic dose of $4-6$ mg/kg/day, toxic manifestations (eg, hepatitis) are infrequent, and blood levels reach an average of 0.5 µg/ml. Isoniazid freely diffuses into tissue fluids, including the CSF. In tuberculous meningitis, $8-10$ mg/kg/day are given for many weeks.

In converters from negative to positive tuberculin skin tests who have no evidence of disease, INH, 300 mg daily for 1 year, may be used "prophylactically."

ETHAMBUTOL

Ethambutol is a synthetic, water-soluble, heat-stable D-isomer of the structure shown below.

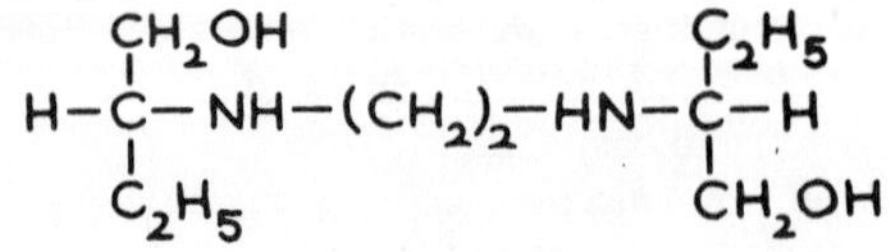

Ethambutol

Many strains of *Mycobacterium tuberculosis* are inhibited in vitro by ethambutol, $1-5$ µg/ml. The mechanism of action is not known.

Ethambutol is well absorbed from the gut. Following ingestion of 25 mg/kg, a blood level peak of 2–5 μg/ml is reached in 2–4 hours. About 20% of the drug is excreted in feces and 50% in urine, in unchanged form. Excretion is delayed in renal failure. About 15% of absorbed drug is metabolized by oxidation and conversion to a dicarboxylic acid. In meningitis, ethambutol appears in the CSF.

Resistance to ethambutol emerges fairly rapidly among mycobacteria when the drug is used alone. Therefore, ethambutol is given in combination with other antituberculosis drugs, most commonly INH.

Ethambutol, 15 mg/kg, is usually given as a single daily dose in combination with INH. At times, the dose is 25 mg/kg/day.

Hypersensitivity to ethambutol occurs infrequently. The commonest side-effects are visual disturbances: reduction in visual acuity, optic neuritis, and perhaps retinal damage occur in some patients given 25 mg/kg/day for several months. Most of these changes apparently regress when ethambutol is discontinued. However, periodic visual acuity testing is mandatory during treatment. With 15 mg/kg/day, visual disturbances are very rare.

RIFAMPIN

Rifampin is a semisynthetic derivative of rifamycin, an antibiotic produced by *Streptomyces mediterranei*. It is active in vitro against some gram-positive and gram-negative cocci, some enteric bacteria, mycobacteria, chlamydiae, and poxviruses. While many meningococci and mycobacteria are inhibited by less than 1 μg/ml, highly resistant mutants occur in all microbial populations in a frequency of 1 in 10^7 or greater. The prolonged administration of rifampin as a single drug permits the emergence of these highly resistant organisms. There is no cross-resistance to other antimicrobial drugs.

Rifampin binds strongly to DNA-dependent RNA polymerase and thus inhibits RNA synthesis in bacteria and chlamydiae. It blocks a late stage in the assembly of poxviruses, perhaps interfering with envelope formation.

Rifampin is well absorbed after oral administration, widely distributed in tissues, excreted mainly through the liver and to a lesser extent into the urine. With oral doses of 600 mg, serum levels exceed 5 μg/ml for 4–6 hours and urine levels may be 10–100 times higher.

In tuberculosis, a single oral dose of 600 mg daily (10–20 mg/kg/day) is administered together with ethambutol, INH, or another antituberculosis drug in order to delay the emergence of rifampin-resistant mycobacteria. A similar regimen may apply to atypical mycobacteria.

An oral dose of 600 mg twice daily for 2 days can eliminate a majority of meningococci from carriers.

Unfortunately, some highly resistant meningococcal strains are selected out by this procedure. In urinary tract infections and in chronic bronchitis, rifampin is not useful.

Rifampin imparts an orange color to urine and sweat, which is harmless. Occasional adverse effects include rashes, thrombocytopenia, and impairment of liver function.

AMINOSALICYLIC ACID (PAS)

p-Aminosalicylic acid closely resembles *p*-aminobenzoic acid and sulfonamides. Most bacteria are not inhibited by PAS, but tubercle bacilli are usually inhibited by PAS, 1–5 μg/ml, while atypical mycobacteria are resistant. In susceptible mycobacterial populations, PAS-resistant mutants tend to emerge. The simultaneous use of a second antituberculosis drug inhibits this development.

Aminosalicylic acid

PAS, 8–12 gm daily by mouth, was commonly given in combination with streptomycin or INH as antituberculosis therapy. However, full oral doses of PAS were commonly associated with severe gastrointestinal side-effects. Therefore, the use of PAS has been largely abandoned.

AMPHOTERICIN B
(Fungizone)

Amphotericin B is a complex antibiotic polyene produced by a Streptomyces species which has negligible antibacterial properties but strongly inhibits the growth of several pathogenic fungi in vitro and in vivo. Amphotericin binds to sterols on the fungal cell membranes and disturbs their function. The microcrystals of the drug are dispensed with sodium deoxycholate and a buffer to be dissolved in dextrose solution. It is injected intravenously in daily doses of 0.5–1.2 mg/kg (with an initial dose of 5 mg/day) and can be given intrathecally up to 1 mg every other day in meningitis. Amphotericin B appears to be the most effective agent available for the treatment of disseminated coccidioidomycosis, blastomycosis, histoplasmosis, cryptococcosis, and candidiasis. It frequently produces marked toxic effects, including fever, chills, nausea and vomiting, renal failure, hypokalemia, and anemia.

FLUCYTOSINE

5-Fluorocytosine is an oral antifungal compound of relatively low toxicity. Flucytosine, 5 μg/ml, inhibits many strains of candida, cryptococcus, and torulopsis and some strains of other fungi. Resistant mutants emerge regularly and rapidly, limiting the usefulness of flucytosine. Oral doses of 100–200 mg/kg/day are well absorbed and widely distributed in tissues, including the CSF. While the drug is relatively well tolerated, prolonged high serum levels often cause depression of bone marrow, loss of hair, skin rashes, and abnormal liver function. With 3–8 gm administered daily in divided doses, there has been prolonged remission of fungemia and meningitis caused by susceptible organisms.

GRISEOFULVIN
(Grifulvin, Fulvicin)

Griseofulvin is an antibiotic obtained from certain Penicillium species. It has no effect on bacteria or fungi producing systemic mycoses but suppresses dermatophytes, particularly *Microsporum audouini* and *Trichophyton rubrum*. Oral daily doses of 0.2–1 gm are given for weeks or months. The absorbed drug is deposited in diseased skin, bound to keratin. Toxic effects include headache, drowsiness, skin rashes, and gastrointestinal disturbances.

CYCLOSERINE

Cycloserine (D-4-amino-3-isoxazolidinone, molecular weight 102) is an antibiotic active against many types of microorganisms, including coliforms, proteus, and tubercle bacilli. It acts by inhibiting the incorporation of D-alanine into peptidoglycan of bacterial cell walls by blocking alanine racemase. It is occasionally used in urinary tract infections (15–20 mg/kg/day orally), but often causes neurotoxic side-effects or shock.

THE NITROFURANS

The nitrofurans are synthetic nitrofuraldehyde compounds which are strongly bactericidal in vitro for many gram-positive and gram-negative bacteria. Most nitrofurans are very insoluble in water. Some compounds (eg, nitrofuraldehyde semicarbazone, Furacin) are effective topical antibacterial agents used in surgical dressings and virtually unabsorbed.

Nitrofurantoin (Furadantin) is absorbed after oral administration and excreted in the urine. With daily doses of 400–600 mg, urine concentrations reach 100–200 μg/ml, sufficient to inhibit most organisms commonly encountered in urinary tract infections. Activity is limited to the urine. In the bloodstream, no antibacterial effect occurs because the drug is bound to blood proteins. Thus, nitrofurantoin has no effect on systemic infections but is a good urinary antiseptic (see below). Sodium nitrofurantoin can be given intravenously but likewise acts only in the urine.

Gastrointestinal intolerance is the commonest side-effect of orally administered nitrofurantoin, but occasionally hemolytic anemia, skin rashes, hepatitis, pneumonitis, and other effects have been observed.

SULFONAMIDES

The sulfonamides are a large group of compounds with the basic formula shown on p 106. By substituting various R-radicals, a series of compounds is obtained with somewhat varying physical, pharmacologic, and antibacterial properties. The basic mechanism of action of all of these compounds appears to be competitive inhibition of para-aminobenzoic acid (PABA) utilization. The simultaneous use of sulfonamides with trimethoprim (co-trimoxazole) results in the inhibition of sequential metabolic steps and possible antibacterial synergism (see p 106).

The sulfonamides are bacteriostatic for some gram-negative and gram-positive bacteria, chlamydiae, nocardia, and some protozoa. Several special sulfones (eg, diaminodiphenylsulfone, DDS) are employed in the treatment of leprosy.

The "soluble" sulfonamides (eg, trisulfapyrimidines, sulfisoxazole) are readily absorbed from the intestinal tract after oral administration in dosages of 4–8 gm daily and are distributed in all tissues and body fluids (required blood levels: 8–12 mg/100 ml). The sodium salts of sulfonamides may be injected intravenously or subcutaneously. Most sulfonamides are excreted rapidly in the urine. Some (eg, sulfamethoxypyridazine, sulfadimethoxine) are excreted very slowly and give high tissue and low urine levels. At present, sulfonamides are particularly useful in the treatment of trachoma, toxoplasmosis, nocardiosis, and first attacks of urinary tract infections due to coliform bacteria. By contrast, many meningococci, shigellae, group A streptococci, and recurrent urinary tract infections are now resistant.

The "insoluble" sulfonamides (eg, phthalylsulfathiazole) are poorly absorbed from the intestinal tract and exert their action largely by inhibiting the microbial population within the lumen of the tract. They are given in a dosage of 8–15 gm orally daily for 4–7 days to prepare the large bowel for surgery.

Resistance

Microorganisms which do not use extracellular PABA but can use preformed folic acid are resistant to sulfonamides.

Side-Effects

The soluble sulfonamides may produce side-effects which fall into 2 categories:

A. Allergic Reactions: Many individuals develop hypersensitivity to sulfonamides after initial contact with these drugs and, on reexposure, may develop fever, hives, skin rashes, and chronic vascular diseases such as polyarteritis nodosa.

B. Direct Toxic Effects: There may be fever, skin rashes, gastrointestinal disturbances, depression of the bone marrow leading to anemia or agranulocytosis, hemolytic anemia, and toxic effects on the liver and kidney. Some of the toxic action on the kidney can be prevented by keeping the urine alkaline and the water intake adequate; by using mixtures of sulfonamides such as trisulfapyrimidines (which are relatively more soluble than a single drug); or by employing sulfisoxazole, which is highly soluble in urine.

Bacteriologic Examination

When culturing specimens from patients receiving sulfonamides, it is necessary to incorporate PABA (5 mg/100 ml) into the medium in order to overcome sulfonamide inhibition.

URINARY ANTISEPTICS

These are drugs with antibacterial effects limited to the urine. They fail to produce significant levels in tissues and thus have no effect on systemic infections. However, they effectively lower bacterial counts in the urine and thus greatly diminish the symptoms of lower urinary tract infection. They are used primarily for the suppression of bacteria in the urine of patients with chronic urinary tract infection.

The most prominent urinary antiseptics are methenamine mandelate (Mandelamine) or hippurate, nitrofurantoin, and nalidixic acid. The active compounds are liberated in the urine only and have no systemic effect. Therefore, it is meaningless to perform and report sensitivity tests with these substances in any systemic infections. Other materials, such as amino acids (methionine) or hippuric acid (cranberry juice), may be ingested in large doses to provide an acid, bacteriostatic urine. Nalidixic acid is effective in the urine, but microbial resistance tends to emerge rapidly. Oxolinic acid appears to be similar.

ANTIVIRAL DRUGS

True viruses, because of their structure and method of replication, are not affected by the common antibacterial drugs. However, viral multiplication may be interrupted by a variety of chemicals at various stages. In addition to specific antibody globulins which block penetration of extracellular virus into the cell, several chemicals have found limited application in the treatment of viral infections. The following substances are currently used in the management of clinical viral disease.

Amantadine Hydrochloride

This tricyclic symmetric amine (and its congener rimantadine) inhibits the penetration into susceptible cells or uncoating of certain myxoviruses, especially influenza A, but not influenza B. A daily oral dose of 200 mg of amantadine hydrochloride for 3 days before and 7 days after influenza A virus infection reduces the incidence and severity of symptoms. The most marked side-effects are insomnia, dizziness, and ataxia.

Several dihydroxyisoquinolines also inhibit the replication of myxoviruses in susceptible cells and can prevent disease due to influenza A and B viruses.

Idoxuridine (5-Iodo-2'-deoxyuridine)

This halogenated pyrimidine can inhibit the replication of DNA viruses by becoming incorporated into viral DNA in place of thymidine. Topical application to herpetic keratitis can result in marked improvement. The topically applied drug remains localized in the avascular cornea and inhibits herpesvirus replication. For the treatment of herpetic keratitis, 1 drop of 0.1% solution is instilled into the conjunctival sac every 2 hours around the clock. Ointments containing 0.5% idoxuridine can be applied less frequently. Some toxic effects on corneal epithelium occur after prolonged use.

Idoxuridine is too severely cytotoxic for use in most generalized virus infections, although it has been employed in herpetic encephalitis (from 40 mg/kg/day IV to 6 gm/day IV). This has now been abandoned.

Cytarabine (cytosine arabinoside, arabinofuranosylcytosine) also inhibits replication of DNA viruses. It has been used topically in herpetic keratitis and systemically in varicella-zoster, but it is more toxic than idoxuridine. In disseminated herpes zoster, it appears to be ineffective. Adenine arabinoside is less toxic and is being investigated with encouraging results in some DNA virus infections.

Methisazone (N-Methylisatin-β-thiosemicarbazone)

This drug can block replication of poxviruses, probably by inhibiting the formation of a structural protein. If administered to contacts of smallpox cases within 1–2 days after exposure, 2–4 gm orally/day for 3–4 days (100 mg/kg/day for children) give striking protection against smallpox.

Generalized or progressive vaccinia in immunodeficient individuals can also be treated with methisazone.

The principal side-effect is vomiting.

Photodynamic Inactivation

Photodynamic inactivation has been attempted in herpesvirus infection of the skin. A dye (neutral red, proflavine, 0.1%) is applied to the denuded skin lesion and irradiated with fluorescent light twice, 6–8 hours apart. The dye becomes bound to the viral DNA and light absorption leads to irreversible DNA damage, resulting in virus inactivation (see p 311). Some success has been reported with this technic by shortening the time of active lesions. Controlled studies do not support the claims for the efficacy of this approach. Photodynamic inactivation of virus in cell cultures can transform cells to neoplastic behavior. Such cells can then produce transplantable tumors in hamsters.

Interferon

Interferon as an antiviral drug is discussed on p 311.

● ● ●

General References

Bauer AW & others: Antibiotic susceptibility testing by a standardized single disc method. Am J Clin Pathol 45:493, 1966.

Bennett WM & others: A guide to drug therapy in renal failure. JAMA 230:1544, 1974.

Cusumano CL, Monif GRG: A word of caution concerning photodynamic inactivation therapy for herpesvirus hominis infection. Obstet Gynecol 45:335, 1975.

Davies JE, Rownd R: Transmissible multiple drug resistance in Enterobacteriaceae. Science 176:758, 1972.

Ericsson HM, Sherris JC: Antibiotic sensitivity testing. Acta Pathol Microbiol Scand [B] 217 (Suppl):1, 1971.

Gale EF & others: *The Molecular Basis of Antibiotic Action.* Wiley, 1972.

Garrod LP, O'Grady F: *Antibiotic and Chemotherapy,* 4th ed. Livingstone, 1973.

Hartmann R & others: Targets of penicillin action. Nature 235:426, 1972.

Hunt TK & others: Antibiotics in surgery. Arch Surg 110:148, 1975.

Jawetz E: The use of combinations of antimicrobial drugs. Annu Rev Pharmacol 8:151, 1968.

Meyers FH, Jawetz E, Goldfien A: *Review of Medical Pharmacology,* 5th ed. Lange, 1976.

Moellering RC Jr, Swartz MN: Drug therapy: The newer cephalosporins. N Engl J Med 294:24, 1976.

Parker CW: Drug allergy. (3 parts.) N Engl J Med 292:511, 732, 957, 1975.

Pestka S: Inhibitors of ribosome function. Annu Rev Microbiol 25:487, 1971.

Stevens DA & others: Cytosine arabinoside in disseminated zoster. N Engl J Med 289:873, 1973.

Strominger JL: The actions of penicillin and other antibiotics on bacterial cell wall synthesis. Johns Hopkins Med J 133:63, 1973.

Weinstein L: Common sense (clinical judgment) in the diagnosis and antibiotic therapy of etiologically undefined infections. Pediatr Clin North Am 15:141, 1968.

Weinstein L, Dalton AC: Host determinants of response to antimicrobial agents. N Engl J Med 279:467, 1968.

11...
Host-Parasite Relationships

A parasite is an organism which resides on or within another living organism in order to find the environment and nutrients it requires for growth and reproduction. This does not imply that a parasite must harm its host. On the contrary, the most successful parasites achieve a balance with the host which ensures the survival, growth, and propagation of both parasite and host. Thus a majority of host-parasite interactions do not result in disease: The infection remains latent or subclinical.

The relationship between parasite and host is determined both by those characteristics of the parasite which favor establishment of the parasite and damage to the host and by the various host mechanisms which oppose these processes. Among the parasite's attributes are infectivity, invasiveness, pathogenicity, and toxigenicity. These are described below. If the parasite injures the host to a sufficient degree, disturbances will result in the host which manifest themselves as disease.

INFECTION

Infection is the process whereby the parasite enters into a relationship with the host. Its essential component steps in man and animals are the following:

(1) Entrance of the parasite into the host—The most frequent portals of entry are the respiratory tract (mouth and nose), the gastrointestinal tract, and breaks in the superficial mucous membranes and skin. Some parasites can penetrate intact mucous membrane and skin; still others are passively introduced by arthropods through these layers directly into the lymphatic channels or the bloodstream.

(2) Establishment and multiplication of the parasite within the host—From the portal of entry the parasite may spread directly through the tissues or may proceed via the lymphatic channels to the bloodstream, which distributes it widely and permits it to reach tissues particularly suitable for its multiplication. The biochemical environment of the tissues ultimately determines the susceptibility or resistance of a certain host to a given parasite.

Although the process of infection is of paramount interest to medicine, there are 2 other requirements for the perpetuation of a parasitic species: a satisfactory portal of exit of the parasite from the host and an effective mechanism for transmission to new hosts.

ATTRIBUTES OF MICROORGANISMS WHICH ENABLE THEM TO CAUSE DISEASE

There is no sharp semantic distinction between the terms "pathogenicity" and "virulence." **Pathogenicity** denotes the ability of microorganisms to cause disease or to result in the production of progressive lesions. **Virulence** introduces the concept of degree, ie, virulent organisms exhibit pathogenicity when introduced into the host in very small numbers. These properties may be subdivided into **toxigenicity** (ability to produce toxic substances) and **invasiveness** (ability to enter host tissues, multiply there, and spread). Different pathogenic microorganisms possess these attributes in varying degrees. Toxigenicity and invasiveness may be under separate genetic control.

Virulence is measured in terms of the number of microorganisms or micrograms of toxin necessary to kill a given host when administered by a certain route. It is usually expressed as LD_{50}, ie, the number of organisms or micrograms which must be administered to kill 50% of the animals.

A few representative substances known to play a role in the production of disease by microorganisms are mentioned below.

Toxins

Microbial toxins are usually grouped as exotoxins or endotoxins. The essential features of each group are listed in Table 11−1.

Pathogenetic Mechanisms in Some Disorders Caused by Microbial Exotoxins

A. Diphtheria: *Corynebacterium diphtheriae* grows in the upper respiratory tract or wounds and produces toxin. The toxin is absorbed, inhibits protein synthesis, and results in necrosis of epithelium, heart muscle, kidney, and nerve tissue.

Table 11—1. Differentiation of exotoxins and endotoxins.

Exotoxins	Endotoxins
Excreted by living cells; found in high concentrations in fluid medium.	Integral part of microbial cell walls of gram-negative organisms liberated upon their disintegration.
Polypeptides, molecular weight 10,000–900,000.	Lipopolysaccharide complexes. Lipid A portion probably responsible for toxicity.
Relatively unstable; toxicity often destroyed rapidly by heat over 60°C.	Relatively stable; withstand heat over 60°C for hours without loss of toxicity.
Highly antigenic; stimulate the formation of high-titer antitoxin. Antitoxin neutralizes toxin.	Do not stimulate formation of antitoxin; stimulate formation of antibodies to polysaccharide moiety.
Converted into antigenic, nontoxic toxoids by formalin, acid, heat, etc.	Not converted into toxoids.
Highly toxic; fatal for laboratory animals in micrograms or less.	Weakly toxic; fatal for laboratory animals in hundreds of micrograms.
Do not produce fever in host.	Often produce fever in host.

Diphtheria toxin is a polypeptide (molecular weight 62,000) which can be lethal in a dose of 40 ng. The essential action is inhibition of peptide chain elongation by inactivating the elongation factor EF-2 (formerly called transferase II). The toxin inactivates EF-2 by catalyzing a reaction which yields free nicotinamide plus an inactive adenosine diphosphate-ribose-EF-2 complex. The arrest of protein synthesis brings about disruption of normal physiologic functions.

B. Tetanus: *Clostridium tetani* contaminates wounds and the spores germinate in an anaerobic environment (devitalized tissue). Vegetative forms produce toxin which reaches the CNS by retrograde axon transport and is bound to gangliosides. Toxin increases reflex excitability in neurons of the spinal cord (by blocking function of inhibitory synapses). The toxin may also affect synaptic transmission at the myoneural junction (perhaps because of accumulation of acetylcholine). Intense muscle spasms result.

C. Gas Gangrene: Spores of *Clostridium perfringens* and other clostridia (especially *Cl novyi, Cl septicum,* and *Cl histolyticum*) are introduced into wounds by soil or feces. In the presence of necrotic tissue (anaerobic environment), spores germinate and cells produce toxins. Many of these are necrotizing and hemolytic and, together with distention of tissue by gas formed from carbohydrates and interference with blood supply, favor the spread of gangrene.

The alpha toxin of *Cl perfringens* is a lecithinase and damages cell membranes by splitting lecithin to phosphocholine and diglyceride. Theta toxin also has a necrotizing effect. Collagenases and DNases are produced by various clostridia. Some strains of *Cl perfringens* also produce an enterotoxin (see below).

D. Botulism: *Clostridium botulinum* grows in anaerobic foods (canned, vacuum-packed, etc) and produces toxin (immunologic types A, B, E). Toxin (molecular weight 70,000) is absorbed from the gut and carried by the blood to motor nerves. Toxin blocks the release (or production) of acetylcholine at synapses and neuromuscular junctions, producing diplopia, dysphagia, respiratory paralysis, and other motor paralyses.

E. Staphylococcal Food Poisoning: Certain strains of *Staphylococcus aureus* produce an enterotoxin while growing in meat, dairy, or bakery products. This enterotoxin (molecular weight 40,000) is resistant to heating at 100° C for 20 minutes. After ingestion, enterotoxin is absorbed in the gut, where it stimulates neural receptors. From there, impulses are transmitted to CNS centers of gut motility. Vomiting, often projectile, results within hours. Diarrhea is less frequent.

F. Cholera: *Vibrio cholerae* from feces of infected persons contaminates food or drink. Vibrios grow in the small intestine, producing a heat-labile enterotoxin (molecular weight 100,000) which binds to ganglioside receptors on villi of the small intestine. The enterotoxin causes a large increase in adenylate cyclase activity and in the concentration of cyclic AMP in the gut. This results in massive hypersecretion of chloride and water and impaired absorption of sodium in the jejunum and ileum. The effect is massive diarrhea and acidosis. Toxin production appears to be under control of a plasmid.

G. Other Food Poisons: Some strains of *Clostridium perfringens, Escherichia coli,* and *Vibrio parahaemolyticus* can produce enterotoxins with actions similar to that of *V cholerae.*

H. Streptococcal Erythrogenic Toxin: Some strains of hemolytic lysogenic streptococci produce a toxin which results in a punctate maculopapular erythematous rash, as in scarlet fever. The precise mode of action is uncertain. Production of erythrogenic toxin is under genetic control of a temperature bacteriophage. If phage is lost, the streptococci cannot produce toxin.

Toxin stimulates antitoxin formation, which neutralizes the toxin effect. Thus, a person possessing antitoxin may have pharyngitis when infected with streptococci producing erythrogenic toxin but not get scarlet fever.

Extracellular Enzymes

Certain bacteria produce substances that are not

directly toxic but which do play an important role in the infectious process.

A. Collagenase: *Clostridium perfringens,* in addition to a lecithinase, also produces proteolytic enzymes (collagenase) capable of disintegrating collagen. This promotes the spread of bacilli in tissues.

B. Coagulase: Many pathogenic staphylococci produce a substance (coagulase) which, in conjunction with certain serum factors, coagulates plasma. Coagulase contributes to the formation of fibrin walls around staphylococcal lesions, which protect the organisms from the defenses of the body and aid in their persistence. Coagulase also causes a deposit of fibrin on the surface of individual staphylococci, which may protect them from phagocytosis or from destruction within phagocytic cells.

C. Hyaluronidases (enzymes hydrolyzing hyaluronic acid, a constituent of the ground substance of connective tissue) are produced by many microorganisms (eg, staphylococci, clostridia, streptococci, pneumococci) and aid in their spread through tissues.

D. Streptokinase (Fibrinolysin): Many hemolytic streptococci produce a substance (streptokinase) which activates a proteolytic enzyme of the plasma (plasminogen → plasmin). This enzyme (also called fibrinolysin) is then able to dissolve coagulated plasma and probably aids in the spread of streptococci through tissues.

E. Hemolysins and Leukocidins: Many microorganisms produce substances which dissolve red blood cells (hemolysins) and probably also tissue cells and leukocytes (leukocidins). Streptolysin O, for example, is produced by group A hemolytic streptococci and is lethal for mice in addition to being hemolytic for a variety of red cells. This substance is readily oxidized and thereby inactivated, but it is reactivated by reducing agents. It is antigenic. The same streptococci also produce oxygen-stable streptolysin S, which is nonantigenic. Clostridia produce a variety of hemolysins, among them the lecithinase previously mentioned. Hemolysins are also produced by staphylococci, pneumococci, and many gram-negative rods.

Factors in the Invasiveness of Microorganisms

A continuous scale of invasiveness could be drawn up for microorganisms. One end of this scale would be occupied by toxin producers like tetanus or diphtheria; the other, by highly invasive organisms like anthrax or plague, with staphylococci and streptococci in between. The toxin producers are pathogenic principally because of elaboration of poisonous chemical substances without much tissue invasion. Plague or anthrax bacilli produce disease and death because they are able to invade tissues rapidly and multiply extensively, with the production of several toxic materials. Pneumococci or meningococci also spread widely throughout the body. The invasiveness of such organisms may be aided by enzymes favoring spread, such as hyaluronidase or streptokinase, but invasiveness is not clearly related to toxic properties. A part of the invasiveness of microorganisms may be attributed to certain surface components which protect the bacteria

from phagocytosis and destruction. Such surface substances may be polysaccharide capsules (eg, pneumococci, *Klebsiella pneumoniae, Haemophilus influenzae*), hyaluronic acid capsules and surface "M" proteins (beta-hemolytic streptococci), or a surface polypeptide (anthrax bacilli). Certain microorganisms may be invasive and "virulent" because they survive within phagocytic cells and are resistant to enzymatic attack. While these various factors contribute to the observed invasiveness of microorganisms, it must be concluded that this behavior is an expression of inherent biochemical properties not yet understood. On the other hand, invasiveness as such is by no means synonymous with disease production. Some infectious agents, eg, viruses, may be widely distributed in the body without causing illness.

How can one prove that a given microorganism really causes a disease? Traditionally, the etiologic relationship between a microorganism and a disease is established by fulfilling "Koch's postulates": (1) The microorganism must regularly be isolated from cases of the illness. (2) It must be grown in pure culture in vitro. (3) When such a pure culture is inoculated into susceptible animal species, the typical disease must result. (4) From such experimentally induced disease the microorganism must again be isolated.

While these postulates were adequate to prove the etiology of some bacterial diseases, they had to be modified for other infections, particularly for virus diseases, which are highly species-specific for man.

ATTRIBUTES OF THE HOST WHICH DETERMINE RESISTANCE TO MICROORGANISMS

The various factors that operate to prevent infection of a host can be arranged in 2 groups: nonspecific factors, operating against a variety of parasites; and specific factors based on immunologic responses toward specific agents.

SOME MECHANISMS OF NONSPECIFIC HOST RESISTANCE

Physiologic Barriers at the Portal of Entry

A. The Skin: Few microorganisms are capable of penetrating the intact skin, but many can enter sweat or sebaceous glands and hair follicles and establish themselves there. Sweat and sebaceous secretions, by virtue of their acid pH and possibly chemical substances (especially fatty acids), have antimicrobial properties which tend to eliminate pathogenic organisms. Lysozyme, an enzyme which dissolves some bacterial cell walls, and perhaps other enzymes are also present on the skin.

Skin resistance may vary with age. In childhood, susceptibility is high to ringworm infection. After puberty, resistance to such fungi increases markedly with the increased content of saturated fatty acids in sebaceous secretions.

B. Mucous Membranes: In the respiratory tract, a film of mucus covers the surface and is constantly being driven by ciliated cells toward the natural orifices. Bacteria tend to stick to this film. Mucus and tears likewise contain lysozyme and other substances with antimicrobial properties. When organisms enter the mucous membrane, they tend to be taken up by phagocytes and to be transported into regional lymphatic channels which carry them to lymph nodes. These act as barriers toward further spread and are capable of disposing of large numbers of bacteria. The mucociliary apparatus for removal of bacteria in the respiratory tract is aided by pulmonary macrophages. This entire defense system can be suppressed by ethyl alcohol, cigarette smoke, hypoxia, acidosis, and other influences. Additional special protective mechanisms include, in the respiratory tract, the hairs at the nares and the cough reflex.

In the gastrointestinal tract, saliva contains numerous hydrolytic enzymes; the acidity of the stomach inactivates many ingested bacteria (eg, *V cholerae*); the small intestine contains many proteolytic enzymes and active macrophages.

In the vagina, an acid pH is maintained by normal lactobacilli which interfere with the establishment of yeasts and other organisms.

It must be remembered that most mucous membranes of the body carry a constant normal microbial flora which itself opposes the establishment of pathogenic microorganisms and has important physiologic functions. (See Bacterial Interference, pp 172 and 251.)

Phagocytosis

Microorganisms (and other particles) which enter the lymphatics, lung, bone marrow, or bloodstream are engulfed by any of a variety of phagocytic cells. Among them are polymorphonuclear leukocytes, phagocytic monocytes (macrophages), and fixed macrophages of the reticuloendothelial system (below). Many microorganisms elaborate chemotactic factors which attract phagocytic cells. Defects in chemotaxis may account for hypersusceptibility to certain infections (eg, Job's syndrome). Phagocytosis can occur in the absence of serum antibodies, particularly if aided by the architecture of tissue. Thus, phagocytic cells are inefficient in large, smooth, open spaces like pleura, pericardium, or joint but may be more effective in ingesting microorganisms which are trapped in small tissue spaces (eg, alveoli) or on rough surfaces. Such "surface phagocytosis" occurs early in the infectious process before antibodies are available.

Phagocytosis is made more efficient by the presence of antibodies (opsonins) which coat the bacterial surface and facilitate the uptake of bacteria by the phagocyte. Opsonization can occur by 3 mechanisms:

(1) Antibody alone can act as opsonin. (2) Antibody plus antigen can activate complement via the classic pathway to yield opsonins. (3) Opsonin may be produced by a heat-labile system where immunoglobulin or other factors activate C3 via the alternative pathway. Macrophages have receptors on their membrane for the Fc portion of antibody and for the C3 component of complement. This aids the phagocytosis of antibody-coated particles.

Hyperosmolality (eg, in the renal medulla) inhibits phagocytosis. Hypophosphatemia depletes ATP in granulocytes and reduces the efficacy of phagocytosis.

The ingestion of foreign particles, eg, microorganisms, has the following effects on phagocytic granulocytes: (1) Oxygen consumption increases and there is an increased generation of superoxide and an increased release of H_2O_2. (2) Glycolysis increases via the hexose monophosphate shunt. (3) Lysosomes rupture and their hydrolytic enzymes are discharged into the phagocytic vacuole to form a digestive vacuole or "phagolysosome." Morphologically, this process appears as "degranulation" of granulocytes. (4) There appear to be no major changes in the synthesis of proteins or nucleic acids.

Granulocytes (polymorphonuclear leukocytes) contain at least 2 types of granules: lysosomes which appear to be "bags" of hydrolytic enzymes and granules consisting of basic proteins which have antibacterial effects but no known enzymatic function, eg, phagocytin or lactoferrin.

The functional mechanisms of intracellular killing of microorganisms in phagocytic granulocytes are not fully known. They include nonoxidative mechanisms (eg, activation of hydrolytic enzymes in contact with microorganisms, action of basic proteins) and oxidative mechanisms. Among the latter, the following have been implicated:

(1) The increased oxidative activity results in accumulation of H_2O_2. In the presence of oxidizable cofactors (halides such as iodine, bromine, chlorine), an acid pH, and the enzyme myeloperoxidase, intensive oxidation results in microbial death.

Children suffering from "granulomatous disease" have granulocytes which ingest microbes normally but lack the subsequent respiratory burst and normal intracellular killing. Such individuals usually die of infection, perhaps because their granulocytes may be specifically deficient in enzymes, eg, myeloperoxidase. In Chédiak-Higashi syndrome, most microorganisms are phagocytosed normally but intracellular killing is impaired, perhaps because myeloperoxidase is not released from (abnormal) lysosomes.

(2) In normal granulocytes, superoxide anion (O_2^-) is generated upon phagocytosis of particles and destroyed by superoxidase dismutase. The superoxide radical may be directly lethal for many microorganisms. "Granulomatous disease" granulocytes have a greatly reduced capacity for generation of superoxide radicals after ingestion of microorganisms. Perhaps this defect is responsible for the impaired killing ability of granulocytes from such patients, which promotes their

susceptibility to infections, especially those due to staphylococci.

Corticosteroids probably increase the stability of lysosomal membranes. This may contribute to the diminished ability of phagocytes to eradicate bacterial and fungal infection in persons receiving high doses of corticosteroids.

In bacterial infections, the number of circulating neutrophilic leukocytes often increases. In addition, these neutrophils reduce colorless nitroblue tetrazolium (NBT) to intracellular blue-black formazan granules. The presence of more than 10% NBT-positive neutrophils strongly suggests the presence of bacterial infection. Depressed NBT responses occur in patients with defective phagocytic immune mechanisms, eg, chronic granulomatous disease.

Circulating phagocytic monocytes (macrophages) are derived from monocyte stem cells in bone marrow, have a longer life span than circulating granulocytic phagocytes, and continue their activity at lower pH.

Macrophages in blood have few lysosomal granules until they become "activated." This "activation" results from interaction with immunologically active T-lymphoid cells as a consequence of bacterial infection. "Activated" macrophages have many lysosomes and are active in phagocytosis and intracellular killing of a variety of bacteria—not only the ones which induced the initial "activation." Thus, the induction of activated macrophages is immunologically specific but their subsequent expression is nonspecific.

Intracellular killing in macrophages probably includes mechanisms similar to those described above for granulocytes. However, the role of superoxide anion appears to be less well defined.

All types of phagocytic cells (granulocytes, macrophages in blood, and fixed macrophages of the reticuloendothelial system) may kill ingested microorganisms or may permit their prolonged survival or even their intracellular multiplication. It is evident that the outcome of phagocytosis is determined by a complex set of factors, including the specific nature of the microorganism, the genetic and functional make-up of phagocytic cells, and the preconditioning of these cells.

Reticuloendothelial (RE) System

This refers to a functional concept of mononuclear, phagocytic cells in blood, lymphoid tissue, liver, spleen, bone marrow, lung, and other tissues which are efficient in uptake and removal of particulate matter from lymph and bloodstream. It includes cells lining blood (Kupffer cells of liver) and lymph sinuses and histiocytes of tissues (macrophages). This system of phagocytic cells is the principal means of clearing particles, including bacteria, from blood and lymph. Phagocytosis by RE cells is greatly enhanced by opsonins.

Biochemical Tissue Constituents

Certain animal tissues are resistant to specific bacteria (eg, *Bacillus anthracis*) because of their content of polypeptides, which have antibacterial properties. Such biochemical constituents may determine tissue resis-

tance to infection. Beta lysin of serum can kill some gram-positive bacteria. The nutritional status of the host plays an important role in susceptibility or resistance to a given infection.

The role of interferon in resistance to virus infections is discussed in Chapter 27.

Many normal tissues have a high inherent ability to inhibit proliferation of microorganisms. This resistance is severely impaired by trauma, foreign bodies, disturbances in fluid and electrolyte balance, and by depressed inflammatory response (x-ray radiation, corticosteroids, antineoplastic drugs, lymphomas).

Inflammatory Response

Any injury to tissue, such as that following the establishment and multiplication of microorganisms, calls forth an inflammatory response. This begins with dilatation of local arterioles and capillaries, from which plasma escapes. Edema fluid accumulates in the area of injury, and fibrin forms a network and occludes the lymphatic channels, tending to limit the spread of organisms. Polymorphonuclear leukocytes in the capillaries stick to the walls, then migrate out of the capillaries toward the irritant. This migration is probably stimulated by substances in the inflammatory exudate (chemotaxis). The phagocytes engulf the microorganisms, and intracellular digestion begins. Soon the pH of the inflamed area becomes more acid, and the cellular proteases tend to induce lysis of the leukocytes. Large mononuclear macrophages arrive on the site and, in turn, engulf leukocytic debris as well as microorganisms and pave the way for resolution of the local inflammatory process.

Several mediators of inflammation have been considered. Prostaglandins (long-chain fatty acids) are vasodilators which are released in inflammation, and their synthesis is inhibited by anti-inflammatory drugs.

Different stages in this inflammatory sequence may predominate with different microorganisms as the inciting cause of the inflammation. The early edema fluid may actually promote bacterial growth. The degree of local fixation depends on the nature of the organism: Staphylococci tend to limit their spread through extensive lymphatic thrombi, fibrin walls, etc, precipitated by coagulase, while hemolytic streptococci, through the activity of streptokinase (fibrinolysin) and hyaluronidase, tend to spread rapidly through the tissue. Phagocytosis and intracellular residence are destructive to some bacteria (some pyogenic cocci), whereas for others (eg, tubercle bacilli) they serve as a means of transport and protection and even of multiplication.

Fever

Fever in itself does not seem to be a helpful mechanism in many acute infections, and suppression of fever is not harmful. It is certainly the most frequently observed systemic manifestation of the inflammatory response and a cardinal symptom of infectious diseases. Possible mechanisms of fever production must therefore be discussed.

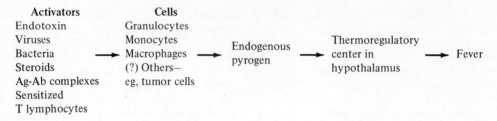

The ultimate regulators of body temperature are the thermoregulatory centers in the brain. They are subject to physical and chemical stimuli. Direct mechanical injury or the application of chemical substances to these centers results in fever. Neither of these obvious forms of stimulation is present in the many types of fever which are associated with infection, neoplasia, hypersensitivity, and other processes which cause inflammation.

Among the substances capable of inducing fever are the endotoxins of gram-negative bacteria and extracts of normal leukocytes, especially granulocytes, called "endogenous pyrogen." These 2 substances differ as follows:

(1) Endotoxins are heat-stable lipopolysaccharides. After intravenous injection, there is a 60- to 90-minute latent period until the onset of fever. During that time, leukopenia usually develops. Repeated intravenous injection of endotoxin makes the recipient **tolerant**: He becomes unresponsive to further injections of endotoxin.

(2) Endogenous pyrogen is heat-labile (destroyed by 90° C for 30 minutes). After intravenous injection, fever begins in a few minutes, even in endotoxin-tolerant recipients, without the development of leukopenia. Repeated injection of endogenous pyrogen does not induce unresponsiveness.

From many observations it is probable that a variety of activators (endotoxins, bacteria, viruses, steroids, antigen-antibody complexes, sensitized T lymphocytes) can act upon several cell types (granulocytes, monocytes, macrophages, perhaps others) and induce them to release endogenous pyrogen. The pyrogen released from different cells may have different characteristics. Endogenous pyrogen is carried by blood to the thermoregulatory center in the hypothalamus, which initiates physiologic responses resulting in fever, eg, increased heat production and heat conservation and reduced heat loss.

The properties of endogenous pyrogen are as follows: It appears to be a protein with a molecular weight of 10,000–20,000 and an isoelectric point near 7.1; it is inactivated at pH above 8.0 or by heat and is stabilized at pH below 4.0 or by sulfhydryl reducing agents. The endogenous pyrogen derived from cells of one mammalian species acts partially on other species; no tolerance develops upon repeated injections; and activity is increased 100-fold upon injection directly into the hypothalamus.

Some Causes of Persistent Fever of Unknown Origin (FUO) Lasting More Than 3 Weeks

If the usual diagnostic procedures (including thorough bacteriologic and serologic studies) fail to reveal the diagnosis, consider early biopsy or exploratory laparotomy.

(1) Infections (bacterial, fungal, parasitic; rarely viral): Especially tuberculosis, liver and biliary tract disease, bacterial endocarditis, abdominal abscess, urinary tract disease.

(2) Neoplasms: Consider especially those involving the kidneys, lungs, thyroid, liver, pancreas; lymphomas, leukemias, myeloma.

(3) Hypersensitivity disease: Visceral angiitis, disseminated lupus erythematosus, polyarteritis nodosa, scleroderma, dermatomyositis, rheumatic fever, drug fever, rheumatoid arthritis.

(4) Granulomatous diseases: Regional enteritis, granulomatous hepatitis.

(5) Neurogenic or endocrine disorders: Consider lesions of brain stem and thalamus; encephalitis, hyperthyroidism; exaggerated circadian temperature variation.

(6) Factitious fever: Malingering.

(7) Miscellaneous: Consider sarcoidosis, thrombophlebitis, infarction, poisons, drugs.

RESISTANCE & IMMUNITY

In the preceding section were described various properties of the host which give nonspecific resistance to infection. The term "immunity" signifies all those properties of the host which confer resistance to a specific infectious agent. This resistance may be of all degrees, from almost complete susceptibility to complete insusceptibility. Therefore, "resistance" and "immunity" are relative terms implying only that one host is more or less susceptible to a given infection than another host. No inference can be drawn regarding the possible mechanisms of this resistance.

Immunity may be natural or acquired. Acquired immunity may be passive or active.

NATURAL IMMUNITY

Natural immunity is that which is not acquired through previous contact with the infectious agent (or with a related species). Little is known about the mechanism responsible for this form of resistance.

Species Immunity

A given pathogenic microorganism is often capable of producing disease in one animal species but not in another. The bacillus of avian tuberculosis causes disease in birds but almost never in man; the anthrax bacillus infects man but not chickens (perhaps because of the higher body temperatures of fowl); gonococci infect man and chimpanzees but no other animal species.

Racial or Genetic Basis of Immunity

Within one animal species there may be marked racial and genetic differences in susceptibility. Some dark-skinned races of man have a 10 times greater chance of developing disseminated coccidioidomycosis following primary infection than light-skinned races. Certain "strains" of mice are highly susceptible to viral and resistant to bacterial infections. With other strains the opposite is true.

In a few instances the biochemical basis of racial (genetic) immunity is known. For example, a hereditary deficiency of glucose-6-phosphate dehydrogenase occurs in the red blood cells of certain individuals. Such persons are markedly less susceptible to *P falciparum* malaria, but more susceptible to red cell hemolysis after certain drugs (sulfonamides, primaquine, nitrofurans) than persons with normal red cell enzyme content. The genetic basis of several specific defects of immune responses is under study.

Individual Resistance

As with any biologic phenomenon, resistance to infection varies with different individuals of the same species and race, following a distribution curve for the host population. Thus certain individuals may be discovered within a "highly susceptible population" who unaccountably cannot be infected with a certain microorganism even though they have had no previous contact with it. Other individuals have genetic defects (see above) in immunologic responsiveness, antibody production, or phagocyte function which make them unusually susceptible to infections. Nutritional status (eg, protein deficiency may enhance susceptibility; microorganisms may be pathogenic by competing for iron with the host), exposure to ionizing radiation or immunosuppressive drugs, and hormonal balance all greatly influence individual susceptibility.

Differences Due to Age

In general, the very young and the elderly are more susceptible to bacterial disease than persons in other age groups. However, resistance to tuberculosis is higher at 5–15 years than before or after. Many age differences in specific infections can be related to physiologic factors. Thus, bacterial meningitis during the first month of life is often caused by coliform bacteria because bactericidal antibodies to these bacteria are IgM and thus fail to cross the placenta. Gonococcal vaginitis occurs mainly in small girls. Near puberty, estrogen production results in epithelial cell cornification and a more acid pH, which induce relative resistance.

Some virus infections (eg, rubella) damage the fetus severely but otherwise produce only mild disease. Rickettsial infections are, by contrast, more severe with advancing age. There are many other examples.

Hormonal & Metabolic Influences

Many known hormones influence susceptibility to infection. Only 2 examples are listed here.

In diabetes mellitus there is increased susceptibility to infections of the urinary tract, vagina, and pyogenic infections of tissue. The latter may be due, in part, to altered metabolism, elevated glucose, lower pH, reduced influx of phagocytic cells, and depression of phagocytosis.

Both in hypoadrenal (Addison's disease) and in hyperadrenal (Cushing's disease) states, susceptibility to infection is increased. Administration of corticosteroids in high doses has similar effects. Bacterial infections are enhanced because of the suppression of the inflammatory response by glucocorticoids. Viral infections (herpes keratitis, varicella) are aggravated by corticosteroids, perhaps due to suppression of interferon production. Huge doses of corticosteroids can directly suppress antibody formation.

Certain clinical associations between an underlying constitutional disorder and a supervening infection are so frequent as to deserve listing:

Sickle cell anemia: salmonella osteomyelitis, pneumococcal bacteremia, meningitis.

Diabetes mellitus (especially ketosis): mucormycosis.

Cirrhosis, nephrosis: pneumococcal peritonitis.

Hypoparathyroidism: candidiasis.

Pulmonary alveolar proteinosis: nocardiosis.

Chronic lymphocytic leukemia: disseminated herpes zoster.

Immunosuppression by drugs: many "opportunistic" infections—viral, bacterial, fungal, protozoal.

ACQUIRED IMMUNITY

Passive Immunity

By "passive immunity" is meant a state of relative temporary insusceptibility to an infectious agent that has been induced by the administration of antibodies against that agent which have been formed in another host rather than formed actively by the individual himself. Because the antibody molecules are decaying steadily while no new ones are being formed, passive protection lasts only a short time—usually a few weeks at most. On the other hand, the protective mechanism is in force immediately upon administration of antibody: There is no lag period such as is required for the formation of active immunity. Antibodies play only a limited role in invasive bacterial infections, and passive immunization (ie, the administration of convalescent serum or globulin) is rarely useful in that type of disease. Where an illness is largely attributable to a toxin, on the other hand (eg, diphtheria, tetanus, botulism), the passive administration of antitoxin is of the greatest use because large amounts of antitoxin can be made immediately available for neutralization of the toxin. In certain virus infections (eg, measles, infectious hepatitis), the administration of specific antibodies (such as human pooled gamma globulin) during the incubation period may result in prevention or modification of the clinical disease.

Passive immunity resulting from the in utero transfer to the fetus of antibodies formed earlier in the mother protects the newborn child during the first months of life against some common infections. This passive immunity (acquired from the mother's blood) may be reinforced by antibodies taken up by the child in mother's milk (particularly colostrum), but the immunity wanes at 4–6 months of age.

Active Immunity

Active immunity is a state of resistance built up in an individual following effective contact with foreign antigens, eg, microorganisms or their products. "Effective contact" may consist of clinical or subclinical infection, injection with live or killed microorganisms or their antigens, or absorption of bacterial products (eg, toxins, toxoids). In all these instances the host actively produces antibodies and his cells learn to respond to the foreign material. Active immunity develops slowly over a period of days or weeks but tends to persist, usually for years. Of the mechanisms which make up the resistance of acquired active immunity, a few can be defined:

A. Humoral Immunity: Active production of **antibodies** against antigens of microorganisms or their products. These antibodies may induce resistance because they (1) neutralize toxins or cellular enzymes or products; (2) have direct bactericidal or lytic effect with complement; (3) block the infective ability of microorganisms or viruses; (4) agglutinate microorganisms, making them more subject to phagocytosis; or (5) opsonize microorganisms, ie, combine with surface antigens which normally interfere with phagocytosis and thus contribute to the ingestion of parasites.

Antibody formation is disturbed in certain individuals with agammaglobulinemia or thymic dysfunction (see Chapter 12).

B. Cellular Immunity: Although antibodies arise in response to foreign antigens, they often play only a minor role in the defense of the organism against invading cells. The central position in such defenses is occupied by cell-mediated immune responses of great complexity combining immunologically specific and nonspecific features. Circulating thymus-dependent lymphoid cells (see T and B cells, Chapter 12) recognize materials as foreign and initiate a chain of responses which include mononuclear inflammatory reactions, cytotoxic destruction of invading cells (microbial, graft, or neoplastic), "activation" of phagocytic macrophages which permits them to destroy intracellular organisms, and delayed type hypersensitivity reactions in tissues. In the course of these events, foreign microorganisms or cells are fixed at their point of entry, thus limiting invasiveness (see Tuberculosis, p 197); the phagocytic capacity of cells (polymorphonuclears, macrophages, reticuloendothelial) is enhanced; ingested microbes or cells are more effectively killed, especially in "activated" macrophages (see p 132); and the biochemical environment in tissues is altered so as to make it less favorable for spread and multiplication of the parasite.

●   ●   ●

General References

Atkins E, Bodel P: Fever. N Engl J Med 286:27, 1972.

Craddock GG & others: Lymphocytes and the immune response. N Engl J Med 285:324, 1971.

DeChatelet LR: Oxidative bactericidal mechanisms of polymorphonuclear leukocytes. J Infect Dis 131:295, 1975.

Dinarella CA & others: Characterization of two distinct human leukocytic pyrogens. J Exp Med 139:1369, 1974.

Douglas SD, Fudenberg HH: Genetically determined defects in host resistance to infection: Cellular aspects. Med Clin North Am 53:903, 1969.

Mackaness GB: Resistance to intracellular infection. J Infect Dis 123:439, 1971.

Matula G, Paterson PY: Reduction of nitroblue-tetrazolium by neutrophils in infection. N Engl J Med 285:311, 1971.

Pearsall NN, Weiser RS: *The Macrophage.* Lea & Febiger, 1970.

Quie PG: Infections due to neutrophil malfunctions. Medicine 52:411, 1973.

Smith H: Biochemical challenge of microbial pathogenicity. Bacteriol Rev 32:164, 1968.

Stossel TP: Phagocytosis. (3 parts.) N Engl J Med 290:717, 774, 833, 1974.

Winkelstein JA: Opsonins. J Pediatr 82:747, 1973.

Wolff SM & others: Unusual etiologies of fever and their evaluation. Annu Rev Med 26:277, 1975.

12 . . .
Immunology: I.
Antigens & Antibodies

DEFINITIONS & CELLULAR BASIS OF IMMUNE RESPONSES

DEFINITIONS

Antigens (Ags) are substances which, when introduced into a foreign species, can elicit the formation of **antibodies (Abs)** in the living animals and can specifically react with such Abs. Most complete Ags are proteins, but some are polysaccharides or polypeptides. Most Ags are macromolecules with a molecular weight of over 10,000. To act as Ags, substances must be recognized as "foreign" or "nonself" by an animal since, in general, animals do not produce Abs to their own ("self") proteins.

Antigenic determinants are those portions of Ag molecules which determine the specificity of Ag-Ab reactions. The size of the antigenic determinant group may be quite small in relation to the size of the whole Ag molecule, eg, 5–7 amino acid residues or 3–6 glucose residues.

Haptens are chemicals of low molecular weight which do not by themselves elicit the formation of Abs but which can combine with Abs elicited by a large molecule which possesses a structural unit similar to or identical with the hapten. Many simple chemicals and drugs can act as haptens. They can bind to host proteins to form a complete antigen.

Antibodies (Abs) are proteins that are formed in response to an Ag and react specifically with that Ag or one very closely related to it. Only vertebrates make Abs. Abs are specialized proteins, the immunoglobulins. The behavior of Abs depends to some extent on the class of immunoglobulins to which they belong.

THE CELLULAR BASIS OF IMMUNE RESPONSES

The capacity to respond to immunologic stimuli rests principally in cells of the lymphoid system. In order to make clear normal immune responses as well as clinically occurring immune deficiency syndromes and their possible management, a brief outline of cur-

rent concepts of the development of the lymphoid system must be presented.

During embryonic life, a stem cell develops in fetal liver and other organs. This stem cell probably resides in bone marrow in postnatal life. Under the differentiating influence of various environments, it can be induced to differentiate along several different lines. Within fetal liver and later in bone marrow, the stem cell may differentiate into cells of the red cell series or of the granulocyte series. Alternatively, the stem cell may turn into a lymphoid stem cell which may differentiate to form at least 2 distinct lymphocyte populations. One population (called T lymphocytes) is dependent on the presence of a functioning thymus; the other (B lymphocytes, analogous to lymphocytes derived in birds from the bursa of Fabricius) is independent of the thymus. Some characteristics of B and T lymphocytes are described below, and some major differences between these 2 types of cells are listed in Table 12–1.

B Lymphocytes

These constitute only a small portion (about

Table 12–1. Some differences between T and B cells.

	T Cells	B Cells
Frequency in blood	80%	20%
Frequency in spleen	65%	35%
Surface appearance by scanning electron microscopy	Smooth	Filamentous projections
Immunoglobulins on surface	±	+++
Method of counting	Rosette formation with sheep red cells	Immunofluorescence with anti-Ig
Secretion of antibody	−	+
Effector in cell-mediated reactions	+	−
Inactivated by x-ray radiation	−	+
Inactivated by anti-lymphocytic serum	+	−
Recognition of determinants on	Carrier	Hapten

20%) of the recirculating pool of small lymphocytes, being mostly restricted to lymphoid tissue. Their life span is short (days or weeks). The mammalian equivalent of the avian bursa is not known, but it is believed that gut-associated lymphoid tissue (eg, tonsils, Peyer's patches, appendix) may be an important source of B lymphocytes. B cells are produced abundantly in the absence of a thymus. B cells have abundant membrane-bound immunoglobulin molecules (about 10^5 per cell). Each cell carries only one type of immunoglobulin, but some carry both IgD and IgM.

B cells can differentiate, proliferate, and mature into plasma cells—large lymphocytes which synthesize specific Abs. Some large lymphocytes can probably revert to small B lymphocytes which have a long life and serve as "memory cells." B cells have various surface receptors, including immunoglobulins and Fc receptors. Attachment of Ag to Ig or of Ag-Ab complex to an Fc receptor provides a stimulus for B cell proliferation. B cell proliferation and "blast cell transformation" can also be stimulated nonspecifically by pokeweed mitogen and lipopolysaccharides from gram-negative bacteria but not by phytohemagglutinin nor concanavalin A.

B cell populations are largely responsible for specific immunoglobulin and Ab production in the host. B cell defects (eg, insufficient numbers, defects in differentiation) lead to inadequate immunoglobulin synthesis but have little to do with cell-mediated immunity. With certain antigens which are large polymers (eg, pneumococcus polysaccharide, anthrax D-glutamic acid polypeptide), B cells alone are stimulated into antibody production, requiring no T cell cooperation. With other antigens which have a smaller number of determinants and require a carrier, T cell cooperation with B cells is needed for antibody production.

T Lymphocytes

These constitute the greater part (65–80%) of the recirculating pool of small lymphocytes. Their life span is long (months or years). While originally derived from bone marrow, they require an intact thymus (at least in early life) before reaching the circulation. A small proportion of T cells have immunoglobulin molecules on their surface (mainly IgM). They have characteristic surface Ags (theta in mouse; homologous MSTA* in man). They tend to give rosette formation with sheep red blood cells. T cells can react with one or a few Ags and then become "immunologically committed" lymphocytes, capable of participating in the cell functions listed below. T cells do not differentiate into immunoglobulin-synthesizing cells and do not produce Ab.

In general, a deficiency of the T cell system manifests itself as a defect in cell-mediated immunity. In view of (E), however (see below), a T cell defect may also result in impaired antibody synthesis in spite of an intact B cell system.

---

*MSTA = an isoantigen homologous to the *mouse* species *t*hymus *a*ntigen.

The precise mechanism by which the thymus controls T cells is not known. In early life, the thymus may be the main intermediate source of T lymphocytes, but their ultimate source is the bone marrow. The thymus may exert some hormonal control over T cells, but such a hormone, if it exists, has not been identified.

T lymphocytes from an individual sensitized to a given Ag can be stimulated by contact with that Ag to replicate and participate in the following functions:

A. Cell-Mediated Immunity: T cells are responsible for delayed type hypersensitivity reactions to bacterial, viral, fungal, and other antigens. They are a major defense mechanism against many infectious agents and perhaps against neoplastic cells.

B. Graft Rejection, Tumor Immunity: T cells are cytotoxic for grafted cells and for tumor cells. They may also mediate graft-versus-host reactions ("killer T cells").

C. Correlates of Delayed Type Hypersensitivity: T cells release soluble factors which inhibit the migration of macrophages, act as transfer factor, transform other lymphocytes, and are lymphotoxic.

D. Immunologic Memory: T cells divide to form a population of Ag-sensitive cells of long life span, thus contributing importantly to immunologic memory.

E. Cooperation With B Lymphocytes: In response to certain Ags (see above), T cells must cooperate with B cells to permit an antibody response. This is particularly true with haptens and their carriers. The hapten reacts with B cells, but the carrier must react with T cells to yield an Ab response.

F. Nonspecific Stimulation: T cells can be nonspecifically stimulated in culture by mitogens, eg, phytohemagglutinin or concanavalin A.

It is probable that some of the functions mentioned above are carried out by defined subpopulations of T cells.

Examples of Clinical Immunodeficiency

In a majority of individuals with clinical immunodeficiency, there are complex functional impairments, often involving both B cell and T cell functions. In a few clinical syndromes, the defect is relatively well defined, as shown in Table 12–2.

Hypersensitivity Reactions

Hypersensitivity or allergic reactions occur in individuals whose reactivity to an Ag has been altered. Reexposure to the same (or a closely related) Ag results in a variety of abnormal reactions. Hypersensitivity reactions are of 2 types: (1) Ab-mediated or immediate type reactions and (2) cell-mediated or delayed type reactions. Some important differences between the 2 groups are listed in Table 12–3.

From the standpoint of pathogenesis, hypersensitivity reactions have been classified by Gell & Coombs into 4 major types:

I. Anaphylactic Type Hypersensitivity: A special class of Ab (cytotropic Ab, mainly IgE) binds to mast cells and basophils through the Fc fragment. When Ag

Table 12–2. Examples of clinical immunodeficiencies.*

Disorder	Postulated Cell Defect		Observed Immunologic Defect
	B	T	
Infantile X-linked agammaglobulinemia (Bruton's)	+	−	Absent plasma cells, all classes of immunoglobulins extremely deficient. Cellular immunity normal.
Transient hypogammaglobulinemia of infancy	+	−	Usually self-limited
Selective immunoglobulin deficiency (IgA)	+	(−)	IgA-producing plasma cells absent, IgA immunoglobulin absent. Cellular immunity normal.
Thymic hypoplasia (DiGeorge's syndrome)	−	+	Immunoglobulins normal but some antibody responses deficient. Cellular immunity defective.
Immunodeficiency with ataxia-telangiectasia	+	+	Variable deficiency in immunoglobulins and antibodies. Cellular immunity defective for some antigens.
Immunodeficiency with thrombocytopenia and eczema (Wiskott-Aldrich syndrome)	(+)	+	Variable deficiency in immunoglobulins and antibodies. Cellular immunity defective for some antigens.
Immunodeficiency (eg, with thymoma; with short-limbed dwarfism; autosomal recessive "Swiss type")	+	+	Extremely deficient antibodies. Cellular immunity defective for all antigens.

*Reference: Cooper MD & others: Classification of primary immunodeficiencies. N Engl J Med 288:966, 1973.
(−) means that there is occasionally a coexisting T cell defect. (+) means that the defect is predominantly T cell but that B cell defects occur also.

reacts with these Abs, vasoactive amines and other mediators are liberated and elicit the reaction (see Chapter 13).

II. Cytotoxic Type Hypersensitivity: Ags on the cell surface combine with Ab. This may lead to opsonization and phagocytosis without complement, may facilitate attack by T cells, or may lead to binding of complement, which promotes immune adherence to phagocytes; or the lytic effect may result in membrane damage by complement (see Chapter 13).

III. Complex-Mediated Hypersensitivity: Ags combine with Ab to form complexes which in turn activate complement and Hageman factor (factor XII in blood coagulation) and aggregate platelets with the following consequences:

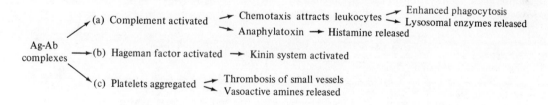

Table 12–3. Differences between immediate and delayed hypersensitivity reactions.

	Ab-Mediated or Immediate Type	Cell-Mediated or Delayed Type
Clinical examples	Anaphylactic shock; allergy to pollen, with asthma; serum sickness; some allergies to antibiotics; asthma reaction.	Tuberculin hypersensitivity, allergy to fungi (histoplasma), parasites (trichina); Rhus plants (poison ivy or oak), chemicals (nickel); skin graft rejection.
Timing	The reaction begins immediately, ie, within minutes after contact with the allergen, and disappears within 1 hour.	The reaction is delayed. It begins within several hours after contact with the allergen and may last for days.
Histology	The main pathologic reaction consists of dilatation of capillaries and arterioles, with prominent erythema and edema and only limited polymorphonuclear leukocyte infiltration.	The main pathologic reaction consists of inflammatory change with predominant mononuclear cell infiltration and tissue induration.
Passive transfer	The reaction is associated with circulating antibodies and can be transferred passively by means of serum.	The reaction is not associated with circulating Abs and cannot be transferred passively by means of serum. It can often be transferred passively by means of lymphoid cells or their extracts.

IV. Cell-Mediated Hypersensitivity: T lymphocytes carrying specific Ag receptors become activated by contact with that Ag, proliferate, transform, and release a variety of mediators which in turn act on macrophages, lymphocytes, and other cells to yield the reactions of delayed type hypersensitivity (see Chapter 13).

ANTIBODIES: STRUCTURE & FORMATION

Antibodies (Abs) are immunoglobulins which can react specifically with the Ag which stimulated their production. Immunoglobulins comprise about 20% of total serum proteins, and a variable proportion of immunoglobulins have Ab activity. Abs may be characterized by their chemical, physical, and immunologic properties. Among the prominent physicochemical properties used for classifying Abs are solubility in salts and solvents, electrophoretic mobility, molecular size, and sedimentation in the ultracentrifuge. Electrophoretically, most Abs move with the gamma and beta$_2$ fractions and a few with alpha globulins.

In terms of molecular weight (by ultracentrifugal analysis), Abs fall into 3 main groups: (1) molecular weight 150,000, 7S; (2) 900,000, 19S; and (3) 170,000–400,000, 7S to 11S.

Electrophoresis permits the separation of proteins by migration in an electrical field in paper, starch, gel, etc. From anode toward cathode, albumins migrate the shortest distance, alpha and beta globulins somewhat farther, and gamma globulins faster and farther than the others. **Immunoelectrophoresis** is an important tool in immunoglobulin and antibody identification. It consists of first separating serum proteins by electrophoresis in an agar gel and then permitting an antiserum to that serum to diffuse from a trough cut into the agar along the line of protein migration. As each serum component encounters its specific antibody, a curved line of precipitate forms in the agar.

The above technics (and others) have indicated that Abs exhibit considerable heterogeneity. Some of this heterogeneity is based on the fact that Abs to the same Ags belong to different immunoglobulin classes. At present, immunoglobulins are arranged into 5 classes (Table 12–4).

STRUCTURE OF IMMUNOGLOBULINS

In response to a single pure antigen, a large, heterogeneous population of antibody molecules arises from different clones of cells. This made study of the chemical structure of immunoglobulins (Igs) virtually impossible until myeloma proteins were isolated. Myelomas are tumors originating as a clone from a single cell. The Igs produced by myelomas are homogeneous and thus permit chemical analysis of IgG, IgA, IgD, and IgE. In Waldenström's macroglobulinemia (clinically distinct from typical myelomas), a monoclonal IgM is produced. From the study of myeloma proteins, the following generalizations about Ig structure are derived.

Table 12—4. Some characteristics of immunoglobulins.

	IgG	IgM	IgA	IgD	IgE
Sedimentation constant	7S	19S	7S or 11S*	7S	8S
Molecular weight	150,000	900,000	170,000 or 400,000*	180,000	200,000
Heavy chain symbol	γ	μ	a	δ	ϵ
Average concentration in normal serum (mg/100 ml)	1000–1500	60–180	100–400	3–5	0.01
Half life in serum (days)	23	5	6	3	2.5
Prominent in external secretions	−	−	++	−	+
Percent carbohydrate	3	12	7	12	10
Crosses placenta	+	−	−	?	−
Fixes complement	+	+	−	−	−
Examples of antibodies	Many Abs to toxins, bacteria, viruses; especially late in Ab response	Many Abs to infectious agents, especially early in Ab response; anti-polysaccharide Ab; cold agglutinins	Important as secretory antibody on mucous membranes	No proved Ab activity; present on lymphocyte surface in newborn or in lymphatic leukemia	Sensitizes skin and other tissues in allergy; reagin; binds to mast cells and basophils; elevated in allergy

*11S, molecular weight 400,000 IgA in external secretions; 7S, molecular weight 170,000 IgA in serum.

All immunoglobulins have similar structural patterns but great diversity of antigenic properties and amino acid sequences. Ig molecules are made up of light (small) and heavy (large) polypeptide chains. Each Ig chain consists of constant and of variable regions each of which, in turn, is genetically determined by at least one gene. Thus, each Ig chain seems to be coded for by at least 2 (probably several) genes—one for the constant and one for the variable region. The chains are held together by disulfide bonds (Fig 12–1) and can be isolated by reduction followed by chromatography at acid pH.

Light (L) Chains

These always belong to one of 2 types: κ (kappa) and λ (lambda), with molecular weights of 25,000. Both types occur in all classes of Ig, but any one molecule contains only one type of L chain. Some myeloma tumors secrete homogeneous L chains, either κ or λ type, called Bence Jones proteins, which are excreted in urine. The hereditary human globulin character "Inv" is located on κ L chains. In primary amyloidosis, the amyloid contains L chains, possibly fragments of autoantibodies.

Heavy (H) Chains

Each of the 5 Ig classes has an antigenically distinct set of H chains (isotypes) with molecular weights of 50,000–70,000. The 5 heavy chain types are called γ in IgG, μ in IgM, α in IgA, δ in IgD, and ε in IgE. The portion of H chains that is not involved in the antibody combining site (Fc fragment) carries the sites for various effector reactions (biologic activity), eg, complement fixation, placental permeability, attachment to phagocytic cells, degranulation of mast cells, and skin fixation. It also is the site of the great majority of the human genetic Gm markers on IgG with which rheumatoid factors react and of most of the carbohydrate moiety of Igs. In "heavy chain disease," H chains linked by disulfide bonds are excreted in urine.

Ig fragments resulting from enzymatic treatment

of Ig molecules are shown schematically in Fig 12–1.

Treatment of a 7S IgG molecule with papain results in the production of 3 fragments. Two of these are identical Ag-binding Fab fragments (each of which is univalent, containing a single Ag-binding site). The third is the Fc fragment, which carries no Ab activity but a variety of effector reactions (see above).

Treatment of the IgG molecule with pepsin results in similar fragments (see Fig 12–1). Thus, Fab fragments are joined to the Fc fragments by peptide bonds which are readily cleaved by proteases.

The piece of heavy chain within the Fab fragment is called the Fd piece.

Combining Site

The biologic activity of an Ab molecule centers on its ability to specifically bind Ags. The combining site is located on the amino terminal end of the Ab molecule (Fig 12–2) and is composed of certain hypervariable segments within the variable regions of both L and H chains. The active sites of certain Abs are estimated to be just large enough to accommodate 4–6 glucose residues. It has been estimated that of the approximately 650 amino acid residues of an L chain-H chain pair, between 15 and 30 amino acid residues may be involved in each Ab combining site. Antibody specificity is a function of both the amino acid sequence and its configuration.

Immunoglobulin G (IgG)

IgG comprises more than 80% of Igs in normal human sera. Each molecule of IgG consists of 2 L chains and 2 H chains (Fig 12–2) linked by 20–25 –S–S– bonds. There are 4 subclasses of IgG (IgG-1 to IgG-4), based on antigenic differences in H chains. Each IgG molecule has only one type of L chain and one type of H chain. IgG is the only Ig to cross the placenta and to produce passive cutaneous anaphylaxis. IgG synthesis in man is about 35 mg/kg/day, and its half-life is about 23 days. Normal adult serum levels (1000–1500 mg/100 ml) are reached at 2 years of age and decrease from the fourth decade onward.

IgG molecules are probably Y-shaped, with a "hinge region" near the middle of the heavy chain connecting the 2 Fab segments to the Fc segment. The IgG molecule can probably assume various angles at the "hinge." Since each Fab segment has one antigen-binding site, an IgG molecule has a valence of 2. Carbohydrate is less abundant in IgG (3%) than in other Ig classes. The function of the carbohydrate (located on the Fc and occasionally also on Fab segments) is uncertain. It may provide binding sites for receptors on various cells.

The heterogeneity between IgG subclasses (in antigenicity or amino acid sequence) is less than that between different Ig classes. There are small differences among subclasses in effector functions due to different H chains.

IgG antibodies can probably attach to various tissues through the Fc fragment and participate in anaphylactic (immediate) type reactions.

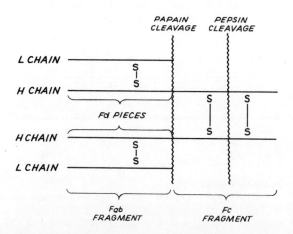

Figure 12–1. Schematic representation of a 7S immunoglobulin (IgG) molecule.

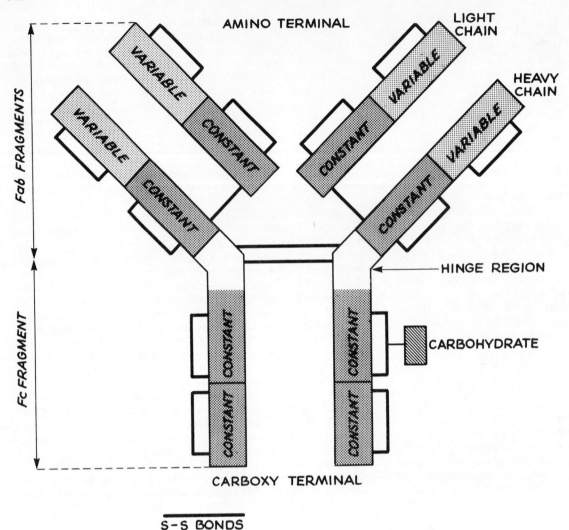

Figure 12—2. Schematic representation of an IgG molecule indicating the location of the constant and the variable regions on the light and the heavy chains.

Immunoglobulin M (IgM)

IgM comprises about 7% of Ig in normal human sera. The greater size of IgM molecules (19S, molecular weight 900,000) is due to 5 units (each similar to one IgG unit) linked through —S—S— bonds near their "hinge regions." Reducing agents (eg, mercaptoethanol) tend to break these linking disulfide bonds and dissociate IgM molecules into 5 subunits of 7—8S, with H chains of molecular weight 70,000. IgM can usually be distinguished from IgG and other Ig classes because treatment with mercaptoethanol results in a loss of agglutinating activity.

Each subunit of IgM consists of 2 L chains and 2 H chains. In addition, there is one J chain (molecular weight 20,000) per 10 L chains of IgM molecules. The J chain is acidic and differs in antigenicity and amino acid composition from the other chains. Its function is uncertain.

Since each IgM molecule has 10 Fab segments, it can combine with up to 10 antigenic sites. It has a valence of 5 (due to steric hindrance) to 10 (Fig 12—3).

IgM molecules are the earliest antibodies synthesized in response to antigenic stimulation. They fix complement well in the presence of antigen. The rate of IgM synthesis is about 8 mg/kg/day, and the half-life in serum is about 5 days. The fetus synthesizes IgM in utero. Since IgM does not cross the placenta, IgM antibodies in the newborn are thus considered a sign of intrauterine infection. Adult serum levels (60—180 mg/100 ml) are reached at 6—9 months after birth.

Immunoglobulin A (IgA)

The basic structural unit of IgA corresponds to that of IgG, with 2 H and 2 L chains. While IgG is uniformly a monomer, IgA can occur as a 7S monomer, a 9S dimer, an 11S trimer, and others. With mild reduction, all of these dissociate into 7S monomers. In

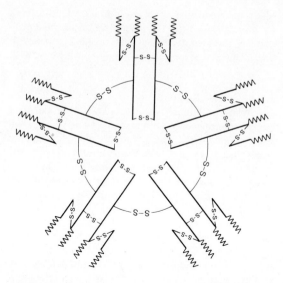

Figure 12–3. Schematic diagram of the pentameric structure of human IgM.

human serum, IgA comprises about 15% of Ig and occurs mostly as the 7S monomer in an average concentration of 100–400 mg/100 ml. The rate of synthesis of serum IgA is about 35 mg/kg/day, and it is rapidly catabolized. In man and other mammals, IgA is the principal Ig in external secretions (eg, mucus of respiratory, intestinal, urinary, and genital tracts, tears, saliva, milk). This secretory IgA is produced by cells in the various body locations. It exists mainly as a multimer (9S, 11S, etc), contains a J chain (see IgM above) in addition to L and H chains, and also another peptide chain called secretory component (molecular weight 60,000). The precise function of the secretory component is not understood. It appears to be synthesized by specialized cells in the epithelium, whereas IgA molecules are synthesized by plasma cells in the mucous membranes or secretory organs. The production of secretory IgA is stimulated more effectively by local than by systemic infection or antigen administration. IgA (serum or secretory) does *not* fix complement in the presence of antigen but may activate C3 by the alternative pathway. Secretory IgA can neutralize viruses and can inhibit attachment of bacteria to epithelial cells.

Immunoglobulin D (IgD)

This immunoglobulin was first encountered as a myeloma protein and then found in concentrations of 3–5 mg/100 ml in normal sera. IgD is rapidly catabolized and has a half-life of only 3 days. IgD has not been proved to have Ab activity, although some antinuclear autoantibodies have been claimed to be IgD. IgD has been demonstrated on the surface of lymphocytes in cord blood and also on cells in lymphatic leukemia.

Immunoglobulin E (IgE)

In normal sera, IgE is found only in minute con-

centration (0.01 mg/100 ml). Intact IgE molecules are 8S, with a molecular weight of 200,000. The H chains of IgE are longer than those of IgG by about 100 amino acid residues, perhaps indicating a special function. IgE mediates allergic reactions in skin and other tissues and, with the Fc fragment, binds to mast cells and basophils. The latter degranulate upon exposure to the specific antigen with the liberation of mediators. (See pp 156–157.) While most Igs are quite heat-stable, IgE loses the ability to sensitize skin after being heated for 4 hours at 56° C.

In persons with allergic reactivity of the antibody-mediated (immediate) type, the serum concentrations of IgE are greatly increased. In such individuals, IgE also appears in external secretions and mediates local allergic reactions. The serum level of IgE is increased in parasitic infections (helminthiases).

One or more immunoglobulins may be present in abnormally high concentration in neoplasms of plasma cells (myelomas), in liver disease, in chronic protozoal or microbial infections, and in autoimmune diseases. Deficiencies of specific immunoglobulins often are on a hereditary basis and can be due to absence of specific cells, impaired synthesis, or increased catabolism (see previous section).

Antibody Formation

The mechanism by which Abs are formed has been debated for years. For some time, the **instructive theory** was in vogue. It proposed that the specificity of an Ab molecule was determined not by its amino acid sequence but by the molding of the peptide chain around the antigenic determinant; the presence of antigen was required to serve as a template. This theory lost favor when it became apparent that Ab-forming cells were devoid of Ag and that Ab specificity was a function of amino acid sequence.

At present, the **clonal selection theory** is widely accepted. It holds that an immunologically responsive cell can respond to only one Ag or a closely related group of Ags and that this property is inherent in the cell before the Ag is encountered. According to the clonal selection theory, each individual is endowed with a very large pool of lymphocytes each of which is capable of responding to a different Ag; when the Ag enters the body, it selects the lymphocyte which has the best "fit" by virtue of a surface receptor. The Ag binds to this Ab-like receptor, and the cell is stimulated to proliferate and form a clone of cells. Thus, selected B cells quickly differentiate into plasma cells and secrete Ab which is specific for the Ag which served as the original selecting agent (or a closely related group of antigens).

It appears that each Ab-producing cell makes only one type of immunoglobulin and only one Ab. The receptors on the surfaces of B cells are specific Igs. When this Ig has been selected and bound by a specific Ag, the surface receptor is lost for several hours while the stimulus sets off cell proliferation and differentiation into plasma cells. Each plasma cell makes only one type of heavy chain and one type of light chain. For each chain, one or more genes code for the variable region and one or more genes for the constant region. It is likely that the DNA sequence encoding the variable and constant regions of each chain is transcribed as one cistron. As protein synthesis proceeds, the building of both L and H chains proceeds continuously, starting from the amino terminal, and the completed Ig molecule is assembled in the cell before release.

While a given cell produces only one Ig type at one time, the so-called **IgM-IgG switch** may occur: initially, IgM is synthesized; later, the genes controlling the variable regions of the H chain of IgM may recombine with genes controlling the constant regions of IgG so that the IgG later produced is of the same specificity as the earlier IgM.

The initial step in Ab formation is the phagocytosis of Ag by macrophages. These cells do not form Ab, but they present Ag in some form (perhaps sticking to their surface) to B cells. Stimulated B cells differentiate into plasma cells, where immunoglobulin chain synthesis begins on polyribosomes. In some instances (eg, myeloma cells), synthesized chains are excreted; in other instances, L and H chains are assembled with disulfide bonds and the sugar moiety is added before release.

With certain Ags, the induction of an Ab response requires the cooperation of B cells with T cells as well as with macrophages. The mechanism of this is not entirely understood (see p 138).

The Primary Response

When an animal or man is injected with an Ag—and if this represents the individual's first contact with that Ag—there is a rise in detectable Ab in serum within several days, depending on the route of injection and the dose and nature of the Ag. The Ab concentration then rises to a peak within 1–10 weeks, then drops, and may fall below detectable levels (Fig 12–4). In general, IgM Abs appear earlier than IgG Abs in the primary response. IgM Ab concentrations decline more rapidly than IgG Ab concentrations because IgM and IgA are normally catabolized more rapidly than IgG.

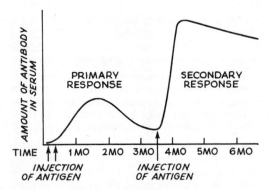

Figure 12–4. Rate of antibody production following initial antigen administration and "booster" injection.

Abs made some time after immunization tend to bind Ag more firmly than Ab made soon after immunization—ie, the affinity and avidity of Ab increase with time. However, cross-reactivity may also increase with time.

The Secondary Response

When an animal is reinjected with the same Ag weeks, months, or even years after the primary Ab levels have subsided, there is a more rapid Ab response to a higher level—and for a longer interval—than in the primary response. This is presumably based on persistence of a substantial number of Ag-sensitive "memory" cells after initial contact with the Ag. The memory for secondary Ab response resides in B cells and for certain antigens in both B and T cells. During the secondary response, IgM antibody production may be similar to that in the primary response, whereas IgG antibody production is usually far greater. A secondary response may be elicited with an Ag which is identical with or related to the Ag eliciting the primary response in that individual. This phenomenon ("original antigenic sin") can be employed in serologic epidemiology of infectious diseases caused by antigenically related but not identical agents (eg, influenza).

Interference With Antibody Formation

When 2 or more Ags are injected simultaneously, the host reacts by producing antibodies to each. Competition of Ags for Ab-producing mechanisms has been observed experimentally, but it plays no practical role, and combined immunization with several Ags is widely used (eg, diphtheria and tetanus toxoids, pertussis vaccine, and mixed live virus vaccines). The passive administration of a specific antibody interferes with the active production of that same specific antibody by the host. A practical application is the injection of human antibody to Rh antigen into Rh-negative women with Rh-positive husbands and children. If the Rh-negative woman is permitted to form antibodies to the fetus's Rh-positive red cells, these antibodies are likely to produce Rh disease in the offspring; but if the Rh-negative woman receives concentrated Rh antibodies before she begins to synthesize Rh antibodies, her antibody production is inhibited and Rh disease of the newborn is prevented (see p 145).

Human Gamma Globulin

Immune human serum globulin USP is a preparation of gamma globulin derived from large pools of human plasma by low temperature ethanol fractionation. The preparation contains about 165 mg of gamma globulin per ml of solution, representing a 25-fold concentration of Ab-containing globulins of plasma, glycine as stabilizer, and an antibacterial agent. Such concentrated gamma globulin is injected intramuscularly or subcutaneously, never intravenously. It may be employed clinically in the following conditions:

A. Hypo- or Dysgammaglobulinemia With Recurrent Bacterial Infections: Inject 0.6–1 ml/kg body weight (100–165 mg/kg gamma globulin) once each month, but twice initially. Antimicrobial drugs must also be used to control active infection.

B. Measles: To prevent clinical disease in non-immunized children (and interfere with development of active immunity), give 0.25 ml/kg as soon as possible after exposure. To attenuate the disease (and permit development of active immunity), give 0.04 ml/kg within 8 days of exposure. Gamma globulin has no effect after the rash has appeared. Attenuation markedly reduces the incidence of complications, but (ideally) all susceptibles should be vaccinated. Gamma globulin (0.02 ml/kg) is administered simultaneously with certain live measles virus vaccines to minimize reactions to the vaccine.

C. German Measles: Susceptible women during the first 4 months of pregnancy may be given 0.6 ml/kg. This will prevent disease in up to 50% of exposed women, but it does not protect the fetus and thus is largely useless.

D. Infectious Hepatitis: Use of 0.02 ml/kg once or twice during the incubation period may prevent or modify the disease without interfering with the development of immunity.

E. Serum Hepatitis: After multiple transfusions, the injection of gamma globulin does not lower the risk of hepatitis. However, the administration of gamma globulin containing very high concentrations of antibody to hepatitis B surface antigen may prevent severe icteric hepatitis.

Specific Human Gamma Globulins

These are obtained from the blood of individuals who have been immunized with a given antigen and have acquired high concentrations of specific antibody. A few specific indications are listed below.

A. Tetanus: For prevention of tetanus after injury in nonimmunized individuals, 250–500 units of human hyperimmune tetanus globulin will yield serum levels of more than 0.01 unit/ml for several weeks (see p 189). Ten thousand units have been injected intravenously for the treatment of tetanus.

B. Vaccinia: Hyperimmune globulin (VIG), 0.6–1 ml/kg, can be used in the rare individual who develops progressive vaccinia gangrenosum after smallpox vaccination. These are usually immunodeficient persons.

C. Rabies: Human rabies immune globulin (HRIG) is prepared from plasma pools with high rabies antibody titer obtained from immunized volunteers. The recommended dose is 20 units/kg. Up to half the dose should be infiltrated around the wound and the rest injected intramuscularly. (Phone Dallas Distribution Center: 214-631-6240.) HRIG may suppress the antibody response to rabies vaccine given prophylactically after exposure. Twenty-one doses of duck embryo vaccine plus 2 booster doses at 10-day intervals should be given.

D. Mumps: Limited evidence suggests that 20 ml of hyperimmune gamma globulin may prevent orchitis in adult males.

E. Chickenpox: Zoster immune globulin (ZIG), 0.15 ml/kg IM, injected into high-risk children within 72 hours of exposure to chickenpox, can prevent the disease.

F. Rh Disease: Specific human anti-Rh immune globulin can be injected into an Rh-negative mother following delivery of an Rh-positive infant. This prevents Rh isoimmunization of the mother and reduces the risk of hemolytic Rh disease in her next Rh-positive infant.

G. Pertussis: 3 ml of hyperimmune globulin may hasten recovery, prevent complications, and reduce mortality in debilitated infants or unimmunized children under 3 years of age.

ANTIGEN-ANTIBODY REACTIONS

Antigens (Ags) have been defined as substances which can elicit the formation of antibodies (Abs) in a living animal. An animal does not generally produce Abs against its own Ags, ie, it differentiates between "self" and "nonself." Exceptions to this generalization are sequestered antigens—eg, thyroid tissue, lens (see below).

Antigenic Specificity

Reactions of Ags with Abs are highly specific. This means that an Ag will react only with Abs elicited by its own kind or by a closely related kind of Ag. The majority of antigenic substances are species-specific, and some are even organ-specific within an animal species. Human proteins can easily be distinguished from the proteins of other animals by Ag-Ab reactions and will cross-react only with the proteins of closely related species (eg, anthropoid apes). Within a single species, kidney protein may be distinguished from lung protein, etc. Exceptions to this species-specificity are certain Ags which are widely distributed among animals, particularly protein of the lens of the eye and the so-called **Forssman** or **heterophil antigen** which is present in the organs of the mouse, dog, cat, horse, fish, and chicken as well as in the red cells of sheep and in some bacteria.

Antigenic specificity is a function of the chemical structure of the Ag. Serologically identical proteins appear to be identical in composition, and Ags showing cross-reactions are closely related in chemical structure. Specificity of Ags may be altered by changing small chemical groups on the large protein molecule or by acetylation, methylation, or esterification. Thus, the specificity of Ags appears to be determined by the chemical structure of small portions of the molecule. Coupling simple chemical groups like $-COOH$, $-SO_3H$, or $-AsO_3H_2$ on a benzene ring with serum protein (by diazo reactions) showed that each of these groups conferred specificity upon the Ag, depending particularly on the position of the radical (ortho-, meta-, or para-) in the aromatic compound.

Ag-Ab reactions are highly specific. Abs usually can distinguish between the homologous Ag (which stimulated their formation) and heterologous, related Ag. The **specificity** of an Ab population depends on its ability to discriminate between Ags of related structure by combining with them to a different extent.

The binding of Ag to Ab does *not* involve covalent bonds but only relatively weak, short-range forces (electrostatic, Coulombic, hydrogen bonding, van der Waals forces, etc). The strength of Ag-Ab bonds depends to a large extent on the closeness of fit between the configuration of the antigenic determinant site and the combining site of the Ab. The combining sites on Ab formed against a given antigenic determinant are not all perfect fits. Any antiserum thus contains some Abs with very close fit and relatively strong binding forces and some with poor fit and weaker binding forces. Abs with the best fit and the strongest binding are said to have high **affinity** for the Ag. They have little tendency to dissociate from Ag after binding it (ie, they have high **avidity**). Abs of low avidity tend to dissociate more readily from Ag. Early in the process of immunization, antibody may have relatively low affinity; as immunization proceeds, antibody of increasingly higher affinity is made.

In spite of the very great antigenic specificity, cross-reactions occur between antigenic determinants of closely related structure and their Abs. The sharing of similar antigenic determinants by molecules of different origin leads to unexpected and unpredictable cross-reactions, eg, between human group A red blood cells and type 14 pneumococci. Many microorganisms share antigens (eg, Haemophilus and *E coli* O75:K100).

When antigenic proteins are denatured by heating or by chemical treatment, the molecular configuration is somewhat changed. This usually results in the loss of the original antigenic determinants and often leads to the uncovering of new antigenic determinants. Formaldehyde-treated proteins acquire an added antigenicity, and their antisera tend to cross-react with other formaldehyde-treated proteins. However, with gentle formaldehyde treatment of toxins, the original antigenicity may also be preserved, whereas the toxicity of the molecule (eg, exotoxins) may be abolished and the molecule thus converted to a "toxoid" which is immunogenic but nontoxic.

Most microorganisms contain not just one but many Ags to each of which Abs may develop in the course of infection. Among these Ags may be capsular polysaccharides, somatic proteins or lipoprotein-carbohydrate complexes, protein exotoxins, and enzymes produced by the organism. All enzymes appear to be antigenic, and in some but not all cases that portion of the molecule which combines with specific Ab appears to be distinct from the portion of the molecule responsible for enzymatic activity. Many hormones are also antigenic.

Alloantigens (Blood Group Substances)

In general, Abs are elicited only by Ags foreign to the injected animal species (heteroantibodies). How-

Table 12–5. Determination of blood group by cross-match.

Group	Ags in Red Cell	Abs in Plasma	Determinant Group of Blood Group Ag
O	. . .	a, b	L-Fucose
A	A	b	*a*-N-Acetyl-galactosaminoyl-galactose
B	B	a	*a*-D-Galactosyl-galactose
AB	AB	. . .	. . .

ever, animals may produce "alloantibodies" against "alloantigens," ie, antigens derived from other individuals of the same species. Outstanding among alloantigens are the blood group substances present in the red cells. There are 4 combinations of the 2 Ags present in erythrocytes. Their presence is under genetic control. The serum contains Ab against the absent Ags. As shown in Table 12–5, Ag and corresponding Ab do not coexist in the same blood. To avoid Ag-Ab reactions which would result in serious transfusion accidents, all bloods must be carefully matched for transfusion.

In addition to these major alloantigens, certain red blood cells contain other blood group substances capable of stimulating antibodies. Among them is the Rh substance. Abs to Rh are developed when an Rh-negative person is transfused with Rh-positive blood or when an Rh-negative pregnant woman absorbs Rh substance from her Rh-positive fetus. The development of high-titer anti-Rh antibodies in this situation can lead to fetal erythroblastosis, abortion, stillbirth, jaundice of the newborn, and other congenital abnormalities.

Apart from certain "sequestered" Ags—eg, thyroid or lens protein—which can definitely serve as autoantigens, it is not clear what may bring about the autoantigenicity of other organ antigens. Perhaps mobilization from the fixed site or slight alteration of structure may predispose to autoimmunization with consequent disease (see Autoimmune Diseases in Chapter 13).

Rate of Absorption & Elimination of Antigen

One of the features which determines the effectiveness of an Ag as a stimulus for antibody production is its rate of absorption and elimination from the site of administration. Ags differ greatly in their rate of excretion, but the major portion of injected Ag is often eliminated from the host within hours or days. In general, Ab response will be higher and more sustained if the Ag is absorbed slowly from its "depot" at the site of injection. For this reason, many immunizing preparations employ physical methods to delay absorption. Toxoids are often adsorbed onto alum, aluminum hydroxide, or aluminum phosphate. Bacterial or viral suspensions are prepared sometimes with adjuvants which delay absorption and promote tissue reaction to "fix" the Ag at its site of injection. (Such adjuvants are discussed in the next chapter.)

Following intravenous injection of a soluble Ag, the following phases in elimination are observed: (1) equilibration between intra- and extravascular compartments; (2) slow degradation of the Ag; (3) rapid immune elimination, as newly formed Ab combines with persisting Ag to form complexes which are phagocytosed by macrophages and digested.

Kinds of Antibodies

Abs are generally described in terms of their reactions with Ag:

A. Antitoxins: Abs to toxins or toxoids which neutralize or flocculate with the antigen.

B. Agglutinins: Abs which aggregate cells, forming clumps. Agglutinins can only be demonstrated if the Ag is particulate or if it is adsorbed onto the surface of a visible particle of uniform size (red blood cell, latex, bentonite, etc).

C. Precipitins: Abs which form complexes with Ag molecules in solution, forming precipitates. Precipitins can only be demonstrated if the Ag is soluble.

D. Lysins: Abs which, usually together with complement, dissolve the antigenic cells.

E. Opsonins: Abs which combine with surface components of microbial and other particles so that they are more readily taken up by phagocytes.

F. Neutralizing (Protective) Abs: Abs which render their antigenic microorganism (commonly viruses) noninfective.

G. Complement-Fixing Abs: Detected by the consumption of complement by the Ag-Ab complex. These reactions are discussed in detail later in the chapter.

H. "Blocking," Inhibitory, and Other Nonprecipitating Abs: These combine with Ag but are not grossly detectable unless they are shown to inhibit or "block" a reaction or unless the protein species of Ab can be identified.

.   .   .

Different types of reactions may sometimes be demonstrated with the same Ag and Ab. Often one reaction may be more efficient than another. In general, Ags are multivalent with respect to Ab. Antibody valence is 2 (for IgG, IgA, IgE) or 5–10 (for IgM). In many reactions, Ag and Ab may combine in multiple proportions (see Danysz Phenomenon).

SEROLOGIC REACTIONS

Serology is the study of reactions between Ags and Abs. It attempts to quantitate these reactions by keeping one reagent constant and diluting the other. Some serologic measurements may be made absolutely quantitative by utilizing the technics of immunochemistry.

Serologic reactions can be used to identify Ags or Abs, if either of these reagents is known. They are also used to estimate the relative quantity of these reactants. Thus, the level or titer of Abs in serum can be determined by means of known Ags, and conclusions can be drawn regarding past contact of the host with the Ag. This is particularly valuable in the diagnosis of infection or of certain forms of hypersensitivity. Conversely, by means of known Abs, the various antigens of a microorganism or other biologic material which characterize it may be identified. Thus, serologic technics permit the definitive identification of microorganisms isolated from an individual with an infection or the classification of red blood cells for blood transfusion or the selection of donor grafts.

The type of Ag-Ab reaction applicable to a given situation depends largely on the physical state of the available Ag (see above). Each of the common types of Ag-Ab reactions is taken up in some detail on the following pages. Because the precipitin reaction permits the most accurate chemical quantitative work, it has been studied in the greatest detail. Some of the characteristics observed in precipitin reactions apply generally to all Ag-Ab reactions.

PRECIPITATION REACTIONS

To demonstrate the presence of Ab against an Ag in solution, the Ag merely has to be layered in a tube over a small volume of antiserum. At the interface of the 2 reagents, precipitation will occur, forming a ring. This gives qualitative evidence of an Ag-Ab reaction, but does not indicate whether one or several Ag-Ab systems are present. If, however, the reaction takes place in a semisolid environment (eg, soft agar), then different Ags and Abs are likely to diffuse at different rates. As a result, optimal proportions for precipitation occur at different sites in the agar and distinct multiple bands of precipitate form. Agar diffusion methods based on this principle (Ouchterlony, Oudin) aid in detecting the number of components in mixtures of Ags or in detecting the identity or diversity of different Ags interacting with a single antibody (Fig 12–5). Agar diffusion can be combined with electrophoretic separation of proteins for their identification (see p 140).

In order to titrate the precipitin content of a serum, serial dilutions of the serum are mixed with a constant amount of Ag (as in most other serologic reactions) or a constant amount of serum is mixed with increasing dilutions of Ag. The latter method is generally preferred because precipitation reactions are markedly inhibited by excess Ag. The precipitin content of the serum is then expressed as the greatest

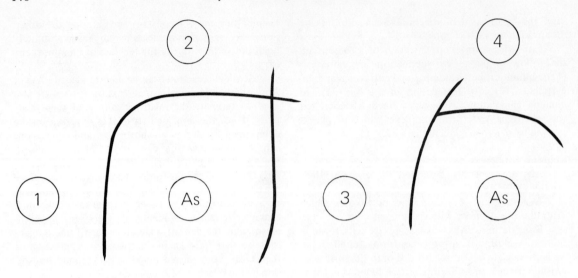

As = Antiserum in wells
1, 2, 3, 4 = Antigen in wells

1 and 2 = Reaction of identity
2 and 3 = Reaction of nonidentity
3 and 4 = Reaction of partial identity (cross-reaction; the "spur" is caused by the fraction of Ab which was not precipitated by Ag 4)

Figure 12—5. Double diffusion precipitin reactions in gel.

dilution of Ag precipitated. Precipitin reactions require the presence of salt, and the pH must be near neutrality. The reaction rate is faster at higher temperatures, but the maximum amount of precipitate is formed at cold temperatures.

Example of Reaction

Serum is obtained from an animal which has been injected repeatedly with a pure Ag solution (eg, crystalline egg albumin). Equal amounts of serum (eg, 1 ml) are distributed into a series of small tubes. To each tube is added a variable graded amount of the Ag (egg albumin), and the tubes are then left at 0° C for 2 hours. At the end of this period, some tubes contain a precipitate and others do not (Table 12—6). This precipitate can be sedimented by centrifugation, washed repeatedly with saline to remove adherent serum, and then analyzed for nitrogen content.

The supernatant from each tube is decanted and distributed into 2 tubes. To one of these is added antigen; to the other, antibody. The occurrence of precipitate in these tubes of supernatant permits 3 zones to be distinguished (see Fig 12—6 and Table 12—6).

(1) A zone of Ab excess, in which uncombined antibody is present.

(2) A zone of equivalence, in which both Ag and Ab are completely precipitated and no uncombined Ag or Ab is present. In this zone there is also maximal complement fixation.

(3) A zone of Ag excess, in which all Ab has combined with Ag and additional uncombined Ag is present. In this zone, precipitation is partly or completely inhibited because soluble Ag-Ab complexes form in the presence of excess Ag.

Micro-Kjeldahl determinations for total nitrogen are then made on the washed precipitate. The precipi-

Table 12—6. Examples of precipitation reactions.

Tube	Serum (ml)	Egg Albumin (mg)	Resulting Precipitation	Test on Supernatant (Zone Formation)	Area of Fig 12—6
1	1	0.015	Minimal	Excess Ab	A. Zone of antibody excess
2	1	0.030	Slight	Excess Ab	
3	1	0.060	Heavy	Slight excess Ab	B. Zone of equivalence
4	1	0.090	Heavy	Neither Ag nor Ab	
5	1	0.120	Heavy	Slight excess Ag	
6	1	0.180	Slight	Excess Ag	C. Zone of antigen excess
7	1	0.240	None	Large excess Ag	

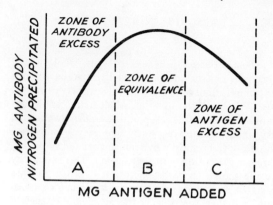

Figure 12–6. The main zones of antigen-antibody interaction.

tate contains both Ab nitrogen and Ag nitrogen. Therefore, the amount of Ab nitrogen contained in the serum (and precipitated completely in the zone of equivalence) can be accurately determined by subtracting the Ag nitrogen added to the tube from the total nitrogen value of the precipitate.

The field of immunochemistry provides methods for absolute quantitative measurement of Ab which can be applied to a large variety of theoretical and practical problems.*

The initial combination of Ag and Ab takes place almost immediately upon mixing of the reactants. The subsequent formation of larger, visible aggregates requires an hour or more and depends somewhat on the temperature and the total volume of the mixture. The reaction is fastest in the zone of equivalence, where optimal proportions between Ag and Ab exist. The speed of gross precipitation is an index of the zone of equivalence, where complete precipitation of both Ag and Ab takes place and neither is present in excess.

Precipitation in gels can be adapted for the quantitation of soluble Ags and Abs. Thus, radial diffusion of immunoglobulins permits their quantitation in an agar containing specific Ab. The diameter of the precipitated ring around a globulin-containing disk under standard conditions can be measured and compared to a known globulin.

gate and finally settle as large, visible clumps, leaving the supernatant clear. If one of the reagents is known, the reaction may be employed for the identification of either Ag or Ab. Thus, the reaction is commonly used to identify, by means of known antisera, microorganisms cultured from clinical specimens. The agglutination reaction is also used to estimate the titer of antibacterial agglutinins in the serum of patients with unknown disease. A rise in Ab titer directed against a specific microorganism occurring during an illness strongly suggests an etiologic relationship.

Microorganisms possess a variety of antigens, and antibodies to one or more of these may be present in antiserum. A simple example is provided by the antibody response to infection by flagellated bacteria. Antibodies may be directed against the flagellar surface antigen, the somatic antigens, or both. The type of macroscopic agglutination may also be distinctive; the flagellar Ag-Ab complex appears coarse and floccular, whereas the somatic complex appears fine and granular.

The agglutination reaction is aided by elevated temperature (37–56° C) and by movement, which increases the contact between Ag and Ab (eg, shaking, stirring, centrifuging). The aggregation of clumps requires the presence of salts. In the zone of Ab excess (ie, concentrated serum), agglutination may be inhibited owing to the presence of blocking Ab. This prozone may give the unwarranted impression that Abs are absent; this error can be avoided only by using serial dilutions of serum.

The agglutination test may be performed microscopically by mixing a loopful of serum with a suspension of microorganisms on a slide and inspecting the result through the low-power objective. This is commonly done for the identification of unknown cultures. For the estimation of the "titer" of agglutinating Ab in an unknown serum, a macroscopic tube dilution test is usually done: A suitable fixed amount of Ag is added to each tube of a series of serum dilutions, and, after thorough shaking, the tubes are incubated at 37° C for 1–2 hours. The result is determined by looking for sedimented clumps and clear supernatant fluid. The "titer" of the serum is the highest dilution with clearly visible agglutination.

AGGLUTINATION REACTIONS

The Ag in agglutination reactions is particulate and commonly consists of suspensions of microorganisms, cells (eg, red blood cells), or uniform particles like latex or bentonite onto which Ags have been adsorbed. When mixed with specific antiserum, these cells or particles become clumped; the clumps aggre-

THE ANTIGLOBULIN (COOMBS) TEST

This is an indirect agglutination test for the detection of blocking or incomplete Abs. Such Abs are by themselves incapable of agglutinating particles but can bind to them firmly. By adding an Ab against the globulin species (eg, antihuman globulin prepared in rabbits), agglutination of the coated particles results. This test has found greatest application in the detection of various anti-red blood cell Abs in hemolytic anemias.

*The technics, accomplishments, and possibilities of immunochemistry are discussed in Kabat EA: *Kabat & Mayer's Experimental Immunochemistry,* 2nd ed. Thomas, 1971.

TOXIN-ANTITOXIN REACTIONS

The toxin-antitoxin reactions described below apply only to exotoxins, as exemplified by the toxins of diphtheria, tetanus, or botulism. The following examples of definitions of units apply to diphtheria toxin:

International Unit of antitoxin (IU): The amount of antitoxin in 0.0628 mg of a standard dried antitoxin maintained at the Serum Institute, Copenhagen.

L+ dose: The smallest amount of toxin which, when mixed with 1 unit of antitoxin and injected subcutaneously into a guinea pig weighing 250 gm, will cause death within 4 days.

Lf dose (flocculating unit): That amount of toxin which flocculates most rapidly with 1 unit of antitoxin in a series of mixtures containing constant amounts of antitoxin and varying amounts of toxin. (This value is calculated from experimental results.)

Antitoxic potency can be measured by the ability to neutralize the toxin when the mixture is injected into animals or to precipitate toxin in vitro.

Any preparation of toxin contains some molecules of full toxicity and others of low or no toxicity but persistent antigenicity (toxoid). Dried antitoxin, however, is constant in its ability to combine with toxin or toxoid molecules. For this reason, antitoxin is taken as the constant standard for biologic estimation of toxic or antitoxic potency. The L+ dose is usually relied upon. The Lf unit is independent of the toxic activity of a given preparation and is only a function of its antigenic combining power. Thus, it remains constant when a toxin is converted to toxoid by formalin or heat. It is of great importance in the standardization of antigenic quantities of toxoid.

Toxin-antitoxin flocculations are similar to precipitin reactions but show a very sharp zone of equivalence. The reaction is inhibited by both Ag excess and Ab excess; soluble complexes result from either.

Danysz Phenomenon

If toxin is added to antitoxin in several fractions with time intervals between them, then more antitoxin (or less toxin) is necessary to give a neutral endpoint in injected animals than if all the toxin had been added at once. This was explained by the ability of toxin to combine with antitoxin in multiple proportions. The first fraction of toxin combines with a relatively large amount of the antitoxin present, so that little antitoxin is left to combine with the second fraction. After some time, however, an equilibrium is again reached. The Danysz phenomenon applies similarly to other Ag-Ab reactions, where the dissociation of Ag-Ab complexes is slow.

ABSORPTION REACTIONS

Sera from animals injected with whole microorganisms or from humans who have passed through several infections tend to react with a variety of related Ags. This raises the question whether the serum contains an Ab specific for a given Ag or merely a related Ab which cross-reacts. Such sera may be rendered specific for one antigen by removing related antibodies through absorption with specific Ags. This is done by mixing the serum with concentrated Ag (eg, a dense bacterial suspension), incubating to permit combination, and then centrifuging the precipitate or agglutinated material and removing the supernatant serum. It is now "absorbed" and should no longer contain Abs specific for the absorbing Ag. Such absorptions may be performed with a series of Ags, finally leaving a serum which will react only with a single remaining Ag for which it is highly specific. This is valuable in "antigenic analysis" of bacteria and other biologic substances.

INHIBITION REACTIONS

In addition to various direct methods of demonstrating and measuring Ag-Ab reactions discussed above, some indirect methods exist which, in essence, use competition for an antibody combining site by 2 antigenic groups or competition for an antigenic group by 2 antibodies. They are especially useful when there is no visible evidence of direct reaction between Ag and Ab. Several of these methods are yielding important information regarding the size of the Ab combining site and the structure of antigenic groups. *Examples:* Inhibition of precipitation by nonprecipitating Ab or by a fragment of digested Ab; inhibition of viral hemagglutination by Ab; inhibition of the Prausnitz-Küstner reaction by blocking Ab.

IMMUNOFLUORESCENCE
(Fluorescent Antibody Tests, FA)

Certain fluorescent dyes (eg, fluorescein isothiocyanate, rhodamine) can be firmly attached to globulin molecules and thus made visible by using ultraviolet light in the fluorescence microscope. If such fluorescent dyes are conjugated with Ab molecules and all excess is carefully eliminated, such "labeled" Ab may be used to locate and identify specific Ag because of the high specificity of the Ag-Ab bond. By means of such "direct immunofluorescence reactions," bacteria may be identified and viral or other Ags may be located inside cells. In bacteriologic diagnosis, specific direct immunofluorescence is valuable for the rapid identification of group A hemolytic streptococci, of *Treponema pallidum,* and other organisms. In special laboratories, immunofluorescence has been applied to the rapid screening of enteric pathogens, of bacteria causing childhood meningitis, and others.

The "indirect immunofluorescence reactions" involve 3 reagents: Ag + its Ab A + a fluorescent-labeled Ab to Ab A. Any one of the 3 reagents can be unknown. For example, in the serodiagnosis of syphilis, *T pallidum* Ag fixed to a slide is overlaid with the patient's unknown serum and then washed. Fluorescein-labeled antihuman globulin (made in an animal) is then placed on the preparation, which is examined by ultraviolet light. If the patient's serum contains specific Abs to *T pallidum,* brightly fluorescent spirochetes are seen. If the spirochetes do not fluoresce, no specific antitreponemal Abs are present. (See FTA Test in Chapter 20.)

Immunofluorescence can be used for the detection of viral and bacterial Ags or Abs, tumor Ags, and many others. The indirect test is often more sensitive than the direct immunofluorescence test because more fluorescein-labeled antibodies adhere per antigenic site.

RADIOIMMUNOASSAY

Radioimmunoassays are the most sensitive and versatile methods for the quantitation of substances which are Ags or haptens and can be radioactively labeled. Radioimmunoassay is particularly applicable to the measurement of serum levels of many hormones, drugs, and other biologic materials. The method is based on competition for specific Ab between the labeled (known) and the unlabeled (unknown) concentration of the material. The complexes which form between Ag (or hapten) and Ab can then be separated and the amount of radioactivity determined. The concentration of the unknown (unlabeled) Ag is determined by comparison with the effect of standards.

OTHER TYPES OF SEROLOGIC REACTIONS

Protection or Neutralization (Nt) Tests

These are widely employed in the determination of antiviral and a few antibacterial antibodies. They utilize the ability of Ab-containing sera to block the infectivity of these agents upon inoculation of the mixture into susceptible hosts.

Immobilization Tests for *Treponema pallidum*

These tests (TPI) detect true antibodies against this organism in the serum of infected persons. The test consists of mixing serum with fresh, motile spirochetes from a rabbit chancre and observing their loss of motility in the darkfield microscope. Similar tests can demonstrate the immune adherence of spirochetes to the surface of red blood cells in the presence of specific antibody.

Opsonophagocytic Tests

In these tests, phagocytic cells from the patient (especially polymorphonuclears) are mixed with viable bacteria of certain species, or with yeasts, in the presence of serum to observe the rate of ingestion and (by subculture) the rate of intracellular killing. By means of such tests, defects in cellular immunity are studied (see Phagocytosis in Chapter 11). Polymorphonuclear cells from patients with specific deficiencies in phagocytosis and intracellular killing (eg, chronic granulomatous disease) also give abnormally depressed responses in the nitroblue tetrazolium dye test (see Chapter 11).

Ferritin-Labeled Antibody Technic

Electron-dense ferritin can be conjugated with Ab molecules which become visible in the electron microscope. This permits localization of Ag in cells and ultrathin sections examined by electron microscopy.

Hemagglutination Tests, Active & Passive

Red blood cells from various animal species may be clumped by certain viruses. This "active hemagglutination" can be specifically inhibited by Ab to virus, and the hemagglutination inhibition is a convenient serologic test. Red cells also present a convenient surface onto which many types of Ags can be adsorbed. Such coated cells will clump when mixed with Abs to these specific Ags ("passive hemagglutination"). Other convenient particles such as latex or bentonite may substitute for red cells. An IgM in the serum of most rheumatoid patients can be measured by a hemagglutination reaction. Red cells coated with human IgG will be clumped by this IgM "rheumatoid factor." Clinically applicable serologic tests for the diagnosis of infection are listed in Chapter 26.

THE COMPLEMENT SYSTEM

The term complement (C) denotes a complex system of proteins and other factors found in normal serum of vertebrates. Some components have enzymatic activity; others are enhancers or inhibitors. Activation of the complement sequence of reactions may occur by the "classic" pathway set off by Ag-Ab reactions or by the "alternative" pathway ("bypass") which does not require Ag-Ab reactions. The sequence of reactions can lead to the production of biologically active factors (eg, chemotactic factors), to damage of cell membranes (eg, lysis of cells), or to various pathologic processes (eg, nephrotoxic nephritis).

The steps in the complement reaction sequence can most easily be illustrated by the events leading to cell lysis. In the sequence shown below, E represents a cell membrane carrying an antigenic site (either an intrinsic or artificially attached Ag) and A represents an Ab to that Ag.

Complement of guinea pigs and humans has been

(1) $E + A \longrightarrow EA$

(2) $EA + C\overline{1} \xrightarrow{Ca^{++}} EAC\overline{1}$. ($C\overline{1}$ represents the activated form of C1 with enzyme activity; Ca^{++} is required for the stability of the complex.)

(3) $EAC\overline{1} + C4 \longrightarrow EAC\overline{1,4}$. (The $C\overline{1}$ enzyme, an esterase, has cleaved C4 and C2, part of which attached to the activated complex or the cell membrane.)

(4) $EAC\overline{1,4}, + C2 \xrightarrow{Mg^{++}} EAC\overline{1,4,2}$. ($Mg^{++}$ is required for stability of the activated complex; the C4,2 moiety is an enzyme, C3 convertase, active in next step.)

Alternative
pathway

(5) $EAC\overline{1,4,2} + C3 \longrightarrow EAC\overline{1,4,2,3} + C3$ fragments with activity of **anaphylatoxin and chemotaxis**. (Cleavage of C3 occurs either by C3 convertase in the classic pathway or by C3 activator in the alternate pathway.)

(6) $EAC\overline{1,4,2,3} + C5,C6,C7 \longrightarrow EAC\overline{1,4,2,3,5,6,7} + C5$ fragments with **anaphylatoxin** activity. (The C5,6,7 complex on the cell membrane is **chemotactic** for polymorphonuclear leukocytes.)

(7) $EAC\overline{1,4,2,3,5,6,7} + C8,C9 \longrightarrow EAC\ \overline{1-9}$. (The final complex results in membrane damage ["holes"], cell damage, or lysis.)

studied most extensively. At present, at least 11 distinct components of guinea pig complement are recognized. Complement must either be kept frozen or used in the form of fresh serum to avoid deterioration of some components. On heating at 56° C, activity is lost completely in 30 minutes. The most heat-sensitive components are C1, C2, C5, C6, C8, and C9. Complement activity depends upon the ionic strength of the medium, pH (optimum 7.2–7.4), volume (inverse relationship), temperature (optimum 30–37° C), and the presence of Ca^{++} (see step 2, below) and Mg^{++} (step 4).

Different animal sera contain different proportions of the various complement components. The component which is lowest in titer or activity in a given serum limits the hemolytic complement activity of that serum. C1 exists in serum as an aggregate of 3 proteins: C1q, C1r, and C1s. C1q can attach to Ag-Ab complexes or to certain aggregated immunoglobulins (eg, IgM, IgG-1) without any activation. All other components are converted one after another from inactive to activated forms. The final step in cytolysis requires only the production of a single membrane lesion induced by complement action.

Alternative Pathway of Complement Activation

While the "classic" pathway depends on starting the reaction sequence by C1q attaching to Ag-Ab complexes, another pathway exists for activating complement-mediated reactions. A variety of substances can bring about the formation of a C3 activator which cleaves C3 in a fashion analogous to that of C3 convertase in the classic pathway. This "alternative pathway" then proceeds C3–C9, as in the classic pathway shown above. Polysaccharides, lipopolysaccharides, and some immunoglobulin aggregates (eg, IgA, IgE,

IgG-4 which do *not* initiate the complement sequence via C1q) activate the **properdin** system as an alternative pathway of complement activation.

The properdin system consists of a unique serum protein (properdin), a glycine-rich beta-glycoprotein (C3 proactivator), and other serum proteins. The activation of this system culminates in cleavage of C3. The reaction sequence then proceeds as in the classic pathway. The properdin system can enhance resistance to gram-negative infections; it is involved in the lysis of erythrocytes from patients with paroxysmal nocturnal hemoglobinuria. The properdin system can also participate in the mediation of immunologic injury (eg, nephritis) and may be defective in sickle cell anemia.

There are other activators of the alternative pathway. Proteolytic enzymes released from lysosomes of phagocytic cells can cleave C3; other proteolytic enzymes involved in the blood coagulation cascade or produced by bacteria can do likewise.

COMPLEMENT-MEDIATED REACTIONS

Immune Hemolysis & Cytolysis

The production of membrane injury of red blood cells by complement acting on Ag-Ab complexes on the membrane is the basis for a sensitive serologic test, the complement fixation (CF) test (see below). Many other types of cells (lymphocytes, tumor cells, etc) are also subject to immune cytolysis.

Some gram-negative bacteria and spirochetes coated with specific Ab go through the sequence of steps (1–7) shown above and exhibit bacteriolysis. It is not clear how often this reaction plays any role in host defenses. Cytolytic reactions may at times cause injury to normal tissues in allergic vasculitis or glomerulitis.

Chemotaxis

Complement bound by Ag-Ab complexes releases chemotactic factors and attracts leukocytes which in turn release lysosomal enzymes and thus cause damage to tissues.

Fragments of C3, C5, and the C5,6,7 complex also attract leukocytes. This may aid in the localization and inactivation of infectious agents or may enhance tissue injury (see step 2, above). This chemotaxis is depressed by alcohol and in cirrhotic patients. Complement components are found attached to Ag-Ab complexes in "complex" diseases, eg, on synovial membranes in rheumatoid arthritis or on glomerular basement membranes in nephritis (see p 158).

Immune Adherence & Opsonization

Fragments of C3 and C5 promote the adherence of Ag-Ab complexes to leukocytes or platelets and the phagocytosis of opsonized (Ab-coated) microorganisms by leukocytes and macrophages.

Anaphylatoxin Effect

Fragments of C3 and C5 can produce degranulation of mast cells with the release of histamine and other mediators. This results in symptoms of vasodilatation, increased capillary permeability, bronchospasm, and others resembling anaphylaxis.

Hereditary Angioedema

Persons with this disorder are deficient in a normal C1 (esterase) inhibitor (a glycoprotein). Consequently, their serum intermittently has increased C1, activity which liberates a vasoactive kinin from C2. This kinin produces acute, transient local accumulations of edema fluid. C1 activation can be prevented by aminocaproic acid or tranexamic acid (1 gm orally 3 times daily).

Low Serum Complement Levels

Low serum complement levels—particularly low C3—are encountered in Ag-Ab complex diseases such as lupus erythematosus and acute glomerulonephritis and in cryoglubulinemia.

Hereditary Deficiencies

Hereditary deficiency of certain complement components may lead to increased susceptibility to infection, while lack of other components is without obvious effect.

THE COMPLEMENT FIXATION TEST

Complement fixation (CF) tests depend upon 2 distinct reactions. The first involves Ag and Ab (of which one is known, the other unknown) plus a fixed amount of pretitrated complement. If Ag and Ab are specific for one another, they will combine; the combination will take up ("fix") the added complement. The second reaction involves testing for the presence of free (unattached) complement. This is done by the addition of red cells "sensitized" with specific hemolysin. If complement has been "fixed" by the Ag-Ab complex, then none will be available for lysis of the sensitized red cells. If the antigen and antibody are *not* specific for each other, or if one of them is lacking, then complement remains free to attach to the sensitized red cells and lyse them. Therefore, a positive CF test gives no hemolysis; a negative test gives hemolysis. This can be written schematically as follows:

I. Specific Ag X + Complement ⟶ Complement not bound

II. Specific Ab anti-X + Complement ⟶ Complement not bound

III. X + Anti-X + Complement ⟶ Complement bound ("fixed")

To detect whether complement is bound or not bound, a hemolytic system (see below) of red blood cells (RBC) + anti-RBC antibody (Ab) is added to each of the mixtures I, II, and III, with these results:

I + RBC + Ab ⟶ Lysis of RBC = Negative test

II + RBC + Ab ⟶ Lysis of RBC = Negative test

III + RBC + Ab ⟶ No lysis of RBC = Positive test

A positive test occurs only if X and anti-X have combined to bind available complement. If Ag (X) does not match specific Ab (Y), no complex will be formed, no complement will be consumed, and lysis of added red cells indicates a negative test. If either Ag X alone or Ab anti-X alone (I or II) inactivates complement, they are unsatisfactory for the test and are called anticomplementary. Anticomplementary Ags or

Table 12-7. Recommended schedule for active immunization and skin testing of children.

Age	Product Administered	Test Recommended
2-3 months	DTP[1]	
	Oral poliovaccine[2], trivalent	
4-5 months	DTP	
	Oral poliovaccine, trivalent	
6-7 months	DTP	
	Oral poliovaccine, trivalent	
12 months	Measles vaccine[3]	
15-19 months	Smallpox vaccine[4] (elective)	Read primary take of
	DTP	smallpox after 1 week
	Oral poliovaccine, trivalent	
2 years	Mumps vaccine[5]	Tuberculin test[6]
4-6 years	DTP	Tuberculin test[6]
	Smallpox vaccine (elective)	
	Oral poliovaccine, trivalent	
8-10 years	Rubella vaccine[7]	Tuberculin test[6]
12-14 years	Td[8]	Tuberculin test[6]
	Smallpox vaccine (elective)	

[1] **DTP**: Toxoids of diphtheria and tetanus, alum-precipitated or aluminum hydroxide adsorbed, combined with pertussis bacterial antigen. Suitable for young children. Three doses of 0.5 ml IM at intervals of 4-8 weeks. Fourth injection of 0.5 ml IM given about 1 year later.

[2] **Oral live poliomeylitis virus vaccine**: Trivalent vaccine given 3 times at intervals of 6-8 weeks and then as a booster 1 year later. Monovalent live vaccine rarely used. Inactive (Salk type) trivalent vaccine is available but not recommended.

[3] **Live measles virus vaccine**, 0.5 ml IM. When using attenuated (Edmonston) strain, give human gamma globulin, 0.01 ml/lb, injected into the opposite arm at the same time, to lessen the reaction to the vaccine. This is not advised with "further attenuated" (Schwarz) strain vaccine. Inactivated measles vaccine should not be used.

[4] **Live smallpox vaccine (vaccinia virus)**, usually supplied as calf lymph or embryonated egg material, must be used fresh, before the expiration date, and must be stored at low temperature. It is administered by multiple pressure technic. Site must be inspected at 7 days for evidence of "primary take" or at 3-4 days for evidence of "accelerated reaction." Some vesicles must be found to indicate immunizing proliferation of virus. Papules without vesication are not acceptable as evidence of "take." Do not vaccinate in the presence of eczema in the child or his siblings, during pregnancy, or when there is known immunologic deficiency. The US Public Health Service recommends that routine smallpox vaccination be abandoned in the USA because the risk of contracting the disease is less than the risk of complications from vaccination. Smallpox vaccination should be limited to those who may travel to places where smallpox has not been eradicated and to health personnel.

[5] **Live mumps virus vaccine (attenuated)**, 0.5 ml IM.

[6] The frequency with which **tuberculin tests** are administered depends on the risk of exposure, ie, the prevalence of tuberculosis in the population group.

[7] **Rubella live virus vaccine (attenuated)** can be given between age 1 year and puberty. Some physicians recommend rubella vaccine only for prepubertal girls. The entire contents of a single-dose vaccine vial, reconstituted from the lyophilized state, are injected subcutaneously. The vaccine must **not** be given to women who are pregnant or likely to become pregnant within 3 months of vaccination. Adult women must also be warned that there is a 40% likelihood of developing arthralgias and arthritis (presumably self-limited) within 4 weeks of vaccination.

[8] **Tetanus toxoid and diphtheria toxoid**, purified, suitable for adults.

sera are detected by suitable controls in the test. Anti-complementary activity can sometimes be removed by heating or dilution.

For the practical performance of the test, it is necessary to control all reagents and environmental conditions carefully. In order to eliminate any complement that might be present in the serum used as source of Ab, all sera must be inactivated by heating for 30 minutes at 56° C. To the Ag and the inactivated serum, a carefully titrated amount of complement is added (usually 1.2-2 units). The mixture is then left at 37° C or in the refrigerator for a specified time to permit interaction of Ag and Ab and "fixation" of complement. Next, the "hemolytic system" is added; this consists generally of a suspension of sheep red cells "sensitized" by the addition of hemolysin (ie, anti-

sheep rabbit serum). The mixture is then incubated at 37° C for 30 minutes and read for hemolysis.

Specific and detailed directions regarding concentrations and amounts of reagents, time and temperature of "fixation," nature of buffer, etc must be followed for each individual CF test. Complete controls must be included in each test.

If properly controlled, the CF test is among the most sensitive and delicate of all the serologic reactions employed in the diagnostic microbiology laboratory. It is used for the identification of antibody and estimation of its titer (with known antigens) or the identification of antigens (with known antibody). The serologic diagnosis of many viral and fungal infections and of some immunologic disorders rests on CF tests (see Chapter 29).

• • •

RECOMMENDED IMMUNIZATION OF ADULTS FOR TRAVEL

Every adult, whether traveling or not, must be immunized with tetanus toxoid. Purified toxoid "for adult use" must be used to avoid reactions. Every adult should also receive primary vaccination for poliomyelitis (oral live trivalent vaccine), for diphtheria (use purified toxoid "for adult use"), and, if traveling, for smallpox. Every traveler must fulfill the immunization requirements of the health authorities of different countries. These are listed in *Health Information for International Travel,* US Public Health Service Publication No. 2045.

The following are suggestions for travel in different parts of the world.

Tetanus

Booster injection of 0.5 ml tetanus toxoid, for adult use, every 7–10 years, assuming completion of primary immunization. (All countries.)

Smallpox

Revaccination with live smallpox vaccine (vaccinia virus) by multiple pressure method every 3 years. WHO certificate requires registration of batch number of vaccine. The physician should ascertain a "take" by observing vesicle formation after administration of either liquid or freeze-dried effective vaccine. (Many countries.) A valid certificate is required in the USA only of arrivals from an area where smallpox is still endemic, but it is required in some other countries at all times.

Typhoid

Suspension of killed *Salmonella typhi.* For pri-

mary immunization, inject 0.5 ml subcut (0.25 ml for children under 10 years) twice at an interval of 4–6 weeks. For booster, inject 0.5 ml subcut (or 0.1 ml intradermally) every 3 years. (All countries.)

Paratyphoid vaccines are not recommended and are probably ineffective at present.

Yellow Fever

Live attenuated yellow fever virus, 0.5 ml subcut. WHO certificate requires registration of batch number of vaccine. Vaccination available in USA only at approved centers. Vaccination must be repeated at intervals of 10 years or less. (Africa, South America.)

Cholera

Suspension of killed vibrios, including prevalent antigenic types. Two injections of 0.5 and 1 ml are given IM 4–6 weeks apart. This must be followed by 0.5 ml booster injections every 6 months during periods of possible exposure. Protection depends largely on booster doses. WHO certificate is valid for 6 months only. (Middle Eastern countries, Asia, occasionally others.)

Plague

Suspension of killed plague bacilli given IM, 2 injections of 0.5 ml each, 4–6 weeks apart, and a third injection 4–12 weeks later. (Middle Eastern countries, Asia, occasionally South America and others.)

Typhus

Suspension of inactivated typhus rickettsiae given subcut, 2 injections of 0.5 ml each, 4–6 weeks apart. Booster doses of 0.5 ml every 6 months may be necessary. (Southeastern Europe, Africa, South America.)

Hepatitis

No active immunization available. Temporary passive immunity may be induced by the IM injection of human gamma globulin, 0.02 ml/kg every 2–3 months.

● ● ●

General References

Bloch KJ & others: Gamma heavy chain disease. Am J Med 55:61, 1973.

Edelman GM: Antibody structure and molecular immunology. Science 180:830, 1973.

Flick JA: Human reagins: Antibody of immediate-type hypersensitivity. Bacteriol Rev 36:311, 1972.

Franklin EC, Frangione B: Immunoglobulins. Annu Rev Med 20:155, 1969.

Fudenberg HH & others: *Basic Immunogenetics.* Oxford Univ Press, 1972.

Gell PGH, Coombs RRA, Lachmann PJ (editors): *Clinical Aspects of Immunology,* 3rd ed. Blackwell, 1974.

Götz O, Müller-Eberhard HJ: Paroxysmal nocturnal hemoglobinuria: Hemolysis initiated by the C3 activator system. N Engl J Med 286:180, 1972.

Kubo RT & others: IgD, an immunoglobulin on the surface of lymphocytes. J Immunol 112:1952, 1974.

Levin WC (editor): Symposium on myeloma. Arch Intern Med 135:27, 1975.

Pensky J & others: Properties of highly purified human properdin. J Immunol 100:142, 1968.

Rowlands DT Jr, Daniele RP: Surface receptors in the immune response. N Engl J Med 293:26, 1975.

Ruddy S & others: The complement system of man. N Engl J Med 287:642, 1972.

Tomasi TB: Secretory immunoglobulins. N Engl J Med 287:500, 1972.

Wybran J, Fudenberg HH: Thymus-derived rosette-forming cells in various human disease states. J Clin Invest 52:1026, 1973.

13...
Immunology: II.
Antibody-Mediated & Cell-Mediated
(Hypersensitivity & Immunity) Reactions

ANTIBODY-MEDIATED HYPERSENSITIVITY

The principal mechanism in a majority of antibody-mediated hypersensitivity reactions is the combination of antibody (Ab) with antigen (Ag) to form complexes which stimulate certain cells to release a variety of mediators. The main reactions in this category are of the anaphylaxis and serum sickness type. Interactions between Ab and red blood cell or platelet Ag usually do not involve the release of mediators.

ANAPHYLAXIS

The experimental demonstration of anaphylaxis involves the following steps:

(1) **Sensitization**: An adequate sensitizing dose of antigen must be absorbed. In the guinea pig, as little as 0.1 μg of a soluble protein is sufficient.

(2) **Waiting period**: A waiting period of 2–3 weeks is required. During this period, cytotropic antibody (in guinea pigs, IgE and some IgG) attaches to mast cells and basophilic leukocytes.

(3) **"Eliciting injection"**: The rapid intravenous injection of a massive dose (0.1–10 mg) of the same antigen as used for sensitization permits the antigen to combine with cell-bound antibody rapidly. The complex stimulates the prompt release of mediators which set off the symptoms of anaphylaxis (eg, bronchospasm) within 3–5 minutes.

(4) **Passive transfer**: If serum is taken after the waiting period (2) from the sensitized animal and injected into the skin of a normal animal, the injected site becomes sensitized in 24 hours (ie, homocytotropic antibodies attach to mast cells and basophils). When Ag is given intravenously to such an animal together with a dye (eg, Evans blue), a local anaphylactic reaction at the sensitized site results in a marked increase in capillary permeability which permits the dye to stain the sensitized area of skin. This **passive cutaneous anaphylaxis** is suitable for quantitation of some anaphylactic events.

Anaphylactic reactivity in man manifests itself as systemic, generalized anaphylaxis or as local anaphylaxis involving skin or respiratory tract or other target tissue.

Generalized anaphylaxis in man begins within 5–30 minutes after administration of the inciting agent with flush, urticaria, paroxysmal cough, dyspnea, wheezing, vomiting, cyanosis, circulatory collapse, and shock. Major causes of death are laryngeal edema, massive airway edema, and cardiac arrhythmias. Major causes of generalized anaphylaxis in man are drugs (eg, penicillins), biologicals (eg, animal sera), insect stings (eg, bee, wasp), and foods (eg, shellfish).

Local anaphylaxis in man begins within a few minutes after contact (inhalation, ingestion) between the responsible antigen and the sensitive shock organ and manifests itself commonly as hay fever, asthma, urticaria, or vomiting. About 10% of the population are prone to become spontaneously sensitized to various environmental Ags (allergens), eg, pollens of ragweed, grasses, or trees, foods, and animal danders. These individuals develop allergic reactions **(atopy)** when exposed to the Ag. There is a marked familial predisposition to this type of disorder, but each individual must become sensitized to the specific allergen before manifesting atopic reactions.

Cutaneous anaphylaxis is seen in the skin test for immediate-type hypersensitivity. Two or 3 minutes after 0.1 ml of Ag is injected intracutaneously (often into the flexor surface of the forearm), itching begins at the site, followed by an elevated, blanched irregular wheal surrounded by a zone of erythema ("flare"). This hive (urticarial reaction) reaches a maximum in 10–15 minutes and subsides within less than 1 hour.

Mechanism of Anaphylaxis

As a result of the original sensitization with Ag, specialized, cytotropic Ab is formed which binds to mast cells and basophils, especially in skin and mucous membranes of the respiratory tract. In man, the cytotropic Ab is IgE. When the same Ag is again absorbed, it reaches these cells and results in aggregation of IgE molecules bound to mast cell surfaces by their Fc fragment. This is the stimulus for the release of pharmacologically active chemical mediators from the cell. Aggregated Fc fragments of IgE proteins can also elicit a cell release of mediators even without the presence of

Ag. Large amounts of soluble Ag-Ab complexes which are capable of binding complement can also evoke anaphylaxis under special circumstances.

Pharmacologically Active Chemical Mediators

Pharmacologically active chemical mediators released during anaphylaxis include the following:

Histamine (formed by decarboxylation of histidine) occurs in platelets and in granules of tissue mast cells and basophils, cells which—in man—bind IgE through special sites of the Fc fragment. The histamine released as a result of anaphylaxis results in vasodilatation, increased capillary permeability (edema), and smooth muscle contraction. The relative amount of histamine and of other mediators determines the efficacy of antihistamine drugs in controlling local anaphylaxis. Antihistamines are relatively effective in allergic rhinitis, relatively ineffective in asthma (in which much more SRS-A [see below] is released than histamine).

Serotonin (5-hydroxytryptamine, formed by decarboxylation of tryptophan) occurs mainly in blood platelets and is released from them during anaphylaxis. It dilates capillaries, increases their permeability, and contracts smooth muscle.

Kinins are basic peptides derived from plasma proteins by enzymatic action. Hageman factor in the blood clotting cascade is activated by various substances (eg, Ag-Ab complexes, endotoxins). One of the resulting products, plasmin, activates an enzyme, kallikrein, which splits the basic peptide bradykinin from an alpha globulin in plasma. Bradykinin levels in blood increase in anaphylaxis and cause vasodilatation, increased capillary permeability, and smooth muscle contraction. Other kinins also participate in anaphylactic reactions.

Slow reacting substance (SRS-A) is an acidic lipid released mainly from lung during anaphylaxis. It causes marked smooth muscle contraction and bronchospasm and is not inhibited by antihistamines. The relatively large amount of SRS-A—compared to histamine—in asthma accounts for the virtual lack of effect of antihistamines in that condition.

Other mediators, including prostaglandins, have been implicated in anaphylaxis. Cellular levels of cyclic AMP probably are important regulators of the release of active mediators in anaphylaxis and may explain the influence of emotional states on the intensity of acute allergic reactions.

The chemical mediators are active for only a few minutes after release. Histamine, serotonin, and bradykinin are enzymatically inactivated, whereas SRS-A is removed by adsorption onto tissues. They are resynthesized at a slow rate. The manifestations of anaphylaxis vary among animal species because mediators are released at different rates and in different amounts, and different tissues ("shock organs") have different sensitivity to mediators. While the respiratory tract (bronchospasm, laryngeal edema) is the principal shock organ in man, the liver (hepatic veins) plays that role in the dog.

Desensitization

Major manifestations of anaphylaxis depend on the sudden release of large amounts of mediators, usually as a result of a massive dose of Ag suddenly combining with cytotropic Ab on many mast cells. If, on the other hand, only very small amounts of Ag are administered at 15-minute intervals, complex formation occurs only on a small scale and not enough mediator is released at a given moment to produce a major reaction. This is the basis of **acute desensitization**, which makes it possible to administer a drug or foreign serum to a hypersensitive person. However, days or weeks later, hypersensitivity is restored.

Chronic desensitization (hyposensitization) relies on a different principle. When small amounts of an Ag (allergen) are administered at weekly intervals to a person hypersensitive to that Ag, IgG antibodies (blocking antibodies) appear in the serum. When a desensitized person is exposed to Ag, the blocking Ab combines with the Ag and prevents their reaching IgE Ab on mast cells and basophils. Consequently, the blocking Ab can prevent allergic reactions.

Blocking antibodies differ from IgE cytotropic Ab (reagins). Reagins are IgE, bind to human skin, persist there for weeks, are heat-labile, and do not cross the placenta. Blocking Abs are IgG, do not bind to human skin, do not persist there, are heat-stable, and cross the placenta.

Passive Transfer of Atopy

The serum of a person with atopic hypersensitivity is injected into the skin of a normal person; IgE antibody binds to skin mast cells and sensitizes them during the next 20 hours. Injection of that sensitized skin site with the Ag produces an immediate type wheal-and-flare anaphylactic response of the skin site. In the normal person, that skin site maintains its ability to react to the antigen for several weeks. This **Prausnitz-Küstner (PK) reaction** is commonly used for the identification of important allergens in atopic patients who may have many positive direct skin tests.

Treatment of Anaphylactic Reactions

This is designed to counteract the effects of released chemical mediators or to block their action. In systemic anaphylaxis, the main efforts are directed at maintaining ventilation and cardiac function. This implies maintenance of a patent airway, assisted ventilation if necessary, and epinephrine (1:1000 solution), 0.1—0.5 ml given subcutaneously or into an intravenous infusion. A soluble corticosteroid may be administered for a later effect, and metaraminol may help to overcome the cardiovascular collapse.

Local anaphylactic reactions tend to respond to epinephrine or aminophylline (7 mg/kg), and their continued activity may be blocked by corticosteroids. Antihistamines are relatively effective in allergic rhinitis but ineffective in asthma.

Anaphylactoid Reactions

These resemble anaphylaxis but are precipitated

by injection of particle suspensions or colloids (kaolin, barium sulfate, inulin, etc) which activate Hageman factor, plasmin, kallikrein, and the alternative pathway of the complement sequence. They are unrelated to Ag-Ab reactions or allergy.

Anaphylaxis in Isolated Tissues

When an organ (eg, uterus, gut) from a sensitized animal is suspended in a salt solution, addition of the specific Ag results in prompt muscular contraction and liberation of mediators into the solution (Schultz-Dale reaction). This is due to the binding of Ag to cytotropic Ab on tissue mast cells.

Prevention of Anaphylaxis

Since anaphylaxis caused by drugs or biologic products may produce serious or life-threatening illness, a careful history of previous exposure or reaction must be taken before such substances are administered. Skin tests (see p 282) or conjunctival tests* can often predict the presence of hypersensitivity and therefore real risk.

ARTHUS REACTION

This antibody-mediated hypersensitivity reaction requires large amounts of Ag-Ab complexes that fix complement, attract polymorphonuclear leukocytes, and are phagocytosed by them. The cells release lysosomal enzymes which cause tissue damage, typically with vasculitis or necrosis of blood vessel walls. The lesions subside within several days.

Any class of Ig can mediate this reaction, but the higher the level of antibody the more intense the lesion; it requires at least 1000 times more Ab than anaphylaxis, and preformed Ag-Ab complexes can elicit it.

Whereas in anaphylaxis the structural changes in tissue are limited to vasodilatation, edema, and a few polymorphonuclear leukocytes, the appearance of the Arthus reaction is much more intensive inflammation. It begins with thrombosis of small vessels surrounded by edema and intense infiltration with polymorphonuclear leukocytes; areas of necrosis then develop in the walls of blood vessels. Neutrophils degenerate, and the debris is taken up by mononuclear cells and eosinophils. The phagocytosed Ag-Ab complexes are broken down and eliminated, and the inflammation subsides. In man, lesions corresponding to the Arthus reaction occur sometimes in serum sickness or in "farmer's lung."

*One drop of dilute material is placed into the conjunctival sac. A positive reaction is indicated by itching, redness, and tearing in a few minutes.

SERUM SICKNESS

Persons who receive a large amount of a drug (eg, penicillin) or of a foreign protein (eg, antiserum) may tolerate these injections well but develop an illness 8–15 days later. Typical serum sickness consists of fever, widespread urticarial eruption, pain and swelling of joints, and enlargement of lymph nodes and spleen. These signs usually subside within a week.

During serum sickness, some tissues exhibit lesions of vasculitis (as in the Arthus reaction) but also vasodilatation and edema and smooth muscle contraction (as in anaphylaxis). The mechanism is as follows: After the injection of a large amount of Ag, its concentration gradually declines and at the same time Ab production starts. The simultaneous presence of Ag and Ab leads to the formation of soluble Ag-Ab complexes which set off the immune response, combining vasculitis with the release of chemical mediators. Serum sickness subsides when the Ag has been eliminated.

IMMUNE COMPLEX DISEASE

Several Ab-mediated hypersensitivity reactions can be elicited by preformed, soluble Ag-Ab complexes (see above). In addition, a number of disease entities are attributed to immune complex deposits initiating tissue disorders—although the Ag often is not established. Examples are glomerulonephritis and rheumatoid arthritis.

Glomerulonephritis

Acute glomerulonephritis usually follows by several weeks the onset of a group A beta-hemolytic streptococcus infection. During acute glomerulonephritis, the levels of serum complement (especially C3) are usually low, suggesting an Ag-Ab reaction. By immunofluorescence, lumpy deposits of Ig and C3 are seen along basement membranes of renal glomeruli—suggesting the presence of Ag-Ab complexes. While streptococcal Ags have been infrequently demonstrated in glomeruli, it is assumed that streptococcal Ag-Ab complexes filtered out in glomeruli initiated the reaction and fixed C3.

An analogous lesion with "lumpy" immunofluorescent deposits containing Ig and C3 occurs in serum sickness caused by a known foreign protein and in the glomerulonephritis associated with bacterial endocarditis.

In systemic lupus erythematosus (SLE), patients have circulating Ab to DNA. In the glomerulonephritis of SLE the lumpy immunofluorescent deposits in glomeruli contain DNA as Ag, Ig (?Ab to DNA), and C3. In other patients with glomerulonephritis (eg, Goodpasture's syndrome), there is linear immunofluorescence along the basement membrane of glomeruli, caused by the combination of basement membrane Ag with Ab and complement (C).

At least in animals, viral infections can cause glomerulonephritis by an immune complex mechanism. In chronically infected mice, lymphocytic choriomeningitis Ag and its antiviral Ab form complexes which are deposited in glomeruli, bind C, and initiate inflammatory lesions. The virus of Aleutian mink disease causes a similar immune complex disease with glomerulonephritis.

Rheumatoid Arthritis

Rheumatoid arthritis is a chronic inflammatory joint disease which is particularly common in young women. The synovial fluid contains high concentrations of Ig aggregates, complement, and polymorphonuclear leukocytes. The nature of the Ag is undetermined. The reaction between human immunoglobulins and rheumatoid factors (IgM and IgG molecules which bind to antigenic determinants on the Fc fragments of IgG) are employed diagnostically and might play an etiologic role.

Autoimmune Diseases

Ag-Ab complexes have been demonstrated in various autoimmune diseases and may participate in their causation (see Chapter 12).

DRUG HYPERSENSITIVITY

Drugs are now among the commonest causes of hypersensitivity reactions, and antibiotics are high on the list. Penicillin hypersensitivity has been studied extensively and is used as an example here.

To induce hypersensitivity, the drug—or a reactive metabolic derivative—must covalently bind to host protein in order to become antigenic. The subsequent allergic reaction is specific for the haptens rather than for the drug itself. Such compounds can induce Ab formation and immediate and delayed type hypersensitivity. The likelihood of any one individual developing hypersensitivity to a given drug is probably influenced by genetic predisposition, the route, duration, and amount of drug exposure, the level of Ab production, and other factors.

In the case of penicillin, some important reactive products are penicilloyl compounds and minor determinant groups. When covalently bound to protein these can induce antibody-mediated hypersensitivity and local or generalized anaphylaxis.

In order to detect possible hypersensitivity to penicillin, skin tests can be performed with penicilloyl polylysine (which will not induce hypersensitivity itself), with alkaline degradation products (containing minor determinants) of penicillin, or with penicillin itself. An immediate type wheal-and-flare reaction suggests that IgE antibodies have become bound to mast cells and that such a reactive person may be subject to generalized anaphylaxis.

In view of the very large number of people who have been given penicillin—many of whom have developed IgE Ab—it is surprising that anaphylactic reactions are so rare. Two possible explanations might be considered: (1) Most persons who develop IgE antipenicilloyl Ab also develop IgG Ab of the same specificity, which may well act as blocking Ab. (2) Penicillin molecules themselves may be univalent for antipenicilloyl Ab and thus may inhibit rather than favor aggregation of IgE Ab.

Penicillin molecules may adsorb onto red blood cells in some persons receiving the drug in large doses for long periods. Such red cells may then be lysed when Ab combines with the Ag on the cell. Such hemolytic anemia is rare with penicillin. Allergic contact dermatitis may develop in persons who handle penicillin (workers in penicillin manufacture). Such persons give typical delayed-type skin reactions.

Penicilloyl Ab and corresponding Ag are presumably the basis for the serum sickness which can follow a brief course of penicillin injections by producing soluble Ag-Ab complexes. Several penicillins are known to induce nephritis. This is most often an Ag-Ab complex disease, with specific localization in the tubular basement membrane. Penicilloyl hapten bound to tubular basement membrane protein may act as antigen to initiate the interstitial nephritis.

Thrombocytopenia has been induced by the sedative apronalide (Sedormid) and by quinine. It appears that these drugs—or their metabolic products—can be selectively bound by proteins on the platelet surface to form a complete antigen. The serum of a hypersensitive person can agglutinate such platelets or, with complement, lyse them. This can account for the marked drop in platelet count and the bleeding tendency. Another example of a drug modifying host tissue and favoring the production of autoantibodies against the tissue antigens as well as against the drug is the formation of antinuclear factors in patients treated with hydralazine or isoniazid.

CELL-MEDIATED HYPERSENSITIVITY & IMMUNITY

The outstanding differences between antibody-mediated and cell-mediated hypersensitivity reactions are shown in Table 12–3. Cell-mediated hypersensitivity reactions begin 1–3 days after contact with Ag, can be transferred by lymphoid cells but not by serum, and consist of inflammatory changes with heavy infiltrates of mononuclear cells. Cell-mediated hypersensitivity is closely related to cell-mediated immunity. For both, the central component is the immunologically committed T lymphocyte, its interactions, and its products. The prototype of cell-mediated hypersensitivity and of "delayed" type skin reactions is seen in tuberculin hypersensitivity.

TUBERCULIN HYPERSENSITIVITY

Koch's Phenomenon

When a tuberculous guinea pig is injected subcutaneously with a suspension of tubercle bacilli, there is a massive inflammatory reaction at the injection site which tends to wall off the injected material and often leads to necrosis; this is called the Koch phenomenon. This reaction does not require living tubercle bacilli but occurs similarly both with filtrates of broth in which tubercle bacilli have been grown (Old Tuberculin, OT) or with tuberculoprotein (PPD). These soluble preparations produce local inflammatory reactions, particularly edema, infiltration with lymphoid cells and macrophages, hemorrhage, and marked enlargement of the regional lymph nodes; and focal reactions, consisting of marked hemorrhagic inflammation and dense cellular infiltration within existing tuberculous lesions. Because focal reactions may "stir up" tuberculous activity, great caution must be exerted, while performing skin tests, to avoid giving excessive doses of tuberculoprotein to hypersensitive individuals.

Delayed Type Skin Reaction

The typical skin test of the delayed type is exemplified by the tuberculin test. There is no immediate reaction following the intracutaneous injection of tuberculoprotein. After a few hours, redness, edema, and induration develop and tend to increase for 24–48 hours. If the reaction is marked, there may be central blanching, hemorrhage, and necrosis. The redness and edema disappear quickly, but the induration of the skin reaction can be felt for days or weeks. Histologically the lesion of the skin test is characterized by initial vasodilatation, edema, and polymorphonuclear cell infiltration; this is followed soon afterward by marked and persistent focal accumulation and diffuse infiltration with lymphoid and mononuclear cells. The intensity of the tuberculin skin reaction in the hypersensitive individual bears no relationship to the level of antibodies that may be demonstrated by complement fixation or other tests. Transfer of lymphoid cells from a skin test positive person can transfer reactivity to a skin test negative person.

PASSIVE TRANSFER OF CELL-MEDIATED HYPERSENSITIVITY

It is not possible to transfer tuberculin or other cell-mediated hypersensitivity with serum. However, viable T lymphocytes taken from a reactive person and transferred to a nonreactive person will temporarily make the recipient reactive (eg, tuberculin-positive). In man—but not in animals—it is also possible to transfer reactivity of cell-mediated hypersensitivity by means of nonviable extracts from T lymphocytes. This material has been called "transfer factor."

Properties of "Transfer Factor"

Transfer factor is stable to repeated freezing and thawing, storage in the lyophilized state, distilled water lysis, and to the action of DNase, RNase, and trypsin. It can be dialyzed and has a molecular weight of less than 10,000. Delayed sensitivity begins 1–7 days after injection of the cell extract and may last more than 1 year. The mechanism of "transfer factor" activity is uncertain. It is involved in the passive transfer of specific delayed hypersensitivity to tuberculin, streptococcal antigens, coccidioidin, allograft (homograft) sensitivity, and others.

In patients with defects in cellular immunity, injection of transfer factor may temporarily restore competence in cellular immunity as well as delayed type hypersensitivity and its associated manifestations described below. Transfer factor therapy has given good results in some patients with Wiskott-Aldrich syndrome and has shown some effect in patients with lepromatous leprosy as well as isolated cases of persons with progressive chronic infection (eg, tuberculosis) and profound defects in cell-mediated responses. If T lymphocytes from a donor showing sensitivity to several antigens are cultured in vitro and then exposed to one antigen, the transfer factor released from these cells will be directed only to the challenge antigen. Thus, it is probable that transfer factors exhibit specificity toward Ag.

INDUCTION OF CELL-MEDIATED HYPERSENSITIVITY

The development of delayed type hypersensitivity is favored by the introduction of small amounts of Ags on cell surfaces or in lipid mixtures called adjuvants. Thus, tuberculin sensitivity can be induced by infection with *Mycobacterium tuberculosis* but also by injection of small amounts of tuberculoprotein together with wax D (a peptidoglycolipid) or tuberculoprotein in complete Freund's adjuvant (see below). If larger amounts of antigen are introduced, there is less cell-mediated hypersensitivity and more Ab response. Whereas very small antigenic determinants (eg, haptens) are effective in inducing Ab responses, cell-mediated responses seem to require larger and more complex structures as determinants of specificity. In other words, cell-mediated responses appear to be carrier-specific.

The first step in the induction of cell-mediated responses may be the uptake of the antigen by macrophages and its subsequent presentation to the receptors on T lymphocytes. Once suitable lymphocytes have been contacted, these may be stimulated to proliferate and become "sensitized" lymphocytes (see below).

When a person carrying such "sensitized" T lymphocytes is again exposed to the Ag (eg, when a tuberculin skin test is applied), only a few sensitized T lymphocytes are necessary to initiate a cell-mediated hypersensitivity response. The few sensitized T lymphocytes can recruit large numbers of other lymphocytes and macrophages to produce the cellular infiltration characteristic of a cell-mediated reaction. They accomplish this, and other effects, through release of the following mediators ("lymphokines"), among others.

A. Mediators Affecting Macrophages:

1. Chemotactic factor, which attracts monocytes which then become macrophages.

2. Aggregation factor, which clumps suspended macrophages in vitro.

3. Migration inhibition factor (MIF), which inhibits the migration of normal macrophages. It is probably an acidic glycoprotein with molecular weight 35,000–50,000. This may be the substance that "activates" macrophages (see p 133).

B. Mediators Affecting Lymphocytes:

1. Blastogenic or mitogenic factor, which causes some lymphocytes to differentiate into large, rapidly dividing blast cells with greatly increased synthesis of DNA. The effect is most readily studied by measuring the incorporation of tritated thymidine into DNA.

2. Transfer factor (see above).

C. Mediators Affecting Cells in Culture, or Viruses:

1. Lymphotoxin, which can damage or lyse many types of cells.

2. Interferon, which can block virus replication in other cells.

TESTS TO EVALUATE CELL-MEDIATED HYPERSENSITIVITY OR IMMUNITY

The assessment of cell-mediated reactivity is increasingly important as greater numbers of persons suffer from spontaneous or medically induced defects of cell-mediated immunity. Increasing numbers of children with congenital defects survive, and in increasing numbers of patients cell-mediated immunity is suppressed by antitumor drugs, corticosteroids, or immunosuppressive drugs used for organ transplants. In the following tests, it is assumed that defects in cell-mediated reactivity probably indicate defects in cell-mediated immunity to infectious agents.

Skin Tests

Skin tests may be used to determine cell-mediated hypersensitivity to commonly encountered antigens. Most normal persons respond with delayed type reactions to skin test antigens of candida, trichophyton, mumps, streptodornase-streptokinase, or PPD.

Tests for Competence to Develop
Cell-Mediated Hypersensitivity

Simple chemicals applied to human skin in lipid solvents induce cell-mediated hypersensitivity in normal persons. One percent 1-chloro-2,4-dinitrobenzene (dinitrochlorobenzene, DNCB) or dinitrofluorobenzene (DNFB) in acetone is applied to the skin and washed off 24 hours later. When a test dose of 0.03–0.1% of the same chemical is applied to the same area 7–14 days later, a delayed type reaction signifies the competence to develop cell-mediated hypersensitivity.

Skin Graft Rejection

A normal person will reject a skin graft from an unrelated individual in a predictable time sequence of reactions (see below). Inability to reject such a skin graft is strong evidence of impaired cell-mediated responses.

In Vitro Evaluation of Responses of Lymphoid Cells

A. Lymphocyte Blast Transformation: When sensitized lymphocytes are exposed to a specific antigen, they transform into large blast cells (the number and proportion of blasts can be counted) with greatly increased DNA synthesis (the incorporation of tritiated thymidine into DNA can be measured). However, only a small number of cells undergo this *specific* blast transformation. A larger number of T lymphocytes undergo *nonspecific* blast transformation when exposed to mitogens such as phytohemagglutinin (a kidney bean extract), pokeweed mitogen, or concanavalin A (a jack bean extract). The measurements in nonspecific and specific blast transformation are the same.

B. Macrophage Migration Inhibitory Factor: Upon challenge by an Ag to which cultured lymphocytes are sensitive, they elaborate macrophage migration inhibitory factor (MIF). This will inhibit the migration of guinea pig peritoneal macrophages from a capillary tube.

C. Rosette Formation: When incubated with sheep red blood cells, most T lymphocytes form rosettes. While the mechanism of this effect is not clear, it permits an estimate of the proportion of circulating lymphocytes which behave in this manner. There is good correlation between rosette-forming and MIF-producing T lymphocytes.

"ALLERGY OF INFECTION": CELL-MEDIATED HYPERSENSITIVITY EMPLOYED IN DIAGNOSIS OF INFECTION

Cell-mediated hypersensitivity develops with many types of infection. Delayed type skin reactivity can be a valuable aid in the diagnosis of many infectious processes if it is cautiously interpreted. A positive skin reaction indicates only that the individual has at some time in the past been infected with the specific agent. It provides information about the nature of a specific illness only if conversion from a negative to a positive skin test occurs during the course of the illness. Blood transfusion may passively transfer delayed hypersensitivity by means of sensitive lymphocytes. Furthermore, the general skin reactivity declines markedly in far-advanced stages of many diseases (anergy). Similar anergy may be encountered during the childhood exanthems (measles, chickenpox); thus a tuberculin-positive child may temporarily give a tuberculin-negative reaction during one of these illnesses. Anergy is also a regular feature of sarcoidosis, Hodgkin's disease, and other advanced neoplasms, as well as uremia. Patients receiving large doses of corticosteroids or immunosuppressive drugs (eg, cancer chemotherapy, organ transplants) have marked depression of cell-mediated hypersensitivity and immunity.

Bacterial Infections

Skin tests are useful to support a diagnosis of tularemia, chancroid, and chlamydial infections (eg, LGV) during the course of the disease. In leprosy, the reaction to lepromin is more an indication of the immunologic state of the disease (ie, tuberculoid) than a help in diagnosis. These and other types of skin tests are described in Chapter 26. Although specific purified protein derivatives are available, mycobacterial infections other than tuberculosis cross-react extensively.

Mycotic Infections

Delayed type skin reactions occur in virtually all deep mycoses. If adequate skin testing material is available and if the concentration used is sufficiently dilute to avoid cross-reactions, the skin tests may be helpful in the diagnosis of past infections such as coccidioidomycosis, histoplasmosis, blastomycosis, and others. Most normal adults give positive skin tests with candida antigens, and a negative test suggests a defect in cell-mediated immunity. In some deep mycoses, application of a skin test may result in a significant rise of specific antibodies and thus may be misleading (eg, histoplasmosis).

Helminthic Infections

In a majority of parasitic infections—including trichinosis, filariasis, and ascariasis—immediate type skin reactions occur with the application of worm extracts. Some delayed type reactions may also be obtained, especially in echinococcus disease with heated hydatid cyst fluid. Skin tests are probably never as specific as refined determinations for antibodies in these disorders.

Viral Infections

Cell-mediated hypersensitivity occurs in many viral infections, including herpes simplex, mumps, and vaccinia. In persons repeatedly vaccinated against smallpox, the inoculation of inactive vaccinia virus results in a delayed type reaction. This denotes hypersensitivity to vaccinia antigens and should not be interpreted as an "immune" reaction.

Combined "Immediate" and "Delayed" Reactions

Skin-testing preparations from many infectious agents may produce both antibody-mediated and cell-mediated responses. This is usually due to the presence of multiple antigens in such preparations, some eliciting one response and some another.

RELATIONSHIP OF CELL-MEDIATED HYPERSENSITIVITY & IMMUNITY & RESISTANCE TO INFECTION

While antibodies provide protection against toxin-induced disorders and to a certain extent against virus infections, they play a limited role in host defenses against microbial infections, except in those whose virulence depends on polysaccharide capsules. Cell-mediated reactions are of paramount importance in maintaining resistance to most microbial infections. In some cell-mediated reactions, antibodies cooperate in processes of recovery, eg, opsonins facilitate phagocytosis and chemotactic fragments of complement enhance inflammatory reactions and localization of infection. One of the most important contributions of cell-mediated reactions to resistance to infection is the "activation" of macrophages (see p 133). Sensitized T lymphocytes act on normal macrophages and "activate" them to a high level of phagocytic activity and intracellular killing ability. While the induction of "activated" macrophages is immunologically specific, their subsequent expression is nonspecific.

The role played by antibody-mediated and by cell-mediated reactions, respectively, can be estimated to some extent by noting the types of infection which develop in persons who have a specified immune defect. Thus, persons with isolated B cell defects and lack of antibody responses may be unusually susceptible to pyogenic coccal (especially pneumococcal) infections but handle intracellular bacterial or fungal and many viral infections normally. Conversely, persons with isolated T cell defects and deficient cell-mediated reactions may be overwhelmed by opportunistic organisms (nocardia, pneumocystis, candida, aspergillus) and incapable of handling mycobacterial or fungal infections. They also permit the widespread dissemination of many viral infections (eg, herpes zoster).

Manifestations of hypersensitivity accompany many infectious processes. At times the hypersensitivity is incidental (eg, erythema nodosum in coccidioidomycosis), but at other times the cell-mediated hypersensitivity may significantly enhance the inflammatory reaction in foci of infection (eg, tuberculosis of the lung) and may lead to increased tissue destruction. In still other situations (see Koch phenomenon, p 160), the cell-mediated hypersensitivity reaction may favor localization of the infectious agent and limitation of its spread.

CONTACT ALLERGY TO DRUGS & SIMPLE CHEMICALS

Common allergic skin disorders in man are attributable to sensitization by contact of skin with many simple chemicals (nickel, formaldehyde), drugs (sulfonamides), cosmetics, plant materials (catechols from poison ivy and poison oak), and others. Chlorogenic acid, a simple phenolic compound of low molecular weight, is a hapten contained in many different plants, eg, coffee beans, castor beans, fruits, and vegetables. It becomes a complete antigen by combining with host protein and can induce respiratory or skin allergy in heavily exposed individuals (eg, coffee workers). Presumably, these materials form covalent bonds with proteins of skin. Induction of cell-mediated hypersensitivity is probably aided by skin lipids or lipid vehicles acting like adjuvants.

Upon skin contact with the offending agent, the sensitized person develops erythema and swelling, itching, vesication, or necrosis in 12–48 hours. Histologically, the reaction is an intense mononuclear cell infiltrate resembling the tuberculin test. Patch testing on a small area of skin reproduces the lesion and can identify the allergen.

ROLE OF LIPIDS, WAXES, & ADJUVANTS IN THE DEVELOPMENT OF CELL-MEDIATED HYPERSENSITIVITY

It has been mentioned above that tuberculoprotein stimulates the development of delayed hypersensitivity reactions only if it is administered together with wax from the tubercle bacillus. The same wax permits sensitization of animals with simple chemicals, such as picryl chloride, which does not elicit hypersensitivity if injected alone. It is conceivable that the strongly allergenic properties of substances applied to the skin (compared with other routes of administration) are aided by the many lipids available in the skin. In general, it appears that the delayed type of hypersensitivity develops best if the allergen is administered in such a fashion as to elicit a focal inflammatory response. Lipids often elicit focal granulomatous tissue lesions.

When weakly antigenic or allergenic materials are mixed with lipids (eg, lanolin or paraffin) and killed tubercle bacilli, they elicit much greater antibody response and hypersensitivity reactions than the antigens alone, and occasionally result in the production of "autoimmune" diseases. Such enhancing mixtures (often lanolin, paraffin oil, and tubercle bacilli) are referred to as "adjuvants" (eg, Freund's adjuvant).

The main role of the adjuvant appears to be maintenance of long-lasting Ag levels in tissue to be taken up by macrophages and presented to lymphocytes.

EXTRINSIC ALLERGIC ALVEOLITIS (CHRONIC RECURRENT LUNG DISEASE)

A large group of recurrent, debilitating pulmonary disorders is caused by hypersensitivity reactions to inhaled Ags in persons hypersensitive to these Ags.

Patients usually have high titers of precipitating Ab against the offending Ag, and immune complex disease has been suspected. However, several features suggest cell-mediated hypersensitivity: delayed onset of reaction, absence of bronchospasm, infiltration of interstitial tissue with mononuclear cells, and, at times, epithelioid cells and granulomas. While the pathogenesis of the disorders appears to be the same, the inciting agent differs: In farmer's lung it is Micropolyspora from moldy hay; in mushroom worker's lung, *Thermoactinomyces vulgaris* from mushroom compost; in maple-bark disease of paper-mill workers, *Cryptostroma corticale* from moldy bark: in the hypersensitivity pneumonitis of office workers, thermophilic actinomycetes contaminating the air-conditioning system; and in sequoiosis of redwood mill workers, moldy dust from Sequoia trees. There are many more.

Opportunistic fungi sometimes establish themselves in the respiratory tract. Aspergillus sp may grow on bronchial surfaces or in tuberculous cavities, but it may also invade pulmonary tissue and produce granulomas in which hypersensitivity probably plays a role. The lung lesions of schistosomiasis and some other parasitic infestations may be caused by cell-mediated hypersensitivity to the parasite's antigens.

INTERFERENCE WITH CELL-MEDIATED OR ANTIBODY-MEDIATED HYPERSENSITIVITY OR IMMUNITY

Interference by Antibody

A. Antilymphocyte Serum (ALS): Antiserum can be made in one animal species against thymus cells (T lymphocytes) of a second species. When such antiserum is injected into the second species, it selectively depresses cell-mediated reactions, including allograft rejection. The practical usefulness of ALS is limited by its being a foreign serum and thus giving rise to anaphylactic reactions.

B. Tumor-Enhancing Antibody: Certain Abs to transplanted tumors interfere with their rejection by the host. This might be attributed to attachment of Ab or Ag-Ab complexes to important tumor cell Ags, thus blocking their recognition or rejection by T lymphocytes.

C. Antibody Formation: Ab present at the time of Ag administration tends to block Ab formation. A practical example is the administration of anti-Rh globulin to Rh-negative mothers at the time of delivery of an Rh-positive infant. The baby's red cells entering the mother's circulation—as the placenta separates—might induce anti-Rh Ab formation in the mother and induce erythroblastosis of a subsequent Rh-positive infant. The anti-Rh globulin usually can prevent this.

Interference by Inhibitors of Inflammation or Lymphocyte Proliferation

Corticosteroids and a variety of "immunosuppressive" drugs (eg, azathioprine) given to prolong the survival of organ transplants suppress cell-mediated hypersensitivity and immunity. They are the principal reason for the marked increase in susceptibility of organ transplant recipients to bacterial, mycotic, and protozoal infections, which are often progressive and lethal. Suppression of Ab formation usually is not important clinically.

Many drugs used in the chemotherapy of neoplasms have similar effects. Corticosteroids alone (in high dosage) in immunologic diseases (rheumatoid arthritis, systemic lupus erythematosus, etc) likewise suppress cell-mediated reactions and therefore open the way for the development of infectious complications.

Other Types of Interference

Lymphoreticular disorders (Hodgkin's disease, sarcoid, lymphosarcoma) or widely disseminated infections (tuberculosis, coccidioidomycosis, lepromatous leprosy) are typically associated with deficient cell-mediated reactions, including anergy to skin tests. Antibody levels are generally normal. If the infection is controlled by treatment, cell-mediated reactivity returns. Transfer factor can accomplish the same result in these disorders for a brief period.

Widespread neoplastic disease also leads to interference with cell-mediated responses. In this situation, cell-mediated skin reactivity has been restored by levamisole, an anthelmintic drug (tetrahydro-6-phenylimidazothiazole). The mechanism is not known.

Interference by Antigen

A. Vertical Transmission of Animal Viruses: Many tumor viruses (as well as lymphocytic choriomeningitis virus) are transmitted from mother to fetus. Viruses multiply in the fetus and persist after birth with little or no antibody or cell-mediated response. The offspring appears to be tolerant to viral antigens that permit tumor development. If, on the other hand, the fetus is not infected in utero, it can be infected as a mature animal, develops an immune reaction to viruses, and resists tumor development.

B. Immune Paralysis: If highly purified polysaccharide or protein Ags are injected into a mature animal in very large or rapidly repeated doses, the animal does not develop Abs. This tolerance apparently depends on large amounts of Ag persisting; when most of the antigenic mass has been metabolized or excreted, Ab production begins. During immunologic paralysis, Ab-producing cells are also absent. B cells, in general, become unresponsive less readily and remain tolerant less long than T cells. The poorer the Ag, the easier it is to induce unresponsiveness. This tolerance ends spontaneously unless Ag injections are continued. Tolerance can be terminated by administering a cross-reacting Ag.

C. Desensitization: Desensitization by repeated Ag administration is quite effective in most antibody-mediated reactions, but it is generally not successful in cell-mediated reactions.

D. Tolerance to Tissue Allografts: (Tolerance means specific inability to mount an immune response to a specific Ag.)

1. If animals of one strain are injected in utero with cells (lymphoid cells, bone marrow) from a second strain, the mature animals of the first strain may permit the survival and growth of tissues derived from the second strain, ie, they accept an allograft.

2. Tolerance is established most readily if the antigenic disparity between donor and recipient is slight, ie, if they differ only in weak or minor antigens. Tolerance is most difficult to establish if donor and recipient differ by several or strong antigens.

3. To establish tolerance, the recipient must be immunologically immature. There is a wide variation among different species of the stage of development (or age) at which immunologic maturity is established. Mice or rats in utero are immunologically immature; sheep and man in utero (in the last third of pregnancy) are immunologically mature.

4. In general, tolerance is more easily established in T lymphocytes than in B lymphocytes. The ease of establishing tolerance is proportionate to the amount of Ag administered to the immature animal and inversely proportionate to its amount of functional lymphoid tissue mass.

5. Risk of graft-versus-host reaction. When lymphoid cells are transferred from an immunologically competent donor (eg, a normal adult) to an allogeneic immunologically incompetent recipient (eg, an immunodeficient child), the transferred cells may establish themselves and grow but "reject" the host. This may result in growth retardation, runting, or death. This presents a serious problem in "immunologic reconstitution" of immunodeficient children. (See bone marrow transplant, p 167.)

AUTOIMMUNE DISEASES

Certain disease states are attributed to immune responses of a host to his own tissues. The mechanism of pathogenesis is speculative—often based on circumstantial evidence rather than definitive proof.

In general, the tissue antigens present during fetal and neonatal life are recognized as "self" and so are tolerated by the host. No antibodies or hypersensitivity reactions are developed to them. On the other hand, Ags not present during fetal or neonatal life are rejected as "not self" and immune responses to them may develop. Very complex interactions are involved.

The differentiation of "self" from "not self" must be an important homeostatic function of the animal body. "Autoimmune disease" may be considered a failure of this homeostatic function, a disorder of immune regulation.

In certain specialized situations, tolerance may be lost and immunologic reaction to host Ags develops. Some possible mechanisms are as follows:

(1) Certain tissues are normally sequestered, so

that their Ags have no access to Ab-forming cells. The lens and uveal tract of the eye, sperm, and CNS tissue are normally isolated from the circulation and are thus not recognized as "self." Entrance of these antigens into the circulation elicits relatively organ-specific Abs. When these Ags are administered with adjuvant, various disorders such as endophthalmitis, aspermatogenesis, thyroiditis, or encephalitis can be produced experimentally (see below).

(2) Although most Ag-Ab reactions are highly specific, cross-reactions between unrelated Ags do occur. Thus, an Ab formed in response to an extrinsic Ag might by chance cross-react with a tissue Ag of the host. Examples are found among vegetable substances which stimulate Abs reacting with red blood cell Ags, or streptococcal Ags which stimulate Abs reacting with human heart tissue Ags.

(3) It is possible that in certain circumstances native tissue Ags are slightly altered (perhaps by combination with extrinsic haptens) and thus assume a new antigenic specificity. The Ab forming against the hapten-Ag complex may likewise react with the native Ag. In other circumstances, a foreign molecule (eg, a drug) might attach to a cell surface. Abs forming to that foreign molecule can combine with it, and the resulting Ag-Ab complex at the cell surface may injure the cell. (See discussion of apronalide purpura, below, for further details.)

(4) In still other situations, it appears that a genetic abnormality determines the ability of certain individuals and their families to manufacture Abs to common host tissue constituents. Thus, in rheumatoid arthritis the IgM or IgG called "rheumatoid factor" may be an Ab to normal human IgG. In systemic lupus erythematosus and related "collagen diseases," Abs are formed to DNA. This may involve an abnormal loss of tolerance.

The following are some oversimplified examples of natural or experimental disorders in which "autoimmune" reactions may be involved.

Chronic Thyroiditis

If rabbits are repeatedly injected with extracts of homologous thyroid gland, they develop Abs and cell-mediated immunity against thyroid Ags. These can be demonstrated by serologic technics. At the same time, many of the animals develop chronic thyroiditis which histologically resembles Hashimoto's thyroiditis in humans. Patients suffering from chronic thyroiditis have in their serum specific Abs against thyroid Ags, whereas persons not suffering from thyroid disease lack such Abs. It is probable, therefore, that human thyroiditis develops as an "autoimmune" disease: Through some insult, thyroid Ags are no longer recognized as "self" by the host; consequently, antibodies and cell-mediated reactions are formed against them. It is likely that lymphoid cells are sensitized to thyroid Ags and that these cells provoke the inflammatory process which, in turn, leads to fibrosis and loss of function of the gland. Abs to thyroglobulin may also play a role.

Allergic Encephalitis

When animal brain substance is mixed with adjuvants (see p 163) and injected into other members of the same animal species, many of these animals will develop encephalitis. The experiment can even be performed successfully by removing the frontal lobe from a monkey, mixing the ground brain material with adjuvant, and injecting it intramuscularly into the same monkey. Such an animal often develops demyelinating disease of the CNS with disseminated lesions in the brain and cord. Histologically, these lesions greatly resemble "postvaccinal" encephalomyelitis, which occurs in persons who have been repeatedly injected with animal brain material, as in rabies vaccine.

Experimental allergic encephalitis cannot be transferred passively by serum but can be passively transferred with lymphoid cells. The severity of lesions bears no relationship to measurable CF anti-brain Abs, and such Abs may even protect against lesions. The likelihood is great that the illness is based on cell-mediated reactions and that a protein of brain acts as allergen. One such encephalitogenic nonapeptide has been characterized and synthesized.

Rheumatic Fever

The development of rheumatic fever is regularly preceded by multiple infections with group A beta-hemolytic streptococci. There exist cross-reactions between Ags of human heart and streptococci. Certain group A streptococci contain a cell membrane Ag which cross-reacts with human cardiac muscle fibers, especially the sarcolemma. Thus, Abs to the streptococci might react with heart muscle. There is also cross-reactivity between structural glycoproteins of heart valves and streptococcal group-specific carbohydrate. The pathogenetic role of these cross-reacting Abs is not established.

Blood Diseases

Various forms of human hemolytic anemias, granulocytopenias, thrombocytopenias, and other blood disorders have been attributed either to the development of autoantibodies directed against antigens in red blood cells or platelets or to the attachment of Ag-Ab complexes to the cell surface. As a result of such Ag-Ab reactions, cells would be destroyed. The responsible antibodies have been demonstrated in a number of instances. For example, in the thrombocytopenic purpura caused by apronalide (Sedormid) or quinine, the sensitive person's serum contains antibody which can lyse platelets onto which the drug has been adsorbed.

Pernicious anemia may represent an "autoimmune" reaction to intrinsic factor, a special protein secreted by parietal cell into the stomach.

Systemic Lupus Erythematosus (SLE) & Other "Collagen Vascular Diseases"

This is a group of human diseases characterized by focal inflammatory lesions, vasculitis, and collagen degeneration. It includes polyarteritis nodosa, scleroderma, dermatomyositis, systemic lupus erythematosus (SLE), and others. The causes of these diseases are not known, but typical cases have followed sensitization by sulfonamides, foreign serum, and other immune stimuli. In these diseases, and particularly in SLE, a variety of Abs against various normal body constituents has been identified, including autoantibodies to red cell Ag, cellular DNA, clotting factors, etc. The typical LE cell is a granulocyte which has taken up an aggregate of DNA-anti-DNA complex. By immunofluorescence, the intracellular DNA can be identified; the complement level in active SLE is low, indicating Ag-Ab reactions which bind complement.

In patients with rheumatoid arthritis, a "rheumatoid factor" can be regularly demonstrated by hemagglutination, latex fixation, or precipitation tests. This is an IgM or IgG which reacts with normal human IgG and may be a true autoantibody to IgG. Rheumatoid arthritis may be a "complex disease" (see p 159).

TRANSPLANTATION IMMUNITY*

Blood groups of the ABO systems are transplantation Ags, but they are carbohydrates (see Chapter 12). Most other transplantation Ags are proteins.

It has long been known that an individual will accept a graft of his own tissue (eg, skin) but not that of another person, except an identical twin. An autograft is a graft of tissue from one individual onto itself, and it "takes" regularly and permanently. An isograft is a graft of tissue from one individual to another genetically identical individual, and it usually "takes" permanently. A heterograft (xenograft) is a graft from one species to another species. It is always rejected. An allograft (homograft) is a graft from one member of a noninbred species to another member, eg, from one human to another human. It is rejected by the homograft reaction. Initial vascularization and circulation of the graft are good, but after 11–14 days marked reduction in circulation and infiltration of the bed of the graft with mononuclear cells occur, and the graft eventually becomes necrotic and sloughs. In the homograft rejection, a cell-mediated reaction with competent lymphoid cells is of primary importance, but Abs can also participate in the reaction. If a second homograft from the same donor is applied to a recipient who has rejected the first graft, an accelerated ("second-set") rejection is observed in 5–6 days.

The problem of tissue transplantation resides in specific "transplantation antigens" which exist in all mammalian cells. These antigens are of a great variety under the control of a number of different "histocompatibility genes." In inbred strains of mice, at least 14 independently segregating genetic loci for transplantation Ags have been recognized. At each of these

*An excellent review of this subject may be found in Russell PS, Winn HJ: New England J Med 282:786, 896, 1970.

loci there exist multiple alleles, so that the number and variety of transplantation Ags are enormous. If inbred mice are cross-mated, the F1 offspring are tolerant of grafts from either parent but either parent rejects the F1 hybrid graft. In man, the major histocompatibility complex involves at least 2 closely associated loci: the first serologically defined (SD-1, formerly "LA") locus and the second serologically defined (SD-2, formerly "four") locus. These genetic loci determine strong transplantation antigens. Several other weaker transplantation antigens are determined by other genetic loci. Antigens determined by these several genetic loci are defined by their interaction with antisera in the lymphocytotoxicity test. The antisera are raised in the course of repeated human pregnancy or as a result of immunization in man.

The major histocompatibility genetic loci occur on each member of a single chromosome pair (in man, probably chromosome 6). For each histocompatibility locus, many alleles exist, controlling expression of specific antigens. Because of this polymorphism, each individual is likely to have at least 4 strong transplantation antigens on cells. The term "haplotype" denotes the products of the major histocompatibility complex in haploid form. Each individual has strong transplantation antigens arranged in pairs of haplotypes, with each haplotype being controlled by the major histocompatibility loci of one chromosome of a pair. More than 13 first locus and more than 15 second locus antigens have now been identified, resulting in thousands of potential haplotypes. Consequently, the likelihood is very small that 2 random individuals would have completely or partly identical haplotypes. Within a family, on the other hand, only 4 haplotypes are involved (2 from each parent), which permits a reasonable opportunity of genetic matching of family members as donors or recipients of transplants. About 25% of siblings are SD-1 identical.

In addition to serologically defined loci, there are lymphocyte defined (LD) loci. These are important in mixed leukocyte culture (MLC) tests.

It is also considered essential that donor and recipient be compatible by matching of ABO blood groups. The following procedures are employed in determining the degree of histocompatibility for "matching" donor and recipient of transplants:

A. Mixed Leukocyte Culture (MLC): This test applies only to living donors and requires 6–7 days to complete. At present, it is not applicable to cadaver organ transplants. For the test, lymphocytes from donor and recipient are separated from blood and then cultured together in vitro for 5 days. On the fifth day, the mixed cell cultures and appropriate controls (ie, cultures of each cell population alone) are labeled with radioactive thymidine. The isotype is incorporated into any DNA being synthesized. Thus, the level of cellular radioactivity becomes an indicator of cellular stimulation as a result of exposure to antigens which are recognized as foreign. The greater the disparity of donor and recipient cells, the higher the stimulation of cell growth and of labeled thymidine incorporation into DNA. The ratio of radioactivity in the mixed cell culture and in the sum of the single cell cultures is a measure of antigenic disparity. Ratios greater than 8 (or 7) are empirically considered indicative of an unsuitable "match."

The MLC described above is a "2-way reaction" since it measures the response of both cell populations to one another. Since the reaction of the recipient's cells to the donor's antigens is most important, a "one-way reaction" can be created by blocking DNA synthesis in donor cells by treating them with mitomycin C or x-ray radiation.

The MLC is particularly useful in selecting the best donor within a family of compatible SD (HLA) types. MLC compatibility, shown by a ratio near 1, takes precedence over the results of HLA typing in donor selection.

B. Histocompatibility Antigen (SD, HLA) Typing by Lymphocytotoxicity: Viable purified lymphocytes from blood of the tissue donor are added to a panel of standard sera and the recipient's serum. Complement is added, then dye (eosin or trypan blue) and formalin. Cell death occurs if an antigen + antibody + complement reaction takes place. Cell death is established by counting the number of viable cells which exclude the dye (whereas dead cells are stained by dye). An alternative method is to preincubate lymphocytes with ^{51}Cr and determine the release of this isotope as an indication of cell death.

If donor and recipient are well matched by MLC and HLA typing, the long-term survival of a transplanted organ or tissue is enhanced. In 1975, the survival rate of kidney transplants from related, matched, living donors was better than 90% for 2 years, whereas the survival rate of cadaver kidney transplants from unrelated donors was 60% for 2 years.

In one center, well-matched transplants of bone marrow from siblings established themselves in 33 of 37 patients with aplastic anemia, half of whom lived with functioning grafts. However, about 70% of patients with successful marrow grafts exhibited graft-versus-host (GVH) disease (see below).

To delay or diminish rejection of transplanted tissue or organs, attempts are made to suppress immunologic rejection mechanisms. At present this involves the administration of corticosteroids, immunosuppressive drugs such as azathioprine, antilymphocytic serum, and radiation. Unfortunately, all of these immunosuppressive measures enhance the recipient's susceptibility to endogenous or exogenous infection. Even "nonpathogenic" microorganisms (bacteria, fungi, viruses, protozoa) may prove fatal to the immunosuppressed transplant recipient. Such disorders as cytomegalovirus pneumonia, *Pneumocystis carinii* pneumonia, or disseminated herpes zoster are prominent examples of endogenous infections which occur almost exclusively in the immunosuppressed.

Histocompatibility antigens also appear to be genetic markers for a variety of diseases. SD antigens appear to contribute to the specific susceptibility to rheumatic diseases. Ankylosing spondylitis and Reiter's disease are associated with antigen HLA-B27. HLA-B8 and HLA-Bw15 antigens are found with unusual frequency in insulin-dependent diabetics. HLA-B13 and HLA-Bw17 antigens may occur with greater than normal frequency in patients with psoriasis vulgaris. The ultimate meaning of this coincidence has yet to be explained.

The longer a tissue or organ graft survives in the recipient, the greater the chance that tolerance to the graft may be established under the cover of immunosuppressive measures. The establishment of tolerance by means of repeated administration of donor cells into recipients has been attempted only rarely. (See Chapter 12.)

In certain experimental situations, the transplantation of immunologically competent lymphoid tissue into an immunosuppressed recipient has resulted in a graft-versus-host reaction. The grafted cells appeared to survive and "took over" by rejecting the host. In immunosuppressed mice, lymphoid tissue transplants from normal mice can result in "runting" and death of the recipient as a form of graft-versus-host reaction. Graft-versus-host (GVH) reactions occur in man following bone marrow transplant into immunodeficient hosts (eg, in cases of aplastic anemia or in leukemia after intensive irradiation and cyclophosphamide treatment). Prominent disturbances of GVH reactions include skin lesions and malfunctions of the liver and the intestinal tract. Less than 25% of patients with major evidence of GVH survive. Antithymocyte globulin may have therapeutic value in GVH.

TUMOR IMMUNITY

Animals carrying chemical-induced or virus-induced tumors develop a certain amount of resistance to that tumor which can be demonstrated experimentally although it is usually insufficient to cause complete regression of the tumor.

In the course of neoplastic transformation of cells, new Ags develop at the cell surface which permit the host's immune responses to recognize such cells as "foreign." (Some tumors in adults contain Ag found in *fetal* but not in adult cells. Thus, a carcinoembryonic antigen is found in the serum of patients with neoplasia of the gut.) Cell-mediated responses (see p 159) attack these "foreign" tumor cells and tend to limit their proliferation. It is probable that these cell-mediated responses are an effective surveillance system which can eliminate some newly arising clones of neoplastic cells.

The tumor antigens also stimulate the development of specific antibodies. Some such antibodies may be cytotoxic. Others interfere with recognition and disposal of tumor cells by cell-mediated immune responses of the host, and such antitumor antibodies (or Ag-Ab complexes) thus produce an enhancement of tumor growth.

Some immunologic features of virus-induced tumors of animals are discussed in Chapter 40.

There is tentative evidence that spontaneously arising human tumors have new cell surface Ags against which the host develops both cytotoxic antibodies and cellular hypersensitivity. The possibility is under investigation that enhancement of such immune responses may permit containment of malignant neoplasms. Enhancement by the administration of BCG into surface tumors (melanomas) has led to tumor regression.

● ● ●

General References

Austen KF: Systemic anaphylaxis in the human being. N Engl J Med 291:661, 1974.

Biggar WD & others: Immunologic reconstitution. Annu Rev Med 24:135, 1973.

Bloom BR, Glade PR: *In Vitro Methods in Cell-Mediated Immunity.* Academic Press, 1971.

Catalona WJ & others: Dinitrochlorobenzene contact sensitization. N Engl J Med 286:399, 1972.

Collins RM: Vaccines and cell-mediated immunity. Bacteriol Rev 38:371, 1974.

Committee on Drugs of the American Academy of Pediatrics: Anaphylaxis. Pediatrics 51:136, 1973.

Dale DC, Petersdorf RG: Corticosteroids and infectious diseases. Med Clin North Am 57:1277, 1973.

Danilevicus Z: HL-A antigens: Markers of many diseases. (Editorial.) JAMA 231:965, 1975.

David JR: Lymphocyte mediators and cellular hypersensitivity. N Engl J Med 288:143, 1973.

Ellis EF: Immunologic mechanisms in allergic disease. Pediatr Clin North Am 19:373, 1972.

Flax MH: Drug-induced autoimmunity. N Engl J Med 291:414, 1974.

Flick AJ: Human reagins: The antibody of immediate type hypersensitivity. Bacteriol Rev 36:311, 1972.

Freda VJ & others: Prevention of Rh hemolytic diseases. N Engl J Med 292:1014, 1975.

Garraty G, Petz LD: Drug-induced hemolytic anemia. Am J Med 58:398, 1975.

Hellström KE, Hellström I: Tumor immunity. Adv Cancer Res 12:167, 1969.

Kaliner M & others: Immunologic release of chemical mediators from human nasal polyps. N Engl J Med 289:277, 1973.

Kaplan SR, Calabresi P: Immunosuppressive agents. N Engl J Med 289:952, 1973.

Leskowitz S: Tolerance. Annu Rev Microbiol 21:157, 1967.

Levin AS & others: Transfer factor therapy in immune deficiency states. Annu Rev Med 24:175, 1973.

McCluskey RT, Klasser J: Immunologically mediated renal disease. N Engl J Med 288:564, 1973.

McCombs RP: Diseases due to immunologic reactions in the lungs. N Engl J Med 286:1186, 1972.

Najarian JS: The clinical use of antilymphocyte globulin. N Engl J Med 285:158, 1971.

Palmer DL, Reed WP: Delayed hypersensitivity skin testing. (2 parts.) J Infect Dis 130:132, 138, 1974.

Parker CW: Drug allergy. (2 parts.) N Engl J Med 292:511, 732, 1975.

Paterson RY: Immune processes and infection factors in CNS disease. Annu Rev Med 20:75, 1969.

Stiller CR & others: Autoimmunity. Ann Intern Med 82:405, 1975.

Stossel TP: Phagocytosis. (3 parts.) N Engl J Med 290:717, 774, 833, 1974.

Thomas ED & others: Bone marrow transplantation. (2 parts.) N Engl J Med 292:832, 895, 1975.

Tripodi D & others: Drug-induced restoration of delayed type hypersensitivity. N Engl J Med 289:354, 1973.

Weiss DW & others: Current aspects of tumor immunology. Isr J Med Sci 9:205, 1973.

Wood WC, Morton DM: Host immune response to cell-surface antigen in human sarcomas. N Engl J Med 284:569, 1971.

14...
Pyogenic Cocci

THE STAPHYLOCOCCI

The staphylococci are gram-positive spherical cells, usually arranged in irregular clusters. They grow readily on a variety of media and are active metabolically, fermenting many carbohydrates and producing pigments which vary from white to deep yellow. The pathogenic staphylococci often hemolyze blood and coagulate plasma. Some are members of the normal flora of the skin and mucous membranes of man; others cause suppuration, abscess formation, a variety of pyogenic infections, and even fatal septicemia. A common type of food poisoning is caused by a heat-stable enterotoxin produced by certain staphylococci. Staphylococci rapidly develop resistance to many antimicrobial agents and present difficult therapeutic problems.

Morphology & Identification

A. Typical Organisms: Spherical cells about 1 μm in diameter arranged in irregular clusters. In liquid cultures single cocci, pairs, and chains are also seen. Young cocci stain strongly gram-positive; on aging, many cells become gram-negative. Staphylococci are nonmotile and do not form spores. Under the influence of certain chemicals (eg, penicillin) they are lysed

or changed into L forms, but they are not affected by bile salts.

Gaffkya tetragena is characteristically arranged in tetrads, often with a wide capsule.

B. Culture: Staphylococci grow readily on most bacteriologic media under aerobic or microaerophilic conditions. They grow most rapidly at 37° C but form pigment best at room temperature (20° C). Colonies on solid media are round, smooth, raised, and glistening, forming varying pigments: *Staphylococcus aureus* is deep golden yellow; *S epidermidis (S albus)* is porcelain white; intermediate shades also occur. Many colonies develop pigment only upon prolonged incubation at 20° C. No pigment is produced anaerobically or in broth. Various degrees of hemolysis are produced by different strains. Anaerobic cocci (Peptococcus) resemble staphylococci in morphology.

C. Growth Characteristics: Staphylococci are able to ferment slowly many carbohydrates, producing lactic acid but not gas. There are great variations among strains. Proteolytic activity also varies greatly. The extracellular substances produced by pathogenic staphylococci are discussed below.

Staphylococci are relatively resistant to drying, to heat (they will withstand 50° C for 30 minutes), and to 9% sodium chloride, but are readily inhibited by certain chemicals, eg, hexachlorophene, 3%. Staphylococci are variably sensitive to sulfonamides and antibiotics, and drug-resistant mutants are found in most strains. Many strains are penicillin-resistant by virtue of the production of penicillinase (β-lactamase), an enzyme that destroys penicillins by breaking the β-lactam ring. Its production is controlled by a plasmid which can be transferred by bacteriophages (transduction). Plasmids also carry genetic control of resistance to other antibiotics, eg, tetracyclines.

D. Variation: Any culture of staphylococci contains certain organisms which differ from the bulk of the population in cultural characteristics (colony type, pigment, hemolysis), in enzyme equipment, in drug resistance, and in pathogenicity.

Antigenic Structure

Staphylococci contain both antigenic polysaccharides and proteins which permit a grouping of strains to a limited extent. Teichoic acids (polymers of glycerol or ribitol phosphate) linked to cell wall peptido-

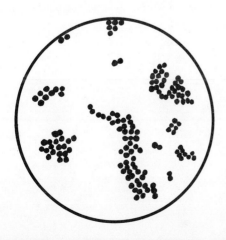

Figure 14—1. Staphylococci from broth culture.

glycan can be antigenic. Surface protein may interfere with phagocytosis. Most of the extracellular substances produced by staphylococci are likewise antigenic. While serologic tests have limited usefulness in identifying strains, this can be done by "phage typing." The method is based on the lysis of organisms by one or a series of specific bacteriophages. Such bacteriophage susceptibility (phage type) is a stable genetic characteristic, based on surface receptors. It permits the epidemiologic tracing of strains.

Many staphylococcal strains are lysogenic. Production of some toxins appears to be phage-mediated.

Toxins & Enzymes

Staphylococci can produce disease both through their ability to multiply and spread widely in tissues and through their production of many extracellular substances. Among the latter are the following:

A. "Exotoxin": A filtrable, thermolabile mixture which is lethal for animals on injection, causes necrosis in skin, and contains several soluble hemolysins which can be separated by electrophoresis. The alpha hemolysin, a protein with a molecular weight of 3×10^4, dissolves rabbit erythrocytes, damages platelets, and is probably identical with the lethal and dermonecrotic factors of exotoxin. Alpha hemolysin also has a powerful action on vascular smooth muscle. Beta hemolysin dissolves sheep erythrocytes (but not rabbit cells) upon incubation for 1 hour at 37° C and then 18 hours at 10° C. These hemolysins (and 2 others, the gamma and delta hemolysins) are antigenically distinct and bear no relationship to streptococcal lysins. Exotoxin treated with formalin gives a nonpoisonous but antigenic toxoid which has been used to stimulate antitoxic immunity to staphylococci.

B. Leukocidin: A soluble material which kills exposed white blood cells of a variety of animal species. It is antigenic but more heat-labile than exotoxin. Its role in pathogenesis is uncertain. Pathogenic staphylococci may not kill white blood cells and may be phagocytosed as effectively as nonpathogenic varieties. However, they are capable of very active intracellular multiplication, whereas the nonpathogenic organisms rapidly die inside the cell. Antibodies to leukocidin may play a role in resistance to recurrent staphylococcal infections.

C. Enterotoxin: A soluble material produced by certain strains of staphylococci, particularly when they are grown in high concentrations of CO_2 (30%) in semisolid media. Enterotoxin is a protein with a molecular weight of 3.5×10^4 that resists boiling for 30 minutes and the action of gut enzymes, and belongs to one of 4 antigenic types. An important cause of food poisoning, enterotoxin is produced especially when certain staphylococci grow in carbohydrate and protein foods. Ingestion of 25 μg of enterotoxin B results in vomiting and diarrhea in man or monkeys. The emetic effect of enterotoxin is probably the result of CNS stimulation (vomiting center) after the toxin acts on neural receptors in the gut. Enterotoxin can be assayed by precipitin tests (gel diffusion).

D. Coagulase: Most staphylococci pathogenic for man produce coagulase, an enzyme-like substance (a protein) which clots oxalated or citrated plasma in the presence of a factor contained in many sera. The coagulase-reactive factor of serum reacts with coagulase to generate both esterase and clotting activities in a manner similar to the activation of prothrombin to thrombin. Coagulase may deposit fibrin on the surface of staphylococci, perhaps altering their ingestion by phagocytic cells or their destruction within such cells.

E. Other Substances: Other extracellular sub-

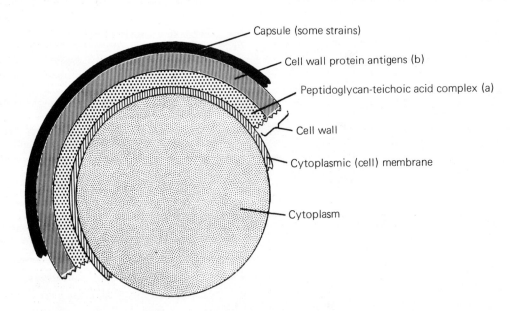

Figure 14—2. Antigenic structure of staphylococci. *(a)* Site of bacteriophage attachment. Species antigens present (antigenic determinant is N-acetylglucosamine linked to polyribitol phosphate). *(b)* Multiple antigens; several widely distributed.

stances produced by staphylococci include a hyaluronidase, or spreading factor; a staphylokinase resulting in fibrinolysis but acting much more slowly than streptokinase; proteinases, lipases, and penicillinase; and an exfoliative toxin causing the "scalded skin" syndrome (the last 2 are under genetic control of plasmids).

Pathogenesis

Staphylococci (particularly *S epidermidis*) are members of the normal flora of the human skin and of the respiratory and gastrointestinal tracts; they are also found regularly in air and human environments. The pathogenic capacity of a given strain of staphylococci is the combined effect of the above-named extracellular factors and toxins together with the invasive properties of the strain, and it covers a wide scale. At one end is staphylococcal food poisoning, attributable solely to the ingestion of preformed enterotoxin; at the other end, staphylococcal bacteremia and disseminated abscesses in all organs. The potential contribution of the various extracellular factors in pathogenesis is evident from the nature of their individual actions.

Pathogenic, invasive staphylococci *(S aureus)* tend to be hemolytic, produce coagulase and yellow pigment, and ferment mannitol. Nonpathogenic, noninvasive staphylococci *(S epidermidis)* tend to be nonhemolytic, white, coagulase-negative, and do not ferment mannitol. *Gaffkya tetragena* may produce suppuration like other staphylococci and occasionally causes pneumonia.

Pathology

The prototype of a staphylococcal lesion is the furuncle or other localized abscess. Groups of staphylococci established in a hair follicle lead to tissue necrosis (dermonecrotic factor). Coagulase is produced and coagulates fibrin around the lesion and within the lymphatics, resulting in formation of a wall which limits the process and which is reinforced by the accumulation of inflammatory cells and, later, fibrous tissue. Within the center of the lesion, liquefaction of the necrotic tissue occurs (enhanced by delayed hypersensitivity) and the abscess "points" in the direction of least resistance. Drainage of the liquid central necrotic tissue is followed by the slow filling of the cavity with granulation tissue and eventual healing.

Focal suppuration is typical of staphylococcal infection. From any one focus, organisms may spread via the lymphatics and bloodstream to other parts of the body. Suppuration within veins, associated with thrombosis, is a common feature of such dissemination.

Staphylococci of low invasiveness are involved in many minor skin infections (eg, acne, impetigo). Staphylococci of phage group II cause bullous exfoliation—the "scalded skin" syndrome—through the production of an exfoliating toxin. In osteomyelitis the primary focus of staphylococcal growth is typically in a terminal blood vessel of the metaphysis of long bones, leading to necrosis of bone and chronic suppuration. Staphylococci may be the causative organ-

isms in pneumonia, meningitis, empyema, endocarditis, or sepsis with suppuration in any organ. Anaerobic cocci (Peptococcus) participate in mixed anaerobic infections.

Clinical Findings

The picture of a localized staphylococcal infection is that of a "pimple," hair follicle infection, or an abscess—usually an intense, localized, painful inflammatory reaction which undergoes central suppuration and which heals quickly when the pus is drained. The wall of fibrin and cells around the core of the abscess tends to prevent spread of the organisms and should not be broken down by manipulation or trauma. If the organisms become disseminated and bacteremia ensues, the clinical picture resembles that seen with other bloodstream infections. The secondary localization within an organ or system is accompanied by the symptoms and signs of organ dysfunction and intense focal suppuration.

Food poisoning due to staphylococcus enterotoxin is characterized by a short (1–8 hours) incubation period, violent nausea, vomiting, and diarrhea, and rapid convalescence. There is no fever.

The suppression of normal bowel flora by antimicrobial drugs favors the development of postoperative staphylococcal enterocolitis which has a high fatality rate.

Diagnostic Laboratory Tests

A. Specimens: Surface swab, pus, blood, tracheal aspirate, or spinal fluid for culture, depending upon the localization of the process. Antibody studies on serum are not commonly performed.

B. Stained Smears: Typical staphylococci are seen in stained smears of pus or sputum. It is not possible to distinguish saprophytic *(S epidermidis)* from pathogenic *(S aureus)* organisms.

C. Culture: Specimens planted on blood agar plates give rise to typical colonies in 18 hours at 37° C, but hemolysis and pigment production may not occur until several days later, preferably at room temperature. From specimens contaminated with a mixed flora, staphylococci can be grown in media containing 7.5% NaCl. Most human staphylococci are not pathogenic for animals. A staphylococcus is generally considered pathogenic if it produces pigment or coagulase, ferments mannitol, liquefies gelatin, or hemolyzes blood.

D. Coagulase Test: Citrated rabbit (or human) plasma diluted 1:5 is mixed with an equal volume of broth culture and incubated at 37° C. A tube of plasma mixed with sterile broth is included as control. The tubes are frequently inspected for clotting over a period of 1–4 hours.

Growth on tellurite medium may be substituted for coagulase tests. Most coagulase-positive staphylococci reduce tellurite with the production of jet black colonies.

All coagulase-positive staphylococci are considered pathogenic for man. Certain types of infections, notably bacterial endocarditis, can be caused by coagulase-negative *S epidermidis*.

E. Serologic Tests, Animal Inoculations: These procedures have little practical value. However, phage typing of staphylococci isolated in hospital environments is a useful epidemiologic tool (see below); antibiotic resistance patterns are also helpful.

Treatment

The impression among clinicians that active resistance to staphylococcal infections can be acquired has led to the use of staphylococcal toxoid in persons suffering from recurrent staphylococcal skin infections. While the increase in antitoxin titer which follows toxoid therapy may be associated with diminution in severity of recurrent infections, there is no good evidence for the efficacy of toxoids in treatment. Staphylococcal vaccines are of even more questionable value.

Many antimicrobial drugs have some effect against staphylococci in vitro. However, the rapid development of resistance to most drugs and the inability of drugs to act in the central necrotic part of the lesions make it difficult to eradicate pathogenic staphylococci from infected persons. Drainage of closed suppurating lesions is essential.

Most persons harbor staphylococci on the skin and in the nose or throat. Even if the skin (eg, in eczema) can be cleared of staphylococci, reinfection by droplets will occur almost immediately. Pathogenic organisms are commonly spread from one lesion (eg, furuncle) to other areas of the skin by fingers and clothing. Scrupulous local antisepsis is therefore of considerable aid.

Serious multiple skin infections (acne, furunculosis) occur most often in adolescents and are believed to be favored by hormonal factors. Similar skin infections occur in patients receiving prolonged courses of corticosteroids. In acne, lipases of staphylococci and corynebacteria liberate fatty acids from lipids and thus cause tissue irritation. Lipases can be inhibited by tetracyclines.

Because of the frequency of resistant variants in most staphylococcal strains and the consequent unpredictability of clinical response to any one antimicrobial drug, all pathogenic staphylococci should be submitted to antibiotic sensitivity testing upon isolation in the laboratory, and adjustments in chemotherapy should be made according to the results. Resistance to drugs of the erythromycin group or novobiocin tends to emerge so rapidly that these drugs should not be used singly for treatment of chronic infection. Tetracycline and penicillin resistance, determined by plasmids, can be transmitted among staphylococci by transducing bacteriophages.

Penicillin G-resistant staphylococci from clinical infections always produce penicillinase. They may be susceptible to β-lactamase-resistant penicillins (eg, methicillin; see p 115), cephalosporins, or vancomycin. Methicillin resistance is independent of β-lactamase and occurs in only a small part of the microbial population. Its basis is uncertain, and its clinical frequency varies

enormously in different countries (USA < 0.1%, Denmark 40%).

In view of the rapid emergence of drug resistance among staphylococci, hospitals have sometimes restricted the use of an antistaphylococcus drug to the treatment of the most seriously ill patients. Such restriction may greatly prolong the useful period of a new drug.

Epidemiology & Control

Staphylococci are ubiquitous human parasites. The chief sources of infection are accessible human lesions, fomites contaminated from them, and the human respiratory tract and skin. Airborne infection has assumed added importance in hospitals, where a large proportion of the staff and patients carry antibiotic-resistant staphylococci in nose or throat or on the skin. Although cleanliness, hygiene, and aseptic management of lesions ordinarily control the spread of skin infections due to staphylococci, only limited methods are available to prevent the wide dissemination of staphylococci from carriers. Aerosols (eg, glycols) and ultraviolet irradiation of air have little effect. The most endangered areas in hospitals are the newborn nursery and the surgical operating rooms. Massive introduction of "epidemic" pathogenic staphylococci into these areas may lead to serious clinical disease. Persons with active staphylococcal lesions and carriers may have to be excluded from these areas. In such individuals the application of topical antiseptics (eg, neomycin cream) to carriage sites (nostrils, perineum, etc) may diminish shedding of dangerous organisms. Antiseptics (eg, hexachlorophene) used on the skin of the newborn diminish colonization by staphylococci, but toxicity presents problems.

In most hospitals, because antibiotics are used extensively, prevalent staphylococci are resistant to commonly employed antimicrobial drugs. Phage typing provides a valuable tool to establish the transmission of "hospital staphylococci" from personnel and patients to newly admitted patients. During outbreaks of staphylococcal disease among newborns or surgical patients, a single phage type (eg, 80/81) usually prevails. Sporadic infections are often caused by several different types. Certain phage types appear to spread much more readily in the environment and acquire drug resistance more rapidly than others. Most drug-resistant staphylococci of hospitals fall into the series of phage types called group III.

Experimentally, it is possible to selectively colonize individuals with nonpathogenic staphylococci (eg, 502A) and thereby prevent colonization with pathogenic staphylococci. This "bacterial interference" can also be applied at times to patients whose lesion-causing staphylococci have been temporarily suppressed by drugs. "Bacterial interference" may have a nutritional basis (eg, competition for a metabolite) or may be attributable to the production of an inhibitor.

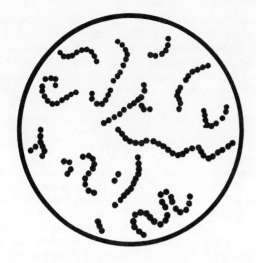

Figure 14—3. Hemolytic streptococci from broth culture.

THE STREPTOCOCCI

The streptococci are spherical microorganisms, characteristically arranged in chains and widely distributed in nature. Some are members of normal human flora; others are associated with important human diseases attributable in part to infection by streptococci, in part to sensitization to them. They produce a variety of extracellular substances and enzymes. Their ability to hemolyze red blood cells to various degrees is one important basis for classification.

Morphology & Identification

A. Typical Organisms: Individual cocci are spherical or ovoid and are arranged in chains. The cocci divide in a plane perpendicular to the long axis of the chain. The members of the chain often have a striking diplococcal appearance, and rod-like forms are occasionally seen. The lengths of the chains vary widely, conditioned largely by environmental factors.

Some streptococci elaborate a capsular polysaccharide which is comparable to that of pneumococci. The majority of group A and group C strains produce capsules composed of hyaluronic acid. The capsules are most noticeable in very young cultures. They impede phagocytosis. The streptococcal cell wall contains proteins (M, T, R antigens), carbohydrates (group-specific), and peptidoglycans (Fig 14—4).

B. Culture: Most streptococci grow in solid media as discoid colonies, usually 1—2 mm in diameter. Group A strains which produce capsular material often give rise to mucoid colonies. Matt and glossy colonies of group A strains are discussed below. Peptostreptococcus grows under anaerobic conditions.

C. Growth Characteristics: Energy is principally obtained from the utilization of sugars. Growth of streptococci tends to be poor on solid media or in broth unless enriched with blood or tissue fluids. Nutritive requirements vary widely among different species. The human pathogens are most exacting, requiring a variety of growth factors. Growth and hemolysis are aided by 10% CO_2.

While most pathogenic hemolytic streptococci grow best at 37° C, group D enterococci grow well between 15° C and 45° C. Enterococci also grow in high (6.5%) sodium chloride concentration and in 0.1% methylene blue. Most streptococci are facultative anaerobes, but some strains from surgical infections are obligate anaerobes (Peptostreptococcus). Other characteristics are discussed below.

D. Variation: Variants of the same streptococcus strain may show different colony forms. This is particularly marked among group A strains, giving rise to either matt or glossy colonies. Matt colonies consist of organisms which give rise to much M protein. Such organisms tend to be virulent and relatively insuscepti-

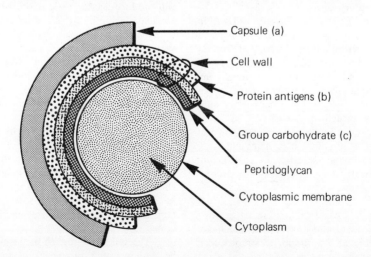

Figure 14—4. Antigen structure of streptococcal cell. *(a)* Capsule is hyaluronic acid. *(b)* Cell wall protein antigens M, T, and R. *(c)* Group carbohydrate for group A streptococci is rhamnose-N-acetylglucosamine.

ble to phagocytosis by human leukocytes. Glossy colonies tend to produce little M protein and are often nonvirulent.

Antigenic Structure

Hemolytic streptococci can be divided into serologic groups (A–O), and certain groups can be subdivided into types. Several antigenic substances are found:

(1) **C Carbohydrate:** This substance is contained in the cell wall of many streptococci and forms the basis of serologic grouping (Lancefield A–O). Extracts of C carbohydrate for "grouping" of streptococci may be prepared by extraction of centrifuged culture with hot hydrochloric acid, nitrous acid, or formamide; by enzymatic lysis of streptococcal cells (eg, with pepsin, trypsin); or by autoclaving cell suspensions at 15 lb pressure for 15 minutes. The serologic specificity of C carbohydrate is determined by an amino sugar. For group A streptococci, this is rhamnose-N-acetylglucosamine; for group C, it is rhamnose-N-acetylgalactosamine; for group F, it is glucopyranosyl-N-acetylgalactosamine.

(2) **M Protein:** This substance is closely associated with virulence of group A streptococci and occurs chiefly in organisms producing matt or mucoid colonies. Repeated passage on artificial media may lead to loss of M protein production, which may be restored by rapidly repeated animal passage. M protein interferes with the ingestion of virulent streptococci by phagocytic cells. Growing L forms of streptococci also produce M protein as well as hyaluronic acid.

M protein is present in extracts of group A streptococci made with hot hydrochloric acid. This protein determines the type specificity of group A streptococci as demonstrated by agglutination or precipitation reactions with absorbed type-specific sera. There are more than 50 types in group A. Types are assigned Arabic numbers. In man, antibodies to an M protein protect against infection with this specific type of group A streptococcus.

(3) **T Substance:** This antigen has no relationship to virulence of streptococci. It is destroyed by acid extraction and by heat and thus is separated from M protein. It is obtained from streptococci by proteolytic digestion (which rapidly destroys M proteins) and permits differentiation of certain types. Other types share the same T substance. Yet another surface antigen has been called R protein.

(4) **Nucleoproteins:** Extraction of streptococci with weak alkali yields mixtures of proteins and other substances of little serologic specificity, called P substances, which probably make up most of the streptococcal cell body.

Toxins & Enzymes

More than 20 extracellular products which are antigenic are elaborated by group A streptococci, including the following:

(1) **Streptokinase (fibrinolysin)** is produced by many strains of beta-hemolytic streptococci. It transforms the plasminogen of human serum into plasmin, an active proteolytic enzyme, which digests fibrin and other proteins. This process of digestion may be interfered with by nonspecific serum inhibitors and by a specific antibody, antistreptokinse, formed in response to previous exposure to streptokinase. In persons with normal cell-mediated immunity, the skin test with streptokinase-streptodornase is virtually always positive.

(2) **Streptodornase (streptococcal deoxyribonuclease)** is an enzyme which depolymerizes DNA. The enzymatic activity can be measured by the lowering in viscosity of known DNA solutions. Purulent exudates owe their viscosity largely to deoxyribonucleoprotein. Streptodornase is employed therapeutically to liquefy viscous exudates. Mixtures of streptodornase and streptokinase are used in "enzymatic debridement." They help to liquefy exudates and facilitate removal of pus and necrotic tissue; antimicrobial drugs thus gain better access, and infected surfaces recover more quickly. An antibody to DNase develops after streptococcal infections (normal limit = 100 units).

(3) **Hyaluronidase** is an enzyme which splits hyaluronic acid, an important component of the ground substance of connective tissue. Thus hyaluronidase aids in spreading infecting microorganisms (spreading factor). Hyaluronidases are antigenic and specific for each bacterial or tissue source. Following infection with hyaluronidase-producing organisms, specific antibodies are found in the serum. Purified hyaluronidase is employed in medical therapy to facilitate the spreading and absorption of fluids injected into tissues.

(4) **Erythrogenic toxin** is soluble and is destroyed by boiling for 1 hour. It causes the rash that occurs in scarlet fever. Only strains elaborating this toxin can cause scarlet fever. Erythrogenic toxin is elaborated only by lysogenic streptococci. Strains devoid of the temperate phage genome do not produce toxin. A nontoxigenic streptococcus, after lysogenic conversion, will produce erythrogenic toxin. Erythrogenic toxin is antigenic, giving rise to the formation of specific antitoxin which neutralizes the toxin. Persons possessing such antitoxin are immune to the rash though susceptible to streptococcal infection. There exist some minor qualitative differences between the erythrogenic toxins produced by different strains.

Susceptibility to erythrogenic toxin can be demonstrated by the **Dick test:** 0.1 ml of standardized, diluted, erythrogenic toxin (broth culture filtrate) is injected intradermally. Similar material, heat-inactivated, is used as a control. In the absence of significant concentration of antitoxin in the blood, a positive Dick test is seen, consisting of the appearance in 8–24 hours of erythema and edema measuring more than 10 mm in diameter. (This test has been largely abandoned.)

The specific nature of the rash of scarlet fever can be demonstrated by means of the **Schultz-Charlton reaction.** This consists of the injection of specific antitoxin into an area of scarlet fever rash. If the rash is caused by erythrogenic toxin of streptococci, the redness will blanch and fade in the injected area where the antitoxin has neutralized the toxin.

(5) Some streptococci elaborate a **diphosphopyridine nucleotidase** into the environment. This enzyme may be related to the organism's ability to kill leukocytes. Proteinases and amylase are produced by some strains.

(6) **Hemolysins:** Many streptococci are able to hemolyze red blood cells in vitro in varying degrees. Complete disruption of erythrocytes with release of hemoglobin is called *beta*-hemolysis. Incomplete lysis of erythrocytes with the formation of green pigment is called *alpha*-hemolysis. "Gamma" sometimes refers to nonhemolytic organisms.

Beta-hemolytic group A streptococci elaborate 2 hemolysins (streptolysins):

Streptolysin O is a protein (molecular weight 60,000) which is hemolytically active in the reduced state (available −SH groups) but rapidly inactivated when oxidized. It combines quantitatively with antistreptolysin O, an antibody which appears in animals or man following infection with any streptococci that produce streptolysin O. This antibody blocks hemolysis by streptolysin O. This phenomenon forms the basis of a quantitative test for the antibody. An antistreptolysin O (ASO) titer of sera in excess of 160−200 units is considered abnormally high and suggests either recent infection with streptococci or persistently high antibody levels following an earlier exposure.

Streptolysin S is the agent responsible for the hemolytic zones around streptococcal colonies on blood agar plates. It is not antigenic. However, sera of man and animals frequently contain a nonspecific inhibitor which is independent of past experience with streptococci.

Classification of Streptococci

A practical arrangement of streptococci into major categories can be based on (1) action on red blood cells, (2) resistance to physical and chemical factors, and (3) biochemical tests. While individual features for each species have only limited value, their consideration as a group permits separation of streptococci into 4 divisions.

A. Hemolytic Streptococci: Produce soluble hemolysins which result in beta-hemolysis on blood agar. They elaborate group-specific C carbohydrates. Acid extracts containing these C carbohydrates give precipitin reactions with specific antisera which permit the arrangement of hemolytic streptococci into groups A−O. The majority of invasive beta-hemolytic streptococci pathogenic for man fall into group A *Streptococcus pyogenes)*, but strains of groups B, C, and G are encountered in respiratory infections, bacteremia, and endocarditis. Group B strains are important in neonatal sepsis and meningitis and occur in the normal flora of the female genital tract. They rapidly hydrolyze sodium hippurate and are rarely bacitracin-sensitive.

B. Viridans Streptococci: Do not produce either soluble hemolysins or beta-hemolysis on blood agar.

Many species induce alpha-hemolysis, ie, they turn hemoglobin green. Some species have no action on blood and are called indifferent (gamma) streptococci. The effect on blood cells depends on the species of erythrocyte, on environmental conditions (eg, pH, temperature, moisture), and on other factors which are not understood. They do not produce C carbohydrate. In contrast to pneumococci (whose colonies they resemble), they are not bile-soluble. Viridans streptococci are the most prominent members of the normal flora of the human respiratory tract and are ordinarily associated with disease only when they settle on abnormal heart valves (subacute bacterial endocarditis) or establish themselves in the meninges or the urinary tract of man. They also occur widely in nature. Some *(S mutans)* synthesize large molecular polysaccharides, eg, dextrans, possibly play a role in dental caries, and sometimes cause endocarditis.

C. Enterococci *(Streptococcus faecalis):* Produce group D-specific C carbohydrate. They are capable of growing at 10° C and 45° C, in 0.1% methylene blue milk, on bile esculin agar, or in 6.5% NaCl concentration. They cause variable hemolysis. They are part of the normal flora of the intestinal tract of man and animals and may cause disease when introduced into tissues, the bloodstream, urinary tract, or meninges. Enterococci are quite resistant to many antimicrobial drugs. Penicillins often inhibit but do not kill them unless an aminoglycoside is also present.

Other group D streptococci *(S bovis, S equinus)* are susceptible to penicillins and are inhibited by 6.5% NaCl or by bile but may also occur in the genitourinary tract and produce endocarditis.

D. Lactic Streptococci: Elaborate group N-specific C carbohydrate. Their hemolytic ability is variable. They grow on bile esculin agar but not at 45° C or in 6.5% NaCl, which differentiates them from enterococci. They do not produce disease but are commonly present in milk and are often responsible for the normal coagulation of milk ("souring").

E. Peptostreptococcus: Peptostreptococcus is a genus of strict anaerobes which act in mixed infections of the abdomen, pelvis, or lung. They occur in the normal flora of the gut and of the female genital tract.

Pathogenesis & Clinical Findings

A variety of distinct disease processes are associated with streptococcal infections. The biologic properties of the infecting organisms, the nature of the host response, and the portals of entry of the infection all greatly influence the pathologic picture. Infections can arbitrarily be divided into several categories.

A. Diseases Attributable to Invasion by Beta-Hemolytic Group A Streptococci *(Streptococcus pyogenes):* The portal of entry determines the principal clinical picture. In each case, however, there is a diffuse and rapidly spreading cellulitis which involves the tissues and extends along the lymphatic pathway with only minimal local suppuration. From the lymphatics the infection rapidly extends to the bloodstream, whereupon bacteremia supervenes.

1. Erysipelas—If the portal of entry is the skin or superficial mucous membranes, erysipelas results, with massive brawny edema and a rapidly advancing margin.

2. Puerperal fever—If the streptococci enter the uterus after delivery, puerperal fever develops, which is essentially a septicemia originating in the infected wound (endometritis).

3. Sepsis—Infection of traumatic or surgical wounds with streptococci results in streptococcal sepsis or surgical scarlet fever.

B. Diseases Attributable to Local Infection With Beta-Hemolytic Group A Streptococci and to Their Products:

1. Streptococcal sore throat—The commonest infection due to beta-hemolytic streptococci is streptococcal sore throat. In the infant and small child it occurs as a subacute nasopharyngitis with a thin serous discharge and little fever but with a marked tendency of the infection to extend to the middle ear, the mastoid, and the meninges. The cervical lymph nodes are usually enlarged. The illness may persist for weeks. In older children and adults, the disease is more acute and is characterized by intense nasopharyngitis, tonsillitis, and intense redness and edema of the mucous membranes, with purulent exudate; enlarged, tender cervical lymph nodes; and (usually) a high fever. Twenty percent of infections are asymptomatic. A similar clinical picture can occur with infectious mononucleosis, adenovirus infection, diphtheria, and fusospirochetal infection. If the infecting streptococci produce erythrogenic toxin and the patient has no antitoxic immunity, scarlet fever rash occurs. Antitoxin to the erythrogenic toxin prevents the rash but does not interfere with the streptococcal infection. With the most intense inflammation, tissues may break down and form peritonsillar abscesses (quinsy) or Ludwig's angina, where massive swelling of the floor of the mouth blocks air passages.

Streptococcal infection of the upper respiratory tract does not usually involve the lungs. Pneumonia due to beta-hemolytic streptococci is most commonly a sequel to viral infections, eg, influenza or measles, which seem to enhance susceptibility greatly.

2. Impetigo—Local infection of the skin's superficial layers, especially in small children, leads to the development of impetigo, superficial blisters which break readily and spread by continuity. The denuded surface is covered with honey-colored crusts. Impetigo is highly contagious in children. Streptococci are usually associated with staphylococci in this infection. Streptococcal skin infection (especially types 49, 57, 59, 60, and 61) may lead to poststreptococcal nephritis but not often to rheumatic fever. Streptococcal pyoderma is favored by a hot, humid climate.

C. Bacterial Endocarditis:

1. Acute bacterial endocarditis—In the course of bacteremia, beta-hemolytic streptococci, pneumococci, staphylococci, or gram-negative bacteria may settle on normal or previously deformed heart valves, producing acute ulcerative bacterial endocarditis. Rapid destruction of the valves frequently leads to a fatal outcome

in days or weeks. Other organisms are encountered occasionally in this disease, particularly in narcotics users.

2. Subacute bacterial endocarditis often involves abnormal valves (congenital deformities and rheumatic or atherosclerotic lesions). Although any organism reaching the bloodstream may establish itself on such valves, subacute bacterial endocarditis is most frequently due to members of the normal flora of the respiratory or intestinal tract which have accidentally reached the blood. After dental extraction, at least 30% of patients have viridans streptococcal bacteremia. These streptococci, ordinarily the most prevalent members of the upper respiratory flora, are also the most frequent cause of subacute bacterial endocarditis. About 5–10% of cases are due to enterococci. The lesion is slowly progressive, and a certain amount of healing accompanies the active inflammation; vegetations consist of fibrin, platelets, blood cells, and bacteria adherent to the valve leaflets. The clinical course is gradual, but the disease is invariably fatal in untreated cases. The typical clinical picture includes fever, anemia, weakness, a heart murmur, embolic phenomena, an enlarged spleen, and renal lesions.

D. Other Infections: Various streptococci, particularly enterococci, are frequently the cause of urinary tract infections. Anaerobic streptococci (Peptostreptococcus) occur in the normal female genital tract, in the mouth, and in the intestine. They may give rise to suppurative lesions, either alone or in association with other anaerobes, particularly bacteroides. Such infections may occur in wounds, postpartum endometritis, following rupture of an abdominal viscus, or in chronic suppuration of the lung. Such pus usually has a foul odor. A variety of other streptococci (groups B–L and O) which are usually found in lower animals may also occasionally produce human infections.

E. Poststreptococcal Diseases (Rheumatic Fever, Glomerulonephritis): Following an acute group A streptococcal infection, there is a latent period of 1–4 weeks, after which nephritis or rheumatic fever occasionally develops. The latent period suggests that these poststreptococcal diseases are not attributable to the direct effect of disseminated bacteria but represent instead a hypersensitivity response which follows streptococcal insult to the affected organs. Nephritis is more commonly preceded by infection of the skin; rheumatic fever, by infection of the respiratory tract.

1. Acute glomerulonephritis develops in some persons 3 weeks following streptococcal infection, particularly with types 12, 4, 49, or 57. Certain strains are particularly nephritogenic. Thus, 23% of children with a skin infection with a type 49 strain developed nephritis or hematuria. However, after random streptococcal infections, the incidence of nephritis is less than 0.5%. Other nephritogenic types are 59–61.

Glomerulonephritis may be initiated by antigen-antibody complexes on the glomerular basement membrane. The most important antigen is probably in the streptococcal protoplast membrane. In acute nephritis, there is blood and protein in the urine, edema, high blood pressure, and nitrogen retention; serum complement levels are low. A few patients die; some develop chronic glomerulonephritis with ultimate kidney failure; the majority recover completely.

2. Rheumatic fever is the most serious sequel to hemolytic streptococcal infection because it results in damage to heart muscle and valves. In some countries (eg, Portugal, Rumania, Bulgaria), rheumatic heart disease still ranks high as a cause of death in young adults. Certain strains of group A streptococci contain cell membrane antigens which cross-react with human heart sarcolemma. Sera from rheumatic fever patients contain an antibody to these antigens.

The onset of rheumatic fever is often preceded by a group A streptococcus infection 1–4 weeks earlier, although the infection may be mild and may not be detected. Untreated streptococcal infections may be followed by rheumatic fever in up to 3% of military personnel and 0.3% of civilian children. In general, patients with more severe streptococcal sore throats have a greater chance of developing rheumatic fever.

Typical symptoms and signs of rheumatic fever include fever, malaise, a migratory nonsuppurative polyarthritis, and evidence of inflammation of all parts of the heart (endocardium, myocardium, pericardium). The carditis characteristically leads to thickened and deformed valves and to small perivascular granulomas in the myocardium (Aschoff bodies) which are finally replaced by scar tissue. Erythrocyte sedimentation rates, serum transaminase levels, electrocardiograms, and other tests are used to estimate rheumatic activity.

Rheumatic fever has a marked tendency to be reactivated by recurrent streptococcal infections, whereas nephritis does not have this characteristic. The first attack of rheumatic fever usually produces only slight cardiac damage, which, however, increases with each subsequent attack. It is therefore of the utmost importance to protect such patients from recurrent group A hemolytic streptococcal infections by prophylactic penicillin administration.

Diagnostic Laboratory Tests

Specimens to be obtained depend upon the nature of the streptococcal infection. A throat swab, pus, or blood is obtained for culture. Serum is obtained for antibody determinations, particularly antistreptolysin O titer.

A. Stained Smears: Smears from pus often show single cocci or pairs rather than definite chains. Cocci are sometimes gram-negative. If smears of pus show streptococci but cultures fail to grow, anaerobic organisms must be suspected. Smears of throat swabs are not contributory because streptococci (viridans) are always present.

Smears from broth cultures of throat swabs 2–3 hours old can be stained with fluorescent group A-specific antibody for the most rapid identification of group A streptococci in clinical disease or carriers.

B. Culture: For rapid identification, all specimens suspected of containing streptococci are cultured on blood agar plates. In addition, if anaerobes are suspected, suitable broth cultures and thioglycollate medium must be inoculated. Blood cultures will grow hemolytic group A streptococci (eg, in sepsis) within hours or a few days. However, because certain alpha-hemolytic streptococci or enterococci may grow very slowly, blood cultures in cases of suspected endocarditis should always be incubated for 1–2 weeks before being discarded as negative. Incubation in 10% CO_2 often speeds hemolysis. Slicing into a blood agar plate has a similar effect. The degree and kind of hemolysis (and colonial appearance) may permit placing an organism in a definite group but serologic grouping and typing by means of precipitin tests should be performed whenever possible for definitive classification and for epidemiologic reasons. Streptococci belonging to group A may be presumptively identified by empirically determined amounts of bacitracin. A bacitracin disk containing 0.2 unit strongly inhibits growth of group A streptococci.

C. Serologic Tests: A rise in antibody titer to many antigens can be estimated, including antistreptolysin O (ASO) (particularly in respiratory disease), antihyaluronidase (particularly in skin infections), antistreptokinase, anti-DNase, "bactericidal" anti-M type-specific antibodies, and others. Antibodies to several streptococcal antigens and enzymes are measured by the sensitive streptozyme test. The antigens are adsorbed onto sheep red blood cells, and agglutination by antibodies occurs within a few minutes on a slide.

Immunity

Resistance against streptococcal diseases is type-specific. Thus a host who has recovered from infection by one group A streptococcal type is relatively insusceptible to reinfection by the same type but fully susceptible to infection by another type. This resistance is associated with type-specific anti-M antibodies. These are demonstrated in the so-called "bactericidal test" which exploits the fact that streptococci are rapidly killed after phagocytosis. M protein interferes with phagocytosis, but in the presence of type-specific antibody to M protein streptococci are killed by leukocytes. The changing patterns of streptococcal disease with increasing age suggest that in the course of infections by beta-hemolytic streptococci the general reactivity to all types is altered, with increasing localization and intensity of inflammatory response.

Immunity against the erythrogenic toxin is based on antitoxin in the blood. This antitoxic immunity protects against the rash of scarlet fever but has no effect on infection with streptococci. Antibody to streptolysin O (antistreptolysin) develops following infection but does not indicate immunity. High titers (> 250 units) indicate recent or repeated infections and are found more frequently in rheumatic individuals than those with uncomplicated streptococcal infections.

Treatment

All beta-hemolytic group A streptococci are sensitive to penicillin G, and most to erythromycin. Some are resistant to tetracyclines. Alpha-hemolytic streptococci and enterococci, on the other hand, vary widely in their susceptibility to antimicrobial agents. Particularly in bacterial endocarditis, antibiotic sensitivity tests are essential to determine which drugs (and in what dosage) may be used for optimal therapy. In these cases, laboratory tests should include determinations of both inhibitory and killing power of drugs or drug combinations. Aminoglycosides often enhance the action of penicillin in killing streptococci, especially enterococci.

Antimicrobial drugs have no effect on established glomerulonephritis and rheumatic fever. However, in acute streptococcal infections, every effort must be made to eradicate streptococci from the patient, eliminate the antigenic stimulus, and thus prevent poststreptococcal disease. Doses of penicillin or erythromycin that result in effective tissue levels for 10 days usually accomplish this. Antimicrobial drugs are also very useful in the prevention or early treatment of reinfection with beta-hemolytic group A streptococci in rheumatic subjects.

Epidemiology, Prevention, & Control

A number of streptococci (viridans streptococci, enterococci, etc) are members of the normal flora of the human body. They produce disease only when established in parts of the body where they do not normally occur (eg, heart valves). To prevent such accidents, particularly in the course of surgical procedures on the respiratory, gastrointestinal, and urinary tracts which result in temporary bacteremia, antimicrobial agents are often administered prophylactically to persons with known heart valve deformity.

The ultimate source of group A streptococci is always a person harboring these organisms. The person may have a clinical or subclinical infection, or he may be a carrier. He usually distributes streptococci directly to other persons via droplets from the respiratory tract or skin. The nasal discharges of a person harboring beta-hemolytic streptococci are the most dangerous source of massive contamination with these organisms. The role of contaminated bedding, utensils, or clothing is doubtful. The infected udder of a cow yields milk which may cause epidemic spread of hemolytic streptococci. Immunologic grouping and typing of streptococci are valuable tools for epidemiologic tracing of the transmission chain.

Control procedures are directed mainly at the human source: (1) Detection and early intensive antimicrobial therapy of respiratory and skin infections with group A streptococci. This requires maintenance of adequate penicillin levels in tissues for 10 days (eg, benzathine penicillin G, 2.4 million units given once IM). Erythromycin is an alternative drug of choice. Prompt eradication of streptococci from early infections can effectively prevent the development of poststreptococcal disease. (2) Antistreptococcal chemoprophylaxis in persons who have suffered an attack of rheumatic fever. This involves giving one injection of benzathine penicillin G, 1.2–2.4 million units IM every 3 weeks, or daily oral penicillin or oral sulfonamide.

The first attack of rheumatic fever infrequently causes major heart damage. However, such persons are particularly susceptible to reinfections with streptococci which precipitate relapses of rheumatic activity and give rise to cardiac damage. Chemoprophylaxis in such individuals, especially children, must be continued for years. Chemoprophylaxis is not used in glomerulonephritis because of the small number of nephritogenic types of streptococci. (3) Eradication of group A streptococci from carriers. This is especially important when carriers are in "sensitive" areas, eg, obstetric delivery rooms, surgical teams, classrooms, or nurseries. Unfortunately, it is often difficult to eradicate hemolytic streptococci from permanent carriers, and individuals may occasionally have to be shifted away from "sensitive" areas for some time. (4) Dust control, ventilation, air filtration, ultraviolet light, and aerosol mists are all of doubtful efficacy in the control of streptococcal transmission. Milk should always be pasteurized.

THE PNEUMOCOCCI

The pneumococci *(Diplococcus pneumoniae, Streptococcus pneumoniae)* are gram-positive diplococci, often lancet-shaped or arranged in chains, possessing a capsule of polysaccharide which permits easy "typing" with specific antisera. They are readily lysed by surface-active agents, eg, bile salts. The organisms are normal inhabitants of the upper respiratory tract of man and can cause pneumonia, sinusitis, otitis, meningitis, and other infectious processes.

Morphology & Identification

A. Typical Organisms: The typical gram-positive, lancet-shaped diplococci (Figs 14–5, 14–6, 14–7) are often seen in specimens of young cultures. In sputum or pus, single cocci or chains are also seen. With age, the organisms rapidly become gram-negative and tend to lyse spontaneously.

Autolysis of pneumococci is greatly enhanced by surface-active agents. Lysis of pneumococci occurs in a few minutes when ox bile (10%) or sodium deoxycholate (2%) is added to a broth culture or suspension of organisms at neutral pH, or when optochin (ethylhydrocupreine hydrochloride, 1:4000) is added to solid media. Viridans streptococci do not lyse. This "bile solubility test" differentiates between pneumococci and other streptococci.

B. Culture: Pneumococci form a small round colony, at first dome-shaped and later developing a central plateau with an elevated rim and alpha-hemolysis on blood agar. Routinely they are best grown in meat-infusion blood broth. Ten percent CO_2 aids growth.

Other identifying points include almost uniform virulence for mice when injected intraperitoneally and the "capsule swelling test" or quellung reaction (Fig 14–7).

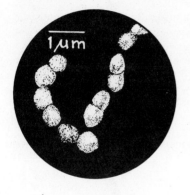

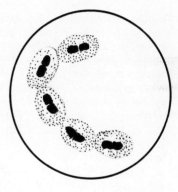

Figure 14–5. Drawing from electron micrograph of pneumococci.

Figure 14–6. Pneumococci in stained smear.

Figure 14–7. Pneumococci mixed with type-specific antiserum (quellung reaction).

C. Growth Characteristics: Most energy is obtained from fermentation of glucose, accompanied by the rapid production of lactic acid, which limits growth. Neutralization of broth cultures with alkali at intervals results in massive growth.

D. Variation: Any culture (bacterial population) of pneumococci contains a few organisms unable to produce capsular polysaccharide, which gives rise to rough colonies. The majority are polysaccharide-producing bacteria, which give rise to smooth colonies. Rough forms predominate if the culture is grown in type-specific antipolysaccharide serum.

E. Transformation: When a rough (polysaccharide-less) organism of one type is grown in the presence of DNA extracted from another pneumococcus type, smooth (encapsulated) organisms of the latter type are formed. Similar transformation reactions have been performed which involve changes in drug resistance.

Antigenic Structure

A. Component Structures: The capsular polysaccharide (SSS = specific soluble substance) is immunologically distinct for each of the more than 85 types. The polysaccharide is an antigen which stimulates B cells only (see p 138).

The somatic portion of the pneumococcus contains an M protein which is characteristic for each type and a C carbohydrate which is common to all pneumococci. The C carbohydrate can be precipitated by C-reactive protein, a substance found in the serum of certain patients (see Chapter 26).

B. Quellung Reaction: When pneumococci of a certain type are mixed with an antiserum against that type (specific antipolysaccharide serum) on a microscopic slide, the capsule swells markedly. This reaction is useful for quick identification and for "typing" of the organisms (Fig 14–7), either in sputum or in cultures. A polyvalent serum containing antibody to more than 80 types ("omniserum") is the best method for establishing the presence of pneumococci in sputum.

Pathogenesis

A. Types of Pneumococci: In adults, types I–IX are responsible for about 80% of cases of pneumococcal pneumonia and for more than half of all fatalities in pneumococcal bacteremia; in children, type XIV is a frequent cause.

B. Production of Disease: Pneumococci produce disease through their ability to multiply in the tissues. They produce no toxins of significance. The "virulence" of the organism is a function of its capsule, which prevents or delays ingestion of encapsulated cells by phagocytes. A serum which contains antibodies against the type-specific polysaccharide (SSS) protects against infection. If such a serum is absorbed with SSS it loses its protective power. Animals or humans immunized with a given type SSS are subsequently immune to that type and possess precipitating and opsonizing antibodies for that type SSS.

C. Loss of Natural Resistance: Since 40–70% of humans are at some time or other carriers of virulent pneumococci, the normal respiratory mucosa must possess great natural resistance to the pneumococcus. Among the factors that probably lower this resistance and thus predispose to pneumococcal infection are the following:

1. Abnormalities of the respiratory tract—Other infections (eg, viral) which damage surface cells; abnormal accumulations of mucus (eg, allergy), which protect pneumococci from phagocytosis; bronchial obstruction (eg, atelectasis); and respiratory tract injury due to irritants disturbing the mucociliary blanket.

2. Alcohol or drug intoxication, which depresses phagocytic activity, depresses the cough reflex, and facilitates aspiration of foreign material.

3. Abnormal circulatory dynamics (eg, pulmonary congestion).

4. Malnutrition, general debility, sickle cell anemia, hyposplenism.

Pathology

Pneumococcal infection causes an outpouring of

fibrinous edema fluid into the alveoli, followed by red cells and leukocytes, which results in consolidation of portions of the lung. Many pneumococci are found throughout this exudate. The alveolar walls remain normally intact during the infection. Later, mononuclear cells actively phagocytose the debris, and this liquid phase is gradually reabsorbed. The pneumococci are taken up by phagocytes and digested intracellularly.

Clinical Findings

The onset of pneumococcal pneumonia is usually sudden, with fever, chills, and sharp pleural pain. The sputum is similar to the alveolar exudate, being characteristically bloody or rusty. Early in the disease, when the fever is high, bacteremia is present in 15–25% of cases. Before the days of chemotherapy, recovery from the disease began between the fifth and tenth days and was associated with the development of type-specific antibodies. With antimicrobial therapy, the illness is terminated promptly; if drugs are given early, the development of consolidation is interrupted.

From the respiratory tract, pneumococci may reach other sites. The sinuses and middle ear are most frequently involved. From the bloodstream (or through extension from the mastoid), the meninges are reached. With the early use of chemotherapy, acute pneumococcal endocarditis has become rare. Pneumococcal pneumonia must be differentiated from pulmonary infarct, atelectasis, neoplasm, congestive heart failure, and pneumonia caused by many other bacteria. Empyema is the commonest complication and requires aspiration and drainage.

Diagnostic Laboratory Tests

Blood is drawn for culture, and sputum is collected for demonstration of pneumococci by smear and culture. It is impractical to test serum for antibodies.

Sputum may be examined in several ways:

(1) **Stained smears**: Gram-stained film of rusty-red sputum shows typical organisms.

(2) **Capsule swelling tests**: Fresh emulsified sputum mixed with antiserum gives "capsule swelling" for identification of pneumococci and possible typing.

(3) **Culture**: Sputum cultured on blood agar in candle jar. Blood culture.

(4) **Injection of sputum intraperitoneally into white mice**: Animals die in 18–48 hours; heart blood gives pure culture of pneumococci. Peritoneal exudate can be used for quellung reaction.

(5) **Pneumococcal meningitis** should be diagnosed by prompt culture of CSF.

Immunity

Immunity to infection with pneumococci is type-specific and depends both on antibodies to SSS and on intact phagocytic function.

Treatment

Type-specific antiserum was formerly administered intravenously to patients who lacked antibodies.

Absence of antibodies was determined by the absence of reaction upon intradermal injection of type-specific polysaccharide (Francis test).

Since pneumococci are sensitive to many antimicrobial drugs, early treatment results in rapid recovery, and antibody response seems to play a much diminished role. The penicillins are the drugs of choice. Recently, some drug resistance has appeared: Pneumococci resistant to tetracyclines, erythromycin, and lincomycin have been isolated from patients. Pneumococci of increased resistance to penicillin have been isolated in New Guinea.

Epidemiology, Prevention, & Control

Pneumococcal pneumonia accounts for ± 80% of all bacterial pneumonias. It is an endemic disease with a high incidence of carriers. The predisposing factors (see above) are more important in the development of illness than exposure to the infectious agent, and the healthy carrier is more important in disseminating infection than the sick patient.

It is possible to immunize individuals with type-specific polysaccharides. Experimental vaccine programs (including types 1–9, 12, 14, 18, 19, and 23) are under way. Such vaccines can probably provide 90% protection against bacteremic pneumonia. In addition, it is desirable to avoid "predisposing" factors, to establish the diagnosis promptly, and to begin adequate chemotherapy early. At present, fatalities (5%) from pneumococcal pneumonia are limited to the very young (infants), persons older than age 45 years, or persons with impaired natural resistance and those with bacteremia.

THE NEISSERIAE

The neisseriae are a group of gram-negative cocci, usually occurring in pairs. Some members of the group are normal inhabitants of the human respiratory tract and occur extracellularly; others (gonococci, meningococci) are human pathogens and typically occur intracellularly.

Morphology & Identification

A. **Typical Organisms**: The typical neisseria organism is a gram-negative diplococcus, approximately 0.8 μm in diameter. Neisseriae are nonmotile and nonsporeforming. Individual cocci are kidney-shaped, with the flat or concave sides adjacent. Older cultures or those exposed to antibiotics may contain swollen, distorted organisms. Meningococci and gonococci autolyze quickly, particularly in an alkaline environment.

B. **Culture**: In 48 hours on enriched media (eg, Mueller-Hinton, Thayer-Martin), gonococci and meningococci form convex, glistening, elevated, creamy, mucoid colonies 1–5 mm in diameter. Colonies are transparent, nonpigmented or yellowish, and nonhemolytic. N flavescens and N flava have a yellowish

Table 14—1. Fermentation reactions of neisseriae.

	Acid Formed From			Growth on Plain Nutrient Agar
	Dextrose	Maltose	Sucrose	
N meningitidis (meningococcus)	+	+	−	−
N gonorrhoeae (gonococcus)	+	−	−	−
N catarrhalis	−	−	−	+
N sicca	+	+	+	+
N flavescens	−	−	−	+

pigment and are less mucoid. *N sicca* produces opaque, brittle, wrinkled colonies.

C. Growth Characteristics: Neisseriae are strict aerobes. They ferment a variety of carbohydrates, forming acid but not gas. Fermentation reactions are summarized in Table 14—1.

Meningococci and gonococci grow best on media containing complex organic substances such as blood or animal proteins and in an atmosphere containing 5% CO_2 (eg, candle jar). They are inhibited by some toxic constituents of the medium, such as fatty acids or salts. They are rapidly killed by drying, sunlight, moist heat, and many disinfectants. They produce indophenol oxidase and autolytic enzymes which result in rapid swelling and dissolution of cultures. This process can be inhibited by cyanide or by heating at 65° C for 30 minutes.

NEISSERIA MENINGITIDIS
(N intracellularis, Meningococcus)

Antigenic Structure

By agglutination and agglutinin-absorption tests, meningococci can be classified into 4 main groups, designated as A, B, C, and D. Additional serogroups are called X, Y, and Z. Most strains from outbreaks are now A, B, C, or Y. Polysaccharides specific for groups A, B, and C have been isolated. The group A polysaccharide is a polymer of N-acetyl-O-acetylmannosamine phosphate. The group C polysaccharide is a polymer of N-acetyl-O-acetylneuraminic acid. Meningococcal antigens are found in blood and CSF of active severe cases.

The nucleoproteins of meningococci (P substance) account for the toxic effect but are not specific for these organisms. Certain nucleic acid extracts are capable of "transformation reactions," inducing streptomycin resistance in meningococci. The composition of cell walls of meningococci resembles that of coliforms; they contain a group-reactive antigen.

Pathogenesis, Pathology & Clinical Findings

Man is the only natural host for whom meningococci are pathogenic. Mice can be infected intraperitoneally if meningococci of any serologic type are suspended in mucin.

The nasopharynx is the portal of entry of meningococci. There the organisms may form part of the transient flora without producing symptoms or may produce an exudative pharyngitis. From the nasopharynx, organisms may reach the bloodstream, producing a bacteremia (meningococcemia) with high fever and a hemorrhagic rash. There may be fulminant sepsis, disseminated intravascular coagulation, and circulatory collapse (Waterhouse-Friderichsen syndrome).

Meningitis is the commonest complication of meningococcemia. It usually begins very suddenly, with intense headache, vomiting, and stiff neck and progresses to coma within a few hours.

During meningococcemia there is thrombosis of many small blood vessels in many organs, with perivascular infiltration and petechial hemorrhages. There may be interstitial myocarditis, arthritis, and skin lesions. In meningitis the meninges are acutely inflamed, with thrombosis of blood vessels and exudation of polymorphonuclear leukocytes so that the surface of the brain is covered with a thick purulent exudate.

It is not known what transforms an asymptomatic infection of the nasopharynx into meningococcemia and meningitis, but this can be prevented by specific bactericidal serum antibodies against the infecting strain. Meningococci are readily phagocytosed in the presence of a specific opsonin.

Diagnostic Laboratory Tests

Specimens of blood are taken for culture, and of spinal fluid for smear, culture, and chemical determinations. Nasopharyngeal swab cultures are suitable for carrier surveys. Puncture material from petechiae may be taken for smear and culture.

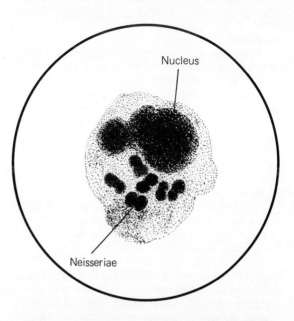

Figure 14—8. Meningococci within a polymorphonuclear leukocyte in spinal fluid.

A. Smears: Gram's stain of the sediment of centri-fuged spinal fluid or of petechial aspirate often shows typical diplococci within polymorphonuclear leuko-cytes or extracellularly. Because meningococci may autolyze rapidly, the fluid must be examined fresh.

B. Culture: Specimens must be promptly plated on heated blood agar (chocolate agar) or Thayer-Martin medium and incubated at 37° C in an atmo-sphere of 5% CO_2 (candle jar). Thayer-Martin medium with antibiotics (VCN: vancomycin, colistin, nystatin) favors the growth of neisseriae and inhibits many other bacteria. Spinal fluid or blood generally yields pure cultures which can be further identified by carbohy-drate fermentation (dextrose +, maltose +, sucrose −) and agglutination with type-specific (or polyvalent) serum.

Direct incubation of freshly drawn spinal fluid at 37° C may give growth of meningococci. It is also possible to obtain rapid growth by inoculation of the yolk sac of 8- to 10-day-old embryonated eggs.

Colonies of meningococci on solid media, partic-ularly in mixed culture, may be identified by the oxidase test: When the plate is sprayed with tetramethylparaphenylenediamine hydrochloride, meningococ-cus (and other neisseria) colonies rapidly turn dark.

C. Serology: Antibodies to meningococcal poly-saccharides can be measured by latex agglutination or hemagglutination tests or by their bactericidal activity.

Immunity

Immunity to meningococcal infection is associ-ated with the presence of specific bactericidal anti-bodies in the serum. These antibodies develop after subclinical infections with different strains or injection of polysaccharides and are type-specific. Infants have passive immunity through IgG antibodies transferred from the mother.

Treatment

Meningococci formerly were uniformly suscep-tible to sulfonamides, and these were the drugs of choice. Sulfonamide-resistant meningococci are now prevalent, comprising 50–70% of all isolates. Penicillin G has become the drug of choice—or chloramphenicol in persons allergic to penicillins. Antimeningococcus serum is no longer employed therapeutically. High levels of meningococcal antigen in CSF are associated with neurologic damage.

Epidemiology, Prevention, & Control

Meningococcal meningitis occurs in epidemic waves (eg, military installations; in Brazil, there were more than 15,000 cases in 1974) and a smaller number of sporadic interepidemic cases. Five to 30% of the normal population may harbor meningococci in the nasopharynx during interepidemic periods. During epidemics the carrier rate goes up to 70 or 80%. A rise in the number of cases is always preceded by an in-creased number of respiratory "carriers." In the past, widespread chemoprophylaxis with sulfonamides was successful. Since the appearance of many sulfonamide-

resistant meningococci, this is no longer possible. Treatment with penicillin suppresses meningococci in the nasopharynx but does not eradicate the carrier state. Rifampin or minocycline can often eradicate the meningococcal carrier state, but some rifampin-resis-tant meningococci are emerging. Sequential use of these 2 drugs is proposed.

Clinical cases of meningitis present only a negli-gible source of infection, and isolation has therefore only limited usefulness. More important is the reduc-tion of personal contacts in a population with a high "carrier" rate. This is accomplished by good ventila-tion and avoidance of crowding. Specific polysaccha-rides of groups A and C can stimulate antibody re-sponse and protect susceptibles against infection. Such vaccines are currently used in selected populations (eg, the military; civilian epidemics).

NEISSERIA GONORRHOEAE
(Gonococcus)

Morphologically and culturally, the gonococcus resembles the meningococcus; however, it does not ferment maltose. The current epidemic of gonorrhea is associated with a great variety of clinical manifesta-tions.

Antigenic Structure

Gonococci are serologically heterogeneous, al-though many freshly isolated strains appear to fall into one group. The pili in colonial types 1 and 2 are im-munologically specific for gonococci. Gonococci pos-sess polysaccharides and nucleoproteins which are similar to those of other neisseriae. Serologic tests are therefore not wholly specific.

Pathogenesis, Pathology, & Clinical Findings

Gonococci exhibit 4 morphologic types of colo-nies. Only types 1 and 2 appear to be virulent and possess pili which attach to epithelial cells and help to resist phagocytosis.

Gonococci attack mucous membranes of the genitourinary tract and the eye, producing acute sup-puration which may lead to tissue invasion; this is followed by chronic inflammation and fibrosis. In the male there is usually urethritis, with yellow, creamy pus and painful urination. The process may extend to the prostate and epididymis. As suppuration subsides, there is fibrosis, sometimes leading to urethral stric-tures. Urethral infection in men can be asymptomatic. In the female the infection extends from urethra and vagina to cervix, giving rise to mucopurulent discharge. It may then progress to the fallopian tubes, causing pelvic inflammatory disease, fibrosis, and obliteration of tubes with consequent sterility. Chronic gonococcal cervicitis or proctitis is often asymptomatic.

Gonococcal bacteremia leads to skin lesions (especially hemorrhagic papules and pustules) and to arthritis and tenosynovitis (especially of the knees, ankles, and wrists). Gonococci can be cultured from only 25% of patients with gonococcal arthritis. Other lesions include proctitis, pharyngitis, endocarditis, meningitis, and eye involvement.

Ophthalmia neonatorum, an infection of the eye of the newborn, is acquired during passage through an infected birth canal. The initial conjunctivitis rapidly progresses to involve all structures of the eye and commonly results in blindness. To avoid this disaster, instillation of silver nitrate into the conjunctival sac of the newborn has been made compulsory.

Diagnostic Laboratory Tests

Pus and secretions are taken from the urethra, cervix, prostate, rectal mucosa, or throat, and occasionally synovial fluid for culture and smear.

A. Stained Smears: In the acute process, Gram's stains of smears reveal many intracellular diplococci within pus cells. These give a presumptive diagnosis. In the later, chronic stages, when the secretions are thinner and contain few pus cells, gonococci are often difficult to find and reliance must be placed on culture. Immunofluorescent staining of smears is more efficient than other stains.

B. Cultures: Immediately after collection, pus or mucus is streaked on a rich selective medium (eg, Thayer-Martin VCN [vancomycin, colistin, nystatin] medium—Public Health Rep 81:559, 1966) and incubated in an atmosphere containing 5% CO_2 (candle jar) at 37° C. Forty-eight hours later, colonies are subjected to the oxidase test (see above). Subcultures of the organisms may be subjected to fermentation reactions (Table 14—1). The gonococcus fails to ferment maltose, and dextrose is the only sugar from which acid is produced. To avoid overgrowth by contaminants, the culture medium should contain vancomycin, 3 μg/ml; colistin, 7.5 μg/ml; and nystatin, 12.5 units/ml (VCN mixture).

C. Serology: CF tests are sometimes performed on persons with negative cultures who are suspected of harboring chronic gonococcal infection. These tests, however, lack specificity and reliability. Detection of antibodies to gonococcal pili is a promising technic in the diagnosis of asymptomatic or culture-negative infection.

Immunity

Immunity to gonococci does not seem to develop in the course of infection, although IgA antibodies occur on mucous membranes. Reinfection is common.

Treatment

Local irrigation of the urethra has little effect.

Many strains of gonococci are now resistant to sulfonamides, and resistance to penicillin is increasing. Recently, strains of gonococci which require 2 units of penicillin per ml for inhibition have been encountered and only 15% of strains are inhibited by 0.5 unit/ml. The minimum acceptable doses of procaine penicillin G are now 4.8 million units IM in acute infections. As alternatives, 5-day courses of oral tetracycline or erythromycin are being used. However, resistance to these drugs is also developing. In established chronic infection (prostatitis, cervicitis), even longer treatment with large doses of drugs is necessary for cure. The basis of drug resistance in gonococci is unknown. It may involve chromosomal transformation controlling cell permeability, or drug binding.

While antimicrobial therapy usually leads to prompt disappearance of symptoms, cure must be established by repeated cultures. Because syphilis may have been acquired simultaneously, treatment and follow-up must be planned accordingly.

Epidemiology, Prevention, & Control

Gonorrhea is worldwide in distribution, and its incidence has risen steadily since 1955. It is almost exclusively transmitted by sexual contact, principally by women and men harboring asymptomatic chronic infections. The infectivity of the organism is such that a single exposure to an infected sexual partner has a 20—30% chance (or greater) of resulting in infection. The infection rate can be reduced by avoiding sexual promiscuity; rapid eradication of gonococci from infected individuals by means of early diagnosis and treatment; and finding of cases and contacts through education and screening of populations at high risk. The development of a specific serologic test will be crucial. Mechanical prophylaxis (condoms) provides only partial protection. Chemoprophylaxis cannot be relied upon because of the rise in antibiotic resistance of the gonococcus.

Ophthalmia neonatorum is prevented by the local application to the conjunctiva of the newborn of a substance bactericidal for gonococci on contact, eg, 1% silver nitrate.

OTHER NEISSERIAE

N catarrhalis and *N sicca* are normal members of the flora of the respiratory tract, particularly the nasopharynx, and do not produce disease. The pigmented neisseriae *(N flava, N flavescens)* occupy a similar position, but these organisms may on rare occasions cause meningitis or endocarditis.

•   •   •

General References

Austrian R: Random gleanings from a life with the pneumococcus. J Infect Dis 131:474, 1975.

Berry FA & others: Transient bacteremia during dental manipulation. Pediatrics 51:476, 1973.

Bisno AL & others: Contrasting epidemiology of rheumatic fever and glomerulonephritis. N Engl J Med 283:561, 1970.

Buchanan TM & others: Quantitative determination of antibody to gonococcal pili. J Clin Invest 52:2896, 1973.

Center for Disease Control: Gonorrhea: Recommended treatment schedules. Ann Intern Med 82:230, 1975.

Devine LF & others: Regimen using minocycline and rifampin sequentially for the elimination of meningococci from healthy carriers. Am J Epidemiol 97:394, 1973.

Ferrieri P & others: Natural history of impetigo. J Clin Invest 51:2851, 1972.

Fraser PL & others: The meningococcal carrier rate. Lancet 1:1235, 1973.

Goldschneider I & others: Immunogenicity of group A and group C meningococcal polysaccharides. J Infect Dis 125:509, 1972.

Handsfield HH & others: Asymptomatic gonorrhea in men. N Engl J Med 290:117, 1974.

Harder EJ & others: *Streptococcus mutans* endocarditis. Ann Intern Med 80:364, 1974.

Hyams PJ & others: Staphylococcal bacteremia and hexachlorophene bathing: An epidemic in a newborn nursery. Am J Dis Child 129:595, 1975.

Lacey RW: Antibiotic resistance plasmids of *Staphylococcus aureus* and their clinical importance. Bacteriol Rev 39:1, 1975.

Melish ME & others: The staphylococcal scalded-skin syndrome. J Infect Dis 125:129, 1972.

Merrill CW & others: Rapid identification of pneumococci. N Engl J Med 288:510, 1973.

Merrill JP: Glomerulonephritis. (3 parts.) N Engl J Med 290:275, 313, 374, 1974.

Moellering RC & others: Endocarditis due to group D streptococci. Am J Med 57:239, 1974.

Punsalang AP, Sawyer WD: Role of pili in virulence of *N gonorrhoeae*. Infect Immun 8:255, 1973.

Schroeter AP: Gonorrhea. Ann Intern Med 72:553, 1970.

Webster B (editor): Symposium on venereal diseases. Med Clin North Am 56:1055, 1972.

Weinstein L: "Modern" infective endocarditis. JAMA 233:260, 1975.

15...
Gram-Positive Bacilli

AEROBIC SPOREFORMING BACILLI

ANTHRAX

The genus Bacillus includes large gram-positive rods occurring in chains. They form spores and are aerobes. Most members of this genus are saprophytic organisms prevalent in soil, water, air, and on vegetation, such as *Bacillus cereus* and *B subtilis*. Some are insect pathogens. Such organisms rarely produce disease in man (eg, meningitis, endocarditis, endophthalmitis, conjunctivitis, or acute gastroenteritis). *B anthracis* is the principal pathogen of the genus.

Morphology & Identification

A. Typical Organisms: The typical cells, measuring $1 \times 3{-}4$ μm, have square ends and are arranged in long chains; spores are located in the center of the nonmotile bacilli.

B. Culture: Colonies are round and have a "cut glass" appearance in transmitted light. Hemolysis is uncommon with anthrax but common with the saprophytic bacilli. Gelatin is liquefied, and growth in gelatin stabs resembles an "inverted fir tree."

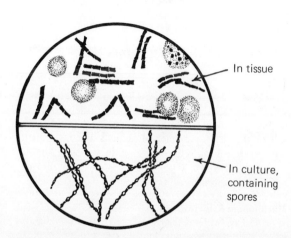

Figure 15—1. Anthrax bacilli in a smear from tissue or culture.

In tissue

In culture, containing spores

C. Growth Characteristics: The saprophytic bacilli utilize simple sources of nitrogen and carbon for energy and growth. The spores are resistant to environmental changes, withstand dry heat and certain chemical disinfectants for moderate periods, and persist for years in dry earth. Animal products contaminated with anthrax spores (eg, hides, bristles, hair) can be sterilized by autoclaving.

D. Variation: Variation occurs with respect to virulence, spore formation, and colony form. (In general, virulence is associated with rough colonies.) To minimize variation, living spore suspensions are employed to preserve unstable properties such as virulence.

Antigenic Structure

The capsular substance of *B anthracis*, which consists of a polypeptide of high molecular weight composed of D-glutamic acid, is a hapten. The bacterial bodies contain protein and a somatic polysaccharide, both of which are antigenic.

Pathogenesis

Anthrax is primarily a disease of sheep, cattle, and horses; man is affected only rarely. The infection is usually acquired by the entry of spores through injured skin or mucous membranes, rarely by inhalation of spores into the lung. In animals the portal of entry is the mouth and gastrointestinal tract. The spores from contaminated soil find easy access when ingested with spiny or irritating vegetation. In humans, scratches in the skin favor infection.

The spores germinate in the tissue at the site of entry, and the growth of the vegetative organisms results in formation of a gelatinous edema and congestion. Bacilli spread via lymphatics to the bloodstream, and bacteria multiply freely in the blood and tissues shortly before and after the death of the animal. In the plasma of animals dying from anthrax a lethal factor has been demonstrated. This material kills mice or guinea pigs upon inoculation and is specifically neutralized by anthrax antiserum. Its nature is still uncertain.

The exudate in anthrax contains a polypeptide, identical with that in the capsule of the bacillus, which is able to evoke histologic reactions similar to those of anthrax infection. Other proteins isolated from exudate stimulate solid immunity to anthrax upon injection into animals. From culture filtrates ("anthrax toxin"), 3 substances have been separated by glass filtration and chromatography: (1) "protective antigen" (a protein), (2) "edema factor," and (3) "lethal factor." Mixtures of (1), (2), and (3) are more toxic in animals, and such mixtures are more immunogenic than single substances.

Pathology

In susceptible animals the organisms proliferate at the site of entry. The capsules remain intact, and the organisms are surrounded by a large amount of proteinaceous fluid containing few leukocytes from which they rapidly disseminate and reach the bloodstream.

In resistant animals the organisms proliferate for a few hours, by which time there is massive accumulation of leukocytes. The capsules gradually disintegrate and disappear. The organisms remain localized.

Clinical Findings

In man anthrax gives rise to an infection of the skin (malignant pustule). A papule first develops within 12–36 hours after entry of the organisms or spores through a scratch. This papule rapidly changes into a vesicle, then a pustule, and finally into a necrotic ulcer from which the infection may disseminate, giving rise to septicemia. Another type of anthrax disease, a primary pneumonia, results from inhalation of spores from the dust of wool, hides, and hair ("woolsorter's disease"). It can be rapidly fatal.

Diagnostic Laboratory Tests

A. Specimens: Fluid or pus from local lesion; blood, sputum.

B. Stained Smears: From the local lesion or blood of dead animals; chains of large gram-positive rods are often seen. Identification of anthrax in smears by immunofluorescent technics is possible at the Center for Disease Control.

C. Culture: When grown on blood agar plates, the organisms produce nonhemolytic gray colonies with typical microscopic morphology. Carbohydrate fermentation is not useful. In semisolid medium anthrax bacilli are always nonmotile, whereas related nonpathogenic organisms (*B cereus*) exhibit motility by "swarming." Virulent anthrax cultures kill mice upon intraperitoneal injection.

D. Ascoli Test: Extracts of infected tissues show a ring of precipitate when layered over immune serum.

E. Serologic Tests: With anthrax antigens adsorbed on tanned red cells, hemagglutinating antibodies can be demonstrated in the serum of vaccinated or infected persons.

Resistance & Immunity

Some animals are highly susceptible (guinea pig) and others are very resistant (rat) to anthrax infection. This fact has been attributed to a variety of defense mechanisms: leukocytic activity, body temperature, and the bactericidal action of the blood. Certain basic polypeptides which kill anthrax bacilli have been isolated from animal tissues. A synthetic polylysine has a similar action.

Active immunity to anthrax can be induced in susceptible animals by vaccination with live attenuated bacilli, with spore suspensions, or with protective antigens from culture filtrates (see above). Immune serum is sometimes injected, together with live bacilli, into animals. Anthrax immunization is based on the classical experiments of Louis Pasteur, who in 1881 proved that cultures which had been grown in broth at 42–52° C for several months lost much of their virulence and could be injected live into sheep and cattle without causing disease; subsequently, such animals proved to be immune. There are great variations in the efficacy of various vaccines, and protection is often far from complete or lasting.

Treatment

Many antibiotics are effective against anthrax in man, but treatment must be started early. Penicillin in moderate doses is satisfactory.

Epidemiology, Prevention, & Control

Soil is contaminated with anthrax spores from the carcasses of dead animals. These spores remain viable for decades. Perhaps spores can germinate in soil at pH 6.5 at proper temperature. Grazing animals, infected through injured mucous membranes, serve to perpetuate the chain of infection. Contact with infected animals or with their hides, hair, and bristles is the source of infection in man. Control measures include (1) disposal of animal carcasses by burning or by deep burial in lime pits, (2) decontamination (usually by autoclaving) of animal products, (3) the use of protective clothing and gloves when handling potentially infected materials, and (4) active immunization of domestic animals and of persons with high occupational risk.

ANAEROBIC SPOREFORMING BACILLI

THE CLOSTRIDIA

The clostridia are anaerobic, gram-positive rods which form spores. Many decompose proteins or form toxins, and some do both. Their natural habitat is the soil or the intestinal tract of animals and man. Most species are saprophytic organisms in the soil. Among the pathogens are the organisms causing botulism, tetanus, and gas gangrene.

Morphology & Identification

A. Typical Organisms: All species of clostridia are large, gram-positive rods, and all can produce spores. The spores are usually wider than the diameter of the rods in which they are formed. In *Clostridium tetani* the spore is located at one end of the rod, giving it a drumstick appearance. In the various species the spore is placed centrally, subterminally, or terminally. Most species of clostridia are motile and possess peritrichous flagella.

B. Culture: Clostridia grow only under anaerobic conditions, established by one of the following means:

1. Agar plates or culture tubes are placed in an airtight jar from which air is removed and replaced by nitrogen with 10% CO_2, or oxygen may be removed by other means.

2. Fluid media in deep tubes containing either fresh animal tissue (eg, chopped cooked meat) or 0.1% agar and a reducing agent such as thioglycollate. Such tubes can be handled like aerobic media, and growth will occur from the bottom up to within 15 mm of the surface exposed to air.

C. Colony Forms: Some organisms produce large raised colonies with entire margins (eg, *Cl perfringens*); others produce smaller colonies which extend in a meshwork of fine filaments (eg, *Cl tetani*). Most species produce a zone of hemolysis on blood agar.

D. Growth Characteristics: The outstanding characteristic of anaerobic bacilli is their inability to utilize oxygen as the final hydrogen acceptor. They lack cytochrome and cytochrome oxidase and are unable to break down hydrogen peroxide because they lack catalase and peroxidase. Therefore it has been suggested that hydrogen peroxide tends to accumulate to toxic concentrations in the presence of oxygen. Alternatively, it has been proposed that clostridia and other strict anaerobes lack superoxide dismutase and thus permit accumulation of the free radical superoxide which may be intensely toxic for them. It has been postulated that such anaerobes can carry out their metabolic reactions only at a negative oxidation-reduction potential (Eh), ie, in an environment which is strongly reducing.

Clostridia can ferment a variety of sugars; many can digest proteins. Milk is turned acid by some, digested by others, and undergoes "stormy fermentation" (ie, clot torn by gas) with a third group (eg, *Cl perfringens*). Various enzymes are produced by different species (see below).

E. Antigenic Characteristics: Clostridia share antigens but also possess specific soluble antigens which permit grouping by means of precipitin tests.

CLOSTRIDIUM BOTULINUM

This microorganism is worldwide in distribution; it is found in soil and occasionally in animal feces.

Types of *Cl botulinum* are distinguished by the antigenic type of toxin they produce. Spores of the organism are highly resistant to heat, withstanding 100° C for at least 3–5 hours. Heat resistance is diminished at acid pH or high salt concentration.

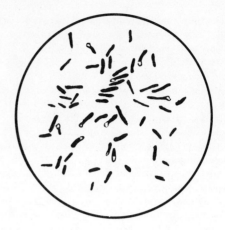

Figure 15–2. *Cl botulinum* from broth grown under anaerobic conditions.

Toxin

During the growth of *Cl botulinum* and during autolysis of the bacteria, toxin is liberated into the environment. Six distinct antigenic varieties of toxin— A, B, C, D, E, and F—are known. Types A, B, and E are most commonly associated with human illness. Type C produces limberneck in fowl; type D, botulism in cattle. Type A, B, and E toxins have been purified and fractionated to yield toxic proteins with a molecular weight of about 70,000. These are among the most highly toxic substances known: 1 mg contains more than 20 million mouse lethal doses. The lethal dose for man is not known but is probably less than 1 μg. The toxins are destroyed by heating for 10 minutes at 100° C. Some toxigenic *Cl botulinum* strains yield bacteriophages which may infect nontoxigenic strains and convert them to toxigenicity.

Pathogenesis

While *Cl botulinum* types A and B have been implicated in a few rare cases of wound infection, they generally do not produce infection in man. Botulism is an intoxication resulting from the ingestion of food in which *Cl botulinum* has grown and produced toxin. The most common offenders are spiced, smoked, vacuum-packed, or canned alkaline foods which are eaten without cooking. In such foods, spores of *Cl botulinum* germinate; under anaerobic conditions, vegetative forms grow and produce toxin.

The toxin probably acts by blocking acetylcholine release or production at synapses and neuromuscular junctions. Flaccid paralysis results.

Clinical Findings

Symptoms begin 18–96 hours after ingestion of the toxic food, with visual disturbances (incoordination of eye muscles, double vision), inability to swallow, and speech difficulty; signs of bulbar paralysis are progressive, and death occurs from respiratory paralysis or cardiac arrest. Gastrointestinal symptoms are not regularly prominent. There is no fever. The patient remains fully conscious until shortly before death. The fatality rate is high. Patients who recover do not develop antitoxin in the blood.

Diagnostic Laboratory Tests

Toxin can occasionally be demonstrated in serum from the patient, and toxin may be found in leftover food. Mice injected intraperitoneally die rapidly. The antigenic type of toxin is identified by neutralization with specific antitoxin. Mice protected with a specific type of antitoxin survive injection of that toxin, while controls not so protected die. *Cl botulinum* may be grown from food remains and tested for toxin production, but this is rarely done and is of questionable significance. Botulinus toxin can occasionally be demonstrated in food by agglutination of red cells coated with specific antiserum.

Treatment

Potent antitoxins to 3 types of botulism toxins have been prepared. Since the type responsible for an individual case is usually not known, trivalent (A, B, E) antitoxin (available from the Center for Disease Control) is administered intravenously as early as possible. Guanidine hydrochloride is given as an adjunct, and respiration is maintained artificially. Patients are occasionally saved by these measures.

Epidemiology, Prevention, & Control

Since spores of *Cl botulinum* are widely distributed in soils, they often contaminate vegetables, fruits, and other materials. When such foods are canned or otherwise preserved, they must be either sufficiently heated to ensure destruction of spores or must be boiled before consumption. Strict regulation of commercial canning has largely overcome the danger of large outbreaks, but commercially canned mushrooms and vichyssoise have caused deaths. At present the chief danger lies in home-canned foods, particularly string beans, corn, spinach, olives, peas, and smoked fish or vacuum-packed fresh fish in plastic bags. Toxic foods may be spoiled and rancid, and cans may "swell"; or the appearance may be innocuous. Home-canned foods should be boiled for more than 10 minutes before consumption. Toxoids are used for active immunization of cattle in South Africa.

CLOSTRIDIUM TETANI

Cl tetani is worldwide in distribution in the soil and in the feces of horses and other animals. Several types of *Cl tetani* can be distinguished by specific flagellar antigens. All share a common O (somatic) antigen, which may be masked, and all produce the same toxin. L forms of *Cl tetani* also produce toxin.

Toxin

Good yields of toxin are obtained when the organism is grown in a semisynthetic medium containing

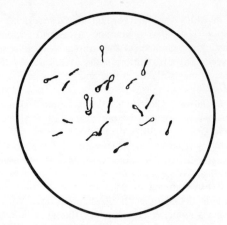

Figure 15–3. *Cl tetani* from blood agar grown under anaerobic conditions.

casein hydrolysate, tryptophan, cysteine, phosphates, trace elements, and growth factors, provided the concentration of iron is held within sharp limits. The toxin is a heat-labile protein (molecular weight 70,000) which is inactivated by 5 minutes' exposure to 65° C and rapidly destroyed by proteolytic enzymes, eg, of the digestive tract. Purified crystalline toxin contains more than 20 million mouse lethal doses per mg.

Pathogenesis

Cl tetani is not an invasive organism. The infection remains strictly localized in the area of devitalized tissue (wound, burn, injury, umbilical stump, surgical suture) into which the spores have been introduced. The volume of infected tissue is small, and the disease is almost entirely a toxemia. Germination of the spore and development of vegetative organisms which produce toxin are aided by (1) necrotic tissue, (2) calcium salts, and (3) associated pyogenic infections, all of which aid establishment of low oxidation-reduction potential. The toxin tetanospasmin probably reaches the CNS by retrograde axonal transport and becomes fixed to ganglioside in the spinal cord and brain stem. The toxin blocks inhibitory synaptic input on spinal motor neurons. This results in the inhibition of antagonists and permits both extreme hyperreflexia and violent spasms of skeletal muscles in response to any stimulus. The toxin may also affect synaptic transmission at myoneural junctions, perhaps by favoring the accumulation of acetylcholine.

Clinical Findings

The incubation period may range from 4–5 days to as many weeks. The disease is characterized by convulsive tonic contraction of voluntary muscles. Muscular spasms often involve first the area of injury and infection and then the muscles of the jaw (trismus, lockjaw), which contract so that the mouth cannot be opened. Gradually, other voluntary muscles become involved, resulting in tonic spasms. Any external stimulus may precipitate a tetanic seizure. The patient is fully conscious, and pain may be intense. Death usually results from interference with the mechanics of respiration. The death rate in generalized tetanus is approximately 50%.

Diagnostic Laboratory Tests

In clinical cases diagnosis rests on the clinical picture and a history of injury. Anaerobic culture of tissues from contaminated wounds may yield *Cl tetani*, but neither preventive nor therapeutic use of antitoxin should ever be withheld pending such demonstration. Proof of isolation of *Cl tetani* must rest on production of toxin and its neutralization by specific antitoxin.

Prevention & Treatment

The results of treatment of tetanus are not satisfactory. Therefore, prevention is all-important. Prevention of tetanus depends upon (1) active immunization with toxoids, (2) proper care of wounds contaminated with soil, etc, (3) prophylactic use of antitoxin, and (4) administration of penicillin.

A. Antitoxin: Tetanus antitoxin, prepared in various animals or in man, can neutralize the toxin, but only before it becomes fixed onto nervous tissue. One International Unit of antitoxin is defined as the activity contained in 0.03384 mg of the Second International Standard for Tetanus Antitoxin.

Because of the frequency of hypersensitivity reactions to foreign serum, and because of the rapidity with which foreign serum is eliminated, the administration of human antitoxin is much preferable. The intramuscular administration of 250–500 units of human antitoxin gives adequate systemic protection (0.01 unit per ml of serum or more) for 2–4 weeks. Human tetanus immune globulin is now commercially available. Only if human antitoxin is not available should heterologous (horse, sheep, rabbit) antitoxin be used in a prophylactic dose of 1500–6000 units. Whenever heterologous antitoxin is to be administered, tests for hypersensitivity to the foreign serum protein must be done. Active immunization with tetanus toxoid should always accompany antitoxin prophylaxis.

Patients who develop symptoms of tetanus always receive muscle relaxants, sedation, and assisted ventilation. Sometimes they are given very large doses of antitoxin (3000–10,000 units of human tetanus immune globulin) intravenously in an effort to neutralize toxin which has not yet been bound to nervous tissue. However, the efficacy of antitoxin for treatment is doubtful except in neonatal tetanus, where it may be lifesaving. In neonatal tetanus, treatment with 10,000 units of equine antitoxin seems equivalent to 500 units of human immune globulin.

B. Surgical Measures: Surgical debridement is vitally important because it removes the necrotic tissue which is essential for proliferation of the organisms. Hyperbaric oxygen has no proved effect.

C. Antibiotics: Penicillin strongly inhibits the growth of *Cl tetani* and stops further toxin production. Antibiotics may also control associated pyogenic infection.

D. "Booster" Shot: When a previously immunized individual sustains a potentially dangerous wound, an additional dose of toxoid should be injected to restimulate antitoxin production. This "recall" injection of toxoid may be accompanied by antitoxin injected into a different area of the body, to provide immediately available antitoxin for the period during which antitoxin levels may be inadequate.

Control

Universal active immunization with tetanus toxoid should be mandatory. Tetanus toxoid is produced by detoxifying the toxin with formalin and then concentrating it. Fluid toxoid or alum-precipitated toxoid is employed. Two injections comprise the initial course of immunization, followed by a third dose about 1 year later. Initial immunization should be carried out in all children during the first year of life. A "booster" injection of toxoid is given upon entry into school. Thereafter, "boosters" can be spaced 7–10 years apart to maintain serum levels of 0.01 unit antitoxin per ml. Tetanus toxoid is often combined with diphtheria toxoid and pertussis vaccine. (For schedule of immunizations, see Table 12–7.)

Control measures are not possible because of the wide dissemination of the organism in the soil and the long survival of its spores. Narcotic addicts are a high-risk group.

THE CLOSTRIDIA OF GAS GANGRENE

The 3 most common species of clostridia to be found in gas gangrene are *Cl perfringens (Cl welchii)*, *Cl novyi (Cl oedematiens)*, and *Cl septicum.* In addition to these, other species are sometimes present in cases of gas gangrene, eg, *Cl bifermentans, Cl histolyticum, Cl ramosum, Cl sporogenes,* and others.

Toxins

The clostridia produce a large variety of toxins

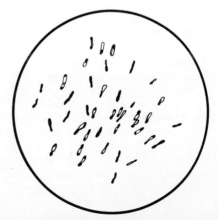

Figure 15–4. Gas gangrene bacilli.

and enzymes which result in a spreading infection. *Cl perfringens, Cl novyi, Cl septicum, Cl histolyticum, Cl bifermentans,* and others produce specific toxins. Many of these toxins have lethal necrotizing and hemolytic properties. In some cases these are different properties of a single substance; in other instances they are due to different chemical entities. The alpha toxin of *Cl perfringens* type A is a lecithinase, and its lethal action is proportionate to the rate at which it splits lecithin (an important constituent of cell membranes) to phosphorylcholine and diglyceride. The theta toxin has similar hemolytic and necrotizing effects but is not a lecithinase. A collagenase which digests collagen of subcutaneous tissue and muscle, hyaluronidase, and DNase are also produced. Some gas gangrene clostridia produce a specific nontoxic antigen ("bursting factor") which enhances infectivity and can immunize animals to gas gangrene.

Some strains of *Cl perfringens* produce a powerful enterotoxin. It is heat-labile, has a molecular weight of 90,000, is distinct from other clostridial toxins, and induces marked hypersecretion in the small intestine, leading to profuse diarrhea.

Pathogenesis

If necrotic tissue is present, gas gangrene develops following the introduction into a wound of soil or fecal matter containing spores. As the organisms multiply, they ferment carbohydrates present in tissue and produce gas. The distention of tissue and interference with blood supply, together with the secretion of necrotizing toxin and hyaluronidase, favor the spread of infection. Tissue necrosis extends, providing an opportunity for increased bacterial growth, hemolytic anemia, and, ultimately, severe toxemia and death.

In gas gangrene a mixed infection is the rule. In addition to the toxigenic clostridia, proteolytic clostridia and various cocci and gram-negative organisms are also usually present. *Cl perfringens* occurs in the genital tract of 5% of women. Clostridial uterine infections may follow instrumental abortions. Clostridial bacteremia is frequent in patients with neoplasms.

The mechanism of *Cl perfringens* enterotoxin is marked stimulation of adenylate cyclase activity in the gut, increase in cAMP concentration, and great hypersecretion in the jejunum and ileum with loss of fluids and electrolytes.

Clinical Findings

From a contaminated wound (eg, a compound fracture, postpartum uterus), the infection spreads in 1–3 days to produce crepitation in the subcutaneous tissue and muscle, foul-smelling discharge, rapidly progressing necrosis, fever, hemolysis, toxemia, shock,

and death. Until the advent of specific therapy, early amputation was the only treatment. At times the infection results only in anaerobic cellulitis. *Cl perfringens* can produce food poisoning with profuse diarrhea lasting 1–3 days.

Diagnostic Laboratory Tests

A. Specimens: Material from wounds, pus, tissue.

B. Smears: The presence of large gram-positive, sporeforming rods in gram-stained smears suggests gas gangrene clostridia, but spores are not always seen.

C. Culture: Material is inoculated into cooked chopped meat medium, thioglycollate medium, and onto blood agar plates incubated anaerobically. The growth from one of the media is transferred into milk. A clot torn by gas in 24 hours is suggestive of *Cl perfringens.* Once pure cultures have been obtained by selecting colonies from anaerobically incubated blood plates, they are identified by biochemical reactions (various sugars in thioglycollate, action on milk), hemolysis, and colony form. Lecithinase activity is evaluated by the precipitate formed around colonies on egg yolk media. Final identification rests on toxin production and neutralization by specific antitoxin.

Treatment

The most important aspect of treatment is prompt and extensive surgical debridement of the involved area and excision of all devitalized tissue, in which the organisms are prone to grow. Administration of antimicrobial drugs, particularly penicillin, is begun at the same time. Hyperbaric oxygen may be of great help in the medical management of clostridial tissue infections. It is said to "detoxify" patients rapidly.

Antitoxins are available against the toxins of *Cl perfringens, Cl novyi, Cl histolyticum,* and *Cl septicum,* usually in the form of concentrated immune globulins. Since the clinical picture is similar with all species of toxin-forming clostridia, polyvalent antitoxin (containing antibodies to several toxins) has been used. While such antitoxin is sometimes administered to individuals with contaminated wounds containing much devitalized tissue, there is no evidence for its efficacy. Food poisoning due to *Cl perfringens* enterotoxin is usually self-limited.

Prevention & Control

Early and adequate cleansing of contaminated wounds and surgical debridement, together with the administration of antimicrobial drugs directed against clostridia (eg, penicillin), are the best available preventive measures. Antitoxins should not be relied on. While toxoids for active immunization have been prepared, they have not come into practical use.

•   •   •

General References

Davis JC & others: Hyperbaric medicine in US Air Force. JAMA 224:205, 1973.

Donado JA & others: Diagnosis and treatment of botulism. J Infect Dis 124:108, 1971.

Ihde DC, Armstrong D: Clinical spectrum of infection due to Bacillus species. Am J Med 55:839, 1973.

Lamb R: A new look at infectious diseases: Anthrax. Br Med J 1:157, 1973.

Loewenstein MS: Epidemiology of *Cl perfringens* food poisoning. N Engl J Med 286:1026, 1972.

Maclennan JD: The clostridia of gas gangrene. Bacteriol Rev 26:177, 1962.

Merson MH & others: Botulism in the United States. JAMA 229:1305, 1974.

Peebles T & others: Tetanus-toxoid emergency boosters: A reappraisal. N Engl J Med 280:575, 1969.

Stark RL: Biological characteristics of *Cl perfringens.* Infect Immun 4:89, 1971.

Weinstein L: Tetanus. N Engl J Med 289:1293, 1973.

16...
Corynebacteria

Corynebacteria are gram-positive rods, nonmotile and nonsporeforming, which often possess club-shaped ends and irregularly staining granules. They are often in characteristic arrangements, resembling "Chinese letters" or palisades. They form acid but not gas in certain carbohydrates. Several species form part of the normal flora of the human respiratory tract, other mucous membranes, and skin. *Corynebacterium diphtheriae* produces a powerful exotoxin which causes diphtheria in man. *C vaginale* from the female genital tract was formerly called Haemophilus (see p 224).

Morphology & Identification

A. Typical Organisms: Corynebacteria are 0.5–1 μm in diameter and several μm long. Characteristically they possess irregular swellings at one end that give them a "club-shaped" appearance. Irregularly distributed within the rod (often near the poles) are granules staining deeply with aniline dyes (metachromatic granules, Babes-Ernst bodies), which give the rod a beaded appearance.

Individual corynebacteria in stained smears tend to lie parallel or at acute angles to one another. True branching is rarely observed in cultures.

B. Culture: On Löffler's coagulated serum medium the colonies are small, granular, and gray, with irregular edges. On McLeod's blood agar containing potassium tellurite, the colonies are gray to black because the tellurite is reduced intracellularly. The 3 types of *C diphtheriae* typically have the following appearance on such media: (1) var *gravis*–nonhemolytic, large, gray, irregular, striated colonies; (2) var *mitis*–hemolytic, small, black, glossy, convex colonies; (3) var *intermedius*–nonhemolytic small colonies with characteristics between the 2 extremes. In broth, var *gravis* strains tend to form a pellicle, var *mitis* strains grow diffusely, and var *intermedius* strains settle as a granular sediment.

C. Growth Characteristics: Corynebacteria grow on most ordinary laboratory media. On Löffler's serum corynebacteria grow much more readily than other respiratory pathogens, and the morphology of organisms is typical in smears. Acid, but not gas, is formed from some carbohydrates as shown in Table 16–1.

D. Variation & Conversion: Corynebacteria tend to pleomorphism in microscopic and colonial morphology. Variation from smooth to rough forms has been described. Variants from toxigenic strains often are nontoxigenic. When some nontoxigenic (avirulent) diphtheria organisms are infected with bacteriophage from certain toxigenic (virulent) diphtheria bacilli, the offspring of the exposed bacteria are lysogenic and toxigenic, and this trait is subsequently hereditary. (See Chapter 4, Genetics; and Chapter 9, Bacteriophage.) When toxigenic diphtheria bacilli are serially subcultured in specific antiserum against the temperate phage that they carry, they tend to become nontoxigenic. Thus, acquisition of phage leads to toxigenicity (lysogenic conversion). The actual production of toxin occurs perhaps only when the prophage of the lysogenic *C diphtheriae* becomes induced and lyses the cell. While toxigenicity is under control of the phage gene, virulence (invasiveness) is under control of the bacterial gene.

Figure 16–1. *C diphtheriae* from Löffler's medium.

Table 16–1.

	Starch	Glucose	Sucrose
C diphtheriae, gravis	+	+	−
C diphtheriae, mitis	−	+	−
C pseudodiphtheriticum	−	−	−
C xerosis	−	+	+

Antigenic Structure

Serologic differences have been observed between types and within each type of *C diphtheriae,* but no satisfactory or useful classification is available. Serologic tests are not generally employed in identification. Diphtheria toxin contains at least 4 antigenic determinants.

Pathogenesis

Some corynebacteria, notably *C pseudodiphtheriticum* and *C xerosis,* are commonly called "diphtheroids." They are normal inhabitants of the mucous membranes of the respiratory tract and the conjunctiva and do not cause disease. A number of other diphtheroids cause infections in animals and, rarely, in man. Anaerobic diphtheroids *(Propionibacterium acnes)* regularly reside in normal skin. They may participate in the pathogenesis of acne. They produce lipases, which split off free fatty acids from skin lipids. These fatty acids can produce tissue inflammation and contribute to acne.

The principal human pathogen of the group is *C diphtheriae.* In nature *C diphtheriae* occurs in the respiratory tract, in wounds, or on the skin of infected persons or normal carriers. It is spread by droplets or contact to susceptible individuals; virulent bacilli then grow on mucous membranes and start producing toxin.

All toxigenic *C diphtheriae* are capable of elaborating the same disease-producing exotoxin. In vitro production of this toxin depends largely on the concentration of iron. Toxin production is optimal at 0.14 μg of iron/ml of medium, but is virtually suppressed at 0.5 μg/ml. Other factors influencing the yield of toxin in vitro are osmotic pressure, amino acid concentration, pH, and availability of suitable carbon and nitrogen sources. The factors which control toxin production in vivo are not well understood.

Diphtheria toxin is a heat-labile polypeptide (molecular weight 62,000) which can be lethal in a dose of 0.1 μg/kg. By breaking disulfide bonds, the molecule can be split into 2 fragments. Fragment B (molecular weight 38,000) has no independent activity but is required for the transport of fragment A into the cell. Fragment A inhibits polypeptide chain elongation—provided nicotinamide adenine dinucleotide (NAD) is present—by inactivating the elongation factor EF-2 (formerly called transferase II). This factor is required for translocation of polypeptidyl-transfer RNA from the acceptor to the donor site on the eukaryotic ribosome. Toxin fragment A inactivates EF-2 by catalyzing a reaction which yields free nicotinamide plus an inactive adenosine diphosphate-ribose-EF-2 complex. The resulting abrupt arrest of protein synthesis presumably brings about a disruption of normal physiologic functions.

Corynebacterium minutissimum (Nocardia minutissima) is the cause of erythrasma, a superficial infection of axillary and pubic skin. The organism produces bright pink fluorescence under ultraviolet light on Mueller-Hinton agar.

Haemophilus vaginalis has been reclassified as a corynebacterium.

Pathology

The toxin is absorbed into the mucous membranes and causes destruction of epithelium and a superficial inflammatory response. The necrotic epithelium becomes embedded in exuding fibrin and red and white cells, so that a grayish "pseudomembrane" is formed—commonly over the tonsils, pharynx, or larynx. Any attempt to remove the pseudomembrane exposes and tears the capillaries and thus results in bleeding. The regional lymph nodes in the neck enlarge, and there may be marked edema of the entire neck. The diphtheria bacilli within the membrane continue to produce toxin actively. This is absorbed and results in distant toxic damage, particularly parenchymatous degeneration, fatty infiltration, and necrosis in heart muscle, liver, kidneys, and adrenals, sometimes accompanied by gross hemorrhage. The toxin also produces nerve damage, resulting often in paralysis of the soft palate, eye muscles, or extremities.

Wound or skin diphtheria occurs chiefly in the tropics. A membrane may form on an infected wound which fails to heal. However, absorption of toxin is usually slight and the systemic effects negligible. The "virulence" of diphtheria bacilli is due to their capacity for establishing infection, growing rapidly, and then quickly elaborating toxin which is effectively absorbed. *C diphtheriae* does not actively invade deep tissues and practically never enters the bloodstream.

Clinical Findings

When diphtheritic inflammation begins in the respiratory tract, sore throat and fever usually develop. Prostration and dyspnea soon follow because of the obstruction caused by the membrane. This obstruction may even cause suffocation if not promptly relieved by tracheostomy. Irregularities of cardiac rhythm indicate damage to the heart. Later, there may be difficulties with vision, swallowing, or movement of the arms or legs. All of these manifestations tend to subside spontaneously.

There is a broad correlation between the type of *C diphtheriae* and the severity of the disease. In general, var *gravis* infections tend to be more severe than var *mitis,* with a correspondingly higher mortality.

Diagnostic Laboratory Tests

These serve to confirm the clinical impression and are of epidemiologic significance. *Note:* Specific treatment must never be delayed for laboratory reports if the clinical picture is strongly suggestive of diphtheria.

A. Specimens: Swabs from the nose, throat, or other suspected lesions must be obtained before antimicrobial drugs are administered.

B. Smears: Smears stained with alkaline methylene blue or Gram's stain show beaded rods in typical arrangement.

C. Culture: Inoculate a blood agar plate (to rule out hemolytic streptococci), a Löffler slant, and a tellurite plate, and incubate all 3 at 37° C. Unless the swab can be inoculated promptly it should be kept moistened with sterile horse serum so the bacilli will remain viable. In 12–18 hours the Löffler slant may yield organisms of typical "diphtheria-like" morphology. In 36–48 hours the colonies on tellurite medium are sufficiently definite for recognition of the type of *C diphtheriae*.

Any diphtheria-like organism cultured must be submitted to a "virulence" test before the bacteriologic diagnosis of diphtheria is definite. Such tests are really tests for toxigenicity of an isolated diphtheria-like organism. They can be done in one of 4 ways as follows:

1. Intracutaneous test—Culture is prepared as for the subcutaneous test (see below) and injected intracutaneously so that each guinea pig (or rabbit) receives 0.1 ml in 2 different skin areas. One control animal is protected with 500 units of antitoxin (see subcutaneous test, below); the other is given 50 units of antitoxin intraperitoneally 4 hours after the skin test to prevent abrupt death. Inflammatory lesions at the site of injection progress to necrosis in 48–72 hours in the unprotected animal, whereas the protected animal must remain completely well to rule out the possibility of other invasive bacteria.

2. Subcutaneous test—A culture is emulsified and injected into each of 2 guinea pigs, one of which has received 500 units of diphtheria antitoxin 18–24 hours previously. The unprotected animal should die in 2–3 days. This test is wasteful of animals.

3. In vitro test—A strip of filter paper saturated with antitoxin is placed on an agar plate containing 20% horse serum. The cultures to be tested for toxigenicity are streaked across the plate at right angles to the filter paper. After 48 hours' incubation the antitoxin diffusing from the paper strip has precipitated the toxin diffusing from toxigenic cultures and resulted in lines radiating from the intersection of the strip and the bacterial growth.

4. Tissue culture test—The toxigenicity of *C diphtheriae* can be shown by incorporation of bacteria into an agar overlay of cell culture monolayers. Toxin produced diffuses into cells below and kills them.

Resistance & Immunity

Since diphtheria is principally the result of the action of the toxin formed by the organism rather than invasion by it, resistance to the disease depends largely on the availability of specific neutralizing antitoxin in the bloodstream and tissues. It is generally true that diphtheria occurs only in persons who possess no antitoxin or only very low levels of it. Similarly, the treatment of diphtheria rests largely on rapid suppression of toxin-producing bacteria and the early administration of specific antitoxin against the toxin formed by the organisms at their site of entry and multiplication. Thus there may be active or passive antitoxic immunity to diphtheria. The relative amount of antitoxin that a person possesses at a given time can be estimated in one of 2 ways:

A. Titration of Serum for Antitoxin Content: (Too complex for routine use.) Serum is mixed with varying amounts of toxin and the mixture injected into susceptible animals. The greater the amount of toxin neutralized, the higher the concentration of antitoxin in the serum.

B. Schick Test: This test is based on the fact that diphtheria toxin is very irritating and results in a marked local reaction when injected intradermally unless it is neutralized by circulating antitoxin. One Schick test dose (amount of standard toxin which, when mixed with 0.001 unit of the US Standard diphtheria antitoxin and injected intradermally into a guinea pig, will induce a 10 mm erythematous reaction) is injected into the skin of one forearm and an identical amount of heated toxin is injected into the other forearm as a control. (Heating for 15 minutes at 60° C destroys the effect of the toxin.) The test should be read at 24 and 48 hours and again in 6 days. Results are interpreted as follows:

1. Positive reaction (susceptibility to diphtheria toxin, ie, absence of adequate amounts of neutralizing antitoxin)—Toxin produces redness and swelling which increase for several days and then slowly fade, leaving a brownish pigmented area. The control site shows no reaction.

2. Negative reaction (adequate amount of antitoxin present; usually in excess of 0.02 unit/ml of serum)—Neither injection site shows any reaction.

3. Pseudoreaction—Schick test reactions may be complicated by hypersensitivity to materials other than the toxin contained in the injections. A pseudoreaction shows redness and swelling on both arms which disappear simultaneously on the second or third day. It constitutes a negative reaction.

4. Combined reaction—A combined reaction begins like a pseudoreaction, with redness and swelling at both injection sites; the toxin later continues to exert its effects, however, whereas the reaction at the control site subsides rapidly. This denotes hypersensitivity as well as relative susceptibility to toxin.

Treatment

Diphtheria antitoxin is produced in various animals (horses, sheep, goats, and rabbits) by the repeated injection of purified and concentrated toxoid. One International Unit of diphtheria antitoxin = 0.0628 mg of International Standard (Copenhagen). Treatment with antitoxin is mandatory when there is strong clinical suspicion of diphtheria. From 20,000–100,000 units are injected IM or IV after suitable precautions have been taken (skin or conjunctival test) to rule out hypersensitivity to the animal serum employed. The antitoxin should be given on the day the clinical diagnosis of diphtheria is made and need not be given again. Intramuscular injection may be used in mild cases.

Antimicrobial drugs (penicillin, erythromycin) inhibit the growth of diphtheria bacilli. While these drugs have virtually no effect on the disease process, they arrest toxin production. They also help to eliminate *C diphtheriae* from the respiratory tracts of patients or carriers.

Antibiotic administration (tetracycline) in acne may inhibit the lipolytic action of anaerobic diphtheroids; this reduces tissue inflammation. Variable benefit has been claimed for this treatment of acne.

Epidemiology, Prevention, & Control

Before artificial immunization, diphtheria was mainly a disease of small children. The infection occurred either clinically or subclinically at an early age and resulted in the widespread production of antitoxin in the population. An asymptomatic reinfection during adolescence and adult life served as a stimulus for maintenance of high antitoxin levels. Thus most members of the population, except children, were immune.

With the introduction of artificial active immunization the situation has changed. After active immunization during the first few years of life, antitoxin levels are generally adequate until adolescence. However, there are very few cases or carriers of diphtheria in the population, so that the stimulus of minimal subclinical infections is lacking. Consequently many adults have no significant amounts of antitoxin and thus are again susceptible to the disease.

Following either natural infection or active immunization, antitoxin levels last only a limited period of time and are subject to great fluctuations. Since the degree of individual resistance varies with the antitoxin titer, all degrees, from complete susceptibility to complete immunity, are likely to be present. This situation is further complicated by the fact that certain Schick-negative individuals may contract the disease, whereas some Schick-positive individuals may be insusceptible.

The principal aim of prevention therefore must be to limit the distribution of toxigenic diphtheria bacilli in the population and to maintain as high a level of active immunization as possible.

A. Isolation: To limit contact with diphtheria bacilli to a minimum, patients with diphtheria must be isolated and every effort made to rid them of the organisms. Without treatment a large percentage of infected persons continue to shed diphtheria bacilli for weeks or months after recovery (convalescent carriers). This danger may be greatly reduced by active early treatment with antibiotics. However, there are some healthy carriers from whom diphtheria bacilli cannot be eradicated with the measures now available. Tonsillectomy is sometimes performed as a last resort.

B. Active Immunization: The following preparations have been employed:

1. Fluid toxoid—A filtrate of broth culture of a toxigenic strain is treated with 0.3% formalin and incubated at 37° C until toxicity has disappeared. Toxoid is standardized in terms of flocculating units (Lf), often as 30 Lf/ml. Three doses of 0.5–1 ml are injected subcutaneously.

2. Alum-precipitated toxoid—Toxoid prepared as above is precipitated with 1–2% potassium alum. This is a somewhat better antigen and remains longer in the subcutaneous tissue. Only 2 injections are required for initial immunization, but the alum-precipitated toxoid may induce hypersensitivity more frequently than fluid toxoid. It is commonly combined with tetanus toxoid and pertussis vaccine in a single injection. Toxoid can also be adsorbed onto aluminum hydroxide or aluminum phosphate for delayed absorption.

Children should receive an initial course of toxoid injections during the first year of life and should have recall ("booster") inoculations at 3–4 and 6–8 years. Adolescents should receive another recall injection. In adults the incidence of hypersensitivity reactions to toxoids is high, and only purified toxoid (Td) should be used.

3. Toxin-antitoxin mixtures—These have been abandoned because of the danger of dissociation of the "neutral" mixture and the serious reactions to the free toxin.

●　　●　　●

General References

Belsey MA & others: *Corynebacterium diphtheriae* skin infections in Alabama and Louisiana: A factor in the epidemiology of diphtheria. N Engl J Med 280:135, 1969.

Collier RJ: Diphtheria toxin: Mode of action and structure. Bacteriol Rev 39:54, 1975.

Kaplan K, Weinstein L: Diphtheroid infections of man. Ann Intern Med 70:919, 1969.

Laird W, Groman N: Tissue culture test for toxigenicity of *C diphtheriae.* Appl Microbiol 25:709, 1973.

Pappenheimer AM, Gill DM: Diphtheria. Science 182:353, 1973.

Rosenberg EW: Bacteriology of acne. Annu Rev Med 20:201, 1969.

17 . . .
Mycobacteria

The mycobacteria are rod-shaped bacteria which do not stain readily but which, once stained, resist decolorization by acid or alcohol and are therefore called "acid-fast" bacilli. In addition to many saprophytic forms, the group includes pathogenic organisms (*M tuberculosis, M leprae*) which cause chronic diseases producing lesions of the infectious granuloma type.

MYCOBACTERIUM TUBERCULOSIS

Morphology & Identification

A. Typical Organisms: In animal tissues, tubercle bacilli are thin straight rods, measuring about 0.4 × 3 μm. On artificial media, coccoid and filamentous forms are seen. Mycobacteria cannot be classified either as gram-positive or gram-negative. Once stained by basic dyes they cannot be decolorized by alcohol, regardless of treatment with iodine. True tubercle bacilli are characterized by "acid-fastness," eg, 95% ethyl alcohol containing 3% hydrochloric acid (acid-alcohol) quickly decolorizes all bacteria except the mycobacteria. Acid-fastness depends on the integrity of the cellular structure. The Ziehl-Neelsen technic of staining is employed for identification of acid-fast bacteria. In sputum or sections of tissue, mycobacteria can be demonstrated by yellow-orange fluorescence after staining with fluorochrome stains (eg, auramine, rhodamine).

B. Culture: Three types of media are employed.

1. Simple synthetic media—Large inocula grow on simple synthetic media in several weeks. Small inocula fail to grow in such media because of the presence of minute amounts of toxic fatty acids. The toxic effect of fatty acids can be neutralized by animal serum or albumin, and the fatty acids may then actually promote growth. Activated charcoal aids growth.

2. Oleic acid-albumin media support the proliferation of small inocula, particularly if Tweens (water-soluble esters of fatty acids) are present. Ordinarily, mycobacteria grow in clumps or masses due to the hydrophobic character of the cell surface. Tweens wet the surface of the tubercle bacilli and thus permit dispersed growth in liquid media. Growth is often more rapid than on complex media.

3. Complex organic media—Small inocula traditionally were grown on media containing complex organic substances, eg, egg yolk, animal serum, tissue extracts. These media often contain penicillin or malachite green.

C. Growth Characteristics: Mycobacteria are obligate aerobes and derive energy from the oxidation of many simple carbon compounds. Increased CO_2 tension enhances growth. Biochemical activities are not characteristic, and the growth rate is much slower than that of most bacteria. The doubling time of tubercule bacilli is 12 hours or more. Saprophytic forms tend to grow more rapidly, proliferate well at 22° C, produce more pigment, and be less acid-fast than pathogenic forms.

D. Reaction to Physical and Chemical Agents: Mycobacteria tend to be more resistant to chemical agents than other bacteria because of the hydrophobic nature of the cell surface and their clumped growth. Dyes (eg, malachite green) or antibacterial agents (eg, penicillin) which are bacteriostatic to other bacteria can be incorporated into media without inhibiting the growth of tubercle bacilli. Acids and alkalies permit the survival of some exposed tubercle bacilli and are used for "concentration" of clinical specimens and partial elimination of contaminating organisms. Tubercle bacilli are fairly resistant to drying, and survive for long periods in dried sputum.

E. Variation: Variation occurs in colony appearance, virulence, and cellular characteristics of tubercle bacilli. "Eugonic" organisms grow luxuriantly on egg media and form rough colonies with irregular edges. Their growth can be enhanced by glycerin. This is the usual appearance of human strains on first isolation. "Dysgonic" cultures grow more slowly, forming flat, circular colonies with entire edges. They are inhibited by the presence of glycerin. This is the usual appearance of bovine strains. "Dysgonic" cultures may assume "eugonic" characteristics of growth. Nonvirulent strains treated with nonionic surface-active agents may acquire virulence and "cord" formation (see below).

F. Types of Tubercle Bacilli: Differences between the 3 main species of tubercle bacilli are particularly evident in their virulence for laboratory animals (Table 17–1).

Human and bovine strains are equally pathogenic for man by either the respiratory or the gastrointestinal route. The route of primary infection determines the pattern and location of tuberculous lesions. Some

Table 17—1. Virulence of tubercle bacilli.

Virulent For	Mycobacterium			
	tuber-culosis	*bovis*	*avium*	"Atypical"
Guinea pigs	+++	+++	−	− to +
Rabbits	+	+++	+++	−
Mice*	+++	+++	−	− to +++
Cattle	−	+++	−	?
Fowl	−	−	+++	?
Man	+++	+++	−	− to +++

*Certain strains.

"atypical" mycobacteria can cause tuberculosis-like disease in man; others are presumed to cause disease rarely. They are described below.

Constituents of Tubercle Bacilli

The constituents listed below are found largely in cell walls. Mycobacterial cell walls can induce delayed hypersensitivity, induce some resistance to infection, and replace whole mycobacterial cells in Freund's adjuvant. Protoplasm does none of these things but can provoke delayed hypersensitivity reactions in previously sensitized animals.

A. Lipids: Mycobacteria are rich in lipids. Many complex lipids, fatty acids, and waxes have been isolated from them. In the cell the lipids are largely bound to proteins and polysaccharides. Some such complexes have been isolated. Lipids are probably responsible for most of the cellular tissue reactions to tubercle bacilli. Phosphatide fractions can produce tubercle-like cellular responses and caseation necrosis. Lipids are to some extent responsible for acid-fastness. When tubercle bacilli are defatted with ether, this staining property is lost. Analysis of the lipids by gas chromatography may reveal species-specific patterns and aids classification.

Virulent strains of tubercle bacilli form microscopic "serpentine cords" in which acid-fast bacilli are arranged in parallel chains. Cord formation is correlated with virulence. A "cord factor" (trehalose-6,6'-dimycolate) has been extracted from virulent bacilli with petroleum ether. It inhibits migration of leukocytes and causes chronic granulomas.

B. Proteins: Each type of tubercle bacillus contains several proteins which elicit the tuberculin reaction. Proteins bound to a wax fraction can, upon injection, induce tuberculin sensitivity. They can also elicit the formation of a variety of antibodies.

C. Polysaccharides: Tubercle bacilli contain a variety of polysaccharides. Their role in the pathogenesis of tuberculosis is uncertain. They can induce the immediate type of hypersensitivity and can interfere with some antigen-antibody reactions in vitro.

Pathogenesis

Tubercle bacilli produce no recognized toxins. The disease results from establishment and proliferation of virulent organisms and interactions with the host. Avirulent bacilli (eg, BCG) survive only for months or years in the normal host. Resistance and hypersensitivity of the host greatly influence the development of the disease.

Pathology

The production and development of lesions and their healing or progression are determined chiefly by (1) the number of tubercle bacilli in the inoculum and their subsequent multiplication, and (2) the resistance and hypersensitivity of the host.

A. Two Principal Lesions:

1. Exudative type—This consists of an acute inflammatory reaction, with edema fluid, polymorphonuclear leukocytes, and, later, monocytes around the tubercle bacilli. This type is seen particularly in lung tissue, where it resembles bacterial pneumonia. It may heal by resolution, so that the entire exudate becomes absorbed; it may lead to massive necrosis of tissue; or it may develop into the second (productive) type of lesion. During the exudative phase, the tuberculin test becomes positive.

2. Productive type—When fully developed, this lesion, a chronic granuloma, consists of 3 zones: (1) a central area of large, multinucleated giant cells containing tubercle bacilli; (2) a midzone of pale epithelioid cells, often arranged radially; and (3) a peripheral zone of fibroblasts, lymphocytes, and monocytes. Later, peripheral fibrous tissue develops and the central area undergoes caseation necrosis. Such a lesion is called a tubercle. A caseous tubercle may break into a bronchus, empty its contents, and form a cavity. It may heal by fibrosis or calcification.

B. Spread of Organisms in the Host: Tubercle bacilli spread in the host by direct extension, through the lymphatic channels and bloodstream, and via the bronchi and gastrointestinal tract.

In the first infection, tubercle bacilli always spread from the initial site via the lymphatics to the regional lymph nodes. The bacilli may spread farther and reach the thoracic duct and the bloodstream, which in turn disseminate bacilli to all organs (miliary distribution). The bloodstream can be invaded also by erosion of a vein by a caseating tubercle or lymph node. If a caseating lesion discharges its contents into a bronchus, they are aspirated and distributed to other parts of the lungs or are swallowed and passed into the stomach and intestines.

C. Intracellular Site of Growth: Once tubercle bacilli establish themselves in tissue they reside principally intracellularly in monocytes, reticuloendothelial cells, and giant cells. The intracellular location is one of the features which makes chemotherapy difficult and favors microbial persistence. Within the cells of immune animals, multiplication of tubercle bacilli is greatly inhibited.

Primary Infection & Reactivation Types of Tuberculosis

When a host has first contact with tubercle bacilli, the following features are usually observed: (1) An

Table 17—2. Identification of acid-fast organisms in sputum specimens.

I. Digest sputum by adding an equal volume of Zephiran-trisodium phosphate* or 4% sodium hydroxide, shaking with glass beads for 20 minutes at room temperature.

II. Restore neutral pH by adding 25% hydrochloric acid, drop by drop.

III. Inoculate Loewenstein-Jensen medium and incubate at 37° C. Inspect at 5-day intervals. When colonies appear, make smears and acid-fast stains. If acid-fast organisms are present, proceed as follows:

    A. Growth in Less Than 5 Days (Rapid Growers): Runyon's group IV.†

        1. Aryl sulfate test*—

            a. Strongly positive—*M fortuitum.*

            b. Negative or weakly positive—Other group IV mycobacteria, to be identified by sugar fermentations (eg, *M smegmatis, M phlei*).

    B. Growth in More Than 5—7 Days (Slow Growers):

        1. Niacin test‡—

            a. Positive; colonies rough—*M tuberculosis.*

            b. Negative—

                (1) Slow, sparse growth; small, flat colonies—*M bovis,* pathogenic for rabbits and guinea pigs. BCG nonpathogenic.

                (2) Smooth hemispherical colonies—Subculture at 37° C in 2 tubes of Loewenstein-Jensen medium. One tube kept in light, the other wrapped in foil and kept in darkness.

                    (a) Yellow to orange in light, nonpigmented in dark—*M kansasii* (Runyon's group I).

                    (b) Yellow to orange in light and dark—Scotochromogens (Runyon's group II).

                    (c) Nonpigmented in light or dark—*M avium, M intracellulare* (Battey bacillus) (Runyon's group III).

*Kubica GP, Dye WE: USPHS Publication No. 1547, 1967.
†Runyon EH: Med Clin North Am 43:273, 1959.
‡Runyon EH & others: Am Rev Tuberc 79:663, 1959.

acute exudative lesion develops and rapidly spreads to the lymphatics and regional lymph nodes. The "Ghon complex" is the primary tissue lesion (usually in the lung) together with the involved lymph nodes. The exudative lesion in tissue often heals rapidly. (2) The lymph node undergoes massive caseation, which usually calcifies. (3) The tuberculin test becomes positive.

This primary infection type occurred in the past usually in childhood but now is seen frequently in adults who have remained free from infection and therefore tuberculin-negative in early life. In primary infections, the involvement may be in any part of the lung but is most often at the base.

The reactivation type is usually caused by tubercle bacilli which have survived in the primary lesion (endogenous reinfection) and rarely by bacilli newly inhaled from the environment (exogenous reinfection). Reactivation tuberculosis is characterized by a more chronic tissue lesion and a predominantly "productive" type of tissue response (the formation of tubercles, caseation, and fibrosis). Regional lymph nodes are only slightly involved, and they do not caseate. Reinfection almost always begins at the apex of the lung.

The contrast between primary infection and reinfection is shown experimentally in the **Koch phenomenon.** When a guinea pig is injected subcutaneously with virulent tubercle bacilli, the puncture wound heals quickly but a nodule forms at the site of injection in 2 weeks. This nodule ulcerates, and the ulcer does not heal. The regional lymph nodes develop tubercles and caseate massively. When the same animal is later injected with tubercle bacilli in another part of the body,

the sequence of events is quite different: there is rapid necrosis of skin and tissue at the site of injection, but the ulcer heals rapidly. Regional lymph nodes do not become infected at all, or only after a delay.

These differences between primary infection and reinfection or reactivation are attributed to (1) resistance and (2) hypersensitivity induced by the first infection of the host with tubercle bacilli. It is not clear to what extent each of these components participates in the modified response in "reinfection" tuberculosis.

Immunity & Hypersensitivity

Unless a host dies during the first infection with tubercle bacilli, he acquires a certain resistance (see Koch phenomenon, above). He has an increased capacity to localize tubercle bacilli, to retard their multiplication, and even to destroy them, limit their spread, and reduce lymphatic dissemination. This can be largely attributed to the ability of mononuclear cells to limit the multiplication of ingested organisms and perhaps to destroy them. Mononuclear cells acquire this "cellular immunity" in the course of initial infection of the host.

Antibodies form against a variety of the cellular constituents of the tubercle bacilli. Antibodies have been determined by precipitation and CF tests and by a hemagglutinating reaction in which sera of tuberculous animals or man clump red cells which have adsorbed tuberculin. None of these serologic reactions bears any definite relation to the state of resistance of the host.

In the course of primary infection, the host also acquires hypersensitivity to the tubercle bacilli. This is made evident by the development of a positive tuberculin reaction (see below). Tuberculin sensitivity can be induced by whole tubercle bacilli or by tuberculoprotein in combination with the chloroform-soluble wax of the tubercle bacillus, but not by tuberculoprotein alone. Hypersensitivity and resistance appear to be separate aspects of the same cellular reaction. However, in man it is not clear what factors determine whether hypersensitivity will aid or hinder the manifestations of resistance.

Tuberculin Test

A. Material: Old tuberculin (OT) is a concentrated filtrate of broth in which tubercle bacilli have grown for 6 weeks. In addition to the reactive tuberculoproteins, this material contains a variety of other constituents of tubercle bacilli and of growth medium. A purified protein derivative (PPD) can be obtained by chemical fractionation of OT and is the preferred material for skin testing. PPD is standardized in terms of its biologic reactivity as "tuberculin units" (TU). By international agreement, the TU is defined as the activity contained in a specified weight of Seibert's PPD Lot #49608 in a specified buffer. This is PPD-S, the standard for tuberculin against which the potency of all products must be established by biologic assay—ie, by reaction size in people. First strength tuberculin has 1 TU; intermediate strength has 5 TU; and second strength has 250 TU. Bioequivalency of PPD products is not based on weight of the material but on comparative activity.

B. Dose of Tuberculin: A large amount of tuberculin injected into a hypersensitive host may give rise to severe local reactions and a flare-up of inflammation and necrosis at the main sites of infection (focal reactions). For this reason tuberculin tests in surveys employ 5 TU; in persons suspected of hypersensitivity, skin testing is begun with 1 TU. More concentrated material (250 TU) is administered only if the reaction to the more dilute material is negative. The volume is usually 0.1 ml injected intracutaneously. Some false-negative skin test reactions with PPD-S were attributed to adsorption of the antigen to glass. This has been avoided by adding Tween 80 or other stabilizer to the bottle during manufacture. Only stabilized liquid PPD should be used.

C. Reactions to Tuberculin: In an individual who has not had contact with tubercle bacilli, there is no reaction to PPD-S. An individual who has had a primary infection with tubercle bacilli develops induration exceeding 10 mm in diameter, edema, erythema in 24–48 hours, and, with very intense reactions, even central necrosis. The skin test should be read in 48 or 72 hours. It is considered positive if the injection of 5 TU is followed by induration 10 mm or more in diameter. Positive tests tend to persist for several days. Weak reactions may disappear more rapidly.

The tuberculin test becomes positive within 4–6 weeks after infection (or injection of avirulent bacilli).

It may be negative in the presence of tuberculous infection when "anergy" develops due to overwhelming tuberculosis, measles, Hodgkin's disease, sarcoidosis, or immunosuppressive drugs. A positive tuberculin test may occasionally revert to negative on the isoniazid treatment of a recent converter. After BCG vaccination, a positive test may last for only 3–7 years. Only the elimination of viable tubercle bacilli results in reversion of the tuberculin test to negative. The reactivity to tuberculin can be transferred only by cells—not by serum—from a tuberculin-positive to a tuberculin-negative person.

D. Interpretation of Tuberculin Test: A positive tuberculin test indicates that an individual has been infected with tubercle bacilli in the past, but it does not indicate present active disease. While tuberculin-positive healthy individuals may have some resistance to widespread disease, in fact most active tuberculosis occurs in persons who have had positive tuberculin tests for months or years. The tuberculin-positive person is at risk of developing disease from activation of the primary infection, whereas the tuberculin-negative person is not at risk.

PPDs from other mycobacteria have been prepared. They exhibit some species specificity in low concentrations and marked cross-reactions in higher concentrations.

Clinical Findings

Since the tubercle bacillus can involve every organ system, its clinical manifestations are protean. Fatigue, weakness, weight loss, and fever may be signs of tuberculous disease. Pulmonary involvement giving rise to chronic cough and spitting of blood usually is associated with far-advanced lesions. Meningitis can occur in the absence of other signs of tuberculosis. Bloodstream dissemination leads to miliary tuberculosis with lesions in many organs and a high fatality rate.

Diagnostic Laboratory Tests

Neither the tuberculin test nor any now available serologic test gives evidence of active disease due to the tubercle bacillus. Only isolation of tubercle bacilli gives such proof.

Specimens consist of fresh sputum, gastric washings, urine, pleural fluid, spinal fluid, joint fluid, biopsy material, or other suspected material.

A. Stained Smear: Sputum, or sediment from gastric washings, urine, exudates, or other material is stained for acid-fast bacilli by the Ziehl-Neelsen technic or a comparable method. If such organisms are found, this is presumptive evidence of tuberculosis. However, saprophytic, nonpathogenic acid-fast bacilli must be ruled out by culture or animal inoculation.

B. Concentration for Stained Smear: If a direct smear is negative, sputum may be liquefied by addition of Clorox (hypochlorite solution), centrifuged, and the sediment stained and examined microscopically. This "digested material" is unsuitable for culture.

C. Culture: Urine, spinal fluid, and materials not contaminated with other bacteria may be cultured directly. Sputum is first treated with sodium hydroxide, sulfuric acid, or other agents bactericidal for contaminating microorganisms but less so for tubercle bacilli. The liquefied sputum is then neutralized and centrifuged and the sediment inoculated into egg media or oleic acid-albumin media (Dubos). Incubation of the inoculated media is continued for 2–8 weeks.

Isolated tubercle bacilli should be tested for drug susceptibility.

D. Animal Inoculation: Part of the cultured material may be inoculated subcutaneously into young guinea pigs, which are tuberculin tested after 3–4 weeks and autopsied after 6 weeks to search for evidence of tuberculosis. In competent hands cultures are just as reliable. The use of both procedures, however, ensures the highest number of positive results. Isoniazid-resistant tubercle bacilli are often nonpathogenic for guinea pigs but grow on artificial media and may be pathogenic for man.

E. Serology: CF and HI tests have little value.

Treatment

Physical and mental rest; nutritional buildup, and various forms of collapse therapy have long been employed but are now of secondary importance. The most widely used antituberculosis drugs at present are isoniazid (isonicotinic acid hydrazide, INH), ethambutol, rifampin, and streptomycin. Unfortunately, resistant variants of tubercle bacilli against each of these drugs emerge rapidly. Treatment is most successful when the drugs are used concomitantly (eg, INH + rifampin; INH + ethambutol; rifampin + ethambutol), thus delaying the emergence of resistant forms. Occasionally, primary infection occurs with tubercle bacilli resistant to one or more drugs. (In the USA, 1–3% of primary infections are caused by INH-resistant *M tuberculosis.*) Other drugs (eg, ethionamide, pyrazinamide, viomycin, cycloserine) are less frequently employed because of their more pronounced side-effects. The available chemotherapeutic drugs result in suppression of tuberculous activity and eradication of most–but not all–tubercle bacilli. Clinical cure can usually be achieved. Host factors are important in control of the residual organisms. The sputum-positive patient becomes noninfective within 2–3 weeks after beginning effective chemotherapy.

The following explanations have been advanced for the particular resistance of chronic tuberculosis to chemotherapy: (1) Most bacilli are intracellular, and some drugs (eg, streptomycin) penetrate cells poorly. (2) The caseous material in lesions, although it is itself inimical to bacterial proliferation, interferes with drug action. (3) In chronic lesions tubercle bacilli are non-proliferating, metabolically inactive "persisters" which are not susceptible to drug action.

Epidemiology

The most frequent source of infection is the human who excretes, particularly from the respiratory tract, large numbers of tubercle bacilli. Close contact (eg, in the family) and massive exposure (eg, in medical personnel) make transmission by droplet nuclei most likely. The milk of tuberculous cows is a source of infection where bovine tuberculosis is not well controlled.

Susceptibility to tuberculosis is a function of 2 risks: the risk of acquiring the infection and the risk of developing clinical disease after infection has occurred. For the tuberculin-negative person, the risk of acquiring tubercle bacilli depends on his exposure to sources of infectious bacilli–principally sputum-positive patients but rarely infected unpasteurized milk. This risk is proportionate to the rate of active infection in the population, crowding, socioeconomic disadvantage, and inadequacy of medical care. These factors, rather than genetic ones, probably account for the significantly higher rate of tuberculous infection in American Indians and blacks than in whites.

The second risk–the development of clinical disease after infection–has a genetic component (proved in animals) and is influenced by age (high risk in infancy and age 16–21), by sex (female risk higher than male), by undernutrition, and by immunologic status, coexisting diseases (eg, silicosis, diabetes), and individual host resistance factors discussed below.

Infection occurs at an earlier age in urban than in rural populations. Disease occurs only in a small proportion of infected individuals. In the USA at present, active disease is discovered most commonly among elderly males.

Prevention & Control

(1) Public health measures designed for early detection of cases and sources of infection (tuberculin test, x-ray) and for their isolation and treatment until noninfectious.

(2) Eradication of tuberculosis in cattle ("test and slaughter") and pasteurization of milk.

(3) Drug treatment of asymptomatic tuberculin "converters" in the age groups most prone to develop complications (eg, young children) and in immunosuppressed tuberculin-positive persons.

(4) Immunization: Various living avirulent tubercle bacilli, particularly BCG (bacille Calmette Guérin, an attenuated bovine organism), have been used to induce a certain amount of resistance in those heavily exposed to infection. Vaccination with these organisms is a substitute for primary infection with virulent tubercle bacilli, without the danger inherent in the latter. The available vaccines are inadequate from many technical and biologic standpoints. Their use is suggested only in tuberculin-negative persons who are heavily exposed (members of tuberculous families, medical personnel, especially in developing countries). Statistical evidence indicates that an increased resistance for a limited period follows BCG vaccination.

The possible immunizing value of nonliving bacterial fractions, especially one derived from bacillary cell walls in oil, is under investigation.

(5) Individual host resistance: Nonspecific factors may reduce host resistance, thus favoring the conversion of asymptomatic infection into disease. Among

such "activators" of tuberculosis are starvation, gastrectomy, and administration of high doses of corticosteroids or immunosuppressive drugs. Such patients receive INH "prophylaxis."

OTHER MYCOBACTERIA

Many acid-fast organisms other than *M tuberculosis* are encountered in man's environment. Many are free-living saprophytes and tend to grow rapidly on simple bacteriologic media. Some are associated with animals, eg, Johne's bacillus (*M paratuberculosis*), which produces a chronic enteritis in cattle and results in severe economic losses; or *M marinum*, which occurs in water, may infect cold-blooded animals, and occasionally produces stubborn "swimming pool granuloma" in patients. It can be treated with rifampin + ethambutol. The preference of that organism for the cool body surface is shared by *M ulcerans,* which produces chronic skin ulcers in man and grows in vitro at 31° C. Other mycobacteria (eg, *M smegmatis*) are regularly found in the sebaceous secretions of the skin of man but are not known to cause disease. They may give rise to confusion with tubercle bacilli.

From human sputum, and occasionally from other sites also, acid-fast mycobacteria are recovered which at times resemble tubercle bacilli in certain respects but are atypical in others. Some of these organisms produce unequivocal disease closely resembling tuberculosis. The tentative grouping of Runyon (Med Clin North Am 43:273, 1959) is widely accepted at present. These **"atypical"** mycobacteria are divided into groups according to pigmentation and growth rate.

Group I consists of photochromogens (growing colonies which produce little pigment in the dark but, after exposure to light for 1 hour, turn yellow-orange in 48 hours), requiring complex media and growing a little faster than tubercle bacilli. The most important representative is *M kansasii,* which definitely produces human pulmonary infection indistinguishable clinically or histologically from tuberculosis. *M kansasii* is treated with rifampin + ethambutol.

Group II, scotochromogens (colonies are yellow-orange in either light or dark), is a very heterogeneous group, most members of which are probably not involved in human disease. They do not grow on plain nutrient agar. *M flavescens* is representative.

Group III consists of buff or light tan colonies which are of softer consistency than most *M tuberculosis* and grow somewhat faster. A representative of this group is *M intracellulare* (Battey bacillus); it definitely causes human disease and appears to be similar to the avian variety of tubercle bacilli. *M intracellulare* appears most commonly as the cause of cervical lymphadenitis in children. Excision of the nodes may be curative. *M intracellulare* may also cause lung involvement, which is treated with INH + rifampin + ethambutol.

Group IV consists of organisms producing nonpigmented colonies which grow very rapidly on simple media. Many such organisms (eg, *M phlei*) are definite saprophytes, but *M fortuitum* can be associated with progressive pulmonary or eye lesions.

Of great practical concern is the relative resistance of many "atypical" mycobacteria to antituberculosis drugs, particularly streptomycin and isoniazid. Most strains are susceptible to rifampin. Treatment consists of combinations of drugs selected in the laboratory.

Extracts equivalent to PPD prepared from such mycobacteria (eg, PPD-B from *M intracellulare;* PPD-Y from *M kansasii*) give delayed skin reactions in many persons, including some who are tuberculin-negative. In the southeastern USA, up to 50% of people appear to have been infected by atypical mycobacteria originating in the environment.

M LEPRAE

Although this organism was described by Hansen in 1873 (9 years before Koch's discovery of the tubercle bacillus), it has never been cultivated with certainty.

Typical acid-fast bacilli—singly, in parallel bundles, or in globular masses—are regularly found in smears or scrapings from skin or mucous membranes (particularly the nasal septum) in lepromatous leprosy. The bacilli are often found within the endothelial cells of blood vessels or in mononuclear cells. The organisms have not been grown on artificial media with certainty. When bacilli from human leprosy (ground tissue, nasal scrapings) are inoculated into foot pads of mice, local granulomatous lesions develop with limited multiplication of bacilli. Inoculated armadillos develop extensive lepromatous leprosy. *M leprae* from armadillo or human tissue contains a unique *o*-diphenoloxidase, perhaps an enzyme characteristic of leprosy bacilli.

Clinical Findings

The onset of leprosy is insidious. The lesions involve the cooler tissues of the body: skin, superficial nerves, nose, pharynx, larynx, eyes, and testicles. The skin lesions may occur as pale, anesthetic macular lesions 1–10 cm in diameter; diffuse or discrete erythematous, infiltrated nodules 1–5 cm in diameter; or a diffuse skin infiltration. Neurologic disturbances are manifested by nerve infiltration and thickening, with resultant anesthesia, neuritis, paresthesia, trophic ulcers, and bone reabsorption and shortening of digits. The disfiguration due to the skin infiltration and nerve involvement in untreated cases may be extreme.

The disease is divided clinically and by laboratory tests into 2 distinct types: lepromatous and tuberculoid. In the lepromatous type, the course is progressive and malign, with nodular skin lesions; slow, symmetric nerve involvement; abundant acid-fast bacilli in the skin lesions; continuous bacteremia; and a negative lepromin (extract of lepromatous tissue) skin test. In the tuberculoid type, the course is benign and nonprogressive, with macular skin lesions, severe asymmetric nerve involvement of sudden onset with few bacilli present in the lesions, and a positive lepromin skin test. Cell-mediated immunity appears to be markedly defective in lepromatous leprosy.

Systemic manifestations of anemia and lymphadenopathy may also occur. Eye involvement is common.

Diagnosis

Scrapings with a scalpel blade from skin, nasal mucosa, or from a biopsy of ear lobe skin, are smeared on a slide and stained by the Ziehl-Neelsen technic. Biopsy of skin or of a thickened nerve gives a typical histologic picture. No serologic tests are of value. Serologic tests for syphilis frequently yield biologic false-positive results in leprosy.

Treatment

Several specialized sulfones (eg, dapsone [diaminodiphenylsulfone, DDS]) and rifampin suppress the growth of *M leprae* and the clinical manifestations of leprosy if given for many months. Sulfone resistance is beginning to emerge in leprosy.

Epidemiology

The mode of transmission of leprosy is uncertain. It is believed that susceptibility to infection is greatest in childhood, that the incubation period may extend over many years, and that infected persons usually develop symptoms and signs only in adult life. Infection is most likely contracted by children from other infected members of the family. Spontaneous leprosy occurs in free-living armadillos.

Prevention & Control

In endemic areas, removal of young children from infected families is employed with some success. Chemotherapy of active cases is good prophylaxis for the community. Chemoprophylaxis with sulfones in close family contacts has been employed. Experimental BCG vaccination has been used in children in endemic areas but with doubtful benefits.

•   •   •

General References

Advisory Committee on Immunization Practices: BCG vaccines. Morbid Mortal Wkly Rep 24:69, Feb 22, 1975.

Bechelli LM & others: BCG vaccination of children against leprosy. Bull WHO 51:93, 1974.

Comstock GW & others: The prognosis of a positive tuberculin reaction in childhood and adolescence. Am J Epidemiol 99:131, 1974.

Gernez-Reiux C, Gervois M: Protection conferred by BCG. Bull WHO 48:139, 1973.

Gunnels JJ & others: Infectivity of sputum-positive tuberculous patients on chemotherapy. Am Rev Respir Dis 109:323, 1974.

Mackaness GB: The immunology of antituberculous immunity. Am Rev Respir Dis 97:337, 1968.

Mitchell RS: Control of tuberculosis. (2 parts.) N Engl J Med 276:842, 905, 1967.

Ribi E & others: Mycobacterial cell walls as vaccine. J Infect Dis 123:527, 1971.

Sheagren JM & others: Immunologic reactivity in patients with leprosy. Ann Intern Med 70:295, 1969.

Shepard CC: Chemotherapy of leprosy. Annu Rev Pharmacol 9:37, 1969.

Storrs EE & others: Leprosy in the armadillo. Science 183:851, 1974.

Wolinsky E: Nontuberculous mycobacterial infections of man. Med Clin North Am 58:639, 1974.

18 ...
Enteric Gram-Negative
Microorganisms

The enteric organisms are a large, heterogeneous group of gram-negative, nonsporeforming rods whose natural habitat is the intestinal tract of man and animals. Some (eg, *Escherichia coli*) form part of the normal flora of the intestinal tract; others (eg, salmonellae, shigellae) are regularly pathogenic for man. Enteric bacteria are aerobes, ferment a wide range of carbohydrates, and possess a complex antigenic structure.

Most gram-negative bacteria possess complex lipopolysaccharides in their cell wall. These substances, endotoxins, have a variety of pathophysiologic effects which are summarized below. Subsequent sections deal with some prominent groups of enteric bacteria. Many enteric gram-negative rods are of particular concern at present as causes of iatrogenic or hospital-borne infections. Anaerobic gram-negative enteric bacteria, eg, Bacteroides, are discussed in Chapter 23.

ENDOTOXINS OF GRAM-NEGATIVE BACTERIA

The endotoxins of gram-negative bacteria are complex lipopolysaccharides derived from bacterial cell walls and often liberated when bacteria lyse. The substances are heat-stable, with molecular weights variously estimated to be between 100,000 and 900,000. The lipopolysaccharide can be extracted (eg, with phenol-water) and has 3 regions (Table 18–1).

Pathophysiologic Effects

The pathophysiologic effects of all endotoxins are similar regardless of their origin.

The administration of endotoxin to animals or man results in a series of events as the endotoxin is taken up by reticuloendothelial or endothelial cells, degraded, or neutralized.

The following are prominently observed clinically or experimentally: fever, leukopenia and hypoglycemia, hypotension and shock, impaired perfusion of essential organs, activation of C3 and complement cascade, intravascular coagulation, and death.

A. Fever: (See p 133.) Normal body temperature is maintained within narrow limits by a balance between heat production and heat loss governed by thermoregulatory centers in the hypothalamus.

Infections (bacteria, viruses, fungi), antigen-antibody complexes, delayed type hypersensitivity reactions, certain steroids, and endotoxins can result in fever production. These insults act on various cells (granulocytes, monocytes, probably others) and result in the release of endogenous pyrogen which acts on the thermoregulatory center to "set" it at a higher level.

Injection of endotoxin gives fever after 60–90 minutes, the time needed to release endogenous pyrogen. Injection of the latter gives fever within 30 minutes. Repeated injection of endogenous pyrogen gives the same fever response each time. Repeated injection of endotoxin gives less and less fever response ("tolerance"–due in part to reticuloendothelial blockade and in part to IgM antibodies to lipopolysaccharide).

Table 18–1. Composition of lipopolysaccharide "endotoxins" in the cell walls of gram-negative bacteria.

Chemistry	Common Name
(a) Repeating oligosaccharide (eg, man-rha-gal) combinations make up type-specific haptenic determinants (outermost on cell wall).	(a) O-specific polysaccharide; "somatic antigen" of "smooth" colonies. Induce specific immunity.
(b) (N-Acetylglucosamine, glucose, galactose, heptose.) Same in all gram-negative bacteria.	(b) Common core polysaccharide ("rough" colony antigen). Induce some nonspecific resistance to gram-negative sepsis.
(c) Backbone of alternating heptose and phosphate groups linked through KDO (2-keto-3-deoxy-octonic acid) to lipid. Lipid is linked to peptidoglycan (by glycoside bonds). (See p 18.)	(c) Lipid A with KDO responsible for primary toxicity.

B. Leukopenia: Bacteremia with gram-negative organisms is often accompanied by early leukopenia. Injection of endotoxins produces early leukopenia. In both instances, a secondary leukocytosis occurs later. The early leukopenia coincides with the temperature rise resulting from liberation of endogenous pyrogen from leukocytes and other cells. Endotoxin enhances glycolysis in many cell types and leads to hypoglycemia.

C. Hypotension: Early in gram-negative bacteremia, there may be widespread arteriolar and venular constriction (chill) followed by peripheral vascular dilatation, increased vascular permeability, decrease in venous return, lowered cardiac output, stagnation in the microcirculation, peripheral vasoconstriction, shock, and impaired organ perfusion and its consequences (eg, anuria). Injection of endotoxins can duplicate this complex sequence. Endotoxins can activate the release of vasoactive substances—eg, serotonin, kallikrein, and kinins—to initiate the sequence. Disseminated intravascular coagulation (DIC; see below) contributes to these vascular changes. However, vascular changes leading to shock may also occur in infections with gram-positive bacteria and viruses which contain no endotoxins.

D. Impaired Organ Perfusion and Acidosis: As a result of vascular reactions, hypotension, and shock, vital organs (kidneys, heart, liver, lungs, and brain) become anoxic and perform inadequately. This in turn may aggravate the vascular problems. Poor perfusion of tissues also results in accumulation of organic acids and metabolic acidosis (especially lactic acidosis).

E. Activation of C3 and Complement Cascade: Endotoxins are among the many different agents that can activate the "alternative pathway" of the complement cascade. C3 can be activated by endotoxins in the absence of preceding activation of C1,4,2, precipitating a variety of complement-mediated reactions (anaphylatoxins, chemotactic responses, membrane damage, etc) and a drop in serum complement components (C3,5–9).

F. Disseminated Intravascular Coagulation (DIC): DIC is a frequent complication of gram-negative bacteremia, although it can also occur in other infections. Endotoxin activates factor XII (Hageman factor)—the first step of the intrinsic clotting system—and thus the "coagulation cascade" is set into motion which culminates in the conversion of fibrinogen to fibrin. At the same time, plasminogen can be activated by endotoxin to plasmin (a proteolytic enzyme) which can attack fibrin with the formation of fibrin split products. Reduction in platelets and fibrinogen and detection of fibrin split products are evidence of DIC.

Injection of endotoxin leads to platelets sticking to vascular endothelium and occlusion of small blood vessels. That, in turn, causes ischemic or hemorrhagic necrosis in various organs. Heparin can prevent lesions of DIC. Clinically, hemorrhagic necrosis of skin occurs frequently in meningococcemia and pseudomonas sepsis, and suggestive DIC occurs frequently in severe gram-negative bacteremias.

Shwartzman phenomenon: This is probably a specialized model for DIC precipitated by endotoxin. If an animal is injected intradermally with endotoxin and injected intravenously with endotoxin the following day, necrosis of the prepared skin site occurs in a few hours. If endotoxin is given intravenously on 2 successive days, DIC occurs. It resembles histologically the DIC seen in gram-negative bacteremias. It has been suggested that the first dose of endotoxin "blocked" the reticuloendothelial system, so that it was unable to efficiently remove the second endotoxin dose. Instead of the first endotoxin dose, the reticuloendothelial system can be "blocked" by carbon particles or corticosteroid treatment.

G. Death: Death may occur as a result of massive organ dysfunction, shock, and DIC. It is not directly related to the amount of endotoxin that can be found circulating in the bloodstream. Endotoxin levels can be assayed by the "limulus test": A lysate of amebocytes from the horseshoe crab (Limulus) gels in the presence of 0.0001 $\mu g/ml$ of endotoxin. However, this test is not entirely specific and has no prognostic value at present.

H. Other Biologic Actions of Endotoxins: Experimentally, small amounts of endotoxins can enhance resistance to ionizing radiation and to infection, perhaps by stimulating the removal of bacteria by the reticuloendothelial system. In pregnant animals, endotoxin can produce decidual hemorrhage, premature labor, and abortions. Pregnant women with active urinary tract infections caused by gram-negative bacteria may have premature labor and consequently a high perinatal mortality rate of offspring. This may be caused by endotoxins originating in the urinary tract.

Immunologic Features of Reactions to Endotoxins

From birth, humans constantly encounter lipopolysaccharides on the surfaces of gram-negative bacteria which form the normal flora of the gut. As a result, antibodies are continually being produced to the many antigenic determinants of lipopolysaccharides, and delayed type hypersensitivity is being established. Immunologic responses occur to the O-specific polysaccharides and the core polysaccharides (linked to proteins).

It is known (from studies on cesarean piglets completely free of antibodies) that true "primary toxicity" of endotoxins exists. However, in man this "primary toxicity" is inseparable from immunologic responses.

A. Immediate Type: Endotoxins combine with antibodies. The Ag-Ab complexes with complement can trigger the same type of reactions as attributed to "primary toxicity" of endotoxins: endogenous pyrogen release, coagulopathy, vasoactive substance release, vascular necrosis, etc.

B. Delayed Type: Cellular hypersensitivity exists to endotoxin antigens. Delayed hypersensitivity can induce reactions attributable to "primary toxicity" of endotoxins: fever, inflammatory lesions, vascular necrosis, etc.

The immune responses can, however, also have a protective role.

C. Tolerance: IgM antibodies to endotoxin can enhance their uptake and degradation by reticuloendothelial cells. This is one form of "tolerance." IgM antibodies may also prevent DIC.

D. Antibodies: High-titer antibodies to the core polysaccharide can protect humans against shock and death from gram-negative bacteremia.

THE COLIFORM BACTERIA

The coliform bacteria are a large and heterogeneous group of gram-negative rods resembling, to some extent, *Escherichia coli.* The complexity of the group, the variations in biochemical test results, and the changing ecologic relationships have led to a confusing profusion of names. Besides *E coli,* derived from the intestinal tract, the following groups of organisms are often included among the "coliforms":

(1) **The Klebsiella-Enterobacter-Serratia group:** Typical *Klebsiella pneumoniae,* originally known as a respiratory pathogen, is now the most commonly encountered member, especially in hospital infections. It is characterized by mucoid growth, large polysaccharide capsules, and lack of motility. *Enterobacter aerogenes* is often motile, exhibits less mucoid growth, has small capsules, and may be found free-living as well as in the intestinal tract, in urinary tract infections, and in sepsis. (Enterobacter was formerly called Aerobacter.) *Serratia marcescens* is a small, usually free-living gram-negative rod which may produce an intense red pigment in culture. Serratia usually ferments lactose very slowly. Hafnia (*E hafniae*) is sometimes associated with gastroenteritis.

(2) **The Arizona-Edwardsiella-Citrobacter group:** These organisms ferment lactose very slowly, if at all, and were called "paracolon bacteria." They resemble salmonellae both in biochemical features and, occasionally, in pathogenicity for man, as when they produce gastroenteritis or sepsis.

(3) **Organisms of the "Providence" group,** formerly included with "paracolon bacteria," are biochemically related to proteus, deaminate amino acids (eg, lysine), and are encountered free-living or in urinary tract infections, sepsis, etc.

The term "paracolon" organisms designates slow lactose fermenters that often have low pathogenicity and produce infections in debilitated hosts or organ systems with impaired function.

Morphology & Identification

A. Typical Organisms: The coliform bacteria are short gram-negative rods which may form chains. Under unfavorable conditions of culture (eg, exposure to antibiotics), long filamentous forms occur. Capsules are rare in *E coli,* more frequent in enterobacter, and large and regular in klebsiella. Motility is present in most strains of *E coli* and some strains of enterobacter; it is absent in klebsiella.

B. Culture: *E coli* forms circular, convex, smooth colonies with distinct edges. Enterobacter colonies are similar but somewhat more mucoid. Klebsiella colonies are large, very mucoid, and tend to coalesce with prolonged incubation. Hemolysis on blood agar is produced by some strains of *E coli.*

C. Growth Characteristics: Escherichia and enterobacter break down many carbohydrates with the production of acid and gas. Escherichia produces approximately equal amounts of CO_2 and H_2 from dextrose; enterobacter produces twice as much CO_2 as H_2. "Paracolon" bacteria characteristically ferment lactose slowly or not at all and differ in other biochemical features. Klebsiella also ferments many carbohydrates, but variations among strains are great. For some typical reactions, see Table 18–6.

The following special tests (IMViC) are employed for differentiation of typical *E coli* and *E aerogenes:*

1. Indole test—*E coli* produces indole in broth containing tryptophan.

2. Methyl red test—This test indicates pH of culture in 0.5% glucose broth after 4 days at 37° C. If below pH 4.5, it is methyl red-positive.

3. Voges-Proskauer reaction—Depends upon production of acetylmethylcarbinol from dextrose. In the presence of alkali it is oxidized to diacetyl and gives a pink color (especially enterobacter).

4. Citrate test—Utilization of sodium citrate as sole source of carbon (free-living organisms).

IMViC, the mnemonic formula for these 4 tests, is for *E coli* ++− −; for *E aerogenes,* − −++. There are many intermediate forms between the typical intestinal *E coli* and the typical free-living *E aerogenes.* The formula for *E freundii,* a free-living organism, is ±+−+.

D. Variation: All cultures contain variants and stable mutants with respect to colonial morphology (rough or smooth), antigenic characteristics, biochemical behavior, and virus resistance. *E coli* strain K12 has been extensively studied from the standpoint of genetics and sexual recombination of inherited characteristics.

Antigenic Structure

Coliform organisms have a complex antigenic structure, and strains are divergent in their serologic behavior. They are classified by heat-stable somatic O antigens (more than 120 different ones), by heat-labile capsular K antigens, and by flagellar H antigens. The K antigens occur on surfaces and often interfere with O agglutination unless they are destroyed by heating. The larger the amount of K antigen on *E coli,* the greater is the likelihood that such a strain would produce neonatal meningitis or invasive urinary tract infection. The antigenic formula of an *E coli* might be O55:K5:H21.

Klebsiellae form large capsules consisting of polysaccharides (K antigens) covering the somatic (O or R) antigens. Klebsiellae can be identified by capsular swelling tests with specific antisera. Human infections of the respiratory tract are caused particularly by capsular types 1 and 2; those of the urinary tract, by types 8, 9, 10, and 24.

Certain O antigens are found in representatives of coliforms, salmonellae, or shigellae. A single organism commonly carries several O antigens. There are many examples of overlapping antigenic structures between coliform and other bacteria. For example, most enterobacteriaceae also share a common enterobacterial antigen first found in *E coli* O14. The type 2 capsular polysaccharide of klebsiellae is very similar to the polysaccharide of type 2 pneumococci. *E coli* O75:K100: H5 can induce antibodies which react with the capsular polysaccharide of *Haemophilus influenzae* type b. Many other examples of cross-reactions are known.

Colicins (Bacteriocins)

Many gram-negative organisms produce bacteriocins (colicins, pyocins). These are antibiotic-like bactericidal substances produced by certain strains of bacteria active against some other strains of the same or closely related species. Their production is controlled by plasmids. Colicins are produced by coliform organisms; pyocins by pseudomonas; marcescins by serratia. Bacteriocin production is accompanied by death and lysis of the producing cell. Bacteriocin-producing strains are resistant to their own bacteriocin; thus, bacteriocins can be used for "typing" of organisms.

Pathogenesis & Pathology

The coliform bacteria constitute a large part of the normal aerobic intestinal flora. Within the intestine, they generally do not cause disease and may even contribute to normal function and nutrition. These organisms become pathogenic only when they reach tissues outside the intestinal tract, particularly the urinary tract, the biliary tract, the lungs, the peritoneum, or the meninges, causing inflammation at these sites. When normal host defenses are inadequate, particularly in early infancy, old age, in the terminal stages of other diseases, after immunosuppression, or with indwelling venous or urethral catheters, coliform bacteria may reach the bloodstream and cause sepsis. In the neonatal period, high susceptibility to coliform sepsis may be caused by the absence of bactericidal IgM antibodies which cannot pass the placenta. *E coli*, especially O serotypes 1, 2, 4, 6, 7, 50, and 75, is the commonest cause of urinary tract infections.

Certain strains of *E coli* belonging to several distinct serologic types (eg, O55, O111, O127) appear to cause infantile diarrhea in certain outbreaks, particularly in newborn nurseries.

Certain other strains of *E coli* produce a potent enterotoxin (see p 130) capable of producing acute diarrhea, without invading intestinal epithelium. Some strains of *E coli* produce a heat-labile toxin (LT) under the control of a plasmid which resembles the cholera enterotoxin and which may be implicated in traveler's diarrhea. Other strains produce both heat-labile and heat-stable toxins (ST) under the control of heterogeneous plasmids. The LT is antigenic; the ST is not. Still other strains of *E coli* penetrate the intestinal epithelium and cause an inflammation resembling that of shigella dysentery.

Arizona-Citrobacter-Edwardsiella resemble salmonellae and can cause enteritis and sepsis. Providencia species are encountered in normal intestinal flora and occasionally in diarrheal disorders. Citrobacter and serratia are common in hospitalized patients as "superinfections." Serratia (usually nonpigmented) can cause pneumonia and sepsis. Erwinia (related to *E coli*) has caused sepsis. All cause urinary tract infections at times and often are resistant to antimicrobial therapy.

Klebsiella pneumoniae occurs in the respiratory tract and in the feces of about 5% of normal individuals and is the etiologic agent responsible for a small proportion (about 3%) of bacterial pneumonias. *K pneumoniae* produces extensive hemorrhagic necrotizing consolidation of the lung, which, if untreated, has a high mortality rate (40–90%). Occasionally it produces urinary tract infection or enteritis in children and bacteremia with focal lesions in debilitated patients. Other coliform organisms may also produce pneumonia. Two other klebsiellae are associated with inflammatory conditions of the upper respiratory tract: *K ozaenae* has been isolated from the nasal mucosa in ozena, a fetid, progressive atrophy of mucous membranes; and *K rhinoscleromatis* from rhinoscleroma, a destructive granuloma of the nose and pharynx.

Calymmatobacterium (Donovania) granulomatis, related to the klebsiellae, causes granuloma inguinale, a venereal disease. It is grown with difficulty on media containing egg yolk. Ampicillin is effective treatment.

Clinical Findings

The clinical manifestations of infections with coliform bacteria depend entirely on the site of the infection and cannot be differentiated by symptoms or signs from processes caused by other bacteria. Coliform bacteremia is often associated with vascular collapse and shock, especially in persons with impaired host defenses subjected to drugs and surgical procedures.

Diagnostic Laboratory Tests

A. Specimens: Urine, blood, pus, spinal fluid, sputum, or other material, as indicated by the localization of the process.

B. Stained Smears: Because gram-negative rods of the coliform group all resemble each other, only the presence of large capsules (klebsiella) is diagnostic. Direct capsule-swelling tests can be performed on klebsiellae visible in fresh specimens.

C. Culture: Specimens are plated both on blood agar and on "differential" media which contain special dyes and carbohydrates; this permits the rapid recognition of lactose-fermenting and nonlactose-fermenting colonies (Table 18–2). On such media, eg, MacConkey's or eosin-methylene blue agar, *E coli* colonies have a distinct metallic sheen. Organisms isolated on "differential" media are further identified by biochemical and serologic tests (Table 18–6). Rapid preliminary identification of gram-negative enteric bacteria is often possible (Table 18–2).

Table 18–2. Identification of gram-negative enteric bacteria.

Lactose Fermented Rapidly	Lactose Fermented Slowly	Lactose Not Fermented
Escherichia coli Metallic sheen on differential media; motile; flat, nonviscous colonies. *Enterobacter aerogenes* Raised colonies, no metallic sheen; often motile; more viscous growth. *Klebsiella pneumoniae* Very viscous, mucoid growth; nonmotile.	Serratia, Citrobacter, Arizona, Providencia	**Shigella species:** Nonmotile; no gas from dextrose. **Salmonella species:** Motile; acid and usually gas from dextrose. **Proteus species:** "Swarming" on agar; urea rapidly hydrolyzed (smell of ammonia). **Pseudomonas species:** Soluble pigments, blue-green, and fluorescing; sweetish smell.

Treatment

No single specific therapy is available. The sulfonamides, ampicillin, chloramphenicol, tetracyclines, polymyxins, and aminoglycosides have marked antibacterial effects against the coliform group, but variation in strain susceptibility is great and laboratory tests for antibiotic sensitivity are essential. Multiple drug resistance is common and is under the control of plasmids which are transmitted by conjugation. Serratia is often resistant to all available systemic antimicrobials except gentamicin. Certain conditions predisposing to infection by these organisms must be corrected surgically, eg, by relief of urinary tract obstruction, closure of perforation in an abdominal organ, or resection of a bronchiectatic portion of lung.

Epidemiology, Prevention, & Control

Coliform bacteria establish themselves in the normal intestinal tract within a few days after birth and from then on constitute a main portion of the normal aerobic microbial flora of the body. *E coli* is the prototype. Finding *E coli* in water or milk is accepted as proof of fecal contamination. *E aerogenes* occurs in the intestinal tract in much smaller numbers and is found free-living on vegetation. Since the enterobacter-klebsiella group of organisms may be present in water in the absence of fecal contamination, tests have been employed to separate them from *E coli* for the purpose of sanitary control. This is a questionable practice because the presence of either Escherichia or Enterobacter species, or their intermediates, in large numbers in drinking water suggests surface contamination.

Control measures are not feasible as far as the normal endogenous flora is concerned. Enteropathogenic *E coli* serotypes and certain "paracolon" bacteria should be controlled like salmonellae. Coliforms constitute a principal problem in hospital infection at present. Rigorous asepsis, sterilization of equipment, disinfection, restraint in ordering intravenous therapy, and strict urinary tract asepsis are helpful.

Immunity

In systemic infections, specific antibodies develop; but it is uncertain whether significant immunity follows infections due to these organisms.

THE PROTEUS GROUP

The proteus organisms are gram-negative, motile, aerobic bacilli. Most species are free-living in water, soil, and sewage. *P vulgaris* commonly occurs in the normal fecal flora of the intestinal tract, and *P morganii* has been incriminated in summer diarrhea in children. *P rettgeri* and *P morganii* are encountered in hospital infections. Proteus does not ferment lactose, decomposes urea with the liberation of ammonia, and tends to "swarm," spreading rapidly over the surface of solid media. "Swarming" can be inhibited by incorporation of phenylethyl alcohol or 0.1% chloral hydrate into the medium. It does not grow well at an acid pH (Table 18–6).

Motile strains of proteus contain H antigen in addition to the somatic O antigen. Certain strains labeled OX share specific polysaccharides with some rickettsiae. The OX strains are agglutinated by sera from patients with rickettsial diseases (Weil-Felix test). Proteus, like the coliform bacilli, produces infections in humans only when it leaves its normal habitat in the intestinal tract. It is frequently found in chronic urinary tract infections and produces bacteremia and focal lesions in debilitated patients or those receiving intravenous infusions. There are great variations among strains of proteus in antibiotic sensitivity; gentamicin is at present the most active drug. *P mirabilis* is often inhibited by penicillin G and ampicillin. Providencia is closely related to proteus.

THE PSEUDOMONAS GROUP

The pseudomonas group is composed of gram-negative motile rods which produce water-soluble pigments that diffuse through the medium. They occur widely in soil, water, sewage, and air.

Pseudomonas aeruginosa is frequently present in small numbers in the normal intestinal flora. It is also found on the human skin. Other Pseudomonas species occur in the environment but rarely cause disease.

Ps aeruginosa grows readily on culture media, does not ferment lactose, and forms smooth round colonies with a fluorescent greenish color and a sweetish aromatic odor. From the colonies, bluish-green pigment diffuses into the medium. Some strains hemolyze blood. Among the pigments produced by *Ps aeruginosa* are pyocyanin, a bluish material soluble in chloroform and water and possessing some antimicrobial activity; and fluorescein, a greenish, fluorescent, water-soluble (but not chloroform-soluble) material (Table 18–6). *Ps aeruginosa* may also produce a heat-labile exotoxin (molecular weight 55,000).

Ps aeruginosa is a pathogen only when introduced into areas devoid of normal defenses or when participating in mixed infections. It produces infection of wounds, giving rise to blue-green pus; meningitis, when introduced by lumbar puncture; urinary tract infection, when introduced by catheters and instruments or in irrigating solutions. Involvement of the respiratory tract, especially from contaminated respirators, results in necrotizing pneumonia. The organism is often found in otitis externa. Infection of the eye, which may lead to rapid destruction of the eyeball, occurs most commonly after injury or surgical procedures. *Ps aeruginosa* (and other species, eg, *Ps cepacia, putida, maltophilia*) is resistant to most antimicrobial agents (especially in the presence of Ca^{++} and Mg^{++}) and therefore becomes dominant and important when more susceptible bacteria of the normal flora are suppressed. In infants or debilitated persons, it may invade the bloodstream and result in fatal sepsis. This occurs commonly in patients with leukemia or lymphoma who have received antineoplastic drugs or radiation, and in severe burns. In *Ps aeruginosa* sepsis, verdoglobin (a breakdown product of hemoglobin) or fluorescent pigment can be detected in wounds, burns, or urine by ultraviolet fluorescence. For epidemiologic purposes, strains can be typed by bacteriophage or by pyocins (see Colicins, above). At least 7 antigenic types of *Ps aeruginosa* have been defined. Lipopolysaccharides carry antigenic specificity. Vaccine from these types administered to high-risk patients provides some protection against pseudomonas sepsis 10 days later. Such treatment is instituted in cases of leukemia, burns, cystic fibrosis, and immunosuppression.

Gentamicin, carbenicillin, polymyxins, and chloramphenicol are the antimicrobial agents most commonly effective against *Ps aeruginosa*.

In debilitated patients Aeromonas sp can produce infections similar to pseudomonas infections.

THE SALMONELLAE

Salmonellae are gram-negative, motile, aerobic rods which characteristically fail to ferment lactose and are pathogenic for man or animals by the oral route. The different species are closely related antigenically.

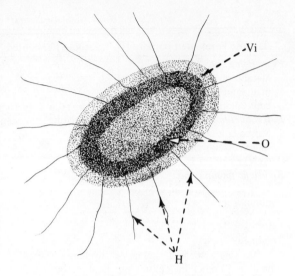

Figure 18–1. Antigenic structure of *Salmonella typhi*.

Morphology & Identification

Salmonellae are gram-negative, nonsporeforming bacilli which vary in length. Most species are motile with peritrichous flagella (except *S pullorum* and *S gallinarum*). Salmonellae grow readily on ordinary media but do not ferment lactose, sucrose, or salicin; they form acid and usually gas from glucose, maltose, mannitol, and dextrin (Table 18–6). Fermentations of sugars form a method of differentiating various species, but this is not as reliable or as rapid as antigenic analysis. Salmonellae are resistant to freezing in water and to certain chemicals, eg, brilliant green, sodium tetrathionate, and sodium deoxycholate; such compounds inhibit coliform bacilli and are, therefore, useful for isolation of salmonellae from feces.

Salmonella species can be identified by biochemical tests and antigenic analysis. Strains within a single species may be identified by lysis by a specific bacteriophage. This "phage typing" helps in epidemiologic tracing of isolates.

Antigenic Structure

A. Antigens: There are 3 main antigens:

1. "H" or flagellar antigens are inactivated by heating over 60° C and also by alcohol and acids. They are best prepared for serologic testing by adding formalin to young motile broth cultures. With sera containing anti-H antibodies, such antigens agglutinate rapidly in large fluffy clumps. These H antigens contain several immunologic constituents. Within a single Salmonella species, flagellar antigens may occur in either or both of 2 forms called phase 1 and phase 2. The organisms tend to mutate from one phase to the other; this is called phase variation. Antibodies to H antigens are predominantly IgG.

2. "O" or somatic antigens are part of the bacterial cell wall and are resistant to prolonged heating at 100° C, to alcohol, and to dilute acids. "O" antigens are prepared from nonmotile bacilli or by treatment

Table 18—3. Representative antigenic formulas of salmonellae.

O Group	Species	Antigenic Formula*
D	*S typhi*	**9, 12,** (Vi):d:—
A	*S paratyphi A*	**1, 2, 12**:a:—
C₁	*S choleraesuis*	**6, 7**:c:1,5
B	*S typhimurium*	**1, 4, 5, 12**:i:1, 2
D	*S enteritidis*	**1, 9, 12**:g, m:—

*O antigens: boldface numerals.
(Vi): Vi antigen if present.
Phase 1 H antigen: lower case letter.
Phase 2 H antigen: numeral.

with heat and alcohol. With sera containing anti-"O" antibodies, such antigens agglutinate slowly in granular masses. Antibodies to O antigens are predominantly IgM. Somatic O antigens are lipopolysaccharides (see p 18 for structure). Some O-specific polysaccharides contain unique sugars, dideoxyhexoses.

3. The "Vi" antigens, specialized capsular K antigens which are present at the extreme periphery of the bacteria, often interfere with agglutination of freshly isolated strains by antisera containing mainly anti-"O" agglutinins. The antigens are destroyed by heating for 1 hour at 60° C and by acids and phenol. Cultures possessing "Vi" antigens tend to be more virulent than those lacking it. Some K antigens resemble capsular polysaccharides of meningococci or haemophilus.

The Kauffmann-White classification of salmonellae is based on agglutination tests with absorbed sera, so that the content of "O" antigens and of phase 1 and phase 2 "H" antigens can be determined in an unknown organism (Table 18—3).

B. Variation: Organisms may lose "H" antigens and become nonmotile. Loss of "O" antigen is associated with change from smooth to rough colony form. "Vi" antigen may be lost partially or completely. Antigens may be acquired (or lost) in the process of transduction (see Chapter 4).

Toxins

As in all gram-negative bacteria, the cell walls of salmonellae contain lipopolysaccharides. These are liberated upon lysis of the cell and act as endotoxins.

Pathogenesis & Pathology

In all forms of salmonella infection, the organisms enter via the oral route and may produce either clinical or subclinical infection. Salmonellae may produce 3 main types of disease, but mixed forms are frequent.

A. The "Enteric Fevers": Typhoid (*S typhi*) and paratyphoid (*S paratyphi, S enteritidis*, etc). Organisms ingested with contaminated food or drink reach the small intestine, from which they enter (perhaps within monocytes) the intestinal lymphatics. They then travel via the thoracic duct into the bloodstream and are disseminated into many organs, including the intestines, where organisms multiply in lymphoid tissue and are excreted in the stool. The infectious dose for man is usually more than 100,000 organisms.

The outstanding lesions are hyperplasia and necrosis of lymphoid tissue (eg, Peyer's patches), hepatitis, focal necrosis in the liver, and inflammation of the gallbladder and occasionally of other sites (eg, periosteum, lungs).

B. Septicemias: Eg, due to *S choleraesuis*. Early invasion of the bloodstream follows infection by the oral route, although intestinal involvement is often absent. The organisms are widely disseminated and tend to cause focal suppuration, abscesses, meningitis, osteomyelitis, pneumonia, and endocarditis, especially in debilitated hosts.

C. Gastroenteritis: (Often called "food poisoning.") Eg, due to *S typhimurium*. Symptoms appear after only 1—3 days' incubation, which suggests that ingestion of large numbers of organisms results in a violent irritation of mucous membranes; usually, however, invasion of the bloodstream and dissemination of infection to other organs do not occur.

Diagnostic Laboratory Tests

Blood for culture must be taken repeatedly. In enteric fevers and septicemias, blood is often positive in the first week of the disease. Bone marrow cultures may be useful. Urine cultures may be positive after the second week.

Stool specimens also must be taken repeatedly. In

Table 18—4. Clinical diseases induced by salmonellae.

	Enteric Fevers	Septicemias	Gastroenteritis
Incubation period	7—20 days	Variable	8—48 hours
Onset	Insidious	Abrupt	Abrupt
Fever	Gradual, then high plateau, with "typhoidal" state	Rapid rise, then spiking "septic" temperature	Usually low
Duration of disease	Several weeks	Variable	2—5 days
Gastrointestinal symptoms	Often early constipation; later, bloody diarrhea	Often none	Nausea, vomiting, diarrhea at onset
Blood cultures	Positive in 1st—2nd week of disease	Positive during high fever	Negative
Stool cultures	Positive from 2nd week on; negative earlier in disease	Infrequently positive	Positive soon after onset

enteric fevers the stools are positive from the second or third week on; in gastroenteritis, during the first week.

Duodenal drainage establishes the location of the organisms in the biliary tract in carriers.

Repeated specimens of blood serum for serology should be taken to demonstrate a rise in titer.

A. Bacteriologic Methods for Isolation of Salmonellae:

1. Enrichment cultures—Put specimen (usually stool) into selenite F or tetrathionate broth, both of which inhibit normal intestinal bacteria and permit multiplication of salmonellae. After incubation for 1–2 days, this is plated on differential and selective media or examined by direct immunofluorescence.

2. Selective medium cultures—The specimen is plated on SS (salmonella-shigella) agar or on deoxycholate-citrate agar, which favors growth of salmonellae and shigellae over coliform organisms.

3. Differential medium cultures—Eosin-methylene blue, MacConkey's, or deoxycholate medium permits rapid detection of lactose nonfermenters (which include not only salmonellae and shigellae but also proteus, pseudomonas, and other organisms). Gram-positive organisms are somewhat inhibited. Bismuth sulfite medium permits rapid detection of *S typhi*, which forms black colonies due to H_2S production.

4. Final identification—Suspected colonies from solid media are identified by biochemical (Table 18–6) and slide agglutination tests with specific sera.

B. Serologic Methods: Serologic technics are used for identification of an unknown culture with a known serum (see below) and detection of antibody titer in patients with unknown illness. Serum agglutinins rise sharply during the second and third week of salmonella infection. At least 2 serum specimens should be obtained at intervals of 7–10 days to prove rise in titer.

1. The rapid slide agglutination test is performed by mixing known serum and unknown culture on a slide and observing the mixture under the low power objective. Clumping, when it occurs, can be observed within a few minutes. This test is particularly useful for preliminary identification of cultures.

2. The tube dilution agglutination test (Widal test)—Serial (2-fold) dilutions of unknown serum are tested against antigens from representative salmonellae. The results are interpreted as follows: (1) High or rising titer "O" (1:160 or more) suggests that active infection is present. (2) High titer "H" (1:160 or more) suggests past vaccination or past infection. (3) High titer "Vi" occurs in carriers.

Immunity

Infection with *S typhi, S paratyphi,* and *S schottmülleri* usually confers a certain degree of immunity. Reinfection may occur but is often milder. Circulating antibodies to O or Vi are related to resistance to infection and disease. However, relapses may occur in 2–3 weeks after recovery in spite of antibodies.

Treatment

In severe diarrhea, replacement of fluids and electrolytes is essential. Opiates may be needed. Among antimicrobials, chloramphenicol or ampicillin is most successful in suppressing the disease but not necessarily in eradicating the organisms, which remains a function of immune processes. Multiple drug resistance transmitted genetically by a plasmid among enteric bacteria plays a role in the problems of treating salmonella infections. Strains of salmonellae resistant to chloramphenicol and ampicillin are becoming more frequent. Trimethoprim-sulfamethoxazole may be a useful drug.

In carriers, the organisms may reside in the intestine or in the gallbladder. Intestinal carriers can sometimes be treated successfully with ampicillin. Biliary carriers require cholecystectomy in addition to ampicillin. While enteric fever can be effectively treated, the course of salmonella gastroenteritis is usually not shortened by antimicrobial drugs and excretion of organisms may even be prolonged.

Epidemiology

A. Sources of Infection: The sources of infection are food and drink which have been contaminated with salmonellae. The following sources are important:

1. Water—Contamination with feces often results in explosive epidemics.

2. Milk and other dairy products (ice cream, cheese, custard)—Contamination with feces or due to inadequate pasteurization or improper handling. Limited outbreaks traceable to source of supply.

3. Shellfish—Contaminated water.

4. Dried or frozen eggs—From infected fowl or contamination during processing.

5. Dried coconut.

6. Meats and meat products—Either from infected animals (poultry) or contaminated with feces by rodents or man. Corned beef has been involved.

7. Animal dyes (eg, carmine) used in drugs, foods, and cosmetics.

8. Household pets, eg, turtles, dogs, and cats.

B. Origin of Contamination: The feces of unsuspected subclinical cases or carriers are a more important source of contamination than frank clinical cases who are promptly isolated. Fecal contamination of this sort is especially dangerous if food handlers are "shedding" organisms. Many animals, including cattle, rodents, and fowl, are naturally infected with a variety of salmonellae and have the bacteria in their tissues (meat), excreta, or eggs. The incidence of typhoid fever has decreased, but the incidence of other salmonella infections has increased markedly in the USA.

C. Carriers: After manifest or subclinical infection, some individuals continue to harbor organisms in their tissues for variable lengths of time (convalescent carriers or healthy permanent carriers). Three percent of survivors with typhoid become permanent carriers, harboring the organisms in the gallbladder, the intestine, or, rarely, the urinary tract.

Prevention & Control

Sanitary measures must be taken to prevent contamination of food and water by rodents or other animals which excrete salmonellae. Infected poultry, meats, and eggs must be thoroughly cooked. Carriers must not be allowed to work as food handlers and should observe strict hygienic precautions. Cholecystectomy or ampicillin may eliminate the carrier state.

Two injections of acetone-killed bacterial suspensions of *S typhi,* followed by a booster injection some months later, give partial resistance to small infectious inocula of typhoid bacilli but not to large ones. The vaccines against other salmonellae give less protection and are not recommended.

THE SHIGELLAE

Shigellae are nonmotile, gram-negative, aerobic rods which, with a few exceptions, do not ferment lactose but which do ferment other carbohydrates, producing acid but not gas. Many species share common antigens with one another and with other enteric bacteria. The natural habitat of shigellae is limited to the intestinal tracts of man and other primates where a number of species produce bacillary dysentery.

Morphology & Identification

A. Typical Organisms: Slender, unencapsulated, nonmotile, nonsporeforming, gram-negative rods. Coccobacillary forms may occur in young cultures.

B. Culture: Shigellae are facultative anaerobes but grow best aerobically. Convex, circular, transparent colonies with intact edges reach a diameter of about 2 mm in 24 hours. They are commonly recognized on differential media by their inability to ferment lactose, thus remaining colorless while lactose fermenters form colored colonies.

C. Growth Characteristics: All shigellae ferment glucose; none ferment salicin. With the exception of *S sonnei* and *S dispar,* they do not ferment lactose. They form acid from carbohydrates but, with the exception of *S newcastle* and *S manchester,* do not produce gas. Shigellae may also be divided into those which ferment mannitol (eg, *S sonnei* and *S flexneri*) and those which do not (eg, *S dysenteriae*) (Table 18—5).

D. Variation: Mutants with different biochemical, antigenic, and pathogenic properties often emerge from parent strains. Variation from smooth (S) to rough (R) colony form is associated with loss of invasiveness.

Antigenic Structure

Shigellae have a complex antigenic pattern. There

is great overlapping in the serologic behavior of different species, and most of them share O antigens with other enteric bacilli.

The somatic O antigens of shigellae are lipopolysaccharides. Their serologic specificity depends on the polysaccharide. The classification of shigellae relies on biochemical and antigenic characteristics. The principal pathogenic species are shown in Table 18—5.

Pathogenesis & Pathology

The natural habitat of dysentery bacilli is the large intestine of man. *S alkalescens* and *S dispar* are almost never associated with bowel disease and are now called escherichiae. Other shigellae can cause bacillary dysentery. Shigella infections are practically always limited to the gastrointestinal tract; bloodstream invasion is quite rare. The essential pathologic process is invasion of the mucosal epithelium; microabscesses in the wall of the large intestine and terminal ileum lead to necrosis of the mucous membrane, superficial ulceration, bleeding, and formation of a "pseudomembrane" on the ulcerated area. This consists of fibrin, leukocytes, cell debris, a necrotic mucous membrane, and bacteria. As the process subsides, granulation tissue fills the ulcers and scar tissue forms.

Toxins

All shigellae release, upon autolysis, their toxic somatic antigen. This endotoxin probably contributes to the irritation of the bowel wall.

In addition, *S dysenteriae* (type 1) produces a heat-labile exotoxin. It is a protein, highly lethal for experimental animals, antigenically distinct from the endotoxin, and stimulates the production of a specific antitoxin. The "neurotoxin" of *S dysenteriae* is probably responsible for some of the clinical severity of some *S dysenteriae* infections and causes the CNS reactions (meningismus, coma) seen in severe cases. The toxin may be identical with an enterotoxin comparable to cholera toxin (see p 130).

Clinical Findings

After a short incubation period (1—4 days) there is a sudden onset of abdominal pain, cramps, diarrhea, and fever. The stools are liquid and contain mucus and blood after the first few movements. Their passage is accompanied by much straining and tenesmus (rectal spasms). Spontaneous recovery generally occurs in a few days, but small children sometimes succumb to dehydration and acidosis. The disease caused by *S dysenteriae* is particularly severe and may be associated

Table 18—5. Pathogenic species of Shigella.

Present Designation	Group and Type	Mannitol	Ornithine Decarboxylase	Earlier Designation
S dysenteriae	A (1—10)	−	−	*S shigae,* Shiga's bacillus
S flexneri	B (1—6)	+	−	*S paradysenteriae,* Flexner subgroup
S boydii	C (1—15)	+	−	*S paradysenteriae,* Boyd subgroup
S sonnei	D 1	+	+	Sonne bacillus

with bacteremia and disseminated intravascular coagulation.

Most persons, on recovery, shed dysentery bacilli for only a short period, but a few remain chronic intestinal carriers and may have recurrent bouts of the disease. Upon recovery from the infection, most persons develop antibodies to shigellae in their blood, but these do not protect against reinfection. Injection of killed dysentery bacilli likewise stimulates the production of antibodies but fails to protect humans against the infection. Live vaccines are experimental.

Diagnostic Laboratory Tests

Specimens consist of fresh stool, mucus flecks, and rectal swabs for culture. Serum specimens, if desired, must be taken 10 days apart to demonstrate rise in titer of agglutinating antibodies.

A. Culture: The materials are streaked on differential selective media (eg, MacConkey's or eosin-methylene blue agar) and on thiosulfate-citrate-bile agar, which suppress coliform and gram-positive organisms. Colorless (lactose-negative) colonies are inoculated into triple sugar iron medium (Table 18–6). Organisms producing acid on the slant and acid and gas in the butt should be discarded; they are either coliforms or paracolon bacilli. Proteus is ruled out by the rapid formation of red color in Christensen's urea medium. Organisms which fail to produce H_2S, which produce acid but not gas in the butt and an alkaline slant and which are nonmotile should be subjected to slide agglutination by specific shigella antisera.

B. Serology: Diagnosis with a single specimen of the patient's serum is impractical because normal persons often have agglutinins against several Shigella species. However, serial determinations of antibody may show a rise of specific antibody. HI tests are promising.

Immunity

A type-specific serologic response occurs with infection. IgA antibodies in the gut may be important in limiting reinfection. They may be stimulated by infection with wild strains or avirulent oral vaccine strains which may have some protective value. Serum antibodies to somatic shigella antigens are IgM.

Treatment

A potent specific antitoxin against *S dysenteriae* exotoxin is available, but convincing proof of its clinical efficacy is lacking. Sulfonamides, ampicillin, tetracyclines, and chloramphenicol are sometimes bacteriostatic for shigellae and can suppress acute clinical attacks of dysentery. They often fail to eradicate the organisms from the intestinal tract, however, and permit the carrier state to establish itself. Multiple drug resistance can be genetically transmitted by a plasmid, and resistant infection is widespread. At present, ampicillin or trimethoprim-sulfamethoxazole (co-trimoxazole) is most apt to be effective.

Epidemiology, Prevention, & Control

Shigellae are transmitted by "food, fingers, feces,

and flies" from man to man. *S dysenteriae* has spread widely in Central and South America. In 1969 in Guatemala, there were 110,000 cases with 8,000 deaths. Mass chemoprophylaxis for limited periods of time (eg, in military personnel) has been tried, but resistant strains of shigellae tend to emerge rapidly. Since man is the main recognized host of pathogenic shigellae, control efforts must be directed at eliminating the organisms from this reservoir by (1) sanitary control of water, food, and milk, sewage disposal, and fly control; (2) isolation of patients and disinfection of excreta; (3) detection of subclinical cases, particularly in food handlers. Live oral vaccines are being investigated.

THE VIBRIOS

Vibrios are curved, gram-negative, aerobic rods; they are motile, possessing a single polar flagellum. *V cholerae* (formerly *V comma*) and related vibrios produce cholera in man. Other vibrios may produce sepsis.

Morphology & Identification

A. Typical Organisms: Upon first isolation vibrios are comma-shaped, curved rods about 2–4 μm long and are very actively motile by means of a single polar flagellum. They do not form spores. On prolonged cultivation vibrios may become straight rods, resembling other gram-negative enteric bacteria.

B. Culture: Vibrios produce convex, smooth, round colonies, opaque and granular in transmitted light. They are oxidase-positive.

Most vibrios grow well at 37° C on defined media containing mineral salts and asparagine as sources of carbon and nitrogen. *Vibrio cholerae* grows well on alkaline taurocholate-tellurite agar or on thiosulfate-citrate-bile salt-sucrose agar. Characteristically, these organisms grow at very high pH (8.5–9.5) but are rapidly killed by acid. Cultures containing fermentable carbohydrates therefore quickly become sterile.

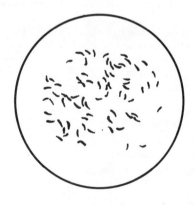

Figure 18–2. Typical organisms of *V cholerae* from broth.

V cholerae regularly ferments sucrose and mannose but not arabinose. When grown in a peptone medium containing adequate amounts of tryptophan and nitrate, it produces indole and reduces nitrate. Upon addition of sulfuric acid a red color develops (nitroso-indol reaction, "cholera red test"). Glucose inhibits this reaction.

C. Toxins: Cholera vibrios produce an enterotoxin which is heat- and acid-labile and has a molecular weight of 90,000. A single antigenic type is known. It causes marked increase in adenylate cyclase activity and cyclic AMP concentration and marked hypersecretion in the small intestine, resulting in massive diarrhea with fluid loss up to 20 liters daily (see p 130).

Some vibrios (eg, El Tor) produce soluble hemolysins. Others (*V cholerae*) digest red blood cells without liberating a soluble hemolysin. They remove myxovirus receptors from the red cell surface by means of a receptor-destroying enzyme (RDE), neuraminidase.

Antigenic Structure

Many vibrios share a single heat-labile flagellar H antigen. Antibodies to the H antigen are probably not involved in the protection of susceptible hosts. Cholera vibrios possess somatic O lipopolysaccharides with polysaccharide fractions that confer serologic specificity which places the O antigen in one of 6 groups. Antibodies to the O antigens tend to protect laboratory animals against infections with *V cholerae*. Both group-specific and type-specific O antigens have been found. In vitro—and perhaps in vivo also—vibrios are converted to a protoplast-like, osmotically fragile form in the presence of specific antibody and complement. Lysis occurs unless osmotic protection is provided (eg, 0.5 M lactose).

Pathogenesis & Pathology

Under natural conditions, cholera vibrios are pathogenic only for man. However, animal models for cholera infection have been devised.

Cholera is not an invasive infection. The organisms never reach the bloodstream but remain localized within the intestinal tract. There they multiply and liberate cholera toxin, and perhaps mucinases and endotoxin. Cholera toxin is adsorbed onto epithelial cell gangliosides and stimulates hypersecretion of water and chloride in all parts of the small intestine while inhibiting absorption of sodium. As a result, there is an outpouring of fluid and electrolytes with resulting diarrhea, dehydration, acidosis, shock, and death. However, the intestine is histologically intact.

Clinical Findings

After an incubation period of 1−4 days, there is a sudden onset of nausea and vomiting and profuse diarrhea with abdominal cramps. The stools resemble "rice water" and contain mucus, epithelial cells, and large numbers of vibrios. There is rapid loss of fluids and electrolytes, which leads to profound dehydration, circulatory collapse, and anuria. The death rate without treatment is between 25 and 50%. El Tor vibrios produce a similar diarrheal disease.

Several other members of the genus Vibrio produce disease in animals, eg, horses and cattle. These localize in the genital tract and may cause abortion. *Vibrio fetus* may produce sepsis and abortion in humans. *V parahemolyticus* may cause food poisoning from contaminated sea foods (eg, crabs) by means of a cholera-like enterotoxin.

The diagnosis of a full-blown case of cholera presents no problem in the presence of an epidemic. How-

Table 18−6. Biochemical reactions of certain gram-negative enteric bacteria.

Organism	Motility	Glucose	Lactose	Sucrose	Mannitol	H₂S Prod.	Triple Sugar Iron Agar Slant	Triple Sugar Iron Agar Butt	Lysine Decarboxylase	Ornithine Decarboxylase	Arginine Decarboxylase
E coli	+	AG	AG	±	AG	−	A	AG	±	±	±
E aerogenes	±	AG	AG	AG	AG	−	A	AG	+	+	−
Edwardsiella	+	AG	−	−	−	+	±	AG	+	±	±
Citrobacter	+	AG	±	±	+	+	±	AG	−	±	±
Serratia	+	A	±	A	A	−	±	A	+	+	−
K pneumoniae	−	AG	±	±	±	−	±	AG	+	−	−
S typhi	+	A	−	−	A	±	Alk	A	+	−	d+
S paratyphi (A)	+	AG	−	−	AG	−	Alk	AG	−	+	d+
S typhimurium	+	AG	−	−	AG	+	Alk	AG	+	+	d+
S dysenteriae	−	A	−	−	−	−	Alk	A	−	−	−
S flexneri	−	A	−	±	±	−	Alk	A	−	−	−
S sonnei	−	A	dA	dA	A	−	Alk	A	−	+	−
P vulgaris	+	AG	−	AG	−	+	±A	AG	−	−	−
P mirabilis	+	AG	−	dA	−	+	±A	AG	−	+	−
V cholerae	+	AG	−	A	A	−	A	A	+	+	−
Ps aeruginosa	+	±	−	±	−	−	Alk	±A	−	−	−
Alcaligenes faecalis	+	−	−	−	−	−	Alk	Alk	−	−	−

(±) Variable   (−) Negative   (AG) Acid and gas   (d) Delayed
(+) Positive   (A) Acid (yellow)   (Alk) Alkaline

ever, sporadic or mild cases are not readily differentiated from other diarrheal diseases.

Diagnostic Laboratory Tests

Specimens for culture consist of mucus flakes from stools and, occasionally, vomitus. Growth is rapid on peptone agar, blood agar with pH near 9.0, or thiosulfate-citrate-bile salt-sucrose agar, and typical colonies can be picked in 18 hours. For enrichment, a few drops of stool can be incubated for 6−8 hours in taurocholate-peptone broth (pH 8.0−9.0) and the organisms stained or subcultured.

Organisms resembling vibrios are further identified by slide agglutination tests, fermentation reactions, and a positive cholera red reaction (see above).

Immunity

Gastric acid provides some protection against cholera vibrios ingested in small numbers.

An attack of cholera is followed by immunity to reinfection, but the duration and actual degree of immunity are not known. In experimental animals, specific antibodies occur in the lumen of the intestine (secretory IgA, "coproantibodies"). Similar antibodies appear in man after infection. IgG vibriocidal antibodies in serum develop after infection but last only a few months. The relative role of vibriocidal and antitoxic antibodies in the circulation and in the gut is not established.

Treatment

The most important part of therapy consists of water and electrolyte replacement to correct the severe dehydration and salt depletion. Many antimicrobial agents are effective against *V cholerae*. Oral tetracycline tends to reduce stool output in cholera and shortens the period of excretion of vibrios.

Epidemiology, Prevention, & Control

Cholera is endemic in India and southeast Asia. From these centers it is carried along shipping lanes, trade routes, and pilgrim migrations. The disease is spread by individuals with mild or early illness and by water, food, flies, and person-to-person contact. In many instances, only 1−5% of exposed susceptible persons develop disease. The carrier state seldom exceeds 3 or 4 weeks, and true chronic carriers are rare. Vibrios survive in water for up to 3 weeks. Since 1960, cholera has spread widely in Africa and the Middle East.

Control rests on education and improvement of sanitation, particularly of food and water. Patients should be isolated, their excreta disinfected, and contacts followed up. Chemoprophylaxis with antimicrobial drugs may have a place. Repeated injection of a vaccine containing either lipopolysaccharides extracted from vibrios or dense vibrio suspensions can confer limited protection to heavily exposed persons (eg, family contacts) but is not effective as an epidemic control measure. Immunization with cholera toxoid is being studied.

●   ●   ●

General References

Alexander JW & others: Immunologic control of pseudomonas infection in burn patients. Arch Surg 102:31, 1971.

Anderson RJ & others: Infectious risk factors in the immunosuppressed host. Am J Med 54:453, 1973.

Aserkoff B & others: Effect of antibiotic therapy in acute salmonellosis. N Engl J Med 281:636, 1969.

Carpenter CJ: Cholera enterotoxin. Am J Med 50:1, 1971.

Cash RA & others: Response of man to infection with *Vibrio cholerae*. J Infect Dis 129:45, 1974.

Cherubin CE & others: Septicemia with non-typhoid salmonella. Medicine 53:365, 1974.

Edwards PR, Ewing WH: *Identification of Enterobacteriaceae,* 3rd ed. Burgess, 1972.

Elin RJ, Wolff SM: Nonspecificity of Limulus amebocyte lysate test. J Infect Dis 128:349, 1973.

Gorbach SL & others: Traveler's diarrhea and toxigenic *Escherichia coli.* N Engl J Med 292:933, 1975.

Hornick RB & others: Typhoid fever. (2 parts.) N Engl J Med 283:686, 739, 1970.

Ketover BP & others: Septicemia due to *Aeromonas hydrophila.* J Infect Dis 127:284, 1973.

Levine MM & others: Pathogenesis of *Shigella dysenteriae* 1 dysentery. J Infect Dis 127:261, 1973.

Lüderitz O & others: Lipid A: Structure and biologic activity. J Infect Dis 128(Suppl):S17, 1973.

McCable WR & others: Humoral immunity to type specific and cross-reactive antigens of gram negative bacilli. J Infect Dis 128(Suppl):S284, 1973.

McCracken GH & others: Relation between *Escherichia coli* K1 capsular polysaccharide antigen and clinical outcome in neonatal meningitis. Lancet 2:246, 1974.

McHenry MC, Hawk WA: Bacteremia caused by gram-negative bacilli. Med Clin North Am 58:623, 1974.

Pennington JE & others: Pseudomonas pneumonia: A retrospective study of 36 cases. Am J Med 55:155, 1973.

Prost E: Food-borne salmonellosis. Annu Rev Microbiol 21:495, 1967.

Sommer A & others: Efficacy of cholera vaccination. Lancet 1:230, 1973.

Tulloch EF & others: Invasive *Escherichia coli* dysentery. Ann Intern Med 79:13, 1973.

Wahab MF & others: Paratyphoid A fever. Ann Intern Med 70:913, 1969.

Wilrowske CJ & others: *Serratia marcescens.* JAMA 214:2157, 1970.

19...

Small Gram-Negative Rods

THE BRUCELLAE

The brucellae are small, aerobic, gram-negative coccobacilli which are nonmotile, nonsporeforming, and relatively inactive metabolically. They are obligate parasites of animals and man and are characteristically located intracellularly. *Brucella melitensis* typically infects goats; *Br suis,* swine; *Br abortus,* cattle; and *Br canis,* dogs (especially beagles). The disease in man, brucellosis (undulant fever, Malta fever), is characterized by an acute septicemic phase followed by a chronic stage which may extend over many years and may involve many tissues.

Morphology & Identification

A. Typical Organisms: The appearance in young cultures varies from cocci to rods 1.2 μm in length, with short coccobacillary forms predominating. The organisms are gram-negative but often stain irregularly. Capsules can be demonstrated on smooth and mucoid variants. The organisms are nonmotile and nonsporeforming.

B. Culture: On enriched media small, convex, smooth colonies appear in 24–48 hours. The colonies are at first translucent; later they often become brownish.

C. Growth Characteristics: Brucellae are adapted to an intracellular habitat, and their nutritional requirements are complex. Some strains have been cultivated on defined media of 18 amino acids, vitamins, salts, and glucose. Fresh specimens from animal or human sources are usually inoculated on trypticase-soy or liver infusion agar. On primary isolation various constituents of the medium may be toxic to the organisms (eg, toxic amounts of sulfur may be liberated from sulfur-containing amino acids in the medium). Other constituents of the medium must neutralize these toxic effects to permit growth of brucellae. *Br abortus* requires 5–10% CO_2 for growth, whereas the other 3 species grow in the presence of air.

Brucellae utilize carbohydrates but produce neither acid nor gas in amounts sufficient for classification. Catalase is produced by some strains and may have some correlation with virulence. Hydrogen sulfide is produced by many strains, and nitrates are reduced to nitrites.

Brucellae are moderately sensitive to heat and acidity. They are killed in milk by pasteurization.

D. Variation: Smooth, mucoid, and rough variants are recognized by colonial appearance and virulence. The typical virulent organism forms a smooth, transparent colony; it tends to mutate to the rough form, which is avirulent. These avirulent (rough) cells agglutinate in 1% acriflavine solution, whereas virulent (smooth) forms do not.

The selection of mutants in vivo appears to be influenced by materials in the environment. Thus the serum of susceptible animals contains a globulin and a lipoprotein which suppress growth of nonsmooth, avirulent types and favor the growth of virulent types. Resistant animal species lack these factors, so that rapid mutation to avirulence can occur. D-Alanine has been shown in vitro to have a similar selective effect.

Antigenic Structure

Different species of brucellae cannot be differentiated by agglutination tests but can be distinguished by agglutinin absorption reactions. It is probable that 2 antigens, A and M, are present in different proportions in 3 species. In addition, a superficial L antigen has been demonstrated which resembles the Vi antigen of salmonellae.

Species differentiations among 3 Brucella species is made possible by their characteristic sensitivity to dyes. (See Table 19–1.)

Bordetella bronchiseptica is a small gram-negative rod often found in the respiratory tracts of canines. It is related both to brucellae and to *Haemophilus influenzae.*

Eikenella corrodens is a small gram-negative rod (related to brucellae) which grows on agar and produces pits. It has been isolated from the human respira-

Table 19–1. Dye sensitivity of brucellae.

	Growth in Presence Of		H_2S Production	CO_2 Requirement
	Thionine (1:50,000)	Basic Fuchsin (1:25,000)		
Br abortus	−	+	++	+
Br melitensis	+	+	±	−
Br suis	+	−	+++	−
Br canis	+	−	++	−

tory tract, wounds, abscesses, meningitis, and endocarditis. It is of uncertain pathogenicity in the normal host.

Pathogenesis & Pathology

Although each species of Brucella has a preferred host, all can infect a wide range of animals, including man.

The common routes of infection in man are the intestinal tract (ingestion of infected milk), mucous membranes (droplets), and skin (contact with infected tissues of animals). The organisms progress from the portal of entry, via lymphatic channels and regional lymph nodes, to the thoracic duct and the bloodstream, which distributes them to the parenchymatous organs. In lymphatic tissue, liver, spleen, bone marrow, and other parts of the reticuloendothelial system, granulomatous nodules form which may develop into abscesses. In such lesions the brucellae are principally intracellular. There is also occasionally osteomyelitis, meningitis, or cholecystitis. The main histologic reaction in brucellosis consists of proliferation of mononuclear cells, exudation of fibrin, coagulation necrosis, and fibrosis. The granulomas consist of epithelioid and giant cells, with central necrosis and peripheral fibrosis.

Persons with active brucellosis react more markedly (fever, myalgia) to injected brucella endotoxin than normal persons. Sensitivity to endotoxin thus may play a role in pathogenesis.

Fetal membranes of many animals contain erythritol, a growth factor for brucellae. This may explain the particularly high susceptibility of pregnant animals. No such susceptibility exists in man, in whom erythritol is absent.

Clinical Findings

The incubation period is 1–6 weeks. The onset is insidious, with malaise, fever, weakness, aches, and sweats. The fever usually rises in the afternoon; its fall during the night is accompanied by drenching sweat. There may be gastrointestinal and nervous symptoms. Lymph nodes enlarge, and the spleen becomes palpable. Hepatitis may be accompanied by jaundice. Deep pain and disturbances of motion, particularly in vertebral bodies, signify osteomyelitis. These symptoms of generalized brucella infection generally subside in weeks or months, although localized lesions and symptoms may continue.

Following the initial infection, a chronic stage may develop characterized by weakness, aches and pains, low-grade fever, nervousness, and other nonspecific manifestations compatible with psychoneurotic symptoms. Brucellae cannot be isolated from the patient at this stage, but the IgG agglutinin titer may be high. The diagnosis of "chronic brucellosis" is difficult to establish with certainty unless local lesions are present. A high IgG antibody titer is suggestive of brucella activity.

Diagnostic Laboratory Tests

Take blood for culture, biopsy material for culture (lymph nodes, bone marrow, etc), and serum for serologic tests.

A. Culture: Blood or tissues are incubated in trypticase-soy broth and on thionine-tryptose agar. At intervals of several days, subcultures are made on solid media of similar composition. All cultures are incubated in 10% CO_2 and should be observed and subcultured for 6 weeks before being discarded as negative.

If organisms resembling brucellae are isolated, they are typed by H_2S production, dye inhibition, and agglutination by absorbed sera. As a rule, brucellae can be cultivated from patients only during the acute phase of the illness or during recurrence of activity.

B. Serology: Early in the disease, IgM antibodies appear; somewhat later, IgG and blocking antibodies. Whereas IgM antibody may persist after recovery (ie, when active infection is terminated spontaneously or by treatment), the finding of a substantial IgG antibody titer indicates active infection and active disease. Usual agglutination tests fail to detect infection with *Br canis.*

1. Agglutination test—To be reliable, agglutination tests must be performed with standardized heat-killed, phenolized, smooth brucella antigens available from brucellosis centers and should be incubated at 37° C for 48 hours. IgG agglutinin titers above 1:80 indicate active infection. Individuals injected with cholera vaccine may develop agglutinin titers to brucellae. If the serum agglutination test is negative in patients with strong clinical evidence of brucella infection, tests must be made for the presence of "blocking" antibodies. These can be detected by adding antihuman globulin to the antigen-serum mixture.

2. Opsonophagocytic test—This test is subject to great variations and is probably not reliable.

3. Blocking antibodies are IgA antibodies which interfere with agglutination by IgG and IgM and cause serologic tests to be negative in low serum dilutions although positive in higher dilutions (prozone). These antibodies appear during the subacute stage of infection, tend to persist for many years independently of activity of infection, and are detected by the Coombs antiglobulin method.

C. Skin Test: When "brucellergen" or a protein brucella extract is injected intradermally, erythema, edema, and induration develop within 24 hours in some infected individuals. The skin test is unreliable. Application of the skin test may stimulate the agglutinin titer.

Immunity

An antibody response occurs with infection, and it is probable that some resistance to subsequent attacks is produced. Immunogenic fractions from brucella cell walls have a high phospholipid content, lysine predominates among 8 amino acids, and there is no heptose (thus distinct from endotoxin).

Treatment

Brucellae may be susceptible to tetracyclines or ampicillin. Symptomatic relief may occur within a few days after treatment with these drugs is begun. However, because of their intracellular location, the organisms are not readily eradicated completely from the host. For best results, treatment must be prolonged. Combined treatment with streptomycin and a tetracycline may be considered.

Epidemiology, Prevention, & Control

Brucellae are essentially animal pathogens transmitted in animal populations by contact with feces, urine, milk, and infected tissues. Infection of man is accidental, through contact with these same infected materials. The common sources of infection for man are unpasteurized milk, milk products, and cheese and occupational contact (eg, farmers, veterinarians, slaughterhouse workers) with infected animals. Occasionally the airborne route may be important. Because of occupational contact, brucella infection is much more frequent in men. The majority of infections remain asymptomatic (latent).

Infection rates vary greatly with different animals and in different countries. In the USA, about 4% of all cattle are infected, about 15% of herds contain infected animals, and infection in hogs is common. Eradication of brucellosis in cattle can be attempted by test and slaughter, active immunization of heifers with avirulent live strain 19, or combined testing, segregation, and immunization. Cattle are examined by agglutination tests and skin tests.

Active immunization of humans against brucella infection is still in the experimental stage. Control rests on limitation of spread and possible eradication of animal infection, pasteurization of milk and milk products, and reduction of occupational hazards wherever possible.

THE PASTEURELLAE

Pasteurellae are short, gram-negative rods showing bipolar staining by special methods. They are nonsporeforming aerobic or microaerophilic organisms. All are nonmotile except *Yersinia (Pasteurella) pseudotuberculosis.* Different species break down a variety of carbohydrates, producing acid but not gas. Some species produce hemorrhagic septicemia in various animals *(Y multocida);* others infect animals and also produce serious disease in man *(Yersinia [P] pestis,* plague; *Francisella [P] tularensis,* tularemia). One species *(Yersinia enterocolitica)* causes enteric disease and bacteremia in man.

Morphology & Identification

A. Typical Organisms: The typical short, ovoid, plump, gram-negative rods are predominant in cultures and in smears from infected tissues. *Y pseudotuberculosis* possesses flagella; other species are nonmotile. Wayson's stain (methylene blue with carbolfuchsin)

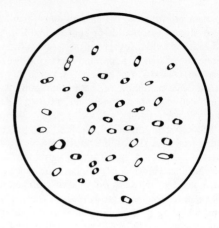

Figure 19–1. Typical organisms of *Y pestis* from smear of lymph node.

brings out the bipolar appearance of pasteurellae, causing them to resemble safety pins. Capsules or "envelopes" around the bacterial body are frequently present. Upon prolonged incubation or in an unfavorable environment, the rods are pleomorphic, varying greatly in size and shape. Long filamentous rods are occasionally seen.

B. Culture: All pasteurellae except *F tularensis* grow on ordinary bacteriologic media, but they grow more rapidly on media containing tissue fluids or blood. Gray, viscous colonies are formed from virulent tissue inocula, but irregular rough colonies occur frequently. *F tularensis* grows from small inocula only on complex media containing blood or tissue extracts and cystine, forming minute drop-like colonies in 48–76 hours at 37° C. All pasteurellae grow readily in the yolk sacs of embryonated eggs.

C. Growth Characteristics: Pasteurellae ferment carbohydrates, forming acid but not gas. There is great variation among strains, and species are not uniform in their biochemical reactions. The temperature for optimal rate of growth is 30° C for *Y pestis* and 37° C for *F tularensis,* but the production of certain antigenic components (eg, the protein-carbohydrate complex of fraction I in *Y pestis*) is greater at 37° C than at 30° C. *Y pseudotuberculosis* grown at 22° C is motile; at 37° C it is nonmotile. Catalase activity is greater in virulent than in avirulent strains of *Y pestis.*

D. Variation: Variants and stable mutants occur commonly with respect to appearance, morphology (eg, motility in *Y pseudotuberculosis*), biochemical characteristics, antigenic makeup, virulence, and drug resistance. Stable, avirulent mutants have been employed for vaccination against plague.

Antigenic Structure

The members of each species of Pasteurella fall into certain antigenic patterns; even within each species, however, there are antigenic differences among strains, and different species may appear interrelated by serologic tests. All pasteurellae possess somatic O antigens which are toxic for animals and which chemically are lipopolysaccharide-protein complexes. These have been subdivided by chemical fractionation into components of varying immunologic and serologic activity. In *Y pestis,* for example, fraction I, precipitated by 33% saturation of ammonium sulfate from aqueous extracts of acetone-dried bacilli, is largely responsible for stimulating antibacterial immunity. This fraction is produced by virulent and by certain avirulent strains at 37° C but much less at 30° C; it appears to be located in the outer "envelope" of the plague bacillus. Organisms virulent for guinea pigs produce, in addition to fraction I, a V-W antigen which makes them resist phagocytosis even in the absence of a visible "envelope." V-W alone suffices for full mouse virulence. A pure toxin has been isolated from *Y pestis* which is homogeneous protein with a molecular weight of 74,000 and an LD_{50} for mice of 1 μg. The "toxin" for mice appears to be distinct from the "toxin" for guinea pigs.

   Yersinia pseudotuberculosis carries an H antigen in its flagella when grown at 22° C. At 37° C this antigen does not form and the organisms are universally nonmotile. At least one of the O antigens of *Y pseudotuberculosis* cross-reacts with that of *Y pestis.* Bacteriophages specific for *Y pestis* tend to lyse many strains of *Y pseudotuberculosis,* but they usually do not lyse *Y multocida* or *F tularensis.* Bacteriophages that lyse *Y pseudotuberculosis* also lyse certain strains of shigellae or salmonellae. *F tularensis* strains are relatively homogeneous serologically but cross-react with some brucellae. All this indicates close relationship of antigenic constituents among many gram-negative bacilli.

Pathogenesis & Pathology

   Some Pasteurella species have narrow host ranges, producing disease in only a few types of animals; others affect a large variety of hosts. Pasteurellae generally produce disease by rapid invasion of the host body, multiplying in many tissues until overwhelming sepsis supervenes. When the population of pasteurellae reaches a high level, autolysis probably liberates sufficient "toxin" to be harmful to the host tissues.

   Purified plague toxins depress respiration of heart mitochondria in vitro, affecting different animal species in different degrees.

Hemorrhagic Septicemia of Animals

   There are varieties of *Y multocida* which are pathogenic for one or more of the following animals: rabbits, rats, horses, sheep, fowl, dogs, cats, and swine. The organisms are usually normal inhabitants of the respiratory tracts of animals and may suddenly assume pathogenicity when the host-parasite balance is disturbed. This occurs either (1) when there is unusually rapid passage from one host to another (eg, in the experimental passage of tissue in series), or (2) when host resistance is impaired through drastic environmental changes or intercurrent infections (particularly those due to viruses). Under such circumstances there

may be acute septicemia with rapid proliferation of bacilli in tissues and bloodstream, high fever, prostration, diarrhea, and death within 12–48 hours. Pathologically there are serous and hemorrhagic inflammatory changes in all organs and vast numbers of bacilli in the blood. In subacute and chronic disease, necrotic foci form in various organs, and the animals often survive. Human infections with *Y multocida* are rare and may follow animal bites. *Y multocida* is susceptible to penicillin.

Plague

   Yersinia (P) pestis is a parasite of various rodents, eg, rats and squirrels. It is transmitted from one rodent to another through the bites of fleas who have become infected by sucking the blood of an infected animal. The plague bacilli proliferate vastly in the intestinal tract of the flea and eventually block the lumen of the proventriculus completely so that no food can pass through. The hungry flea bites ferociously, and the aspirated blood is regurgitated, with an admixture of plague bacilli, into the bite wound. Thus, plague infection is transmitted from rodent to rodent and, occasionally, from rodent to man. It is not transmitted from man to man by fleas. When in the course of human infection pneumonia develops, droplets containing plague bacilli are coughed up. Such droplets are highly infectious by the airborne route and result in primary pneumonic plague in man, which is always fatal without chemotherapy and is readily transmitted from person to person. Some plague strains are so highly virulent that infection with a single organism may be lethal.

   When plague bacilli enter the host via the mucous membranes or through the bite of a flea, they extend via the lymphatic channels to the regional lymph node. Along the lymphatics and in the lymph nodes there is a rapidly spreading hemorrhagic inflammation and the node becomes greatly enlarged, forming a "bubo." Such buboes are usually located in the groin or axilla and may undergo necrosis and become fluctuant. In the lesser forms of plague the infective process stops there. Often, however, organisms progress via efferent lymphatics and the thoracic duct to the bloodstream, which rapidly disseminates them to all organs, especially to the spleen, liver, and lungs. In parenchymatous organs hemorrhagic inflammation is followed by development of focal necrosis. There are serosanguineous effusions in the pleura, the peritoneum, and the pericardium, and there may be (plague) meningitis. Terminally, plague bacilli may proliferate freely in the bloodstream.

Pseudotuberculosis

   Yersinia (P) pseudotuberculosis produces an infection of birds, rodents, and other animals which is rarely transmitted to man. The route of transmission has not been established, but it is probable that animals become infected through ingestion of contaminated droppings. Typical lesions consist of whitish nodules, grossly resembling tubercles, in the intestines and the parenchymatous organs. They consist of a necrotic center surrounded by inflammatory cells, but there are no giant or epithelioid cells. The disease tends to be chronic and to progress slowly, but there may be sepsis with rapidly fatal outcome. One clinical form in man presents as appendicitis, enteritis, and regional lymphadenitis, which tend to subside spontaneously. Serious *Y pseudotuberculosis* sepsis is associated with liver disease.

Yersinia (P) enterocolitica is an occasional member of the human gut flora. It grows best at 25° C. It can produce febrile diarrhea in dogs and man with person-to-person spread on close contact. Severe abdominal pain may suggest appendicitis and lead to operation. There may be ileitis, mesenteric adenitis, hepatic or splenic abscesses, and, rarely, bacteremia or endocarditis. Swine may be a source of infection.

Tularemia

Francisella (P) tularensis is essentially a parasite of rodents which is adapted to transmission by biting flies (Chrysops), ticks (Dermacentor and others), and a rabbit louse, all of which transmit the infection among the rodent population and thus maintain the reservoir of infection. Hares, rabbits, and muskrats are the main sources of disease in man. Handling, skinning, or eating such infected animals may result in human infection. *F tularensis* may enter the host via the skin or mucous membranes, through the bites of arthropods, or via the respiratory or gastrointestinal tracts. An ulcerating papule often develops at the site of penetration of the skin or mucous membranes, and the regional lymph nodes enlarge and suppurate. Transitory bacteremia establishes the organisms in various parenchymatous organs, where granulomatous nodules form which often undergo necrosis. As the disease progresses, tularemic pneumonia and septicemia develop which are fatal if untreated. Often the localizing signs are limited to the portal of entry. Thus the clinical picture may be "oculoglandular," following infection via the conjunctiva; "ulceroglandular," following entry through the skin; or "pneumonic," following primary inhalation of infectious droplets. At other times there may be no localizing symptoms whatever and only a febrile systemic illness.

Clinical Findings

Sporadic cases of pasteurella infection usually present difficult diagnostic problems, whereas in epidemics (eg, of plague) the diagnosis is readily apparent. Usually the clinical features of a local lesion, adenopathy, and a bubo in a febrile illness with a history suggestive of exposure warrant the performance of laboratory procedures which can establish the diagnosis unequivocally.

Diagnostic Laboratory Tests

Blood for culture should be collected repeatedly, as well as blood serum for serologic tests; after an initial specimen in the acute stage, subsequent specimens should be obtained at 12- to 21-day intervals.

Sputum for smear and culture must be obtained when pulmonary involvement is probable, and material from local lesions or aspirated material from a suppurating lymph node will be required for smear, culture, and animal inoculation. Strict aseptic precautions must be maintained because some pasteurellae are highly infective.

A. Stained Smears: Gram-stained films often show pleomorphic gram-negative organisms ranging from coccal forms to long rods. When plague or tularemia is suspected, immunofluorescent staining can identify the organism rapidly.

B. Cultures: Materials are cultured in rich blood culture media and on blood agar (plates), incubated both aerobically and with 10% CO_2. If tularemia is suspected, specimens should also be cultured on blood-glucose-cysteine agar, as cysteine is a growth requirement for *F tularensis*. If growth occurs, bacteria may be identified by biochemical and serologic tests, susceptibility to specific bacteriophages, subculture at 20° C for motility *(Y pseudotuberculosis),* and animal inoculation. *Note:* Great caution is necessary in handling highly infectious cultures. Sometimes it is difficult or impossible to assign a species designation to a pasteurella organism recovered from clinical or pathologic material because pasteurellae do not always fit rigidly into the described species characteristics. The pasteurellae may be thought of as a broad group of organisms in which host affinity and susceptibility and ecologic relationships influence the behavior of the "strains" recovered from a given host at a given time.

C. Animal Inoculations: One of the important classifying characteristics of the pasteurella group is its ability to cause disease and specific lesions in a variety of laboratory animals (eg, *Y pestis* is pathogenic for white rats and guinea pigs; *Y pseudotuberculosis* for guinea pigs but not for rats). Laboratory animals must be kept in strict isolation and must be rid of ectoparasites before being injected. Animal inoculation is particularly valuable when the specimen is contaminated with other organisms which tend to outgrow pasteurellae in culture. Such organisms frequently are nonpathogenic for laboratory animals and thus permit pasteurellae to produce specific lesions.

D. Serology: In subacute or chronic infections with pasteurellae, recovery of the organism in culture is rarely possible. Diagnosis often depends on the outcome of serologic tests. To be reliable the antigen must be obtained from a standard source, eg, a state health department. A rise in titer is more significant in establishing diagnosis than is a single high titer.

Agglutination and CF tests can be performed for antibodies to each of the pasteurellae. Very low serum titers are of questionable significance, since some cross-reactions occur with different types of organisms (brucellae, shigellae). A single high titer indicates only that infection has occurred at some time in the past; it does not establish the cause of the current disease. Only by a definite rise in serum titer in 2 specimens taken 2 weeks apart can the diagnosis be established. Antiplague sera agglutinate *Y pseudotuberculosis,* but usually not the reverse. Precipitin tests with chemical fractions of *F tularensis* and *Y pestis* can be performed. Precipitins appear in humans after infection but not after injection of killed vaccines. Such precipitins may be associated with immunity. Their development may be suppressed by antimicrobial therapy early in the infection.

E. Skin Test: Intradermal injection of an extract of *P tularensis* gives a delayed positive (tuberculin-like) reaction within 2–4 weeks after infection and for years thereafter. The skin test is specific and rarely causes a rise in agglutination titer.

Immunity

A solid immunity to plague and tularemia follows infection and recovery in each case.

Treatment

Most pasteurellae are sensitive to streptomycin, tetracyclines, and other antimicrobial drugs. Streptomycin, either alone or in combination with one of the tetracyclines, is rapidly curative in most patients if treatment is begun early in the disease.

Prevention

Vaccines have been prepared from various pasteurellae for the protective inoculation of exposed hosts. Attenuated cultures or killed suspensions of *Y multocida* are sometimes employed in the hope of preventing hemorrhagic septicemia in domestic animals. Vaccines against plague and tularemia can be prepared from (1) avirulent live bacteria; (2) heat-killed or formalin-inactivated suspensions of virulent bacteria; or (3) chemical fractions of the bacilli. The first 2 of these have been used on millions of persons in endemic areas and have given some protection which, however, is incomplete and of relatively short duration. Therefore, repeated vaccination of exposed individuals is essential in maintaining effective resistance. Reinfection following recovery from natural plague is quite rare, and immunity is thus presumed to be solid.

No practical or useful vaccines are available for pseudotuberculosis. A living, avirulent vaccine against tularemia has been used in Russia on a large scale.

In endemic areas plague can be efficiently prevented (even in persons exposed to patients with pneumonic involvement) by the daily administration of 2–4 gm of a sulfonamide or tetracycline. No spontaneously emerging drug-resistant plague bacilli have as yet been reported.

Epidemiology & Control

Pasteurella infections are animal diseases and are only accidentally transmitted to man. The risk to man can be reduced if the animal infection rate can be kept low. This is the principle of control measures. Infections of man with *Y multocida* and *Y pseudotuberculosis* are so rare that active measures against the animal reservoir of infection are not carried out. Tularemia is maintained in wild rodents away from human habitation. Proper precautions when dealing with wild rabbits or muskrats, and thorough cooking, are adequate safeguards in the majority of instances. In some parts of the world (eg, Russia, USA), water, grain, or hay contaminated by infected wild rodents or bites of the deerfly (Chrysops) may convey *F tularensis* to man.

Plague, on the other hand, presents an enormous epidemiologic problem. It is essentially an infection of wild rodents (squirrels, field mice, voles, gerbilles, etc) and occurs in many parts of the world. The chief enzootic areas are India, East Asia, South Africa, South America, and the western states of North America and Mexico. In these regions reservoirs of infection are always present in wild rodents and, intermittently, many animals die from the infection. The infection is transmitted by infective fleas among wild rodents. When the rate of infection rises in wild rodents, rats in urban environments become infected; the rat flea *(Xenopsylla cheopis)* is the chief vector in transmitting the disease to man. Once plague pneumonia occurs in man, direct man-to-man transmission through droplets constitutes a serious threat. From cities and harbors, infected rats have been transported across oceans on ships to start new outbreaks in other seaports.

Control measures are directed toward breaking the infection chain at several points: (1) Reduction of wild rodent populations and continuous survey of the rate of plague infection. Practical measures include shooting, trapping, and poisoning. (2) Reduction of rat populations in cities and continuous survey for plague infection in trapped rats. Measures are directed against rats on ships and in harbors. (3) Widespread application of insecticides to kill fleas, eg, DDT. (4) Chemoprophylaxis (tetracycline) in all contacts whenever plague is suspected. (5) Prompt and efficient chemotherapy of cases. (Human plague carriers are exceedingly rare.) (6) Active immunization as a supplementary measure in highly endemic areas, in troops, and in persons who may be forced into situations of potential exposure. (7) Strict isolation of plague cases and observation for pneumonic involvement.

THE HEMOPHILIC BACTERIA

This is a heterogeneous group of small, gram-negative, aerobic bacilli which are nonmotile and nonsporeforming and which require enriched media, usually containing blood or its derivatives, for isolation. Some are among the normal flora of the mucous membranes; others *(H influenzae, B pertussis)* are important human pathogens.

HAEMOPHILUS INFLUENZAE

Morphology & Identification

A. Typical Organisms: In specimens from acute infections the organisms are short (1.5 μm) coccoid bacilli, sometimes occurring in short chains. Long rods and large spherical bodies are also found. In cultures the morphology depends both on age and on the medium. At 6–8 hours in rich medium, coccobacillary forms predominate. Later there are longer rods, lysed bacteria, and very pleomorphic forms.

Organisms in young cultures (6–18 hours) on rich medium have a definite capsule. This capsule is rapidly dissolved by autolytic enzymes and therefore is poorly seen in older cultures. Capsule swelling tests are employed for "typing" *H influenzae* (see below).

B. Culture: On brain-heart infusion agar with blood, small, round, convex colonies with a strong iridescence develop in 24 hours. The colonies on "chocolate" (heated blood) agar take 36–48 hours to develop diameters of 1 mm. Isovitalex in media enhances growth. There is no hemolysis. Around staphylococcal (or other) colonies, the colonies of *H influenzae* grow much larger ("satellite phenomenon").

C. Growth Characteristics: Identification of organisms of the haemophilus group depends in part upon demonstrating the need for certain growth factors called X and V. Factor X acts physiologically as hemin; factor V can be replaced by coenzyme I or II or by nicotinamide nucleoside. The requirements for X and V factors of various Haemophilus species are listed in Table 19–2. Carbohydrates are fermented poorly and irregularly.

D. Variation: In addition to morphologic variation, *H influenzae* has a marked tendency to lose its capsule and the associated type specificity. Nonencapsulated variant colonies lack iridescence.

E. Transformation: Under proper experimental circumstances, the DNA extracted from a given type of *H influenzae* is capable of transferring that type specificity to other cells. Antibiotic resistance has been similarly transmitted by DNA (transformation).

Antigenic Structure

Encapsulated *H influenzae* contains capsular polysaccharides of one of 6 types (a–f); these polysaccharides (molecular weight > 150,000) resemble those

Table 19–2. Characteristics and growth requirements of some hemophilic organisms.

Organism	Hemolysis	Requires X	Requires V	Capsule
H influenzae	−	+	+	+
H parainfluenzae	−	−	+	+
H haemolyticus	+	+	+	−
H suis	−	+	+	+
H haemoglobinophilus	−	+	−	−
Bordetella pertussis	+	−	−	+

of pneumococci and sometimes give serologic cross-reactions with pneumococcal types 6, 29, and others. The capsular antigen of type b is a polyribose phosphate.

The somatic antigen of *H influenzae* consists of at least 2 proteins: the P substance constitutes much of the bacterial body, whereas the M substance is a labile surface antigen. Filtrable endotoxins can be derived from many fluid cultures of *H influenzae*, but their antigenic nature is not clear.

Encapsulated *H influenzae* can be typed by a capsule swelling test with specific antiserum; this test is analogous to the "quellung test" for pneumococci.

Pathogenesis

H influenzae produces no exotoxin, and the role of its toxic somatic antigen in natural disease is not clearly understood. The nonencapsulated organism is a regular member of the normal respiratory flora of man. The encapsulated forms of *H influenzae*, particularly type b, produce suppurative respiratory infections (sinusitis, laryngotracheitis, epiglottitis, otitis) and, in young children, meningitis. Over the age of 3 years, the blood of many individuals has strong bactericidal power for *H influenzae*, and clinical infections are less frequent. Recently, however, bactericidal antibodies have been absent from 25% of adults, and clinical infections are occurring more often in adults.

The role of *H influenzae* in human influenza of the pandemic type (particularly as occurred in 1918–1919) is not definitely known. This organism may well have been only a secondary invader producing pneumonitis in the respiratory tract already damaged by influenza virus. On the other hand it may have been definitely contributory to pandemic influenza in man, just as *H suis* is an essential etiologic component of swine influenza. Swine influenza is caused by a virus related to influenza type A but requires in addition the presence of *H suis* for the development of clinical symptoms. *H influenzae* is not pathogenic for laboratory animals.

Clinical Findings

H influenzae type b enters by way of the respiratory tract in small children and produces a nasopharyngitis, often with fever. Other types rarely produce disease. There may be local extension with involvement of the sinuses or of the middle ear. *H influenzae* type b is the commonest cause of otitis media, with pneumococcus the second most common. The organisms may reach the bloodstream and be carried to the meninges or, less frequently, may establish themselves in the joints. The meningitis thus induced does not differ clinically from other forms of bacterial meningitis in children under 3 years of age, and diagnosis rests on bacteriologic demonstration of the organism. Haemophilus meningitis is increasing in incidence.

Occasionally, a fulminating obstructive laryngotracheitis with swollen, cherry-red epiglottis develops in babies and requires prompt tracheostomy as a lifesaving procedure. Pneumonitis and epiglottitis due to

H influenzae may follow upper respiratory tract infections in small children and old or debilitated people.

Diagnostic Laboratory Tests

Specimens consist of nasopharyngeal swabs, pus, blood, and spinal fluid for smears and cultures.

A. Direct Identification: When organisms are present in large numbers in specimens, they may be identified by immunofluorescence or may be mixed directly with specific rabbit antiserum (type b) and a capsule swelling test performed. A direct precipitin test may be done on spinal fluid in which no bacteria can be seen. This test is performed by layering the spinal fluid over specific type b rabbit antiserum in a small test tube. A precipitate developing rapidly at the interface constitutes a positive test. It indicates that the fluid contains high concentrations of specific polysaccharide from *H influenzae* type b.

B. Culture: Specimens are grown in meat infusion blood broth or on enriched "chocolate" agar until typical colonies can be identified with the capsule swelling test (in 36–48 hours). *H influenzae* is differentiated from related gram-negative bacilli by observing the requirements for X and V factors and hemolysis on blood agar (Table 19–2).

Immunity

Immune persons have anticapsular antibody in blood; susceptibles lack it. Many persons over the age of 3–4 years are immune to infection because of the bactericidal complement-dependent antibodies against *H influenzae*. Injection of *H influenzae* type b capsular polysaccharide (polyribose phosphate) induces the same antibodies as active infection. The same antibodies can be induced by cross-reacting *E coli* O75:K100:H5 carried in the gut.

Treatment

The mortality rate of untreated *H influenzae* meningitis may be up to 90%. Some strains of *H influenzae* type b are susceptible to ampicillin, but an increasing proportion is resistant by virtue of beta-lactamase production. All strains appear to be susceptible to chloramphenicol. These drugs are effective in therapy. Greatest emphasis must be placed on early diagnosis and treatment, for if there is a delay in chemotherapy the incidence of late neurologic and intellectual impairment is high. Prominent among late complications of influenzal meningitis is the development of a localized subdural accumulation of fluid which requires surgical drainage.

Epidemiology, Prevention, & Control

Encapsulated *H influenzae* type b is transmitted from person to person by the respiratory route. The patient with influenzal meningitis is not an important source of infection. An increasing number of adults lack bactericidal antibody and are susceptible to systemic haemophilus infections. Therefore, immunization with capsular polysaccharides is now being considered for infants whose mothers lack antibody.

BORDETELLA (HAEMOPHILUS) PERTUSSIS

Morphology & Identification

A. Typical Organisms: Short, ovoid, gram-negative bacilli, resembling but less pleomorphic than *H influenzae*. With toluidine blue stain, bipolar metachromatic granules can be demonstrated. A capsule is present.

B. Culture: Primary isolation of *B pertussis* requires complex, enriched media. Commonly employed is Bordet-Gengou's medium (potato-blood-glycerol agar), on which small, convex, smooth colonies with a pearl-like luster develop in 36–72 hours. The colonies are mucoid and tenacious, and on blood agar there is a narrow zone of hemolysis.

C. Growth Characteristics: The organism is not very active metabolically and forms acid but not gas in glucose and lactose. It does not require X and V factors on subculture.

D. Variation: When isolated from patients and cultured on enriched media, *B pertussis* is in the smooth, encapsulated, virulent phase I. Phase IV is the designation for a rough, nonencapsulated, avirulent form. Phases II and III are intermediates.

Antigenic Structure

B pertussis cells possess many antigens. Most external are an agglutinogen and a hemagglutinin. The cell wall contains a heat-stable toxin, the protective antigen, and a histamine-sensitizing factor (the last 2 may be identical). Upon disruption of the cell, the protoplasm contains a heat-labile endotoxin, which is destroyed by 56° C for 30 minutes, and several other antigens. Phase I variants contain larger amounts of the protective and other antigens than other variant phases. There are several serotypes of *B pertussis* which may have epidemiologic significance.

Pathogenesis & Pathology

B pertussis survives for only brief periods outside the human host. There are no vectors. Transmission is largely by the respiratory route from early cases and possibly via carriers. The organism adheres to and multiplies rapidly on the surface of the epithelium in the trachea and bronchi and interferes with ciliary action. The blood is not invaded. Disintegrating organisms liberate an endotoxin which irritates surface cells, giving rise to catarrhal symptoms and causing marked lymphocytosis. Later there may be necrosis of parts of the epithelium and polymorphonuclear infiltration with peribronchial inflammation and interstitial pneumonia. Secondary invaders like staphylococci or *H influenzae* may give rise to bacterial pneumonia. Obstruction of the smaller bronchioles by mucous plugs results in atelectasis and diminished oxygenation of the blood. This probably contributes to the frequency of convulsions.

Clinical Findings

After an incubation period of about 2 weeks the

"catarrhal stage" develops, with mild coughing and sneezing. During this stage, large numbers of organisms are sprayed in droplets and the patient is highly infectious but not very ill. During the "paroxysmal" stage the cough develops its explosive character and the characteristic "whoop" upon inhalation. This leads to rapid exhaustion and may be associated with vomiting, cyanosis, and convulsions. The WBC is high (16,000–30,000/cu mm), with an absolute lymphocytosis. Convalescence is slow. Rarely, whooping cough is followed by encephalitis of unknown origin. Several types of adenovirus can produce a clinical picture indistinguishable from that caused by *B pertussis*.

Diagnostic Laboratory Tests

Specimens consist of nasopharyngeal swab or cough droplets for culture. A "cough plate" (Bordet-Gengou) is held 6 inches from the mouth of the patient during paroxysms.

A. Culture: The swab is passed through a drop of penicillin solution (1000 units/ml) before streaking. This tends to inhibit other microorganisms but permits growth of *B pertussis* in 2–4 days. Typical colonies are identified by agglutination with specific antiserum.

B. Serology: During the third week of the disease, agglutinating, precipitating, and complement-fixing antibodies develop for phase I *B pertussis*. A positive skin test to the agglutinogen also develops.

Immunity

Recovery from whooping cough or adequate vaccination is followed by immunity. Second infections may occur but are mild; reinfections occurring years later in older adults usually are severe.

Treatment

Hyperimmune globulin (prepared from the sera of immune persons repeatedly injected with pertussis vaccine) administered early in the course of the illness can make the illness milder, especially in children under 2 years of age. *B pertussis* is susceptible in vitro to many antimicrobial agents. Treatment with erythromycin or ampicillin may not change the course of the paroxysmal cough stage of the disease, but it eliminates the infectious organisms in a few days.

Prevention

During the first year of life every infant should receive 3 injections of killed phase I organisms in proper concentration. This vaccine is usually administered in combination with toxoids of diphtheria and tetanus. An infant exposed to whooping cough without prior immunization can obtain temporary passive protection with hyperimmune gamma globulin.

Epidemiology & Control

Whooping cough is endemic in most densely populated areas all over the world and also occurs intermittently in epidemic outbreaks. The source of infection is usually a patient in the early catarrhal stage of the disease. The communicability is high, ranging from 30–90%. The majority of cases occur in children under 5 years of age; most deaths occur during the first year of life.

Control of whooping cough rests mainly on adequate active immunization of all infants.

OTHER ORGANISMS OF THE HAEMOPHILUS GROUP

Bordetella (Haemophilus) parapertussis

May produce a disease similar to whooping cough even though it differs from typical *B pertussis* in certain bacteriologic criteria and resembles *B bronchiseptica* bacteriologically. Infection is often subclinical.

Eikenella corrodens (See p 215.)

May be present in upper respiratory tract.

Haemophilus parainfluenzae

Resembles *H influenzae* and is a normal inhabitant of the human respiratory tract; it has been encountered in disease only in bacterial endocarditis. (Am J Clin Pathol 37:319, 1962.)

Haemophilus haemoglobinophilus

Requires X but not V factor and has been found in dogs but not in human disease.

Haemophilus suis

Resembles *H influenzae* bacteriologically. Acts synergistically with swine influenza virus to produce the disease in hogs.

Haemophilus haemolyticus

The most markedly hemolytic organism of the group in vitro; it occurs both in the normal nasopharynx and in association with rare upper respiratory tract infections of moderate severity in childhood.

Haemophilus aphrophilus

This organism is encountered rarely in bacterial endocarditis and pneumonia. It is present in the normal oral and respiratory tract flora. It is related to *Actinobacillus actinomycetemcomitans* and is occasionally mistaken for actinomyces. Tiny colonies adhere to the sides of broth tubes.

Haemophilus aegyptius (Koch-Weeks Bacillus, *Haemophilus conjunctivitidis*)

Resembles *H influenzae* closely and has been found to be associated with a highly communicable form of conjunctivitis.

Moraxella lacunata (Morax-Axenfeld Bacillus)

A large gram-negative diplobacillus which is grown with difficulty from purulent exudates in eye infections, especially conjunctivitis. It is found in association with trachoma.

Haemophilus ducreyi

The causative organism of chancroid (soft chancre), a venereal disease. The chancroid consists of a ragged ulcer on the genitalia, with marked swelling and tenderness. The regional lymph nodes are enlarged and painful.

The small gram-negative rods occur in strands in the lesions, usually in association with other pyogenic microorganisms. They are grown with considerable difficulty and only in the presence of blood. Injection of pure cultures into the skin of rabbits or humans results in local ulcerative lesions. Suspensions of killed *H ducreyi* serve as a useful skin test antigen for the diagnosis of chancroid (Ducrey's skin test). The test may become positive 1–2 weeks after infection and may remain positive for years. There is no permanent immunity following chancroid infection.

Haemophilus vaginalis

A serologically distinct organism isolated from the normal female genitourinary tract and also associated with vaginitis. X and V factors are not essential for growth, and the organism is now reclassified as *Corynebacterium vaginale.*

Bordetella bronchiseptica

A small gram-negative bacillus which inhabits the respiratory tracts of canines and may be associated with pneumonitis. It resembles *B parapertussis* bacteriologically.

• • •

General References

Aftandelians RV, Connor JD: *Bordetella pertussis* serotypes in a whooping cough outbreak. Am J Epidemiol 99:343, 1974.

Bass JW & others: Antimicrobial treatment of pertussis. J Pediatr 75:768, 1969.

Buchanan TM & others: The tularemia skin test. Ann Intern Med 74:336, 1971.

Dorff GJ & others: Infections with *Eikenella corrodens:* A newly recognized human pathogen. Ann Intern Med 80:305, 1974.

Gutman LT & others: Outbreak of *Yersinia enterocolitica* enteritis. N Engl J Med 288:1372, 1973.

Hall WH & others: Blocking by hyperimmune rabbit IgA. J Immunol 107:41, 1971.

Honig PJ & others: *H influenzae* pneumonia in children. J Pediatr 83:215, 1973.

Hubbert WT, Rosen MN: *Pasteurella multocida* infection. Am J Public Health 60:1103, 1970.

Kendrick PL: Can whooping cough be eradicated? J Infect Dis 132:707, 1975.

Klock LE & others: Tularemia epidemic associated with the deerfly. JAMA 226:149, 1973.

Lewis JF & others: *C vaginale* vaginitis. Am J Obstet Gynecol 112:87, 1972.

Medeiros AA, O'Brien TF: Ampicillin-resistant *Haemophilus influenzae.* Lancet 1:716, 1975.

Meyer KF: Effectiveness of plague vaccines. Bull WHO 42:653, 1970.

Palmer DL & others: Clinical features of plague in the U.S. J Infect Dis 124:367, 1971.

Rabson AR & others: Generalized *Yersinia enterocolitica* infection. J Infect Dis 131:447, 1975.

Reddin JL & others: Significance of 7S and 19S brucella agglutinins in human brucellosis. N Engl J Med 272:1263, 1965.

Schneerson R, Robbins JB: Induction of serum *H influenzae* type b capsular antibodies in adult volunteers fed cross-reacting *Escherichia coli* 075:K100:H5. N Engl J Med 292:1093, 1975.

Schwirrenberger PR & others: Brucellosis in an Illinois abattoir. Arch Environ Health 24:337, 1972.

Street L & others: Brucellosis in childhood. Pediatrics 55:416, 1975.

Williams E: Brucellosis. Br Med J 1:791, 1973.

Young LS & others: Tularemia epidemic, Vermont 1968. N Engl J Med 280:1253, 1969.

20...
Spirochetes & Other Spiral Microorganisms

The spirochetes are a large, heterogeneous group of spiral, motile organisms. (See Chapter 3 for general morphologic characteristics.)

One family (Spirochaetaceae) of the order Spirochaetales includes 3 genera of free-living, large spiral organisms. The other (Treponemataceae) includes 3 genera pathogenic for man: (1) Treponema, which causes syphilis, bejel, yaws, and pinta; (2) Borrelia, which causes relapsing fever; and (3) Leptospira, which causes systemic infections with fever, jaundice, and meningitis.

TREPONEMA PALLIDUM

Morphology & Identification

A. Typical Organisms: Slender spirals measuring about 0.2 μm in width and 5–15 μm in length. The spiral coils are regularly spaced at a distance of 1 μm from each other. The organisms are actively motile, rotating steadily around their long axes. The long axis of the spiral is ordinarily straight but may sometimes bend so that the organism forms a complete circle for moments at a time, returning then to its normal straight position.

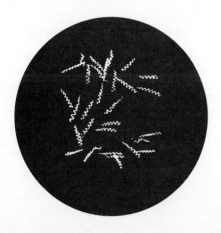

Figure 20–1. Typical organism of *Treponema pallidum* from tissue fluid in dark field.

The spirals are so thin that they are not readily seen unless darkfield illumination or immunofluorescent stain is employed. They do not stain well with aniline dyes, but they do reduce silver nitrate to metallic silver which is deposited on the surface so that treponemes can be seen in tissues (Levaditi silver impregnation).

Treponemes ordinarily reproduce by transverse fission, and divided organisms may adhere to one another for some time.

B. Culture: *Treponema pallidum* pathogenic for man has never been cultured with certainty on artificial media, in fertile eggs, or in tissue culture. The strains of purported *T pallidum* (eg, Reiter) cultured anaerobically in vitro are probably merely saprophytes, but they appear to be related to *T pallidum.*

C. Growth Characteristics: Because *T pallidum* cannot be grown, no studies of its physiology have been made. The growth requirements for one cultured probably saprophytic strain (Reiter) have, however, been established. A defined medium of 11 amino acids, vitamins, salts, minerals, and serum albumin supports its growth.

In proper suspending fluids and in the presence of reducing substances *T pallidum* may remain motile for 3–6 days at 25° C. In whole blood or plasma stored at 4° C, organisms remain viable for at least 24 hours, which is of potential importance in blood transfusions.

D. Reactions to Physical and Chemical Agents: Drying kills the spirochete rapidly, as does elevation of the temperature to 42° C also. This fact formed, in part, the basis for fever therapy of syphilis. Treponemes are rapidly immobilized and killed by trivalent arsenicals, mercury, and bismuth. This killing effect is accelerated by high temperatures and can be partially reversed and the organisms reactivated by compounds containing –SH (eg, cysteine, BAL). Penicillin is treponemicidal in minute concentrations, but the rate of killing is slow, presumably because of the metabolic inactivity and slow multiplication rate of the organism (estimated division time is 30 hours).

E. Variation: A life cycle has been postulated for *T pallidum,* including granular stages and cyst-like spherical bodies in addition to the spirochetal form. The occasional ability of *T pallidum* to pass through bacteriologic filters has been attributed to the filtrability of the granular stage.

Antigenic Structure

The antigens of *T pallidum* are unknown. In the human host the spirochete stimulates the development of antibodies capable of staining *T pallidum* by indirect immunofluorescence, of immobilizing and killing live motile *T pallidum,* and of fixing complement in the presence of suspensions of *T pallidum.* The spirochetes also cause the development of a distinct antibody-like substance, reagin, which gives positive complement fixation and flocculation tests with aqueous suspensions of lipids extracted from normal mammalian tissues. Either reagin or antitreponemal antibody is used for the serologic diagnosis of syphilis.

Pathogenesis, Pathology, & Clinical Findings

A. Acquired Syphilis: Natural infection with *T pallidum* is limited to the human host. Human infection is usually transmitted by sexual contact and the infectious lesion is on the skin or mucous membranes of genitalia. In about 10% of cases, however, the primary lesion is extragenital (usually oral). *T pallidum* can probably penetrate intact mucous membranes, or it may enter through a break in the epidermis.

Spirochetes multiply locally at the site of entry, and some spread to nearby lymph nodes and then reach the bloodstream. In 2–10 weeks after infection a papule develops at the site of infection which breaks down to form an ulcer with a clean, hard base ("hard chancre"). The inflammation is characterized by a predominance of lymphocytes and plasma cells. This "primary lesion" always heals spontaneously, but 2–10 weeks later the "secondary" lesions appear. These consist of a red maculopapular rash anywhere on the body, and moist, pale papules (condylomas) in the anogenital region, axillas, and mouth. There may also be syphilitic meningitis, chorioretinitis, nephritis (immune complex type), or periostitis. The secondary lesions also subside spontaneously. Both primary and secondary lesions are rich in spirochetes and are highly infectious. Contagious lesions may recur within 3–5 years after infection, but thereafter the individual is not infectious. Syphilitic infection may remain subclinical, and the patient may pass through the primary or secondary stage (or both) without symptoms or signs yet develop tertiary lesions.

In about 25% of cases early syphilitic infection progresses spontaneously to complete cure without treatment. In another 25% the untreated infection remains latent (principally evident by positive serologic tests). In the remainder the disease progresses to the "tertiary stage," characterized by the development of granulomatous lesions (gummas) in skin, bones, and liver, degenerative changes in the CNS (paresis, tabes), or syphilitic cardiovascular lesions, particularly aortitis (sometimes with aneurysm formation) and aortic valve insufficiency. In all tertiary lesions treponemes are very rare, and the exaggerated tissue response must be attributed to some form of hypersensitivity to the organisms. However, treponemes can occasionally be found in the eye or CNS of late syphilis.

B. Congenital Syphilis: A pregnant syphilitic woman can transmit *T pallidum* to the fetus through the placenta. Some of the infected fetuses die and miscarriages result; others are stillborn at term. Others are born live but develop the signs of congenital syphilis in childhood: interstitial keratitis, Hutchinson's teeth, saddle nose, periostitis, and a variety of CNS anomalies. Adequate treatment during the first half of pregnancy prevents congenital syphilis. The reagin titer in the blood of the child rises if he is infected but falls with time if antibody was passively transmitted from the mother. In congenital infection the child makes IgM antitreponemal antibody.

C. Experimental Disease: Rabbits can be experimentally infected in the skin, testis, and eye with human *T pallidum.* The animal develops a chancre rich in spirochetes, and organisms persist in lymph nodes, spleen, and bone marrow for the entire life of the animal, although there is no progressive disease.

Diagnostic Laboratory Tests

A. Specimens: Tissue fluid expressed from early surface lesions for demonstration of spirochetes; blood serum for serologic tests.

B. Darkfield Examination: A drop of tissue fluid or exudate is placed on a slide and a coverslip pressed over it to make a thin layer. The preparation is then examined under oil immersion with darkfield illumination for typical motile spirochetes.

Treponemes disappear from lesions within a few hours after the beginning of antibiotic treatment.

C. Immunofluorescence: Tissue fluid or exudate is spread on a glass slide, air dried, and mailed to the laboratory. It is fixed, stained with a fluorescein-labeled antitreponeme serum, and examined by ultraviolet microscopy for typical fluorescent spirochetes.

D. Serologic Tests for Syphilis: These are basically of 2 kinds: the detection of reagin or of antitreponemal antibody.

1. Tests for reagin—"Reagin" appears to be a mixture of IgM and IgA antibodies directed against some tissue antigens which are widely distributed. Reagin is found in the patient's serum after the second or third week of infection, or in the spinal fluid after the fourth to eighth week of infection. The "antigens" for estimation of reagin are lipids extracted from mammalian tissues. The purified cardiolipin from beef heart is a diphosphatidyl-glycerol. It requires the addition of lecithin and cholesterol or other "sensitizers" to react with syphilitic reagin. The most commonly used tests are flocculation tests and CF tests.

a. Flocculation tests (Hinton, Kahn, Kline, Mazzini, VDRL [Venereal Disease Research Laboratory], etc) are based on the fact that the particles of the lipid antigen remain dispersed in normal serum but combine with reagin to form visible aggregates, particularly when shaken or centrifuged. Positive VDRL tests revert to negative 6–24 months after effective treatment of syphilis.

b. CF tests (Wassermann, Kolmer) are based on the fact that reagin-containing sera fix complement in the presence of cardiolipin "antigen." It is necessary to ascertain that the serum is not "anticomplementary" (ie, that it does not destroy complement in the absence of antigen). An estimate of the amount of reagin present in a serum can be made by performing a serologic test with 2-fold dilutions of serum and expressing the "titer" as the highest dilution which still gives a positive result.

Biologic false-positive (BFP) results may occur (1) because of the technical complexities of the tests and (2) because certain sera regularly give positive flocculation or CF tests in the absence of syphilitic infection. BFP occur with other infections (eg, malaria, leprosy, measles), smallpox vaccination, in collagen diseases (disseminated lupus erythematosus, polyarteritis nodosa), and other conditions.

2. **Tests for antitreponemal antibodies—**

a. **Fluorescent treponemal antibody (FTA-ABS) test**—A test employing indirect immunofluorescence (killed *T pallidum* + patient's serum + labeled antihuman gamma globulin) shows excellent specificity and sensitivity for syphilis antibodies if the patient's serum, prior to the FTA test, has been absorbed with sonicated Reiter spirochetes. The FTA-ABS test is the first to become positive in early syphilis, and it usually remains positive many years after effective treatment of early syphilis. The test cannot be used to judge the efficacy of the treatment. The presence of IgM FTA in the blood of newborns is good evidence of in utero infection (congenital syphilis).

b. **TPI tests—**Demonstration of *T pallidum* immobilization (TPI) by specific antibodies in the patient's serum after the second week of infection. Dilutions of serum are mixed with complement and with live, actively motile *T pallidum* extracted from the testicular chancre of a rabbit, and the mixture is observed microscopically. If specific antibodies are present, spirochetes are immobilized; in normal serum, active motion continues. This test requires live treponemes from infected animals and is hard to perform.

c. ***Treponema pallidum* complement fixation test—**Spirochetes extracted from syphilomas of rabbits form specific antigens for complement fixation tests which probably measure the same antibody as the TPI test, above. Such spirochetal suspensions are difficult to prepare. Antigens prepared from cultured Reiter spirochetes are occasionally employed in the Reiter complement fixation test.

STS and FTA-ABS can also be performed on spinal fluid. Antibodies do not reach the CSF from the bloodstream but are probably formed in the CNS in response to syphilitic infection.

Immunity

A person with active syphilis or yaws appears to be resistant to superinfection with *T pallidum*. However, if early syphilis or yaws is treated adequately and the infection is eradicated, the individual becomes again fully susceptible.

Treatment

Arsenicals and bismuth salts were the drugs of choice for the treatment of syphilis until the advent of antibiotics. However, they have now been abandoned. Penicillin in concentrations of 0.003 unit/ml has definite treponemicidal activity, and penicillin is now the treatment of choice. In early syphilis, penicillin levels are maintained for 2 weeks (eg, a single injection of benzathine penicillin G, 2.4 million units IM); in late syphilis, for 3–4 weeks. Other antibiotics can occasionally be substituted. Prolonged follow-up is essential.

Epidemiology, Prevention, & Control

At present, the incidence of syphilis (and all other venereal diseases) is rising in most parts of the world. With the exceptions of congenital syphilis and the rare occupational exposure of medical personnel, syphilis is acquired through sexual exposure. An infected person may remain contagious for 3–5 years during "early" syphilis. "Late" syphilis, of more than 5 years' duration, is usually not contagious. Consequently, control measures depend on (1) prompt and adequate treatment of all discovered cases; (2) follow-up on sources of infection and contacts so they can be treated; (3) sex hygiene; and (4) prophylaxis at the time of exposure. Both mechanical prophylaxis (condoms) and chemoprophylaxis (eg, penicillin after exposure) have great limitations. Washing the genitalia after exposure may afford some protection to the male. Several venereal diseases can be transmitted simultaneously. Therefore, it is important to attempt diagnosis of syphilis when any one venereal disease has been found.

DISEASES RELATED TO SYPHILIS

These diseases are all caused by treponemes indistinguishable from *T pallidum*. All give biologic true-positive serologic tests for syphilis, and some cross-immunity can be demonstrated in experimental animals and perhaps in man. All are nonvenereal diseases and are commonly transmitted by direct contact. None of the etiologic organisms have been cultured on artificial media.

Bejel

Bejel occurs chiefly in Africa, particularly among children, and produces highly infectious skin lesions; late visceral complications are rare. Penicillin is the drug of choice.

Yaws (Frambesia)

Yaws is endemic, particularly among children, in many humid, hot tropical countries. It is caused by *Treponema pertenue*. The primary lesion, an ulcerating papule, occurs usually on the arms or legs. Transmission is by person-to-person contact in children under the age of 15. Transplacental, congenital infection does not occur. Scar formation of skin lesions and bone destruction are common, but visceral or nervous system complications are very rare. It has been debated whether yaws represents a variant of syphilis adapted to nonvenereal transmission in hot climates. There appears to be cross-immunity between yaws and syphilis. Diagnostic procedures and therapy are similar to those for syphilis. The response to penicillin treatment is dramatic.

Pinta

Pinta is caused by *Treponema carateum* and occurs endemically in all age groups in Mexico, Central and South America, the Philippines, and some areas of the Pacific. The disease appears to be restricted to dark-skinned races. The primary lesion, a nonulcerating papule, occurs on exposed areas. Some months later, flat, hyperpigmented lesions appear on the skin; depigmentation and hyperkeratosis take place years afterward. Late cardiovascular and nervous system involvement probably occurs. Transmission is nonvenereal, either by direct contact or through the agency of a fly (Hippelates). Diagnosis and treatment are the same as for syphilis.

Rabbit Syphilis

Rabbit syphilis (*Treponema cuniculi*) is a natural venereal infection of rabbits producing minor lesions of the genitalia. The etiologic organism is morphologically indistinguishable from *T pallidum* and may lead to confusion in experimental work.

OTHER SPIROCHETAL ORGANISMS

BORRELIA RECURRENTIS

Morphology & Identification

A. Typical Organisms: *B recurrentis* is an irregular spiral 10–30 μm long and 0.3 μm wide. The distance between turns varies from 2–4 μm. The organisms are highly flexible and move both by rotation and by twisting. *B recurrentis* stains readily with bacteriologic dyes as well as with blood stains such as Giemsa's or Wright's stain.

B. Culture: The organism can be cultured in fluid media containing blood, serum, or tissue, but it rapidly loses its pathogenicity for animals when transferred repeatedly in vitro. Multiplication is rapid in chick embryos when blood from patients is inoculated into the chorioallantoic membrane.

C. Growth Characteristics: Virtually nothing is known of the metabolic requirements or activity of borreliae. At 4° C, the organisms survive for several months in infected blood or in culture. In some ticks (but not in lice), spirochetes are passed from generation to generation.

D. Variation: The only significant variation of borrelia is with respect to its antigenic structure.

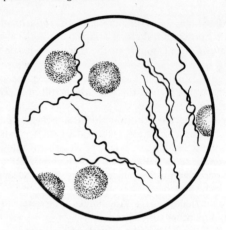

Figure 20–2. *Borrelia recurrentis* in blood smear.

Antigenic Structure

Many strains of *B recurrentis* have been isolated from different parts of the world (erroneously given different names), from different hosts, and from different vectors (lice or ticks). Some strains grow preferentially in one vector and some in another, but these are not stable differences.

Agglutinins, complement-fixing antibodies, and lytic antibodies develop in high titer after infection with borreliae. Apparently the antigenic structure of the organisms changes in the course of a single infection. The antibodies produced initially may act as a selective factor which permits the survival only of antigenically distinct variants. It has been suggested that the relapsing course of the disease is due to the multiplication of such variants, against which the host must then develop new antibodies. Ultimate recovery (after 3–10 relapses) might, if this is true, be associated with the presence of antibodies against several antigenic variants.

Pathology

Fatal cases show spirochetes in great numbers in the spleen and liver, necrotic foci in other parenchymatous organs, and hemorrhagic lesions in the kidneys and the gastrointestinal tract. Spirochetes have been occasionally demonstrated in the spinal fluid and brains of persons who have had meningitis. In experimental animals (guinea pigs, rats), the brain may serve as a reservoir of borreliae after they have disappeared from the blood.

Pathogenesis & Clinical Findings

The incubation period is 3–10 days. The onset is sudden, with chills and an abrupt rise of temperature. During this time spirochetes abound in the blood. The fever persists for 3–5 days and then declines, leaving the patient weak but not ill. The afebrile period lasts from 4–10 days and is followed by a second attack of chills, fever, intense headache, and malaise. There are from 3–10 such recurrences, generally of diminishing severity. During the febrile stages (especially when the temperature is rising), organisms are present in the blood; during the afebrile periods they are absent. Organisms appear less frequently in the urine.

Antibodies against the spirochetes appear during the febrile stage, and it is possible that the attack is terminated by their agglutinating and lytic effects. These antibodies may select out antigenically distinct variants which multiply and cause a relapse. Several distinct antigenic varieties of borreliae may be isolated from a single patient's several relapses, even following experimental inoculation with a single organism.

Diagnostic Laboratory Tests

A. Specimens: Blood obtained during the rise in fever, for smears and animal inoculation.

B. Stained Smears: Thin or thick blood smears stained with Wright's or Giemsa's stain reveal large, loosely coiled spirochetes among the red cells.

C. Animal Inoculation: White mice or young rats are inoculated intraperitoneally with blood. Stained films of tail blood are examined for spirochetes 2–4 days later.

D. Serology: Spirochetes grown in culture can serve as antigens for CF tests, but the preparation of satisfactory antigens is difficult. Patients suffering from epidemic (louse-borne) relapsing fever may develop high titers of agglutinins for proteus OXK.

Immunity

Immunity following infection is usually of short duration.

Treatment

The great variability of the spontaneous remissions of relapsing fever makes evaluation of chemotherapeutic effectiveness difficult. Tetracyclines and penicillin have been claimed to be capable of terminating individual attacks and preventing relapses.

Epidemiology, Prevention, & Control

Relapsing fever is endemic in many parts of the world. Its main reservoir is the rodent population, which serves as a source of infection for ticks of the genus Ornithodorus. The distribution of endemic foci and the seasonal incidence of the disease are largely determined by the ecology of the ticks in different areas. In the USA, infected ticks are found throughout the West, especially in mountainous areas, but clinical cases are rare. In the tick, borrelia may be transmitted transovarially from generation to generation.

Spirochetes are present in all tissues of the tick and may be transmitted by the bite or by crushing the tick. The tick-borne disease is not epidemic. However, when an infected individual harbors lice, the lice become infected by sucking blood; 4–5 days later, they may serve as a source of infection for other individuals. The infection of lice is not transmitted to the next generation, and the disease is the result of rubbing crushed lice into bite wounds. Severe epidemics may occur in louse-infested populations, and transmission is favored by crowding, malnutrition, and cold climate.

In endemic areas human infection may occasionally result from contact with the blood and tissues of infected rodents. The mortality of the endemic disease is low, but in epidemics it may reach 30%.

Prevention is based on avoiding exposure to ticks and lice and on delousing (cleanliness, DDT, insecticides). No vaccines are available.

LEPTOSPIRAE

Morphology & Identification

A. Typical Organisms: Tightly coiled, thin, flexible spirochetes 5–15 μm long, with very fine spirals 0.1–0.2 μm wide. One end of the organism is often bent, forming a hook. There is active rotational motion, but no flagella have been discovered. Electron micrographs show a thin axial filament and a delicate membrane. The spirochete is so delicate that in the dark field it may appear only as a chain of minute cocci. It does not stain readily but can be impregnated with silver.

B. Culture: Leptospirae grow best aerobically at 30° C in peptone broth with 10% inactivated serum. On semisolid media, round colonies 1–3 mm in diameter develop if agar contains 10% serum and hemoglobin. Leptospirae also grow on chorioallantoic membranes of embryonated eggs.

C. Growth Requirements: Metabolic activity or requirements have not been studied. The organisms are able to survive for long periods in water, particularly at an alkaline pH.

Antigenic Structure

The main strains of leptospirae isolated from man or animals in different parts of the world and designated as different species (Table 20–1) are all serologically related and exhibit marked cross-reactivity in serologic tests. This indicates considerable overlapping in antigenic structure, and quantitative tests and antibody absorption studies are necessary for a specific serologic diagnosis. From many strains of leptospirae, a serologically reactive lipopolysaccharide has been extracted which has group reactivity.

Pathogenesis & Clinical Findings

Human infection results usually from ingestion of water or food contaminated with leptospirae. More rarely, the organisms may enter through mucous membranes or breaks in the skin. After an incubation period of 1–2 weeks, there is a variable febrile onset during which spirochetes are present in the bloodstream. They then establish themselves in the parenchymatous organs (particularly liver and kidneys), producing hemorrhage and necrosis of tissue and resulting in dysfunction of those organs (jaundice, hemorrhage, nitrogen retention). The CNS is frequently invaded, and this results in a clinical picture of "aseptic meningitis." There may be lesions in skin and muscles also. Often there is episcleral injection of

Table 20–1. Principal leptospiral diseases.

Leptospiral Species	Source of Infection	Disease in Man	Clinical Findings	Distribution
L autumnalis	?	Pretibial fever or Ft. Bragg fever	Fever, rash over tibia	USA, Japan
L ballum	Mice	—	Fever, rash, jaundice	USA, Europe, Israel
L bovis	Cattle, voles	—	Fever, prostration	USA, Israel, Australia
L canicola	Dog urine	Infectious jaundice	Influenza-like illness, aseptic meningitis	Worldwide
L grippotyphosa	Rodents, water	Marsh fever	Fever, prostration, aseptic meningitis	Europe, USA, Africa
L hebdomadis	Rats, mice	Seven-day fever	Fever, jaundice	Japan, Europe
L icterohaemorrhagiae*	Rat urine, water	Weil's disease	Jaundice, hemorrhages, aseptic meningitis	Worldwide
L mitis	Swine	Swineherd's disease	Aseptic meningitis	Australia
L pomona	Swine, cattle	Swineherd's disease	Fever, prostration, aseptic meningitis	Europe, USA, Australia

*In the view of some investigators, the other organisms listed in this table are not different species but serotypes of *L icterohaemorrhagiae*.

the eye. The degree and distribution of organ involvement vary in the different diseases produced by different leptospirae in various parts of the world (Table 20–1). Many infections are mild or subclinical. Hepatitis is particularly frequent in patients with leptospirosis. It is often associated with elevation of serum creatine phosphokinase, whereas that enzyme is present in normal concentrations in viral hepatitis.

Kidney involvement in many animal species is chronic and results in the elimination of large numbers of leptospirae in the urine; this is probably the main source of contamination and infection of man. Human urine also may contain spirochetes in the second and third weeks of disease.

Agglutinating, complement-fixing, and lytic antibodies develop during the infection. Serum from convalescent patients protects experimental animals against an otherwise fatal infection. Immunity resulting from infection in man and animals appears to be specific for leptospirae. Dogs have been artificially immunized with killed cultures of leptospirae.

Diagnostic Laboratory Tests

Specimens consist of blood for microscopic examination, culture, and inoculation of young hamsters or guinea pigs; and serum for agglutination tests.

A. Microscopic Examination: Darkfield examination or thick smears stained by Giemsa's technic occasionally show leptospirae in fresh blood from early infections. Darkfield examination of centrifuged urine may also be positive.

B. Culture: Whole fresh blood can be cultured in diluted serum or on Korthof's medium.

C. Animal Inoculation: A sensitive technic for the isolation of leptospirae consists of the intraperitoneal inoculation of young hamsters or guinea pigs with fresh plasma or urine. Within a few days, spirochetes

become demonstrable in the peritoneal cavity; on the death of the animal (8–14 days), hemorrhagic lesions with spirochetes are found in many organs.

D. Serology: Agglutinating antibodies attaining very high titers (1:10,000 or higher) develop slowly in leptospiral infection, reaching a peak at 5–8 weeks after infection. For agglutination tests, cultured leptospirae are used live or fixed with formalin. Gross absorption of sera may permit identification of a species-specific antibody response. With live suspensions, agglutination is often followed by lysis. Leptospiral extracts sensitize sheep erythrocytes in the presence of specific antibodies, so that these sheep red blood cells are lysed by complement. These reactions are group-specific.

Immunity

A solid species-specific immunity (directed against individual serotypes) follows leptospiral infection.

Treatment

In very early infection, antibiotics (penicillin, tetracyclines) have some therapeutic effect but do not eradicate the infection.

Epidemiology, Prevention, & Control

The leptospiroses are essentially animal infections; human infection is only accidental, following contact with water or other materials contaminated with the excreta of animal hosts. Rats, mice, wild rodents, dogs, swine, and cattle are the principal sources of human infection. They excrete leptospirae in urine and feces both during the active illness and during the asymptomatic carrier state. Leptospirae remain viable in stagnant water for several weeks; drinking, swimming, bathing, or food contamination may lead to human infection. Persons most likely to come in contact with water contaminated by rats (eg, miners, sewer workers, farmers, fishermen) run the greatest risk of infection. Children acquire the infection from dogs more frequently than do adults. Control consists of preventing exposure to potentially contaminated water and reducing contamination by rodent control. Vaccination of dogs has been proposed.

SPIRILLUM MINUS
(Spirillum morsus muris)

Spirillum minus causes one form of rat-bite fever (sodoku). This very small (3–5 μm) and rigid spiral organism is carried by rats all over the world. The organism is inoculated into humans through the bite of a rat and results in a local lesion, regional gland swelling, skin rashes, and fever of the relapsing type. The frequency of this illness depends upon the degree of contact between humans and rats. The spirillum can be isolated by inoculation of guinea pigs or mice with material from enlarged lymph nodes or blood. In the USA and Europe, this disease has been recognized only infrequently. Several other motile gram-negative spiral aerobic organisms can produce spirillum fever. (Kowal J: N Engl J Med 264:123, 1961.)

SPIROCHETES OF THE NORMAL MOUTH & MUCOUS MEMBRANES

A number of spirochetes occur in every normal mouth. Some of them have been named (eg, *Borrelia buccalis*), but neither their morphology nor their physiologic activity permits definitive classification. On normal genitalia, a spirochete called *Borrelia refringens* is occasionally found which may be confused with *T pallidum*. These organisms are harmless saprophytes under ordinary conditions. Most of them are strict anaerobes which can be grown in petrolatum-sealed meat infusion broth tubes to which some tissue has been added.

FUSOSPIROCHETAL DISEASE

Under certain circumstances, particularly injury to mucous membranes, nutritional deficiency, or concomitant infection (eg, with herpes simplex virus) of the epithelium, the normal spirochetes of the mouth, together with cigar-shaped, banded, anaerobic fusiform bacilli (fusobacteria) find suitable conditions for vast increase in numbers. This occurs in ulcerative gingivostomatitis (trench mouth), often called Vincent's stomatitis or Vincent's infection. When this type of process produces ulcerative tonsillitis and massive tissue involvement, it is often called Vincent's angina. It also occurs in lung abscesses where pyogenic microorganisms and Bacteroides sp have broken down tissue; in bronchiectasis, where anatomic and physiologic disturbances interfere with normal drainage; in leg ("tropical") ulcers with mixed infection and venous stasis; and similar situations.

In all of these instances, necrotic tissue provides the anaerobic environment required by the fusospirochetal flora. The latter in turn prevents rapid healing and may contribute to tissue breakdown. Fusiform bacilli (fusobacteria) coexist with other anaerobes (bacteroides, peptostreptococcus; see Chapter 23). The fusospirochetal flora is readily inhibited by antibiotics. Thus antibiotic therapy may control gingivostomatitis or angina. However, the fusospirochetal organisms are not primary pathogens. Effective treatment must direct itself against the initial cause of tissue breakdown.

Fusospirochetal disease is generally not transmissible through direct contact, since everybody carries the organisms in the mouth. However, outbreaks occur occasionally in children or young adults. This is attributed to the transmission of a viral agent (eg, herpes simplex virus) in a susceptible population group or to nutritional deficiency and poor oral hygiene ("trench mouth").

● ● ●

General References

Babudieri B: The agglutination-absorption test of leptospira. Bull WHO 44:795, 1971.

Clark EG, Danbolt N: The Oslo study of the natural course of untreated syphilis. Med Clin North Am 48:613, 1964.

Dunlop EMC: Persistence of treponemes after treatment. Br Med J 2:577, 1972.

Southern PM, Sanford JP: Relapsing fever. Medicine 48:129, 1969.

Sparling PF: Diagnosis and treatment of syphilis. N Engl J Med 284:642, 1971.

Termini BA, Music SI: The natural history of syphilis. South Med J 65:241, 1972.

Turner LH: Leptospirosis. Br Med J 1:537, 1973.

Webster B (editor): Symposium on venereal diseases. Med Clin North Am 56:1055, 1972.

21...
Rickettsial Diseases

The rickettsiae were at one time considered closely related to the viruses because they are smaller than bacteria and because their growth, like that of viruses, occurs within cells. It is now clear that the rickettsiae are small, obligately parasitic, true bacteria, showing in thin sections all of the structural features of bacteria as well as possessing most of the enzymes of bacteria and a typical bacterial cell wall. The natural reservoir of these organisms is the arthropods, in which they propagate without, usually, producing any disease. When transmitted to an unnatural host such as man, they are likely to cause disease.

Except for Q fever organisms, the rickettsiae are transmitted by arthropods and produce infections in human beings characterized by fever and rash. The rickettsial diseases can be divided into groups on the basis of their clinical features, epidemiologic aspects, and immunologic characteristics.

Classification*

A. Typhus Group:
1. Epidemic typhus, louse-borne—*R prowazekii.*
2. Endemic typhus, murine flea-borne—*R typhi* (formerly *R mooseri*).

B. Spotted Fever Group:
1. Rocky Mountain spotted fever (RMSF)—*R rickettsii.*
2. Mediterranean fever (boutonneuse fever), South African tick bite fever, Kenya tick typhus, Indian tick typhus—*R conorii.*
3. North Asian tickborne rickettsiosis—*R sibirica.*
4. Queensland tick typhus—*R australis.*
5. Rickettsialpox, Russian vesicular rickettsiosis—*R akari.*
6. *R canada*—Transmitted by ticks in North America; causes a disease resembling Rocky Mountain spotted fever.

C. Scrub Typhus (Tsutsugamushi Fever): *R tsutsugamushi* (formerly *R orientalis*).

D. Q Fever: *Coxiella burnetii.*

E. Trench Fever: *R quintana.*

Properties of Rickettsiae

Rickettsiae are pleomorphic, appearing either as

*The spelling of the names of rickettsiae are based on Buchanan RE, Gibbons NE: *Bergey's Manual of Determinative Bacteriology*, 8th ed. Williams & Wilkins, 1974.

short rods, 600 × 300 μm in size, or as cocci, and they occur singly, in pairs, in short chains, or in filaments. When stained, they are readily visible under the optical microscope. With Giemsa's stain they stain blue; with Macchiavello's stain they stain red and contrast with the blue-staining cytoplasm in which they appear.

A wide range of animals are susceptible to infection with rickettsial organisms. Rickettsiae grow readily in the yolk sac of the embryonated egg (yolk sac suspensions contain up to 10^9 rickettsial particles per ml). Pure preparations of rickettsiae can be obtained by differential centrifugation of yolk sac suspensions. Many rickettsial strains also grow in cell culture.

Purified rickettsiae contain both RNA and DNA in a ratio of 3.5:1 (similar to the ratio in bacteria). Rickettsiae have cell walls consisting of peptidoglycans containing muramic acid, resembling cell walls of gram-negative bacteria. Rickettsiae divide like bacteria.

Unlike viruses, purified rickettsiae contain enzymes concerned with metabolism. Thus they oxidize intermediate metabolites like pyruvic, succinic, and glutamic acids and can convert glutamic acid into aspartic acid. Rickettsiae lose their biologic activities (toxicity, hemolytic activity, infectivity, and respiratory activity) when they are stored at 0° C; this is due to the progressive loss of nicotinamide adenine dinucleotide (NAD). All of these properties can be restored by subsequent incubation with NAD. They may also lose their biologic activity if they are starved by incubation for several hours at 36° C. This loss can be prevented by the addition of glutamate, pyruvate, or adenosine triphosphate (ATP). Subsequent incubation of the starved organism with glutamate at 30° C leads to partial or complete recovery of activity. Analysis of the ATP content of the rickettsiae during the starvation and recovery process indicates that the ATP level falls to zero during starvation and rises again on addition of glutamate.

Rickettsiae may grow in different parts of the cell. Those of the typhus group are usually found in the cytoplasm; those of the spotted fever group, in the nucleus. Thus far, one of the rickettsiae, *R quintana,* has been grown on cell-free media. It has been suggested that rickettsiae grow best when the metabolism of the host cells is low. Thus, their growth is enhanced when the temperature of infected chick embryos is lowered to 32° C. If the embryos are held at 40° C, rickettsial multiplication is poor. Conditions which influence the metabolism of the host can alter its susceptibility to rickettsial infection.

Rickettsial growth is enhanced in the presence of sulfonamides, and rickettsial diseases are made more severe by these drugs. Para-aminobenzoic acid (PABA), the structural analogue of the sulfonamides, inhibits the growth of rickettsial organisms. This inhibition is reversed by parahydroxybenzoic acid, which may be the metabolite whose function is interfered with by PABA.

Chloramphenicol and the tetracycline drugs inhibit the growth of rickettsiae and are excellent therapeutic agents.

In general, rickettsiae are quickly destroyed by heat, drying, and bactericidal chemicals. Although rickettsiae are usually killed by storage at room temperature, dried feces of infected lice may remain infective for months at room temperature.

The organism of Q fever is the rickettsial agent most resistant to drying. This organism may survive pasteurization at 60° C for 30 minutes and has been recovered from the commercially pasteurized milk of infected herds.

Rickettsial Antigens & Antibodies

A variety of rickettsial antibodies are known; all of them participate in the reactions discussed below. The antibodies which develop in man after vaccination generally are more type-specific than the antibodies developing after natural infection.

A. Agglutination of *Proteus vulgaris* (Weil-Felix Reaction): The Weil-Felix reaction is commonly used in diagnostic work. Rickettsiae and proteus organisms appear to share certain antigens. Thus during the course of rickettsial infections, patients develop antibodies which agglutinate certain strains of *Proteus vulgaris*. For example, the proteus strain OX19 is agglutinated strongly by sera from persons infected with epidemic or endemic typhus; weakly by sera from those infected with Rocky Mountain spotted fever;

Table 21–1. Serologic tests for rickettsial diseases.

Disease	Weil-Felix	Immunofluorescence or CF With Yolk Sac Antigen
Epidemic typhus	OX19	+
Endemic typhus	OX19	+
Scrub typhus	OXK	+
Rocky Mountain spotted fever	OX19 and OX2	+
Mediterranean (boutonneuse) fever)	OX19 and OX2	+
South African tick fever	OX19 and OX2	+
Rickettsialpox	Negative	+
Q fever	Negative	+

and not at all by those infected with Q fever. Convalescent sera from scrub typhus patients react most strongly with the proteus strain OXK (Table 21–1).

B. Agglutination of Rickettsiae: Rickettsiae are agglutinated by specific antibodies. This reaction is very sensitive and can be diagnostically useful when heavy rickettsial suspensions are available.

C. Complement Fixation With Rickettsial Antigens: Complement-fixing antibodies are commonly used in diagnostic laboratories. A 4-fold or greater antibody titer rise is usually required as laboratory support for the diagnosis of acute rickettsial infection. Convalescent titers often exceed 1:64. Group-reactive antigens are available for the typhus group, the spotted fever group, and Q fever. They consist of mixtures of particulate and soluble antigens (proteins and nucleoproteins). Some of the latter may give species-specific reactions. All antigens are derived from rickettsiae grown in the yolk sacs of embryonated eggs.

D. Immunofluorescence Test With Rickettsial Antigens: Suspensions of rickettsiae can be partially purified from infected yolk sac material and used as antigens in indirect immunofluorescence tests (see p 151) with patient's serum and a fluorescein-labeled antihuman globulin. The results indicate the presence of partly species-specific antibodies, but some cross-reactions are observed. Antibodies after vaccination are IgG; early after injection, IgM.

E. Neutralization of Rickettsial Toxins: Rickettsiae contain toxins which produce death in animals within a few hours after inoculation. These toxins are complex lipopolysaccharides. Toxin-neutralizing antibodies appear during infection, and these are specific for the toxins of the typhus group, the spotted fever group, and scrub typhus rickettsiae. Toxins exist only in viable rickettsiae (inactivated rickettsiae are nontoxic) and somewhat resemble bacterial endotoxins.

Pathology

Rickettsiae multiply in endothelial cells of small blood vessels. The cells become swollen and necrotic; there is thrombosis of the vessel, leading to rupture and necrosis. Vascular lesions are prominent in the skin, but vasculitis occurs in many organs. In the brain, aggregations of lymphocytes, polymorphonuclear leukocytes, and macrophages are associated with the blood vessels of the gray matter; these are called typhus nodules. The heart shows similar lesions of the small blood vessels. Other organs may also be involved.

Clinical Findings

Except for Q fever, in which there is no skin lesion, rickettsial infections are characterized by fever, headache, malaise, prostration, skin rash, and enlargement of the spleen and liver.

A. Typhus Group:

1. Epidemic typhus—In epidemic typhus, systemic infection and prostration are severe, and fever lasts for about 2 weeks. The disease is more severe and is more often fatal in patients over 40 years of age. During epidemics, the case mortality has been 6–30%.

2. Endemic typhus—The clinical picture of endemic typhus has many features in common with that of epidemic typhus, but the disease is milder and is rarely fatal except in elderly patients.

B. Spotted Fever Group: The spotted fever group resembles typhus clinically; however, unlike the rash in other rickettsial diseases, the rash of the spotted fever group usually appears first on the extremities, moves centripetally, and involves the palms and soles. Some, like Brazilian spotted fever, may produce severe infections; others, like Mediterranean fever, are mild. The case mortality rate varies greatly. In untreated Rocky Mountain spotted fever, it is usually much greater in older age groups (up to 60%) than in younger people. Rickettsialpox is a mild disease with a rash resembling that of varicella. About a week before onset of fever, a firm red papule appears at the site of the mite bite and develops into a deep-seated vesicle which in turn forms a black eschar (see below).

C. Scrub Typhus: This disease resembles epidemic typhus clinically. One feature is the eschar, the punched-out ulcer covered with a blackened scab which indicates the location of the mite bite. Generalized lymphadenopathy and lymphocytosis are common. Localized eschars may also be present in the spotted fever group.

D. Q Fever: This disease resembles influenza, primary atypical pneumonia, or hepatitis rather than typhus. There is no rash or local lesion. The Weil-Felix reaction is negative, and transmission appears to be airborne rather than through the skin.

E. Trench Fever: The disease is characterized by headache, exhaustion, pain, sweating, coldness of the extremities, and fever associated with a roseolar rash. Relapses occur, and it may take over a year for the disease to run its course. Trench fever has been known only among armies during wars in central Europe.

Laboratory Findings

Isolation of rickettsiae is technically quite difficult and so is of only limited usefulness in diagnosis. Whole blood (or emulsified blood clot) is inoculated into guinea pigs, mice, or eggs. Rickettsiae are recovered most frequently from blood drawn soon after onset, but they have been found as late as the 12th day of the disease.

If the guinea pigs fail to show disease (fever, scrotal swellings, hemorrhagic necrosis, death), either "blind" passages to other animals are made or, more often, serum of the guinea pig is collected for antibody tests to determine if the animal has had an inapparent infection.

The agent of scrub typhus grows readily in the mouse. Regardless of the animal used for isolation of this agent, material should be passed through the mouse, for rickettsiae are readily seen in smears of peritoneal exudate.

Serologic tests of choice for the various rickettsial diseases are indicated in Table 21–1. An antibody rise should be demonstrated during the course of the illness.

Treatment

The tetracyclines and chloramphenicol are effective. The total amount of either antibiotic given in the first 24 hours of therapy is 4–6 gm by mouth. For seriously ill patients, give initially 1 gm tetracycline or chloramphenicol IV. The daily dose thereafter is 2–3 gm divided into 4 doses. Response should be observed within 1–2 days, and the progression of the clinical disease is usually halted at the stage where treatment is started. To avoid relapses, continue treatment for 3–5 days after the temperature is normal.

Sulfonamides enhance the disease and are contraindicated.

The antibiotics do not free the body of rickettsiae, but they do suppress their growth. Recovery depends upon the immune mechanisms of the patient, which usually take 2 weeks to develop to the stage where they can control the parasite. If treatment is begun after the sixth day of illness, the immunity develops as in the untreated infection and relapses do not occur. If antibiotics are given earlier in the disease and a short course of treatment used, the immune mechanism is not properly stimulated and relapses occur. Such relapses can usually be prevented by giving effective drugs for more than 10 days.

Epidemiology

A variety of arthropods, especially ticks and mites, harbor rickettsia-like organisms which do not harm the host. They are found in the cells which line the alimentary tract; from there they reach the genital tract and are transmitted from one generation to the next.

Rickettsiae, like other microorganisms, appear to be in a state of continuous evolution. They seem to be "bacteria" of arthropods which have become limited to an intracellular life cycle.

The life cycles of different rickettsiae vary according to the stage of their evolution:

(1) *R prowazekii* has achieved a greater degree of parasitism for man than any other member of the group. Its life cycle is limited to man and to the human louse *(Pediculus corporis* and *P capitis).* The louse obtains the organism by biting infected human beings and transmits the agent by fecal excretion on the surface of the skin of another person. Whenever a louse bites, it defecates at the same time. It is the scratching of the area of the bite which allows the rickettsiae excreted in the feces to penetrate the skin. As a result of the infection the louse dies, but the organisms remain viable for some time in the dried feces of the louse. Rickettsiae are not transmitted from one generation of lice to another. Typhus epidemics have been controlled by delousing large proportions of the population with insecticides like DDT.

Brill's disease is a recrudescence of an old typhus infection. The rickettsiae can persist for many years in the body of an individual without any symptoms being manifest. The rickettsiae isolated from such cases behave like classical *R prowazekii*; this suggests that man himself is the reservoir of the rickettsiae of epidemic typhus. Epidemic typhus epidemics have been associated with war and the lowering of standards of personal hygiene, which in turn have increased the opportunities for human lice to flourish. If this occurs at the time of recrudescence of an old typhus infection, an epidemic may be set off. Brill's disease occurs in local populations of typhus areas as well as in persons who migrate from such areas to places where the disease does not exist. Serologic characteristics readily distinguish Brill's disease from primary epidemic typhus. Antibodies arise earlier and are IgG rather than the IgM detected after primary infection. They reach a maximum by the tenth day of disease. The Weil-Felix reaction is usually negative. This early IgG antibody response and the mild course of the disease suggest that partial immunity is still present from the primary infection.

(2) *R typhi* has its reservoir in the rat, in which the infection is inapparent and long-lasting. The agent can be recovered from the rat for at least a year after exposure. Rat fleas carry the rickettsiae from rat to rat and sometimes from rat to man, who develops endemic typhus. Cat fleas can serve as vectors. In endemic typhus, the flea cannot transmit the rickettsiae through the egg.

(3) *R tsutsugamushi* has its true reservoir in the mites which infest rodents. Rickettsiae can persist in rats for over a year after infection. Mites transmit the infection transovarially. Occasionally infected mites or rat fleas bite man, and scrub typhus results. The rickettsiae persist in the mite-rat-mite cycle in the scrub or secondary jungle vegetation which has replaced the virgin jungle in areas of partial cultivation. Such areas may become infested with rats and trombiculid mites.

(4) *R rickettsii* may be found in healthy wood ticks *(Dermacentor andersoni)* and is passed transovarially. Vertebrate hosts such as deer and man are occasionally bitten by infected ticks in the western USA. In order to be infectious, the tick carrying the rickettsiae must be engorged with blood, for this increases the number of rickettsiae in the tick. Thus, there is a delay of 45–90 minutes between the time of the attachment of the tick and its becoming infective. In the eastern USA, Rocky Mountain spotted fever is transmitted by the dog tick *Dermacentor variabilis.* Dogs are hosts to dog ticks but do not serve as a continuing source of tick infection. Most Rocky Mountain spotted fever in the USA now occurs in the eastern and the southeastern regions.

(5) *R akari* has its vector in blood-sucking mites of the species *Allodermanyssus sanguineus.* These mites may be found on the mice *(Mus musculus)* trapped in apartment houses where rickettsialpox has occurred. Transovarial transmission of the rickettsiae occurs in the mite. Thus the mite may act as a true reservoir as well as a vector. *R akari* has also been isolated from a vole in Korea.

(6) *R quintana* is the etiologic agent of trench fever; it is found in lice and in man, and its life cycle is like that of *R prowazekii.* The disease has been limited to fighting armies. This organism can be grown on blood agar in 10% CO_2.

(7) *Coxiella burnetii* is found in ticks, which transmit the agent to sheep, goats, and cattle. Workers in slaughterhouses and in plants which process wool and cattle hides have contracted the disease as a result of handling infected animal tissues. *C burnetii* is transmitted by the respiratory pathway rather than through the skin. There may be a chronic infection of the udder of the cow. In such cases the rickettsiae are excreted in the milk and occasionally may be transmitted to man by ingestion or inhalation.

Infected sheep may excrete *C burnetii* in the feces and urine. The placentas of infected cows and sheep contain the rickettsiae, and parturition creates infectious aerosols. The soil may be heavily contaminated from one of the above sources, and the inhalation of infected dust leads to infection of man and livestock. Coxiella infection is now widespread in cattle herds in the USA. Coxiella can cause endocarditis.

Geographic Occurrence

A. Epidemic Typhus: Potentially worldwide, it has disappeared from the USA, Britain, and Scandinavia. It is still present in the Balkans, Asia, Africa, Mexico, and the Andes. In view of its long duration in man as a latent infection (Brill's disease), it can flourish quickly under proper environmental conditions, as it did in Europe during World War II as a result of the deterioration of community sanitation.

B. Endemic, Murine Typhus: Worldwide, especially in areas of high rat infestation, such as seaports. It may exist in the same areas as—and may be confused with—epidemic typhus or scrub typhus.

C. Scrub Typhus: Far East, especially Burma, India, Ceylon, New Guinea, Japan, and Taiwan. *Trombicula pallida,* the chigger most often found in Korea, maintains the infection among the wild rodents of Korea *(Apodemus agrarius)*, but only infrequently does it transfer scrub typhus to man.

D. Spotted Fever Group: These infections occur around the globe, exhibiting as a rule some epidemiologic and immunologic difference in different areas. Transmission by a tick of the Ixodidae family is common to the group. The diseases which are grouped together include Rocky Mountain spotted fever (western and eastern RMSF), Colombian, Brazilian, and Mexican spotted fevers; Mediterranean (boutonneuse), South African tick, and Kenya fevers; North Queensland tick typhus; and North Asian tick-borne rickettsiosis.

E. Rickettsialpox: The human disease has been found among inhabitants of apartment houses in the northern USA. However, the infection also occurs in Russia, Africa, and Korea.

F. Q Fever: Since 1935, the disease is recognized around the world.

Seasonal Occurrence

Epidemic typhus is more common in cool climates, reaching its peak in winter and waning in the spring. This is probably a reflection of crowding, lack of fuel, and low standards of personal hygiene, which favor louse infestation.

Rickettsial infections which must be transmitted to the human host by vector reach their peak incidence at the time the vector is most prevalent—the summer and fall months.

Control

Control is achieved by breaking the infection chain or by immunizing and treating with antibiotics.

A. Prevention of Transmission by Breaking the Chain of Infection:

1. Epidemic typhus—Delousing with DDT or other insecticide.

2. Murine typhus—Rat-proofing buildings and using rat poisons.

3. Scrub typhus—Clearing from campsites the secondary jungle vegetation in which rats and mites live.

4. Spotted fever—Similar measures for the spotted fevers may be used: clearing of the infested land; personal prophylaxis in the form of protective clothing such as high boots, socks worn over trousers; tick repellents, etc.

5. Rickettsialpox—Elimination of rodents and their parasites from human domiciles.

B. Prevention of Transmission of Q Fever by Adequate Pasteurization of Milk: Heating of *C burnetii* in whole raw milk for 30 minutes at 62.5° C (144.5° F) is sufficient to destroy all the viable rickettsiae. The presently recommended conditions of "high-temperature, short-time" pasteurization at 71.5° C (161° F) for 15 seconds are adequate.

C. Prevention by Vaccination: Active immunization may be carried out using formalinized antigens prepared from the yolk sacs of infected chick embryos or from cell cultures. Such vaccines are available for epidemic typhus *(R prowazekii)*, Rocky Mountain spotted fever *(R rickettsii)*, and some others. A live vaccine (strain E) for epidemic typhus is effective and used experimentally but produces a self-limited disease.

D. Chemoprophylaxis: Chloramphenicol has been used as a chemoprophylactic agent against scrub typhus in endemic areas. Oral administration of 3 gm doses at weekly intervals controls infection so that no disease occurs even though rickettsiae appear in the blood. The antibiotic must be continued for a month after the initiation of infection to keep the person well. Tetracyclines may be equally effective.

●   ●   ●

General References

Anacker RL & others: Immunological properties of *R rickettsii* purified by zonal centrifugation. Infect Immun 11:1203, 1975.

Berman SJ, Kundin WD: Scrub typhus in South Vietnam. Ann Intern Med 79:26, 1973.

Brezina R & others: Rickettsiae and rickettsial diseases. Bull WHO 49:433, 1973.

DuPont HL & others: Rocky Mountain spotted fever: Study of active immunity. J Infect Dis 128:340, 1973.

Hand WL: Rocky Mountain spotted fever: A vascular disease. Arch Intern Med 125:879, 1970.

Ormsbee RA: Rickettsiae as organisms. Annu Rev Microbiol 23:275, 1969.

Philip RN & others: Microimmunofluorescence test for Rocky Mountain spotted fever and typhus. J Clin Microbiol 3:51, 1976.

Sheehy TW & others: Scrub typhus: Comparison of chloramphenicol and tetracycline. Arch Intern Med 132:77, 1973.

Torres J & others: Rocky Mountain spotted fever in the mid-South. Arch Intern Med 132:340, 1973.

Tsianabos T & others: Origin and structure of the group-specific complement-fixing antigen of *Rickettsia rickettsii.* Appl Microbiol 28:481, 1974.

Wisniewski HJ & others: Q fever in Milwaukee. Arch Environ Health 21:58, 1970.

Wisseman CL, Waddell AD: In vitro studies of rickettsia-host cell interactions. Infect Immun 11:1391, 1975.

Woodward TE: A historical account of the rickettsial diseases. J Infect Dis 127:583, 1973.

22...
Chlamydiae
(Agents of the Psittacosis-LGV-TRIC Group)

The agents of psittacosis, lymphogranuloma venereum (LGV), trachoma, and inclusion conjunctivitis (TRIC) are a large group of nonmotile, gram-negative, obligate intracellular parasites possessing a similar morphology and a common group antigen which multiply in the cytoplasm of their host cells by a distinctive developmental cycle. The group includes some important human and animal pathogens. In the interest of brevity, the generic term chlamydiae will be used here to denote agents of the psittacosis-LGV-TRIC group (formerly called bedsoniae).

Because of their obligate intracellular parasitism, these organisms were once considered viruses. However, the chlamydiae differ from true viruses in the following important characteristics:

(1) Like bacteria, they possess both RNA and DNA.

(2) They multiply by binary fission; viruses never do.

(3) They possess bacterial type cell walls with peptidoglycans containing muramic acid.

(4) They possess ribosomes; viruses never do.

(5) They have a variety of metabolically active enzymes, eg, they can liberate CO_2 from glucose. Some can synthesize folates.

(6) Their growth can be inhibited by many antimicrobial drugs.

Chlamydiae can be viewed as gram-negative bacteria which lack some important mechanisms for the production of metabolic energy. This defect restricts them to an intracellular existence, where the host cell furnishes energy-rich intermediates.

Development Cycle

All chlamydiae share a general sequence of events in their reproduction. The infectious particle is a small cell ("elementary body") about 0.3 μm in diameter with an electron-dense nucleoid. It is taken into the host cell by phagocytosis. A vacuole, derived from the host cell surface membranes, forms around the small particle. This small particle is reorganized into a large one ("initial body") measuring about 0.5–1 μm and devoid of an electron-dense nucleoid. Within the membrane-bound vacuole, the large particle grows in size and divides repeatedly by binary fission. Eventually the entire vacuole becomes filled with small particles derived by binary fission from large bodies to form an "inclusion" in the host cell cytoplasm. The newly formed small particles may be liberated from the host cell to infect new cells. The developmental cycle takes 24–48 hours.

Structure & Chemical Composition

Examination of highly purified suspensions of chlamydiae, washed free of host cell materials, indicates the following: The outer **cell wall** resembles the cell wall of gram-negative bacteria. It has a relatively high lipid content, and the peptidoglycan contains muramic acid. Cell wall formation is inhibited by penicillins and cycloserine, substances which inhibit peptidoglycan synthesis in bacteria. **Both DNA and RNA** are present in both small and large particles. In small particles, most DNA is concentrated in the electron-dense central nucleoid. In large particles, the DNA is distributed irregularly throughout the cytoplasm. Most RNA probably exists in ribosomes, in the cytoplasm. The large particles contain about 4 times as much RNA as DNA, whereas the small, infective particles contain about equal amounts of RNA and DNA.

The protein content of small particles is about 60%, with at least 18 amino acids present. Chlamydiae contain large amounts of **lipids**, especially phospholipids, which are well characterized.

A toxic principle is intimately associated with infectious chlamydiae. It kills mice after the intravenous administration of more than 10^8 particles. Its chemical nature is not known.

Staining Properties

Chlamydiae have distinctive staining properties (similar to those of rickettsiae) which differ somewhat at different stages of development. Single mature particles (elementary bodies) stain purple with Giemsa's stain and red with Macchiavello's stain, in contrast to the blue of host cell cytoplasm. The larger, noninfective bodies (initial bodies) stain blue with Giemsa's stain. The gram reaction of chlamydiae is negative or variable, and Gram's stain is not useful in the identification of the agents.

Fully formed, mature intracellular inclusions are compact masses near the nucleus which are dark purple when stained with Giemsa's stain because of the densely packed mature particles. If stained with dilute Lugol's iodine solution, the inclusions formed by some

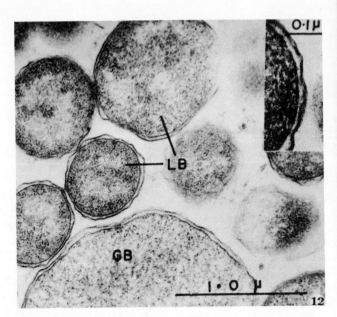

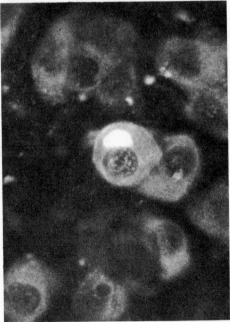

Figure 22—1. Chlamydiae. *Left:* Chlamydiae in various stages of intracellular development. LB, "elementary body" particles with cell walls. GB, "reticulate large body," "initial body." *Right:* Fluorescent inclusion body of TRIC agent in epithelial cell (conjunctival scraping) stained with specific fluorescein-labeled antiserum.

chlamydiae (mouse pneumonitis, LGV, TRIC) appear brown because of the glycogen-like matrix which surrounds the particles.

Antigens

Chlamydiae possess 2 types of antigens. Both are probably located in the cell wall. **Group antigens** are shared by all members of the group of chlamydiae. These are lipopolysaccharides, resistant to heat, nucleases, and proteinases but inactivated by periodate and lecithinase and removed in part by treatment with deoxycholate. They contain 2-keto-3-deoxyoctanoic acid like other lipopolysaccharides of gram-negative bacteria. **Specific antigens** remain attached to cell walls after group antigens have been largely removed by treatment with fluorocarbon or deoxycholate. Specific antigens can best be detected by immunofluorescence. Specific antigens are shared by only a limited number of chlamydiae, but a given organism may contain several specific antigens. Fifteen immunotypes of chlamydiae have been identified (A, B, Ba, C–K, L1, L2, L3), of which 3 are LGV immunotypes. The toxic effects of chlamydiae are associated with antigens. Specific neutralization of these toxic effects of antiserum permits similar antigenic grouping of organisms.

A very unstable hemagglutinin capable of clumping some chicken and mouse erythrocytes is present in chlamydiae. This hemagglutination is blocked by group antibody.

Growth & Metabolism

Chlamydiae require an intracellular habitat, pre-

sumably because they lack some essential feature of energy metabolism. All types of chlamydiae proliferate in embryonated eggs, particularly in the yolk sac. Some also grow in cell cultures and in various animal tissues.

Different chlamydiae differ somewhat in amino acid requirements, at times requiring fewer amino acids than their host cells. Chlamydiae appear to have an endogenous metabolism similar to that of some bacteria but participate only to a limited extent in potentially energy-yielding processes. They can liberate CO_2 from glucose, pyruvate, and glutamate; they also contain dehydrogenases. Nevertheless, they require energy-rich intermediates from the host cell to carry out their biosynthetic activities.

Reactions to Physical & Chemical Agents

Chlamydiae are rapidly inactivated by heat. They lose infectivity completely after 10 minutes at 60° C and partly after 3–12 hours at 37° C. They maintain infectivity for years at −50° C to −70° C. During the process of freeze-drying, much of the infectivity is lost, but successfully lyophilized preparations are stable for years. Some air-dried chlamydiae may also remain infective for long periods.

Chlamydiae are rapidly inactivated by ether (in 30 minutes), by formalin (0.1% for 24 hours), or by phenol (0.5% for 24 hours).

The replication of chlamydiae can be inhibited by many antibacterial antibiotics. Cell wall inhibitors such as penicillins and cycloserine result in the production of morphologically defective forms but are not very effective in clinical diseases. Inhibitors of protein synthesis (tetracyclines, erythromycins, chloramphenicol) are effective in laboratory models and at times in clinical infections. Some chlamydiae synthesize folates and are susceptible to inhibition by sulfonamides. Aminoglycosides and polymyxins have only minimal inhibitory activity for chlamydiae.

Characteristics of Host-Parasite Relationship

The outstanding biologic feature of infection by chlamydiae is the balance that is often reached between host and parasite, resulting in prolonged, often lifetime latency. Subclinical infection is the rule—and overt disease the exception—in the natural hosts of these agents. Spread from one species (eg, birds) to another (eg, man) more frequently leads to disease. Antibodies to several antigens of chlamydiae are regularly produced by the infected host. These antibodies have little protective effect. Commonly the infectious agent persists in the presence of high titers of antibodies. Treatment with effective antimicrobial drugs (eg, tetracyclines) for prolonged periods may eliminate the chlamydiae from the infected host. Very early, intensive treatment may suppress antibody formation. Late treatment with antimicrobial drugs in moderate doses may suppress disease but permit persistence of the infecting agent in tissues.

The immunization of susceptible animals with various inactivated or living vaccines tends to induce protection against death from the toxic effect of living challenge organisms. However, such immunization in animals or man has been singularly unsuccessful in protecting against infection. At best immunization, or prior infection, has induced some resistance which resulted in milder disease after challenge or reinfection.

Classification

Historically, chlamydiae have been arranged according to their pathogenic potential and their host range. Antigenic differences are being defined by specific antigen-antibody reactions studied by immunofluorescence. Chlamydiae can also be grouped according to the nature of the intracytoplasmic inclusion and the susceptibility to sulfonamides. TRIC agents, LGV, mouse pneumonitis, and other organisms of this group (group A) are inhibited by sulfonamides, and their intracellular inclusions are very compact and contain glycogen. These agents are classified as *Chlamydia trachomatis*. In contrast, the agents of psittacosis, meningopneumonitis, feline pneumonitis, and other organisms of this group (group B) are usually resistant to sulfonamides, and their inclusions are diffuse and contain no glycogen. These agents are classified as *Chlamydia psittaci*. Nucleic acid hybridization experiments, however, suggest that these 2 "species" are not closely related.

PSITTACOSIS
(Ornithosis)

Psittacosis is a disease of birds which may be transferred to man. In man, the agent produces a spectrum of clinical manifestations ranging from severe pneumonia and sepsis with a high mortality rate to a mild inapparent infection.

Properties of the Agent

A. Size and Staining Properties: Similar to other members of the group (see above).

B. Animal Susceptibility and Growth of Agent: Psittacosis agent can be propagated in embryonated eggs, in mice and other animals, and in cell cultures. In all these host systems, growth can be inhibited by tetracyclines and, to a limited extent, by penicillins. However, in intact animals and in man, antimicrobial drugs may not be able to eliminate the infectious agent or to terminate the carrier state.

C. Antigenic Properties: The heat-stable group-reactive complement-fixing antigen resists proteolytic enzymes but is destroyed by potassium periodate. It is probably a lipopolysaccharide.

Infected tissue contains a toxic principle, intimately associated with the agent, which rapidly kills mice upon intravenous or intraperitoneal infection. This toxic principle is active only in particles which are infective.

Specific serotypes characteristic for certain mammalian and avian species may be demonstrated by cross-neutralization tests of toxic effect. Neutralization of infectivity of the agent by specific antibody or cross-protection of immunized animals can also be used for serotyping.

D. Cell Wall Antigens: Walls of the infecting agent have been prepared by treatment with deoxycholate followed by trypsin. The deoxycholate extracts contained group-specific complement-fixing antigens, while the cell walls retained the species-specific antigens. The cell wall antigens were also associated with toxin neutralization and infectivity neutralization.

Pathogenesis & Pathology

The agent enters through the respiratory tract, is found in the blood during the first 2 weeks of the disease, and may be found in the sputum at the time the lung is involved.

Psittacosis causes a patchy inflammation of the lungs in which consolidated areas are sharply demarcated. The exudate is predominantly mononuclear. Only minor changes occur in the large bronchioles and bronchi. The lesions are similar to those found in pneumonitis caused by some viruses and mycoplasma. Liver, spleen, heart, and kidney are often enlarged and congested.

Clinical Findings

A sudden onset of illness taking the form of influenza or atypical pneumonia in a person exposed to birds is suggestive of psittacosis. The incubation period averages 10 days. The onset is usually sudden, with malaise, fever, anorexia, sore throat, photophobia, and severe headache. The disease may progress no further and the patient may improve in a few days. In severe cases the signs and symptoms of bronchial pneumonia appear at the end of the first week of the disease. The clinical picture often resembles that of influenza, atypical pneumonia, or typhoid fever. The fatality rate may be as high as 20% in untreated cases, especially in the elderly.

Laboratory Diagnosis

A. Recovery of Agent: Laboratory diagnosis is dependent upon the recovery of psittacosis agent from blood and sputum, or, in fatal cases, from lung tissues. Specimens are inoculated intra-abdominally into mice, into the yolk sacs of embryonated eggs, and into x-irradiated cell cultures. Infection in the test systems is confirmed by the serial transmission of the infectious agent, its microscopic demonstration, and serologic identification of the recovered agent.

B. Serology: A variety of antibodies may develop in the course of infection. In humans, complement fixation with group antigen is the most meaningful diagnostic test. Acute and later phase sera should be run in the same test in order to establish an antibody rise. In birds the indirect CF test may provide additional diagnostic information. Although antibodies usually develop within 10 days, the use of antibiotics may delay their development for 20–40 days or suppress it altogether.

Sera of patients with other chlamydial infections may fix complement in high titer with psittacosis antigen. In patients with psittacosis, the high titer persists for months and, in carriers, even for years. Infection of live birds is suggested by a positive CF test and by the presence of an enlarged spleen or liver. This can be confirmed by demonstration of particles in smears or sections of organs and by passage of the agent in mice and eggs.

Immunity

Immunity in animals and man is incomplete. A carrier state in man can persist for 10 years after recovery. During this period the agent may continue to be excreted in the sputum.

Skin tests with group reactive antigen are positive soon after infection with any member of the group. Specific dermal reactions may be obtained by the use of some skin-testing antigens prepared by extracting suspensions of agent with dilute hydrochloric acid or with detergent.

Live or inactivated vaccines induce only partial resistance in animals.

Treatment

Tetracyclines are the drugs of choice. Psittacosis agents are not sensitive to streptomycin, and most strains are not susceptible to sulfonamides. While antibiotic treatment may control the clinical evidence of disease, it may not free the patient from the agent, ie, he may become a carrier. Intensive antibiotic treatment may also delay the normal course of antibody development. Strains may become drug-resistant.

With the introduction of antibiotic therapy, the case fatality rate has dropped from 20% to 2%. Death occurs most frequently in patients from 40–60 years of age.

Epidemiology

The term psittacosis is applied to the human disease acquired from contact with birds and also the infection of psittacine birds (parrots, parakeets, cockatoos, etc). The term ornithosis is applied to infection with similar agents in all types of domestic birds (pigeons, chickens, ducks, geese, turkeys, etc) and freeliving birds (gulls, egrets, petrels, etc). Outbreaks of human disease can occur whenever there is close and continued contact between man and infected birds which excrete or shed large amounts of infectious agent. Birds often acquire infection as fledglings in the nest; may develop diarrheal illness or no illness; and often carry the infectious agent for their normal life span. When subjected to stress (eg, malnutrition, shipping), birds may become sick and die. The agent is present in tissues (eg, spleen) and is often excreted in feces by healthy birds. The inhalation of infected dried bird feces is a common method of human infection. Another source of infection is the handling of infected tissues (eg, in poultry rendering plants) and inhalation of an infected aerosol.

Birds kept as pets have been an important source of human infection. Foremost among these were the many psittacine birds imported from South America, Australia, and the Far East and kept in aviaries in the USA. Latent infections often flared up in these birds during transport and crowding, and sick birds excreted exceedingly large quantities of infectious agent. Control of bird shipment, quarantine, testing of imported birds for psittacosis infection, and prophylactic tetracyclines in bird feed help to control this source. Pigeons kept for racing or as pets or raised for squab meat have been important sources of infection. Pigeons populating civic buildings and thoroughfares in many cities are not infrequently infected but shed relatively small quantities of agent.

Among the personnel of poultry farms involved in the dressing, packing, and shipping of ducks, geese, turkeys, and chickens, subclinical or clinical infection is relatively frequent. Outbreaks of disease among birds have at times resulted in heavy economic losses and have been followed by outbreaks in humans.

Persons who develop psittacosis may become infectious for other persons if the evolving pneumonia results in expectoration of large quantities of infectious sputum. This has been an occupational risk to hospital personnel.

Control

Shipments of psittacine birds should be held in quarantine to ensure that there are no obviously sick birds in the lot. A proportion of each shipment should be tested for antibodies and examined for agent. An intradermal test has been recommended for detecting ornithosis in turkey flocks. The incorporation of tetracyclines into bird feed has been used to reduce the number of carriers. The source of human infection should be traced, if possible, and infected birds should be killed.

LYMPHOGRANULOMA VENEREUM (LGV)
(Lymphopathia Venereum)

LGV is a venereal disease, characterized by suppurative inguinal adenitis, which is common in tropical and temperate zones. The agent is related to that of psittacosis.

Properties of the Agent

A. Size and Staining Properties: Similar to other members of the group.

B. Animal Susceptibility and Growth of Agent: The agent can be transmitted to monkeys and mice and can be propagated in tissue cultures or in chick embryos. It does not infect birds readily. Most strains grow in cell cultures; their infectivity for cells is not enhanced by pretreatment with DEAE-dextran and is inhibited by neuraminidase.

C. Antigenic Properties: The particles contain complement-fixing antigens and also serve as a skin-testing antigen (see Frei test, below). The agent possesses a heat-stable group-reactive antigen (resistant to boiling) which it shares with other members of the psittacosis group. At least 3 antigenic types of LGV chlamydiae have been defined by immunofluorescence. Infectious particles contain a toxic principle.

Clinical Findings

Several days to several weeks after exposure, a small, evanescent papule or vesicle develops on any part of the external genitalia, anus, or rectum. The lesion may ulcerate, but usually—especially in women—it remains unnoticed and heals in a few days. Soon thereafter, the regional lymph nodes enlarge and tend to become matted and often painful. In males, inguinal nodes are most commonly involved both above and below Poupart's ligament, and the overlying skin often turns purplish as the nodes suppurate and eventually discharge pus through multiple sinus tracts. In females, the perirectal nodes are prominently involved, with proctitis and a bloody mucopurulent anal discharge. This is also seen in homosexual males.

During the stage of active lymphadenitis, there are often marked systemic symptoms including fever, headaches, meningismus, conjunctivitis, skin rashes, nausea and vomiting, and arthralgias. Meningitis, arthritis, and pericarditis occur rarely. Unless effective antimicrobial drug treatment is given at that stage, the chronic inflammatory process progresses to fibrosis, lymphatic obstruction, and rectal strictures. The lymphatic obstruction may lead to elephantiasis of the penis, scrotum, or vulva. The chronic proctitis of women or homosexual males may lead to progressive rectal strictures, rectosigmoid obstruction, and fistula formation.

Laboratory Diagnosis

A. Smears: Pus, buboes, or biopsy material may be stained but particles are rarely recognized.

B. Isolation of Agent: Suspected material is inoculated into the yolk sacs of embryonated eggs, into cell cultures, or into the brains of mice. Streptomycin (but not penicillin or ether) may be incorporated into the inoculum to lessen the bacterial contamination. The agent is identified by its morphology and serologic tests.

C. Complement Fixation Test: The CF reaction is the simplest serologic test for the presence of antibodies. Antigen is prepared from infected yolk sac. The test becomes positive 2–4 weeks after onset of illness, at which time skin hypersensitivity can sometimes also be demonstrated. In a clinically compatible case, a rising antibody level or a single titer of more than 1:64 is good evidence of active infection. If treatment has eradicated the LGV infection, the complement fixation titer falls.

D. Frei Test (for Dermal Hypersensitivity): 0.1 ml of heat-inactivated agent is injected intradermally. The same amount of control material (prepared in the same way from normal yolk sac) is injected at a separate site. Readings are made after 48–96 hours. An inflammatory nodule at the site of injection measuring at least 6 mm more than the control site constitutes a positive test (7–40 days after infection). The erythema accompanying the skin test has no significance.

Because the important antigen in the inactivated preparation is the heat-stable antigen which the agent shares with the other members of the group, the Frei test is not specific for LGV; a positive test also occurs in persons infected with chlamydiae other than LGV. Treatment of the agent with dilute acid (0.02 N HCl) has been found to extract skin-testing antigen. The reactions evoked by such acid extracts appear to be specific for each member of the group.

The Frei test remains positive long after the acute infection has passed, perhaps for life. A positive test means only that infection has occurred; unless it is negative in the acute stage and becomes positive later, the test cannot be used to support a clinical diagnosis of LGV. Some commercial antigens have given unreliable results.

Immunity

Untreated infections tend to be chronic with persistence of the agent for many years. Little is known about active immunity. The coexistence of latent infection and antibodies is typical of all agents of the group.

Treatment

The sulfonamides and tetracyclines have been

used with good results, especially in the early stages. In some drug-treated persons there is a marked decline in antibody level, which may indicate that the infective agent has been eliminated from the body.

Epidemiology

The disease is most often spread by venereal contact, but not exclusively so. The portal of entry may sometimes be the eye (conjunctivitis with an oculoglandular syndrome). The genital tracts and rectums of chronically infected (but at times asymptomatic) persons serve as reservoirs of infection.

While the highest incidence of LGV has been reported from subtropical and tropical areas, the infection occurs all over the world.

Control

The measures used for the control of other venereal diseases apply also to the control of LGV. Case-finding and early medical care and control of infected persons are essential.

TRACHOMA & INCLUSION CONJUNCTIVITIS (TRIC AGENTS)

These 2 eye diseases differ somewhat in clinical and epidemiologic features but are caused by agents very closely related to each other and almost indistinguishable in the laboratory. The TRIC agents are typical chlamydiae.

Trachoma is a chronic keratoconjunctivitis characterized by the development of follicles, papillary hypertrophy, and pannus, typically leading to scar formation and sometimes to blindness. Inclusion conjunctivitis is an acute purulent conjunctivitis of the newborn and a follicular conjunctivitis of the adult which produces only minor corneal involvement and scarring. The usual habitat of the agent of the inclusion conjunctivitis is the human genital tract, and in adults a venereal disease results.

Properties of TRIC Agents

A. Size and Staining Properties: Similar to other members of the group.

B. Animal Susceptibility and Growth of TRIC Agents: The natural host for the TRIC agents is man, and they produce disease only in the eye and the genital tract of man and other primates. All TRIC agents multiply in the yolk sacs of embryonated hens' eggs and result in death of the embryo when the titer is sufficient. TRIC agents can also be serially passaged in irradiated, nonmultiplying human cells in culture.

When TRIC agents multiply in cells they go through a well defined growth cycle. Elementary bodies enter the cell and soon cannot be visualized clearly. After some time, larger "initial bodies" appear near the nucleus of the cell, followed by the development of vacuoles, which gradually enlarge and fill with "elementary body" particles embedded in a matrix of

carbohydrate resembling glycogen. This is the picture of the typical intracytoplasmic (Halberstaedter-Prowazek) inclusion which is diagnostic of TRIC infection in conjunctival epithelial cells. Occasional cells contain multiple inclusions. After disruption of cells, free elementary or initial bodies may be found in conjunctival exudates.

A toxic factor is associated with viable TRIC particles. After intravenous inoculation of 10^8 particles into mice, a shock-like state develops in 2–8 hours; this phase is followed by death. Vaccination of mice can specifically protect against this toxic death, and by this method at least 9 distinct antigenic types of TRIC agents have been delineated. The same types can be identified by immunofluorescence.

Clinical Findings

The incubation period in experimental TRIC infection is 2–9 days, depending upon the infectious dose. Inclusion conjunctivitis of the newborn begins between the fifth and twelfth days of life. The incubation period of naturally occurring trachoma is uncertain because the onset is often insidious.

A. Trachoma: The early symptoms of trachoma are lacrimation, mucopurulent discharge, and irritation. Early signs include conjunctival hyperemia and follicular hypertrophy. Biomicroscopic examination of the cornea reveals epithelial keratitis, subepithelial infiltration, and extension of limbal vessels into the cornea (pannus).

Progression of pannus across the cornea, scarring of subepithelial tissues, lid deformities, secondary bacterial infection, and blindness may occur over a period of months to years. There are no systemic symptoms or signs of infection. Endemic trachoma is most commonly caused by TRIC serotypes A, B, or C.

B. Inclusion Conjunctivitis: Inclusion conjunctivitis is most commonly seen as an acute purulent conjunctivitis of the newborn, involving particularly the lower lids. After several weeks of intense inflammation, the disease gradually subsides and the conjunctiva may become normal in several months. However, some children gradually develop pannus and scarring indistinguishable from trachoma. In adults, eye infection ("swimming pool conjunctivitis") is manifested by follicular conjunctivitis with corneal subepithelial infiltration which usually resolves spontaneously. The genital infection in adults either produces no symptoms and signs or causes cervicitis and urethritis. Naturally occurring eye infection of adults with inclusion conjunctivitis agent may produce a clinical picture indistinguishable from trachoma.

Genital TRIC infection and inclusion conjunctivitis are commonly caused by TRIC serotypes D–K.

Laboratory Diagnosis

A. Recovery of TRIC Agents: Typical cytoplasmic inclusions are found in epithelial cells obtained in conjunctival scrapings stained by Giemsa's method or with fluorescent antibody. These are most frequent in early active disease. In trachoma they are most prevalent in the upper tarsal conjunctiva; in inclusion conjunctivitis, the lower lid conjunctiva is more intensively involved.

TRIC agents can be isolated in embryonated eggs inoculated by the yolk sac route. Often several passages are necessary to build up uniformly high titers. The susceptibility of embryonated eggs fluctuates intermittently, even when the eggs are derived from antibiotic-free poultry. X-irradiated, nonmultiplying human cells or cell cultures treated with DEAE-dextran or idoxuridine can be used for isolating the agent and for supporting its growth through multiple passages. Sensitivity can be increased by centrifuging the agent into the cells.

The most sensitive method of establishing the diagnosis appears to be finding typical inclusions in conjunctival cells by immunofluorescence or isolation of agent centrifuged onto idoxuridine-treated cell cultures.

B. Serology: TRIC agents share a common antigen with other chlamydiae. Individuals infected with TRIC agents often develop antibodies to the group antigen, but these antibodies do not protect against reinfection. Type-specific antibodies can be demonstrated in infected persons' sera and tears by immunofluorescence.

Treatment

A. Trachoma: In endemic areas trachoma must be diagnosed and treated in children because it can be affected by drugs before scarring occurs. The tetracyclines and sulfonamides have been most widely used. The tetracyclines are often applied topically and sulfonamides given orally. Treatment schedules are determined largely by convenience, cost, and feasibility. In holoendemic areas, it may be practical to treat the entire community every month for 6 months with topical tetracycline ointment twice daily for 5 days. The most effective treatment of acute infections may be a combination of systemic sulfonamides for 3 weeks and ophthalmic tetracycline applied 4 times daily for 6 weeks. In chronic infection, full systemic doses of either sulfonamides or tetracyclines can suppress clinical signs but fail to eradicate the infection. Drug-resistant chlamydiae have thus far been encountered only in the laboratory. Topical application of corticosteroids is not indicated and can reactivate latent, persistent trachoma infection. The effect of antimicrobial drugs may partly be attributed to elimination of bacterial infections. TRIC agents may persist during and after drug treatment, and relapse is common.

B. Inclusion Conjunctivitis: Inclusion conjunctivitis is similarly susceptible to therapy, and often responds rapidly in the acute stage. Genital TRIC infection responds to tetracycline treatment.

Epidemiology

A. Trachoma: It is believed that over 400 million people throughout the world are infected with trachoma and that 20 million have been blinded by it. Trachoma is spread mechanically from eye to eye by fingers and fomites, eg, shared cosmetics or towels. The disease is most prevalent in Africa and Asia, particularly where hygienic conditions are poor and water is scarce. In such endemic areas infection may be universally acquired in childhood. In the USA trachoma occurs sporadically in many areas, and endemic foci are found on many Indian reservations.

B. Inclusion Conjunctivitis: The epidemiology of inclusion conjunctivitis is quite different from that of trachoma. Inclusion conjunctivitis is fundamentally an infection of the adult human genital tract and is spread primarily by sexual contact. In the female, the agent grows in the epithelium of the cervix. The agent enters the eye of the newborn during passage through the birth canal and produces acute conjunctivitis. Adults are occasionally infected by eye-to-eye transfer from the newborn, but most adult infections originate by sexual contact and subsequent finger-to-eye spread. Thus inclusion conjunctivitis is a typical venereal disease, occasionally manifest in the eye. In the past, infection may have occurred in swimming pools contaminated with genital secretions. However, chlorination has apparently limited this method of spread.

C. Nongonococcal ("Nonspecific") Urethritis: This clinical syndrome in males involves dysuria, thin discharge, and negative cultures for gonococci. About 50% of cases demonstrate *Chlamydia trachomatis.* Chlamydiae grow in the urethral epithelium of the male and are the source of female cervical infection and "inclusion conjunctivitis." Sometimes the chlamydial involvement of the genital tract is called "genital trachoma." There is no doubt that genital infection with chlamydiae is a common sexually transmitted disease, at times coexisting with other etiologic agents—gonococci, herpesviruses, trichomonas, etc.

Control

A. Trachoma: Control of trachoma depends upon improvement of hygienic standards and drug treatment. Experimental vaccines have been prepared from egg-grown purified TRIC agents and can give significant protection to primates. Field studies with such vaccines have given variable and not often promising results. Experimental infection of volunteers and of subhuman primates suggests that resistance is type-specific and partial.

B. Inclusion Conjunctivitis: Chlorination of swimming pools and drug treatment of the genital and ocular infection of adults are the principal control measures. Penicillin or silver nitrate instillation into the newborn's eye does not prevent inclusion conjunctivitis.

C. Nongonococcal Urethritis: Tetracycline treatment of both sex partners is advised.

OTHER AGENTS OF THE GROUP

Many mammals carry infectious agents which are members of the psittacosis-LGV-TRIC group. Common animal disease entities are pneumonitis, arthritis, enteritis, and abortion, but infection is often latent. Some of these agents may also be communicated to man and cause disease in man.

Similar agents have been isolated from Reiter's disease in man, both from the involved joints and from the urethra. The etiologic role of these agents remains uncertain.

In nonbacterial regional lymphadenitis (cat scratch fever), a skin test with heat-inactivated pus gives a delayed positive reaction. Chlamydiae have been proposed as a possible cause but without proof. The usefulness of tetracyclines in this syndrome is questionable.

● ● ●

General References

Abrams AJ: Lymphogranuloma venereum. JAMA 205:59, 1968.

Christoffersen G, Manire GP: The toxicity of meningopneumonitis organisms *(Chlamydia psittaci)* at different stages of development. J Immunol 103:1085, 1969.

Dunlop EMC & others: Chlamydiae in non-specific urethritis. Br J Vener Dis 48:425, 1972.

Grayson JT, Wang SP: New knowledge of chlamydiae and the diseases they cause. J Infect Dis 132:87, 1975.

Holmes KK & others: Etiology of nongonococcal urethritis. N Engl J Med 292:1199, 1975.

Jawetz E: Chemotherapy of chlamydial infections. Adv Pharmacol Chemother 7:253, 1969.

Moulder JW: The contribution of model systems in infectious diseases (biochemistry of chlamydiae). Perspect Biol Med 14:486, 1971.

Schachter J & others: Are chlamydial infections the most prevalent venereal disease? JAMA 231:1252, 1975.

Schachter J & others: Comparison of Frei test, complement fixation, and isolation of agent in lymphogranuloma venereum. J Infect Dis 120:372, 1969.

Schaffner W & others: The clinical spectrum of endemic psittacosis. Arch Intern Med 119:433, 1967.

Wang SP, Grayston JT: Immunologic relationship between TRIC, LGV and related organisms. Am J Ophthalmol 70:367, 1970.

23...
Miscellaneous
Pathogenic Microorganisms

MYCOPLASMAS (PPLO) & WALL-DEFECTIVE MICROBIAL VARIANTS

Mycoplasmas (previously called pleuropneumonia-like organisms, or PPLO) are a group of organisms with the following characteristics: (1) The smallest reproductive units have a size of 125–250 nm. (2) They are highly pleomorphic because they lack a rigid cell wall and instead are bounded by a triple-layered "unit membrane." (3) They are completely resistant to penicillin but inhibited by tetracycline. (4) They can reproduce in cell-free media; on agar the center of the whole colony is characteristically embedded beneath the surface. (5) Growth is inhibited by specific antibody. (6) Mycoplasmas do not revert to, or originate from, bacterial parental forms. (7) Mycoplasmas have an affinity for cell membranes.

Wall-defective microbial forms (WDMF) can be categorized as follows: **Protoplasts** are WDMF with external surfaces free of cell wall constituents, spherical, osmotically fragile, usually derived from gram-negative rods. **Spheroplasts** are WDMF with external surfaces containing some cell wall material. **L phase variants** are WDMF which can replicate serially as nonrigid cells and produce colonies on solid media. Some are stable; others are unstable and revert to bacterial parent forms. WDMF can result from spontaneous mutation or from the effects of chemicals such as enzymes and antimicrobials (eg, penicillins).

Morphology & Identification

A. Typical Organisms: Mycoplasmas cannot be studied by the usual bacteriologic methods because of the small size of their colonies, the plasticity and delicacy of their individual cells (due to the lack of a rigid cell wall), and their poor staining with aniline dyes. The morphology appears different according to the method of examination (eg, darkfield, Giemsa-stained films from solid or liquid media, agar fixation).

Growth in fluid media gives rise to many different forms, including rings, bacillary and spiral bodies, filaments, and granules. Growth on solid media consists principally of plastic protoplasmic masses of indefinite shape, easily distorted and often appearing as disks or globules which contain "chromatin bodies" and dense

granules. All of these structures vary greatly in size, ranging from 50–300 nm in diameter.

B. Culture: Many strains of mycoplasma grow in heart infusion peptone broth of 2% agar (pH 7.8) to which about 30% human ascitic fluid or animal serum (horse, rabbit) has been added. Following incubation at 37° C for 48–96 hours, there may be no turbidity; but Giemsa stains of the centrifuged sediment show the characteristic pleomorphic structures, and subculture on solid media yields minute colonies.

After 2–6 days on special agar medium incubated in a Petri dish which has been sealed to prevent evaporation, isolated colonies measuring 20–500 μm can be detected with a hand lens. These colonies are round, with a granular surface and a dark center nipple typically buried in the agar. They can be subcultured by cutting out a small square of agar containing one or more colonies and streaking this material on a fresh plate or dropping it into liquid medium. The organisms can be stained for microscopic study by placing a similar square on a slide and covering the colony with a coverglass onto which an alcoholic solution of methylene blue and azure has been poured and then evaporated (agar fixation). Such slides can also be stained with specific fluorescent antibody.

C. Growth Characteristics: Mycoplasmas are unique in microbiology because of (1) their extremely small size and (2) their growth on complex but cell-free media.

Filtration studies with gradocol membranes indicate that the smallest reproductive units measure about 125–250 nm and thus are in the range of magnitude of the larger viruses.

All parasitic strains of mycoplasma require for growth a protein from serum or yeast extract as well as cholesterol, but are resistant to thallium acetate, 1:10,000. Many human mycoplasmas produce peroxides and hemolyze red blood cells. In cell cultures mycoplasmas develop predominantly at cell surfaces. Many established cell lines carry mycoplasmas as contaminants.

D. Variation: The extreme pleomorphism of mycoplasmas is one of their principal characteristics. There is no genetic relationship between mycoplasmas, WDMF, and their parent bacteria. The characteristics of WDMF are similar to those of mycoplasmas, but, by definition, mycoplasmas do not revert to parent bacteria or originate from them. WDMF continue to synthesize some antigens which are normally located in the cell wall of the parent bacteria (eg, streptococcal L forms produce M protein and capsular polysaccharide; see Chapter 11). Reversion of L forms to the parent bacteria is enhanced by growth in the presence of 15–30% gelatin or 2.5% agar, whereas reversion is inhibited by inhibitors of protein synthesis.

Antigenic Structure

From animals (eg, mice, chicken, turkeys), many antigenically distinct species of mycoplasmas have been isolated. In man, 6 distinct antigenic types are presently recognized: *Mycoplasma hominis, M salivarium, M orale, M fermentans,* and *M pneumoniae.* The complement-fixing antigens of mycoplasmas are glycolipids. *M hominis* has at least 7 serotypes.

Diseases Due to Mycoplasmas

It is doubtful that WDMF cause tissue reactions resulting in disease. They may be important for the persistence of microorganisms in tissues and recurrence of infection after antimicrobial treatment.

The parasitic mycoplasmas appear to be strictly host-specific, being communicable and potentially pathogenic only within a single host species. In vivo mycoplasmas appear to be intracellular parasites with a predilection for mesothelial cells (pleura, peritoneum, synovia of joints). Several extracellular products are known to be elaborated, eg, hemolysins and at least one neurotoxin. In human respiratory tract infections, mucous membranes are inflamed and there may be interstitial pneumonia and necrotizing bronchiolitis.

A. Diseases of Animals: Bovine pleuropneumonia is a contagious disease of cattle producing pulmonary consolidation and pleural effusion, with occasional deaths. The disease probably has an airborne spread. Mycoplasmas are found in inflammatory exudates.

Agalactia of sheep and goats in the Mediterranean area is a generalized infection with local lesions in the skin, eyes, joints, udder, and scrotum; it leads to atrophy of lactating glands in females. Mycoplasmas are present in blood early; in milk and exudates later.

In poultry, several economically important respiratory diseases are caused by mycoplasmas. The organisms can be transmitted from hen to egg and chick. Swine, dogs, rats, mice, and other species harbor mycoplasmas which can produce infection involving particularly the pleura, peritoneum, joints, respiratory tract, and eye. In mice, a mycoplasma-like agent of spiral shape (spiroplasma) can induce cataracts.

B. Diseases of Man: Mycoplasmas have been cultivated from human mucous membranes and tissues, particularly from the genital, urinary, and respiratory tracts and from the mouth. Some mycoplasmas are inhabitants of the normal genitourinary tract, particularly in females. While found in association with inflammatory processes, eg, cervicitis, urethritis, or prostatitis, *Mycoplasma hominis* and T strains (tiny colonies, requiring 10% urea for growth) probably have no etiologic role in these disorders. However, in preg-

nant women, carriage of T strains on the cervix was associated with low birth weight of children and chorioamnionitis. Infrequently, mycoplasmas have been isolated from brain abscess and pleural or joint effusion. Mycoplasmas are part of the normal flora of the mouth and can be grown from normal saliva, oral mucous membranes, sputum, or tonsillar tissue. By means of volunteer inoculation, 2 species of mycoplasmas (*M hominis* and *M pneumoniae*) have been shown to be capable of causing human disease.

M hominis can produce an acute, afebrile respiratory illness with sore throat and tonsillar exudate. It has also been isolated from blood after vaginal delivery in women who carried it as normal flora in the genital tract. The frequency of natural infection with clinical disease is uncertain, but over half of normal adults have specific antibodies to this agent.

M pneumoniae is one of the causative agents of the syndrome "primary atypical pneumonia" (see below). The effects in man of infection with *M pneumoniae* range from inapparent infection to mild or severe upper respiratory disease, ear involvement (myringitis), and bronchial pneumonia.

C. Diseases of Plants: Aster yellows, corn stunt, and other plant diseases appear to be caused by mycoplasmas. They are transmitted by insects and can be suppressed by tetracyclines.

Diagnostic Laboratory Tests

Specimens consist of throat swab, sputum, inflammatory exudates, and respiratory, urethral, or genital secretions.

A. Microscopic Examination: Direct examination of a specimen is useless. Cultures are examined as described above.

B. Culture: The material is inoculated onto special solid media (above) and incubated for 3–10 days at 37° C (often under anaerobic conditions), or into special broth (above) incubated aerobically. One or 2 transfers of media may be necessary before growth appears, suitable for microscopic examination by staining or immunofluorescence. Colonies may have a "fried egg" appearance on agar.

C. Serology: Antibodies develop in humans infected with mycoplasmas and can be demonstrated by several methods. CF tests can be performed with glycolipid antigens extracted with chloroform-methanol from cultured mycoplasmas. HI tests can be applied to tanned red cells with adsorbed mycoplasma antigens. Indirect immunofluorescence may be used. Most specific is the test which measures growth inhibition by antibody. With all these serologic technics, there is adequate specificity for different human Mycoplasma species, but a rising antibody titer is required for diagnostic significance because of the high incidence of positive serologic tests in normal individuals.

Treatment

Many strains of mycoplasma are inhibited by a variety of antimicrobial drugs, but most strains are resistant to penicillins, cephalosporins, and vancomycin. Tetracyclines and erythromycins are effective both in vitro and in vivo and are, at present, the drugs of choice in mycoplasmal pneumonia.

Epidemiology, Prevention, & Control

Isolation of infected livestock will control the highly contagious pleuropneumonia and agalactia in limited areas. No vaccines are available. Primary atypical pneumonia caused by *M pneumoniae* behaves like a communicable viral respiratory disease (see next section).

Primary Atypical Pneumonia & Mycoplasmal Pneumonia

Primary atypical pneumonia (PAP) is an acute, usually self-limited respiratory syndrome characterized by malaise, fever, cough, and pulmonary infiltration demonstrated far more readily by x-ray than by physical signs. It is a syndrome of multiple etiology; adenoviruses, influenza viruses, respiratory syncytial virus, parainfluenza type 3 virus, the chlamydia of psittacosis, and the rickettsia of Q fever have been implicated as important causes. However, the single most prominent etiologic agent is *M pneumoniae*. In military populations, up to 65% of cases of PAP have been associated with mycoplasmal infection, but in college populations of the same age no more than 25% of PAP cases are due to mycoplasmas.

Infection in man may range from asymptomatic to serious bronchial pneumonia. An association between *M pneumoniae* infection and Stevens-Johnson syndrome has been noted. Typical cases in epidemics and in volunteers experimentally infected with *M pneumoniae* showed the following picture:

The incubation period varies from 1–3 weeks. The onset is usually insidious, with malaise, fever, headache, sore throat, and cough. Initially the cough is nonproductive. Later there may be mucopurulent or blood-streaked sputum and chest pain. Early in the course, the patient appears only moderately ill, and physical signs of pulmonary consolidation are often negligible compared to the striking consolidation seen on x-rays. Later, when the infiltration is at a peak, the illness may be severe. Resolution of pulmonary infiltration and clinical improvement occur slowly for 1–4 weeks. While the course of the illness is exceedingly variable, death is very rare, usually attributable to cardiac failure. Complications are uncommon. Myringitis has occurred in many inoculated volunteers. The most common pathologic findings are interstitial and peribronchial pneumonitis and necrotizing bronchiolitis.

The following laboratory findings apply to *M pneumoniae* pneumonia: The white and differential counts are within normal limits. The etiologic mycoplasma can be recovered by culture early in the disease from the pharynx and from sputum. Immunofluorescent stains of mononuclear cells from the throat may reveal the agent. There is a rise in specific antibodies to *M pneumoniae* which is demonstrable by complement fixation, immunofluorescence, passive hemagglutination, and growth inhibition.

A variety of nonspecific reactions can be observed. Cold hemagglutinins for group O human erythrocytes appear in about 50% of untreated patients, in rising titer, with the maximum reached in the third or fourth week after onset. A titer of 1:32 or more supports the diagnosis of *M pneumoniae* infection.

Tetracyclines or erythromycins in full systemic doses (2 gm daily for adults) can result in clinical improvement but do not eradicate the mycoplasma.

M pneumoniae infections are endemic all over the world. In populations of children and young adults where close contact prevails, and in families, the infection rate may be high (50–90%), but the incidence of pneumonitis is variable (3–30%). For every case of frank pneumonitis, there exist several cases of milder respiratory illness. *M pneumoniae* is apparently transmitted mainly by direct contact involving respiratory secretions. Second attacks are infrequent. The presence of antibodies to *M pneumoniae* is associated with resistance to infection. Experimental vaccines have been prepared from agar-grown *M pneumoniae*. Certain live, temperature-sensitive strains have induced a degree of protection, but most killed vaccines have aggravated subsequent disease.

STREPTOBACILLUS MONILIFORMIS

Streptobacillus moniliformis is an aerobic, gram-negative, highly pleomorphic organism which forms irregular chains of bacilli interspersed with fusiform enlargements and large round bodies. It grows best at 37° C in media containing serum protein, egg yolk, or starch, but ceases to grow at 22° C. In most cultures of the organism, L forms can easily be demonstrated. Subculture of pure colonies of L forms in liquid media often yields the streptobacillus again. All strains of streptobacilli appear to be antigenically identical.

S moniliformis is a normal inhabitant of the throats of rats, and humans can be infected by rat bites. The human disease (rat-bite fever) is characterized by septic fever, blotchy and petechial rashes, and polyarthritis. Diagnosis rests on cultures of blood, joint fluid, or pus; on mouse inoculation; and on serum agglutination tests.

This organism can also produce infection after being ingested in milk—a disease called Haverhill fever which has occurred in epidemics. Penicillin, streptomycin, and perhaps other antibiotics are therapeutically effective.

LISTERIA MONOCYTOGENES

Listeria monocytogenes is a short, gram-positive, nonsporeforming, motile rod in its smooth form; in its rough form it is long and filamentous. Growth on simple media is enhanced by the presence of blood, ascitic fluid, or glucose. Listeria is isolated more readily from pathologic specimens if the tissue is kept at 4° C for some days before inoculation into bacteriologic media. The organism is a facultative anaerobe and is catalase-positive. Most strains produce a zone of hemolysis on blood agar plates. Listeria produces acid but not gas in a variety of carbohydrates. There are at least 7 antigenic types.

Spontaneous infection occurs in many animals (domestic and wild) and in man. In smaller animals (rabbits, chickens) there is a septicemia with focal abscesses in liver and heart muscle and marked monocytosis. A glyceride extracted from listeria can likewise induce monocytosis in rabbits. This cellular reaction, however, is not related to human infectious mononucleosis. Listeria infection leads to the production of cold agglutinins for human and sheep red cells as well as specific agglutinating antibodies.

In man and in ruminants (eg, sheep), listeria may produce meningoencephalitis with or without bacteremia. Listeriosis may be superimposed on lymphoma or immunodeficiency. The diagnosis rests on isolation of the organism in cultures of blood and spinal fluid. A second form of human listeriosis, granulomatosis infantiseptica, is an intrauterine infection with a high mortality for the infant before or after birth. There is generalized infection with focal necroses in many organs. The route of infection for adults is sometimes the genital tract. It is probable that asymptomatic infection is rather widespread. Many antimicrobial drugs inhibit listeria in vitro. Penicillin, ampicillin, and tetracyclines have resulted in clinical cures.

ERYSIPELOTHRIX INSIDIOSA (RHUSIOPATHIAE)

This organism resembles listeria bacteriologically but produces an entirely different disease. In its smooth form it grows as clear, minute colonies in which short, nonsporeforming, nonmotile rods are arranged in short chains; in its rough form, long filaments predominate.

Growth is aided by blood and glucose in the medium. On blood agar only slight hemolysis is produced. Carbohydrates are fermented irregularly, and catalase is not produced. The antigenic pattern is not established.

Infection with *E insidiosa* occurs in worldwide distribution in a variety of animals, especially hogs. Infection in man follows skin abrasions from contact with fish, shellfish, meat, or poultry. The infection, called erysipeloid, is limited to the skin. There are pain, edema, and purplish erythema with sharp margins which extends peripherally but clears centrally. Relapses and extension of the lesions to distant areas are common, but there is usually no fever. Rare cases of endocarditis have occurred. There is no permanent

immunity following an attack. The diagnosis rests on isolation of the organism in cultures from a skin biopsy. The fragment should be incubated in glucose broth for 24 hours, then subcultured on blood agar plates. Typical clinical appearance in a person with occupational exposure is highly suggestive of infection due to this organism.

Penicillin appears to be the antibiotic of choice.

MIMEAE (ACINETOBACTER)

A group of aerobic gram-negative bacteria (often resembling neisseriae on smears because diplococcal forms predominate on solid media) have been recovered from meningitis and sepsis and have been confused with meningococci. However, they are oxidase-negative. They also have been isolated from blood, sputum, skin, pleural fluid, and urine, but their pathogenic role is not clearly established. In patients with burns or with immunologic deficiency, these organisms become opportunistic pathogens and can produce sepsis. By precipitin tests with enzymatic digests of organisms and specific antisera, mimeae can be grouped into at least 10 antigenic types. They are fairly inactive metabolically and often are antibiotic-resistant, responding most commonly to tetracyclines, kanamycin, or gentamicin. Herellea and Mima are the most frequently encountered varieties. Infections are occasionally induced in hospitals, but the source of sepsis is variable.

BARTONELLA BACILLIFORMIS

This is a gram-negative, very pleomorphic, motile organism which causes **Oroya fever,** a serious infectious anemia, and **verruga peruana,** a skin disorder in man. The infection is limited to the mountainous areas of the American Andes in tropical Peru, Colombia, and Ecuador, and is transmitted by the sandfly Phlebotomus.

Bartonella grows in semisolid nutrient agar containing 10% rabbit serum and 0.5% hemoglobin. After about 10 days' incubation at 28° C, some turbidity develops in the medium and rod-shaped and granular organisms can be seen in Giemsa-stained smears.

Human infection is characterized by the rapid development of severe anemia due to blood destruction, enlargement of spleen and liver, and hemorrhage into the lymph nodes. Masses of bartonellae fill the cytoplasm of cells lining the blood vessels, and endothelial swelling may lead to vascular occlusion and thrombosis. The mortality of untreated Oroya fever is about 40%. The diagnosis is made by examining stained blood smears and blood cultures in semisolid medium.

Verruga peruana is a vascular granulomatous skin lesion which occurs in successive crops, lasts for about 1 year, and produces little systemic reaction and no fatalities. Bartonella can be seen in the granuloma; blood cultures are often positive, but there is no anemia. Verruga often occurs in persons who have recovered from Oroya fever.

Penicillin, streptomycin, and chloramphenicol are dramatically effective in Oroya fever and greatly reduce the fatality rate, particularly if blood transfusions are also given. Control of the disease depends upon the elimination of the sandfly vectors. Insecticides, DDT insect repellents, and elimination of breeding areas are of value. Prevention with antibiotics may be useful.

BACTEROIDES

This is a large group of nonsporeforming, strictly anaerobic, usually gram-negative bacteria which are very pleomorphic. They may appear as slender rods, branching forms, or round bodies. They grow most readily on complex media, eg, brain-heart infusion agar, in an anaerobic atmosphere containing 10% CO_2.

Bacteroides are normal inhabitants of the upper respiratory, genital, and intestinal tracts. They constitute more than 95% of the normal fecal flora. The most commonly encountered species are *B fragilis* (particularly in the lower intestine), *B melaninogenicus* (particularly in the oropharynx), and *B oralis*. Classification is based on colonial and biochemical features and characteristic appearance in gas chromatography.

In anaerobic infections (lung, brain, peritoneum, pelvis), bacteroides are often associated with other anaerobic organisms, particularly anaerobic streptococci (Peptostreptococcus) and fusiform bacteria (Fusobacterium sp), as well as gram-negative aerobic enteric organisms.

Bacteroides may be associated with ulcerative lesions of the skin and mucous membranes; they may produce lung and brain abscesses and empyema; they may cause suppuration in surgical infection such as peritonitis following injury to the bowel. In such anaerobic infections, the pus is often foul-smelling. Bacteremia is common, and endocarditis may develop.

Most bacteroides are susceptible to penicillin G in massive doses. *B fragilis* is relatively resistant to penicillin but susceptible to clindamycin. Tetracycline and chloramphenicol may also be drugs of choice, depending on susceptibility tests. Metronidazole is markedly bactericidal for many bacteroides and fusobacteria but may be oncogenic.

Veillonellae are small, anaerobic, gram-negative cocci which are part of the normal mouth flora. They ferment few sugars and probably are not pathogens.

PSEUDOMONAS (ACTINOBACILLUS) MALLEI & PSEUDOMONAS PSEUDOMALLEI

Pseudomonas mallei is a small, nonmotile, gram-negative, aerobic rod which grows readily on most bacteriologic media and does not ferment lactose. It causes glanders, a disease of horses transmissible to man. Human infection (often fatal) usually begins as an ulcer of the skin or mucous membranes followed by lymphangitis and sepsis. Inhalation of the organisms may lead to primary pneumonitis.

The disease has been controlled by slaughter of infected horses and mules, and at present is very rare. In many countries laboratory infections are the only source of the disease.

The diagnosis is based on rising agglutinin titers, the mallein skin test, or culture of the organism from local lesions of man or horse. Human cases can be treated effectively with sulfonamides.

Melioidosis, a disease resembling glanders in man, occurs in Burma, Vietnam, Guam, the Philippines, and perhaps also in the Western Hemisphere. It is caused by *Pseudomonas pseudomallei*, which resembles other nonpigmented pseudomonads but is antigenically distinct. The infection occurs spontaneously in rats, guinea pigs, and rabbits, and may be transmitted to man by arthropod vectors or by food and water contaminated by rodent excreta. The epidemiology of this disorder is still uncertain.

Melioidosis may manifest itself as an acute or a chronic lung disease and has a high fatality rate if untreated. *Pseudomonas pseudomallei* is susceptible to many antibiotics in vitro. Chloramphenicol (2 gm daily) or gentamicin, alone or in combination, may be the treatment of choice. Trimethoprim-sulfamethoxazole (co-trimoxazole) may be effective. Drug resistance emerges frequently.

AEROMONAS HYDROPHILA

Aeromonas hydrophila is a motile gram-negative rod isolated commonly from water, soil, or foods, and rarely from the human intestinal tract. It can be found in bacteremia in persons with seriously impaired host defenses. It is occasionally isolated from the feces of patients with diarrhea. Most strains are susceptible to tetracyclines, aminoglycosides, and polymyxins.

● ● ●

General References

Bartlett JG, Finegold SM: Anaerobic pleuropulmonary infections. Medicine 51:413, 1972.

Ciba Foundation Symposium: *Pathogenic Mycoplasmas.* Excerpta Medica, 1972.

Gantz NM & others: Listeriosis in immunosuppressed patients. Am J Med 58:637, 1975.

Gorbach SL, Bartlett JG: Anaerobic infections. N Engl J Med 290:1177, 1974.

Gravenitz A, Mensch AH: The genus Aeromonas in human bacteriology. N Engl J Med 278:245, 1968.

McCormack WM & others: The genital mycoplasmas. N Engl J Med 288:78, 1973.

Medoff G & others: Listeriosis in humans. J Infect Dis 123:247, 1971.

Piggott JA, Hochholzer L: Human melioidosis. Arch Pathol 90:101, 1970.

Rotheram EB & others: Nonclostridial anaerobes in septic abortion. Am J Med 46:80, 1969.

Shurin PA & others: Chorioamnionitis and colonization of the newborn infant with genital mycoplasmas. N Engl J Med 293:5, 1975.

Steinberg P & others: Ecology of *Mycoplasma pneumoniae.* Am J Epidemiol 89:62, 1969.

24...
Normal Microbial Flora of the Human Body

The skin and mucous membranes always harbor a variety of microorganisms which can be arranged into 2 groups: (1) The resident flora consists of relatively fixed types of microorganisms regularly found in a given area at a given age; if disturbed, it promptly re-establishes itself. (2) The transient flora consists of nonpathogenic or potentially pathogenic microorganisms which inhabit the skin or mucous membranes for hours, days, or weeks; it is derived from the environment, does not produce disease, and does not establish itself permanently on the surface. Members of the transient flora are generally of little significance so long as the normal resident flora remains intact. However, if the resident flora is disturbed, transient microorganisms may proliferate and produce disease.

ROLE OF THE RESIDENT FLORA

The microorganisms that are constantly present on body surfaces are commensals. Their flourishing in a given area depends upon physiologic factors of temperature, moisture, and the presence of certain nutrients and inhibitory substances. Their presence is not essential to life because "germ-free" animals can be reared in the complete absence of a normal microbial flora. Yet the resident flora of certain areas plays a definite role in maintaining health and normal function. Members of the resident flora in the intestinal tract synthesize vitamin K and aid in the absorption of nutrients. On mucous membranes and skin, the resident flora may prevent colonization by pathogens and possible disease through "bacterial interference" (see Chapter 14).

On the other hand, members of the normal flora may themselves produce disease under certain circumstances. These organisms are adapted to the non-invasive mode of life defined by the limitations of the environment. If forcefully removed from the restrictions of that environment and introduced into the bloodstream or tissues, these organisms may become pathogenic. For example, streptococci of the viridans group are the commonest resident organisms of the upper respiratory tract. If large numbers of them are introduced into the bloodstream (eg, following tooth extraction or tonsillectomy), they may settle on abnormal heart valves and produce subacute bacterial endocarditis. Small numbers occur transiently in the bloodstream with minor trauma (eg, dental scaling or vigorous toothbrushing). Bacteroides are the commonest resident bacteria of the large intestine and are quite harmless in that location. If introduced into the free peritoneal cavity or into pelvic tissues along with other bacteria, as a result of trauma, they cause suppuration and bacteremia. Spirochetes, fusiform bacilli, and *Bacteroides melaninogenicus* are resident in every normal mouth. In the presence of tissue damage through trauma, nutritional deficiency, or infection they proliferate vastly in the necrotic tissue, producing "fuso-spirochetal" disease. There are many other examples, but the important point is that microbes of the normal resident flora are harmless and may be beneficial in their normal location in the host and in the absence of coincident abnormalities. They may produce disease if introduced into foreign locations in large numbers and if predisposing factors are present. For these reasons, members of the resident flora that are found in disease are sometimes referred to as "opportunists."

NORMAL FLORA OF THE SKIN

Because of its constant exposure to and contact with the environment, the skin is particularly apt to contain transient microorganisms. Nevertheless there is a constant and well-defined resident flora, modified in different anatomic areas by secretions, habitual wearing of clothing, or proximity to mucous membranes (mouth, nose, and perineal areas).

The predominant resident microorganisms of the skin are aerobic and anaerobic diphtheroid bacilli (eg, Corynebacterium, Propionibacterium); nonhemolytic aerobic and anaerobic staphylococci (S epidermidis, Peptococcus); gram-positive, aerobic, sporeforming bacilli which are ubiquitous in air, water, and soil; alpha-hemolytic streptococci *(S viridans)* and enterococci *(S faecalis)*; and gram-negative coliform bacilli and mimeae. Fungi and yeasts are often present in skin folds; acid-fast, nonpathogenic mycobacteria occur in areas rich in sebaceous secretions (genitalia, external ear).

Among the factors that may be important in eliminating nonresident microorganisms from the skin are the low pH, the fatty acids in sebaceous secretions, and the presence of lysozyme. Neither profuse sweating nor washing and bathing can eliminate or significantly modify the normal resident flora. The number of superficial microorganisms may be diminished by vigorous surgical "scrubbing," but the flora is rapidly replenished from sebaceous and sweat glands even when contact with other skin areas or with the environment is completely excluded.

NORMAL FLORA OF THE MOUTH & UPPER RESPIRATORY TRACT

The mucous membranes of the mouth and pharynx are often sterile at birth but may be contaminated by passage through the birth canal. Within 4—12 hours after birth, alpha-hemolytic streptococci (*S viridans*) become established as the most prominent members of the resident flora and remain so for life. They probably originate in the respiratory tracts of the mother and attendants. Early in life aerobic and anaerobic staphylococci, gram-negative diplococci (neisseriae), diphtheroids, and occasional lactobacilli are added. When teeth begin to erupt, the anaerobic spirochetes, bacteroides (especially *Bacteroides melaninogenicus*), and fusiform bacteria and some anaerobic vibrios and lactobacilli establish themselves. Actinomyces species are normally present in tonsillar tissue and on the gingivae in adults. Yeasts occur in the mouth.

In the pharynx and trachea, a similar flora establishes itself, whereas few bacteria are found in normal bronchi. Small bronchi and alveoli are normally sterile. The predominant organisms in the upper respiratory tract, particularly the pharynx, are nonhemolytic and alpha-hemolytic streptococci and neisseriae. Staphylococci, diphtheroids, haemophilus, pneumococci, mycoplasma, and bacteroides are also encountered.

The flora of the nose consists of prominent corynebacteria, staphylococci *(S aureus, S epidermidis),* and streptococci.

The Role of the Normal Mouth Flora in Dental Caries

Caries is a disintegration of the teeth beginning at the surface and progressing inward. First the surface enamel, which is entirely noncellular, is demineralized. This has been attributed to the effect of acid products of bacterial fermentation. Subsequent decomposition of the dentin and cement involves bacterial digestion of the protein matrix.

An essential first step in caries production appears to be the formation of "plaque" on the hard smooth enamel surface. The "plaque" consists mainly of gelatinous deposits of high molecular weight dextrans and levans in which acid-producing bacteria adhere to the enamel. The dextran-levan polymers are produced mainly by streptococci (*S mutans,* Peptostreptococcus) from sucrose and other sugars as substrate. There appears to be a strong correlation between the presence of *S mutans* and caries on specific enamel areas. The essential second step in caries production appears to be the formation of large amounts of acid from carbohydrates by streptococci and lactobacilli in the plaque. High concentrations of acid demineralize the adjoining enamel and initiate caries.

In experimental "germ-free" animals, cariogenic streptococci can induce the formation of plaque and of caries. Adherence to smooth surfaces requires both the synthesis of water-insoluble dextran-levan polymer by cell-bound enzymes and the participation of a binding site on the surface of *S mutans* cells. Adherence may be inhibited by salivary IgA antibody to *S mutans.* Certain diphtheroids and streptococci which produce levans can induce specific soft tissue damage and bone resorption typical of periodontal disease. Proteolytic organisms, including actinomycetes and bacilli, play a role in the microbial action on dentin which follows damage to the enamel. The development of caries also depends on genetic, hormonal, nutritional, and many other factors. Control of caries involves physical removal of "plaque," limitation of sucrose intake, good nutrition with adequate protein intake, and reduction of acid production in the mouth by limitation of available carbohydrates and frequent cleansing. The application of fluoride to teeth or its ingestion in water results in enhancement of acid resistance of the enamel. Control of periodontal disease requires removal of calculus (calcified deposit) and good mouth hygiene.

NORMAL FLORA OF THE INTESTINAL TRACT

At birth the intestine is sterile, but organisms are soon introduced with food. In breast-fed children, the intestine contains large numbers of lactic acid streptococci and lactobacilli. These aerobic and anaerobic, gram-positive, nonmotile organisms (eg, bifidobacterium) produce acid from carbohydrates and tolerate pH 5.0. In bottle-fed children, a more mixed flora exists in the bowel, and lactobacilli are less prominent. As food habits develop toward the adult pattern, the bowel flora changes. Diet has a marked influence on the relative composition of the intestinal and fecal flora.

In the normal adult, the esophagus contains microorganisms arriving with saliva and food. The stomach's acidity keeps the number of microorganisms at a minimum ($10^3 - 10^5$/gm of contents) unless obstruction at the pylorus favors the proliferation of gram-positive cocci and bacilli. As the pH of intestinal contents becomes alkaline, the resident flora gradually increases. In the adult duodenum, there are $10^3 - 10^6$

bacteria/gm; in the jejunum and ileum 10^5-10^8 bacteria/gm; and in the cecum and transverse colon, 10^8-10^{10} bacteria/gm of contents. In the upper intestine, lactobacilli and enterococci predominate, but in the lower ileum and cecum the flora is fecal. In the sigmoid colon and rectum, there are about 10^{11} bacteria/gm of content, constituting 10–20% of the fecal mass. In diarrhea, the bacterial content may diminish greatly, whereas in intestinal stasis the count rises.

In the adult normal colon, the resident bacterial flora consists of 96–99% anaerobes (bacteroides—especially *B fragilis;* anaerobic lactobacilli, eg, bifidobacterium; clostridia [*Cl perfringens* 10^2-10^4/gm] ; and anaerobic streptococci) and only 1–4% aerobes (gram-negative coliforms, enterococci, and small numbers of proteus, pseudomonas, lactobacilli, candida, and other organisms). More than 100 distinct types of organisms occur regularly in normal fecal flora. Minor trauma (eg, sigmoidoscopy, barium enema) may induce transient bacteremia in about 10% of procedures.

Intestinal bacteria are important in synthesis of vitamin K, conversion of bile pigments and bile acids, absorption of nutrients and breakdown products, and antagonism to microbial pathogens. The intestinal flora produces ammonia and other breakdown products which are absorbed and can contribute to hepatic coma.

Antimicrobial drugs taken orally can, in man, temporarily suppress the drug-susceptible components of the fecal flora. This is commonly done for the preoperative "sterilization" of the bowel by drugs such as neomycin. For several days the count of fecal bacteria declines greatly, but at the end of 1–2 weeks the total count returns to normal or becomes higher than normal and the drug-susceptible microorganisms are replaced by drug-resistant ones, particularly staphylococci, enterobacter, enterococci, proteus, pseudomonas, and yeasts.

The feeding of large quantities of *Lactobacillus acidophilus* may result in the temporary establishment of this organism in the gut and the concomitant partial suppression of other gut microflora.

Growth of young chickens, turkeys, and pigs is greatly accelerated by admixture of antibiotics to the feed. The nature of this phenomenon is not clear; it probably does not occur in man or ruminants.

NORMAL FLORA OF THE VAGINA

Soon after birth, aerobic lactobacilli (Döderlein's bacilli) appear in the vagina and persist as long as the pH remains acid (several weeks). When the pH becomes neutral (remaining so until puberty), a mixed flora of cocci and bacilli is present. At puberty, lactobacilli reappear in large numbers and contribute to the maintenance of acid pH through the production of acid from carbohydrates, particularly glycogen. This appears to be an important mechanism in preventing the establishment of other, possibly harmful microorganisms in the vagina. If lactobacilli are suppressed by the administration of antimicrobial drugs, yeasts or various bacteria increase in numbers and cause irritation and inflammation. After the menopause, lactobacilli again diminish in numbers and a mixed flora returns. The normal vaginal flora often includes clostridia, anaerobic streptococci (peptostreptococcus), aerobic group B hemolytic streptococci, and others. The cervical mucus has antibacterial activity and contains lysozyme.

NORMAL FLORA OF THE EYE (CONJUNCTIVA)

The predominant organisms of the conjunctiva are diphtheroids *(Corynebacterium xerosis),* neisseriae, and gram-negative bacilli resembling haemophilus (Morax-Axenfeld bacillus, Moraxella species). Staphylococci and nonhemolytic streptococci are also frequently present.

• • •

General References

Bentley DW & others: The microflora of the human ileum and colon. J Lab Clin Med 79:421, 1972.

Finegold SM: Intestinal bacteria: Their role in physiology. Calif Med 110:455, 1969.

Glickman I: Periodontal disease. N Engl J Med 284:1071, 1971.

Gorbach SL, Bartlett JG: Anaerobic infections. N Engl J Med 290:1177, 1974.

Mukasa H, Slade HD: Mechanism of adherence of *Streptococcus mutans* to smooth surfaces. Infect Immun 8:555, 1973.

Scherp HW: Dental caries. Science 173:1199, 1971.

Swenson RM & others: The bacteriology of intra-abdominal infections. Arch Surg 109:398, 1974.

Thadepalli H & others: Anaerobic infections of the female genital tract. Am J Obstet Gynecol 117:1034, 1973.

25...
Medical Mycology

For purposes of convenience, fungal infections of man are divided into superficial, subcutaneous, and deep (or systemic) mycoses. Superficial fungal infections of skin, hair, and nails are often chronic and resistant to treatment but rarely affect the general health of the patient. The deep mycoses, on the other hand, often produce systemic involvement and are sometimes fatal. Actinomycetes and nocardiae are not fungi but eubacteria. However, they produce disease pictures resembling fungal infections and are therefore discussed here.

Fungi are frequent causes of plant diseases, but only about 50 of the thousands of known species of fungi cause disease in man or animals and only the superficial mycoses (dermatophytoses) are transmitted from man to man.

Most of the deep mycoses are caused by organisms that live free in nature. Infection is frequently limited to certain geographic areas. In such areas, a majority of inhabitants may acquire the fungal infection; most infected persons, however, develop no (or only minor) symptoms, and only a small minority progress to the full-blown serious or fatal disease.

Pathogenic fungi generally produce no toxins. In the host they regularly induce hypersensitivity to their chemical constituents. In systemic mycoses, the typical tissue reaction is a chronic granuloma with varying degrees of necrosis and abscess formation.

With few exceptions, most of the fungi pathogenic for man are classified as **fungi imperfecti,** so named because they produce only asexual spores and have no known sexual spore development in the highly specialized structures that are found in other classes of fungi. Recently, the sexual form of some of the dermatophytes has been discovered, thereby causing these fungi to be reclassified.

The general morphology of fungi has been described in Chapter 1. Some typical structures of pathogenic fungi are mentioned below; others are given with the descriptions of specific disease entities.

STRUCTURES OF FUNGI

When grown on suitable media, many fungi produce long branching filaments. Each filament is called a **hypha**. Hyphae may become divided into a chain of cells by the formation of transverse walls, or septa. These are called septate hyphae. As the hyphae continue to grow and branch, a mat of growth develops called a **mycelium**. That part of the growth which projects above the surface of the substrate is called an **aerial** mycelium; the part which penetrates into the substrate and absorbs food is known as the **vegetative** mycelium.

Fungi reproduce by spores of various types, many of which develop on the aerial mycelium, which is then called the **reproductive** mycelium. Spores are called **asexual** when no fusion of nuclei takes place in their formation; when such fusion does take place, they are called **sexual**. In the majority of fungi of medical importance, sexual spore development has not yet been identified. The following sexual spores are encountered in fungi of medical interest:

(1) Zygospores: In certain phycomycetes the tips of approximating hyphae come together and their contents fuse, thus developing large, thick-walled bodies called zygospores.

(2) Ascospores: Usually 4 spores form within a specialized cell called an ascus in which nuclear fusion has taken place.

Other Common Types of Spores in Fungi of Medical Interest

A. Blastospore: A simple asexual spore which develops by budding and subsequent separation of the bud from the parent cell (eg, in candida, cryptococcus, other yeasts).

B. Chlamydospores: Cells in a hypha enlarge and develop thick walls. These asexual spores are resistant to unfavorable environmental conditions and germinate when conditions become more favorable for vegetative growth.

C. Arthrospores: Asexual spores resulting from a hypha fragmenting into individual cells (eg, in coccidioides).

D. Conidia: Spores produced on specialized hyphae (called conidiophores) by "pinching off" at the point of attachment. When more than one kind of conidium is produced within a given colony, the small, single-celled conidia are called microconidia, and the large, often multicelled conidia are designated macroconidia.

THE ACTINOMYCETES

The actinomycetes are a heterogeneous group of filamentous microorganisms clearly related to "true bacteria" (corynebacteria and mycobacteria), while superficially resembling fungi. The characteristic growth is a branched mycelium which tends to fragment into bacteria-like pieces. Some actinomycetes are acid-fast. Many are free-living, particularly in soil. The anaerobic species *Actinomyces israelii* and some of the aerobic Nocardia and Streptomyces species produce disease in man and animals.

Morphology & Identification

A. Typical Organisms: In culture, *A israelii* is a gram-positive, nonacid-fast, nonmotile, filamentous organism which shows characteristic branching. The filaments break easily into short bacillary fragments with observable branching in the form of a V or Y. In tissues, "sulfur granules" are formed which consist of a central mass of filamentous mycelia. A peripheral array of swollen eosin-staining "clubs" may be present.

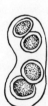

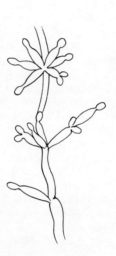

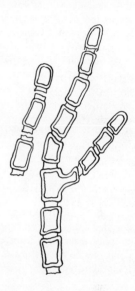

Figure 25–1. Ascospores in an ascus.

Figure 25–2. Blastospores budding from pseudomycelium.

Figure 25–3. Arthrospores.

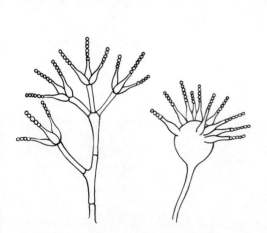

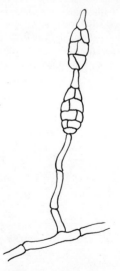

Figure 25–4. Chains of conidia on conidiophores.

Figure 25–5. Chlamydospores.

Figure 25–6. Macroconidia.

[Figs 25–1 to 25–6 redrawn, with permission, from Conant NF & others: *Manual of Clinical Mycology*, 2nd ed. Saunders, 1954.]

A israelii differs in certain respects from *A bovis;* eg, *A bovis* hydrolyzes starch whereas *A israelii* does not, and the cell wall composition of the 2 species differs significantly. However, from a medical and bacteriologic standpoint, they are sufficiently similar to be considered together.

B. Culture: Rough, heaped-up, small, irregular, dead-white colonies form on blood agar or brain-heart infusion agar with 1% glucose after 48 hours of anaerobic incubation. Smooth, glossy colonies are formed less frequently. Thioglycollate medium or chopped-meat infusion broth are the best liquid media. In these, *A israelii* grows as small fluffy balls below the surface of the medium. Strains can be maintained best if grown alternately in different media.

C. Growth Characteristics: Fermentation of carbohydrates varies with different strains, but the presence of sugars favors growth. Most strains are anaerobic but may grow under microaerophilic conditions, particularly if reducing substances are present. Most strains are nonhemolytic and nonproteolytic.

D. Variation: Rough forms are most commonly isolated from actinomycosis in man. Smooth colonial forms isolated from lesions in cattle have been called *A bovis.* Occasionally this form has been isolated from man.

Antigenic Structure

By gel diffusion technics, *A israelii* can be differentiated from *A bovis.* Species-specific antigens (mainly polysaccharides from cell wall) occur in acetone concentrates of culture fluid supernate. There are at least 2 serotypes of *A israelii.*

Pathogenesis & Pathology

Single injections of cultures of *A israelii* do not regularly produce disease in laboratory animals. Perhaps hypersensitivity is necessary for the development of lesions.

Typical *A israelii* can be recovered from the teeth (especially the calculus deposits), pharynx, and tonsils of many normal persons. It is uncertain whether trauma (eg, tooth extraction, human bite), pyogenic infection, or hypersensitivity precipitate disease due to these organisms.

The typical lesion consists of an abscess with central necrosis, surrounded by granulation tissue and fibrous tissue; the pus often contains "sulfur granules" and an abundance of leukocytes. Histologically, the lesions are not typical unless sulfur granules can be found.

Clinical Findings

The characteristic appearance of actinomycosis is a hard, red, relatively nontender swelling which usually develops slowly. It becomes fluctuant, points to a surface, and eventually drains, forming a chronic sinus tract which has little tendency to heal. The lesion tends to extend locally, and there may also be dissemination via the bloodstream.

In about half the cases of actinomycosis the initial lesion is cervicofacial, involving the tissues of the face, neck, tongue, and often the mandible. About one-fifth of cases show predominant involvement of the lungs with abscesses and empyema (thoracic actinomycosis). An equal number have abdominal actinomycosis, where the primary lesion is in the cecum, appendix, or in the pelvic organs; multiple draining fistulas may develop. *Arachnia propionica* may produce identical disease.

Diagnostic Laboratory Tests

Animal inoculation, skin tests, and serologic procedures are not useful in diagnosis.

Specimens consist of pus from lesion or sinus tract, discharge from fistula, and sputum; biopsy specimens are occasionally taken.

A. Microscopic Examination: Every effort must be made to find "sulfur granules" in the specimen. Wash one in saline, place it on a slide, and crush with a coverglass for wet mount examination. The appearance of the central mycelium and peripheral clubs is characteristic. If no "sulfur granules" are found, the demonstration of branching rods and filaments is suggestive.

B. Culture: Material is inoculated into thioglycollate medium, streaked onto blood agar or brain-heart

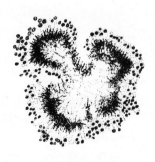

Sulfur granule
in pus

Branching filaments
in pus

Diphtheroid-like and
branching in culture

Figure 25–7. *Actinomyces israelii.*

infusion agar plates, and incubated anaerobically for at least 2 weeks. The small, heaped-up opaque colonies of *A israelii* (or the "fluff-ball" colonies in thioglycollate) can then be examined microscopically for branching mycelia or "twig-like" gram-positive rods.

Immunity

Actinomycetes are part of the normal body flora. It is uncertain whether any immunity is produced by infection with actinomycetes.

Treatment

Prolonged administration of penicillin or sulfonamides is effective in many cases. However, drugs may penetrate poorly into the abscesses and some of the tissue destruction may be irreversible. Surgical drainage and surgical removal are accepted forms of treatment.

Epidemiology

Because of the many free-living actinomycetes and the occurrence of "lumpy jaw" in cattle, it was at one time believed that actinomycosis in man was acquired from grasses, straws, etc, which acted by traumatizing the mucous membranes and introducing the etiologic organism. However, it is now established that potentially pathogenic *A israelii* is a common inhabitant of mucous membranes in the mouth, so that no introduction from the outside need be postulated. The disease is never communicable.

Virtually all isolates from human sources are *A israelii;* most isolates from bovine sources are *A bovis.*

NOCARDIA ASTEROIDES & RELATED SPECIES

Morphology & Identification

A. Typical Organisms: Nocardia and Streptomyces species have narrow, gram-positive, branching filaments. Nocardia may fragment into bacillary or coccal forms, and some may be acid-fast. Streptomyces does not fragment into bacillary forms and is not acid-fast. Bacillary and filamentous forms may be seen in tissue exudates or in pus; white or colored (yellow, red, or black) mycelial granules which may not have peripheral clubs may also be seen.

B. Culture: Nocardiae grow aerobically very slowly, on many simple media. Colonies are most often dry, wrinkled, and crumbling, resembling acid-fast bacilli, but are sometimes soft and mucilaginous. Varying pigmentation, ranging from yellow to red, is produced by different strains. In liquid media a wrinkled surface pellicle is produced.

C. Growth Characteristics: Most strains of nocardiae ferment no carbohydrates; some (but not *N asteroides*) coagulate milk and liquefy gelatin.

D. Variation: Variation among strains is great with regard to all cultural and biologic properties. However, 5 species have been proposed: *N asteroides,* *S madurae,* *S pelletieri,* *N brasiliensis,* and *S paraguayensis.*

Antigenic Structure

Serologic tests demonstrate at least one antigen which is shared by all aerobic actinomycetes, but species cannot be differentiated by serologic means. By immunodiffusion, at least 4 antigenic types can be established. Rabbits infected with *N asteroides* give specific delayed skin reactions to protein and polysaccharide fractions of the organism.

Pathogenesis

N asteroides injected intravenously into rabbits causes a generalized infection with miliary abscesses in many organs. Guinea pigs injected intraperitoneally develop diffuse, fatal peritonitis.

Pathology & Clinical Findings

In man, either localized or generalized infection may occur with *N asteroides* or *N brasiliensis. N asteroides* may occasionally reside on skin or in the respiratory tract without producing disease.

(1) A localized, chronic suppurating granuloma of subcutaneous tissues and bones, with draining sinuses which discharge pus containing the pigmented "granules." This occurs particularly in the extremities (Madura foot, or mycetoma) and leads to progressive bone destruction and deformity but little systemic illness. The clinical picture is indistinguishable from maduromycosis (Madura foot) caused by *Monosporium apiospermum.*

(2) A systemic infection with infiltration and suppuration of the lungs extending via the bloodstream to the meninges, brain, or other organs. The presenting symptoms may be fever without localizing manifestations; headache, nausea, and vomiting, suggestive of brain abscess; or fever, night sweats, cough and sputum, and weight loss similar to those of tuberculosis. Systemic nocardiosis occurs frequently as a complication of lymphoma or immunosuppression.

(3) *Nocardia minutissima (Corynebacterium minutissimum)* causes a superficial skin infection, erythrasma.

Diagnostic Laboratory Tests

Serologic tests are unreliable at present. A polypeptide extracted from nocardia cells gives a specific positive skin test (delayed) experimentally.

Specimens consist of pus from sinus, biopsy material, sputum, or spinal fluid, depending upon type of localization.

A. Microscopic Examination: Pigmented granules should be looked for. They may resemble the actinomycotic "sulfur granules" or may consist only of a tangled mass of hyphae. Wet mounts in 10% potassium hydroxide and Gram-stained smears should be examined. The latter may show only coccal forms and short, branching gram-positive rods. Acid-fast stains are also indicated.

B. Culture: Both aerobic and anaerobic cultures

must be made, and Sabouraud's glucose agar slants should be inoculated to detect other fungi. Intravenous inoculation of rabbits or intraperitoneal injection of guinea pigs may be useful to determine pathogenicity.

Treatment

Surgical treatment is similar to that for actinomycosis (see above). The pulmonary disease caused by aerobic nocardia responds less satisfactorily than that caused by anaerobic actinomyces. The sulfonamides are currently the drugs of choice, or occasionally minocycline.

Epidemiology

Potentially pathogenic nocardia of all types are ubiquitous in soil and probably enter the body by the respiratory route or through trauma. Nocardiosis is not communicable. Many household pets and farm animals carry nocardia.

SUPERFICIAL MYCOSES (DERMATOPHYTOSES)

The dermatophytes are a group of closely related fungi, now classified into 3 genera: Epidermophyton, Microsporum, and Trichophyton. They infect only superficial keratinized tissues, particularly the skin, hair, and nails, but do not invade deeper tissues and do not become disseminated. In keratinized tissues they form only hyphae and arthrospores. In culture on

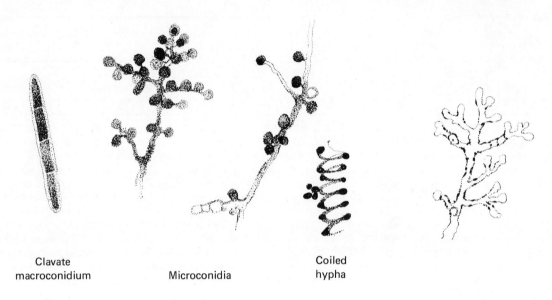

Clavate
macroconidium   Microconidia

Coiled
hypha

Figure 25—8. *Trichophyton mentagrophytes.*

Figure 25—9. *Trichophyton schoenleini* showing "favic chandeliers."

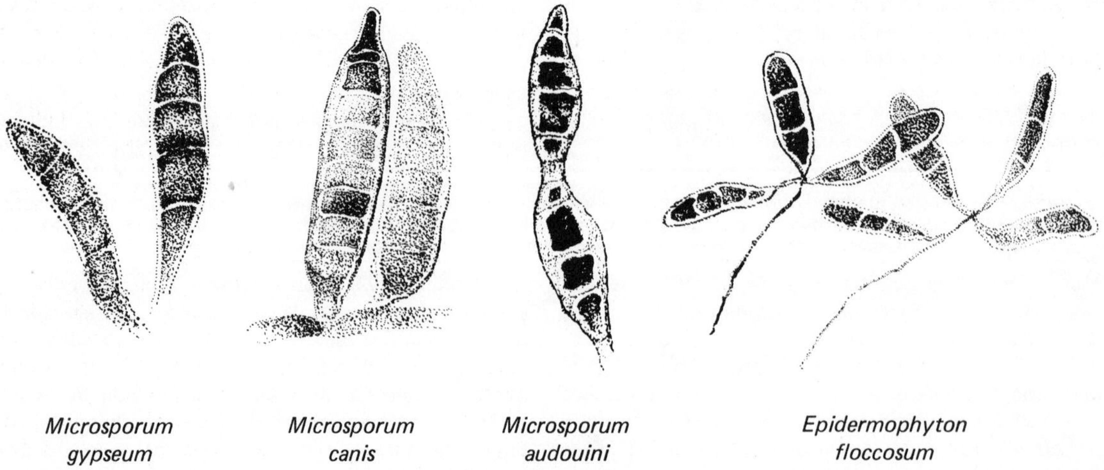

Microsporum gypseum   *Microsporum canis*   *Microsporum audouini*   *Epidermophyton floccosum*

Figure 25—10. Macroconidia.

Table 25—1. Cultural and clinical features of dermatophytes.

Organism	Characteristics of Culture		Clinical Features and Epidemiology
	Colonies	Morphology	
Trichophyton mentagrophytes	White to tan; powdery or cottony.	Coiled hyphae; spherical microconidia in grape-like clusters or along sides of hyphae.	Common cause of athlete's foot; also infections of hair, nails, skin, beard. Worldwide.
T rubrum	Velvety, white, reddish, or purple. Pigmentation on reverse of colony.	Club-shaped regular microconidia along sides of hyphae.	Chronic, treatment-resistant lesions of skin and nails. Worldwide. Very common in tropics. Griseofulvin is useful.
T tonsurans	Creamy or yellow, with central furrows	Elongated irregular microconidia along sides of hyphae.	Endothrix infections, common in Mexico, increasing incidence in USA.
T schoenleini	Smooth, waxy, irregularly folded; brownish.	Hyphal swellings, chlamydospores; "favic chandelier," ie, antler-like processes on ends of hyphae.	Favus on scalp and skin. Common in Europe and Near East; rare in USA.
T concentricum	Similar to *T schoenleini.*		Tinea imbricata. In tropics only.
T violaceum	Violet; otherwise similar to *T schoenleini.*		Ringworm in eastern Europe and Asia.
T ferrugineum	Orange; otherwise similar to *T schoenleini.*		Ringworm in Far East and eastern Europe.
Microsporum audouini	Velvety, brownish, with light orange pigmentation in agar.	Rare macroconidia; microconidia club-shaped.	Epidemic ringworm of scalp. In humans only.
M canis	Cottony white mycelium, with brilliant orange pigmentation in agar.	Many large macroconidia, spindle-shaped, multicelled; thick-walled.	Infects dogs, cats, horses, man. About half of ringworm in USA.
M gypseum	Fast-growing, powdery, cinnamon-colored colony.	Many macroconidia, spindle-shaped, multicelled.	Ringworm. Frequently isolated from soil.
Epidermophyton floccosum	Greenish, powdery colony.	Club-shaped macroconidia in clusters predominate.	Skin and nail infections.

Sabouraud's glucose agar at 20° C, they develop characteristic colonies and spore forms by means of which they are classified. Sexual spores of some species (Trichophyton, Microsporum) have been found.

Most dermatophytes are worldwide in distribution, but some species show a higher incidence in certain regions than in others (eg, *T schoenleini* in the Mediterranean area, *T rubrum* in tropical climates). Many domestic and other animals have dermatophyte infections, and a few of them (eg, *M canis*) are transmitted from dogs or cats to children. Some dermatophytes may be acquired by man from the soil.

Morphology & Identification

The representative colony forms on Sabouraud's agar and the predominant spore forms seen in slide culture are listed in Table 25—1. Some generic characteristics are as follows:

A. Trichophyton (Arthroderma sp): Colonies may be powdery, velvety, or waxy, with pigmentation ranging from white, pink, red, and purple to brown and yellow. Microconidia are the predominant spore forms. They may be arranged in clusters on the sides of hyphae or on conidiophores (see above). Macroconidia are few and elongated, with blunt ends. Fungus invades hair, skin, and nails.

B. Microsporum (Nannizia sp): Colonies are white to tan or brown in color. Macroconidia are the predominant spore forms. They are single, large, multicellular, and spindle-shaped, and occur on the ends of

hyphae (Fig 25—10). This fungus invades hair and skin but rarely the nails.

C. Epidermophyton: Colonies are velvety to powdery and greenish-yellow in color. Oval or club-shaped macroconidia having 2—6 cells are typically arranged in clusters (Fig 25—10). Thus, fungus invades skin and nails but not hair.

Antigenic Structure

Dermatophytes contain both group-specific and species-specific antigens. Both of these are contained in trichophytin, a preparation derived from cultures of dermatophytes which is analogous to tuberculin. A positive trichophytin test (a delayed reaction) merely indicates present or past infection and is of no diagnostic value. The skin test is positive in those individuals who manifest hypersensitivity by developing "dermatophytids."

Clinical Findings

A. Tinea Pedis (Athlete's Foot): This is the most prevalent of all dermatophytoses. The toe webs are infected with a Trichophyton species or with *Epidermophyton floccosum*. Initially there is itching between the toes and the development of small blisters which rupture and discharge a thin fluid. The skin of the toe webs becomes macerated and peels, whereupon cracks appear which are prone to secondary bacterial infection. When secondary infection does occur, lymphangitis and lymphadenitis develop. When the fungal infection becomes chronic, peeling and cracking of the skin are the principal manifestations. Sometimes the nails become brittle, thickened, yellow, and irregular (tinea unguium).

In the course of a chronic dermatophytosis the individual becomes hypersensitive to constituents or products of the fungus and may develop allergic manifestations, called dermatophytids (usually vesicles), elsewhere on the body (most often on the hands). The trichophytin skin test is markedly positive in such persons.

B. Tinea Corporis (T Glabrosa, T Cruris) (Ringworm): This is a dermatophytosis of the nonhairy skin of the body which gives rise commonly to the annular lesions of ringworm, with a clearing, scaly center surrounded by a raised, red advancing border which often contains vesicles.

C. Tinea Capitis (Ringworm of the Scalp): This occurs in childhood and heals spontaneously at puberty, perhaps because of the elaboration, during adult life, of higher fatty acids which are fungistatic. The dermatophytes grow in or on the hair and the keratinized epithelium of dead skin. They produce inflammatory changes, with redness, edema, scaling, vesicle formation, and thickening of the keratinized layer. The deeper layers of the epidermis show vesication and cellular infiltration. The gross appearance varies with the infecting microorganism: In microsporum infections, the hair is broken off a short distance from the surface of the scalp, resulting in circumscribed spots of discolored hair stubs. There may also be a pronounced inflammation of the scalp, even resembling pyogenic infection, called kerion (especially with *M canis* or *M gypseum*).

In some trichophyton infections the hair shaft itself is invaded and the hair broken off at the surface of the scalp. The follicle is left with a black hair stub center surrounded by scaling skin. Scalp infection with *T schoenleini* gives cup-like structures (scutula) formed by crusts around infected follicles. Microsporum-infected hairs (except with some strains of *M gypseum* and *M canis*) fluoresce and appear green under Wood's light. Trichophyton-infected hairs do not fluoresce.

Trichophyton species may involve the bearded region of man (tinea barbae); they closely resemble pyogenic infections of that area.

D. Tinea Versicolor: An infection of the skin which usually produces brownish-red scaling patches on the neck, trunk, and arms. It is caused by *Malassezia furfur,* a fungus which appears microscopically in the skin as clusters of round, budding cells intermixed with short fragments of hyphae.

E. Piedra: An infection of the hair resulting in hard black nodules (*Piedraia hortai*) or soft white nodules (*Trichosporon beigelii*) attached to hair.

F. Erythrasma: A superficial infection of axillary or pubic skin caused by *Nocardia minutissima (Corynebacterium minutissimum).*

Diagnostic Laboratory Tests

Specimens consist of scrapings of skin and nails

and hair plucked from involved areas. Microsporum-infected hairs are best located by observing the fluorescent areas under Wood's light in a darkened room.

A. Microscopic Examination: Specimens are placed on a slide in a drop of 10–20% potassium hydroxide, covered with a coverslip, and examined immediately as well as after 10–30 minutes. In skin or nails, branching hyphae only are seen. In hairs, microspora often form dense sheaths of spores in a mosaic pattern around the hair; trichophyta form parallel rows of spores outside (ectothrix) or inside (endothrix) the hair shaft.

B. Culture: All final identification of dermatophytes must be made in cultures. Specimens are inoculated onto Sabouraud's glucose agar slants, incubated for 2–3 weeks at room temperature, and then further examined in slide cultures if necessary.

Treatment

Therapy consists of adequate removal of infected and dead epithelial structures and application of a topical antifungal chemical. Harmful overtreatment must be avoided, and attempts must be made to prevent reinfection. In serious or widespread involvement, oral administration of griseofulvin for 2–4 weeks has been strikingly effective.

A. Scalp Infections: In scalp infections, if griseofulvin is not given, the hair should be either plucked manually, clipped, or otherwise epilated. Frequent thorough washing with soap, application of ointments containing salicylic acid, salicylanilide, or undecylenates; and the wearing of cotton stocking caps to prevent shedding of infected hair—all have their place in adequate therapy. Treatment must be continued for months. Systemic griseofulvin has been particularly useful in *T rubrum* infections.

B. Body Infections: Use antifungal ointments, eg, ammoniated mercury, 5%; undecylenic acid, 5%; salicylic acid, 3%; benzoic acid, 5%. In tinea versicolor, sodium thiosulfate is also effective.

C. Foot Infections:

1. Acute phase—Soak in potassium permanganate, 1:4000, until the acute inflammation subsides. Then use antifungal chemicals as mentioned below.

2. Subacute or chronic phases—Apply antifungal chemicals as creams (at night) and powders (during the day), eg, undecylenic acid, 5%, and zinc undecylenate, 20%; salicylic acid, 3%, and benzoic acid, 5%. Many other preparations may be used with comparable success.

Epidemiology & Control

Only sporadic cases of ringworm infection come from cats or dogs (*M canis*). The majority of cases arise from contact with infected children or infected hair and skin. Epidemics of *M audouini* infection in children have been traced to the use of common barber shop clippers and the transfer of infected hairs on theater seats as well as to person-to-person contact. Only a concerted public health approach involving proper treatment of children, sterilization of instruments (hot paraffin oil), and reduction of contacts can accomplish control.

Athlete's foot spreads through the use of common showers and dressing rooms, where infected, desquamated skin serves as a source of infection. No really effective control measures (other than widespread use of local treatment) are available. In many persons, chronic athlete's foot is asymptomatic and becomes activated only in excessive heat, moisture, or with unsuitable footwear.

DEEP MYCOSES

CANDIDA ALBICANS

Candida (Monilia) albicans is an oval, budding, yeast-like fungus which produces a pseudomycelium both in culture and in tissues and exudates. It is a member of the normal flora of the mucous membranes in the respiratory, gastrointestinal, and female genital tracts. In such locations it may gain dominance and be associated with pathologic conditions. Sometimes it produces systemic progressive disease in debilitated or immunosuppressed patients. It may produce bloodstream infection, thrombophlebitis, endocarditis, or infection of the eyes and other organs when introduced intravenously (tubing, needles, hyperalimentation, narcotic addiction, etc). Other yeasts (eg, *Torulopsis glabrata*) may be pathogenic under similar circumstances.

Morphology & Identification

In smears of exudates, candida appears as a gram-positive, oval, budding yeast, measuring 2–3 × 4–6 μm, and gram-positive, elongated budding cells resembling hyphae (pseudohyphae). On Sabouraud's glucose agar incubated at room temperature, soft cream-colored colonies develop which have a yeast-like odor. The surface growth consists of oval budding cells. The submerged growth consists of pseudomycelium. This is composed of pseudohyphae, forming blastospores at the nodes and sometimes chlamydospores terminally. *C albicans* ferments glucose and maltose, producing both acid and gas, produces acid from sucrose, and does not attack lactose. These carbohydrate fermentations, together with colonial and morphologic characteristics, differentiate *C albicans* from the other species of Candida *(C krusei, C parapsilosis, C stellatoidea, C tropicalis, C pseudotropicalis,* and *C guilliermondii),* which are also occasionally members of normal human flora and occasionally implicated in disease. *Torulopsis glabrata*—an occasional opportunistic pathogen—is a yeast-like organism found in the normal vagina or on the skin.

Antigenic Structure

By agglutination tests with absorbed sera, all *C*

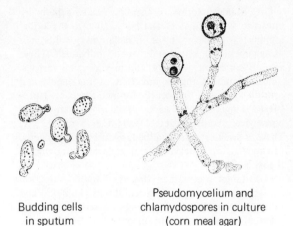

Budding cells in sputum

Pseudomycelium and chlamydospores in culture (corn meal agar)

Figure 25–11. *Candida albicans.*

albicans strains fall into 2 distinct groups: A and B. Group A appears to be antigenically identical with *C tropicalis;* group B, with *C stellatoidea.*

Pathogenesis & Pathology

Upon intravenous injection into rabbits dense suspensions of *C albicans* result in widespread abscesses, particularly in the kidney, and death in less than one week.

Histologically the various skin lesions in man show inflammatory changes. Some resemble abscess formation; others resemble chronic granulomata. Large numbers of candida are sometimes found in the intestinal tract following administration of oral antibiotics, eg, tetracyclines, but this usually causes no symptoms. Candida may be carried by the bloodstream to many organs, including the meninges, but in general is not able to establish itself and cause miliary abscess formation except in a grossly debilitated host. Dissemination and sepsis occur sometimes in lymphoma or immunosuppression.

Clinical Findings

Among the principal predisposing factors to *C albicans* infection are the following: diabetes mellitus, general debility, immunosuppression, indwelling urinary or intravenous catheters, intravenous narcotic abuse, administration of antimicrobials (which alter the normal bacterial flora), and corticosteroids.

A. Mouth: Infection of the mouth (thrush) occurs, mainly in children, as white adherent patches on the buccal mucous membranes which consist largely of pseudomycelium and desquamated epithelium with only minimal erosion of the membrane. Growth of candida in saliva is enhanced by glucose, antibiotics, and corticosteroids.

B. Female Genitalia: Vulvovaginitis resembles thrush but produces irritation, intense itching, and discharge. Its development is favored by alkaline pH, humid heat, and nonabsorbing clothing. It is counteracted normally by vaginal lactobacilli.

C. Skin: Infection of the skin occurs principally in moist, warm parts of the body, such as the axilla, intergluteal folds, groin, or inframammary folds; it is most common in obese and diabetic individuals. These areas become red, weeping, and may develop vesicles.

D. Hands: Candida infection of the hands and nails is seen most frequently following repeated prolonged immersion in water; it is most common in housewives, cooks, vegetable and fish handlers, etc. There is swelling of the nailbed, resembling a pyogenic paronychia, and thickening and transverse grooving of the nails.

E. Lungs and Other Organs: Candida infection may be a secondary invader of lungs, kidneys, and other organs where a preexisting disease is present (eg, tuberculosis or cancer). In uncontrolled leukemia and in immunosuppressed or surgical patients, candidal lesions may occur in many organs. Candida endocarditis occurs particularly in narcotic addicts.

F. Chronic Mucocutaneous Candidiasis: This disorder may be a sign of deficiency of cellular immunity.

Diagnostic Laboratory Tests

Specimens consist of swabs and scrapings from surface lesions, sputum, and exudates.

A. Microscopic Examination: Sputum, exudates, thrombi, etc may be examined by Gram's stains for yeast-like cells. Skin or nail scrapings are first placed in a drop of 10% potassium hydroxide.

B. Culture: All specimens are cultured on Sabouraud's glucose agar at room temperature and at 37° C; typical colonies are examined for yeast-like cells and pseudomycelia. Production of chlamydospores of *C albicans* is an important differential test: these can be produced on either corn meal agar or the chlamydospore agar of Nickerson and Mankowski.

C. Serology: A carbohydrate extract of group A candida gives positive precipitin reactions with sera of 50% of normal persons and of 70% of persons with mucocutaneous candidiasis. In systemic candidiasis, the titer of antibodies to candida (agglutination, indirect immunofluorescence, precipitation) may rise. High antibody titers detected by immunodiffusion tests suggest continuing activity of a deep infection.

D. Skin Test: A candida skin test is almost universally positive in normal adults. It is used therefore as an indicator of competent cellular immunity.

Immunity

Animals can be immunized actively and are then resistant to disseminated candidiasis. Human sera often contain IgG antibody which clumps candida in vitro and may be candidicidal.

Treatment

Orally administered nystatin does not reach tissues and thus is of no avail in disseminated candida infections. Soluble amphotericin B (0.5–1.2 mg/kg/day IV) has been successful in some patients.

Local lesions are best treated by removing the cause: avoid moisture; keep areas cool, powdered, and dry; and withdraw antibiotics. Both serum and vaccine therapy has been advocated, but there is no convincing evidence of their effectiveness. Various chemicals have been employed with more or less success, eg, 1% gentian violet for thrush, and parahydroxybenzoic acid esters, sodium propionate, or candicidin for vaginitis. Nystatin suppresses intestinal and vaginal candidiasis.

Epidemiology & Control

The most important preventive measure is to avoid interfering with the normal balance of microbial flora and with normal host defenses. Candida infection is not communicable, since most individuals harbor the organism under normal circumstances.

CRYPTOCOCCUS NEOFORMANS
(Torula histolytica)

Cryptococcus neoformans is a yeast-like, budding fungus characterized by a wide capsule both in culture and exudates. It is free-living in the soil and is found frequently in pigeon feces. In man, primary pulmonary infection is occasionally followed by meningitis.

Morphology & Identification

In spinal fluid or tissue, the organism is spherical or ovoid, 5–12 μm in diameter, often budding, and enclosed in a wide capsule. On Sabouraud's agar at room temperature, the colonies are glistening and mucoid, and cream-colored organisms appear as in tissue. No mycelium is produced. Cultures produce no gas from carbohydrates. However, they assimilate glucose, maltose, sucrose, and galactose (but not lactose). They hydrolyze urea. In contrast to nonpathogenic cryptococci, *C neoformans* grows readily at 37° C on most laboratory media.

Antigenic Structure

At least 3 serologic types of capsular polysaccharide material—A, B, and C—have been identified among different strains. Some of the capsular material is dissolved in spinal fluid and gives a precipitate with specific anticryptococcal serum. Such serum also gives a capsular swelling reaction. Patients with progressive cryptococcal infection may develop specific antibodies. Antipolysaccharide antibodies are not associated with increased resistance.

Pathogenesis

Intraperitoneal or intracerebral injection of *C neoformans* into mice leads to a fatal infection from which organisms can be recovered in pure culture. Infection in man occurs through the respiratory tract. Primary pulmonary disease may be followed by systemic dissemination and establishment of the infection in the CNS.

Histologically, the reaction varies from mild inflammation to typical granulomas.

Suspension
of culture

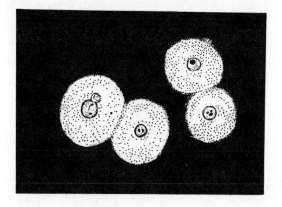

India ink preparation
of spinal fluid

Figure 25—12. *Cryptococcus neoformans.*

Clinical Findings

In man, infection with *C neoformans* often remains subclinical. The commonest clinical manifestation is a slowly developing chronic meningitis with frequent spontaneous remissions and relapses. The meningitis may resemble a brain tumor, brain abscess, tuberculous meningitis, or degenerative disease of the CNS. The pressure and protein content of the spinal fluid may be greatly increased; the cell count may be mildly elevated; the spinal fluid sugar is normal or low. In addition, there may be lesions of skin and of the lungs or other organs.

The course of cryptococcal meningitis may extend over many years, often with long remissions, but ultimately all untreated cases appear to be fatal. The disease is not communicable. Pathogenic cryptococci have been isolated from soil, but bird feces are the main source of infection.

Diagnostic Laboratory Tests

Specimens consist of spinal fluid, exudates, and sputum.

A. Microscopic Examination: Specimens are examined in wet mount, either directly or after mixing with India ink (which makes the large capsules stand out clearly around the budding yeast cells), or by immunofluorescence. Filtration of CSF through Millipore filters may reveal the organism.

B. Culture: Growth is rapid at 20–37° C on both Sabouraud's glucose agar and other laboratory media.

Urea is hydrolyzed. Cultured cells should be injected into mice to determine their pathogenicity. C neoformans colonies produce brown pigment on media which contain substrate for phenol oxidase (eg, potato extract).

C. Serology: Tests for both antigen and antibody can be performed on CSF and serum. The latex slide agglutination test reveals antigen. With effective treatment, the antigen titer drops. Cryptococcal antibody agglutinates whole cells or antigen-coated latex particles. No serologic test is highly sensitive or completely specific.

Treatment

Amphotericin B (0.5—1.2 mg/kg/day IV), although toxic, has resulted in several apparent cures. Flucytosine (100—150 mg/kg/day orally) has also been effective, but resistant mutants present a problem.

Epidemiology & Control

Soil or bird droppings containing *C neoformans* are the source of infection for both animals and man. The organism grows luxuriantly in pigeon feces, but the birds do not appear to be infected. At present, the only method of control is reduction of the pigeon population and site decontamination with alkali.

BLASTOMYCES DERMATITIDIS

Blastomyces (Ajellomyces) dermatitidis is a yeast-like fungus which consists of thick-walled, budding spherical forms in tissues or when cultured at 37° C but which shows filamentous growth at room temperature. It causes a chronic granulomatous disease, North American blastomycosis, which may be limited to the skin or lung or may be widely disseminated in the body.

Morphology & Identification

Blastomyces organisms exhibit striking dimorphism. In tissues, pus, or exudates, the organism appears as a round, budding sphere, 8—20 μm in diameter, with a thick, doubly refractile wall. Each cell shows only a single bud. Colonies on blood agar at 37° C are wrinkled, waxy, and soft, and the cells are morphologically similar to the tissue stage, although short hyphal segments may also be present. On the other hand, when grown at room temperature on Sabouraud's glucose agar, a white to brownish filamentous colony develops which consists of branching, septate hyphae with lateral spherical or pear-shaped spores (Fig 25—13). The organism ferments no sugars. The yeast phase produces a hemolysin. The sexual stage of *B dermatitidis* has recently been discovered.

Antigenic Structure

Carbohydrates and proteins isolated from the yeast phase of *B dermatitidis* give positive skin tests in infected patients or animals. A delayed tuberculin-like reaction is also shown to blastomycin, a skin test material prepared from the filtrate of a synthetic medium in which the organism has grown. Antibodies can be demonstrated by immunodiffusion or CF tests mainly in individuals with widespread or progressive infection.

Pathogenesis & Pathology

Many laboratory animals can be experimentally infected. The mechanism and route of human infection are not known, but the organism probably enters via the respiratory tract. Dissemination usually involves the skin, bones, genitourinary tract, and meninges.

Histologically, there are both small abscesses and distinct granulomas resembling tubercles. The budding, thick-walled spheres are commonly seen in pus or tissues.

Clinical Findings

A. Skin: The primary skin lesion is a pustule which breaks down in the center and spreads peripherally, forming an irregular ulcer with a raised red border studded with small abscesses. This lesion may occur anywhere on the body but occurs most frequently on exposed areas.

B. Lungs: Primary pulmonary blastomycosis is probably the commonest form of infection and is usually benign and self-limited.

C. Skin Test: The blastomycin skin test is positive in some patients but is not entirely specific. The skin test may stimulate complement-fixing antibodies.

Diagnostic Laboratory Tests

Specimens consist of sputum, pus, exudates, and biopsy from skin lesions.

A. Microscopic Examination: Wet mounts of specimens may show budding, thick-walled, yeast-like organisms which may also be apparent in histologic sections.

B. Culture: Colonial and cellular morphology is

typical on blood agar at 37° C and on Sabouraud's glucose agar at 20° C.

C. Animal Inoculation: Massive doses of yeast phase cultures injected intravenously or intraperitoneally into mice, guinea pigs, or rabbits are fatal in 3–20 days.

D. Serology: The complement fixation or immunodiffusion tests with blastomycin may be positive. Cross-reactions with histoplasmin may occur.

Treatment

The acute pulmonary form usually requires no treatment. The aromatic diamidines (eg, dihydroxystilbamidine) induce prolonged remissions even of extensive lesions and may result in permanent cure. Amphotericin B injected intravenously for many weeks can also be curative in disseminated disease. Surgical removal of lesions is occasionally valuable.

Epidemiology

Infection with *B dermatitidis* probably occurs mainly in the USA, Canada, Mexico, and some parts of Africa. The organism has been isolated from soil, and spontaneously infected dogs have been found.

It is probable that *B dermatitidis* occurs in soil or on vegetation. Infection probably follows inhalation of spores in soil dust or trauma. The disease is not communicable from person to person.

BLASTOMYCES BRASILIENSIS
(Paracoccidioides brasiliensis)

Blastomyces brasiliensis is a yeast-like fungus which causes South and Central American blastomycosis (paracoccidioidomycosis). This organism occurs only in South America, the majority of cases being noted between Brazil (south) and Colombia (north). The disease appears in the geographical area located between the 2 countries. In tissues and in culture at 37° C, it forms thick-walled spheres with both single and multiple buds. At room temperature, cultures develop an aerial mycelium.

Morphology & Identification

B brasiliensis resembles *B dermatitidis* in both tissue and culture; the principal difference is that *B brasiliensis* forms thick-walled cells (10–60 μm in tissue, 6–30 μm in culture) which characteristically have multiple buds.

Pathogenesis & Clinical Findings

The infective organism is usually inhaled, and early lesions occur in the respiratory tract and lungs. Occasionally, the site of entry is the skin or mucous membrane, with spread to regional lymph nodes.

A different form of the infection begins in the lymphoid tissue of the intestine and spreads first to the mesenteric lymph nodes and then to the other abdomi-

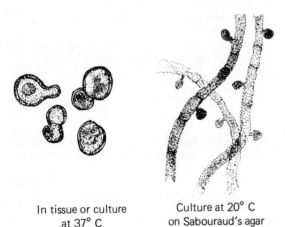

In tissue or culture
at 37° C

Culture at 20° C
on Sabouraud's agar

Figure 25–13. *Blastomyces dermatitidis.*

In tissue or culture at 37° C; multiple budding

Figure 25—14. *Blastomyces brasiliensis.*

nal viscera. Histologically, there is either abscess formation or granuloma with central caseation. Organisms are frequently seen in tissue, giant cells, or pus and are always characterized by their multiple budding.

Skin tests with "paracoccidioidin" are analogous to those with blastomycin in the North American disease. The same material is used as antigen for immunodiffusion tests, which are positive in extensive involvement and are specific in endemic areas.

Diagnostic Laboratory Tests

These are essentially the same as for *B dermatitidis.* Animal inoculation is best carried out by the intratesticular injection of guinea pigs and culture of the developing lesion.

Treatment

South American blastomycosis responds strikingly to prolonged administration of sulfonamides. All forms of the disease have shown improvement. Amphotericin B has proved curative in some patients.

Epidemiology

South American blastomycosis occurs mainly in rural areas, particularly among farmers. The disease is much more frequent in males than females, which suggests that the men acquire the infection while working in the fields. The fungus has been isolated from soil. The disease is not communicable.

HISTOPLASMA CAPSULATUM

Histoplasma capsulatum is a yeast-like fungus which causes histoplasmosis. In tissues and on blood agar at 37° C, it is seen as a small, ovoid, budding organism by Giemsa or Gomori stain. In cultures at room temperature, it produces filamentous colonies.

Morphology & Identification

Within phagocytic cells and on sealed blood agar slants incubated at 37° C, *Histoplasma capsulatum* forms oval, yeast-like budding cells measuring 2—4 μm. On blood agar at 37° C, colonies are smooth and white. On Sabouraud's glucose agar incubated at room temperature, white, cottony colonies develop, with large (8—20 μm), thick-walled, spherical spores having finger-like projections. The appearance of these tuberculate spores is diagnostic of *H capsulatum* infection.

Antigenic Structure

Patients with histoplasmosis give positive skin tests with histoplasmin, a filtrate of broth in which *H capsulatum* has been grown. The reaction is delayed and tuberculin-like. From yeast phase or mycelium, polysaccharides with precipitating and complement-fixing activity can be isolated.

Pathogenesis & Clinical Findings

Infection with *H capsulatum* usually occurs through the respiratory tract. It is often asymptomatic, in which case the small inflammatory or granulomatous foci in the lungs heal with calcification. Such miliary calcification has been observed in many tuberculin-negative, histoplasmin-positive individuals in the endemic area in the USA. With heavy respiratory exposure, clinical pneumonia and protracted illness can develop.

Disseminated histoplasmosis develops in a small minority of infected individuals, but more frequently in white males over 40 than in dark-skinned persons. The reticuloendothelial system is particularly involved, with lymphadenopathy, enlarged spleen and liver, high fever, anemia, and a high fatality rate. Tumor-like ulcers of the nose, mouth, tongue, and intestine can occur. In such individuals the histologic lesion shows focal areas of necrosis in small granulomas in many organs. Phagocytic cells (mononuclear or polymorphonuclear leukocytes of the blood, fixed reticuloendothelial cells of liver, spleen, and bone marrow) contain the small, oval yeast-like cells.

Many animals, including dogs and rodents, are spontaneously infected in endemic areas. Mice and guinea pigs can be infected experimentally with cultures.

Diagnostic Laboratory Tests

Specimens consist of sputum, scrapings from lesions, and buffy coat blood cells for culture; biopsies from bone marrow, skin, lymph nodes; and blood for serology.

A. Microscopic Examination: In histologic sections, the small ovoid cells may be detected intracellularly. The same is true for smears of blood or bone marrow.

B. Culture: Specimens are cultured at 22° C on blood and Sabouraud's agar; cultures must be kept for 3 weeks.

C. Serology: Latex agglutination, complement fixation, or precipitin tests are positive within a few weeks after infection, reach a peak titer in 2—3 months, and then fall to low levels if the disease is inactive. With progressive disease, the complement fixation test remains positive in high titer (> 1:32). Two precipitin bands can be formed in serum. One (H) connotes active histoplasmosis; the other (M) may arise from repeated skin testing or past contact.

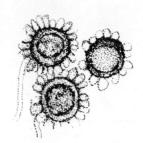

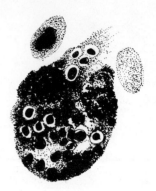

Yeast phase in
culture at 37° C

Tuberculate spores in
culture at 20° C

Showing
intracellular bodies

Figure 25–15. *Histoplasma capsulatum.*

D. Skin Test: The histoplasmin skin test becomes positive soon after infection and remains positive if the disease is arrested. It may be negative in disseminated, progressive disease. Repeated skin tests stimulate complement-fixing antibodies which may cross-react with other fungal antigens.

Immunity

Some degree of immunity appears to follow infection with histoplasma.

Treatment

Symptomatic therapy in primary pulmonary histoplasmosis suffices for the recovery of most infected persons. In disseminated histoplasmosis, amphotericin B has been of some benefit.

Epidemiology & Control

The endemic area for *H capsulatum* in the USA includes the central and eastern states, where small epidemics have occurred and where the fungus has been recovered from the soil, from animals, and from certain locations on farms (eg, silos). The fungus grows abundantly in bird feces (chicken houses) and bat guano (caves). Exposure in such places may result in massive infection with severe disease (eg, cave disease). In endemic areas it must be assumed that very small infective inocula are spread by dust. A large proportion of inhabitants (about 65%) apparently become infected, without symptoms, during childhood, develop positive histoplasmin skin tests, and occasionally have healed miliary calcifications in the lungs. The disease is not communicable. Spraying of formaldehyde on infected soil may destroy histoplasma.

COCCIDIOIDES IMMITIS

Coccidioides immitis is a fungus which is endemic in the southwestern USA and causes coccidioidomyco-
sis. In tissue it is a large, thick-walled spherule filled with endospores. Cultured at room temperature, it produces a cottony colony with hyphae which fragment into highly infectious arthrospores.

Morphology & Identification

In histologic sections of tissues or in pus or sputum, *C immitis* appears as a spherule, 15–75 μm in diameter, with a thick, doubly refractile wall. The spherule is filled with minute endospores which occasionally can be seen to have erupted into surrounding tissues. Spherules can be produced in vitro by using specialized culture media. When grown at room temperature on common laboratory media or on Sabouraud's glucose agar, a fluffy, cottony white colony develops. The hyphae of this growth contain rectangular arthrospores, which are freed in old cultures through fragmentation of the hyphae. These spores are very light, float readily in air, and are highly infectious. When inoculated into tissues, these spores develop into spherules.

Antigenic Structure

Coccidioidin is produced from the filtrate of a broth culture in which *C immitis* has been grown and may be derived from the mycelial coccidioidin or spherule phase spherulin. It gives positive skin tests (in dilutions up to 1:10,000) in infected persons and acts as antigen in precipitin and complement fixation tests. A polysaccharide has been isolated from it which also gives positive skin and precipitin tests. In low dilutions of coccidioidin (1:10), there are cross-reactions with histoplasmin and with the antigens of some other fungi (eg, Paracoccidioides).

Pathogenesis & Clinical Findings

Infection is acquired through the inhalation of air- and dust-borne arthrospores. There follows a respiratory infection which may be asymptomatic and may manifest itself only by the development of a positive coccidioidin skin test in 3 weeks. Otherwise, the indi-

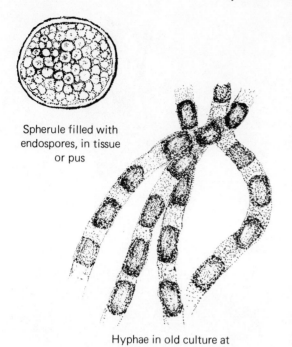

Spserule filled with
endospores, in tissue
or pus

Hyphae in old culture at
room temperature breaking
up into arthrospores

Figure 25—16. *Coccidioides immitis.*

vidual may have an influenza-like illness, with fever, malaise, cough, aches, pains, and sweats, from which he recovers. About 3–5% of individuals who have had such an illness develop, 1–2 weeks later, hypersensitivity reactions in the form of erythema nodosum or erythema multiforme. This symptom complex is referred to as "valley fever" or "desert rheumatism" and is self-limited. Thin-walled cavities occasionally develop in the lungs at this time; these also tend to subside spontaneously.

Fewer than 1% of persons who have been infected progress to the disseminated, highly fatal form called "coccidioidal granuloma." This occurs 10 times more frequently in dark-skinned than in light-skinned individuals. Dissemination, when it occurs, develops usually within 1 year of the initial infection, either by direct extension of the process or by endogenous spreading. Dissemination may occur in pregnancy. Dissemination denotes some defect in the individual's ability to localize and control infection with *C immitis*. Most individuals can be considered immune to the organism once their skin test has become positive.

Disseminated coccidioidomycosis is entirely comparable to tuberculosis, with lesions in all organs and in the CNS. Histologically, these lesions are typical granulomas which are indistinguishable from tuberculosis unless spherules can be detected in them. The clinical course often involves remissions and exacerbations.

Diagnostic Laboratory Tests

Specimens consist of sputum, pus, gastric wash-ings, spinal fluid, biopsy specimens, and blood.

A. Microscopic Examination: All materials should be examined fresh (after centrifuging, if necessary) for typical spherules; histologic sections must be stained.

B. Cultures: Culture can be done on blood agar at 37° C and on Sabouraud's agar at room temperature. *Use extreme caution—cultures are highly infectious.*

C. Animal Inoculations: Mice injected intraperitoneally develop progressive disease.

D. Serology: Precipitating IgM antibodies in titers of diagnostic significance develop soon after infection and then diminish. Complement-fixing IgG antibodies become positive in high titer only in progressive disseminated disease; when this happens, the prognosis is poor. In coccidioidal meningitis, the complement-fixing antibody titer may be high in CSF, low in serum.

E. Skin Test: (See Antigenic Structure.) The coccidioidin test (1:100) is specific when read at 48 hours. It is often negative in disseminated disease. Cross-reactions with other fungi occur with 1:10 dilution.

Immunity

Immunity usually follows infection with *C immitis*. Experimental vaccines are under study.

Treatment

For the primary infection, only symptomatic treatment and rest are necessary because most persons recover completely. For disseminated coccidioidomycosis, long-term intravenous amphotericin is the best treatment, resulting in some remissions.

Epidemiology & Control

The endemic area of *C immitis* in the USA includes the dry, arid regions of the southwestern states, particularly the San Joaquin and Sacramento Valleys of California, the area around Tucson and Phoenix in Arizona, and west Texas. Some spread of the endemic area is being noted. It also occurs in Central and South America in a "lower sonoran life zone." In those areas the fungus is found in soil, dust, and in rodents, and the majority of residents (up to 90%) give evidence, by positive coccidioidin skin tests, of past infection. The infection rate is highest during the dry months of summer and autumn, when dust is most prevalent.

Infection can be diminished by dust control measures: paving roads and airfield runways, planting lawns, and using oil sprays. The disease is not communicable, and there is no evidence that infected animals contribute to its spread.

GEOTRICHUM CANDIDUM

Geotrichum candidum is a yeast-like fungus which produces geotrichosis, an infection of bronchi, lungs, and mucous membranes.

Morphology & Identification

In sputum, *G candidum* appears as rectangular

arthrospores 5 × 10 μm or thick-walled, ovoid, yeast-like cells. Characteristically, both are present. Cultures on Sabouraud's agar produce slow-growing, membranous, flat, soft, white colonies. The hyphae segment into arthrospores.

Pathogenesis & Clinical Findings

The natural habitat of the fungus is not known for certain, but it may be a normal inhabitant of the mouth and gut of man. It is associated with chronic bronchitis with the x-ray appearance of diffuse peribronchial thickening, diffuse pulmonary infiltration resembling tuberculosis, or thrush-like lesions in the mouth. The sputum is mucoid and occasionally blood-streaked and contains the organisms. The prognosis is generally good.

Diagnostic Laboratory Tests

Examination of sputum by microscopy and culture.

Treatment

Potassium iodide by mouth is claimed to result in improvement. One percent gentian violet suppresses oral lesions.

SPOROTHRIX (SPOROTRICHUM) SCHENCKII

Sporothrix (Sporotrichum) schenckii is a fungus producing a leathery colony with typical clusters of pear-shaped conidia on the hyphae. It causes sporotrichosis, a chronic granulomatous infection of skin, lymphatics, and other tissues in animals and man.

Morphology & Identification

The organisms are only rarely seen in pus and tissues from human infections but may appear as small, spindle-shaped, single, gram-positive budding cells. In cultures on Sabouraud's agar, cream-colored to black, folded, leathery colonies develop within 3–5 days. (The pigment formations of different strains of *S schenckii* are variable.) They consist of thin, septate, branching hyphae which carry clusters of pear-shaped conidia at the ends of lateral branches.

Antigenic Structure

Heat-killed saline suspensions of cultures (or carbohydrate fractions from them) give positive delayed skin tests in infected man or animals. A variety of antibodies is also produced.

Pathogenesis & Clinical Findings

The fungus is introduced into the skin of the extremities through trauma. A local lesion develops as a pustule, abscess, or ulcer, and the lymphatics leading from it become thickened and cord-like. Multiple subcutaneous nodules and abscesses occur along the

Figure 25–17. *Sporothrix (Sporotrichum) schenckii* in culture, showing clusters of conidia on conidiophores.

lymphatics. Usually there is little systemic illness associated with these lesions, but dissemination of the infection sometimes occurs, especially in debilitated patients. Rarely, primary infection in man occurs through the lung. A variety of animals (rats, dogs, mules, and horses) are found naturally infected.

Histologically, the lesions show both chronic inflammation and specific granulomas which undergo necrosis. In disseminated disease, complement-fixing antibodies rise.

Diagnostic Laboratory Tests

Specimens consist of pus or biopsy from lesions.

A. Microscopic Examination: In human lesions, the organism can rarely be seen, whereas the fusiform cells are common in infections of rats or mice.

B. Culture: On Sabouraud's agar, typical colonies and clusters of conidia are diagnostic. The organism will grow on most laboratory media and can be identified by immunofluorescence.

C. Serology: Immunodiffusion tests with sporothrix extracts reveal specific antibodies in infected patients.

Immunity

It is not definite whether immunity develops with infection.

Treatment

In the majority of cases the infection is self-limited although very chronic. Potassium iodide administered orally for weeks has a therapeutic effect in the cutaneous-lymphatic form. Amphotericin B intravenously is used in systemic involvement.

Epidemiology & Control

S schenckii occurs worldwide in nature on plants,

moss, thorns, and timber; in dust, and on infected animals. In the USA, the principal endemic area is the Mississippi Valley. Occupational exposure of gardeners, miners, and persons in contact with animals accounts for the majority of cases. Prevention of trauma in these occupations is effective, since the organism must be passively introduced into the skin to produce disease.

CHROMOBLASTOMYCOSIS

Chromoblastomycosis is a chronic, slowly progressive, granulomatous infection of skin and lymphatics caused by the fungi *Fonsecaea (Cladosporium) pedrosoi, F (Cladosporium) compactum, Phialophora verrucosa,* and others.

Morphology & Identification

In exudates and tissues, these fungi produce dark-brown septate bodies, 6–12 μm in diameter, which reproduce by splitting. On Sabouraud's glucose agar the following characteristics are noted:

A. *F pedrosoi:* Colonies are dark green to brown or black, with felt-like aerial mycelia. Conidia may be in branching chains, may surround the swollen ends of hyphae, or may be produced from flask-shaped conidiophores.

B. *F compactum:* Colonies are brittle, heaped-up, and black, with a coarse aerial mycelium. Spherical conidia are arranged in compact sporulating heads.

C. *P verrucosa:* Colonies are brown or black with a short, felt-like, gray aerial mycelium. Conidia are produced within the ends of flask-shaped conidiophores which are laterally attached to hyphae.

Pathogenesis & Clinical Findings

The fungus is introduced by trauma into the skin, usually of the lower extremities. Slowly, over a period of weeks or months, wart-like growths develop and extend gradually along the lymphatics. Cauliflower-like

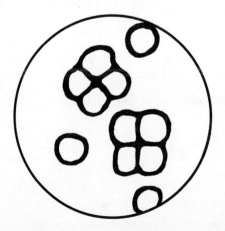

Figure 25–18. *Fonsecaea (Cladosporium) pedrosoi* in tissue.

nodules eventually cover part of the leg, and elephantiasis may result from fibrosis and obstruction of lymph channels. Dissemination to other parts of the body is very rare.

Histologically, the lesions are granulomas; within leukocytes or giant cells the dark-brown, round fungus bodies may be seen.

Diagnostic Laboratory Tests

Specimens consist of scrapings or biopsy from the lesions.

A. Microscopic Examination: Specimens are placed in a 10% potassium hydroxide solution and examined for the dark, round, splitting fungus bodies.

B. Culture: Culture should be made on Sabouraud's agar to observe the characteristic conidial structures and arrangements necessary for identification of organisms.

Treatment

Amphotericin B injected directly into the lesions results in improvement but does not eradicate the infection. Local removal is the only other feasible treatment.

Epidemiology

Chromoblastomycosis is worldwide but occurs mainly in the tropics. The fungi are saprophytic in nature, probably occurring on vegetation and in the soil. The disease occurs chiefly on the legs of barefooted farm laborers, presumably following traumatic introduction of the fungus. It is not communicable. Some animals have been found to be spontaneously infected. No control measures are known.

MADUROMYCOSIS

Maduromycosis is a slowly progressive infection of the subcutaneous tissue, usually of the foot; it is also called mycetoma and Madura foot. It can be caused by Nocardia and Streptomyces species, by *Monosporium apiospermum, Allescheria boydii,* and several filamentous fungi. It is principally a disease of the tropics and is particularly prevalent in India.

Morphology & Identification

Monosporium apiospermum is found in tissues or exudates as a yellowish granule, composed of septate hyphae with many chlamydospores around the periphery. Grayish-white, cottony colonies are formed on Sabouraud's agar at room temperature; they have single ovoid conidia at the ends of conidiophores. Other species may produce black granules composed of dark septate hyphae. Each species has its own characteristic colonial morphology.

Pathogenesis & Clinical Findings

After the traumatic introduction of one of the

causative fungi into the subcutaneous tissue of the foot, deep-seated nodules or abscesses form which increase in size and eventually drain, establishing chronic sinuses. The infection extends from the subcutaneous tissue to muscles and bones, causing deformity and loss of function.

Histologically, the lesions resemble actinomycosis, with prominent abscess formation, granulation tissue, necrotic foci, and fibrosis.

Diagnostic Laboratory Tests

Materials from sinuses or biopsy specimens should be examined for characteristic granules and should be cultured. Skin tests with a protein from *Nocardia brasiliensis* are positive in mycetoma patients, and precipitin tests in their sera can be performed with a polysaccharide from that organism.

Treatment

Antibiotics have been of no avail except to reduce secondary bacterial infection. Sulfonamides and sulfones have proved effective for some cases of nocardia and streptomyces infections.

Epidemiology & Control

The fungi producing maduromycosis occur free in nature, in the soil, or on vegetation. The disease is produced when they are introduced into tissues through trauma. Barefoot farm laborers are therefore most exposed. Wearing shoes is a reasonable control measure.

ASPERGILLOSIS

Aspergillus species are dimorphic fungi: in tissue, they grow as long filaments which branch dichotomously; in culture media (or on body surfaces), they form mycelia which support complex conidiophores. When growing on peanuts, aspergillus produces aflatoxins (see p 90).

Aspergillus fumigatus and other Aspergillus sp have become a frequent cause of systemic fungal infection in an altered host. Patients with leukemia or lymphoma, immunosuppressed persons (especially after organ transplants), and those receiving intensive corticosteroid therapy are particularly susceptible to aspergillosis. The portal of entry is the respiratory tract, and in most cases of aspergillosis pulmonary manifestations occur, predominantly necrotizing bronchopneumonia, hemorrhagic pulmonary infarction, or granulomas (aspergillomas). The fungus is best demonstrated in biopsies of lung tissue by the methenamine silver stain.

At other times, aspergillus grows as a "fungus ball" in sinuses, lung cavities, or bronchiectatic areas without actual tissue invasion. Patients with the latter manifestation have no immunologic response to the fungus; patients with invasive disease may exhibit precipitating antibodies in gel diffusion tests.

Since aspergillus is a ubiquitous organism, it sometimes grows as a saprophyte on body surfaces (eg, otitis externa) without tissue invasion or disease manifestations. When aspergillus is not invasive, antifungal treatment is not required but only management of the underlying condition. In systemic aspergillosis with tissue invasion and dissemination to various organs, treatment with amphotericin B (0.5–1.2 mg/kg/day) is usually attempted with marginal success. The same applies to the occasional postsurgical aspergillus endophthalmitis which usually leads to rapid loss of the eye.

PHYCOMYCOSIS

Saprophytic phycomycetes (eg, Mucor, Rhizopus) occasionally invade the tissues of hosts with compromised defenses. In persons suffering from diabetes mellitus with acidosis, extensive burns, tuberculosis, leukemia, lymphoma, or other chronic illnesses or persons who are given immunosuppressive drugs, Rhizopus sp, Mucor sp, and other phycomycetes may proliferate in the walls of blood vessels, producing thrombosis. This occurs commonly in the paranasal sinuses, lungs, and gastrointestinal tract and results in ischemic necrosis of surrounding tissue with an intense polymorphonuclear infiltrate.

The organisms are infrequently cultured during life but are seen in histologic preparations as long nonseptate hyphae in thrombosed blood vessels or sinuses, with surrounding leukocytic and giant cell response.

If diagnosed during life, intense treatment with surgical removal of infected tissue (eg, nephrectomy) and with systemic amphotericin B has occasionally resulted in remissions and possible cure.

HYPERSENSITIVITY TO FUNGI

Several types of pneumonitis (eg, farmer's lung, maple bark disease) are caused by hypersensitivity reactions to inhaled antigens of a variety of fungi. These are discussed in Chapter 13.

MYCOTOXINS

Many fungi produce poisonous substances, called mycotoxins, which can cause acute or chronic damage in animals or man. Acute poisoning may occur, such as in acute mushroom poisoning caused by the ingestion of some types of mushrooms. Chronic damage to the liver or bone marrow may be produced, and neoplasms may be induced in animals (eg, aflatoxin from *Aspergillus flavus)*. Derivatives of fungal products may cause profound mental derangement (eg, lysergic acid diethylamide).

• • •

General References

Bach MC & others: Fungal and nocardial infections in renal-transplant patients. Lancet 1:180, 1973.

Bennett JE: Chemotherapy of systemic mycoses. (2 parts.) N Engl J Med 290:30, 320, 1974.

Burton JR & others: Aspergillosis in renal transplant patients. Ann Intern Med 77:383, 1972.

Campbell CC: Use and interpretation of serologic and skin tests in the respiratory mycoses. Dis Chest 54:305, 1968.

Conant NF & others: *Manual of Clinical Mycology,* 3rd ed. Saunders, 1971.

Gaines JD, Remington JS: Disseminated candidiasis in surgical patients. Surgery 72:730, 1972.

Gehlbach SH & others: Coccidioidomycosis: An occupational disease in cotton mill workers. Arch Intern Med 131:254, 1973.

Kammer RB, Utz JP: Aspergillus species endocarditis: The new face of a not so rare disease. Am J Med 56:506, 1974.

Lewis JL, Rabinovich S: The wide spectrum of cryptococcal infections. Am J Med 53:315, 1972.

Louria DB: Deep-seated mycotic infections: Allergy to fungi and mycotoxins. N Engl J Med 277:1065, 1967.

Palmer DL & others: Diagnostic and therapeutic considerations in *Nocardia asteroides* infection. Medicine 53:391, 1974.

Pankey GA, Daloviso JR: Fungemia caused by *Torulopsis glabrata.* Medicine 52:395, 1973.

Peeters F & others: Observations on candidal vaginitis. Am J Obstet Gynecol 112:80, 1972.

Restrepo A, Moncada LH: Characterization of the precipitin bands detected in the immunodiffusion test for paracoccidioidomycosis. Appl Microbiol 28:138, 1974.

Satir AA & others: Systemic phycomycosis. Br Med J 1:440, 1971.

Vanek J, Schwarz J: The gamut of histoplasmosis. Am J Med 50:89, 1971.

Werner SB & others: Epidemic of coccidioidomycosis among archeology students. N Engl J Med 286:507, 1972.

Young LS & others: *Nocardia asteroides* infection complicating neoplastic disease. Am J Med 50:356, 1971.

Young RC & others: Fungemia with compromised host resistance: A study of 70 cases. Ann Intern Med 80:605, 1974.

26...
Principles of Diagnostic Medical Microbiology

Diagnostic medical microbiology is concerned (1) with the etiologic diagnosis of infectious disease by means of the isolation and identification of infectious agents and the demonstration of immunologic responses (antibody, skin reactivity) in the patient; and (2) with the rational selection of antimicrobial therapy on the basis of laboratory tests.

In the field of infectious diseases, the results of laboratory tests depend largely on the quality of the specimen, the timing of its collection and the care with which it is collected, and the technical proficiency and experience of the laboratory personnel. Although any general physician should be competent to perform a few simple, crucial microbiologic tests—make and stain a smear, examine it microscopically, and streak a culture plate—the technical details of the more involved procedures are usually left to the bacteriologist or virologist and the technicians on his staff. Any physician who deals with infectious processes must know when and how to take a specimen, what laboratory examinations to request, and how to interpret the results.

COMMUNICATION BETWEEN PHYSICIAN & LABORATORY

When a physician sends a blood specimen to the laboratory and requests a chemical determination, the laboratory has no alternative but to employ a single chemical procedure and report the result to the physician. While that value may be reported higher or lower depending upon variations in the specimen, in the skill and experience of the technician, or in the equipment at hand in the laboratory, the physician generally accepts that value and takes it into account in making his clinical diagnosis. Little would be gained, in this situation, by further communication between the physician and the laboratory.

In microbiologic laboratory diagnosis the situation is different. No one method is available which will permit the isolation of all possible pathogenic organisms or differentiate them from nonpathogenic ones. Before the laboratory personnel can select the one technic best suited to the isolation of one or another

organism, the physician must inform the laboratory of his tentative clinical diagnosis and of the type of infection he suspects. This forces the clinician to reason more closely than if he merely suspects "infection" and defers all attempts at etiologic diagnosis until the laboratory results are returned. Clinical information from the physician can often aid the laboratory in selecting the best methods available for the identification of an etiologic agent.

In contrast with chemical determinations, microbiologic laboratory procedures are often slow, requiring a series of sequential steps before the answer is reached. Many pathogenic microorganisms grow slowly, and days or even weeks may elapse before their identification. However, it is almost never possible to defer treatment until this laborious process is complete. It is therefore essential that the physician obtain proper specimens, inform the laboratory of his tentative clinical diagnosis, and then begin appropriate treatment with or without drugs aimed at the organism he supposes is responsible for the patient's illness. As the laboratory begins to derive information of clinical significance, it can feed it back to the physician so that he may reevaluate his diagnosis, along with the clinical course of the patient, and perhaps make changes in the therapeutic program. This "feedback" information will consist of preliminary reports of the results of individual steps in the isolation and identification of the etiologic agent.

SPECIMENS

The results of many diagnostic tests in infectious diseases depend largely upon the selection, timing, and method of collection of specimens. These factors are often more crucial for microbiologic specimens than for those designed to yield chemical data. Microbial agents grow and die, are susceptible to many chemicals, and can be found at different anatomic sites and in different body fluids and tissues during the natural history of most infectious disorders. In general, the successful isolation of an infectious agent carries much more diagnostic weight in the formulation of a diagnosis than failure to do so. Therefore, the specimen must be obtained from the site most likely to yield the infectious agent at that particular stage of illness and must be handled in such a way as to favor survival and growth of the agent. For each type of specimen, suggestions for optimal handling are given in the following paragraphs.

Recovery of an infectious agent is most significant if the agent is isolated from a site normally devoid of microorganisms. Any type of microorganism cultured from blood, cerebrospinal fluid, or joint fluid or from the pleural cavity is a significant diagnostic finding. Conversely, many parts of the body have a normal microbial flora which may be altered by endogenous or exogenous influences. The recovery of potentially pathogenic microorganisms from the respiratory, gastrointestinal, or genitourinary tracts, from wounds, or from the skin must be considered in the context of the normal flora of each particular site. The situation is often further complicated by the presence of mixtures of different microorganisms each of which may or may not participate in a disease process of that particular tissue. Correlation of bacteriologic information with medical experience is then required to arrive at meaningful interpretation of results.

A few general rules apply to all specimens:

(1) A sufficient quantity of specimen must be provided to permit thorough study.

(2) The sample should be representative of the infectious process (eg, sputum, not saliva; pus from the underlying lesion, not from its sinus tract; a swab from the depth of the wound, not from its surface).

(3) Care must be taken to avoid contamination of the specimen by using only sterile equipment and aseptic precautions.

(4) The specimen must be taken to the laboratory and examined promptly.

(5) Meaningful specimens must be secured before antimicrobial drugs are administered. If antimicrobial drugs are given before specimens are taken for microbiologic study, drug therapy may have to be stopped and repeat specimens obtained several days later.

The above comments apply particularly to specimens intended for the isolation of bacterial or fungal agents. The isolation of viruses, rickettsiae, or chlamydiae is usually performed only in specialized laboratories. Specimens are often shipped to such laboratories in well-stoppered containers packed in dry ice. All specimens must be accurately labeled and accompanied by adequate instructions, a clearly worded statement of the information desired, and background information.

The type of specimen to be examined is determined by the presenting clinical picture. If symptoms or signs point to involvement of one organ system, specimens are obtained from that source. In the absence of localizing signs or symptoms, repeated blood samples for culturing are taken first. Specimens from other sites are then considered in sequence, depending in part upon the likelihood of involvement of a given organ system in a given patient and in part upon the ease of obtaining the specimen.

SELECTION OF LABORATORY INVESTIGATIONS

Diagnostic tests in infectious diseases fall into 4 classes:

(1) The demonstration of an infectious agent (bacterial, mycotic, viral, protozoal, or helminthic) in specimens obtained from the patient.

(2) The demonstration of a meaningful antibody response in the patient. This frequently involves proof of a rise in specific antibody titer, and therefore requires 2 serum specimens usually obtained at an interval of 10–20 days. In some instances, a longer interval between collections of specimens may be required.

(3) The demonstration of meaningful skin reactivity, as evidence of hypersensitivity to antigens of a particular infectious agent.

(4) The demonstration of deviations in a variety of clinical laboratory determinations which nonspecifically suggest or support a suspicion of infectious diseases.

In the following paragraphs, some important applications of these principal classes of tests will be described.

THE DEMONSTRATION OF AN INFECTIOUS AGENT

Laboratory examinations usually include microscopic study of fresh unstained and stained materials and preparation of cultures under environmental conditions which are suitable for growth of a wide variety of microorganisms, including the type of organism most suspect on clinical grounds. If a microorganism is seen or isolated, the physician is notified of its preliminary identification. Complete identification may then be pursued by bacteriologic, mycologic, or other technics. Isolated microorganisms may be tested for susceptibility to antimicrobial drugs or combinations of drugs. In certain types of diseases, assay of antibacterial activity in the patient's serum or urine during treatment may be more informative than drug susceptibility tests (see Chapter 10 and p 287). In all cases where significant pathogenic microorganisms are isolated before treatment, follow-up examinations during and after treatment are mandatory.

Blood

In the febrile ill patient, with or without localizing signs or symptoms, blood culture is the most useful and most frequently performed test for the detection of systemic infection due to bacteria. Proof of bacteremia is also essential in all persons suspected of having bacterial endocarditis even when they do not appear acutely or severely ill. In addition to its diagnostic significance, recovery of an infectious agent from the blood provides invaluable aid in guiding antimicrobial therapy. Every effort should therefore be made to isolate the etiologic organism in bacteremia.

In healthy persons, properly obtained blood cultures remain sterile. Although microorganisms from the normal respiratory and gastrointestinal flora enter the blood occasionally, they are rapidly removed by the reticuloendothelial system. These transients rarely affect the interpretation of blood culture results. If a blood culture yields microorganisms, this fact is of great clinical significance provided that technical error can be excluded. Proper technic in performing the procedure is therefore all-important.

Tissues, tissue fluids, or reducing substances must be used in such a way that the bottom part of the blood culture bottle will provide sufficiently low oxygen tension to permit growth of anaerobes while the top part permits growth of aerobes.

The following rules, rigidly applied, yield reliable results:

(1) Use only sterile equipment and strict aseptic technic.

(2) Apply a tourniquet and locate a fixed vein by touch to minimize probing after insertion of the needle.

(3) Prepare the skin by applying 2% tincture of iodine in widening circles, beginning with the site of proposed skin puncture. Remove iodine with 70% alcohol. Do not touch the skin with the fingers after it has been prepared.

(4) Perform venipuncture and withdraw 12–15 ml blood.

(5) Add 1–2 ml of blood to a sterile tube containing 1 ml of 1.8% sodium citrate and mix well. Add the remainder of the blood to a flask containing 50–100 ml of a rich nutrient medium, which will permit the growth of fastidious organisms.

(6) Take the specimens to the laboratory promptly.

At the laboratory, a measured quantity of citrated blood is added to melted agar and poured into plates for quantitative cultures. The plates and the blood culture bottles are incubated at 37° C for up to 2 weeks. They are examined for bacterial growth every 2–3 days by inspection, smears, and subcultures. Colonies appearing on the poured plates are counted to give the number of bacteria per ml of blood in the original specimen. Anaerobic cultures should also be obtained.

In general, there is no significant advantage in arterial over the usual venous blood specimens.

If microorganisms grow from blood cultures, it then becomes necessary to determine their significance by ruling out technical error. Although it is not possible to state conclusively that any given positive blood culture does not reflect bacteremia, the following criteria may be helpful in differentiating "true" positives from contaminated specimens:

(1) Growth of the same type of organism in repeated cultures: bacteremia.

(2) Growth of large numbers of a single type of organism in quantitative cultures: bacteremia.

(3) Small numbers of several different organisms: suggestive of contamination.

(4) Common skin flora (white staphylococci [*Staphylococcus epidermidis; S albus*], diphtheroids [Propionibacterium]) occurring in only one of several cultures: suggestive of contamination. (The presence of such organisms in more than one culture, or in bone marrow culture in addition to blood culture, enhances the likelihood of clinically significant bacteremia.)

(5) "Expected" organisms (eg, viridans streptococci or enterococci) in suspected endocarditis are more apt to be etiologically significant than organisms commonly found as contaminants.

The number of blood specimens for cultures that should be drawn, and over what period, depends upon the severity of the clinical illness. In hyperacute sepsis, only 2 or 3 blood cultures can be taken in as many hours before antimicrobial therapy, based on the clinician's "best guess" regarding etiology, is begun. On the other hand, with a chronically ill patient who has suspected endocarditis, one or 2 cultures may be taken daily for 3–5 days before drugs are administered. In patients who eventually yield positive blood cultures, growth is usually obtained in the first few cultures taken, although there may be much delay until growth becomes evident. About 90–95% of positive blood cultures in proved cases of bacterial endocarditis are encountered among the first 5 cultures taken. Consequently, it is reasonable to begin treatment after 5–6 specimens have been obtained.

Virtually every microorganism other than viruses, rickettsiae, and chlamydiae has been grown in blood culture at some time. The following are most commonly found: Viridans streptococci, *Streptococcus faecalis,* staphylococci (*S aureus* and others); gram-negative enteric bacteria, including *Escherichia coli, Enterobacter aerogenes,* and *Klebsiella pneumoniae;* Proteus species, Pseudomonas species, pneumococci, meningococci, gonococci, bacteroides, salmonellae, brucellae, pasteurellae, *Haemophilus influenzae,* vibrios, leptospirae, candida, and others.

In most types of bacteremia listed above, examination of direct blood smears contributes little. However, in some spirochetal infections (eg, leptospirosis, relapsing fever) and parasitic infections (eg, malaria, trypanosomiasis), the etiologic organism can be detected in stained blood films. In some infections (eg, rickettsioses, leptospirosis, spirillosis, psittacosis), inoculation of blood into experimental animals may give positive results more readily than culture.

Urine

At present, bacteriologic examination of the urine is done mainly when signs or symptoms point to urinary tract infection, renal insufficiency, or hypertension. It should always be done in persons with suspected systemic infection or fever of unknown origin. It may some day become part of the routine periodic health examination.

Urine secreted in the kidney is sterile unless the kidney is infected. Uncontaminated bladder urine is also normally sterile. The urethra, however, contains a normal flora, so that normal voided urine contains small numbers of bacteria. Because it is necessary to distinguish contaminating from etiologically important organisms, only *quantitative* urine examination can yield meaningful results.

The following steps are essential in proper urine examination:

A. Proper Collection of Specimen: Because of the danger of introducing microorganisms into the bladder, catheterization is to be avoided whenever possible. Satisfactory specimens from males can usually be obtained by cleansing the meatus with soap and water and collecting midstream urine in a sterile container. Satisfactory midstream specimens from females can sometimes be obtained after cleansing the vulva and spreading the labia, but catheterization is sometimes unavoidable. Separate specimens from the right and left kidneys and ureters can be obtained by the urologist at cystoscopy using a catheter. When an indwelling catheter and closed collection system are in place, urine is best obtained by sterile aspiration of the catheter with needle and syringe.

For most types of examinations, 0.5 ml of ureteral urine or 5 ml of voided urine is sufficient. Urine specimens must be delivered to the laboratory and examined within 1 hour, or refrigerated not longer than overnight. At room or body temperature, many types of microorganisms multiply rapidly in urine. To resolve diagnostic problems, urine can be aspirated directly from the full bladder through suprapubic puncture of the abdominal wall.

B. Microscopic Examination: A great deal can be learned from the simple microscopic examination of urine. A drop of fresh uncentrifuged urine placed on a slide, covered with a coverglass, and examined with restricted light intensity under the high-dry objective of an ordinary clinical microscope reveals not only leukocytes and epithelial cells, but also bacteria if more than 10^4-10^5 organisms per ml are present. This procedure informs the physician promptly that significant numbers of organisms are present and also indicates whether cocci (often *Streptococcus faecalis*) or motile rods (often gram-negative coliform organisms) are causing the infection. Similar semiquantitative observations can be made with dried smears of urine stained with methylene blue or Gram's stain.

Bacteria are not sedimented by short (3–5 minutes) centrifugation at the usual speeds of the clinical centrifuge. However, brief centrifugation does readily sediment pus cells which may carry along bacteria and thus may help in rapid microscopic diagnosis of infection. The presence of other formed elements in the sediment—or the presence of proteinuria—is of little direct aid in the specific identification of active urinary tract infection. Pus cells may be present without bacteria and, conversely, bacteriuria may be present without pyuria. The presence of many squamous epithelial cells, lactobacilli, or mixed flora on culture suggests improper urine collection.

C. Urine Cultures: As explained above, culture of the urine, to be meaningful, must be performed quantitatively. Properly collected urine is cultured in measured amounts on solid media, and the number of colonies appearing after incubation is counted to indicate the number of bacteria per ml. The usual procedure is to spread 0.1 ml of undiluted urine, 0.1 ml of 1:100 dilution, and 0.1 ml of 1:10,000 dilution on blood agar plates or to incorporate these amounts into agar pour plates for quantitative culture. If desired, a loopful of urine can be cultured anaerobically and inoculated onto a blood agar plate for direct disk sensitivity tests. All media are incubated overnight at 37° C; colonies are then counted and the number of bacteria per ml of urine is estimated. Several simplified methods are available to estimate the number of bacteria in urine (Dip-Slide; spoon with agar, etc).

In active pyelonephritis, the number of bacteria in urine collected by ureteral catheter is relatively low. While accumulating in the bladder, bacteria multiply rapidly and soon reach numbers in excess of 10^5/ml, far more than could occur as a result of contamination by urethral or skin flora or from the air. Therefore, it is generally agreed that if more than 100,000 organisms per ml are cultivated from a properly collected and properly examined urine specimen, this constitutes strong evidence of active urinary tract infection. The presence of more than 10^5 bacteria of the same type per milliliter in 2 consecutive specimens establishes a diagnosis of active infection of the urinary tract with 95% certainty. If fewer bacteria are cultivated, repeated examination of urine is indicated to establish the presence of infection.

If fewer than 10,000 colonies per ml are present (especially if, as is often the case, there are several types), this suggests that the organisms come from normal flora or are contaminants. Intermediate counts (eg, 10,000–100,000 colonies per ml) do not permit definitive interpretation from a single specimen and must be repeated with a fresh specimen. Such counts obtained repeatedly suggest persistent, chronic, or suppressed infection. If found only in a single specimen, they suggest contamination. If cultures are negative but clinical signs of urinary tract infection are present, tuberculosis, anaerobic infection, ureteral obstruction, or "abacterial bladder syndrome" must be considered.

Bacteria most commonly found in urinary tract infections are coliforms, other gram-negative rods, and enterococci.

Cerebrospinal Fluid (CSF)

The early, rapid, and precise diagnosis of meningitis ranks high among medical emergencies. It depends upon maintaining a high index of suspicion; securing adequate specimens properly; and examining the specimens promptly. Because the risk of death or irreversible tissue damage is great unless treatment is started immediately, there is rarely a second chance to obtain pretreatment specimens—which are essential for specific etiologic diagnosis and optimal management.

The most urgent diagnostic issue is the differentiation of acute purulent bacterial meningitis from "aseptic" and granulomatous meningitis. The immediate decision is usually based on the results of cell count and glucose content of CSF (see Table 26–1) and of microscopic search for microorganisms. It is subsequently modified by the results of culture, CSF protein content, serologic tests, and other laboratory procedures. Table 26–1 illustrates some typical findings. In evaluating the results of CSF glucose determinations, the simultaneous blood glucose level must be considered. In some CNS neoplasms, the CSF glucose is low.

A. Specimens: As soon as infection of the CNS is suspected, blood cultures are taken and CSF is secured. Lumbar puncture is performed with strict aseptic technic, taking care not to risk compression of the medulla by too rapid withdrawal of fluid when the intracranial pressure is markedly elevated. CSF is usually collected in 3 or 4 portions (2–5 ml each) in sterile tubes. This permits the most convenient and most reliable examination for the several different values which determine the physician's course of action.

B. Microscopic Examination: Smears are made from fresh uncentrifuged CSF which appears cloudy; otherwise from the sediment of centrifuged CSF. Smears are stained with Gram's stain and occasionally with Ziehl-Neelsen stain. Ziehl-Neelsen stain is particularly indicated if a pellicle forms on the surface of the fluid, trapping acid-fast organisms. Study of stained smears under the oil immersion objective may reveal intracellular gram-negative diplococci (meningococci),

intra- and extracellular lancet-shaped gram-positive diplococci (pneumococci), or small gram-negative rods (*Haemophilus influenzae* or coliform organisms). In *H influenzae* meningitis, layering of CSF on specific type b antiserum may yield a precipitate at the interface, providing an etiologic diagnosis promptly even when no organisms are seen. Cryptococci are organisms best seen in India ink preparations. Common bacterial causes of meningitis can be rapidly identified by specific immunofluorescence. Initial treatment is usually aimed at the type of organism seen microscopically.

C. Culture: The culture methods used must be those which will favor the growth of microorganisms most commonly encountered in meningitis. Virus isolation can be attempted in aseptic meningitis or meningoencephalitis. It is often successful in infections caused by mumps and echo- or coxsackieviruses, but not usually so in the arthropod-borne encephalitides, herpes simplex encephalitis, or lymphocytic choriomeningitis infections.

D. Follow-Up Examination of CSF: The return of CSF glucose and CSF cell count toward normal levels is the most reliable evidence of adequate initial therapy.

Respiratory Secretions

Symptoms or signs often point to involvement of a particular part of the respiratory tract, and specimens are chosen accordingly. In interpreting the laboratory results it is necessary to consider the normal microbial flora of the area from which the specimen was collected.

Table 26–1. Cerebrospinal fluid findings.

Diagnosis	Some Etiologic Microorganisms	Cells/ cu mm	Protein (mg/100 ml)	Glucose (mg/100 ml)	Remarks
Normal	. . .	0–5 lymphocytes	10–45	50–85	Glucose 20 mg/ 100 ml lower than blood level
Acute purulent meningitis (bacterial)	Meningococci, pneumococci, *Haemophilus influenzae,* streptococci, staphylococci, coliform organisms, etc.	200–20,000 or more PMNs	Increased: 50–1000 or more	Low: 0–45	Organisms found in smear or culture
Viral meningo-encephalitis ("aseptic")	Viruses of mumps, herpes simplex, lymphocytic choriomeningitis, poliomyelitis, coxsackievirus, echovirus, arboviruses.	100–1000 or more, mostly lymphocytes	Normal or increased	Normal	Virus isolation or titer rise in paired serum specimen
Granulomatous (tuberculous or fungal) meningitis	*Mycobacterium tuberculosis,* cryptococcus, coccidioides, histoplasma, etc.	10–1000 or more, mostly lymphocytes	Increased: 45–500 or more	Low: 0–45	Organisms found in smear or culture
Syphilitic or leptospiral meningitis	*Treponema pallidum,* Leptospira species.	25–2000 or more, mostly lymphocytes	Increased: 45–400 or more	15–75	Serologic tests positive
"Neighborhood reaction" (eg, epidural or brain abscess, thrombosis)		Increased	Normal or increased	Normal	Cultures negative

A. Specimens:

1. Throat—Most "sore throats" are due to viral infection. Only 5–10% of such complaints in adults and 15–20% in children are associated with bacterial infections. The finding of a follicular yellowish exudate or a grayish membrane must arouse the suspicion of hemolytic streptococcal, diphtherial, fusospirochetal (Vincent's), or candidal infection; but such signs may also be present in infectious mononucleosis, adenovirus, and other virus infections.

Throat swabs must be taken from each tonsillar area before a swab is taken from the posterior pharyngeal wall. The normal throat flora includes an abundance of viridans streptococci, neisseriae, diphtheroids, staphylococci, small gram-negative rods, and many other organisms. Microscopic examination of smears from throat swabs is of no value in streptococcal infections because all throats harbor a predominance of streptococci, but it can rapidly identify fusospirochetal disease and may suggest diphtheria. By immunofluorescence, group A streptococci can sometimes be identified rapidly as the predominant organism.

Cultures of throat swabs are most reliable if inoculated promptly after collection, although special swabs are available which permit survival of important pathogens for days. When streaking culture plates (blood agar is used), it is essential to spread a small inoculum thoroughly and avoid overgrowth by normal flora. This can be done readily by touching the throat swab to one small area of the plate and using a second sterile applicator (or sterile bacteriologic loop) to streak the plate from that area. Incubation at 37° C must often be continued for 48 hours until hemolytic colonies can be clearly identified.

Reports on throat cultures should state the types of prevalent organisms. If potential pathogens (eg, beta-hemolytic streptococci) are cultured, their approximate number is important. A few colonies of beta-hemolytic streptococci may well represent only "transients" in the throat without pathogenic meaning. In "strep throat," the group A streptococci prevail. On a blood plate bearing massive growth, the "bacitracin 0.2 unit disk" method most easily establishes the group A nature of the organisms.

2. Nasopharynx—Specimens from the nasopharynx are studied infrequently because they must be obtained by special technics. (See Viral Diagnosis, below.)

3. Middle ear—Specimens are rarely obtained because puncture of the drum is necessary. In acute otitis media, 30–50% of aspirated fluids are bacteriologically sterile. The most frequently isolated bacteria are pneumococci, *Haemophilus influenzae,* and hemolytic streptococci.

4. Sputum—Bronchial and pulmonary secretions or exudates are usually studied by examining sputum. The most misleading aspect of sputum examination is the almost inevitable contamination with saliva and mouth flora. Thus, finding candida or *Staphylococcus aureus* in the sputum of a patient with pneumonitis has no etiologic significance unless supported by the clinical picture. Meaningful sputum specimens should be expectorated in the physician's presence from the lower respiratory tract and should be grossly distinct from saliva. The presence of many squamous epithelial cells suggests heavy contamination with saliva. Sputum may be induced by inhalation of heated hypertonic saline aerosol for several minutes. Specimens can sometimes be obtained by catheter aspiration, bronchoscopy, or bronchial brushing. In pneumonia accompanied by pleural fluid, examination of the latter may yield the etiologic organisms more reliably than sputum. Most bacterial pneumonias are caused by pneumococci. In suspected tuberculosis or fungal infection, gastric washings (swallowed sputum) may yield organisms when expectorated material fails to do so. Semi-quantitative cultures are helpful.

5. Transtracheal aspiration—The flora in such specimens often reflects accurately the events in the lower respiratory tract. Lung puncture or open biopsy of lung tissue may be necessary (eg, in the diagnosis of pneumocystis pneumonia).

B. Microscopic Examination: Smears of purulent flecks or granules from sputum stained by Gram's stain or by acid-fast methods may reveal etiologic organisms. Some mycotic organisms (eg, actinomyces) are best seen in unstained wet preparations. A direct "quellung" test for pneumococci with polyvalent serum can be performed on sputum.

C. Cultures: The media used must be suitable for the growth of bacteria (eg, pneumococci, klebsiella), fungi (eg, *Coccidioides immitis*), anaerobes (eg, bacteroides), mycobacteria (eg, *Mycobacterium tuberculosis*), mycoplasma, and others. The relative prevalence of different organisms in the specimen must be estimated. Only a finding of one predominant organism or the simultaneous isolation of an organism from both sputum and blood can clearly establish its role in a pneumonic or suppurative process.

D. Viral Diagnosis: Most respiratory tract infections are caused by viruses. Throat swabs, throat washings, and sputum are fertile sources of virus if specialized laboratory facilities for virus isolation are available. Throat swabs immersed in broth, garglings with broth, or sputum must be brought to the virus laboratory promptly or kept frozen until they are inoculated into cell cultures, embryonated eggs, or animals. To support the possible etiologic role of viral agents, a rise in specific antibody titer must be demonstrated. Serum specimens are obtained aseptically as early as possible in the disease and again 2–3 weeks later. The first serum specimen is stored in the refrigerator until the second specimen has been secured. Both serum samples are then submitted to the virus laboratory—with an adequate clinical description—for specific serologic diagnosis.

Gastrointestinal Tract Specimens

Acute symptoms referable to the gastrointestinal tract—particularly nausea, vomiting, and diarrhea—are commonly attributed to infection. In reality most such attacks are caused by food intolerance, intoxication, neurogenic impulses, or systemic illnesses. This is an important consideration if one is to avoid the error of administering antimicrobial drugs to everyone who has acute gastrointestinal symptoms. The objectives of management in such patients should be to restore water and electrolyte balance, restrict oral intake, and establish an etiologic diagnosis. The diagnosis must often be based on individual and community history.

Most cases of acute infectious diarrheas are due to viruses. On the other hand, many viruses (eg, adenoviruses, enteroviruses) can multiply in the gut without causing gastrointestinal symptoms. Similarly, some enteric bacterial pathogens may establish persistent residence in the gut following an acute infection. Thus, it is often difficult to assign significance to a microbial or viral agent cultured from the stool, especially in subacute or chronic illness.

These considerations should not discourage the physician from attempting laboratory isolation of enteric organisms but should warn him of some common difficulties in interpreting the results.

The lower bowel has an exceedingly high normal bacterial flora. The most prevalent organisms are anaerobes (bacteroides, lactobacilli, clostridia, and streptococci), coliform gram-negative rods, and *Streptococcus faecalis.* Any attempt to recover pathogenic bacteria from feces involves their separation from the normal flora, usually through the use of differential selective media and enrichment cultures. The most prominent bacterial pathogens are salmonellae, shigellae, vibrios, toxigenic *Escherichia coli,* and "paracolon bacteria" (see Chapter 18).

A. Specimens: Feces and rectal swabs are the most readily available specimens. Bile obtained by duodenal drainage may reveal infection of the biliary tract. The presence of blood, mucus, or helminths must be noted on gross inspection of the specimen. Special technics must be used in searching for ova and parasites. Stained smears may reveal a prevalence of certain abnormal organisms, eg, candida or staphylococci, but cannot differentiate enteric bacterial pathogens from normal flora.

B. Culture: Specimens are suspended in broth and cultured on ordinary as well as selective differential media (eg, MacConkey's, EMB agar) to permit separation of nonlactose-fermenting organisms from coliform bacteria. If salmonella infection (typhoid fever or paratyphoid fever) is suspected, the specimen is also placed in an enrichment medium (eg, selenite F broth) for 18 hours before plating. Identification of bacterial colonies proceeds by standard bacteriologic examination, and blood is drawn for serologic diagnosis. The agglutination of bacteria from suspected colonies by pooled specific antiserum is often the fastest way to establish the presence of salmonellae or shigellae in the intestinal tract. Elevation of the specific serum antibody titer often supports the diagnosis of salmonella infection.

Gastric washings represent swallowed sputum and may be cultured for tubercle bacilli and other mycobacteria on special media (eg, Dubos' medium). For virus isolation, frozen fecal specimens are submitted to special laboratories, accompanied by paired serum specimens.

Intestinal parasites and their ova are discovered by repeated microscopic study of fresh fecal specimens subjected to specialized handling in the laboratory. (See Appendix.)

Puncture Fluids

Exudates which have collected in the pleural, peritoneal, or synovial spaces must be aspirated with the most meticulous aseptic technic to avoid superinfection. If the material is frankly purulent, smears and cultures are made directly. If the fluid is clear, it should be centrifuged at high speed for 10 minutes and the sediment used for stained smears and cultures. The culture method used must be suitable for the growth of organisms suspected on clinical grounds—eg, mycobacteria, anaerobic organisms, neisseriae—as well as the commonly encountered pyogenic bacteria.

Although direct tests for etiologic microorganisms yield the most important answers, indirect supportive evidence of infection is also helpful. These include tests on oxalated puncture fluids. The following results are suggestive of infection: specific gravity over 1.018; protein content over 3 gm/100 ml, often resulting in clotting; and cell counts over 500–1000/cu mm. Polymorphonuclear leukocytes predominate in acute untreated pyogenic infections; lymphocytes or monocytes predominate in chronic infections. Transudates resulting from neoplastic growth may grossly resemble infectious exudates in appearing bloody or purulent and in clotting on standing. Cytologic study of smears or of sections of centrifuged cells may prove the neoplastic nature of the process.

Genital Lesions

Prominent among the infections associated with local lesions of the external genitalia, discharge, and regional adenopathy are syphilis, gonorrhea, chancroid, lymphogranuloma venereum, granuloma inguinale, and herpes simplex. Each has a characteristic natural history and evolution of lesions, but one can mimic another. The laboratory diagnosis of most of these infections is covered elsewhere in the text. A few diagnostic tests are listed below.

A. Gonorrhea: Urethral or cervical exudate shows intracellular gram-negative diplococci in stained smear. Culture of freshly collected pus yields *Neisseria gonorrhoeae.* Serologic tests are not helpful.

B. Syphilis: Darkfield or immunofluorescence examination of tissue fluid expressed from the base of the chancre may reveal typical *Treponema pallidum.* Serologic tests for syphilis (STS) become positive 3–6 weeks after infection. A positive immunofluorescence treponemal antibody (FTA-ABS) test (see Chapter 20) proves syphilitic infection.

C. Chancroid: Smears and cultures from a suppurating ulcer usually show a mixed bacterial flora, including gram-negative rods in chains. Serologic tests are rarely done. The Ducrey skin test (*Haemophilus* *ducreyi* suspension) usually is positive within 3–5 weeks after infection. A positive skin test, however, cannot distinguish between old and recent infection.

D. Lymphogranuloma Venereum (LGV): While it is possible to grow the chlamydia (see Chapter 22) by inoculating pus from suppurating lymph nodes into embryonated eggs or cell cultures, the procedure is infrequently tried. Serologic tests (usually complement fixation) can demonstrate a diagnostic rise in antibody titer of paired sera obtained 2 weeks apart. The Frei test is often employed to support the clinical diagnosis. This skin test may become positive within 2–3 weeks after infection and remain positive for life, but recently the test has been negative in some proved LGV infections. The skin test indicates reactivity to a group-specific antigen. Thus, past infection with psittacosis or trachoma may give rise to a positive Frei test as readily as past infection with lymphogranuloma venereum.

E. Other Chlamydial Infections (TRIC Agent, Inclusion Conjunctivitis): This infection usually manifests itself as an acute conjunctivitis of the newborn or as a venereal disease and eye infection of adults. Immunofluorescence or Giemsa-stained smears of scrapings from the eye, the cervix, or the male urethra may reveal typical crescent-shaped inclusion bodies in epithelial cells (see Chapter 22). Culture in treated cells may permit isolation of chlamydiae. Fluorescent antibody tests are available.

F. Granuloma Inguinale: The etiologic agent of this hard granulomatous proliferating lesion *(Calymmatobacterium [Donovania] granulomatis)* can be grown in complex bacteriologic media, but this is rarely attempted in practice. Histologic demonstration of intracellular "Donovan bodies" in biopsied material most frequently supports the clinical impression. Serologic tests are not helpful.

G. Herpes Progenitalis: Primary or recurrent herpetic vesicles, evolving to ulcers and crusts and resembling the common "cold sores" on lips or skin, may occur on the genitalia. A positive diagnosis depends upon finding typical multinucleated giant cells or positive immunofluorescence in scrapings from the ulcer base, or isolation and identification of herpes simplex virus from the aspirated contents of the vesicle.

H. *Trichomonas vaginalis* **Vaginitis or Urethritis:** Typical organisms can be seen or cultured from genital discharges.

Wounds, Tissue Biopsies, Bone & Joint Infections, Abscesses

Microscopic study of smears and cultures of specimens from wounds or abscesses may often give early and important indications of the nature of the infecting organism and thus help in the choice of antimicrobial drugs. Specimens from diagnostic tissue biopsies should be submitted to bacteriologic as well as histologic examination. They are kept away from fixatives and disinfectants, minced and finely ground, and cultured by a variety of methods.

In closed undrained abscesses, the pus frequently contains only one organism as etiologic agent—most commonly staphylococci, streptococci, anaerobes, or coliforms. The same is true in acute osteomyelitis, where the organisms can often be cultured from the blood before the local lesion has become chronic. However, in open wounds, a multitude of microorganisms are frequently encountered, which makes it difficult to decide which are significant. When deep suppurating lesions drain onto exterior surfaces through a sinus or fistula, the flora of the surface drainage must not be mistaken for that of the deep lesion.

Only with reservations can organisms obtained from sinus tracts be used to guide therapy. Bacteriologic study of pus from closed or deep lesions must always include anaerobic methods. Anaerobic bacteria (bacteroides, streptococci) sometimes play an essential etiologic role, whereas aerobes may represent surface contaminants. The typical wound infections due to clostridia are readily suspected in gas gangrene. Pseudomonas in wounds gives rise to blue-green pus.

The methods employed must be suitable for the semiquantitative recovery of common bacteria and also for specialized microorganisms such as anaerobes, mycobacteria, and fungi. Eroded skin and mucous membranes are frequently the sites of yeast or fungus infection. Candida, aspergillus, and others can be seen microscopically in smears or scrapings from suspicious areas and can be grown in cultures.

Viral antigens can sometimes be demonstrated directly in specimens from surface lesions by the fluorescent antibody method.

· · ·

ANAEROBIC INFECTIONS

A large majority of the bacteria which make up the normal human flora are anaerobes. When displaced from their normal sites into tissues or body spaces, they may produce disease. Certain characteristics are suggestive of anaerobic infections: (1) They tend to involve mixtures of organisms, frequently several types of anaerobes. (2) They tend to form closed-space infections, either as discrete abscesses (lung, brain, pleura, peritoneum) or by burrowing through tissue layers. (3) Pus from anaerobic infections often has a foul odor. (4) Septic thrombophlebitis and metastatic suppuration occur frequently and require surgical drainage in addition to antimicrobial drugs. (5) Most of the pathogenetically important anaerobes except *Bacteroides fragilis* are highly sensitive to penicillin G. (6) Anaerobic infections are favored by reduced blood supply, necrotic tissue, and a low oxidation-reduction potential—all of which also interfere with delivery of antimicrobial drugs. (7) It is essential to use special collection methods and sensitive anaerobic technics and media to isolate the organisms. Otherwise, bacteriologic examination may be negative or yield only incidental aerobes.

The following are sites of important anaerobic infections.

Respiratory Tract

Periodontal infections, sinusitis, and mastoiditis may involve predominantly *B melaninogenicus,* Fusobacterium, and Peptostreptococci—all susceptible to penicillin. Aspiration of saliva (containing up to 10^8 of these organisms) may result in aspiration pneumonia, necrotizing pneumonia, lung abscess, and empyema. Penicillin and energetic drainage are essential for treatment.

Central Nervous System

Anaerobes rarely produce meningitis but are a common cause of brain abscess, subdural empyema, and septic thrombophlebitis. The organisms usually originate in the respiratory tract (via extension or hematogenous spread) and require similar management.

Intra-abdominal & Pelvic Infections

The flora of the colon consists predominantly of 10^{11} anaerobes per gram of feces. *B fragilis*, Clostridia, and peptostreptococci play a main role in abscess formation originating in perforation of the colon or gallbladder and in abscesses of the pelvis originating in the female genital organs. *B fragilis* is often relatively resistant to penicillin; therefore, chloramphenicol or clindamycin is important.

Bacteremia & Endocarditis

About 5–10% of these infections are now caused by anaerobes originating in the gut or the female genital tract. Specific bacteriologic diagnosis is essential for optimal treatment. Otherwise, the rate of treatment failure may be high.

Skin & Soft Tissue Infections

Anaerobes and aerobic bacteria often join to form synergistic infections (gangrene, necrotizing fasciitis, cellulitis). Surgical drainage, excision, and improved circulation are the most important forms of treatment, while antimicrobials act as adjuncts. It is usually difficult to pinpoint one specific organism as being responsible for the progressive lesion since mixtures of organisms are usually involved.

SEROLOGIC TESTS & THE DEMONSTRATION OF SPECIFIC ANTIBODY

In the course of many infections, serum antibodies are acquired relatively early, as microorganisms multiply, and these antibodies may persist for months or years. Thus, the serologic demonstration of anti-body indicates effective exposure (by infection or vaccination) at some time in the past but may have no bearing on the current illness. For the diagnosis of a current infection it is often necessary to demonstrate an increase in antibody concentration, ie, a rise of antibody level in the second of 2 blood specimens obtained at an interval of 10–20 days. The 2 specimens of sera must be examined simultaneously in the same test for meaningful results. Blood specimens must be taken aseptically and the serum separated with sterile precautions.

Diagnostic antibody titers are sometimes obtained in the following infections.

Amebiasis

Latex particles coated with *Entamoeba histolytica* antigens are agglutinated by serum in invasive amebiasis.

Blastomycosis

Complement-fixing antibodies appear principally in disseminated and progressive disease.

Brucellosis

During the acute infection, agglutinating antibodies appear; later, blocking (prozone, see p 216) IgA and IgG antibodies. Agglutinating IgM antibodies persist for years without manifest activity of the disease. The diagnosis of active brucellosis is suggested by the presence of IgG (over 1:80) agglutinating antibodies. CF tests are rarely employed.

Coccidioidomycosis

Soon after the initial infection, precipitating and complement-fixing antibodies to *Coccidioides immitis* appear. In the absence of complications, these tend to subside to very low levels within months. Dissemination of the infection is accompanied by a rising titer of complement-fixing antibodies (more than 1:32), which carries a grave prognosis.

Mycoplasmal Pneumonia
(Primary Atypical Pneumonia)

In some cases of pneumonitis not caused by common bacteria, cold agglutinins develop in the serum during the illness. These are substances which are capable of agglutinating human group O cells at 4° C but not at 20° or 37° C. Patients who develop cold agglutinins are usually infected with *Mycoplasma pneumoniae*. Antibodies to *M pneumoniae* can be detected by complement fixation, growth inhibition, or hemagglutination inhibition.

Histoplasmosis

Precipitating and complement-fixing antibodies to antigens of *Histoplasma capsulatum* appear usually within 3–4 weeks of acute infection and, in the absence of complications, revert to low levels. If the infection disseminates and progresses, the complement fixation titer rises (more than 1:32), However, serologic tests are less reliable than isolation of the fungus.

Infectious Mononucleosis

This disease is caused by the EB herpes virus. Diagnosis of the clinically suggestive case rests usually on the identification of representative "atypical" lymphocytes in blood smears and on the "heterophil agglutination" test of Paul and Bunnel. This is a nonspecific reaction: persons suffering from infectious mononucleosis develop a high titer (usually more than 1:112) of antibodies which agglutinate fresh washed sheep red blood cells or horse red cells. Similar agglutinating antibodies appear in a variety of hypersensitivity reactions but can be differentiated by absorption tests. The mononucleosis agglutinins cannot be absorbed by boiled guinea pig kidney, whereas agglutinins following other reactions are removed by this absorption. Commercial mononucleosis spot tests combine these reactions and yield sensitive and specific results.

In special laboratories, antibodies to EB (Epstein-Barr) virus can be demonstrated in sera of mononucleosis patients by immunofluorescence. (See Chapter 38.)

Leptospirosis

Microscopic agglutination tests give very high titers (often over 1:1000) following infection.

Parasitic Diseases

In cysticercosis, trichinosis, echinococcosis, and other parasitic infections, CF, precipitin, or HI tests are occasionally employed for diagnosis.

Pasteurellosis (Plague, Tularemia)

Agglutination titers of 1:20 or higher, particularly with rising titers, can support the clinical diagnosis of acute infection. Low titers suggest cross-reactions (eg, with brucella or shigella organisms) or long-past infection.

Psittacosis (Ornithosis), Lymphogranuloma Venereum, Trachoma, Inclusion Conjunctivitis

Antibodies to the group antigen often become demonstrable by CF tests within 2–4 weeks after symptoms appear. These antibodies cannot differentiate one infection of the group from another. Some species-specific antibodies can be found by immunofluorescence.

Rheumatoid Factor

In many disorders of possible "autoimmune" etiology, antibodies to the host's own antigens are encountered. Antithyroid antibodies are demonstrated in several thyroid disorders; antibodies which fix complement in the presence of nucleoproteins are found in disseminated lupus erythematosus. Anti-DNA antibodies are also demonstrated by immunofluorescence. In rheumatoid arthritis, an IgM ("rheumatoid factor") is present which reacts with human IgG. This can be demonstrated as an agglutination of red cells or other particles coated with IgG by diluted sera from rheumatoid patients. It is of interest that more than half of individuals with bacterial endocarditis exhibit a very high titer of such "rheumatoid factor." These substances disappear with bacteriologic cure of endocarditis.

Rickettsioses

CF tests permit the demonstration of type-specific antibody rise if specific antigens are available. Various special strains of proteus organisms share antigens with the rickettsiae, and suspensions of these proteus organisms are agglutinated in high titer by the serum of infected persons (Weil-Felix test).

See Chapter 21 for further details about the diagnosis of rickettsial infections.

Salmonellosis
(Typhoid Fever, Paratyphoid Fever, Etc)

A rising agglutination titer to O antigens is suggestive of active infection. Antibodies to H antigens occur commonly with vaccination and may persist for years. In carriers, antibody to Vi antigen may be more prominent than that to O or H. In previously vaccinated individuals with residual O or H titers, there may be no further titer rise with active infection.

Staphylococcal Infections

Persons with deep, active, suppurating staphylococcal infections frequently develop antibodies against a variety of staphylococcal antigens and extracellular products. In view of the ubiquity of many staphylococci, most such antibodies have little diagnostic meaning. However, a rise in antibody titer to staphylococcal leukocidin and staphylococcal alpha-hemolysin may indicate activity of a deep chronic lesion.

Streptococcal Infections &
Poststreptococcal Disease

Persons infected with beta-hemolytic streptococci develop antibodies to a variety of streptococcal antigens and extracellular products. Most conveniently, antibodies to streptolysin O can be detected. If antistreptolysin O (ASO) is repeatedly found to be present in titers exceeding 166 units, this suggests recent or persistent infection with beta-hemolytic streptococci. Antistreptolysin formation is readily suppressed by early and adequate penicillin therapy. Type-specific bactericidal antibody may also be measured.

Syphilis

Common serologic tests for syphilis (STS) are based on the accidental relationship between lipid extracts of mammalian tissue and reagin, a substance developing in the serum of persons after treponemal infection. Flocculation tests (VDRL, Kahn, Kline, Hinton, Mazzini, etc) are simpler and more commonly employed than CF tests (Kolmer, Wassermann). All of these tests estimate the presence of reagin and are therefore subject to false-positive results. The latter are particularly frequent in various infectious and febrile disorders, in "collagen diseases," and after vaccinations. STS can be performed in a quantitative manner if desired. Most biologic false-positive results are of low titer.

The *Treponema pallidum* immobilization (TPI) test and the fluorescent treponemal antibody (FTA-ABS) test measure specific antibodies to the etiologic agent. The latter is cheaper to perform because it requires no living spirochetes. Positive TPI and FTA-ABS reactions occur only in syphilis or infections with closely related treponemes (yaws, bejel, pinta). Positive FTA-ABS reactions develop within a few weeks after infection and persist long after adequate therapy for syphilis whereas STS often revert to negative.

Toxoplasmosis

Toxoplasma gondii, a crescent-shaped protozoon, can be isolated with difficulty by inoculating lymph node material taken from patients with acute infection into mice. Three serologic tests can be applied. The dye test depends upon the ability of antibodies to prevent the uptake of methylene blue by living toxoplasma organisms. The test results become positive (frequently more than 1:1000) in 2–4 weeks after acquired toxoplasmosis and may remain positive for years. In congenital toxoplasmosis, the dye test is often positive. The CF test becomes positive (up to 1:100) in 4–8 weeks and declines to very low levels in a few months. Immunofluorescence antibody tests in low titer indicate only past infection, but high titers (1:10,000 or more) suggest recent infection. Immunofluorescence tests for IgM antibody reveal congenital infection in newborns. Positive tests in single samples of serum of adults must take into account the high frequency of asymptomatic infection.

Trichinosis

For the diagnosis of acute trichinosis, a bentonite flocculation test is useful. Bentonite particles coated with *Trichinella spiralis* antigen may be agglutinated to high titer by the serum of persons infected for 2 weeks or more.

Viral Infections

The diagnosis of viral infections is discussed in detail in Chapters 28 and 29.

SKIN TESTS

Under the antigenic stimulus of an infectious agent, the host may develop hypersensitivity, manifested by skin reactivity, to one or more antigens of that agent. The controlled application of known antigens can therefore give evidence of infection and serve as a valuable diagnostic aid. A positive skin reaction indicates only that the individual has, at some time in the past, been infected with the specific agent. It provides information about the relationship of a specific agent to a *current* illness only if conversion from a

negative to a positive skin test occurs during or just preceding the current illness. The general skin reactivity declines markedly (anergy) during far-advanced stages of many infections and is a regular feature of sarcoidosis, Hodgkin's disease, and some childhood exanthematous diseases (eg, measles). Similarly, skin reactivity may be suppressed by the administration of corticosteroids or immunosuppressant drugs.

Most skin test reagents are not pure antigens but a complex mixture of potentially reactive substances. For proper interpretation, it is essential to include suitable control materials in the test. Both immediate and delayed skin reactions may occur with some skin test preparations. In general, the delayed reaction is the only meaningful one for the diagnosis of specific infection.

In a properly performed test the entire test volume (usually 0.1 ml) of the standardized preparation must be injected intracutaneously. Unless the injection raises a well circumscribed bleb, it is likely that part of the test volume has escaped into the subcutaneous tissue or onto the surface. This will diminish the reliability of the test. (Patch tests occasionally used in small children are not reliable.) In most instances the test should be read at 48 hours; additional readings at 24 and 72 hours are sometimes helpful.

The size of induration is the only important criterion of positive readings; erythema alone is not meaningful. When several strengths of test preparation are available, the smallest concentration of antigen must be injected initially, followed by increasingly higher concentrations if the previous test result was negative.

Diagnostic skin tests are frequently applied in the following clinical conditions.

Blastomycosis

Blastomycin is a filtered, concentrated broth in which *Blastomyces dermatitidis* has been grown for long periods. A test dilution of 1:100 gives 5 mm induration in persons with past infection. Interpretation is analogous to interpretation of the histoplasmin test (see below), but cross-reactions are very frequent.

Brucellosis

Filtrates of old broth cultures of brucella (brucellin) or a brucella nucleoprotein extract (brucellergen) have been used for skin testing. Such preparations cannot be well standardized, and proper controls are not available. Therefore, the usefulness of the skin test is doubtful. Serologic tests are much to be preferred for diagnosis.

Candida

Candida antigens are used in skin tests to ascertain the individual's ability to respond with a delayed type hypersensitivity reaction. Virtually all normal adults react positively.

Cat Scratch Fever

Pus from active cases, diluted 1:5 and heated at

60° C for 10 hours, can be used as a skin test antigen. It gives a positive reaction in some individuals with a typical clinical picture. The nature of the etiologic agent and the significance of the test are not known.

Chancroid

A positive Ducrey test, a delayed skin reaction following the injection of a treated suspension of *Haemophilus ducreyi,* indicates past infection. A positive reaction may persist for years.

Coccidioidomycosis

Coccidioidin is a filtered, concentrated broth in which *Coccidioides immitis* has been grown for long periods. The usual test dilution is 1:100, and a positive reaction (more than 5 mm induration) occurs in 24–48 hours. In 1:10 dilution the material often gives cross-reactions with other fungal antigens. Positive skin tests commonly denote past subclinical infection and significant specific resistance to reinfection.

Echinococcosis

The injection of inactivated hydatid fluid (Casoni reaction) obtained from human or animal cases may give both immediate and delayed reactions in individuals with echinococcus infection. The test is less reliable than antibody demonstrated by immunoelectrophoresis.

Filariasis

Dirofilaria immitis antigens often give positive delayed skin test reactions in infected persons.

Herpes Simplex

Injection of a soluble antigen obtained from growing virus gives a positive result in 18–24 hours in individuals who have had a primary infection with the virus and may develop local recurrences.

Histoplasmosis

Histoplasmin is a concentrated filtrate prepared from broth in which *Histoplasma capsulatum* has been grown for long periods. The usual test dilution is 1:100 and a positive reaction (more than 5 mm induration) occurs in 24–48 hours. Cross-reactions with other fungal products occur relatively frequently. Positive skin tests commonly denote past subclinical infection and significant specific resistance to reinfection. The skin test may raise the antibody titer.

Leishmaniasis

Leishmanin is an inactivated suspension of cultured flagellate leishmania. A positive delayed skin test to this preparation develops within 6–12 weeks after many leishmania infections and remains positive for life. The test is often negative in active kala-azar but becomes positive after effective chemotherapy.

Leprosy

Lepromin, a standardized homogenate of lepromatous skin nodules, has no diagnostic value. Normal persons may react. However, in a person with known leprosy, a positive lepromin test is diagnostic of tuberculoid leprosy and a negative test indicates lepromatous (anergic) leprosy.

Lymphogranuloma Venereum

The Frei test antigen is a chlamydial suspension prepared from infected chick embryo yolk sacs. An injection of uninfected yolk sac material must be used as a control. A positive reaction consists of induration at least 6 mm larger than the control site. A positive Frei test may occur following infection with any member of the psittacosis-LGV-TRIC group at any time in the past.

Mumps

Intradermal injection of inactivated mumps vaccine gives a delayed positive skin test reaction in 18–36 hours provided the individual has had a past infection. A negative mumps skin test has limited value in permitting identification of susceptibles and does not correlate well with neutralizing serum antibodies. It does permit demonstration of the ability to respond with a delayed-type hypersensitivity reaction.

Sarcoidosis

An extract of sarcoid tissue injected into the skin of a person with sarcoidosis results in a papule which persists for months. Excision after 4–8 weeks reveals a histologic pattern of sarcoid (Kveim test). The basis of the reaction is not certain. Reliability depends on standardized materials. (Editorial: N Engl J Med 292:859, 1975.)

Toxoplasmosis

Toxoplasmin is prepared from a suspension of killed *Toxoplasma gondii* and evokes a delayed reaction in some individuals who also give positive serologic tests. Positive reactors are presumed to have been infected at some time in the past. The test has little diagnostic value, but has been employed in epidemiologic surveys.

Trichinosis

Antigens derived from trichinae (trichinella skin test) may give both immediate and delayed reactions in infected individuals, but most commercial antigens are too insensitive.

Tuberculosis

The tuberculin skin test is performed with a purified protein derivative (PPD-S) standardized accurately in terms of tuberculin units (TU) (see Chapter 17).

The initial test dose is usually 5 TU (intermediate strength PPD). Larger doses are injected when smaller doses have given negative results. The test is considered positive if induration 10 mm in diameter or more occurs in 48–72 hours following injection of 5 TU. In hypersensitive persons with erythema nodosum or phlyctenular conjunctivitis, not more than 1 TU should be injected to avoid serious reactions.

PPD (-B, -Y) prepared from other mycobacteria are used in epidemiologic surveys. Many of them cross-react.

Tularemia

Antigens extracted from *Francisella (Pasteurella) tularensis* give a delayed skin reaction in persons who have been infected in the past. The test is quite specific and remains positive longer than antibody titers.

. . .

Toxin-Neutralization Tests

A. Schick Test: Although it is not designed for the diagnosis of infection, the Schick test is a valuable aid in the determination of probable susceptibility or resistance to diphtheria. The test consists of the intradermal injection of a standard skin test dose of active diphtheria toxin and of an identical amount of heated toxin as control. The test is usually read in 24 and 48 hours. A positive reaction consists of redness and swelling at the active toxin site which increases for 48 hours and then fades, leaving a brownish pigmented area. The control site shows no reaction. A positive reaction denotes the absence of an adequate amount of neutralizing circulating antitoxin and therefore susceptibility to diphtheria toxin. A negative reaction at both sites suggests the presence of adequate amounts of circulating neutralizing antitoxin and insusceptibility to diphtheria toxin.

The Schick test is at times complicated by individual hypersensitivity to constituents other than toxin contained in the injections.

Individuals who have positive Schick tests should be immunized with diphtheria toxoids. However, even if the Schick test is negative, diphtheria infection can sometimes occur.

B. Schultz-Charlton Reaction: If specific antitoxin to the erythrogenic toxin of beta-hemolytic group A streptococci is injected intradermally into a patient with scarlet fever, the rash will blanch and fade at the injection site because the antitoxin has neutralized the toxin. This test is rarely employed.

NONSPECIFIC CLINICAL LABORATORY TESTS

The usual laboratory procedures performed on most patients who undergo detailed medical examination frequently contain clues concerning possible infectious processes. Anemia and leukocytosis are suitable examples. Such abnormalities are compatible with a large variety of diagnoses and are helpful only if integrated with other findings into a meaningful pattern. No attempt is made here to list the many different laboratory findings which can thus aid in the diagnosis of infection. A few specific items will be discussed briefly for the sake of illustration.

Red Cell Count & Packed Cell Volume (PCV)

Anemia is a feature of many protracted infections, eg, bacterial endocarditis and malaria. Conversely, in acute diarrheal diseases, there may be dehydration with elevated PCV.

White Cell Count

In most suppurative infections the white count is elevated and the proportion of young polymorphonuclear cells is increased. A low white count in pneumococcal or staphylococcal pneumonia, especially in elderly patients, is an unfavorable prognostic sign.

In some infections caused by gram-negative bacilli there is a fall in the total white count and relative lymphocytosis. Similar findings occur in some viral infections (eg, myxoviruses). However, arbovirus infections with encephalitis commonly give rise to high white counts. In whooping cough, the white count is frequently high, with absolute lymphocytosis. Sudden widespread dissemination of any bacterial or fungal pathogen may be accompanied by a very rapid rise in the white count, at times to leukemoid levels. On the other hand, persons with depressed marrow activity do not develop white count elevations with infections.

These examples should indicate the complexity of interpreting white cell counts.

Erythrocyte Sedimentation Rate (ESR)

In many acute infections the ESR is normal; in prolonged infections it becomes accelerated. However, a rapid ESR can be associated with so many different processes which produce cell injury or derangements of blood proteins that it is rarely helpful in establishing the diagnosis of infection. It may be of use in evaluating therapeutic response.

C-Reactive Protein (CRP)

CRP is a substance in the serum of certain patients which reacts with the somatic C polysaccharide of pneumococci in vitro but is commonly measured by precipitation with a specific antiserum prepared in rabbits. It is a beta-globulin not found in normal sera but occurring frequently in sera of patients with inflammatory, neoplastic, or necrotizing processes. The laboratory test for the presence of CRP thus constitutes a nonspecific test for the presence of inflammation or tissue injury.

Tests for several mucoproteins in serum are likewise entirely nonspecific and so are of little help in diagnosis.

Transaminase & Similar Enzyme Tests

Glutamic oxaloacetic transaminase (SGOT), glutamic pyruvic transaminase (SGPT), lactate dehydrogenase (SLDH), and others are intracellular enzymes involved in amino acid or carbohydrate metabolism. In the course of many disease processes

Table 26–2. Bacteriologic diagnosis of specific microorganisms from clinical infections.

Organism	Principal Sources of Clinical Specimens	Preferred Culture Media	Special Conditions and Additional Tests Usually Required
Staphylococcus	Pus or exudate from site of infection; bloodstream, spinal fluid, urine.	Blood agar plates; trypticase-soy broth; brain broth (3 weeks).	Aerobic or micro-aerophilic. Presence of hemolysis; coagulase reaction; mannitol fermentation.
Streptococcus			Aerobic or anaerobic. Type of hemolysis; growth in 6.5% NaCl broth—enterococci.
Pneumococcus	Sputum, bloodstream, spinal fluid, exudates, pus.	Blood agar plates; trypticase-soy broth; blood broth.	Hemolysis—alpha type; solubility in bile; typing with specific serum.
Gonococcus	Exudates from genitalia, eye, joints; blood.	"Chocolate" agar plates incubated in 10% CO_2 (candle jar).	Intracellular diplococci on smear. Oxidase test.
Meningococcus	Bloodstream, spinal fluid, nasopharynx, skin petechiae.		Intracellular diplococci on smear. Oxidase test; maltose fermented.
C diphtheriae	Nasopharynx, wounds, eye.	Löffler's slants; potassium tellurite medium; blood agar plates.	Typical morphology on smear. Virulence test; Schick skin test.
Clostridium	Wounds, exudates, pus, bloodstream.	Blood agar plates; thioglycollate medium; chopped meat broth.	Strictly anaerobic. Type of hemolysis; milk coagulation.
M tuberculosis	Sputum, exudates, pus, spinal fluid, urine.	Petragnani's, Loewenstein's, or Dubos' media (2–4 weeks).	Guinea pig inoculation. Acid-fast stain; concentration.
Actinomyces	Sputum, exudates, pus.	Thioglycollate medium; blood agar plates.	"Sulfur granules" in specimen. Aerobic and anaerobic culture.
E coli-E aerogenes group	Urine, bloodstream, spinal fluid, exudates, pus.	Blood agar plates. MacConkey's or eosin-methylene blue (EMB) agar.	Lactose fermented (paracolon bacilli ferment lactose slowly).
Salmonella	Feces, bloodstream, urine, exudates.	MacConkey's or EMB agar plates; tetrathionate broth; triple sugar iron agar.	Identified by slide agglutination with specific serum; patient's serum for agglutination test—H and O agglutination.
Shigella	Feces.		Identified by slide agglutination with specific serum.
K pneumoniae (Friedländer's bacillus)	Sputum, bloodstream, spinal fluid, exudates.	Blood agar plates; blood broth.	Typing with specific serum.
Proteus-Pseudomonas group	Urine, exudates, bloodstream, spinal fluid.	Blood agar plates; EMB agar.	Characteristic pigment, odor, "swarming"; lactose not fermented.
Pasteurella	Bloodstream, sputum, exudates, pus.	Blood agar plates; cysteine agar.	Patient's serum for agglutination test.
Brucella	Bloodstream, exudates.	Trypticase-soy agar and broth, incubated in 10% CO_2 (candle jar).	Patient's serum for agglutination or precipitin tests.
Haemophilus species	Spinal fluid, bloodstream, sputum, exudates.	"Chocolate" agar plates; blood agar plates with Isovitalex.	Typing with specific serum. Precipitin test in spinal fluid.
Bacteroides	Exudates, bloodstream.	Chopped meat broth; thioglycollate medium; blood agar plates.	Strictly anaerobic. Typical morphology.
T pallidum	Primary or secondary syphilitic lesion, blood serum.	None.	Immunofluorescence microscopy; serologic tests.
Leptospira	Bloodstream, urine.	Serum broth.	Darkfield microscopy.
B recurrentis	Bloodstream.	Blood broth.	Stained blood film; serologic tests.
Yeasts and fungi	Skin, nails; exudates, pus; sputum, blood, CSF.	Blood agar plates; Sabouraud's medium.	Serologic tests on patient's serum.

involving cellular injury, the enzyme concentration in blood serum increases markedly. Consequently, elevated enzyme levels are found in acute infections, neoplasms, infarctions, and many degenerative processes and are not necessarily due to hepatic insult or myocardial infarction, with which they are commonly associated.

Serum Bilirubin

The serum bilirubin may be elevated, indicating jaundice, particularly in infections of the newborn and in infections caused by gram-negative enteric organisms.

Biopsy

In many cases of protracted fever of unknown origin, all tests to establish the presence of infection fail to yield a definitive diagnosis. Surgical exploration and histologic examination of tissues may give the final answer. (See Petersdorf & Beeson reference.)

Table 26–3. Diagnostic features of some acute exanthems.

Disease	Prodromal Signs and Symptoms	Nature of Eruption	Other Diagnostic Features	Laboratory Tests
Measles (rubeola)	3–4 days of fever, coryza, conjunctivitis, and cough.	Maculopapular, reddish-brown; begins on head and neck, spreads downward. In 5–6 days rash brownish, desquamating.	Koplik's spots on buccal mucosa.	WBC low; specialized CF and virus neutralization in tissue culture.
German measles (rubella)	Little or no prodrome.	Maculopapular, pink; begins on head and neck, spreads downward, fades in 3 days. No desquamation.	Lymphadenopathy, post-auricular or occipital.	WBC normal or low; virus neutralization in tissue culture or HI tests.
Chickenpox (varicella)	0–1 day of fever, anorexia, headache.	Rapid evolution of macules to papules, vesicles, crusts; all stages simultaneously present; lesions superficial, distribution centripetal.	Lesions on scalp and mucous membranes.	Specialized CF and virus neutralization in tissue culture. Immunofluorescence in smear of lesion.
Smallpox (variola)	3 days of fever, severe headache, malaise, chills.	Slow evolution of macules to papules, vesicles, pustules, crusts; all lesions in same stage; lesions deep-seated, distribution centrifugal.		Virus isolation on chorioallantoic membranes of chick embryos, CF, or cell cultures.
Scarlet fever	½–2 days of malaise, sore throat, fever, vomiting.	Generalized, punctate, red; prominent on neck, in axilla, groin, skin folds; circumoral pallor; fine desquamation involves hands and feet.	Strawberry tongue, exudative tonsillitis.	Group A hemolytic streptococci cultures from throat; antistreptolysin O titer rise.
Exanthem subitum (roseola infantum)	3–4 days of high fever.	As fever falls by crisis pink maculopapules appear on chest and trunk; fade in 1–3 days.		WBC low.
Fifth disease (erythema infectiosum)	None.	Red, flushed cheeks; circumoral pallor; maculopapules on extremities.	"Slapped face" appearance.	WBC low.
Meningococcemia	Hours of fever, vomiting.	Maculopapules, petechiae, purpura.	Meningeal signs, shock.	Cultures of blood, CSF.
Rocky Mountain spotted fever	3–4 days of fever, chills, severe headaches.	Maculopapules, petechiae, distribution centrifugal.	History of tick bite.	Agglutination (OX19, OX2), CF.
Typhus fevers	3–4 days of fever, chills, severe headaches.	Maculopapules, petechaie, distribution centripetal.	Endemic area, lice.	Agglutination (OX19), CF.
Infectious mononucleosis	Fever, adenopathy, sore throat.	Maculopapular rash resembling rubella, rarely papulovesicular.	Splenomegaly, adenopathy.	Atypical lymphs in blood smears; heterophil agglutination; Mononucleosis spot test.
Enterovirus infections (echo, coxsackie)	1–2 days of fever, malaise.	Maculopapular rash resembling rubella, rarely papulovesicular.	Aseptic meningitis.	Virus isolation from stool or CSF; CF titer rise.
Drug eruptions	Occasional fever.	Maculopapular rash resembling rubella, rarely papulovesicular.		Eosinophilia.
Eczema herpeticum	None.	Vesiculopustular lesions in area of eczema.		Herpes simplex virus isolated in tissue culture; serology.

Nonspecific Organ System Response to Infections

Whenever an infectious process involves primarily one organ system, nonspecific laboratory tests may show abnormal values. For example, in renal infections, proteinuria and abnormal urinary sediment may be present even without bacteriuria. In CNS infections, abnormal values of CSF composition are of great help in diagnosis. In infections of the external eye, the cell picture of the conjunctival exudate assists in etiologic diagnosis. The roentgenographic appearance of bone or lung may not only support a diagnosis of infection but may even point to the etiologic agent.

Radioisotope Scanning Methods

Infective processes may alter blood supply to an area, produce necrotic foci, and change tissue cell behavior. Consequently, localized infections in some organs (eg, the liver, spleen, brain) may be found by concentration or by exclusion of isotopes such as gallium, technetium, and others. The technology of scanning methods and the interpretation of results tend to change very rapidly.

LABORATORY AIDS IN THE SELECTION OF ANTIMICROBIAL THERAPY

The first drug used is chosen on the basis of clinical impression after the physician is convinced that a microbial infection exists and has made a tentative etiologic diagnosis on clinical grounds. On the basis of this "best guess," he can readily select a probable drug of choice (see Chapter 10). Before the probable drug of choice is administered, specimens are often obtained for laboratory isolation of the etiologic agent. The results of these examinations may necessitate selection of a different drug. The identification of certain microorganisms which are uniformly drug-susceptible eliminates the necessity for further testing and permits the selection of optimally effective drugs solely on the basis of experience. Under other circumstances, tests for drug susceptibility of isolated microorganisms may be helpful (see Chapter 10).

The commonly performed "disk test" must be used judiciously and interpreted with restraint. Only one member of each major class of drugs should be represented. For gram-negative rods, the following disks are used: ampicillin, cephalothin, chloramphenicol, tetracycline, kanamycin, gentamicin, and polymyxin (or colistin). For gram-positive organisms, penicillin G, cloxacillin, kanamycin, erythromycin, tetracycline, cephalothin, and clindamycin may be used. Vancomycin and methicillin may be tested against staphylococci; ampicillin against enterococci; clindamycin and chloramphenicol against bacteroides and other anaerobes. Nitrofurantoin disks are useful only against organisms isolated from the urine because the drug is only active in the urine—not systemically. Mandelamine disks are never used. Testing with sulfonamide disks or trimethoprim-sulfamethoxazole (cotrimoxazole) is rarely indicated and requires PABA-free media.

The sizes of zones of growth inhibition vary with the molecular characteristics of different drugs. Thus zone size of one drug cannot be compared to the zone size of another drug acting on the same organism. However, for any one drug the zone size can be compared to a standard, provided media, inoculum size, and other conditions are carefully standardized. Then it is possible to list for each drug a minimum zone size which denotes "susceptibility" (Kirby-Bauer).

The disk test measures the ability of drugs to *inhibit* the growth of microorganisms. Its results correlate reasonably well with therapeutic response in those disease processes where body defenses can frequently eliminate infectious microorganisms.

In a few types of human infections, the results of disk tests are of little assistance (and may be misleading) because a *bactericidal* drug effect is required for cure. Outstanding examples are bacterial endocarditis, acute osteomyelitis, and severe infections in a host whose antibacterial defenses are inadequate, eg, persons with neoplastic diseases which have been treated with radiation and antineoplastic chemotherapy, or persons who are being given corticosteroids in high dosage and are immunosuppressed.

The selection of a bactericidal drug or drug combination for each patient can be guided by specialized laboratory tests. (See Jawetz reference.)

Evaluation of the chemotherapeutic regimen in vivo can be performed by serum assay (see Chapter 10). This procedure consists of the following steps:

(1) An etiologic microorganism is isolated.

(2) Antimicrobial therapy is started.

(3) Blood is drawn from the patient receiving treatment.

(4) Dilutions of the separated serum are tested for their ability to kill in vitro the microorganisms isolated from the patient.

This test can sometimes help decide whether the patient is receiving the proper drug in adequate amounts or whether the regimen should be altered.

In urinary tract infections the antibacterial activity of urine is far more important than that of serum. The disappearance of infecting organisms from the urine during treatment can serve as a partial drug level assay.

Instead of the disk test, a semiquantitative test tube procedure can be employed. This test measures more exactly the concentration of an antibiotic necessary to inhibit growth of a standardized inoculum under defined conditions. A series of broth tubes containing graduated amounts of an antibiotic is inoculated with a dilution of fresh broth culture of the test organism. After incubation, the tubes are examined for turbidity. The end point is considered to be that concentration of antibiotic contained in the last tube remaining clear. Upon this basis a rough estimate of the in vivo dose necessary to inhibit growth of the test organism can be arrived at. In addition, bactericidal effect may be determined by the tube dilution method, if tubes without growth are subcultured on drug-free media.

In persons with renal impairment who must receive nephrotoxic drugs, concentration of drug in serum can be estimated by an assay of serum against special test microorganisms.

. . .

GRAM & ACID-FAST STAINING METHODS

Gram Stain (Hucker Modification)

(1) Fix smear by heat.

(2) Cover with crystal violet for 1 minute.

(3) Wash with water. Do not blot.

(4) Cover with Gram's iodine for 1 minute.

(5) Wash with water. Do not blot.

(6) Decolorize for 10–30 seconds with gentle agitation in acetone (30 ml) and alcohol (70 ml).

(7) Wash with water. Do not blot.

(8) Cover for 10–30 seconds with safranin (2.5% solution in 95% alcohol).

(9) Wash with water and let dry.

Ziehl-Neelsen Acid-Fast Stain

(1) Fix smear by heat.

(2) Cover with carbolfuchsin, steam gently for 5 minutes over direct flame (or for 20 minutes over a water bath).

(3) Wash with water.

(4) Decolorize in acid-alcohol until only a faint pink color remains.

(5) Wash with water.

(6) Counterstain for 10–30 seconds with Löffler's methylene blue.

(7) Wash with water and let dry.

Kinyoun Carbolfuchsin Acid-Fast Stain

(1) Formula: Basic fuchsin, 4; phenol crystals, 8; alcohol (95%), 20; distilled water, 100.

(2) Stain fixed smear for 3 minutes (no heat necessary) and continue as with Ziehl-Neelsen stain.

● ● ●

General References

Bauer AW & others: Antibiotic susceptibility testing by a standardized single disc method. Am J Clin Pathol 45:493, 1966.

Ericsson HM, Sherris JC: Antibiotic sensitivity testing: Report of an international collaborative study. Acta Pathol Microbiol Scandinav [B] 217(Suppl):1, 1971.

Fox HA: Immunofluorescence in the diagnosis of acute bacterial meningitis. Pediatrics 43:44, 1969.

Gorbach SL, Bartlett JG: Anaerobic infections. (3 parts.) N Engl J Med 290:1177, 1237, 1289, 1974.

Jawetz E & others: Laboratory test for antibiotic combinations. Am J Clin Pathol 25:1016, 1955.

Kalinske RW & others: Diagnostic usefulness and safety of transtracheal aspiration. N Engl J Med 276:604, 1967.

Kunin CM: *Detection, Prevention, and Management of Urinary Tract Infections,* 2nd ed. Lea & Febiger, 1974.

Lennette EH, Spaulding EH, Truant JP (editors): *Manual of Clinical Microbiology,* 2nd ed. American Society for Microbiology, 1974.

Levison ML, Frank PF: Differentiation of group A from other beta hemolytic streptococci with bacitracin. J Bacteriol 69:284, 1955.

Petersdorf RG, Beeson P: Fever of unexplained origin: Report of 100 cases. Medicine 40:1, 1961.

27...
General Properties of Viruses

DEFINITIONS

Viruses are the smallest infectious agents (20–300 nm in diameter), containing a molecule of nucleic acid (RNA or DNA) as their genome. The nucleic acid is encased in a protein shell, and the entire infectious unit is termed a virion. Viruses replicate only in living cells. The viral nucleic acid contains information necessary for programming the infected host cell to synthesize a number of virus-specific macromolecules required for the production of virus progeny. During the replicative cycle, numerous copies of viral nucleic acid and coat proteins are produced. The coat proteins assemble together to form the capsid, which encases and stabilizes the viral nucleic acid against the extracellular environment and facilitates the attachment, and perhaps penetration of the virus upon contact with new susceptible cells.

The nucleic acid, once isolated from the virion,

can be hydrolyzed by either ribo- or deoxyribonuclease, whereas the nucleic acid within the intact virus is not affected by such treatment. In contrast, viral antiserum will neutralize the virion because it reacts with the antigens of the protein coat. However, the same antiserum has no effect on the free infectious nucleic acid isolated from the virion.

The spectrum of hosts which viruses infect is broad in general, although the host range for a given virus may be extremely limited. Viruses are known to infect unicellular organisms such as mycoplasmas, bacteria, and algae and all higher plants and animals.

Much information on virus-host relationships has been obtained from studies on bacteriophages, the viruses which attack bacteria. This subject is discussed in Chapter 9. Properties of individual viruses are discussed in Chapters 30–39.

Some Useful Definitions in Virology (Fig 27–1)

Capsid: The symmetric protein shell which encloses the nucleic acid genome. Often, empty capsids are by-products of the viral replicative cycle.

Nucleocapsid: The capsid together with the enclosed nucleic acid.

Structural units: The basic protein building blocks of the capsid.

Capsomeres: Morphologic units seen in the electron microscope on the surface of virus particles. Capsomeres represent clusters of polypeptides, which when completely assembled form the capsid.

Virion: The complete infective virus particle, which in some instances (adenoviruses, papovaviruses, picornaviruses) may be identical with the nucleocapsid. In more complex virions (herpesviruses, myxoviruses), this includes the nucleocapsid plus a surrounding envelope.

Defective virus: A virus particle which is functionally deficient in some aspect of replication. Defective virus may interfere with the replication of normal virus.

Pseudovirions: During viral replication the capsid sometimes encloses host nucleic acid rather than viral nucleic acid. Such particles look like ordinary virus particles when observed by electron microscopy, but they do not replicate.

Pseudovirions contain the "wrong" nucleic acid.

Primary, secondary, and tertiary nucleic acid structure: Primary structure refers to the sequence of bases in the nucleic acid chain. Secondary structure refers to the spatial arrangement of the complete nucleic acid chain, ie, whether it is single- or double-stranded, circular or linear in conformation. Tertiary structure refers to other elements of fine spatial detail in the helix, eg, presence of supercoiling, breakage points, deletions, gaps, catenation, regions of strand separation.

Transcription: The mechanism by which specific information encoded in a nucleic acid chain is transferred to messenger RNA.

Translation: The mechanism by which a particular base sequence in messenger RNA results in production of a specific amino acid sequence in a protein.

EVOLUTION OF VIRUSES

Three hypotheses have been proposed to explain the origin of viruses.

(1) Viruses are descendants of ancient precellular organisms which became parasites of the first cellular organisms. As organisms and animals evolved, viruses evolved with them. It is of interest in this connection that human beings may be harmlessly infected with latent herpes simplex virus for life and that monkeys may be infected in similar fashion with another type of herpesvirus. These viral species probably had a common origin; however, if man is accidentally infected with the monkey herpesvirus B—with which he has had no evolutionary experience—the infection is usually fatal.

(2) Viruses have evolved from pathogenic bacteria through a retrograde evolutionary process. While rickettsiae and chlamydiae are examples of intracellular organisms which have undergone parasitic degeneration, they are not viruses. There is at present no evidence to support the theory that true viruses have evolved from bacteria.

(3) Viruses are components of normal cells which sometimes become autonomous. Within the cell, the virus might exert an autocatalytic influence so that replicas of itself are formed from the materials within the cell. Viruses might be said to resemble genes which have escaped regulatory control and continue to multiply as long as there is building material available. Cells of certain plant species, for example, contain what appear to be completely normal constituents of the species. However, when extracts of such cells are inoculated into other plants, the recipient host, if susceptible, behaves as if it has been inoculated with a true virus. If the second (susceptible) host were not known, it would never have been recognized that the

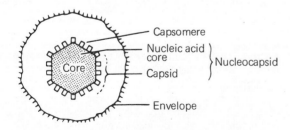

Figure 27–1. Schematic diagram illustrating the components of the complete virus particle or the virion.

first host contained material of a viral nature. A superficially similar phenomenon is known in human virology: normal-appearing cell cultures derived from infants who acquired rubella infection in utero produce rubella virus which is cytopathic for other cell lines.

A corollary of this hypothesis is that viruses are derivatives of normal cellular genes (nucleic acids) which eons ago became capable of autonomous replication and acquired the genetic information for coding for capsid protein. The capsid is essential in order to stabilize the nucleic acid of the subcellular organelle in its travel from cell to cell. Cancer viruses may exist in normal cells as repressed genes.

Analysis of the patterns of nearest neighbor base sequences in the nucleic acid of mammalian viruses suggests that small viruses (parvo-, picorna-, and papovaviruses) which contain very little information conform closely in their frequency pattern to the doublet pattern of host cell DNA. Doublet patterns of larger viruses (pox- and herpesviruses) show only a limited resemblance to that of mammalian DNA. These results suggest that the small viruses, all of which have nucleic acid with a molecular weight of $< 5 \times 10^6$ and a G + C content of 41–48%, might have evolved from cells of their hosts. In contrast, herpes- and poxviruses are probably of external origin; their DNA has a molecular weight of 70–160 $\times 10^6$ and their G + C contents range from 35–74%. These considerations make it unlikely that one evolutionary theory will explain the origin of all viruses.

CLASSIFICATION OF VIRUSES

Basis of Classification

The following properties, listed in the order of preference or importance, have been used as a basis for the classification of viruses. The amount of information available in each category is not uniform for all viruses. For some agents, knowledge is at hand about only a few of the properties listed.

(1) Nucleic acid type: RNA or DNA; single-stranded or double-stranded.

(2) Size and morphology, including type of symmetry, number of capsomeres, and presence of membranes.

(3) Susceptibility to physical and chemical agents, especially ether.

(4) Immunologic properties.

(5) Natural methods of transmission.

(6) Host, tissue, and cell tropisms.

(7) Pathology, including inclusion body formation.

(8) Symptomatology.

Classification by Symptomatology

The oldest classification of viruses is based on the diseases they produce, and this system offers certain

conveniences for the clinician. However, it is not satisfactory for the biologist because the same virus may appear in several groups, since it causes more than one disease depending upon the organ attacked.

A. Generalized Diseases: Diseases in which virus is spread throughout the body via the bloodstream and in which multiple organs are affected. Skin rashes may occur. These include smallpox, vaccinia, measles, rubella, chickenpox, yellow fever, dengue, Colorado tick fever, West Nile fever, sandfly fever, pleurodynia, and exanthem subitum; and rash due to enteroviruses, especially echoviruses 4, 9, 16, and 18, and coxsackieviruses A9, A19, B1, and B3.

B. Diseases Primarily Affecting Specific Organs: The virus may spread to the organ through the bloodstream, along the peripheral nerves, or by other routes.

1. Diseases of the nervous system—Poliomyelitis, meningitis caused by the enteroviruses (polio-, coxsackie-, and echoviruses), rabies, encephalitis lethargica, arthropod-borne encephalitides, lymphocytic choriomeningitis, herpes simplex, herpes B, meningoencephalitis of mumps, measles, vaccinia, and others, subacute sclerosing panencephalitis (SSPE), progressive multifocal leukoencephalopathy (PML), and kuru.

2. Diseases of the respiratory tract—Influenza, bronchial pneumonia of children (RS virus, parainfluenza), bronchiolitis (RS virus, parainfluenza), laryngotracheobronchitis (parainfluenza), pharyngoconjunctival fever (adenovirus), common cold (caused by a number of different viruses, eg, rhinoviruses, parainfluenza viruses), and primary atypical pneumonia.

3. Localized diseases of the skin or mucous membranes—Herpes simplex, herpes progenitalis, molluscum contagiosum, warts, herpangina, and herpes zoster.

4. Diseases of the eye—Adenovirus conjunctivitis, Newcastle virus conjunctivitis, herpes keratoconjunctivitis, and epidemic hemorrhagic conjunctivitis (enterovirus-70).

5. Diseases of the liver—Hepatitis type A (infectious hepatitis), type B (serum hepatitis), yellow fever, and, in the neonate, enteroviruses, herpesviruses, and rubella virus.

6. Diseases of the salivary glands—Mumps and cytomegalovirus.

7. Diseases of the gastrointestinal tract—Gastroenteritis A virus and gastroenteritis B virus.

Classification by Biologic, Chemical, & Physical Properties (Table 27–1)

Viruses can be clearly separated into families on the basis of the type and form of the nucleic acid genome and the size, shape, substructure, and mode of replication of the virus particle. Table 27–1 shows one widely used scheme by which these criteria are used for classification. However, there is not complete agreement among virologists on the relative importance of the criteria used to classify viruses. Fig 27–2 illustrates a virus classification scheme which gives first priority to the division of viruses into enveloped and nonenveloped geometric subdivisions.

Table 27–1. Classification of viruses into families based on chemical and physical properties.

Nucleic Acid Core	Capsid Symmetry	Virion: Enveloped or Naked	Ether Sensitivity	No. of Capsomeres	Virus Particle Size (nm)*	Molecular Weight of Nucleic Acid in Virion (× 10^6)	Physical Type of Nucleic Acid	No. of Genes (Approx.)	Virus Family
DNA	Icosahedral	Naked	Resistant	32	18–26	1.5–1.8	SS	7	Parvoviridae
				72	45–55	2.4–5	DS circular	10	Papovaviridae
				252	70–90	20–30	DS	50	Adenoviridae
		Enveloped	Sensitive	162	100†	54–92	DS	180	Herpetoviridae
	Complex	Complex coats	Resistant‡		230 × 300	160	DS	400	Poxviridae
RNA	Icosahedral	Naked	Resistant	32	20–30	2–2.8	SS	12	Picornaviridae
				?§	60–80	12–15	DS segmented	40	Reoviridae
		Enveloped	Sensitive	32?	40–70	3–4	SS	15	Togaviridae
	Unknown or complex	Enveloped	Sensitive		50–300	3–5	SS segmented	15	Arenaviridae
					80–130	9	SS	30	Coronaviridae
					~100	5–10	SS segmented	50	Retroviridae
	Helical	Enveloped	Sensitive		90–100	7	SS segmented	15	Bunyaviridae
					80–120	4	SS segmented	15	Orthomyxoviridae
					150–300	6–8	SS	30	Paramyxoviridae
					70 × 175	3–4	SS	20	Rhabdoviridae

*Diameter, or diameter × length.

†The naked virus, ie, the nucleocapsid, is 100 nm in diameter; however, the enveloped virion varies up to 200 nm.

‡The genus *Orthopoxvirus,* which includes the better studied poxviruses, eg, vaccinia, variola, alastrim, cowpox, ectromelia, rabbitpox, monkeypox, is ether-resistant. Some of the poxviruses belonging to other genera have been found to be ether-sensitive.

§Reoviruses contain an outer and an inner capsid. The inner capsid appears to contain 32 capsomeres, but the number on the outer capsid has not been definitely established. A total of 92 capsomeres has been suggested.

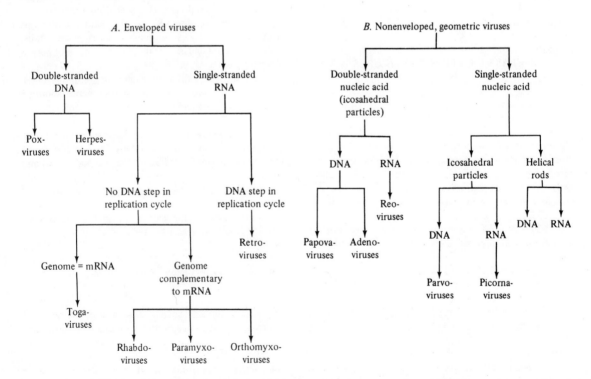

Figure 27–2. Matthews' classification system based on the relationship between size of genome and size of virion (dry mass or particle volume). For the enveloped viruses, those with large genomes have double-stranded DNA and those with smaller genomes have single-stranded RNA. For the nonenveloped viruses, those with genomes above a certain size have double-stranded nucleic acid (DNA or RNA); those below that size have single-stranded nucleic acid (DNA or RNA). (After Matthews, J Gen Virol 27:135, 1975.)

Within each family, genera are usually based on antigenicity. Properties of the major families of animal viruses are summarized in Table 27–1, are discussed briefly below, and are considered in greater detail in the chapters that follow.

DNA-Containing Viruses

A. Parvoviridae Family: The members of this family are very small viruses, with a particle size of about 20 nm; they contain single-stranded DNA and have cubic symmetry, with 32 capsomeres 2–4 nm in diameter. They have no envelope and are ether-resistant. Some members of the group are resistant to high temperatures (60° C for 30 minutes). Replication and capsid assembly take place in the nucleus of the infected cell. Genus *Parvovirus* includes the autonomously replicating parvoviruses: hamster osteolytic H viruses, latent rat viruses (Kilham rat virus, X14 virus), minute virus of mice, and a parvovirus of swine. Genus *Adenosatellovirus* consists of the adeno-associated satellite viruses which are defective and cannot multiply in the absence of a replicating adenovirus which serves as a "helper virus." Herpesvirus can act as a partial helper; in cells co-infected with herpesvirus, infectious satellite DNA and capsid proteins are made, but they are not assembled into satellite virions. Some satellite serotypes are known to be indigenous to man. (See Chapter 37.) Genus *Densovirus* includes the arthropod parvoviruses.

B. Papovaviridae Family: These are small (45–55 nm), ether-resistant viruses containing double-stranded circular DNA and exhibiting cubic symmetry, with 72 capsomeres. The human representatives are the papilloma or wart virus and SV40-like viruses isolated from the brain tissue of patients with progressive multifocal leukoencephalopathy (PML) (JC virus) or from the urine of immunosuppressed renal transplant recipients (BK virus). (See Chapter 33.) Other members include papilloma viruses of rabbits and cattle, polyoma and K viruses of mice, and vacuolating viruses of monkeys (SV40) and of rabbits. These viruses have relatively slow growth cycles characterized by replication within the nucleus. Papovaviruses produce latent and chronic infections in their natural hosts. All are tumorigenic in at least some animal host species. (See Chapter 40.)

C. Adenoviridae Family: These are medium-sized (70–90 nm) viruses containing double-stranded DNA and exhibiting cubic symmetry, with 252 capsomeres. They are not enveloped and are ether-resistant. Thirty-one types are known to infect man; they have a predilection for mucous membranes and may persist for years in lymphoid tissue. Some of these agents cause acute respiratory diseases, febrile catarrhs, pharyngitis, and conjunctivitis. Human adenoviruses rarely cause disease in laboratory animals, but certain types produce tumors in newborn hamsters. A number of distinct serotypes are known for simian, bovine, canine, avian, and murine species. (See Chapters 37 and 40.)

D. Herpetoviridae Family: These are medium-sized viruses containing double-stranded DNA. The viral nucleocapsid, about 100 nm in diameter, possesses cubic symmetry with 162 capsomeres and is surrounded by a lipid-containing envelope. The enveloped virion is 150–200 nm in diameter. Latent infections may occur and last for the life span of the host, even in the presence of circulating antibodies.

Herpes simplex types 1 and 2, varicella-zoster, EB, and cytomegaloviruses infect man. Other members occur in monkeys, rabbits, cattle, horses, pigs, dogs, frogs, shrews, fowl, and snakes. (See Chapters 38 and 40.)

E. Poxviridae Family: These are relatively large, brick-shaped or ovoid viruses (230 X 300 nm) containing a double-stranded DNA genome and proteins, enveloped by double membranes. All poxviruses share a common nucleoprotein antigen and contain several enzymes, including a DNA-dependent RNA polymerase, within the virion. This is the major DNA-containing virus family which replicates solely within the cytoplasm.

This family includes members which are chiefly pathogenic for the skin not only in man (smallpox [variola], vaccinia, molluscum contagiosum) but also in lower animals (eg, cowpox, monkeypox, ectromelia or mousepox, fowlpox, fibroma and myxoma of rabbits). Some of the animal poxviruses (eg, cowpox, monkeypox) can infect man. (See Chapter 36.)

RNA-Containing Viruses

A. Picornaviridae Family: The genera whose members infect man are *Enterovirus* and *Rhinovirus.* At least 70 human enteroviruses are known; these include the polio-, coxsackie-, and echoviruses. Other types exist throughout the animal kingdom. More than 100 rhinoviruses have been isolated and are the most common cause of colds in man. Rhinoviruses are known to exist in other species, eg, foot-and-mouth disease virus of cattle.

Picornaviruses are small (20–30 nm), ether-resistant viruses, containing single-stranded RNA and exhibiting cubic symmetry. The enteroviruses and some rhinoviruses are stabilized by $MgCl_2$ against thermal inactivation. The rhinoviruses are acid-labile and have a high density in CsCl (1.39–1.45 gm/ml), 2 properties which distinguish them from the enteroviruses, which are acid-resistant and have a density of 1.32–1.35 gm/ml. (See Chapter 31.)

B. Reoviridae Family: Reoviruses were the first viruses shown to have double-stranded RNA. They are medium-sized (60–80 nm), ether-resistant viruses with cubic symmetry. Reovirus strains recovered from lower animals are similar to those of man. The association of human reoviruses with disease is not clear.

The family **Reoviridae** contains 2 genera: *Reovirus* and *Orbivirus.* Members of the genus *Reovirus* are characterized by capsids having a double layer of capsomeres. Members of the genus *Orbivirus* are arboviruses which (unlike most arboviruses) are ether-resistant, are serologically interrelated but are unrelated to reoviruses or other virus groups, and are more sensitive to low pH than the reoviruses.

Orbiviruses have an indistinct outer capsid and an inner capsid whose surface has 32 capsomeres. The outer layer capsomeres are unusually large (10–15 nm wide) and are doughnut-shaped. The proposed name refers to these unusual capsomeres (Latin *orbis* ring). The orbivirus genus includes bluetongue and African horse sickness viruses, Colorado tick fever virus, and a number of other agents of animals, insects, and plants.

C. Arbovirus Group: This is an ecologic grouping of more than 350 viruses which survive through a complex cycle involving vertebrate hosts and arthropods which serve as vectors, transmitting the viruses by their bites. Members infect a variety of species, including man, horses, domestic and wild birds, bats, snakes, and insects (mosquitoes, ticks). Common arboviruses pathogenic for man include the viruses of dengue; eastern, western, and Venezuelan encephalitis; Japanese encephalitis; St. Louis encephalitis; and yellow fever.

Arbovirus is not one of the groups listed in Table 27–1 since the grouping is based primarily upon ecologic factors and its members have diverse physical and chemical properties. However, considering together the viruses which are arthropod-transmitted serves a number of useful purposes. (See Chapter 30.)

D. Togaviridae Family: Members of this family include most arboviruses of antigenic groups A and B, rubella virus, and LDH (lactic dehydrogenase) virus of mice. These viruses possess a lipid-containing, ether-sensitive envelope and have a genome of single-stranded RNA; the enveloped virion is 40–70 nm in diameter. The virus particles mature by budding from the cytoplasmic and surface cell membranes. Some togaviruses, eg, Sindbis and Semliki Forest viruses, possess a nucleocapsid 35 nm in diameter. Within the nucleocapsid, a further spherical structure 12–16 nm in diameter has been suggested as the central core component. Sindbis virus probably has 32 capsomeres in an icosahedral surface lattice. Togaviruses constitute a large virus family with 4 genera: *Alphavirus* (group A arboviruses), with Sindbis virus as the type species; *Flavivirus* (group B arboviruses), with yellow fever virus as the type species; *Rubivirus*, with rubella virus as the type species; and *Pestivirus*, with mucosal diarrhea virus as the type species. (See Chapters 30 and 35.)

E. Arenaviridae Family: This grouping of viruses has been established because of the morphologic and biologic similarities and the common antigen shared by arboviruses of the Tacaribe complex (including the Junin and Machupo viruses of South American hemorrhagic fevers), Lassa virus, lymphocytic choriomeningitis (LCM) virus, and Pichinde virus. These RNA-containing, enveloped viruses have a mean diameter of 110 nm, with a range of 50–300 nm. The virions contain a number of electron-dense, RNA-containing granules about 20–30 nm in diameter which are indistinguishable in size, shape, and density from ribosomes. The group is named for these granules (Latin *arenaceus* sandy). Some members of this group produce "slow" virus infections. (See Chapters 30 and 33.)

F. Coronaviridae Family: Members are enveloped, 80–130 nm in size, and contain a genome of single-stranded RNA; the nucleocapsid is thought to be helical, 7–9 nm in diameter. They thus resemble the orthomyxoviruses morphologically except that the surface projections of coronaviruses are petal-shaped; this fringe of projections, resembling the solar corona, suggested the family name. Coronavirus nucleocapsids develop in the cytoplasm and mature by budding into cytoplasmic vesicles. The human coronaviruses have been isolated from patients with acute upper respiratory tract illness, primarily through the use of human embryonic tracheal and nasal organ cultures. Coronaviruses are known for lower animals: avian infectious bronchitis virus (IBV), mouse hepatitis virus, transmissible gastroenteritis virus and hemagglutinating encephalitis virus of swine, neonatal calf diarrhea virus, and probably rat pneumonotropic virus. (See Chapter 34.)

G. Retroviridae Family: Members of this family, which includes all of the RNA tumor viruses, superficially resemble the orthomyxoviruses in size and shape but have a more complicated internal structure (see Fig 40–4). They contain a high molecular weight RNA and traces of DNA. Various enzymes (ie, reverse transcriptase [RNA → DNA] and nucleases) have been associated with purified virions. The family has been divided into 3 subfamilies: **Oncovirinae**, which includes the leukemia and sarcoma viruses of mice, cats, fowl, and monkeys (see Chapter 40); **Spumavirinae**, which includes the foamy viruses of primates, cats, cattle, and man; and **Lentivirinae**, which includes visna and maedi viruses of sheep (slow viruses) (see Chapter 33).

H. Bunyaviridae Family: All the members of this family are arboviruses. They are spherical, enveloped particles 90–100 nm in diameter. These viruses replicate in the cytoplasm and acquire an envelope by budding through the cytoplasmic membrane. They are sensitive to ether, acid, and heat. About 70 members of the family are serologically related to Bunyamwera virus, the type species. An additional 50 viruses are included as possible members of the family; they are morphologically, but not serologically, related. (See Chapter 30.)

I. Orthomyxoviridae Family: These are medium-sized enveloped viruses containing single-stranded RNA and essential lipids and exhibiting helical symmetry. The enveloped virions vary in size from 80–120 nm. The particles are pleomorphic; roughly spherical forms predominate, but filamentous forms also are common. Most orthomyxovirus particles have a layer of surface projections or spikes as a part of their outer wall. The diameter of the internal ribonucleoprotein (RNP) helix is 6–9 nm, and the RNA is made up of 6 components. An RNA-dependent RNA polymerase is associated with purified virions. During replication, the helical nucleocapsid is first detected in the nucleus whereas the hemagglutinin and neuraminidase are formed in the cytoplasm. The virus matures by budding at the cell surface membrane. The orthomyxoviruses are sensitive to dactinomycin.

All orthomyxoviruses recognized to date are considered influenza viruses; they include the viruses of human, equine, and swine influenza and of fowl plague. They are classed as type A, B, or C on the basis of their RNP antigen, which does not cross-react between types. (See Chapter 34.)

J. Paramyxoviridae Family: Members are morphologically similar to orthomyxoviruses but are generally somewhat larger (150–300 nm). The diameter of the helical nucleocapsid is 18 nm, and the molecular weight of the single-stranded, nonsegmented paramyxovirus RNA is about 4 times greater than that of orthomyxovirus RNA. Also in contrast to orthomyxoviruses, both the nucleoprotein and the hemagglutinin antigens of paramyxoviruses are confined to the cytoplasm. The paramyxoviruses are resistant to dactinomycin. The virions of this group also contain enzymes such as RNA-dependent RNA polymerase and neuraminidase.

Paramyxoviruses of man include parainfluenza, measles, and mumps viruses. Paramyxoviruses of lower animals include simian paramyxoviruses and the viruses of Newcastle disease, distemper, and rinderpest.

Pneumonia virus of mice (PVM) and respiratory syncytial (RS) virus are also paramyxoviruses but differ in some aspects and have been placed in a separate genus, *Pneumovirus*. The diameters of their helical nucleocapsids are 12–15 nm, intermediate between the orthomyxoviruses and paramyxoviruses. Cells infected by RS or PVM viruses contain dense intracytoplasmic inclusions (presumably representing internal viral components), in contrast to the inclusions composed of loosely arranged nucleocapsids found in the cytoplasm of cells infected with other paramyxoviruses. (See Chapter 35.)

K. Rhabdoviridae Family: Members of this family have enveloped virions which are rod-shaped, resembling a bullet, flat at one end and rounded at the other (Fig 27–34). The diameter of the cylinder is 70 nm and the length about 175 nm. The envelope bears spikes 10 nm long. An internal helix, resembling the nucleoprotein helix of the paramyxoviruses, has been observed for several members of this group. The genome is single-stranded RNA. Virus particles are formed by budding from the cell surface membrane. Members include rabies virus, 6 arboviruses (vesicular stomatitis virus of cattle and several bat viruses), hemorrhagic septicemia of rainbow trout (Egtved virus), sigma virus of Drosophila, and a number of viruses of plants.

L. Other Viruses: Some viruses exist for which there are insufficient data to permit their inclusion in any of the above families. These include viruses which cause infectious and serum hepatitis (hepatitis A and B, respectively) and viruses responsible for certain immune complex diseases and neurologic disorders characterized by a long latent period ("slow" virus diseases).

M. Viroids: A class of infectious agents smaller than viruses, termed viroids, has recently been discovered. These agents cause several diseases of plants (eg, potato spindle tuber disease) and may ultimately be found to cause disease in man and higher animals (eg, scrapie disease of sheep). Viroids exhibit the characteristics of nucleic acids in crude extracts, ie, they are insensitive to heat and organic solvents but sensitive to nucleases, and they do not appear to possess a protein coat. Presently known viroids consist solely of a short strand of RNA with a molecular weight of 75,000–100,000.

CULTIVATION; QUANTIFICATION; INCLUSION BODIES; CHROMOSOME DAMAGE

Cultivation of Viruses

In the early years of virus research, the use of animals was mandatory for the recognition of viruses, and rapid, quantitative results were often difficult. For example, poliomyelitis research was limited as long as the presence of the virus could be detected only by monkey inoculation. At present, many viruses can be grown in cell cultures or in fertile eggs under strictly controlled conditions. Growth of virus in animals is still used for the primary isolation of certain viruses and for the study of pathogenesis of viruses and of viral oncogenesis.

A. Chick Embryos: Virus growth in an embryonated chick egg may result in the death of the embryo (eg, encephalitis virus), the production of pocks or plaques on the chorioallantoic membrane (eg, herpes, smallpox, vaccinia), the development of hemagglutinins in embryonic fluids or tissues (eg, influenza), or the development of infective virus (eg, poliovirus type 2).

B. Tissue Cultures: The availability of cells grown in vitro has facilitated the identification and cultivation of newly isolated and previously known viruses. There are 3 basic types of cell culture. Primary cultures are made by dispersing cells (usually with trypsin) from host tissues. In general, they are unable to grow for more than a few passages in culture, as secondary cultures. Diploid cell strains are secondary cultures which have undergone a change that allows their limited culture (up to 50 passages) but which retain their normal chromosome pattern. Continuous cell lines are cultures capable of more prolonged (perhaps indefinite) culture which have been derived from cell strains or from malignant tissues. They are invariably aneuploid, ie, they have altered and irregular numbers of chromosomes.

The type of cell culture used for virus cultivation depends on the sensitivity of the cells to that particular virus. The multiplication of the virus can be followed by determining the following:

1. The cytopathic effect, or necrosis of the cells in the tissue culture (polio, herpes, measles, adenovirus, cytomegalovirus, etc).

2. The inhibition of cellular metabolism, or failure of virus-infected cells to produce acid (eg, enteroviruses).

3. The appearance of a hemagglutinin (eg, mumps, influenza) or complement-fixing antigen (eg, poliomyelitis, varicella, measles).

4. The adsorption of erythrocytes to infected cells, called hemadsorption (parainfluenza, influenza). This reaction becomes positive before cytopathic changes are visible, and in some cases it is the only means of detecting the presence of the virus.

5. Interference by a noncytopathogenic virus (eg, rubella) with replication and cytopathic effect of a second, indicator virus (eg, echovirus).

6. Morphologic transformation by an oncogenic virus (eg, SV40, Rous sarcoma virus), usually accompanied by the loss of contact inhibition and the piling up of cells into discrete foci. Such alterations are a heritable property of the transformed cells.

Quantification of Virus

A. Physical Methods: Virus particles can be counted directly in the electron microscope by comparison with a standard suspension of latex particles of similar small size. However, a relatively concentrated preparation of virus is necessary for this procedure, and infectious virus particles cannot be distinguished from noninfectious ones.

Hemagglutination: The red blood cells of man, chickens, and other animals can be agglutinated by a number of different viruses. Hemagglutination by viruses has led to rapid and inexpensive quantitative methods of virus assay. Since both noninfective and infective viruses give the reaction, the test measures the total number of virus particles present.

The orthomyxoviruses contain a hemagglutinin which is an integral part of the viral envelope. Once these viruses have agglutinated with the cells, spontaneous dissociation of the virus from the cells can occur. The dissociated cells can no longer be agglutinated by the same virus species, but the recovered virus is able to agglutinate fresh cells. (See Chapter 34.) This is due to the destruction of specific mucopolysaccharide receptor sites on the surface of the erythrocyte by the enzyme neuraminidase associated with the virus particles. The hemagglutination reaction can be inhibited by mucopolysaccharides since they compete with erythrocytes for the virus.

The reaction of red blood cells with virus can also be used as an indicator of the growth of paramyxoviruses in chick embryos or tissue cultures. The erythrocytes will hemadsorb to the infected cells and can be observed visually.

A second group of viruses also agglutinates red cells, but in this group (poxviruses) the hemagglutinin is separable from the intact, infective virus particle. The hemagglutinin, a phospholipid-protein complex, is smaller than the virus and is not so readily sedimented in the centrifuge.

A third group of viruses (arboviruses and others) have hemagglutinins which appear to be identical with the virus. The union between hemagglutinin and red blood cells is irreversible.

B. Biologic Methods: Quantal assays depend on the measurement of animal death, animal infection, or cytopathic effects in tissue culture upon endpoint dilution of the virus being tested. The titer is expressed as the 50% infectious dose (ID_{50}), which is the reciprocal of the dilution of virus that produces the effect in 50% of the cells or animals inoculated. Precise assays require the use of a large number of test subjects.

Pock assays, ie, quantification of the number of pocks produced on chorioallantoic membranes of embryonated eggs inoculated with dilutions of virus, can be used to determine the amount of infectious virus for those viruses which produce such lesions, eg, herpes, vaccinia, smallpox.

The most widely used assay for infectious virus is the plaque assay. Monolayers of host cells are inoculated with suitable dilutions of virus and after adsorption are overlaid with medium containing agar or carboxymethylcellulose to prevent virus spreading. After several days, the cells initially infected have produced virus that spreads only to surrounding cells, producing a small area of infection, or plaque. Under controlled conditions a single plaque can arise from a single infectious virus particle, termed a plaque-forming unit (PFU). The cytopathic effect of infected cells within the plaque can be distinguished from uninfected cells of the monolayer, with or without suitable staining, and plaques can usually be counted macroscopically. The ratio of infectious particles varies widely, from near unity to less than 1 per 1000.

Inclusion Body Formation

In the course of virus multiplication within cells, virus-specific structures called inclusion bodies may be produced. They become far larger than the individual virus particle and often have an affinity for acid dyes such as eosin or acid fuchsin. They may be situated in the nucleus, in the cytoplasm, or in both (as in measles). In many viral infections, the inclusion bodies are believed to be the site of development of the virions (the virus factories). In some infections (molluscum contagiosum), the inclusion body consists of masses of virus particles which can be seen in the electron microscope to ripen to maturity within the inclusion body. In still others, as in the intranuclear inclusion body of herpes, the virus appears to have multiplied within the nucleus early in the infection, and the inclusion body appears to be a remnant of virus multiplication. Variations in the appearance of inclusion material depend largely upon the fixative used.

The presence of inclusion bodies may be of considerable diagnostic aid. The intracytoplasmic inclusion in nerve cells, the Negri body, is pathognomonic for rabies. A mild case of smallpox may be difficult to differentiate clinically from a severe case of chickenpox. Histologic examination of the skin lesion permits a rapid diagnosis; with smallpox, intracytoplasmic inclusions will be present; with chickenpox, intranuclear inclusions will be found.

Chromosome Damage

One of the consequences of infection of cells by

viruses is derangement of the karyotype. Most of the changes observed are random in nature. Frequently, breakage, fragmentation, and rearrangement of the chromosomes occurs; abnormal chromosomes and changes in chromosome number have also been observed. Herpes zoster virus induces a colchicine-like effect in human cells; the mitotic cycle is interrupted at metaphase, the chromosomes overcontract, and micronuclei form. Some of the chromosomes undergo fragmentation. Chromosome breaks have also been observed in leukocytes from patients with chickenpox and from patients with measles. These viruses, as well as rubella virus, cause similar aberrations when inoculated into cultured cells. Cells infected with or transformed to malignancy by papovaviruses SV40 and polyoma, and cells exposed to adenovirus type 12, also exhibit random chromosomal abnormalities. Many of these findings are preliminary, and analysis of the effect of various viruses on chromosomes is continuing.

Special studies have been carried out with the Chinese hamster cell, which has the advantage for cytogenetic studies of a stable karyotype composed of only 22 chromosomes. Inoculation of these hamster cells with herpes simplex virus results in chromosome aberrations that are not random in distribution. Most of the breaks occur in region 7 of chromosome No. 1 and in region 3 of the X chromosome. The Y chromosome is unaffected. Replication of the virus is necessary for induction of the chromosome aberrations. To date, no pathognomonic chromosome alterations have been identified in either virus-infected or virus-transformed cells.

STRUCTURE & SIZE OF VIRUSES

Virus Particles

Advances in x-ray diffraction technics and electron microscopy have made it possible to resolve fine differences in the basic morphology of viruses. The study of virus symmetry in the electron microscope requires the use of heavy metal stains (eg, potassium phosphotungstate) to emphasize surface structure. The heavy metal permeates the virus particle as a cloud and brings out the surface structure of viruses by virtue of "negative staining." While some particles can be seen in great detail, others such as the lipid-containing RNA tumor viruses only represent amorphous "blobs" using this simple technic.

Such studies made possible the grouping of virus architecture into 3 types based on the arrangement of morphologic subunits: (1) those with helical symmetry, eg, paramyxo- and orthomyxoviruses; (2) those with cubic symmetry, eg, adenoviruses; and (3) those with complex structures, eg, poxviruses. All cubic symmetry observed with animal viruses to date is of the icosahedral pattern. The icosahedron has 20 faces (each an equilateral triangle), 12 vertices, and 5-fold, 3-fold, and 2-fold axes of rotational symmetry. Capso-

meres can be arranged to comply with icosahedral symmetry in a limited number of ways expressed by the formula $N = 10(n-1)^2 + 2$, where N is the total number of capsomeres and n the number of capsomeres on one side of each equilateral triangle. Table 27–2 shows the number of capsomeres where n varies from 2–6, in several virus groups.

Icosahedral structures can be built from one simple, asymmetric building unit, arranged as 12 pentamer units and x number of hexamer units. The smallest and most basic capsid is that of the phage ϕX-174, which simply consists of 12 pentamer units.

Viruses exhibiting icosahedral symmetry can also be grouped according to their triangulation number, T, which is the number of small triangles formed on the single face of the icosahedron when each adjacent morphologic subunit is connected by a line. One class has T values of 1, 4, 9, 16, and 25; a second class, values of 3 and 12; and a third class, values of 7, 13, 19, and 21. The number of morphologic units (capsomeres) is expressed by the formula $M = 10T + 2$. Table 27–2 shows the triangulation number for several virus groups. This formula for triangulation number originated in the idea that those viruses would be formed from the small subunits in such a way as to give a surface lattice representing the minimum-energy design for closed shells arranged from identical units. All virus structures require that they have 60 × T structural subunits.

An example of icosahedral symmetry is seen in Fig 27–3. The adenovirus ($n = 6$) model illustrated shows the 6 capsomeres along one edge (Fig 27–3[a]). Degradation of this virus with sodium lauryl sulfate releases the capsomeres in groups of 9 (Fig 27–3[b], [c]) and possibly groups of 6. The groups of 9 lie on the faces, plus one capsomere from each of the 3 edges of the face, and the groups of 6 would be from the vertices. The groups of 9 from the faces of the 20 triangular facets making the adenovirus icosahedron account for 180 subunits, and the groups of 6 which form the 12 vertices account for 72 capsomeres, thus totaling 252.

Measuring the Sizes of Viruses

Small size and ability to pass through filters which hold back bacteria are classic attributes of viruses. However, because some bacteria may be

Table 27–2.

Virus Family	n	T	Capsomeres
Phage (ϕX-174)	2	1	12
Picorna*	2	3	32
Papova†	3	7	72
Reo	4	9	92(?)
Herpes	5	16	162
Adeno	6	25	252

*Picornaviruses are a special case and, for $n = 2$, fit the formula $N = 30(n-1)^2 + 2$.

†Capsomeres in a skew arrangement.

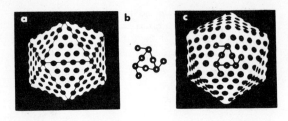

Figure 27–3. *(a)* Representation of the capsomere arrangement of an adenovirus particle, as viewed through the 2-fold axis of symmetry. *(b)* Arrangement of capsomere group of 9, obtained by treatment of an adenovirus with sodium lauryl sulfate. *(c)* Orientation of the capsomere group of 9 on the adenovirus particle. If the model were marked to show the maximum number of small triangles formed on one face of the icosahedron by drawing a line between each adjacent morphologic subunit, it would yield the triangulation number for the adenovirus particle, which in this case turns out to be 25.

smaller than the largest viruses, filtrability is no longer regarded as a unique feature of viruses.

The following methods are used for determining the sizes of viruses and their components.

A. Filtration Through Collodion Membranes of Graded Porosity: These membranes are available with pores of different sizes. If the virus preparation is passed through a series of membranes of known pore size, the approximate size of any virus can be measured by determining which membranes allow the infective unit to pass and which hold it back. The size of the limiting APD (average pore diameter), multiplied by 0.64, yields the diameter of the virus particle. It should be noted that the passage of a virus through a filter will also depend on the physical structure of the virus; thus, only a very approximate estimate of size is obtained.

B. Sedimentation in the Ultracentrifuge: If particles are suspended in a liquid, they will settle to the bottom at a rate which is proportionate to their size. In an ultracentrifuge, forces of more than 100,000 times gravity may be used to drive the particles to the bottom of the tube. The relationship between the size and shape of a particle and its rate of sedimentation permits determination of particle size. Once again, the physical structure of the virus will affect the size estimate obtained.

C. Direct Observation in the Electron Microscope: As compared with the light microscope, the electron microscope uses electrons rather than light waves and electromagnetic lenses rather than glass lenses. The electron beam obtained has a much shorter wavelength than that of light, so that objects much smaller than the wavelength of visible or ultraviolet light can be visualized. Viruses can be visualized not only in preparations made from tissue extracts but also in ultrathin sections of infected cells. Electron microscopy is the most widely used method for estimating particle size.

D. Ionizing Radiation: When a beam of charged particles such as high-energy electrons, alpha particles, or deuterons passes through a virus, it causes an energy loss in the form of primary ionization. The release of ionization within the virus particle inactivates certain biologic properties of the virus particle such as infectivity, antigenicity, and hemagglutination.

From the number of ionizations per unit volume or area which will destroy all but 37% of the biologic activity of the virus, the average sensitive volume or area per ionization can be determined. This is the point at which, according to the Poisson distribution, there has been an average of one hit per sensitive target, and so the volume or area per ionization is equivalent to the volume or area of the sensitive unit measured. Knowing the volume or area, one can readily calculate the diameter or area of the infective unit (or other biologic unit) in the virus particle. If the virus particle has properties other than infectivity, the rate of loss of each property will be proportionate to the size of the unit which governs the property in question. In this way, the sizes of viral genome segments coding for complement-fixing antigens and for hemagglutinins have been determined for certain viruses.

E. Comparative Measurements: (See Table 27–1.) For purposes of reference, it should be recalled that: (1) Staphylococcus has a diameter of about 1000 nm. (2) Bacterial viruses (bacteriophages) vary in size (10–100 nm). Some are spherical or hexagonal and have short or long tails. (3) Representative protein molecules range in diameter from serum albumin (5 nm) and globulin (7 nm) to certain hemocyanins (23 nm).

It should also be pointed out that particles with a 2-fold difference in diameter have an 8-fold difference in volume. Thus, the mass of a poxvirus is about 1000 times greater than that of the poliovirus particle, and the mass of a small bacterium is 50,000 times greater.

Throughout this text, in accordance with modern terminology, the term **nanometer (nm)** is used to express a length of 10^{-9} meter, instead of the old term millimicron (mμ), and the term **micrometer** (μm; 10^{-6} meter) is used instead of the old term micron (μ).

CHEMICAL COMPOSITION OF VIRUSES

Viral Protein

The structural proteins of viruses have several important functions. They serve to protect the viral genome against inactivation by nucleases, participate in the attachment of the virus particle to a susceptible cell, and are responsible for the structural symmetry of the virus particle. Also, the proteins determine the antigenic characteristics of the virus. The structural proteins of many viruses have been studied by the technic of sodium dodecyl sulfate-polyacrylamide gel electrophoresis (SDS-PAGE). In this technic, the proteins of the virus particle are dissociated by a detergent (SDS), then separated by electrophoresis through a polyacrylamide gel matrix. This allows description of virus particles in terms of their constituent proteins.

Poliovirus contains 4 structural polypeptides; these few polypeptides (one copy each) make up the structural units or protamers which are joined together in groups of 5, and then the groups of 5 form the 12 pentamers. Thus, there are the expected 60 structural units in the icosahedral shell.

The protein shell forms a compact and highly stable structure which encases the infectious RNA. Thus, the RNA does not contribute to the surface properties of the virus, eg, electrophoretic mobility and serologic specificity. Each infective poliovirion contains a single linear molecule of RNA with a molecular weight of 2.5 million. Little is known of the binding of the RNA to the protein.

Virus structural proteins may be very specialized molecules designed to perform a specific task: (1) vaccinia virus carries many enzymes within its particle to perform certain functions early in the infectious cycle; (2) some viruses have specific proteins for attachment to cells, eg, influenza virus hemagglutinin; and (3) RNA tumor viruses contain an enzyme, reverse transcriptase, that makes a DNA copy of the virus RNA, which is an important step in transformation by these viruses.

Viral Nucleic Acid

Viruses contain a single kind of nucleic acid, either DNA or RNA, in which is encoded the genetic information necessary for the replication of the virus. The RNA or DNA genome may be single-stranded or double-stranded and, as mentioned previously, the strandedness, the type of nucleic acid, and the molecular weight are major characteristics used for classifying viruses into families (Table 27–1). Most major families of RNA-containing animal viruses have single-stranded RNA genomes with the notable exception of the reoviruses, which have double-stranded RNA. Most major families of DNA-containing animal viruses have double-stranded DNA genomes, with the exception of single-stranded DNA-containing parvoviruses. The range of molecular weights found for DNA viruses is wider than that found for RNA viruses.

The molecular weight of the viral DNA genome ranges from $1.5–1.8 \times 10^6$ (parvoviruses) to 160×10^6 (poxviruses). The molecular weight of the viral RNA genome ranges from as low as 1×10^6 (for bromegrass mosaic virus) to as large as $10–15 \times 10^6$ (for reoviruses and retroviruses).

The type of nucleic acid can be determined by a number of methods, using either the intact virus particle or the free nucleic acid. Both the type of nucleic acid and the strandedness can be determined in the fluorescence microscope by staining with acridine orange (pH 4.0, dye concentration 0.01%) and the nucleic acids identified by color reactions and enzyme digestion tests (Table 27–3).

Uranyl acetate is a specific stain for DNA while having no affinity for RNA by electron microscopy. To characterize its physicochemical properties, it is necessary to isolate the nucleic acid from the virion. The usual procedure involves (1) lysis of the virus pro-

Table 27–3. Identification of viral nucleic acids with acridine orange (AO).

Carnoy-Fixed Virus Smear	Color Reaction With 0.01% AO At pH 4.0	Enzyme Susceptibility	
		DNase	RNase
Double-stranded DNA virus	Yellow	+	–
Single-stranded DNA virus	Red	+	–
Single-stranded RNA virus	Red	–	+
Double-stranded RNA virus	Yellow	–	+

tein coat by a detergent such as sodium dodecyl sulfate and (2) deproteinization by pronase and phenol.

After purification, the nucleic acid can be characterized for the type of sugar (ribose or deoxyribose), strandedness, size, and composition by technics involving nuclease treatment, centrifugation in solutions of cesium salts, column chromatography, electron microscopy, etc. The sequence and composition of nucleotides of each viral nucleic acid are distinct from that of any other. One of the properties useful for characterizing a viral nucleic acid is its guanine + cytosine (G + C) content. This can be computed from direct base composition analysis and from the relationships of G + C content to the buoyant density of the DNA in CsCl and to the melting point of the DNA.

Most viral genomes are quite fragile once they are removed from their protective protein capsid, but some nucleic acid molecules have been examined in the electron microscope without disruption, and their lengths have been measured. Using linear densities of approximately 2×10^6 per μm for double-stranded nucleic acid and 1×10^6 per μm for single-stranded forms, molecular weights of viral genomes can be calculated from direct measurements (Table 27–1).

All of the major DNA virus families in Table 27–1 have genomes that are single molecules of DNA and which for a given family have a linear or a circular configuration. This circle is often hypercoiled (Fig 27–4) in the virion. Most of the base sequences in DNA genomes are unique, but examples of cohesive ends and terminal or internal redundancy or repetition of sequences are found in certain DNA virus families. Studies of large DNA molecules have been aided in recent years by the use of enzymes isolated from bacteria and known as host-restriction endonucleases. These enzymes recognize certain specific base sequences in DNA molecules and cut the DNA within those sequences, yielding smaller DNA fragments which are easy to isolate and separate using agarose gel electrophoresis. The fragments are important in the mapping of genes in the larger DNA genome and in determining the molecular basis of DNA replication and function.

Viral RNAs exist in several forms. The RNA may be a single linear molecule, as found with picorna-, toga-, paramyxo-, and rhabdoviruses. For other viruses, eg, orthomyxo- and reoviruses, the genome consists of several molecules or segments of RNA which may be loosely linked together in some fashion within the

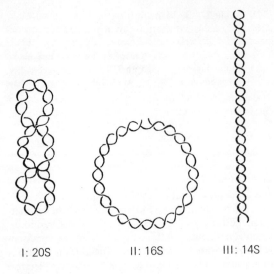

I: 20S   II: 16S   III: 14S

Figure 27—4. Diagrammatic representation of hypercoiled (I), circular (II), and linear (III) forms of polyoma DNA. Each morphologic form is associated with a specific sedimentation coefficient S.

virion. The isolated RNA of picornaviruses and togaviruses is infectious, and the entire molecule functions as a messenger RNA within the infected cell. The isolated RNA of other RNA viruses, including those with segmented and nonsegmented genomes, is not infectious. For these virus families, the virions carry an RNA polymerase which in the cell transcribes the genome RNA molecules into several complementary RNA molecules, less than genomic size, each of which may serve as a messenger RNA.

A detailed knowledge of molecular events following infection by different viruses has resulted from recent advances in molecular hybridization technics (DNA to DNA, DNA to RNA, or RNA to RNA), which have made it possible to study the extent of transcription of the viral genome within the infected cell as well as the relatedness of different viruses.

The number of genes in a virus can be approximated (Table 27—1) if one assumes the following: (1) the genetic code is triplet and nonoverlapping; (2) nucleic acid of 10^6 molecular weight in the form of a single strand (ie, the replicating form) contains 6000 nucleotides; and (3) the viral genes code for proteins, each of which contains about 200 amino acids.

Viral Lipids

A number of different viruses contain lipids as part of their structure. Electron microscopic studies of the enveloped Sindbis virus have yielded a proposed structure of the virion as seen in Fig 27—5. Such lipid-containing viruses are sensitive to treatment with ether and other organic solvents (Table 27—1), indicating that disruption or loss of lipid results in loss of infectivity. Nonlipid-containing viruses are generally resistant to the action of ether. The lipid composition of the viral envelope is probably similar to the lipid of the host membrane through which the virus buds. When the lipid composition of paramyxovirus SV5 was analyzed after the virus was grown in different cultured cell lines, the SV5 envelope had a phospholipid and glycolipid composition similar to that of the plasma membrane of the respective host cell. In contrast, there are other studies which suggest that the phospholipid and fatty acid composition of mature virus particles is partially virus-specific and does not necessarily reflect the lipid composition of the host cell surface membrane. These divergent trends may partially be the consequence of technologic problems encountered in attempts to isolate pure membrane fractions for analysis.

In a study of influenza virus obtained from

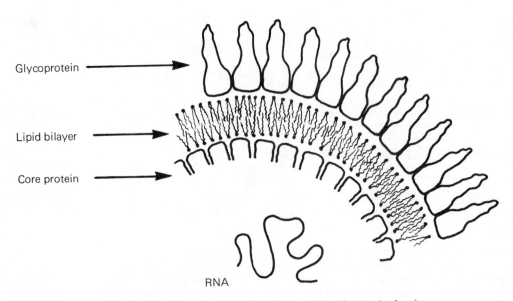

Glycoprotein

Lipid bilayer

Core protein

RNA

Figure 27—5. Proposed structure of Sindbis virus. (After Harrison & others.)

cultured chick embryo cells, the fatty acid composition of the isolated virus was found to be different from the host plasma membrane, but the phospholipid composition of vesicular stomatitis virus, another virus which buds from the plasma membrane, was the same as that of the plasma membrane of the host. In another study, the phospholipids of Newcastle disease virus, Sindbis virus, Rous sarcoma virus, and Sendai virus—all grown in chick embryo fibroblasts—were compared to the phospholipids of the plasma membrane of chick embryo fibroblasts. The phospholipid patterns of the virion envelopes of all 4 viruses were the same, but they differed from the host plasma membrane phospholipid composition. These results suggest that the requirements for "budding" during viral maturation, or adsorption to host cells at the onset of viral penetration, include a specific phospholipid composition of the virion envelope for a given cell type.

Recent studies on the phospholipid composition of herpes simplex virus, a virus which buds through the nuclear membrane (Fig 27–6), suggest that the phospholipid composition of the purified virion is more closely related to the inner nuclear membrane than to the outer nuclear membrane or cytoplasmic membrane.

The diverse ways in which different viruses acquire their envelopes is emphasized in Fig 27–7. Therefore, it seems unlikely that any unified theory of envelopment and lipid composition will emerge which will encompass all animal virus groups. Budding of virus particles (Fig 27–7) occurs only at sites in which virus-specific proteins have been inserted into the cell membrane.

Glycosphingolipids comprise a significant portion of the surface, or plasma, membrane of most animal cells. When cultured cells are transformed by either SV40, polyoma, or Rous sarcoma viruses, significant changes in the relative amounts of the various sphingoglycolipids result. There is a reduction in the amount of enzymes responsible for putting sugars on glycolipid. The changes in sphingoglycolipid composition may be related to loss of contact inhibition and to surface antigen changes which result from viral transformation.

Viral Carbohydrates

In addition to lipid and protein constituents, the

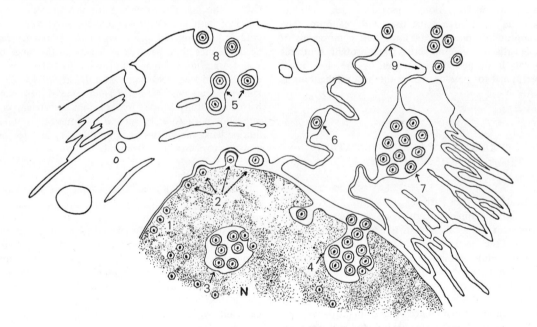

Figure 27–6. Envelopment and release of herpesvirus from infected cells. The numbers refer to specific steps in the process as discussed below. (Darlington & Moss.) Herpesvirus nucleocapsids are assembled in the cell nucleus and acquire envelopes from the nuclear rather than cytoplasmic membrane. Virus is assembled in the nucleus and approaches the nuclear membrane *(1)*. At the point of contact, the inner nuclear membrane becomes thicker and progressively envelops the virus particle *(2)* and finally pinches off, leaving the nuclear membrane intact and the enveloped particle free in the perinuclear cisterna. Nucleocapsids may also acquire envelopes by budding into nuclear vacuoles *(3)*. These vacuoles seem to be indentations of the nuclear membrane cut in cross section and are continuous with the perinuclear cisterna *(4)*. The virus particle is now transported from the vicinity of the nucleus toward an extracellular location in the following sequence: The outer lamella of the nuclear envelope wraps around the enveloped nucleocapsid and sequesters it from the cell cytoplasm *(5)*. When the vacuole reaches the cytoplasmic membrane, the enveloped virion is released outside the cell *(8)*. An additional route seems to be through the cisternae of the endoplasmic reticulum *(6, 7)* to the exterior of the cell *(9)*. Later in the infection, unenveloped particles may also appear in the cytoplasm where they may be enveloped, but breaks in the nuclear membrane are also present at this time. The envelopment process occurs whenever the nucleocapsid comes into contact with a cell membrane and may represent a cellular defense mechanism. Since the nuclear membrane is the first membrane encountered, it would be the primary site of envelopment.

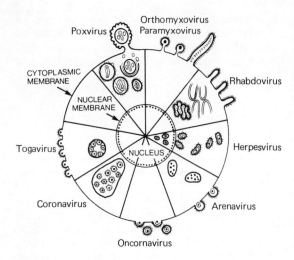

Figure 27—7. Diagrammatic relationship between lipid-containing viruses and host cell membranes. (From Blough & Tiffany.)

viral envelope also contains a significant amount of carbohydrate, mainly in glycoproteins. These glycoproteins may contain various monosaccharides, including glucosamine, fucose, galactose, and mannose. The glycoproteins appear to be important components of viral antigenic determinants. Glycoprotein synthesis appears to be partially controlled by the virus but is determined to some degree by the host cell genome as well.

PURIFICATION & IDENTIFICATION OF VIRUSES

Purification of Virus Particles

With the application of tissue culture methods to the growth and assay of virus infectivity, quantities of materials such as never existed before became available for purification studies. In addition, large quantities of viral material may be produced in the naturally infected host in virus diseases for which a tissue culture system has not been developed. A prime example of this situation is the presence of large quantities of viral particles in the blood of people infected with hepatitis type B. In general, the starting material is usually large volumes of tissue culture medium, body fluids, or infected cells. The first step usually involves concentration of the virus particles by precipitation with ammonium sulfate, ethanol, or polyethylene glycol or by ultrafiltration. Hemagglutination can also be used as the basis of a method for concentrating myxoviruses. After the virus has been adsorbed onto erythrocytes, it can be eluted into a small volume of buffer and the erythrocytes removed by centrifugation. Once concentrated, virus can be separated from host materials by differential centrifugation, density gradient centrifugation, column chromatography, and electrophoresis.

Rate-Zonal Centrifugation

A sample of concentrated virus is layered onto a preformed linear density gradient of sucrose or glycerol, and during centrifugation the virus sediments as a band at a rate determined primarily by the size and weight of the virus particle. Samples are collected by piercing a hole in the bottom of the centrifuge tube. The band of purified virus may be detected by optical methods, by radiolabeling the virus, or by assaying for infectivity.

Equilibrium Density Gradient Centrifugation

Viruses can also be purified by high-speed centrifugation in density gradients of cesium chloride (CsCl), potassium tartrate, potassium citrate, or sucrose. The gradient material of choice is the one that is least toxic to the virus. A density gradient is either preformed mechanically or in some cases (eg, CsCl) can be established during centrifugation. Virus particles migrate to an equilibrium position where the density of the solution is equal to their buoyant density and the virus particles form a visible band. Virus bands may be harvested by puncture through the bottom of the plastic centrifuge tube and then assayed for infectivity. CsCl is the material of choice for this procedure because of its high density and low viscosity. Relatively crude preparations of viruses with cubic symmetry can be used since they band at a density in the range of 1.3–1.4 gm/ml, whereas cell proteins float at a density of 1.25 and free DNA bands at a density of 1.7. Certain viruses are unstable in CsCl and some of these have been successfully banded in potassium tartrate and citrate and in sucrose. In sucrose or potassium citrate, murine leukemia viruses band at a density of 1.16 and most myxoviruses at 1.20 gm/ml.

Criteria of Purity

There can be no absolute criteria, but one would at least require (1) that the particles appear homogeneous in the electron microscope, (2) that uninfected cells that are radioactively labeled show no radioactive material which "purifies with virus" (that is to say, when added to a virus suspension, which is then purified, no radioactive label contaminates the fraction containing the purified virus), and (3) that additional purification procedures fail to remove additional contaminants without reducing infectivity.

Identification of a Particle as a Virus

When a characteristic physical particle has been obtained from various tissues, it should fulfill as many of the following criteria as possible before it is identified as the virus particle. In brief, these are as follows:

(1) The particle can be obtained only from infected cells or tissues.

(2) Particles obtained from various sources are identical, regardless of the cellular species in which the virus is grown.

(3) The degree of infective activity of the virus varies directly with the number of particles present.

(4) The degree of destruction of the physical

particle by chemical or physical means is associated with a corresponding loss of virus activity.

(5) Certain properties of the particles and infectious virus must be shown to be identical, such as their sedimentation behavior in the ultracentrifuge and their pH stability curves.

(6) The absorption spectrum of the purified physical particle in the ultraviolet range should coincide with the ultraviolet inactivation spectrum of the virus.

(7) Antisera prepared against the infective virus should react with the characteristic particle and vice versa. Direct observation of an unknown virus can be accomplished by electron microscopic examination of aggregate formation in a mixture of antisera and crude virus suspension.

(8) The particles should be able to induce the characteristic disease in vivo (if such experiments are feasible).

(9) Passage of the particles in tissue culture should result in the production of progeny with biologic and serologic properties of the virus.

REACTION TO PHYSICAL & CHEMICAL AGENTS

Heat & Cold

Virus infectivity is generally destroyed by heating at 50–60° C for 30 minutes, although there are some notable exceptions (eg, serum hepatitis virus, adeno-satellite virus, scrapie virus).

Viruses can be preserved by storage at subfreezing temperatures, and some may withstand lyophilization and can thus be preserved in the dry state at 4° C or even at room temperature. Viruses which withstand lyophilization are more heat-resistant when heated in the dry state. Enveloped viruses tend to lose infectivity after prolonged storage even at −90° C and are particularly sensitive to repeated freezing and thawing; however, in the presence of dimethyl sulfoxide (DMSO) at concentrations as low as 5%, these viruses are effectively stabilized.

Stabilization of Viruses by Salts

Many viruses can be stabilized by molar concentrations of salts, ie, they are not inactivated even by heating at 50° C for 1 hour. The mechanism by which the salts stabilize virus preparations is not known. Viruses are preferentially stabilized by certain salts (Table 27–4).

The stability of viruses is important in the preparation of vaccines. The ordinary nonstabilized poliovaccine must be stored at freezing temperatures to preserve its potency. However, with the addition of salts for stabilization of the virus, potency can be maintained for weeks at ambient temperatures, even in the high temperatures of the tropics.

Heating of some virus preparations in the

Table 27–4. Stabilization of viruses by salts.

Molar MgCl₂	Molar MgSO₄	Molar Na₂SO₄
Picornaviruses	Orthomyxo-viruses	Herpesvirus
Polioviruses	Influenza virus	Herpes
Echoviruses	Paramyxoviruses	simplex virus
Coxsackie-viruses	Parainfluenza virus	
Rhinoviruses	Measles virus	
Reoviruses	Rubella virus	

presence of high salt concentrations can be used to remove adventitious agents. For example, heating poliovirus suspensions in molar $MgCl_2$ will inactivate such simian contaminants as SV40, foamy virus, and herpes B virus but has no deleterious effect on the infectivity and potency of poliovirus.

pH

Viruses are usually stable between pH values of 5.0 and 9.0. Because of the electrostatic forces in the hemagglutination reactions, variations of a few tenths of a pH unit may be the deciding factor in obtaining positive or negative results in this test.

Radiation

Ultraviolet, x-ray, and high-energy particles inactivate viruses. The dose varies for different viruses.

Vital Dyes

Viruses are penetrable to a varying degree by vital dyes such as toluidine blue, neutral red, and proflavine. These dyes unite with the viral nucleic acid, and the virus then becomes susceptible to inactivation by visible light. A gradient of photodynamic inactivation ranges from viruses which are impenetrable and therefore not inactivated (eg, polioviruses) through those which are moderately susceptible (adenovirus, reovirus) to those which are readily inactivated (herpesvirus, vaccinia). Impenetrable viruses like poliovirus, when grown in the dark in the presence of vital dyes, incorporate the dye into their nucleic acid and are then susceptible to photodynamic inactivation. The coat antigen is unaffected by the process. Photodynamic inactivation has recently been introduced as a method of treating herpetic lesions.

Ether Susceptibility

Ether susceptibility has been useful for distinguishing viruses that possess a lipid-rich envelope from those that do not. The following viruses are inactivated by ether: herpes-, orthomyxo-, paramyxo-, rhabdo-, corona-, retro-, arena-, toga-, and bunyaviruses. The following viruses are resistant to ether: parvo-, papova-, adeno-, picorna-, and reoviruses. The poxviruses are unique in that members vary in sensitivity to ether.

Antibiotics

Antibacterial antibiotics and sulfonamides have no effect on viruses. Rifampin and some of its derivatives can inhibit poxvirus replication.

Metabolic analogues or antibiotics that interfere with synthesis of DNA or RNA will inhibit viral replication. These analogues also interfere with the metabolic processes of the host cell and are therefore too toxic to be of any chemotherapeutic value in the treatment of most virus infections. However, investigative work is continuing in this area.

Antibacterial Agents

Under usual conditions, quaternary ammonium compounds are effective against only a few viruses. Larger concentrations of chlorine are required to destroy viruses than to kill bacteria. For example, the chlorine treatment of stools recommended for typhoid carriers is inadequate to destroy poliomyelitis virus present in feces. Dilute hydrochloric acid and formalin destroy resistant viruses like those of the poliomyelitis and coxsackie groups.

Organic iodine compounds are also relatively ineffective against viruses because tiny amounts of contaminating organic matter rapidly deplete the active iodine.

REPLICATION OF VIRUSES

Viruses require a living cell to multiply. The host cell must provide not only the energy and synthetic machinery but also the low molecular weight precursors for the synthesis of viral proteins and nucleic acids. The viral nucleic acid carries the genetic specificity to code for all the virus-specific macromolecules in a highly organized fashion. In many instances, as soon as the viral nucleic acid enters the host cell, the cellular metabolism is redirected exclusively toward the synthesis of new virus particles. In other cases, however, the metabolic processes of the host cell are not altered significantly, although the cell synthesizes viral proteins and nucleic acids. The ability of a virus to control its host's metabolic processes depends both upon the nature of the virus and the type of the host cell.

During the replicative cycle, viruses use several different methods to transfer genetic information from one generation to another. The essential theme, however, is that specific mRNAs must be transcribed from the viral nucleic acid for successful expression and duplication of genetic information. Once this is accomplished, viruses use cell components to translate the mRNA. Various classes of viruses use different pathways to synthesize the mRNAs depending upon the structure of the viral nucleic acid. Some viruses (eg, vaccinia virus, rhabdoviruses, orthomyxoviruses, paramyxoviruses) carry RNA polymerases to synthesize mRNAs. Table 27–5 summarizes the various pathways of transcription (but not necessarily that of replication) of the nucleic acids of different classes of viruses.

Most of the viral mRNAs possess a sequence of polyadenylic acid [Poly (A)] at their 3'-end. Though it has been postulated that Poly (A) sequences in mRNAs may be necessary for conservation, translation, or even transport of the mRNAs, the precise function of these sequences is yet to be elucidated.

Virus multiplication was first studied successfully in bacteriophages. These studies have resulted in a fairly complete picture of the mechanism of phage replication—in particular, the T-even series of bacteriophages—which is presented in Chapter 9. The studies of animal viruses have not been so fruitful, but some of the steps of the interaction between the infecting virus and susceptible cells have now been elucidated.

The following 2 sections describe the replication of an RNA and a DNA virus that have been studied in some detail.

RNA Virus Replication (Fig 27–8)

The replication of poliovirus, which contains a single-stranded RNA as its genome, provides a useful

Table 27–5. Pathways of nucleic acid transcription for various virus classes.

Type of Viral Nucleic Acid	Intermediates	Type of mRNA	Example	Comments
± DS DNA	None	+ mRNA	Most DNA viruses (eg, herpesvirus, T4 bacteriophage)	
+ SS DNA	± DS DNA	+ mRNA	φX bacteriophage	See Chapter 9.
± DS RNA	None	+ mRNA	Reovirus	
+ SS RNA	± DS RNA	+ mRNA	Picornavirus	Viral nucleic acid is infectious and serves as mRNA
+ SS RNA	None	− mRNA	Rhabdoviruses, paramyxoviruses, orthomyxoviruses	Viral nucleic acid is not infectious; virion contains RNA polymerase
+ SS RNA	− DNA, ± DNA	? mRNA	Retroviruses	Noninfectious nucleic acid; virion contains reverse transcriptase

DS = double-stranded
SS = single-stranded

− indicates negative strand
+ indicates positive strand

± indicates a helix containing a positive and a negative strand

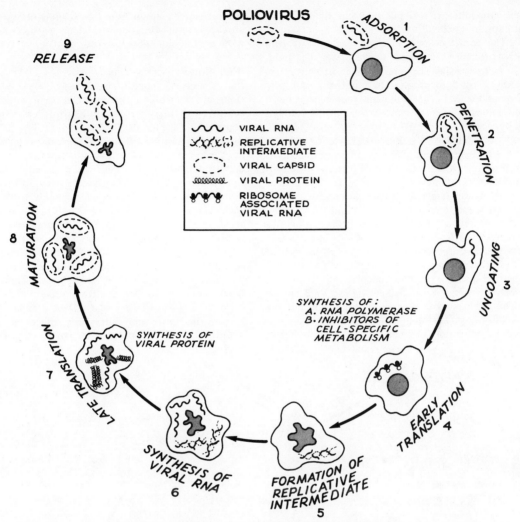

POLIOVIRUS

9 RELEASE

1 ADSORPTION

2 PENETRATION

3 UNCOATING

	VIRAL RNA
	REPLICATIVE INTERMEDIATE
	VIRAL CAPSID
	VIRAL PROTEIN
	RIBOSOME ASSOCIATED VIRAL RNA

8 MATURATION

7 LATE TRANSLATION

SYNTHESIS OF VIRAL PROTEIN

SYNTHESIS OF:
A. RNA POLYMERASE
B. INHIBITORS OF CELL-SPECIFIC METABOLISM

4 EARLY TRANSLATION

6 SYNTHESIS OF VIRAL RNA

5 FORMATION OF REPLICATIVE INTERMEDIATE

Figure 27—8. Replication of poliovirus, which contains an RNA genome.

example. All of the steps are independent of host DNA and occur in the cell cytoplasm. Polioviruses adsorb to cells at specific cell receptor sites (step 1), losing in the process one virus polypeptide (VP 4) which may, therefore, be important in adsorption. The sites are specific for virus coat-cell interactions. This is evidenced by the fact that intact poliovirus infects only primate cells in culture, whereas the isolated RNA will also infect nonprimate cells (rabbit, guinea pig, chick) and complete one cycle of multiplication. Multiple cycles of infection are not observed in nonprimate cells because the resulting progeny possess protein coats and will again infect only primate cells. After attachment, the virus particles are taken into the cell by viropexis (similar to pinocytosis) (step 2), and the viral RNA is uncoated (step 3). The single-stranded RNA can then serve as its own messenger RNA. This messenger RNA is translated (step 4), resulting in the formation of an RNA polymerase—a protein which has not yet been identified. The RNA polymerase catalyzes the production of a replicative intermediate (RI), a partially

double-stranded molecule consisting of a complete RNA strand and numerous partially completed strands (step 5). At the same time, inhibitors of cellular RNA and protein synthesis of unknown origin and nature are produced. It is not yet absolutely clear how synthesis of (+) and (−) strands of RNA comes about, but it appears likely that the mechanism is similar for both, although only completely elucidated for (+) strands. Here the RI consists of one complete (−) strand and many small pieces of newly synthesized (+) strand RNA (step 6).

Another form of RNA is produced in the infected cell. The replicative form (RF) consists of 2 complete RNA strands, one (+) and one (−). It appears likely at present that this is a byproduct of RNA synthesis.

The single (+) strand RNA is made in large amounts and may perform any one of 3 functions: (a) serve as messenger RNA for synthesis of structural proteins, (b) serve as template for continued RNA replication, or (c) become encapsidated, resulting in mature progeny virions. The synthesis of viral capsid proteins (step 7) is initiated at about the same time as RNA synthesis.

The entire poliovirus genome acts as its own mRNA, forming a polysome of ~350S, and is translated to form a single large polypeptide which is subsequently cleaved to produce the various viral capsid polypeptides. Thus, the poliovirus genome serves as a polycistronic messenger molecule. Poliovirus contains 4 polypeptides: VP 1 (MW = 3.5×10^4), VP 2 (MW = 2.8×10^4), VP 3 (MW = 2.4×10^4), and VP 4 (MW = 6×10^3). Polyacrylamide gel electrophoresis analysis has also been carried out on virus particles devoid of their RNA that have been separated from infectious virus by density gradient centrifugation. These particles were found to contain only VP 1 and VP 3, as well as a new polypeptide, VP 0. It is believed that this RNA-free particle (or procapsid) may be important in the regulation of virus functions and is a precursor of the infectious virus, and that as the RNA becomes associated with the procapsid in some as yet unknown fashion (step 7), VP 0 is cleaved to yield VP 2 and VP 4. The mechanism of cleavage is unknown, but the possibility exists that one of the 3 procapsid polypeptides (VP 0, VP 1, or VP 3) may possess an appropriate

enzyme activity. Completion of encapsidation (step 8) produces mature virus particles which are then released when the cell undergoes lysis (step 9).

DNA Virus Replication (Fig 27–9)

In poxvirus replication, synthesis of virus components and assembly of virus particles occur within the cytoplasm of the infected cell. Poxvirus replication is described in Chapter 36.

The replication of other DNA viruses (including the adeno-, herpes-, and papovavirus families) differs in that viral DNA is replicated in the nucleus, whereas viral proteins are synthesized in the cytoplasm followed by their migration to, and assembly within the nucleus. Fig 27–9 shows the steps in the replication of adenovirus, a double-stranded DNA tumor virus. In general, the adsorption (step 1) and penetration (step 2) of the virus into the cell are similar to steps described for poliovirus. After the virus enters the cell, the protein coat is removed (step 3), presumably by cellular enzymes, and the viral DNA is released into the nucleus. In most cases one of the DNA strands is transcribed (in SV40 and herpesvirus infections, both strands of a small part of the DNA may be transcribed)

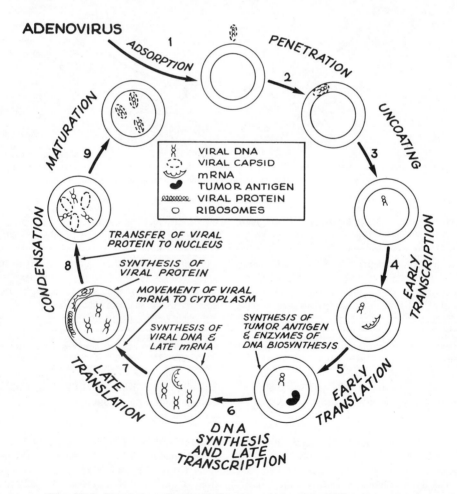

Figure 27–9. Steps in the replication of adenovirus, which contains DNA in its genome.

Figure 27–10. Diagrammatic representation of replicating SV40 papovavirus DNA. The salient features of the molecule are that (1) both parental DNA strands (solid lines) are covalently closed, and (2) the 2 newly synthesized DNA strands (broken lines) are not covalently linked to the parental DNA nor are they linked together. (From Sebring, Kelly, Thoren, & Salzman.)

(step 4) into specific mRNA, which in turn is translated (step 5) to synthesize virus-specific proteins, such as tumor antigen and enzymes necessary for biosynthesis of virus DNA. This period encompasses the early virus functions. Host cell DNA synthesis is temporarily elevated and is then suppressed as the cell shifts over to the manufacture of viral DNA (step 6). As the viral DNA continues to be transcribed, late virus functions become apparent. Messenger RNA transcribed during the later phase of infection (step 6) migrates to the cytoplasm and is translated (step 7). Proteins for virus capsids are synthesized and are transported to the nucleus to be incorporated into the complete virion (step 8). The migration of some structural proteins of certain viruses from the cytoplasm to the nucleus can be inhibited when arginine is absent from the growth medium. Assembly of the protein subunits around the viral DNA results in the formation of complete virions (step 9), which are released after cell lysis.

The replication of SV40 circular DNA has been well characterized. There is a single unique origin for DNA synthesis; the synthesis is RNA-primed and discontinuous (giving rise to short fragments which are joined together by a ligase), and it proceeds bidirectionally. (See Fig 27–10.)

It has been shown that early and late mRNA is transcribed off different strands of the papovavirus genome. Regulatory controls responsible for such a strand switch during transcription are unknown.

Summary of Viral Replication

The molecular events that have been discussed above are summarized in Fig 27–11. Viruses with

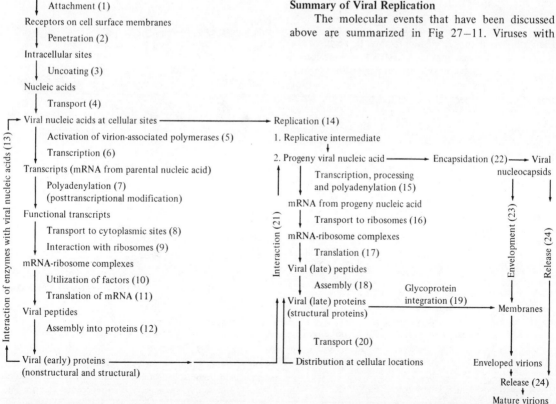

Figure 27–11. Molecular events in the replication of viruses. (From Becker, Monogr Virol, vol 11, 1976.)

genomes containing double-stranded (ds) nucleic acid proceed along most of the steps shown in the figure. Viruses with single-stranded (ss) nucleic acid utilize only some of the steps. For the orthomyxoviruses, the RNA template is utilized for the synthesis of a complementary RNA strand which produces the replicative form of the nucleic acid. This in turn serves as the template for the synthesis of the progeny viral RNA. For the retroviruses, the ssRNA acts as a template for the RNA-dependent DNA polymerase (reverse transcriptase) to synthesize dsDNA. The dsDNA molecules are then used as templates for the transcription and synthesis of ssRNA molecules which serve either as viral mRNA molecules or as viral genomes for encapsidation by the viral structural proteins.

In Vitro Synthesis of Infectious Viral DNA

Several infectious RNAs and DNAs have been synthesized for small viruses. Recent studies with small DNA phages have shed some light on DNA replication in the prokaryotic host cell. Since these phages are so small, they have limited genetic information and rely on host cell enzymes for DNA replication. The in vitro replication of phage DNA has been used to determine what enzymes are involved for various replication steps. The replication of phage DNA serves as a model for the replication of host DNA since the same enzymes are involved.

DNA replication is divided into 3 stages: initiation, elongation, and termination (Fig 27–12). The first stage requires the synthesis of small pieces of RNA which act as a primer for the elongation of DNA along the DNA template. For different small phage DNAs, different proteins and enzymes are required. In the simplest case, phage G4, only RNA polymerase of the host is required. In a more complex case, as many as 5 different proteins of the bacteria are required for this step. In all cases, it is essential that all the DNA except the initiation site be coated with proteins of high affinity for DNA which have no other enzymatic function. Elongation of DNA using the RNA primer requires only DNA polymerase III of the host.

Termination requires DNA polymerase I which removes the RNA primer and fills the gap with DNA. Another enzyme, ligase (joining enzyme), then seals the new replacement DNA to that previously made.

Thus, what once seemed a relatively simple mechanism for making phage DNA requires a complex series of enzymes including some, if not all, of those required for host DNA replication.

Control Mechanisms in Virus Replication

In the course of virus replication, all the virus-specified macromolecules are synthesized in a highly organized sequence, although virus components are usually made in excess. In some virus infections early viral proteins are synthesized soon after infection and late proteins are made only late in infection after viral DNA synthesis. Early genes may or may not be shut off when late products are made. In addition to these temporal controls, quantitative controls also exist,

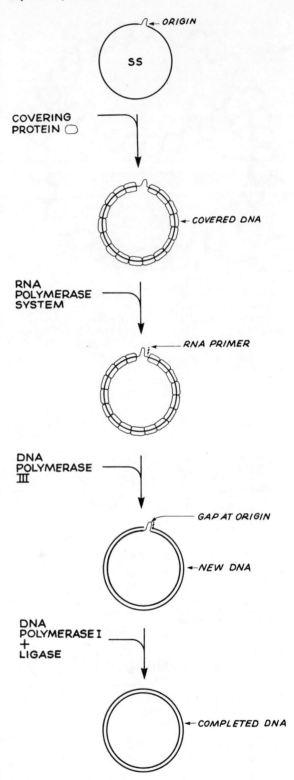

Figure 27–12. Model for the synthesis of phage DNA. (Reproduced, with permission, from Schekman R, Weiner A, Kornberg A: Multi-enzyme systems of DNA replication. Science 186: 987, 1974. Copyright © 1974 by the American Association for the Advancement of Science.)

since not all virus proteins are made in the same amounts. Virus-specific proteins may regulate the extent of transcription of genome or the translation of viral messenger RNA.

The presence of such control mechanisms makes animal viruses attractive models for studying eukaryotic gene expression. Reovirus is one animal virus whose genetic material (double-stranded RNA) is arranged in 10 separate pieces. Synthesis of proteins from messenger RNA species transcribed from all 10 pieces of RNA has been demonstrated in vitro in cell-free systems. Thus, this virus at least does not appear to contain any RNA with an exclusively regulatory role.

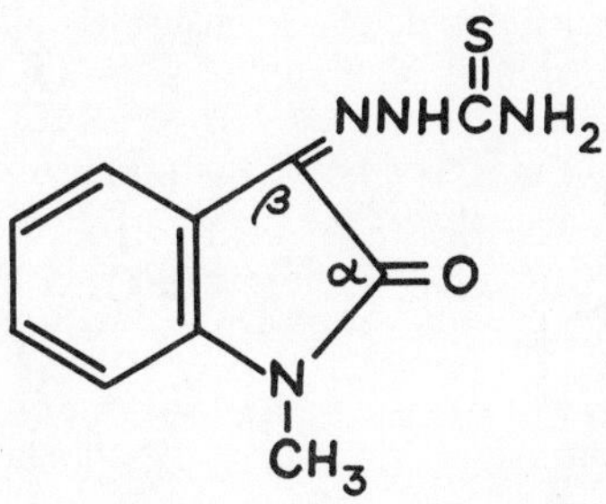

Figure 27–13. Methisazone (N-methylisatin-β-thiosemicarbazone, Marboran), an inhibitor of poxvirus replication.

EXPERIMENTAL CHEMOPROPHYLAXIS OF VIRUS INFECTIONS

It is possible in the infected cell to inhibit some processes leading to the synthesis of viral constituents or to inhibit adsorption, penetration, or release of infectious virus from the host cell. A number of different types of compounds have been described whose actions are directed toward metabolic reactions of the host cell. However, in order to be considered for chemoprophylaxis, they must have a greater specificity for virus-directed reactions than for normal host cell reactions. The inhibitors range from those which are highly virus-specific to those which are only slightly virus-specific. At this time, no inhibitors are available that can be used in the routine treatment of viral infections in man.

Very few inhibitors have been found which have a specific effect on virus penetration or release from the host cell. **Amantadine (Symmetrel)**, a synthetic amine, specifically inhibits certain orthomyxoviruses by blocking viral penetration into the host cell or by blocking virus uncoating. When administered prophylactically, amantadine is reported to have a significant protective effect in experimental animals and man against influenza A strains but not against influenza B or other viruses. This protection consists mainly of a modification of the disease to a milder form.

Guanidine and **2-(a-hydroxybenzyl)-benzimidazole (HBB)** inhibit the replication of many picornaviruses in vitro. The action of the 2 compounds is similar, but not identical, since some viruses can be inhibited by one but not by the other. In experimentally infected animals, neither of the inhibitors has any protective effect. This is probably due to rapid production of drug-resistant mutants. Both drug-resistant and drug-dependent virus mutants have been isolated. The mechanism of action is not certain, but there are 3 probably related effects: (1) cleavage of capsid proteins does not occur normally, (2) empty capsids appear, and (3) viral RNA is not released from the replicative intermediate.

Methisazone (Marboran) (see Fig 27–13 and p

127) is an inhibitor of many members of the poxvirus and adenovirus families. This compound is the N-methyl derivative of isatin-β-thiosemicarbazone (IBT). Methisazone is highly virus-specific and does not affect normal cell metabolism. Viral DNA synthesis occurs normally in the presence of this inhibitor, but not all viral proteins are synthesized. The result is that immature, noninfectious virus particles are formed. Methisazone blocks poxvirus replication in experimental animals. It has reported prophylactic value for smallpox in man if given within 24–48 hours after exposure.

N-ethyl IBT can block the production of Rous sarcoma virus by transformed cells. However, cells transformed by Rous sarcoma virus continue to produce virus particles in the presence of the drug, though the particles are noninfectious. Both N-ethyl and N-methyl IBT—but not the parent IBT molecule itself—interact directly with the virus particle and inactivate a variety of oncornaviruses (Rous sarcoma virus, avian leukosis virus, mouse sarcoma virus). The mechanism is not known.

Many **purine** and **pyrimidine analogues** inhibit both RNA and DNA synthesis. By the incorporation of ribose or deoxyribose into the molecule to make the corresponding riboside or deoxyriboside, the activity of the analogue can be directed preferentially toward the inhibition of RNA or DNA viruses.

Pyrimidine analogues may exert an action according to their structural similarities to either uracil or thymine (Fig 27–14). With halogenated pyrimidines, it has been found that the size of the particular halogen atom attached determines the character of the compound. The Van der Waals radii of fluorine and bromine resemble closely those of hydrogen and the methyl group, respectively; thus, the size and shape of 5-bromouracil is very similar to that of thymine, and that of 5-fluorouracil is similar to that of uracil. 5-Bromouracil is an effective inhibitor of the synthesis of DNA-containing bacteriophage, but is without effect on the synthesis of RNA-containing tobacco mosaic virus. In contrast, 5-fluorouracil (FU) inhibits the growth of the RNA virus; the action of FU is reversed by uridine but not by thymidine.

FU exerts an inhibitory effect on DNA viruses as well. In the presence of FU, herpesvirus-infected cells

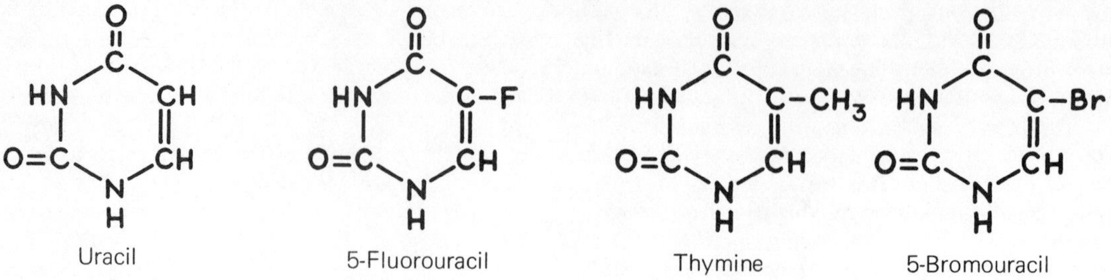

Figure 27–14. Structures of uracil, 5-fluorouracil, thymine, and 5-bromouracil.

produce virus particles that are noninfectious because they lack DNA cores. With papovavirus SV40, large amounts of viral antigen are produced in the nucleus but are not assembled into the capsid.

5-Fluoro-2′-deoxyuridine (FUDR) inhibits DNA synthesis by interfering with the enzymatic synthesis of thymidylic acid; **5-bromo-2′-deoxyuridine (BUDR)** and **5-iodo-2′-deoxyuridine (IUDR)** are incorporated into DNA, resulting in the production of a faulty nucleic acid which does not function normally. These compounds also interfere with enzymatic synthesis of DNA precursors. All 3 of these halogenated deoxyuridines inhibit replication of members of the major DNA virus families: papova-, adeno-, herpes-, and poxviruses. Drug-resistant mutants of some viruses have been obtained, however, by growth in the presence of IUDR or BUDR. Topical administration of IUDR is used, but with limited success, in man in the treatment of corneal lesions due to herpes simplex virus. Because of its toxicity and lack of efficacy in systemic herpes infections, intravenous infusion of IUDR has been abandoned.

The treatment of papovavirus- or herpesvirus-infected cells with IUDR arrests the synthesis of new infectious virus but not of viral components. Large amounts of viral antigen are found in IUDR-treated infected cells so that structurally imperfect herpesvirus particles can be observed in the presence of IUDR. Perhaps the antiviral activity of IUDR is due to a faulty assembly of viral components.

5′-Amino-2′,5′-dideoxy-5-iodouridine, a new thymidine analogue, inhibits replication of herpes simplex virus but is much less toxic to normal cells.

Another pyrimidine analogue is **cytarabine (1-β-D-arabinofuranosylcytosine monohydrochloride, Ara-C, cytosine arabinoside)**. In vivo, Ara-C is converted to Ara-CTP, which can be incorporated into DNA. Ara-CTP can also inhibit mammalian cell DNA polymerase. It is not known which of these mechanisms is responsible for the block in DNA synthesis. Ara-C inhibits cellular DNA synthesis and viral DNA synthesis about equally and, therefore, exhibits little viral specificity. The compound has a differential inhibitory effect during the growth of certain viruses in cell culture. In the presence of inhibitory concentrations of cytarabine, the tumor antigens of both SV40 and adenoviruses are synthesized, but viral capsid pro-

teins and infectious virus are not formed. Synthesis of the tumor antigens probably does not require replication of viral DNA, whereas formation of progeny viral DNA is a prerequisite to the formation of virus coat protein and new infectious virus. Ara-C has been disappointing as a systemic drug in virus infections.

A purine analogue, **9-β-D-arabinofuranosyladenine (Ara-A, adenosine arabinoside, vidarabine)**, has been introduced into clinical therapeutics. The precise mechanism of action of Ara-A is not clear, but it differs from the pyrimidine analogues IUDR and Ara-C. The therapeutic dosage in man is 10–15 mg/kg of body weight given intravenously in 5% dextrose and saline over a 12-hour period. It is relatively nontoxic but may cause nausea and phlebitis. It is not immunosuppressive. It is metabolized slowly in man by deamination to the primary metabolite arahypoxanthine (Ara-Hx). This metabolite (85% of the excreted product) has some antiviral activity but less than the parent compound. The clinical effectiveness of Ara-A against herpes simplex, varicella-zoster, and cytomegalovirus infection in man has been striking. Ara-A is the current drug of choice in serious systemic infections with these viruses.

Dactinomycin (actinomycin D) inhibits DNA-dependent RNA synthesis and thus the multiplication of DNA viruses but not of most RNA viruses. However, dactinomycin inhibits the multiplication of some myxoviruses and retroviruses. The mechanism of this inhibition is not clear for myxoviruses, although the demonstration of a DNA intermediate in the replication of retrovirus RNA is now established.

Phosphonoacetic acid inhibits herpes simplex virus replication. It is a potent inhibitor of herpes simplex virus-induced DNA polymerase, has no significant effect on cellular DNA polymerases, and may have some promise as a chemotherapeutic agent specific for herpesviruses.

Virazole (1-β-D-ribofuranosyl-1,2,4-triazole-3-carboxamide, Ribavirin) is a synthetic nucleoside which is effective against a variety of DNA- and RNA-containing viruses both in vitro and in experimental animals. Its antiviral effect apparently results from its inhibitory effect on guanosine-5′-phosphate synthesis and consequently on the synthesis of both viral DNA and RNA. Clinical trials have not yet been completed in the USA, but the drug is available in Latin America.

Photodynamic inactivation is currently being evaluated for treatment of herpes simplex infections of the skin and mucous membranes in man. Treatment consists of (1) rupture of the very early vesicular lesion and (2) application of proflavine dye, followed by (3) exposure to light of 450 nm wavelength (peak absorption by proflavine) for 30 minutes. The dye immediately combines with the DNA of preformed extracellular virus, and the DNA-dye complex is then inactivated by the light. (4) On the following morning, new infectious virus that develops from virions located intracellularly at the time of the first treatment has the dye incorporated into its structure. Such virus is exceedingly photosensitive and is destroyed even if located intracellularly. Therefore, a second treatment with light is applied at this time.

Although not practical as chemotherapeutic agents, protein inhibitors have been useful in the study of viral replication. For example, **puromycin, cycloheximide,** and **p-fluorophenylalanine** all inhibit synthesis of both viral and cell proteins. They have proved useful in interrupting the cycle of virus replication at different stages.

With all specific inhibitors, it is necessary to demonstrate that inhibition is not due merely to direct cytotoxicity of the compound. The action of competitive inhibitors (cytarabine, IUDR, etc) can be reversed by the addition of the analogous normal metabolic compounds. Resumption of normal activity by the cell after reversal is indicative of the specificity of action of the drug employed.

Also being tested for antiviral activity in animals and man are compounds such as **levamisole** and **isoprinosine (inosiplex),** which act not as antimetabolites but as immunostimulants. They have been reported as being somewhat effective against both RNA and DNA viruses. The activity of such drugs is blocked by antilymphocyte serum.

INTERFERENCE PHENOMENON & INTERFERON

Interference

Infection of either cell cultures or whole animals with 2 viruses often leads to an inhibition of multiplication of one virus, an effect called interference. The phenomenon has caused much interest because of its potential in viral prophylaxis. Interference in animals should be distinguished from specific immunity resulting from antibody stimulation by the infecting virus. Furthermore, interference has not been observed for all virus combinations; 2 viruses may infect and multiply within the same cell (eg, vaccinia and herpesviruses; measles and polioviruses) as efficiently as in single infections.

Two mechanisms may be ascribed to the interference phenomenon:

(1) The initial virus may alter either the host cell surface or its metabolic pathways, thus making them unavailable to the superinfecting virus. This can occur between related as well as unrelated viruses. In some systems, a virus will interfere with its own replication (autointerference). In this case, defective interfering particles are produced at the expense of standard virus when high multiplicities of infection are used. These particles differ in physical properties from the standard virus, and it is often possible to purify them. Defective particles generally lack a portion of their normal complement of nucleic acid and are unable to replicate in the absence of standard virus, since, for their synthesis, they utilize standard virus precursors. This may represent the method by which defective viruses interfere with standard virus replication, ie, by competition for units of the replicative machinery. Autointerference occurs in infections with many viruses, including influenza (the von Magnus phenomenon) and vesicular stomatitis virus. It may have a role in the establishment of persistent virus infections.

(2) The first virus may stimulate the production of an inhibitor (interferon) which prevents the replication of the second virus.

Interference has been used as a basis for controlling outbreaks of infection with virulent strains of poliovirus by introducing into the population an attenuated poliovirus which interferes with the spread of the virulent virus. Theoretically, it would appear possible to use the interference phenomenon as a sort of immunization technic: Viruses of low virulence might be used to prevent subsequent infection with more virulent organisms. Infection with a mild respiratory virus produces a 2- to 6-week refractory period to infection by a related or unrelated respiratory virus. Unfortunately, interference is generally short-lived; when the first virus disappears from the cells, the cells are again susceptible to infection. Also, the unpredictability of using a virus of supposed "low virulence" in man militates against this therapeutic approach.

Interferon

Interferons are a class of proteins which inhibit virus replication and which are produced by intact animals or cultured cells in response to virus infection or other inducers.

Interferon is characterized as protein, possibly a glycoprotein, which is acid-stable (pH 2.0), trypsinsensitive, nondialyzable, and nonsedimentable by ultracentrifuge forces sufficient to pellet viruses. Interferon is effective as an antiviral substance on cells from the species of animal in which it was produced but is ineffective on cells from other species. Thus, interferon produced by the intact mouse or by mouse cells in tissue culture will protect other mouse cells from virus infection but has practically no protective effect for chicken cells. Although interferon activity is specific for the species of cells in which it is effective, it is not specific for a given virus. Interferon production stimulated by one virus will effectively inhibit the replication of a wide variety of viruses.

Interferons appear to be a primary response to

virus infection. Within 12–48 hours after virus titers reach a maximum, interferon in the infected animal is produced in large quantities and virus production rapidly decreases. Antibody does not appear in the blood of the animal until several days after virus production has abated. This temporal relationship of virus production to the appearance of interferon and then of antiviral antibody strongly suggests that interferon plays a major role in the defense of the animal against virus infections.

Interferons are produced by cells in tissue culture, or by the intact animal when stimulated with viruses, rickettsiae, protozoa, bacterial endotoxins, or by synthetic double-stranded polynucleotides. Many agents that are potent interferon inducers either contain double-stranded RNA or cause the production of double-stranded RNA within the infected cell. When stimulated, the host cell genome directs the synthesis of interferon which is released from the infected cell.

When interferon is added to cells prior to infection, there is marked inhibition of virus replication, while the cell functions normally. Interferon does not act directly on the virus. The production of a second protein appears to be required since new messenger RNA and protein synthesis must occur after interferon treatment before a viral inhibitory state is achieved.

The viral inhibitory protein in some way interferes with the translation of viral messenger RNA. Cellular messenger RNA is translated normally. This permits normal cell functions to continue but prevents the synthesis of virus-directed protein. Without the production of necessary enzymes and coat protein for progeny virus, new virus is not formed. In a few systems, there is evidence that interferon may inhibit viral transcription as well. A schematic diagram of the mechanism of interferon action is presented in Fig 27–15.

All of the cells of the intact animal are probably capable of producing interferon; however, the elements of the reticuloendothelial system seem to provide the bulk of interferon during most virus infections.

Studies on purified interferon have indicated that it may have several molecular forms with molecular weights ranging from 12×10^3 to 100×10^3. The molecular weights of interferons vary from species to species. There is some evidence that the high molecular weight forms are polymers of a 12×10^3 to 19×10^3 molecular weight monomer. A certain class of interferon with higher molecular weight may be preformed and is released into the bloodstream within 2 hours after injection of endotoxins.

The low antigenicity and potent antiviral effect of

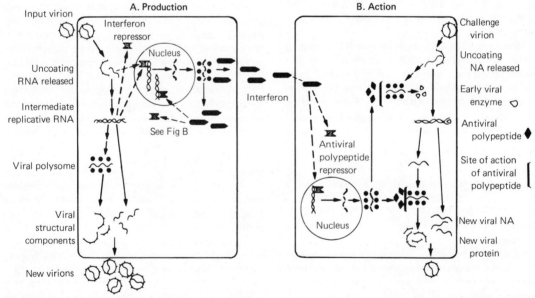

Figure 27–15. Schematic summary of recent concepts in the *(A)* production and *(B)* action of interferon. In production *(A)*, an infectious single-stranded RNA virus serves as the example of an active inducer of interferon. Its single strand of RNA may act as the inducing principle, although the principle is more likely to be the intermediate replicative double-stranded RNA form produced after infection. Subsequent steps in viral replication are shown to indicate that cellular products may be new virions as well as interferon. The interferon inducer binds to the repressor of the interferon gene located in the host DNA. Binding of repressor permits derepression of the host genome for the production of the specific messenger RNA, which is then translated into interferon proteins by means of normal ribosomal machinery. Interferons are then released rapidly from cells to affect neighboring cells or may induce antiviral resistance in the same cell. In action *(B)*, interferon proteins either act at the cell surface or may enter cells to bind the repressor of the host cistron coding for the antiviral polypeptide. After derepression by the interferon protein, the antiviral polypeptide is then produced by the usual cell machinery to inhibit viral replication, most probably at the ribosomal level. The production of early viral enzymes, viral nucleic acids, and viral structural proteins is thereby inhibited, resulting in reduced viral yield. (Reproduced, with permission, from Grossberg: N Engl J Med 287:79, 1972.)

interferon have created much interest in its possible application in controlling viral diseases of man. In experimental animals, and in limited trials in man, it has been possible to demonstrate the efficacy of exogenous interferon in preventing or decreasing the severity of virus infections. However, the difficulties in producing sufficient quantities of the material for human use are great and the cost is prohibitive. Interferon does not appear to be effective once the infection is well established.

Present hope for the application of interferon to the control of human disease lies in the development of interferon inducers. There have been some clinical trials of attenuated live virus vaccines as inducers of interferon, and a number of synthetic inducers of interferon activity are being investigated. Among the most promising is a synthetic double-stranded RNA called Poly I:C, which is formed by the complexing of 2 homopolymers: polyriboinosinic acid and polyribocytidylic acid. Poly I:C, other synthetic polynucleotides, and other inducers have been extensively tested in animals. Poly I:C has had clinical trials with indefinite results. No inducer is yet available for general use.

VIRAL GENETICS & VIRAL INTERACTIONS

Meaningful genetic studies with animal viruses have been possible only in the past few years. Two factors have made these studies possible. The first was the development of the plaque assay of virus infectivity. Since genetic interactions are relatively rare phenomena, it is necessary that a sensitive and accurate assay method be available. The second factor was the development of stable genetic markers, which, ideally, should be easily recognized and should result from single mutations. Some markers commonly used include plaque size, specific virus-induced antigens, drug resistance, host range, and inability to grow at elevated temperatures. Virus mutants that possess these markers are obtained either after spontaneous mutation, or, more frequently, after treatment of the virus population with a mutagen.

The use of conditional-lethal mutants provides a powerful tool for the study of the genetics and molecular biology of viruses. Conditional-lethal mutants are mutants which are lethal (in that no infectious virus is produced) under one set of conditions—termed nonpermissive conditions—but which yield normal infectious progeny under other conditions—termed permissive conditions. Conditional-lethal mutants may be either temperature-sensitive *(ts)* or host range *(hr)* mutants. *Ts* mutants have been isolated from nearly all of the families of animal viruses; they grow at low (permissive) temperatures but not at high (nonpermissive) temperatures. At the molecular level, these mutants are defective, apparently because an altered amino acid sequence in some essential virus-specified protein renders that protein incapable of assuming or maintaining a functional configuration at the nonpermissive temperature. *Hr* mutants are able to grow and form plaques in one kind of cell (permissive cell), while abortive infection occurs in another type (nonpermissive cell). *Hr* bacterial virus mutants possess altered nucleic acid base sequences which are read as nonsense mutations by the nonpermissive host cell, resulting in polypeptide chain termination and consequently abortive infection. The permissive host cell, on the other hand, carries a transfer RNA which recognizes the altered sequence as a codon and inserts an amino acid, resulting in the formation of a functional polypeptide. Whether this mechanism is operative in host range mutants of animal viruses remains to be established. Following the induction and isolation of a set of conditional-lethal mutants, mixed infection studies with pairs of mutants under permissive and nonpermissive conditions can yield information concerning gene function, gene sequence (genetic mapping), and mechanisms of virus replication at the molecular level.

Mutagens widely used for the induction of mutants fall into 3 classes: (1) base analogues which can replace the normal bases of DNA during replication; (2) substances which chemically alter the bases of resting DNA; and (3) those whose action is to remove DNA bases. An example of the first class of mutagens is 5-bromouracil, which replaces thymine quantitatively and which also binds with guanine. This substance can thus induce mutations by causing 2 types of base pair transitions depending upon whether the pairing error occurs during incorporation or during replication following incorporation. Nitrous acid is an example of the second class of mutagens. Its mutagenic action lies in its ability to oxidatively deaminate either adenine or cytosine. Representative of the third class of mutagens is ethylene ethanesulfonate, which is thought to act by removing guanine bases.

When 2 different virus particles infect the same host cell, they may interact in a variety of ways. The types of interactions are summarized in Table 27–6, and the mechanisms are shown in Table 27–7. Genetic interaction results in some progeny which are **heritably** (genetically) different from either parent. Progeny produced as a consequence of nongenetic interaction are similar to the parent viruses. In genetic interactions the actual **nucleic acid molecules** interact, whereas it is the **products** of the genes which are involved in nongenetic interactions.

The following terms are basic to the discussion of genetics, the study of heredity. **Genotype** refers to the genetic constitution of an organism. **Phenotype** refers to the observable properties of an organism which are produced by the genotype in cooperation with the environment. A **mutation** is a heritable change in the genotype. The **genome** is the sum of the genes of an organism.

Several types of interaction can occur simultaneously under the proper conditions.

Genetic Interactions

Recombination results in the production of prog-

Table 27—6. Types and characteristics of interactions between animal viruses.

Type of Interaction	Viability of Parental Viruses	Some Progeny Different From Parental	Progeny Genetically Stable	Example
I. Genetic				
A. Recombination	Active + active	Yes	Yes	Influenza, herpesvirus
B. Cross-reactivation	Active + inactive	Yes	Yes	Influenza
C. Multiplicity reactivation	Inactive + inactive	Yes	Yes	Vaccinia
II. Nongenetic				
A. Phenotypic mixing	Active + active	Yes	No	Picornaviruses
B. Genotypic mixing	Active + active	Yes	No	Paramyxoviruses
C. Interference	Active + active	No	Yes	Coxsackieviruses
	Defective + active	No	Yes	Satellite + adenovirus
D. Enhancement	Active + active	No	Yes	NDV + parainfluenza
E. Complementation	Active + inactive	No	Yes	Poxviruses
	Active + defective	No*	Yes	(a) Rous-associated virus + Rous sarcoma virus†
				(b) Murine leukemia + sarcoma†
				(c) SV40 + adenovirus
				(d) Adenovirus + satellite
	Defective + defective	No*	Yes	(a) PARA (SV40-adeno) + adenovirus
				(b) MAC-adeno + adenovirus

*In those cases in which the helper virus is supplying the coat (RSV-RAV, MSV-MLV, PARA-adenovirus, MAC-adenovirus), the progeny defective virus will be antigenically different if a heterologous helper virus is present and transcapsidation or pseudotype formation occurs.

†Shares certain similarities with an extreme form of phenotypic mixing.

eny virus (recombinant) which carries traits not found together in either parent. This type of interaction is said to occur when both parental viruses are viable (active). It is postulated that the nucleic acid strands break, and part of the genome of one parent is joined to part of the genome of the second parent. The recombinant virus is genetically stable, yielding progeny like itself upon replication. For example, a recombinant influenza virus was recognized because its hemagglutinin was antigenically identical with that of the type A parent while the antigenicity of its neuraminidase corresponded to that of the type A2 parent. In the case of viruses with segmented genomes, eg, influenza virus, the formation of recombinants may be due to reassortment of individual genome fragments, rather than to an actual cross-over event.

Cross-reactivation occurs between the genome of an active virion and the genome of a virus particle which has been inactivated in some way. A portion of the genome of the inactivated virus recombines with that of the active parent, so that certain markers of the inactivated parent are rescued and appear in the viable progeny. None of the progeny produced are identical to the inactivated parent. The progeny carrying the rescued markers of the inactivated parent are genetically stable. Cross-reactivation was used to obtain an A2 influenza virus suitable for vaccine production. Inactivated type A (with the capacity to grow well in eggs) was mixed with an active Asian (A2) isolate. A recombinant was obtained with the desired A2 antigenicity and the ability of the parental type A to grow in eggs.

Multiplicity reactivation occurs when an inactive virus particle is rendered active by interaction with another inactive virus particle in the same cell. In this case, 2 different parental viruses can be damaged or a single heavily damaged parental virus can be used to infect cells at high multiplicity of infection. Recombination occurs between the damaged nucleic acids of the parents, producing a viable genome which can replicate. The greater the damage to the parental genomes, the larger the number of inactive particles required per cell to ensure the formation of such a viable genome.

Nongenetic Interactions

Phenotypic mixing is the association of a phenotype with a heterologous genotype. This occurs when the genome of one virus becomes randomly incorporated within the capsid of a different virus or a capsid consisting of components of both viruses. It is not a stable genetic change because, upon replication—since protein synthesis is controlled by the virus genome—the phenotypically mixed parent will yield progeny encased in capsids homologous to the genotype.

Genotypic mixing, or heterozygosis, is distinguished by a single virus particle which can give rise to progeny of 2 distinct parental types. This is not a stable genetic change and probably occurs when 2 complete genomes are accidentally incorporated within a single virus capsid. It has been reported only for the paramyxoviruses.

Interference occurs when the multiplication of a superinfecting virus is inhibited because of the presence of the initially infecting virus. This phenomenon

Table 27–7. Mechanistic representations of types of genetic and nongenetic interactions between animal viruses. (After Butel.)

| Type of Interaction | Parental Types | | Progeny | | |
	I	II	Parental Types I	II	Recombinants or Other
I. GENETIC					
Recombination	(a₁b₁) active	+ (a₂b₂) active	(a₁b₁)	(a₂b₂)	(a₁b₂) (a₂b₁)
Cross-reactivation	(a₁b₁) active	+ (a₂b₂) inactive ⟶	(a₁b₁)	none	(a₁b₂) or (a₂b₁)
Multiplicity reactivation	(a₁b₁) inactive	+ (a₂b₂) inactive ⟶	none	none	(a₁b₂) or (a₂b₁)
II. NONGENETIC					
Phenotypic mixing	(A) active	+ [B] active ⟶	(A)	[B]	A or A → replication → (A)
Genotypic mixing	(A) active	+ [B] active ⟶	(A)	[B]	(A, B) → replication → (A) and [B]
Interference 1.	(A) active	+ [B] active ⟶	(A)	[B] Less than usual	Possible
2.	(A) active	+ [B] defective ⟶	(A)	[B] Less than usual	Possible
Enhancement	(A) active	+ [B] active ⟶	(A)	[B] More than usual	Possible
Complementation 1.	(A) active ↓ single infection (A)	+ [B] inactive ↓ no growth	(A)	[B]	Possible
2.	(A) active ↓ single infection (A)	+ [B] defective ↓ no growth	(A)	[B]	Possible
3.	(A) defective ↓ single infection no growth	+ [B] defective ↓ no growth	(A)	[B]	Possible

can be mediated either by interferon or by an alteration of cell receptor sites or metabolic pathways necessary for replication of the second virus. Interference
may be either reciprocal (markedly reduced yields of
both agents) or nonreciprocal (reduced yield of only
one agent). (For additional details, see p 311.)

Enhancement, in contrast to interference, is the
increased production of one virus as the result of coinfection with a second virus. All the progeny will be
like the parental viruses. Again, the basic mechanisms
vary; one reported mechanism is the ability of the
second virus to inhibit the synthesis of interferon. The
helper activity which permits replication of a defective
virus has been termed "potentiation."

Complementation is the functional interaction
between 2 viruses, one or both of which may be defective, which results in the multiplication of one or both
under conditions in which replication would not
ordinarily occur. The progeny produced are like the
parental viruses. Neither the genotype nor the phenotype of either virus is affected. A variety of different
types of complementation may occur, as indicated in
Table 27—6, and the mechanisms permitting complementation vary depending on the system. Examples
include (1) the stimulation, by an active poxvirus
(fibroma), of an uncoating enzyme necessary for the
release of the genome of an inactive poxvirus (myxoma); and (2) the production by active adenovirus, of
coat protein utilized by defective SV40 (PARA). In
the other examples cited, one or both of 2 defective
viruses may act by inducing some essential gene
product—as yet unidentified—which the other requires
for replication but is unable to provide for itself.

Virus-Mediated Gene Transfer in Mammalian Cells

There is mounting interest in the development of
methods by which external genetic information can be
stably introduced into eukaryotic cells. Such methods
could potentially be applied to attempts to repair
genetic defects in cells of persons suffering from congenital metabolic disorders and to other problems of
human genetics. Approaches to the problem of gene
transfer have involved viral transduction, transformation, and cell hybridization technics. Gene transfer
between bacteria is known to occur by bacteriophage
transduction (see Chapter 4). Suggestive evidence that
transduction can occur between mammalian cells using
an animal virus as the transducing agent has been reported. For example, mouse cell DNA within polyoma
pseudovirus particles enters nuclei of recipient human
cells, without loss of physical integrity of the respective DNA.

Successful transduction of eukaryotic cells by
viruses has been reported with the transduction of
human cells by bacteriophage lambda (λ). The gal$^+$
gene from *Escherichia coli* bacterial cells has been
transferred to gal$^-$ human cells from a patient with
galactosemia by the transducing phage λ. Not only was
the enzyme demonstrated in the transduced cells after
repeated subculture, but λ-specific mRNA was also
detected, indicating that both transcription and trans-

lation of the newly introduced viral DNA had occurred.

A second approach to the introduction of external genetic material into eukaryotic cells involves
transformation by UV-inactivated virus. In this case, a
viral gene itself is transferred after the particle has been
rendered noninfectious by UV inactivation. Mouse
cells lacking thymidine kinase (TK) activity have been
stably transformed to a TK-positive phenotype by
infection with UV-irradiated, TK-positive herpes
simplex virus. Transformed cells maintained in culture
for more than 8 months continued to produce the
enzyme. The new enzyme possessed properties which
differed from those of normal, TK-positive mouse
cells, suggesting that the new enzyme activity resulted
from the transfer of a herpesvirus-TK gene.

Inherent problems involved in a virus-mediated
method for correction of genetic defects in mammalian
cells include (1) the possible immunologic incompat-
ibility of the new gene product and (2) the transfer of
undesirable genes simultaneously with the desired
gene. A third and crucial difficulty concerns regulation
of gene expression. If the proper regulatory mechanisms are not active in the recipient cells, the transfer
may be deleterious to the host either by overproduction or underproduction of the new gene product.

Recombinant DNA

Recently developed technics allow DNA to be
cleaved into specific pieces using enzymes from bacteria called restriction endonucleases. These distinct fragments have importance in 2 areas: (1) the physical
mapping of genes in large, complicated DNA genomes,
and (2) genetic engineering. In the latter case, a specific fragment with a desired gene can be coupled to a
rapidly replicating DNA, such as bacterial, viral, or
plasmid DNA. These new genetic combinations can be
inserted into bacterial cultures, allowing the production of vast amounts of the new genetic material (Fig
27—16). (See Chapter 4, Fig 4—15.) Research in this
area must proceed with great caution and under tight
containment because of the dangers inherent in such
technics. For example, by combining fragments of
DNA from different sources, an organism might be
produced endowed with unpredictable biologic properties. The bacterium most commonly used in genetic engineering is a laboratory strain of *E coli*, which is normally present in the human gut. Therefore, the possibility exists that *E coli* containing recombinant DNA
from a toxin-producing bacterium, or from primate
cancer viruses, or from hormone-producing cells may
escape from the laboratory and colonize human beings.
Investigators contemplating recombinant DNA studies
must work in proper isolation facilities and with organisms that cannot grow in human beings or lower animals.

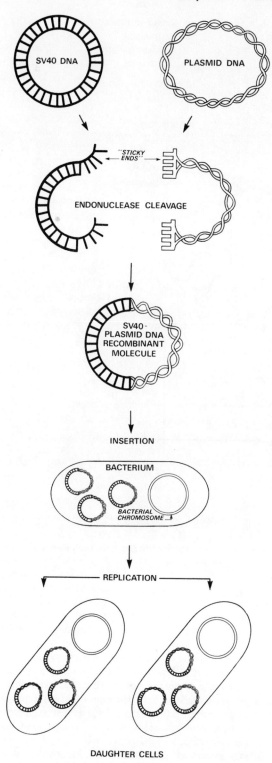

Figure 27—16. Formation of recombinant DNA molecules. SV40 DNA and plasmid DNA are cleaved by enzymes into fragments with "sticky ends." The 2 different DNA fragments combine at their "sticky ends" to form a new, composite DNA molecule. The plasmid containing SV40 DNA is introduced into a bacterium and SV40 DNA is replicated into many copies.

PATHOGENESIS OF VIRUS DISEASES

Virus implantation and multiplication occur in different tissues as the infectious agent travels to the target organ from the portal of entry. In the target organ, virus multiplication must reach a critical level before cell necrosis occurs and disease becomes manifest. Viruses call forth a different tissue response than do pathogenic bacteria, not only in the parenchymatous cells but also in cellular infiltration. Whereas polymorphonuclear leukocytes form the principal cellular response to the acute inflammation caused by pyogenic bacteria, infiltration with mononuclear cells and lymphocytes characterizes the inflammatory reaction of uncomplicated viral lesions. In Fig 27—17 are shown examples of mousepox, a disease of the skin, and of human poliomyelitis, a disease of the CNS.

In mousepox, the virus enters the body through minute abrasions of the skin and multiplies in the epidermal cells. At the same time it is carried by the lymphatics to the regional lymph nodes, where multiplication also occurs. The few virus particles entering the blood by way of the efferent lymphatics are taken up by the macrophages of the liver and spleen. In both organs the virus multiplies rapidly. Following release of virus from the liver and spleen it moves by way of the bloodstream and localizes in the basal epidermal layers of the skin, in the conjunctival cells, and near the lymph follicles in the intestine. The virus may occasionally also localize in the epithelial cells of the kidney, lung, submaxillary gland, and pancreas. A primary lesion occurs at the site of entry of the virus. It appears as a localized swelling which rapidly increases in size, becomes edematous, ulcerates, and goes on to scar formation. A generalized rash follows which is responsible for the release of large quantities of virus into the environment.

In poliomyelitis, virus enters by way of the alimentary tract and multiplies locally at the initial sites of viral implantation (tonsils, Peyer's patches) or the lymph nodes which drain these tissues, and begins to appear in the throat and in the feces. Secondary virus spread occurs by way of the bloodstream to other susceptible tissues, namely, other lymph nodes, brown fat, and the CNS. Within the CNS the virus spreads along nerve fibers. If a high level of multiplication occurs as the virus spreads through the CNS, motor neurons are destroyed and paralysis occurs. The shedding of virus into the environment does not depend upon secondary virus spread to the CNS. Secondary spread to the CNS is readily interrupted by the presence of antibodies, induced by prior infection or vaccination.

Persistent Viral Infections & Immune Complex Diseases

Certain viruses do not invariably kill the cells they infect. The immunologic response of the host to these viruses may be responsible for the observed pathologic changes and the clinical illness. This phenomenon is

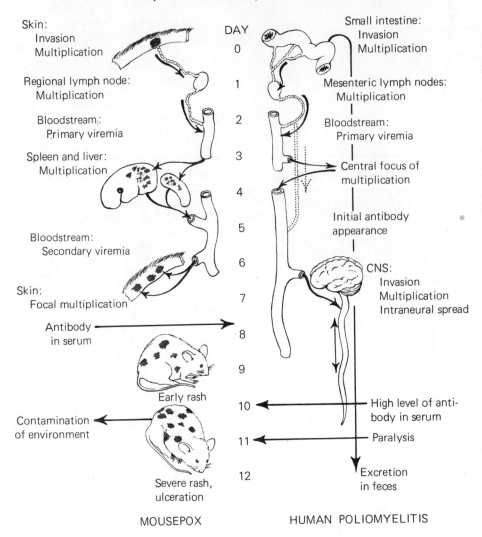

Figure 27—17. Schematic illustrations of the pathogenesis of mousepox and poliomyelitis. (Modified from Fenner.)

exemplified in lymphocytic choriomeningitis virus infection of mice. If adult mice are rendered immunologically incompetent by x-irradiation, immunosuppressive drugs, or antiserum directed against the lymphoid elements of the mouse, they do not become ill when infected with the virus. The virus replicates in the animal and establishes a chronic infection which persists until the competence of the immunologic response is restored, at which time the animal becomes ill. Infection of newborn mice before they develop immunologic competence results in a lifelong viral infection which is not associated with acute illness; however, after 10 months to 1 year of life, many of the persistently infected mice develop a fatal debilitating disease involving the CNS. These animals exhibit chronic glomerulonephritis and hypergammaglobulinemia; the glomerular lesions are thought to be due to deposition of antigen-antibody complexes (see Chapter 33). Persistent infections occur with a number of animal viruses, and the persistence in certain instances

depends upon the age of the host when infected. In human beings, rubella virus and cytomegalovirus infections acquired in utero characteristically result in viral persistence which is of limited duration, probably because of the development of the immunologic capacity to react to the infection as the infant matures.

Persistent ("slow") viral infections may play a far-reaching role in human disease. Persistent viral infections are associated with leukemias and sarcomas of chickens and mice (see Chapter 40) as well as progressive degenerative diseases of the CNS of man and animals (see Chapter 33).

A persistent viral disease of Aleutian mink is associated with alterations of serum immunoglobulins very similar to the changes observed in human multiple myeloma. These alterations in immunoglobulins are thought to represent overreactivity of certain immunocytes in the host's response to the chronic presence of the viral agent. The infected mink also have pathologic alterations of their blood vessels and kidneys similar to those seen in certain human connective tissue disorders. The host's immunologic response to the infecting virus does not appear to always be beneficial to the host. It is probable that virus antigen-antibody complexes deposited in the kidney lead to glomerulonephritis.

Another type of immunopathologic disorder has been observed in human beings previously immunized with vaccines containing killed measles or respiratory syncytial virus. Such immunized persons may develop unusual antibody responses that give rise to serious consequences when these persons later are exposed to the naturally occurring infective virus. Dengue hemorrhagic fever with shock syndrome, which develops in dengue infection of persons who already have had at least one prior infection with another dengue serotype, may be a naturally occurring manifestation of the same type of immunopathology. The syndrome may develop because the body's complement system, activated by immune complexes formed quickly after the second dengue infection, produces "anaphylatoxins," which in turn give rise to vascular permeability leading to hemorrhagic shock.

Experimentally, administration of formalin-inactivated Aleutian disease (AD) vaccine to mink, followed by challenge with live AD virus, leads to marked enhancement of tissue lesions and to increased susceptibility to infection. There may, therefore, be similarities in the underlying mechanisms of pathogenesis in Aleutian disease and in the human immunopathologic developments described above.

Viruses as Causes of Congenital Defects

Viral infection during pregnancy may be a significant cause of fetal damage and loss. Three principles involved in the production of congenital defects are (1) the ability of the virus to infect the pregnant animal and be transmitted to the fetus; (2) the stage of gestation at which infection occurs; and (3) the ability of the virus to cause damage to the fetus directly, by infection of the fetus, or indirectly, by infection of the mother resulting in an altered fetal environment (eg, fever). The sequence of events which may occur prior to and following viral invasion of the fetus is shown in Fig 27–18.

While a variety of viruses are reportedly capable of inducing fetal abnormalities, rubella and cytomegaloviruses are presently considered to be the primary agents responsible for congenital defects in humans. Recent evidence has suggested that congenital infection with herpes simplex, varicella-zoster, and coxsackie B viruses may also be of significance in inducing teratogenic effects in the fetus. Congenital rubella, however, has become the prototype of virus-induced malformation and is discussed more extensively in Chapter 35.

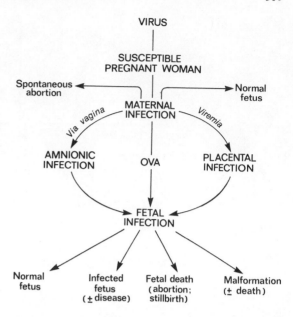

Figure 27–18. Viral infection of the fetus. (After Catalano & Sever.)

LATENT VIRAL INFECTIONS

Inapparent infection covers, at the host-parasite level, the whole field of infections which give no overt sign of their presence. "Subclinical" can be used as an alternative term, particularly in the discussion of human infections.

Latent infections are inapparent infections which are chronic and in which a certain virus-host equilibrium is established. The term occult virus is used in cases where virus particles cannot be detected and in which the actual state of the virus cannot as yet be ascertained.

Whenever it has been shown that viruses of animals or higher plants go through cycles as described for bacteriophage (see Chapter 9), the terms provirus, vegetative virus, and infective virus are appropriate for the corresponding stages. Infective virus is the fully formed virus particle.

A moderate virus (corresponding in some measure to a temperate phage) is one growing in a cell while still permitting the continued survival and multiplication of the cell. Some viruses may be moderate in one cell system and cytocidal in another. **Slow viral infections** are characterized by a prolonged incubation period lasting months or years, during which virus continues to multiply, producing increasing destruction of tissue.

Latency in tissue culture systems: The growth of cells in culture for many generations may be accompanied by a concomitant multiplication of virus. The number of cells supporting viral infection in such optimally growing cultures is usually only a small portion of the entire population.

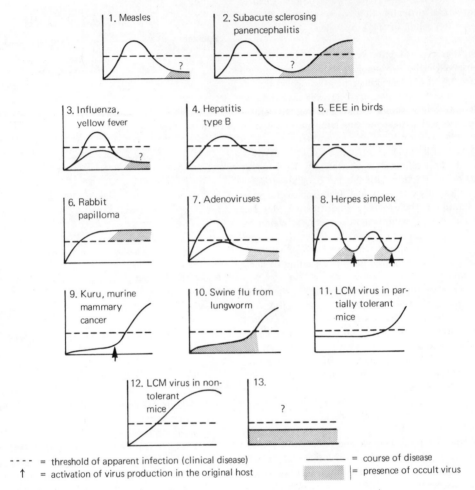

Figure 27–19. Apparent, inapparent, latent, and occult virus infections. *(1)* Measles runs an acute, almost always clinical course resulting in long-lasting immunity. *(2)* Measles may also be associated with persistence of latent infection in sclerosing panencephalitis (see Chapter 35). *(3)* Yellow fever and influenza show a similar pattern except that infection may be more often subclinical than clinical. *(4)* In viral hepatitis type B, recovery from clinical disease may be associated with latent infection in which fully active virus persists in the blood. *(5)* Some infections are, in a particular species, always subclinical, such as equine encephalomyelitis in some species of birds which then act as reservoirs of the virus. *(6)* In rabbit papilloma, the course of infection is chronic, and chronicity is associated with the virus's becoming occult. *(7)* Infection of man with certain adenoviruses may be clinical or subclinical. There may be a long latent infection during which virus is present in small quantity; virus may also persist after the illness. *(8)* The periodic activation of latent herpes simplex virus, which may recur throughout life in man, often follows an initial acute episode of stomatitis in childhood. *(9)* In many instances, infection is wholly latent for long periods of time before it is activated. Examples of such "slow" virus infections characterized by long incubation periods are mammary cancer virus in mice, scrapie virus in sheep, and kuru in man. *(10)* In pigs which have eaten virus-bearing lung worms, swine "flu" is occult until the appropriate stimulus induces virus production and, in turn, clinical disease. *(11)* Lymphocytic choriomeningitis (LCM) virus may be established in mice by in utero infection. A form of modified immunologic tolerance develops in which only low levels of antibody are produced. This antibody and circulating LCM virus form antigen-antibody complexes which ultimately produce immune complex disease in the partially tolerant host. The presence of LCM virus in this latent infection (circulating virus with little or no apparent disease) may be readily revealed by transmission to an indicator host, eg, nontolerant adult mice from a virus-free stock. All nontolerant mice develop classic acute symptoms of LCM and die *(12)*. *(13)* The possibility is shown of latent infection with an occult virus which is not readily activated. Proof of the presence of such a virus remains a difficult task which, however, is attracting cancer investigators (see Chapter 40).

Cells infected with some viruses can divide and grow into infected clones. In these respects, these infections resemble infections by moderate viruses, but there is no evidence that the viral nucleic acid has any real interaction with the host cell nucleic acid. In most of the cells of an actively growing virus-carrier culture, the virus seems to be under some control or repression, eg, local interferon. Culture manipulations that have been found to shift the virus-cell complex toward virus release (cell crowding, medium exhaustion, lowering of temperature) have been of the kind that also slow cell multiplications.

In Fig 27–19 are presented examples of apparent, inapparent, latent, and occult virus infections.

NATURAL HISTORY (ECOLOGY) & MODES OF TRANSMISSION OF VIRUSES

Viruses may be transmitted in the following ways: (1) Direct transmission from person to person by contact, in which droplet or aerosol infection may play the major role (eg, influenza, measles, smallpox). (2) Transmission by means of the alimentary tract (intimate association with carrier, food, and drink) (eg, enterovirus infections, infectious hepatitis). (3) Transmission by bite (eg, rabies). (4) Transmission by means of an arthropod vector (eg, arboviruses).

Some of the viruses may be conveyed in several different ways and may therefore manifest a variable epidemiology.

The following cycles have been recognized among the arthropod-borne viruses:

1. Man-arthropod cycle—*Example:* Urban yellow fever.

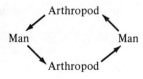

2. Lower vertebrate-arthropod cycle with tangential infection of man—*Examples:* Jungle yellow fever, equine encephalitis.

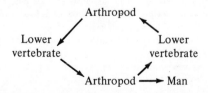

3. Arthropod-arthropod cycle with occasional infection of man and lower vertebrates—*Example:* Colorado tick fever.

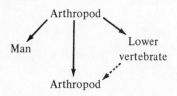

In (3) the virus may be transmitted from the adult arthropod to its offspring by means of the egg (transovarian passage); thus, the cycle may continue with or without intervention of a vertebrate host.

In vertebrates the invasion of most viruses evokes a violent reaction, usually of short duration. The result is decisive. Either the host succumbs or it lives through the production of antibodies that neutralize or kill the virus. Regardless of the outcome, the sojourn of the active virus is usually short (although latent virus infections may occur, as in herpes-, adeno-, and cytomegalovirus infections). In arthropod vectors of the virus, the relationship is usually quite different. The viruses may produce little or no ill effect and remain active in the arthropod throughout the latter's natural life. Thus arthropods, in contrast to vertebrates, act as permanent hosts and reservoirs.

VIRUS VACCINES

The use of vaccines is described in detail in the chapters dealing with specific virus families and diseases and is summarized in Table 27–8. Certain general principles, however, apply to most virus vaccines, both those presently available and those anticipated for future use in the prevention of human disease.

It must be kept in mind that neither vaccination nor recovery from natural infection always results in total protection against a later infection with the same virus. This situation holds for diseases for which successful control measures are available, including polio, smallpox, influenza, rubella, measles, mumps, and adenovirus infections. Control can be achieved by limiting the multiplication of virulent virus upon subsequent exposure and preventing its spread to target organs where the pathologic damage is done (eg, polio and measles viruses kept from the brain and spinal cord; rubella virus from the embryo). Recently, Marek's disease, a widespread lymphoproliferative tumor of domestic chickens, has been brought under control by an attenuated virus vaccine. The vaccine results in a lifelong active infection of the chicken and does not prevent superinfection of the vaccinated animal with the virulent virus, but it does prevent the appearance of the tumor. This is the first practical cancer vaccine that has been developed.

The recommendations for vaccine usage in man given in Table 27–8 apply chiefly to developed countries where health care is readily available and the population is considered "well protected." In a new departure from public health practices of long stand-

Table 27–8. Principal vaccines used in prevention of virus diseases of man.

Disease	Source of Vaccine	Condition of Virus	Route of Administration
Recommended Immunization for General Public (in USA and Other Developed Countries)			
Poliomyelitis	Tissue culture (human diploid cell line, monkey kidney)	Live attenuated	Oral
Measles*	Tissue culture (chick embryo)	Live attenuated†	Subcutaneous‡
Mumps*	Tissue culture (chick embryo)	Live attenuated	Subcutaneous
Rubella*§	Tissue culture (duck embryo, rabbit, or human diploid)	Live attenuated	Subcutaneous
Immunization Recommended Only Under Certain Conditions (Epidemics, Exposure, Travel, Military)			
Smallpox and alastrim**	Lymph from calf or sheep (glycerolated, lyophilized)	Active	Intradermal: multiple pressure, multiple puncture, or (with specially prepared vaccine) by jet injection
	Chorioallantois, tissue cultures (lyophilized)	Active	
Yellow fever	Tissue cultures and eggs (17D strain)	Live attenuated	Subcutaneous or intradermal
Influenza	Highly purified or subunit forms of chick embryo allantoic fluid (formalinized or UV-irradiated)	Inactive	Subcutaneous or intradermal
Rabies	Duck embryo treated with phenol or ultraviolet light	Inactive	Subcutaneous
Adenovirus††	Human diploid cell cultures	Live attenuated	Oral, by enteric-coated capsule
Japanese B encephalitis††	Mouse brain (formalinized), tissue culture	Inactive	Subcutaneous
Venezuelan equine encephalomyelitis‡‡	Guinea pig heart cell culture	Live attenuated	Subcutaneous
Eastern equine encephalomyelitis††	Chick embryo cell culture	Inactive	Subcutaneous
Western equine encephalomyelitis††	Chick embryo cell culture	Inactive	Subcutaneous
Russian spring-summer encephalitis††	Mouse brain (formalinized)	Inactive	Subcutaneous

*Available also as combined vaccines.
†Inactivated measles vaccine was available for a short period. However, a serious delayed hypersensitivity reaction often occurs when children who have received primary immunization with inactive measles vaccine are later exposed to live measles virus. Because of this complication, inactivated measles vaccine is no longer recommended.
‡With less attenuated strains, gamma globulin is given in another limb at the time of vaccination.
§Neither monovalent rubella vaccine nor combination vaccines incorporating rubella should be administered to a postpubertal susceptible female unless she is not pregnant and understands that it is imperative not to become pregnant for at least 3 months after vaccination. (The time immediately postpartum has been suggested as a safe period for vaccination.)
**If administration of smallpox vaccine to pregnant women is essential, vaccinia immune globulin (VIG) should be given simultaneously to reduce the risk of fetal vaccinia.
††Not available in the USA except for the Armed Forces or for investigative purposes.
‡‡Available for use in domestic animals (from the US Department of Agriculture) and for investigative purposes.

ing, general smallpox immunization is no longer recommended in the USA and other countries where the disease is not endemic and is seldom if ever imported. In developing countries, mass immunization programs for smallpox have achieved notable success, and it appears that smallpox might soon be eradicated from the world.

Inactivated Virus Vaccines

Inactivated vaccines prepared from whole virions generally stimulate the development of circulating antibody against the coat proteins of the virus, conferring some degree of resistance. For some diseases, inactivated vaccines are currently the only ones available. Certain disadvantages (listed below) have been inherent in the use of inactivated vaccines, though some of these problems are being solved by new inactivated vaccines (eg, influenza and rabies) which are highly purified or which are prepared from subviral antigens.

(1) Extreme care is required in their manufacture to make certain that no residual live virulent virus is present in the vaccine.

(2) The immunity conferred is often brief and must be boostered, which not only involves the logistic problem of repeatedly reaching the persons in need of immunization but also has caused concern about the possible effects (hypersensitivity reactions) of repeated administration of foreign proteins.

(3) Parenteral administration of inactivated vaccines, even when it stimulates circulating antibody to satisfactory levels, has sometimes given disappointing results in terms of actual protection because local resistance is not induced in significant amounts at the natural portal of entry or primary site of multiplication of the wild virus infection—eg, nasopharynx for respiratory viruses, alimentary tract for poliovirus (see Chapters 31 and 34).

Live Attenuated Virus Vaccines

Attenuated vaccines have the advantage of acting like the natural infection with regard to their effect on immunity. They multiply in the host, and tend to stimulate longer-lasting antibody and also to induce antibody and resistance at the portal of entry. The disadvantages of live attenuated vaccines include the risk of reversion to greater virulence during multiplication within the vaccinee. While reversion has not proved to be a problem in practice, its potential cannot be overlooked. The approved vaccines should be utilized fully, but alert monitoring should be continued.

A further disadvantage of a live vaccine is that unrecognized adventitious agents latently infecting the culture substrate (eggs, primary cell cultures) may enter the vaccine stocks. Viruses that have been found in vaccines have included avian leukosis virus, simian papovavirus SV40, and simian cytomegalovirus.

The problem of adventitious contaminants is being circumvented through the use of normal cells serially propagated in culture (eg, human diploid cell lines) as substrates for cultivation of vaccine viruses. Vaccines prepared in such cultures have been in use in various countries for over 8 years and have been administered to more than 12 million persons. Poliovaccine prepared in a human diploid cell line, WI-38, was licensed in the USA in 1972.

The development of virus strains suitable for live virus vaccines previously was done chiefly by selection of naturally attenuated strains or by cultivating the virus serially in various hosts and cultures in the hope of deriving an attenuated strain. The search for such strains is now being approached more rationally by laboratory manipulations aimed at specific, planned, genetic alterations in the virus (eg, rabies, influenza, respiratory syncytial virus).

Present Vaccines

A. Proper Usage: One fact cannot be overemphasized: A successful vaccine does not protect against disease until it is administered in the proper dosage to susceptible individuals. The failure to reach all sectors of the population with complete courses of immunization is reflected in the USA and elsewhere in the failure to eradicate wild virulent strains of poliovirus and in the continued occurrence of paralytic poliomyelitis in unvaccinated persons. Likewise, after the first decline in measles cases following mass immunization programs in the USA, failure to provide the vaccine to susceptibles led to a sharp upsurge of the disease (75,000 cases) in 1971. With renewed emphasis on vaccination, the number of cases dropped to 32,000 in 1972, and in 1974 only 22,000 cases were recorded. Preschool children in poverty areas are the least adequately vaccinated group in the USA.

B. Simultaneous Administration of Live Vaccines: An interval of 1 month between inoculations of live virus vaccines was originally recommended. This was based on the theoretical consideration that adverse reactions might be more frequent or severe, that antibody response might be diminished, or that interference might occur if 2 or more live vaccines were given at the same time.

In practice, however, simultaneous administration of live vaccines can be safe and effective. There is no evidence of significantly diminished response or adverse reactions accompanying simultaneous administration of smallpox (by multiple pressure), DTP (by subcutaneous inoculation), and live oral poliovaccine. Similar results were obtained with a combined live measles, rubella, mumps vaccine, given by injection, and trivalent oral poliovirus vaccine.

Combination live virus vaccines (measles-mumps-rubella; measles-rubella; and rubella-mumps) were licensed in 1971 in the USA. These vaccines incorporate specific virus strains shown to be effective and safe when administered simultaneously. Antibody response to each component of these combination vaccines is comparable with antibody response to the individual vaccines given separately.

Future Prospects

A. Local Administration of Vaccine to Stimulate Local Antibody at the Portal of Entry: Intranasally

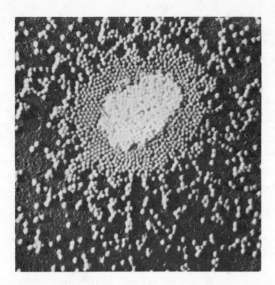

Figure 27—20. Electron micrograph typical of purified preparations of a spherical virus (20,000 X). Shown are human wart virus particles (papovavirus family) having a diameter of 45 nm. (Melnick & Bunting.)

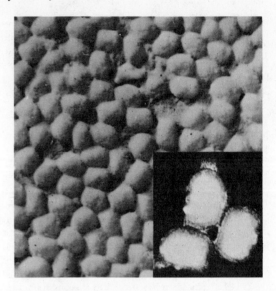

Figure 27—22. Electron micrograph of a purified sample of a brick-shaped poxvirus, molluscum contagiosum (20,000 X). The virus particles, purified from human skin lesions by differential centrifugation, measure about 330 X 230 nm. (Melnick, Bunting, & Strauss.) *Inset:* Uranyl acetate stain of DNA-containing core of the virus (47,000 X).

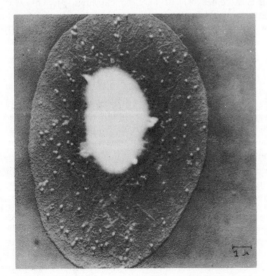

Figure 27—21. Influenza virus particles, PR8 strain, adsorbed on the membranes of a chicken erythrocyte. The particles are about 100 nm in diameter. (Werner & Schlesinger.)

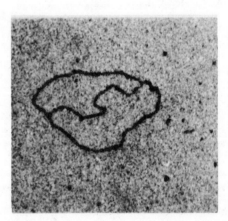

Figure 27—23. Replicating molecule of papovavirus SV40 DNA (schematically shown in Fig 27—10). The electron micrograph shown above represents about 10% of the population of replicating DNA molecules. Most of the replicating molecules also contain a superhelical branch which is so tightly twisted that in electron micrographic preparations it is usually not possible to distinguish individual DNA duplexes. (Salzman & others.)

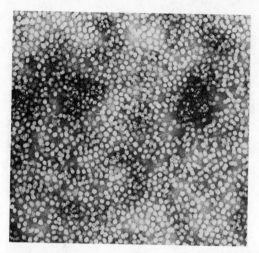

Figure 27–24. Purified hepatitis B surface antigen (HB$_S$Ag) (55,000 ×). (McCombs & Brunschwig.)

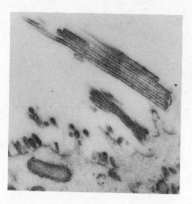

Figure 27–26. Influenza virus at the cell surface (31,000 ×). Two bundles of filaments (one cut longitudinally, the other obliquely) extend into the extracellular space. At left, short filaments seem to be budding from the cell. (Morgan, Rose, & Moore.)

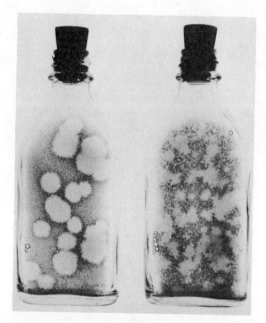

Figure 27–25. Plaques produced by poliovirus *(left)* and by an echovirus *(right)*. Both viruses are cultivated in bottle cultures of monkey kidney cells. After the viruses are seeded, the epithelial sheet is covered with an agar overlay containing a vital dye (neutral red). As the cytopathic effect of the virus becomes manifest, the cells lose their vital stain and clear areas appear in the culture. The progeny of a single virus particle are located in each clear area. The plaque morphology of each of the viruses shown is sufficiently clear so that the 2 virus groups can readily be distinguished from each other by this method. (Hsiung & Melnick.)

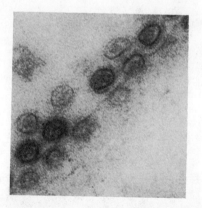

Figure 27–27. Spherical forms of influenza virus (116,000 ×). The cell wall passes diagonally across the field, with host cell cytoplasm to the right. Several particles just beneath the cell membrane seem to be undergoing differentiation toward the mature extracellular form. (Morgan, Rose, & Moore.)

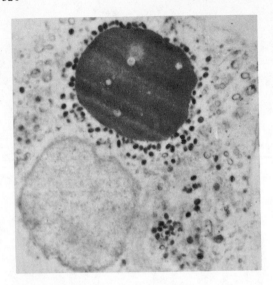

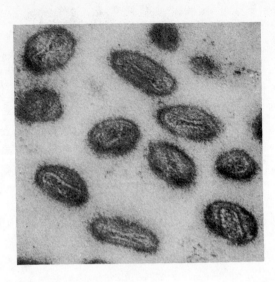

Figure 27—28. Mousepox virus within the infected cell (7400 ×). Nucleus at lower left; above it can be seen a dark cytoplasmic inclusion body surrounded by virus particles. A colony of virus particles in the process of development is located to the right of the nucleus. (Gaylord & Melnick.)

Figure 27—30. Ultrathin section of vaccinia virus particles within the cytoplasm of an infected cell (74,000 ×). The internal structure of the mature virus is evident. (Morgan, Rose, & Moore.)

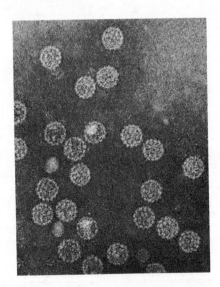

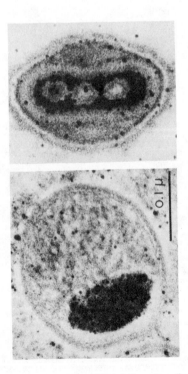

Figure 27—29. Papovavirus SV40. Purified preparation negatively stained with phosphotungstate (150,000 ×). (McGregor & Mayor.)

Figure 27—31. Localization of DNA in immature *(bottom)* and mature *(top)* vaccinia particles. After hydrolysis with HCl, a silver methenamine solution has been applied to Epon sections of the virus. Silver granules are specifically deposited at the sites of DNA. Other structures are made visible by counterstaining with uranyl acetate (170,000 ×). (Peters.)

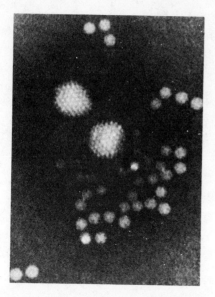

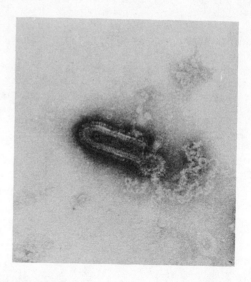

Figure 27–32. A group of satellite viruses surrounding 2 adeno-virions which function as helpers for the defective satellites (250,000 ✕). (Mayor, Jordan, & Melnick.)

Figure 27–34. Electron micrograph of bullet-shaped particle typical of the rhabdovirus family (100,000 ✕). Shown here is vesicular stomatitis virus negatively stained with potassium phosphotungstate. (McCombs, Benyesh-Melnick, & Brunschwig.)

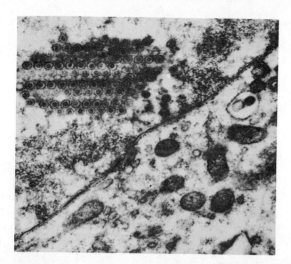

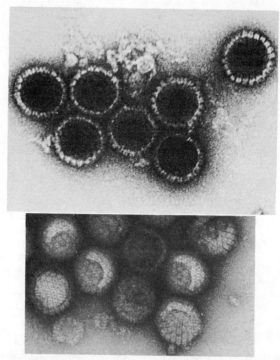

Figure 27–33. Herpesvirus in human amnion cell. The nuclear membrane runs from lower left to upper right. A regular array of virus particles, each possessing a dense central body and a single peripheral membrane, is present within the nucleus (27,000 ✕). (Morgan.)

Figure 27–35. *Top:* Herpesvirus particles from human vesicle fluid, stained with uranyl acetate to show DNA core (140,000 ✕). *Bottom:* Virions stained to show protein capsomeres of the virus coat (140,000 ✕). (Smith & Melnick.)

administered aerosol vaccines are being developed, particularly for respiratory disease viruses.

B. Purification of Vaccines by New Methods (eg, Zonal Centrifugation): This is being used to eliminate nonviral proteins and thus reduce the possibility of adverse reactions to the vaccine. In some instances, purified material can also be administered in more concentrated form, containing greatly increased amounts of the specifically desired antigen.

C. Subunit Vaccines: Subviral components are being obtained by breaking apart the virion to include in the vaccine only those viral components that are needed to stimulate protective antibody.

D. Attenuation of Viruses by Genetic Manipulation: This is being utilized to produce recombinants or temperature-sensitive mutants which can then serve as live virus vaccines.

●   ●   ●

General References

Bablanian R: Structural and functional alterations in cultured cells infected with cytocidal viruses. Prog Med Virol 19:40, 1975.

Baltimore D: Expression of animal virus genomes. Bacteriol Rev 35:235, 1971.

Becker Y: Antiviral drugs: Mode of action and chemotherapy of viral infections of man. Monogr Virol, vol 11, 1976.

Berg P & others: Summary statement of the Asilomar Conference on recombinant DNA molecules. Proc Natl Acad Sci USA 72:1981, 1975.

Bishop JM, Levintow L: Replicative forms of viral RNA structure and function. Prog Med Virol 13:1, 1971.

Blattner RJ, Williamson AP, Heys FM: Role of viruses in the etiology of congenital malformations. Prog Med Virol 15:1, 1973.

Butel JS: Infectious nucleic acids of tumor viruses. Methods Cancer Res 8:287, 1973.

Cheville NF: Cytopathology in viral diseases. Monogr Virol, vol 10, 1975.

Cockburn WC: The programme of the World Health Organization in medical virology. Prog Med Virol 15:159, 1973.

Cole CN: Defective interfering (DI) particles of poliovirus. Prog Med Virol 20:180, 1975.

Dalton AJ, Haguenau F (editors): *Ultrastructure in Biological Systems.* Vol 5: *Ultrastructure of Animal Viruses and Bacteriophages: An Atlas.* Academic Press, 1973.

Fenner F: The classification and nomenclature of viruses. Intervirology, vol 6, issue 1, 1975/1976.

Foege WH, Eddins DL: Mass vaccination programs in developing countries. Prog Med Virol 15:205, 1973.

Grossberg SE: The interferons and their inducers: Molecular and therapeutic considerations. N Engl J Med 287:79, 1972.

Higashi N: Electron microscopy of viruses in thin sections of cells grown in culture. Prog Med Virol 15:331, 1973.

Kilham L, Margolis G: Problems of human concern arising from animal models of intrauterine and neonatal infections due to viruses. Prog Med Virol 20:113, 1975.

Levine AJ: The replication of papovavirus DNA. Prog Med Virol 17:1, 1974.

Lonberg-Holm K, Philipson L: Early interaction between animal viruses and cells. Monogr Virol, vol 9, 1974.

Matthews REF: A classification of virus groups based on the size of the particle in relation to genome size. J Gen Virol 27:135, 1975.

Melnick JL: Taxonomy of viruses, 1975. Prog Med Virol 20:208, 1975.

Mims CA: Pathogenesis of viral infections of the fetus. Prog Med Virol 10:194, 1968.

Munyon W & others: Transfer of thymidine kinase to thymidine kinaseless L cells by infection with ultraviolet-irradiated herpes simplex virus. J Virol 7:813, 1971.

Mussgay M & others: Growth cycle of arboviruses in vertebrate and arthropod cells. Prog Med Virol 19:257, 1975.

Neurath AR, Rubin BA: Viral structural components as immunogens of prophylactic value. Monogr Virol, vol 4, 1971.

Oldstone MBA: Virus neutralization and virus-induced immune complex disease. Prog Med Virol 19:84, 1975.

Proceedings of the International Conference on the Application of Vaccines Against Viral, Rickettsial, and Bacterial Diseases of Man. Scientific publication No. 226. Pan American Health Organization, Washington, DC, 1971.

Russell WC, Winters WD: Assembly of viruses. Prog Med Virol 19:1, 1975.

28 . . .
Isolation of Viruses
From Clinical Specimens

Viruses can be isolated and identified during the course of many diseases, thus establishing the etiologic diagnosis. Generally, however, a specific diagnosis cannot be made in the first few days of the infection; the results of many diagnostic tests for viral diseases frequently do not become available until the patient has recovered or died.

The time and cost entailed in isolating and identifying viruses necessitate careful selection of patients and proper collection and handling of specimens. As a general rule, the indications for attempting to isolate a virus from patients include the following: (1) Instances where the established diagnosis will directly affect the management of the patient, eg, laboratory-proved rubella in the first trimester of pregnancy would favor a decision to terminate pregnancy. (2) Instances where the diagnosis is vital to the health of the community, eg, laboratory confirmation of smallpox, poliomyelitis, influenza, or arbovirus encephalitis will provide the necessary information for instituting immunization programs or insect control measures. (3) Instances where the etiologic agent of a disease is being sought. Studies of patients for etiologic association require prior planning and cooperation between the physician, the public health worker, and the virologist and must include the study of samples from control patients.

The laboratory procedures used in the diagnosis of viral diseases in human beings include the following:

(1) Isolation and identification of the agent.

(2) Measurement of antibodies developing during the course of the infection.

(3) Histologic examination of infected tissues. This should be performed on all fatal cases of virus infections and on animals suspected of infection with rabies virus (Negri inclusion bodies). Biopsy material is useful for distinguishing severe varicella (intranuclear inclusions present) from mild variola (cytoplasmic inclusions present).

(4) Detection of viral antigens in lesions. This method is useful today for detecting the antigen of variola in skin lesions and, using fluorescein-labeled antibodies, in the detection of rabies virus antigen. Myxovirus antigens (hemagglutinins) are detectable in respiratory secretions.

(5) Electron microscopic examination of vesicular fluids or tissue extracts treated with negative and positive stains to identify and count DNA and RNA virus

particles (see Chapter 27). This procedure in the hands of trained personnel has provided diagnoses in a matter of hours in patients with vesicular diseases such as those produced by pox-, herpes-, or varicella viruses. In addition, myxoviruses in respiratory secretions can be identified by this method.

CONSIDERATIONS IN THE
DIAGNOSIS OF VIRAL DISEASES

The choice of methods used for laboratory confirmation of a virus infection depends upon the illness in question. While antibody tests are more readily and economically performed than virus isolations, they usually require adequately spaced serum samples, and the diagnosis is not confirmed until the recovery phase of the illness. In addition, antibody tests can be carried out only for those illnesses for which the etiologic viruses have been grown in the laboratory. Virus isolation is required (1) when new epidemics occur, as with A_2 (Hong Kong) influenza in 1968; (2) when serologic tests overlap and do not allow one to distinguish between 2 viruses, as with smallpox and vaccinia; (3) when it is necessary to confirm a diagnosis made by direct microscopic observation, eg, detecting a herpesvirus in vesicle fluid; and (4) when the same clinical illness may be caused by many different agents.

In undertaking the diagnostic evaluation of a patient with a suspected viral disease, one must bear in mind that the same clinical syndromes may be produced by a variety of agents. For example, aseptic (nonbacterial) meningitis may be caused by many different viruses as well as by spirochetes; similarly, respiratory disease syndromes may be caused by many viruses as well as mycoplasma and other agents.

The isolation of a virus is not necessarily equivalent to establishing the etiology of a given disease. A number of other factors have to be taken into consideration. Some viruses persist in human hosts for long periods of time, and therefore the isolation of herpes, poliomyelitis, echoviruses, or coxsackieviruses from the secretions or cells of a patient with an obscure illness does not necessarily indicate that the virus is the cause of his disease. A consistent clinical and epidemiologic pattern must be established by repeated studies before one can be sure that a particular agent is responsible for a specific clinical picture.

Dual infections present still another problem in interpreting the result of virus isolation studies. Different viruses may have the same seasonal and geographic occurrence. Enteroviruses and arboviruses sometimes frequent the same area at the same time. Thus in one summer a patient may have inapparent infection with one virus and clinical infection with the other. If the clinical infection is mild, the syndrome (eg, aseptic meningitis) may be such that it could be produced by either virus. If antibody studies were made only for the virus which produced the inapparent infection, the diagnosis might be missed altogether. Isolation of 2 viral agents similarly confuses the etiologic significance of each agent unless their role in causation of the illness has been established by prior experience.

DIRECT EXAMINATION
OF CLINICAL MATERIAL

The viral diseases for which direct microscopic examination of imprints or smears has been proved useful include rabies, herpes, and varicella/zoster. The procedure for staining viral antigens by immunofluorescence in a smear from a rabid animal has developed to such an extent that it has now become the method of choice for routine diagnosis of rabies. The procedure is carried out as follows:

Two impression smears on a glass slide are made with the suspect brain. The slide is fixed in acetone at −20° C. One smear (control) is flooded with fluorescein-labeled antirabies globulin mixed with mouse brain containing rabies virus. The other smear (test) is flooded with the same fluorescein-labeled antirabies globulin mixed with normal mouse brain. The slide is incubated at 37° C for 30 minutes in a moist chamber, then washed for 10 minutes in buffered saline, air dried, mounted, and examined in the fluorescent microscope by ultraviolet light. The positive test smear gives bright fluorescence, whereas the control smear gives no fluorescence because the specifically labeled antibodies have been bound by the rabies antigen added in mouse brain.

The same principle of identifying viral antigens using immunofluorescence has proved useful in rapid diagnosis of certain respiratory virus diseases by examination of smeared epithelial cells from the nasopharynx, and of herpetic lesions by examining cells scraped from the base of the lesion. Buffy coat leukocytes or leukocytes of the CSF obtained during the acute illness contain viral antigens (eg, enteroviruses), and this offers a rapid method for obtaining an accurate diagnosis of some viral diseases.

Immunofluorescence has also been used for the early detection of mumps virus, either adsorbed directly from clinical specimens onto guinea pig erythrocytes or after isolation in cell culture. With this method, a specific diagnosis of mumps meningoencephalitis can be made in hours (or 2 days if virus isolation is necessary), in contrast to the 6 days required for the standard methods.

VIRUS ISOLATION TECHNIC

The demonstration or isolation of active virus requires the proper collection of appropriate specimens, their preservation both en route to and in the laboratory, and the inoculation of suitable cell cultures, susceptible animals, or embryonated eggs. Prior to the inoculation of the specimen, several preliminary procedures designed to eliminate bacteria from the specimen may be necessary (see below). The presence of a virus is demonstrated by the appearance of characteristic histologic lesions, inclusion bodies, or viral antigens (hemagglutinating and complement-fixing) in the inoculated test system. Isolated viruses are specifically identified using known antibodies which inhibit or neutralize the biologic effects of the virus or react with viral antigens (inhibiting hemagglutination, fixing complement, or inducing specific fluorescence).

SPECIMENS FOR STUDY

In the collection of material for virus identification studies, it is well to remember that many viruses are most readily demonstrated in the first few days of the illness. (See Table 28−1.)

Throat swabs, vesicle fluid, spinal fluid, urine, unfixed biopsy tissue, sputum, nasal washings, stools, and blood serve as sources of virus material for viral isolation from clinical cases (Tables 28−1 and 28−2). Tissues obtained at autopsy may also serve this purpose.

Table 28−1. Relation of stage of illness to presence of virus in test materials and to appearance of specific antibody.

Stage or Period of Illness	Virus Detectable in Test Materials	Specific Antibody Demonstrable*
Incubation	Rarely	No
Prodrome	Occasionally	No
Onset	Frequently	Occasionally
Acute phase	Frequently	Frequently
Recovery	Rarely	Usually
Convalescent	Very rarely	Usually

*Antibody may be detected very early in previously vaccinated or naturally infected persons.

Table 28–2. Specimens for isolation of viruses.

Clinical Manifestations and Common Etiologic Agents	Source of Specimen for Virus Isolation	
	Clinical	Postmortem or Biopsy
Upper respiratory tract infections		
Rhinovirus	Throat swab or nasal secretions	. . .
Parainfluenza		
Respiratory syncytial		
Adenovirus	Throat swab and feces	. . .
Enterovirus		
Reovirus		
Lower respiratory tract infections		
Influenza	Throat swab and sputum	Lung
Adenovirus		
Parainfluenza		
Rhinovirus		
Respiratory syncytial		
Pleurodynia		
Coxsackievirus	Throat swab and feces	. . .
Cutaneous and mucous membrane diseases		
Vesicular		
Smallpox and vaccinia	Vesicle fluid	Liver, spleen, and lung
Herpes simplex		
Varicella/zoster		
Enterovirus	Vesicle fluid, feces, and throat swab	. . .
Exanthematous		
Measles	Throat swab and blood	. . .
Rubella		
Enterovirus	Throat swab and feces	. . .
CNS infections		
Enterovirus	Feces and CSF	Brain tissue and intestinal contents
Herpes simplex	Throat swab and CSF	Brain tissue
Mumps	Throat swab, CSF, urine	Brain tissue
Lymphocytic choriomeningitis	Blood and CSF	Brain tissue
Arboviruses		
Western equine encephalitis	Blood and CSF	Brain tissue
Eastern equine encephalitis		
Venezuelan equine encephalitis		
California encephalitis	Usually not possible to isolate virus from clinical specimens	Brain tissue
St. Louis encephalitis		
Japanese B encephalitis		
Rabies	Saliva	Brain tissue
Chronic CNS infections		
Measles (subacute sclerosing panencephalitis)	. . .	Brain tissue
Human papovavirus (progressive multifocal leukoencephalopathy)	. . .	Brain tissue
Parotitis		
Mumps	Throat swab (Stensen's duct) and urine	. . .
Cytomegalovirus		
Severe undifferentiated febrile illnesses		
Colorado tick fever	Blood	. . .
Yellow fever		
Dengue		
Congenital anomalies		
Cytomegalovirus	Urine and throat swab	Kidney, lung, and other tissues
Rubella	Throat swab and CSF	Lymph nodes, lung, spleen, other tissues

Owing to the variability of different viral types, care must be taken at the outset to prepare the inoculum in the proper manner and to determine which cell types or animals are to be inoculated (Table 29–12). There may be an unavoidable lapse of time between the collection of the material and its inoculation into a suitable cell culture or animal; it is not enough, in such instances, to leave the material at the usual refrigerator temperature in the hope that the virus may survive for 1–2 days until it can be inoculated. This is particularly true if the material is left in a fluid state.

Material should, in general, be frozen at $-20°$ C or lower temperatures if there is a delay in bringing it to the laboratory. The principal exceptions to this rule are (1) whole blood drawn for antibody determination, which must have the serum separated before freezing; and (2) tissue for organ or cell culture (or urine for cytomegalovirus isolation), which should be placed at $4°$ C and taken to the laboratory as soon as possible for prompt processing.

The choice of specimens for viral study is of utmost importance. The specimens most likely to yield virus from common illnesses are listed in Table 28–2 along with the etiologic agents commonly associated with the diseases.

Generally, respiratory illnesses are associated with excretion of virus in pharyngeal or nasal secretions. Virus can be demonstrated in the fluid of vesicular rashes. Illnesses manifested as encephalitis are usually diagnosed more readily by serologic means. If an enterovirus is the etiologic agent, however, it can be isolated readily. Arboviruses and herpesvirus are not usually recovered from clinical specimens in most instances of CNS disease, although autopsy specimens of brain tissue from patients with viral encephalitis who died early in the course of the disease often yield the etiologic virus. Other illnesses associated with enteroviruses, such as acute pericarditis, myocarditis, and fatal neonatal illness, are readily diagnosed by studying feces and throat swabs.

PRESERVATION OF VIRUSES

Freezing

A large wide-mouthed thermos jar or insulated carton, half-filled with pieces of solid CO_2 (dry ice), is useful for the transportation and temporary preservation of material containing viruses. The temperature within a dry ice storage cabinet can be maintained close to $-76°$ C. Electric deep-freeze cabinets can maintain temperatures of -50 to $-105°$ C.

Lyophilization

This procedure consists of rapid freezing at low temperature (in a bath containing alcohol and dry ice) and dehydration from the frozen state at high vacuum. Ten to 50% of normal rabbit serum or other plasma or serum in the fluid menstruum protects the virus to be frozen and dried. The plasma or serum must not contain antibodies which might neutralize the virus. Skimmed milk is another "protective" menstruum in which virus-containing material may be suspended. If tissues are to be preserved by these methods, they may be ground to a paste and then desiccated in the same manner as are blood and other biologic suspensions.

Dried virus should be stored in the refrigerator. To reconstitute the virus, the sealed ampule containing the dried material is opened and a volume of distilled water equal to the original or desired volume is added.

Glycerol

This is the oldest and simplest method of preserving viruses. Small pieces of tissue or fecal material and suspensions of mucus can be preserved in 50% glycerol. The majority of pathogenic bacteria do not survive in glycerol after 5 or 6 days. Some viruses remain viable in glycerol longer than others.

PREPARATION OF INOCULA

Bacteria-free fluid materials such as CSF, whole blood, plasma, or serum may be inoculated into cell cultures, animals, or eggs, directly or after dilution with buffered phosphate solution (pH 7.6).

Preparation of Tissues

Tissue is placed in a sterile Petri dish, washed in media or sterile water, drained, and weighed. Using sterile equipment and materials, it is minced into small pieces with scissors, placed in a mortar with sand (or particles of Alundum), and ground with a pestle to make a homogeneous paste. Diluent should be added in amounts sufficient to make up a concentration of 10–20%. This suspension can be centrifuged at low speed (not more than 2000 rpm) for 10 minutes to sediment insoluble cellular debris. The supernatant fluid may be inoculated; if bacteria are present, they are eliminated as discussed below.

Tissues may also be trypsinized and a cell suspension prepared. This cell suspension may then be (1) inoculated on an existing tissue culture cell monolayer, (2) co-cultivated with another cell suspension of cells known to be virus-free, or (3) used as an organ culture.

Removal of Bacteria

If the material to be tested contains bacteria—as occurs with oral washings or with suspensions of stools, infected tissue, or insects—these bacteria must be removed before inoculation.

A. Bactericidal Agents:

1. Antibiotics—Antibiotics are commonly employed in combination with differential centrifugation (see below).

2. Ether—If it is not harmful to the virus in question (eg, enteroviruses, vaccinia), ether may be added in concentrations of 10–15%.

B. Mechanical Methods:

1. Filters—Earthenware, porcelain, and asbestos filters reduce the virus concentration by adsorption and are therefore used infrequently.

2. Differential centrifugation—This is a convenient method of removing many bacteria from heavily contaminated preparations of the small viruses. It consists of sedimenting the bacteria at speeds which do not sediment the virus: 18,000 rpm for 20 minutes in a 6-inch rotor has been recommended for viruses less than 100 nm in size. If the material is suspected of containing minimal quantities of infective virus, these may be concentrated by spinning the suspension in a vacuum ultracentrifuge at forces sufficient to sediment the virus into a small gelatinous pellet at the bottom of the tube. Centrifugation at 40,000 rpm (100,000 times gravity) for 60 minutes in a 6-inch rotor will sediment most viruses. The supernatant from such a run contains less than 1% of the original virus. The virus-containing sediment is then resuspended in a small volume.

ANIMAL INOCULATION

The laboratory animals employed for virus isolation include mice, hamsters, cotton rats, guinea pigs, rabbits, and monkeys. For certain viruses, infant mice (less than 48 hours old) are used. The animal of choice and the recommended route of inoculation for specific viruses are included in Table 29—12. Only the intracerebral and intranasal routes will be discussed here.

Intracerebral Inoculation

This is the method of choice for many neurotropic viruses. The inoculum must be relatively free from pathogenic bacteria, for the brain is more susceptible to bacterial infection artificially introduced than are many other parts of the body. Mice are used in groups of at least 6; they should be anesthetized before inoculation. The technic consists of injecting 0.03 ml of inoculum above the orbital ridge into the brain.

Each day after inoculation all animals should be examined closely for signs of illness, and this daily observation should be pursued for an appropriate length of time (3—4 weeks). If the inoculated animal dies during the period of observation, bacterial cultures should be made of the brain and heart blood in order to rule out or confirm the possibility of supervening bacterial infection. If the animal survives without signs of illness until the end of the period of observation, it should be sacrificed and a careful autopsy performed.

Intranasal Inoculation or Instillation

Animals should be anesthetized and the material dropped in the nares with a capillary pipet.

Autopsies of inoculated animals should be performed with great care. Histologic sections are usually required to complete the examination.

CULTIVATION IN CELL CULTURE

Viruses replicate only in living cells, and cell culture technics are the most widely used for isolating viruses from clinical specimens. When viruses multiply in cell culture, they produce biologic effects (cytopathic changes, viral interference, or the production of a hemagglutinin) which permit identification of the agent.

Test tube cultures are prepared by adding cells suspended in 1—2 ml of nutrient fluid which contains balanced salt solutions and various growth factors (usually serum, glucose, amino acids, and vitamins). Cells of fibroblastic or epithelial nature attach and grow on the wall of the test tube where they may be examined with the aid of a low power microscope.

With many viruses, growth of the agent is paralleled by a degeneration of these cells. (See Fig 28—1.) Some viruses produce characteristic cytopathic effects in cell culture, making a rapid presumptive diagnosis possible when the clinical syndrome is known. As examples, measles, mumps, parainfluenza, and respiratory syncytial viruses characteristically produce multinucleated giant cells, while adenoviruses produce grape-like clusters of large round cells, rhinoviruses produce focal areas of rounding and dendritic forms, and herpes simplex virus produces diffuse uniform rounding of cells.

Some viruses (eg, rubella virus) produce no direct cytopathic changes but rather can be detected by their interference with the cytopathic effect of a second challenge virus (viral interference).

Influenza virus as well as other orthomyxoviruses may be detected within 24—48 hours if erythrocytes are added to infected cultures. Viruses maturing at the cell membrane produce a hemagglutinin enabling the erythrocytes to adsorb at the cell surface (hemadsorption).

Organ cultures of ferret and human tracheal epithelium may support the growth of a wide variety of viruses which cause upper respiratory tract disease, including some new viruses which do not grow in conventional cell cultures (eg, coronaviruses). Viruses may cause general or focal necrosis of the ciliated epithelial cells or may be detected by a decline in ciliary movement.

Confirmation of the identity of a virus isolate requires use of type-specific antiserum, which inhibits both virus growth and the biologic (or cytopathic) effect.

EMBRYONATED EGGS

Embryonated eggs of varying age may be inoculated by several routes. After inoculation, the eggs are reincubated for several days at 36—38° C and examined daily.

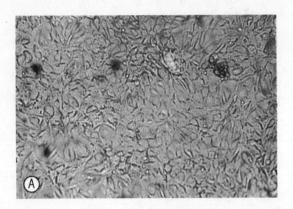

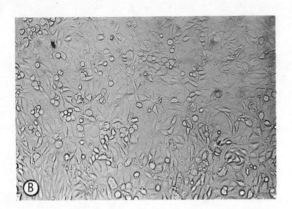

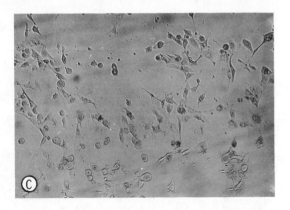

Figure 28–1. *A:* Monolayer of normal unstained monkey kidney cells in culture (120 ×). *B:* Unstained monkey kidney cell culture showing early stage of cytopathic effects (CPE) typical of enterovirus infection (120 ×). Approximately 25% of the cells in the culture show CPE indicative of virus multiplication (1+ CPE score). *C:* Unstained monkey kidney cell culture illustrating more advanced enteroviral cytopathic effect (3+ to 4+ CPE) (120 ×). Almost 100% of the cells are affected, and most of the cell sheet has come loose from the wall of the culture tube.

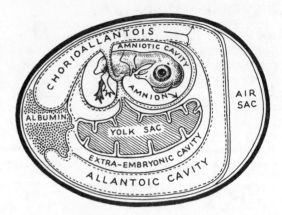

Figure 28–2. Schematic diagram showing developing chick embryo and indicating cavities and other structures used for various routes of inoculation.

Chorioallantoic Inoculation

This is performed in 10- to 12-day-old chick embryos. An area free of vessels is selected by candling and marked at the greatest circumference of the egg. The air sac is also located. An artificial air sac is made by chipping the shell with a sharp-pointed instrument over the marked area. The intact shell membrane is carefully exposed and slit by gentle pressure. The chorioallantois lying immediately beneath must not be ruptured in the process. A second hole is made in the air sac end of the egg. When gentle suction is applied through this opening, the chorioallantois will drop away from the shell membrane beneath the first hole. The inoculum may be placed on top of the first hole and be drawn in when the membrane is dropped, or it may be placed later onto the membrane.

Amniotic Sac Inoculation

Embryos 7–14 days old have been used. After the chorioallantois is dropped, the side opening is enlarged. A forceps is then thrust through the chorioallantois and a small part of the amniotic membrane drawn through the chorioallantois, so that the inoculum can be introduced directly into the amniotic sac.

Allantoic Sac Inoculation

This procedure is performed in 10-day-old embryos through an opening made in the shell and underlying membranes over an avascular area of the chorioallantois. A hole is made in the air sac end to prevent back pressure of the inoculum.

Yolk Sac Inoculation

This is performed in 3- to 8-day-old embryos. At this age the yolk sac fills almost the entire egg. A hole is made in the air sac end, and the inoculum is introduced directly into the yolk sac.

Other Types of Inoculation

Intraembryonic, intravenous, and intracelomic inoculations may also be done in special instances.

EXAMINATION OF EMBRYOS

The shell over the artificial air space is chipped away and the shell membrane removed with sterile scissors and forceps. This exposes the ectodermal surface of the chorioallantois, on which lesions may have developed.

The membrane is removed, placed in sterile water, and examined for lesions against a dark background. If the virus is to be passed, the membrane is first ground to make a suspension. For some agents the whole embryo (minced and ground) may be used as a source of virus. Yolk sacs and the allantoic or amniotic fluid are also sometimes used as sources.

•   •   •

General References

Bradstreet CMP, Pereira MS, Pollock TM: The organization of a national virological diagnostic service. Prog Med Virol 16:241, 1973.

Hermann EC Jr: New concepts and developments in applied diagnostic virology. Prog Med Virol 17:221, 1974.

Hoorn B, Tyrrell DAJ: Organ cultures in virology. Prog Med Virol 11:408, 1969.

Hsiung GD: *Diagnostic Virology.* Yale Univ Press, 1973.

Lennette DA, Emmons RW, Lennette EH: Rapid diagnosis of mumps virus infections by immunofluorescence methods. J Clin Microbiol 2:81, 1975.

Lennette EH, Melnick JL, Magoffin RL: Clinical virology: Introduction to methods. Pages 667–677 in: *Manual of Clinical Microbiology,* 2nd ed. American Society for Microbiology, 1974.

Rahman A: Early detection of influenza virus in cell culture by means of immunofluorescence. J Clin Pathol 26:503, 1973.

Rapp F, Melnick JL: Applications of tissue culture methods in virus laboratories. Prog Med Virol 6:268, 1964.

Schmidt NJ: Tissue culture techniques for diagnostic virology. Pages 79–178 in: *Diagnostic Procedures for Viral and Rickettsial Infections,* 4th ed. American Public Health Association, 1969.

Sulkin SE, Pike RM: Prevention of laboratory infections. Pages 66–78 in: *Diagnostic Procedures for Viral and Rickettsial Infections,* 4th ed. American Public Health Association, 1969.

Taber LH & others: Rapid diagnosis of enterovirus meningitis by immunofluorescent staining of CSF leukocytes. Intervirology 1:127, 1973.

29...
Serologic Diagnosis
& Immunologic Detection
of Virus Infections

Procedures Available

Typically, a virus infection is characterized by an immune response directed against one or more viral antigens. Both cellular and humoral immune responses usually develop, and measurement of either may be used to diagnose a virus infection. Cellular immunity may be assessed by dermal hypersensitivity; this test is described at the end of this chapter and has limited usefulness. Humoral immune responses are of major diagnostic importance. Antibodies of the IgM class appear initially and are followed by IgG antibodies. The IgM antibodies disappear in several weeks, while the IgG antibodies persist for many years. Establishing the diagnosis of a virus infection is accomplished serologically by demonstrating a rise in antibody titer to the virus or by demonstrating antiviral antibodies of the IgM class.

Procedures for quantifying antibodies in virus diseases are based on classic antigen-antibody reactions (see Chapter 12), with some modifications for certain viruses. The commonly used methods include the neutralization (Nt) test, the complement fixation (CF) test, the hemagglutination inhibition (HI) test, and the immunofluorescence test. Less commonly used methods include passive hemagglutination, immunodiffusion, counterimmunoelectrophoresis, and radioimmunoassay. This chapter will deal with methods chosen to illustrate some principles. A summary of the tests available for viruses is presented in Table 29—12.

Antibodies measured by different methods do not necessarily give parallel results. This is illustrated in Table 29—1. Antibodies are detected by complement

fixation during an enterovirus infection and in the convalescent period, but they do not persist. Antibodies detected by neutralization appear during infection and persist for many years. Assessment of antibodies by several methods in individuals or groups of individuals provides diagnostic information as well as information about epidemiologic features of the disease.

Collection of Blood Specimens

Serial samples of serum are essential for diagnostic purposes if antibodies are to be adequately tested and evaluated. In general, the first sample should be collected as soon as possible after the onset of the illness; the second, 2—3 weeks after onset. A third sample may be required later for special study. Antibodies appear earlier in some viral infections than in others, and so the times of collecting specimens must be varied according to circumstances.

Blood specimens should be drawn with aseptic precautions and without anticoagulants and the serum separated and stored at 4° C or −20° C. Before performing serologic tests it may be necessary to heat the serum (56° C for 30 minutes) to remove nonspecific interfering or inhibiting substances and complement. This is essential for CF tests and also, with certain viruses, for Nt tests.

If paired sera are not available, a presumptive diagnosis can sometimes be made by demonstrating IgM antibodies to the virus. IgM antibodies may be detected by sensitivity to 2-mercaptoethanol (2-ME), by immunofluorescence, or by physical separation of IgM from IgG, using density gradient centrifugation. IgM is relatively more sensitive to degradation by 2-ME than is IgG. A significant fall in antibody titer after treatment of a serum sample with 2-ME indicates the presence of IgM and signifies a current or recent infection. High-speed centrifugation of serum on a sucrose density gradient separates IgM, which sediments toward the bottom of the tube, from IgG, which remains near the center of the tube. Following centrifugation, demonstration of antibody activity associated with the bottom fractions collected from the tube indicates a recent infection. Using fluorescein-labeled antibody to IgM, antibodies to viral antigens of the IgM class can be detected by the indirect immunofluorescent method.

Table 29—1. Interpretation of laboratory data in enterovirus infection.

Virus Isolation	Complement-fixing Antibody	Neutralizing Antibody	Antibody of IgM Class	Interpretation of Infection
−	−	−	−	None
+	−	−	−	Early
+	+	+	+	Current
−	+	+	+	Recent
−	−	+	−	Old

NEUTRALIZATION (Nt) TESTS

Virus-neutralizing antibodies are measured by adding serum containing these antibodies to a suspension of virus and then inoculating the mixture into susceptible cell cultures. The presence of neutralizing antibodies is demonstrated if the cell cultures fail to develop cytopathic effects (CPE), while control cell cultures, which had received virus plus a serum free of antibody, develop CPE. In some instances, the virus-antiserum mixture may be inoculated into susceptible experimental animals (as with type A coxsackieviruses) or embryonated eggs (as with mumps virus). The failure of virus to grow in the presence of the antiserum and its growth in the control cultures indicate the presence of protective or neutralizing antibody in the antiserum.

The virus in a neutralized mixture is not destroyed, since it is possible to treat many virus-antibody mixtures with acid (pH 2.0), which denatures the antibody and liberates the virus in its original, fully infectious state.

The level of such antibodies can be determined by using a constant amount of virus and falling concentrations of serum. In certain instances undiluted serum may be tested against falling concentrations of virus. In order to establish a diagnosis, one must be able to show a significant rise in antibody titer during the course of the infection.

A positive test in a single sample of serum is not of diagnostic value in acute recent infections. Neutralizing antibodies can persist for years, and their mere presence may indicate a past infection in a given individual. Thus, Nt tests are useful in serologic epidemiology, where one is interested in knowing which viral agents have infected a given population in the past.

Although simple in principle, Nt tests are expensive in time and in materials and may be difficult to interpret, chiefly because of the variability in the titration endpoint and the possible nonspecificity of the neutralization. The technic of performing the test for neutralizing antibodies must be standardized for each viral agent. Among the variables which must be considered are (1) the selection of the cell culture, experimental animal, or embryonated egg; (2) the route of inoculation of the virus-serum mixture; (3) the age of the test animals; (4) the stability of the test virus; (5) the reproducibility of the endpoint; (6) the relative heat-stability of the specific antibody and of possible interfering substances in serum; (7) the addition of an accessory factor found in fresh normal serum of the homologous species; (8) the use of one concentration of virus and varying dilutions of serum, or vice versa (and the relationship between varying concentrations of each); (9) the temperature of the neutralizing mixture; and (10) the time of incubation of the mixture.

QUANTITATIVE NEUTRALIZATION TESTS

Mouse Test

A stock of mice of known uniform susceptibility and standard age is selected. The mice are inoculated by a standard route with the virus-serum mixture. They are observed daily for signs of illness, such as weakness or paralysis, to establish specificity of the deaths. Illness and deaths are recorded daily for 21 days. Deaths within 24 hours after inoculation are attributed to traumatic or nonviral causes.

Titration of Virus

It is necessary to titrate the virus each time a test is performed. The 50% endpoints (50% tissue culture infectious dose, $TCID_{50}$; 50% infectious dose, ID_{50}; or 50% lethal dose, LD_{50}) are calculated according to the method of Reed and Muench or the method of Kaerber. A variation of this expression is the PD_{50}, the dose which paralyzes 50% of the animals.

A. Calculation of LD_{50} Titer by Reed-Muench Method: The proportionate distance between the 2 dilutions (in the example shown in Tables 29–2 and 29–3, between 10^{-3} and 10^{-4}), wherein the 50% endpoint lies, equals

$$\frac{\% \text{ mortality above } 50 - 50\%}{\% \text{ mortality above } 50\% - \% \text{ mortality below } 50\%} =$$

$$\frac{90 - 50}{90 - 22} = \frac{40}{68} = 0.6$$

Table 29–2. Animal mortality data.

Virus Dilution	Mortality Ratio	Died*	Survived*
10^{-1}	8/8	8	0
10^{-2}	8/8	8	0
10^{-3}	7/8	7	1
10^{-4}	2/8	2	6
10^{-5}	0/8	0	8

*Arrows indicate direction of addition for accumulated values.

Table 29–3. Accumulated values from mortality data.

Virus Dilution	Died	Survived	Mortality Ratio	Mortality Percent
10^{-1}	25	0	25/25	100
10^{-2}	17	0	17/17	100
10^{-3}	9	1	9/10	90
10^{-4}	2	7	2/9	22
10^{-5}	0	15	0/15	0

Negative logarithm of LD_{50} titer =

$$\left(\begin{array}{c}\text{Negative log of dilution}\\ \text{above 50\% mortality}\end{array}\right) + \left(\begin{array}{c}\text{Proportionate}\\ \text{distance}\end{array}\right)$$

Negative logarithm of LD_{50} titer =
$$3.0 + 0.6 = 3.6$$
$$LD_{50}\text{ titer} = 10^{-3.6}$$

The same procedure is used for calculating $TCID_{50}$ titers. In the tissue culture calculations, the mortality ratio (number of mice dead per number of mice inoculated) is replaced by the cytopathogenic ratio (number of cultures showing cytopathic changes per number of cultures inoculated).

B. Calculation of LD_{50} Titer by the Kaerber Method:

$$\text{Log } LD_{50} = 0.5 + \left(\begin{array}{c}\text{Log of highest concentration}\\ \text{of virus used}\end{array}\right)$$
$$- \frac{\text{Sum of \% of dead animals}}{100}$$

For the example shown above in Table 29–2,

$$\text{Log } LD_{50}\text{ titer} = 0.5 + (-1.0)$$
$$- \frac{100 + 100 + 88 + 25}{100}$$

$$\text{Log } LD_{50}\text{ titer} = 0.5 - 1.0 - 3.1$$
$$\text{Log } LD_{50}\text{ titer} = -3.6$$
$$LD_{50}\text{ titer} = 10^{-3.6}$$

The same procedure is used for calculating $TCID_{50}$ titers. In the tissue culture titrations the "sum of percent of dead animals" is replaced by "sum of percent of cultures showing cytopathic changes."

Neutralization Index

The neutralization index is the expression of the ratio of the virus control LD_{50} titer to the LD_{50} titer of the serum-virus mixtures in which virus has been added to undiluted serum. The logarithm of the LD_{50} titer of the virus control minus the logarithm of the LD_{50} titer of the serum-virus mixture equals the logarithm of the neutralization index. The antilogarithm of this difference equals the neutralization index. A neutralization index of less than 10 is considered to indicate the absence of antibodies.

If the above virus titration had been that of the control sample (ie, virus plus normal serum), a positive serum might give the reaction shown in Table 29–4. (Each virus dilution is mixed with an equal volume of serum and the mixture incubated for 1 hour at room temperature before inoculation.)

A. Calculation of Neutralized Virus LD_{50} by the Reed-Muench Method: (Using accumulated values in Table 29–5.)

$$\text{Proportionate distance} = \frac{56 - 50}{56 - 8} = \frac{6}{48} = 0.1$$

Negative logarithm of LD_{50} titer =
$$1.0 + 0.1 = 1.1$$
$$LD_{50}\text{ titer} = 10^{-1.1}$$

B. Calculation of Neutralized Virus LD_{50} by the Kaerber Method: (Using data in Table 29–4.)

$$\text{Logarithm of } LD_{50}\text{ titer} = 0.5 + (-1.0) - \frac{50 + 13}{100}$$
$$= 0.5 - 1.0 - 0.6 = -1.1$$
$$LD_{50}\text{ titer} = 10^{-1.1}$$

C. Calculation of Neutralization Index: Logarithm of neutralization index = neg log of control titer minus neg log of serum-virus mixture. Neutralization index = antilog of above value. A neutralization index may be calculated from the above examples using the control titer based on data in Tables 29–2 and 29–3 and the serum-virus mixture titer based on data in Tables 29–4 and 29–5. The formula would appear as follows: $3.6 - 1.1 = 2.5$.

Neutralization index = Antilog of 2.5 = 320

Interpretation

As neutralizing antibodies for many viruses persist for a long time, it is essential to demonstrate a rise in titer in paired sera in order to establish recent infection by the virus. A positive test in a single specimen may be the result of an earlier and perhaps subclinical infection and is not useful for clinical diagnosis of the acute disease. For diagnostic purposes, the increase in neutralization index during convalescence should be at least 100. When antibodies are present in acute phase sera, their increase during the course of the disease is often more readily demonstrated by using a constant amount of virus and varying the dilutions of serum.

Table 29–4. Animal mortality data.

Virus Dilution Present in Each Virus-Serum Mixture*	Mortality Ratio	Died†	Survived
10^{-1}	4/8	4	4
10^{-2}	1/8	1	7
10^{-3}	0/8	0	8

*An equal volume of undiluted serum is added to each virus dilution 1 hour before inoculation of the mixture.

†Arrows indicate direction of addition for accumulated values.

Table 29–5. Accumulated values from mortality data.

Virus Dilution	Died	Survived	Mortality Ratio	Mortality Percent
10^{-1}	5	4	5/9	56
10^{-2}	1	11	1/12	8
10^{-3}	0	19	0/19	0

THE NEUTRALIZATION TEST IN CELL CULTURE

The details of performing this test vary in different laboratories, but the same principle underlies all of them: The viral antibody specifically neutralizes the cytopathogenic effects of the virus.

With each series of Nt tests, control titrations of virus are made, the starting concentration being the highest dose (100 $TCID_{50}$) used in the serum-virus mixtures. It is also advisable to test the highest concentration of each serum in a cell culture tube for possible nonspecific cell toxicity. A few tubes are left uninoculated to serve as cell controls. The typical results of sera obtained from a patient infected with type 1 poliovirus are shown in Table 29—6. The cultures were incubated at 36° C for 3 days and then examined microscopically. At the end of that time the virus titration showed that 100 $TCID_{50}$ doses had been added to each serum.

Suspensions of monkey kidney cells or cells from a continuous cell line may be used directly in Nt tests. The same basic principle which underlies any virus Nt test, ie, antibody specifically neutralizes the infectivity of the virus, also applies to the color (or metabolic inhibition) test. The color test employs known quantities of cell suspensions which are added to test tubes or plastic panel cups 1 hour after the serum-virus mixture. This eliminates the need for cultures in which cells have already grown out on glass. The color test utilizes the fact that, with continued cellular growth in control tubes or in the presence of an immune serum-virus mixture, acidic products of metabolism lower the pH of the medium. This effect is readily observed by incorporating the indicator dye phenol red into the medium. This dye is red at pH 7.4—7.8. It becomes salmon pink and finally yellow as the pH drops below 7.0. Conversely, cell necrosis induced by the virus leaves the medium red, for the dying cultures fail to reach the degree of acidity exhibited by the control cultures. The test can thus be read by color change alone rather than by the presence or absence of cellular degeneration as determined microscopically. Neutralizing antibodies are measured by determining the serum dilution which, in the presence of added virus, will allow the cells to metabolize normally and the pH to fall as in the controls.

The test described in the above paragraph is used with the enteroviruses. Because adenoviruses cause a stimulation of cellular metabolism and more rapid lowering of the pH than that of the control cultures, the color reaction is the opposite of that described above.

NEUTRALIZATION TESTS IN EGGS

The embryonated egg may also be used as an indicator system in virus Nt tests. With influenza and mumps viruses, after the inoculation of the virus-serum mixtures, the endpoint is measured by determining whether viral hemagglutinins have developed in the allantoic fluid.

For viruses such as herpes or vaccinia, which produce pocks or plaques on the chorioallantoic membrane, neutralization may be measured by comparing the number of pocks produced by the virus alone with the number produced in the presence of the serum. Such pock reduction or plaque neutralization technics are available for many viruses grown in cell culture, and are commonly used where greater accuracy of quantitation is required.

COMPLEMENT FIXATION (CF) TESTS

Analogous to bacterial complement fixation, it has been shown that antiviral sera fix complement in

Table 29—6. Cell culture neutralization test with paired sera of patient infected with type 1 poliovirus.

Virus*	Serum (Day After Onset)	Cellular Degeneration (Cytopathic Effect) Final Serum Dilution					50% Serum Titer	
		1:2	1:10	1:50	1:250	1:1250	Logarithm	Antilog
Type 1	1	000	+++	+++	+++	+++	0.7	5
	20	000	000	000	00+	+++	2.5	320
Type 2	1	000	+++	+++	+++	+++	0.7	5
	20	000	000	0++	+++	+++	1.5	32
Type 3	1	+++	+++	+++	+++	+++	0	0
	20	+++	+++	+++	+++	+++	0	0
None	1	000						
	20	000						

*100 $TCID_{50}$ doses of each virus used in test.

the presence of their homologous antigens. Such tests are being employed for most viral diseases. The difficulty with viral CF tests lies in the problem of preparing concentrated antigens free of nonspecific interfering substances. Infected tissue has often been employed in the past. At present, most antigens are derived from the allantoic fluid of the embryonated egg or from cell culture fluids after infection with viruses. In some instances (eg, rubella), antigens are prepared from 10–20% suspensions of virus-infected cells which are disrupted by freezing and thawing or by sonication.

Preparation of Antigen

Various test procedures have been devised. A brief review of the Casals technic for the viral encephalitides follows; it illustrates principles common to many viral CF tests. The antigens are often virulent, and caution should therefore be observed in handling them.

Antigen is prepared from mouse brains harvested at the first signs of infection. The weighed tissue is blended with 20 volumes of chilled acetone for 2 minutes. Following centrifugation, the sediment is re-extracted once with a mixture of equal parts of acetone and anhydrous ethyl ether and twice more with ether. After the last extraction, the ether is decanted and the residual material evaporated under vacuum. The ether-insoluble residue is resuspended in 3 volumes of physiologic saline solution and the suspension centrifuged. The supernatant constitutes the antigen.

Other methods have been advocated for the preparation of neurotropic virus antigens. These include the use of infected chick embryos as source material and the extraction with benzene of lyophilized chick embryos or mouse brains followed by their resuspension in saline. For optimal reactivity, Veronal buffer with added Mg^{++} and Ca^{++} may offer certain advantages over saline as a suspending medium for viral antigens.

Procedure

Complement should be titrated in the presence of each antigen under the same conditions as prevail in the test proper. A preliminary titration is made in saline. Another titration is set up at the same time with antigen and saline as control, and this is incubated along with the test for antibodies.

The test is run as follows: Inactivated sera (60° C

for 20 minutes) are diluted 2-fold, beginning with the 1:2 dilution, and 0.25 ml is placed in a series of test tubes (13 X 100 mm). Then 0.25 ml of antigen is added plus 2 units of complement in 0.5 ml. The mixture of serum, antigen, and complement is incubated at 37° C for 1–2 hours or, for greater sensitivity, at 2–4° C for 18 hours. Following incubation the hemolytic system is added; this consists of 0.25 ml of a 3% suspension of sheep erythrocytes plus 0.25 ml of rabbit antisheep erythrocyte serum (hemolysin) diluted to provide 3 minimal hemolytic doses. The total volume of fluid in each tube is now 1.5 ml. The tubes are incubated at 37° C for 20 minutes and read visually: 4+ represents no hemolysis, which indicates complement fixation. A micro-modification using micro-titer equipment is available in which each volume of reagent is reduced by a factor of 10. The micro-procedure has supplanted the macro-method in most laboratories in recent years.

Interpretation

The titer is defined as the highest dilution of serum giving a 2+ or better fixation. Control tubes, in which 0.25 ml of saline replaces the serum or the antigen respectively, used in the test proper, are included for each antigen and for each serum as a measure of their anticomplementary activity.

SOLUBLE & VIRAL ANTIGENS

Some viruses have been shown to possess 2 serologically distinct complement-fixing antigens, one being intimately associated with the virus and the other being much smaller ("soluble") and found in infected tissues. These observations have been of diagnostic value in mumps, particularly during the early stage of the disease. Antibodies against the soluble or S-antigen appear earlier in the infection than do those against the virus-bound or V-antigen. Furthermore, anti-V bodies persist for much longer periods than anti-S bodies.

Thus, if the serum of an acutely ill patient has a high titer against the S-antigen and a negligible titer against the V-antigen of mumps virus, the illness is probably mumps. High levels of both antibodies indicate a recent infection or one of several days' duration.

Table 29–7. An example of a complement fixation test response.

Time of Taking Serum	Serum Dilution						Titer
	1:5	1:10	1:20	1:40	1:80	1:160	
Acute phase	0	0	0	0	0	0	0
Recovery phase	4+	3+	0	0	0	0	1:10
Convalescent	4+	4+	4+	3+	2+	0	1:80

4+ indicates complement fixation (no hemolysis); 0 indicates complete hemolysis.

Low titers against V-antigen indicate long-past apparent or inapparent infection. With both S- and V-antigens, a presumptive diagnosis of infection with mumps virus often may be made in the first days of illness, for this is the only period when there occurs a high titer of anti-S and a low titer of anti-V. This has permitted the recognition of mumps meningoencephalitis in the absence of parotitis as early as 2 days after onset.

HEMAGGLUTINATION
INHIBITION (HI) TESTS

There are a number of viruses which agglutinate erythrocytes, and this reaction may be specifically inhibited by immune or convalescent sera. As shown in Table 29–12, this reaction forms the basis of a number of diagnostic tests for viral infections.

Diseases in Which an Antibody Response May Be Demonstrated by the HI Test

    Influenza
    Rubella
    Mumps
    Measles
    Newcastle disease
    Variola
    Vaccinia
    California virus encephalitis
    St. Louis encephalitis
    Western equine encephalitis
    Japanese B encephalitis
    West Nile fever
    Dengue
    Adenovirus infections
    Some enterovirus infections
    Reovirus infections

As the same general principles apply for the HI tests used with different viral agents, the details will be presented only for influenza. However, it should be noted that a distinct species of erythrocytes may be necessary to agglutinate certain viruses, eg, some of the adenovirus types agglutinate only rat erythrocytes.

STANDARDS & TITRATION

Standard Erythrocyte Suspension

This suspension consists of 0.5% human type O erythrocytes in physiologic saline solution. The blood may be either freshly collected or preserved with sterile precautions in Alsever's solution for not longer than 1 month at 5° C. Formalinized chicken erythrocytes may also be used for measurement of influenza

antibody. They may be stored for 3 months with no loss of hemagglutinating activity.

Standard Antigens

Standard influenza virus antigens types A, A1, A2, and B may be obtained from commercial sources. These consist of allantoic fluids from infected eggs and are distributed in lyophilized form.

Titration of Antigens

The hemagglutinating unit of antigen is defined as 0.5 ml of the highest dilution of antigen which completely agglutinates the 0.5 ml of standard human erythrocyte suspension. The virus-red cell mixture is read and recorded on the basis of the pattern of agglutination.

(1) Positive agglutination is indicated by a red, granular, diffused lining on the bottom of the tube.

(2) Absence of agglutination is indicated by the formation of a compact red button at the bottom of the tube.

(3) Partial agglutination is indicated by something in between a diffused lining on the bottom of the tube and a red button. This takes the form of a ring with a hollow center. The rings are of varying sizes, depending upon the extent of agglutination.

THE DIAGNOSTIC AGGLUTINATION
INHIBITION TEST

Procedure

Two serum specimens from each patient must be tested with all types of antigen. The first of these (acute phase) is obtained within 2–3 days after the onset of illness; the second (convalescent phase) is obtained 10–14 days after the onset of illness. The tests are set up as follows:

(1) 0.3 ml amounts of the sera to be tested are inactivated at 53° C for 30 minutes; they are then diluted 1:8 by adding 2.1 ml of saline solution.

(2) For each serum to be tested set up 3 rows of tubes, preferably in a rack with 3 rows of 10 holes each. Saline solution in 0.75 ml amounts is added to the second to tenth tubes in the front row. The first tube on the far left in the front row and all the tubes in the middle and back rows are left empty. The inactivated 1:8 dilution of serum in 0.25 ml amounts is transferred to the first tube of each of the 3 rows and 0.75 ml of the same solution of the serum is placed in the second tube of the front row. This is mixed thoroughly, and 0.25 ml is transferred to the second tube of the middle and back rows and 0.75 ml is placed in the third tube of the front row. The operation is repeated in this manner until 3 identical series of 2-fold dilutions have been prepared. Each tube contains 0.25 ml and the serum dilutions range from 1:8 through 1:4096.

(3) After the serum dilutions have been prepared,

0.25 ml amounts containing 4 hemagglutinating units of the 3 test antigens are added to the tubes in the first, second, and third rows respectively.

(4) Shake well and then add 0.5 ml of the 0.5% erythrocyte suspension to the serum-antigen mixtures.

(5) Shake well and incubate at room temperature for 60 minutes. Be careful not to bump or move the racks.

(6) The tests are read and recorded in terms of degree of inhibition of agglutination by each serum using each antigen. The titer of a given serum using a given antigen is defined as the highest dilution of serum which effects complete inhibition of agglutination.

Controls

Known antisera to A, A1, A2, and B influenza are set up in the same manner as are the unknown sera, except that a 1:100 initial dilution of the standard titrated serum is used instead of the 1:8 dilution in the human sera described.

The test antigens must be re-titrated at the same time that the agglutination inhibition tests are performed.

Interpretation

Results are reported in terms of the titers of each of the paired sera obtained with each antigen. An example is shown in Table 29–8. A 4-fold or greater increase in titer during convalescence is considered of diagnostic significance.

As noted with the CF test, micro-methods are used in most laboratories today for hemagglutination and HI tests.

PASSIVE HEMAGGLUTINATION TEST

The use of a coupling reagent, chromic chloride, to attach proteins to indicator erythrocytes has made possible the hemagglutination of red cells by antigens which otherwise do not demonstrate this property. Use of this indirect or passive hemagglutination test has simplified the serologic diagnosis of rhinovirus infections and has made possible the rapid measurement of hepatitis B antigen (HBAg) and antibody in type B

viral hepatitis. The method described below for the diagnosis of rhinovirus infections offers a useful epidemiologic tool for the study of respiratory diseases. The technic is group-specific for rhinoviruses; however, cross-reactivity with echovirus 11 has been demonstrated.

Method

One volume (0.1 ml) of washed guinea pig or human group O erythrocytes is mixed with one volume of virus antigen (10^3 $TCID_{50}$) and one volume of a 1:20 dilution of stock chromic chloride ($CrCl_3 \cdot 6H_2O$) solution. The cells, antigen, and $CrCl_3 \cdot 6H_2O$ are prepared in phosphate-free 0.15 M saline. The stock solution of $CrCl_3 \cdot 6H_2O$ is 1% in distilled water and is kept in a brown, light-proof bottle at 5° C. The mixture of cells, antigen, and chromic chloride is allowed to react for 5 minutes at room temperature and is then washed 4 times in phosphate-buffered saline (PBS), using 30-second periods of centrifugation. The washed cells are reconstituted as a 0.1% suspension in PBS containing 0.1% bovine serum albumin.

Micro-titer plates ("V" type) are used. A diluent containing PBS, Tween 80 (1:20,000), and polyvinyl-pyrrolidone (2.5 mg/100 ml) is added to each well, and an equal volume of each serum under test is added to the first well of the micro-titer trays and serially diluted with a micro-titer loop. Control tests are done in the last 2 wells of each row for all experiments; these include antigen-coated cells without test serum, and noncoated erythrocytes with test serum. All test wells then receive an equal volume of the 0.1% suspension of virus-coated erythrocytes. The titration plates are covered with clear tape to minimize evaporation and left at room temperature for 1 hour. They are then spun for 1 minute at 1000 rpm in a centrifuge equipped with special carriers for micro-titer trays. The clear tape is removed and the plates are inclined at a 60-degree angle on an illuminated platform for 20 minutes. Cells that remain as a button at the bottom of a well signify a positive reaction, and smooth-running patterns of erythrocytes denote negative reactions.

In lieu of centrifuge adaptors, constant volume deliverers, serial dilutors, micro-titer trays, etc, the procedure can be done in test tubes employing "settling patterns" as endpoint determinants.

Table 29–8. An example of a hemagglutination inhibition test response.

Time of Taking Serum	Serum Dilution						Titer
	1:8	1:16	1:32	1:64	1:128	1:256	
Acute phase	0	+	+	+	+	+	1:8
Recovery phase	0	0	0	+	+	+	1:32
Convalescent	0	0	0	0	0	+	1:128

+ = Agglutination. 0 = No agglutination.

OTHER TESTS

MIXED HEMADSORPTION TEST

This test has been used to detect and identify viral antigens at the cell surface of monolayer cultures infected with a variety of viruses. The principle of the test is similar to the indirect immunofluorescence test except that specially prepared erythrocytes are used as an indicator instead of fluorescence. Erythrocytes are coated with red cell antibody made in the same animal species used to prepare antibodies against the virus. To the coated erythrocytes is added antiglobulin antibody. Viral antibody is then added to the infected cells, coating the cell surface if virus antigens are present. The erythrocytes with their external coat of gamma globulin are added, and attach to those cells coated with viral antibody.

The test can be used to quantitate antigen or viral antibody. There is a good correlation between the mixed hemadsorption and the Nt and CF tests. Although the mixed hemadsorption titers are about 100–1000 times higher than in the corresponding CF and Nt tests, the test is not yet widely used in the diagnosis of human disease.

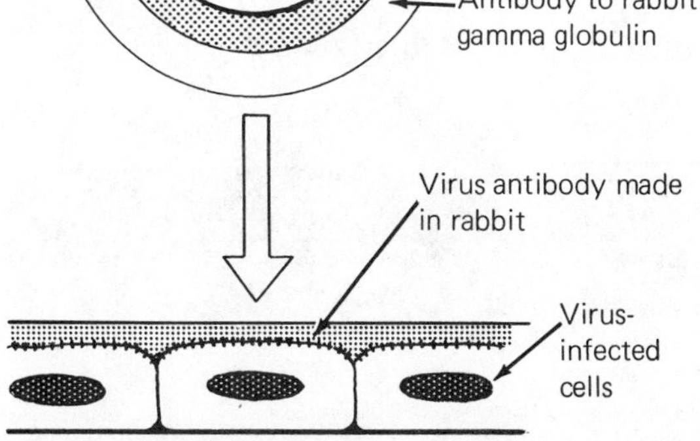

IMMUNOFLUORESCENCE TEST

The indirect immunofluorescence technic has been effectively applied for quantitating antibodies to certain viruses (eg, rubella). Cultured cells on the coverslips are infected with the virus and the culture incubated to allow virus replication. The coverslips are washed, fixed in acetone, and covered with 2-fold dilutions of the test serum along with known positive and negative control sera. The excess antibody is removed after 30 minutes by washing with buffer, and the coverslips are covered with fluorescent antibody against human globulin. (Before use, this indicator antibody is labeled with fluorescein isothiocyanate.) The excess labeled antibody is removed after 30 minutes by washing; the coverslips are then dried, mounted, and examined in the darkfield microscope under ultraviolet light. The presence of viral antibody in the test serum produces a distinct fluorescence in the infected cells.

Alternatively, this method has been simplified by the use of rubella-infected cells, which are trypsinized, washed, and resuspended in high concentration. Drops of the rubella-infected cell suspension are then placed on standard microscope slides, allowed to dry, fixed and handled as described above.

With the direct immunofluorescence test, the virus antibody is labeled. The diagnosis of influenza can be established within 2 hours by direct staining of sputum. Diagnosis can also be made in 36 hours by culturing infected cells (monkey kidney or human trachea).

IMMUNODIFFUSION TEST

In immunodiffusion tests, the antigen and antibody are allowed to diffuse toward each other in a semisolid medium such as agar. A line of precipitate is formed at the zone of optimal proportions. The number of precipitation lines formed will depend upon the number of distinct antigen-antibody reactions taking place; each line represents one antigen-antibody system. The technic is well suited for the analysis of soluble antigens associated with viruses. The test, commonly performed with the Ouchterlony technic, provided the basis for demonstrating the surface antigen of hepatitis type B (HB$_s$Ag). Microscopic slides are covered with 1% agarose containing 0.1 M NaCl, 0.01 M tris buffer, 0.0001 M EDTA, and 1 mg protamine sulfate. After the agarose has hardened, wells are cut in it. The center well is filled with a rabbit serum or a human serum containing antibodies to the antigens. Opposite wells are filled with serum from persons with acute or chronic hepatitis. The slides are incubated in a moist chamber for 24–48 hours. The appearance of a precipitation line indicates the presence of the antigen. Similar technics have been used to detect antigens or

Figure 29–1. Espmark's schematic representation of the postulated principles underlying the mixed hemadsorption reaction. In the given example the test antibody is of rabbit origin and the indicator red cells are prepared accordingly.

antibodies to a number of viruses. Additional wells must be filled with normal control serum to ascertain that the precipitin line is specific for the viral antigen. The test is more sensitive and rapid if combined with electrophoresis (see Counterimmunoelectrophoresis Test, below).

of HB_S antigen, it is applicable for other systems in which the virus or viral antigens are negatively charged.

RADIOIMMUNOASSAY METHOD

COUNTERIMMUNOELECTROPHORESIS TEST

The counterimmunoelectrophoresis method has been developed to detect HB_SAg in the serum of patients with type B viral hepatitis. The methodology is relatively simple, the results are available in 1–2 hours, and the sensitivity is similar to that obtained by the more complex complement fixation assay. Agarose dissolved in buffer (pH 8.4 or above) is applied to glass slides and allowed to gel. Parallel rows of wells are cut into the agarose and the agarose plugs removed by suction. Reference antigen or the unknown samples are placed in the wells nearest the cathode, while antibody is added to the anode wells (Fig 29–2). The slide is connected to electrophoresis chambers by paper wicks and subjected to a constant current. The method is based on the principle that at an alkaline pH, HB_S antigen is negatively charged and migrates toward the anode in an electrophoresis apparatus. Conversely, gamma globulin is close to its isoelectric point and moves toward the cathode by endosmotic forces. As a result of this countermigration in an electrical field, a precipitin line forms whenever equivalent concentrations of antigen and its specific antibody occur. Although this technic has been used chiefly for detection

Radioimmunoassay (RIA) technics measure immunologic rather than biologic activity. Recently, they have become widely adapted to the detection and measurement of viral antigens and antibodies in picogram concentrations. Two basic assay procedures have been utilized depending on whether the specific compound to be labeled is antigen or antibody. Conventional RIA systems are based on the principle of saturation analysis in which the protein or polypeptide to be measured competes with a labeled antigen for a limited amount of antibody. The final ratio of labeled antigen for the specific antibody depends on the proportion of unlabeled antigen present in the system. In order to quantify the amount of unlabeled antigen in the system, a means of separating the residual free radioactivity from that complexed with the antibodies is necessary. Such separation technics include adsorption methods (silicates, coated charcoal), fractional precipitation using staphylococcal protein A which binds the Fc fragment of IgG, and immunologic precipitation of the bound fraction with a second antibody (double antibody) directed against the antigenic determinants of IgG in the first antibody.

Table 29–9 illustrates the general procedure for the double antibody RIA method as applied to the detection of hepatitis B surface antigen (HB_SAg) or its antibody (anti-HB_S). Antigen detection is based on

CATHODE (−)

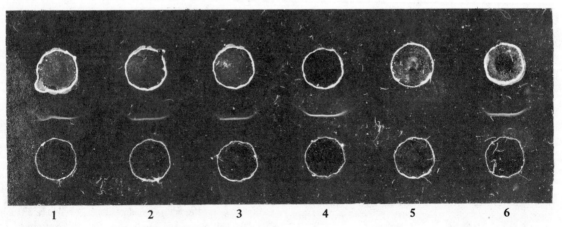

ANODE (+)

Figure 29–2. Counterimmunoelectrophoresis showing formation of precipitin lines between test samples and HB_S antibody (anti-HB_S). Human serum samples were placed in the top row of wells, and anti-HB_S was placed in all wells of the bottom row. In the top row, wells 1–4 contain 4 serum samples from patients with viral hepatitis type B. Well 5 contains a negative normal human serum control; well 6 contains a known positive for HB_SAg.

Table 29–9. Double antibody radioimmunoassay.

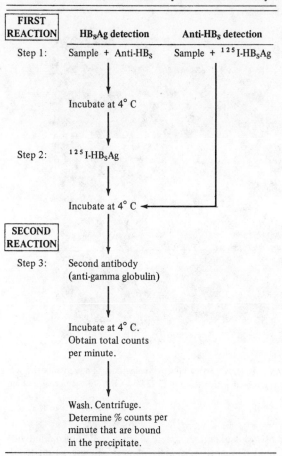

FIRST REACTION	HB$_S$Ag detection	Anti-HB$_S$ detection
Step 1:	Sample + Anti-HB$_S$	Sample + ^{125}I-HB$_S$Ag
	Incubate at 4° C	
Step 2:	^{125}I-HB$_S$Ag	
	Incubate at 4° C	
SECOND REACTION		
Step 3:	Second antibody (anti-gamma globulin)	
	Incubate at 4° C. Obtain total counts per minute.	
	Wash. Centrifuge. Determine % counts per minute that are bound in the precipitate.	

Table 29–10. Two-site immunoradiometric assay.

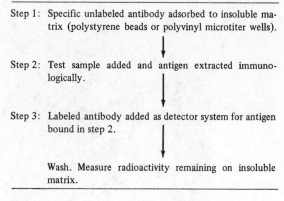

Step 1: Specific unlabeled antibody adsorbed to insoluble matrix (polystyrene beads or polyvinyl microtiter wells).

Step 2: Test sample added and antigen extracted immunologically.

Step 3: Labeled antibody added as detector system for antigen bound in step 2.

Wash. Measure radioactivity remaining on insoluble matrix.

The RIA technic is 100–200 times more sensitive than the CF test.

IMMUNE ELECTRON MICROSCOPY

Viruses not detectable by conventional technics may be observed by immune electron microscopy (IEM). In sophisticated laboratories, IEM appears to be as sensitive as tissue culture methods, but it is more rapid and lends itself to detection of noncytolytic agents (gastroenteritis virus, hepatitis A virus).

In the IEM technic, antiserum is employed to enhance sensitivity and specificity. Antigen-antibody complexes or aggregates formed between virus particles in suspension and added homologous antiserum are detected more readily and with greater assurance than individual virus particles. Fig 29–3 shows the IEM examination of human stool filtrates in which the virus responsible for hepatitis type A is characterized.

With the direct IEM technic, the sample is first clarified by centrifugation and then mixed with specific or convalescent serum and incubated for 1 hour at 37° C and overnight at 6° C. Following incubation, the complexes formed are sedimented by centrifugation; the supernatant is discarded and the pellet is resuspended in distilled water, mixed with 3% phosphotungstic acid, and adjusted to pH 6.0. The mixture is applied to a copper grid and examined by electron microscopy. The indirect IEM technic, in which gamma globulin is added prior to overnight incubation, is 4–32 times more sensitive than the direct method.

In a recent study, 19 of 25 throat washings from patients with respiratory disease were found to be positive for adenovirus by indirect IEM within 24 hours. A number of these specimens were positive in tissue culture but only after one or 2 blind passages. Likewise, 3 of 6 influenza patients had positive throat washings by direct IEM within a 24-hour period but only 2 were positive by conventional tissue culture and egg inoculation. Such rapid identification of influenza virus would permit immediate preventive measures to limit the spread of the disease.

determining whether a significant reduction occurs in the percentage of counts bound by the test sample when compared with the negative control samples. The amount of reduction is a function of the concentration of unlabeled antigen present. Conversely, antibody detection depends on finding an increased number of counts in the precipitate of the test specimens when compared with the counts observed in the control samples that do not contain antibody.

The second method of immunoassay, which has become a powerful analytic tool for the diagnostic laboratory, is illustrated in Table 29–10. This 2-site, solid-phase immunoradiometric assay involves adsorption of unlabeled antibody to an insoluble matrix, eg, polystyrene beads or polyvinyl microtiter wells. The test sample containing antigen is allowed to complex with the antibody-coated surface. Antigen is literally extracted immunologically from the test specimen by specific binding to its surface; it is measured following a second reaction, now with radioactive labeled antibody. The amount of radioactivity measured is proportionate to the concentration of antigen bound by the initial reaction. The test offers increased sensitivity and specificity and can be completed in a relatively short time.

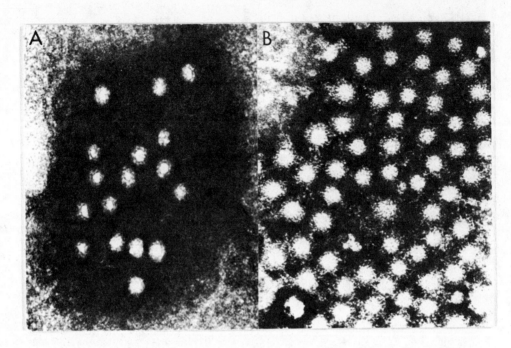

Figure 29—3. Electron micrographs of 27 nm hepatitis A virus (HAV). *A:* HAV particles not treated with antibody, demonstrating the presence of core-like structures (222,000 ✕). *B*: HAV particles aggregated with antibody (222,000 ✕). Note the presence of an antibody "halo" around each particle. (Bradley, Hornbeck, & Maynard.)

With the IEM technic, it should be possible to use convalescent sera from patients with fever of undetermined etiology, construct antigen-antibody complexes with serum obtained during the acute phase, and determine if microbial agents were associated with the illness. This technic offers a sensitive method of identifying new agents and subsequently determining their role in infectious disease.

IEM has also been used to demonstrate the morphology of rubella virus and rhinoviruses and has facilitated the detection of hepatitis virus type B surface antigen and the inner component of the associated Dane particle.

DIAGNOSIS OF INFECTIOUS MONONUCLEOSIS

In patients with infectious mononucleosis, the development of antibodies against a herpes-type virus has been demonstrated by an indirect immunofluorescence test in which the antigen is a virus-bearing cell line derived from a Burkitt lymphoma. Similar cell lines have been obtained from peripheral blood and bone marrow of patients with infectious mononucle-

osis or leukemia, as well as from some normal individuals. The antibodies, absent in pre-illness serum specimens, usually appear very early in the acute disease, rise to peak levels within a few weeks, and remain at relatively high levels during convalescence. They are distinct from heterophil antibodies and, unlike the latter, they persist for years (probably for life).

Complement-fixing antibodies also develop, quickly against the virus-associated antigen but slowly against the soluble nonviral antigen present in infected cell lines.

Infectious mononucleosis is accompanied by the appearance of unique sheep cell hemagglutinins. The serologic procedure for detecting the hemagglutinins of infectious mononucleosis has long been used for diagnosis and is described below. It has, however, been replaced in most laboratories by the simpler and reliable mononucleosis spot test (see below).

HETEROPHIL AGGLUTINATION TEST

Collection of Specimen

It is desirable to have matched specimens of serum, the first taken as soon as infectious mononucleosis is suspected, the second taken in the second week of the disease, and the third taken during the third or fourth week after the onset of the disease. If only one specimen is available it may yield more valuable information if obtained in the second or third week of the disease than if obtained in the first week.

Procedure

Blood is drawn and serum is separated from the clot by centrifugation, removed, and inactivated at 56° C for 30 minutes. Inactivation is necessary because some normal sera possess a relatively high lytic titer for sheep cells.

For the antigen a 1% suspension of sheep erythrocytes, washed with physiologic saline 3 times, is used. Freshly washed cells are used or citrated blood (10 volumes of blood plus 2 volumes of sterile 3.8% sodium citrate solution) up to 1 week old may be used. For serial tests, blood from the same sheep should be used.

Two-fold serial dilutions (1:2.5–1:1280) of inactivated serum in amounts of 0.5 ml each with an equal volume of 1% sheep red blood cell suspension yield a final serum dilution of 1:5–1:2560, and all titers should be reported on this basis. For a control, 0.5 ml of the cell suspension is added to 0.5 ml of saline. The tubes are incubated at 37° C in the water bath for 2 hours and then placed in the refrigerator overnight. Readings are made the following morning, after shaking, and the highest final serum dilution showing agglutination is taken as the titer. It is essential that the tests be read after the times specified.

Interpretation

There is some disagreement concerning the diagnostic titer of sheep cell agglutinins in infectious mononucleosis serum; this can be explained, in part at least, by the fact that variable technics have been used. Titers which range from 1:10–1:40 should be considered negative; titers from 1:80–1:160 are suspicious; and agglutination titers of 1:160 or more are considered as definitely elevated and may be regarded as positive. The best criterion in the early stages is that of a rising titer, especially after the adsorption tests described below are performed.

ADSORPTION TEST FOR INCREASED SPECIFICITY

Sheep cell agglutinins in infectious mononucleosis are adsorbed by bovine erythrocytes but are not reduced significantly by adsorption with guinea pig kidney. Sheep cell agglutinins in serum sickness are completely adsorbed by both guinea pig kidney and bovine erythrocytes. Sheep cell agglutinins in normal human serum are almost completely adsorbed by guinea pig kidney (Table 29–11).

Procedure

One ml of guinea pig kidney suspension is added

Table 29–11. Adsorption reactions of agglutinins in human serum.

Type of Serum	Agglutinins Adsorbed By	
	Guinea Pig Kidney	Bovine Erythrocytes
Normal	Yes	No
Infectious mononucleosis	No	Yes
Serum sickness	Yes	Yes

to 1 ml of a 1:2.5 dilution of the serum to be tested. The mixture is incubated at 37° C for 30 minutes and then centrifuged at 4000 rpm for 15 minutes. The supernatant is tested in serial dilutions for sheep cell agglutinins, as described above. If agglutinins remain, a second adsorption with bovine red cells may be done. To 1 ml of the serum dilution adsorbed with guinea pig kidney, 0.5 ml of packed bovine red cells is added, mixed, and incubated at 37° C for 30 minutes. After centrifugation the supernatant is tested for sheep cell agglutinins as before.

Interpretation

The relationships of the different types of sheep cell agglutinins in human serum are shown in Table 29–11. Agglutinins, which may be present in normal serum to a titer of 1:160 and in serum sickness to a titer of 1:20,000, are removed by adsorption with guinea pig kidney. The failure of guinea pig kidney to affect the sheep cell agglutinin titer of the patient's serum is adequate evidence of infectious mononucleosis in most cases; adsorption with bovine red cells is rarely required for confirmation.

MONONUCLEOSIS SPOT TEST

A reliable, simple, and specific slide test (Monospot, Monotest, Monostico, Mono-Diff) has replaced the traditional sheep cell agglutination test as the most frequently used serologic test in diagnosing infectious mononucleosis. In this test, serum is adsorbed with guinea pig kidney and boiled ox erythrocytes, and a single drop of serum is mixed with horse erythrocytes. Agglutination of the horse erythrocytes indicates the presence of infectious mononucleosis.

TESTS FOR DERMAL HYPERSENSITIVITY (SKIN TESTS)

When available, tests for dermal hypersensitivity offer certain advantages in determining, easily and

Table 29–12. Laboratory diagnosis of viral diseases.

(CC, cell culture. Nt, neutralization. CF, complement fixation. HI, hemagglutination inhibition. CAM, chorioallantoic membrane. ID, immunodiffusion. IF, immunofluorescence. CIE, counterimmunoelectrophoresis. RIA, radioimmunoassay. CPE, cytopathic effect.)

Disease	Human Specimens to Be Tested	Primary Isolation of Virus				Diagnostic Serologic Tests	
		CC or Animals to Be Inoculated	Route	Tissue to Be Harvested for Passage	Positive Result in Test System: Signs and Pathology	Type of Test	Source of Virus or Antigen
ARTHROPOD-BORNE							
Encephalitides	Brain, blood	Mice	Intracerebral	Brain	Encephalitis		
California						Nt in mice or CC	Mouse brain or CC
St. Louis						CF	Mouse brain or CC
Japanese B						HI	Infant mouse brain
Western equine							
Eastern equine							
Venezuelan equine							
Russian spring-summer							
West Nile fever							
Bwamba, etc							
Yellow fever	Blood, viscera	Monkeys	Intraperitoneal	Viscera	Hepatic necrosis	Nt	Mouse brain
		Mice	Intracerebral	Brain	Encephalitis		
Rift Valley fever	Blood	Mice	Intraperitoneal	Liver	Hepatitis	Nt, CF	Mouse liver
Dengue	Blood	Mice (difficult)	Intracerebral	Brain	Encephalomyelitis	Nt, CF	Mouse brain
Sandfly fever	Blood	Infant mice	Intracerebral	Brain	Encephalomyelitis	Nt, CF	Mouse brain
Colorado tick fever	Blood	Hamsters	Intraperitoneal	Brain	Encephalitis	Nt	Mouse brain
		Mice	Intracerebral	Brain	Encephalitis	CF	Mouse brain
NEUROTROPIC, NONARTHROPOD-BORNE							
Poliomyelitis	Spinal cord, feces, throat swabs	CC		Fluid of infected culture	CPE	Nt, CF	CC
Rabies	Brain	Mice	Intracerebral	Brain	Encephalitis, Negri inclusion bodies in cytoplasm	IF	
Lymphocytic choriomeningitis	Brain, blood, spinal fluid	Mice	Intracerebral	Brain	Encephalitis and choroiditis	Nt	Mouse brain
		Guinea pig	Intraperitoneal	Spleen	Death with pneumonia, focal infiltration in liver	CF	Guinea pig spleen
B virus infection (Herpes B)	Brain, spleen	Rabbit	Intracutaneous	Spinal cord	Necrosis of skin, myelitis, intranuclear inclusion bodies	CF, Nt	Rabbit kidney CC
		Rabbit kidney CC		CC fluid	CPE	CF, Nt	Rabbit kidney CC
Human papovavirus	Brain	CC			CPE	HI	CC
Measles	Brain	Direct exam (or co-cultivation in cell culture)				IF	

DERMOTROPIC

Disease	Material from patient	System for isolation	Route	Material harvested	Method of recognition	Serologic tests	Antigen / remarks
Variola (smallpox)	Skin lesions, vesicle fluid, blood	Embryonated egg	CAM	CAM	Pocks on membrane, cytoplasmic inclusion bodies	CF, HI, ID	Vesicle fluid or crusts from patient against standard serum for rapid results
Vaccinia	Skin lesions, vesicle fluid	Embryonated egg	CAM	CAM	Pocks on membrane	CF	CAM, rabbit skin or testicle, mouse brain, CC
		Rabbit	Intracutaneous	Skin	Skin lesion, cytoplasmic inclusion bodies	Nt in eggs, rabbits, mice, CC; HI	
Varicella (chickenpox)	Vesicle fluid	CC		CC fluid	CPE		
		CC		Cells of infected culture	Intranuclear inclusions in skin lesions and in CC	CF, Nt	CC
Zoster	Vesicle fluid	CC		Cells of infected culture	Intranuclear inclusions	CF	CC
Measles	Nasopharyngeal secretions, blood	CC		CC fluid	Multinucleate giant cells and intranuclear inclusions	CF, Nt	CC
Rubella (German measles)	Nasopharyngeal secretions, blood, amniotic fluid	CC		CC fluid	Interference, or CPE	Nt, CF, HI, IF, ID	CC
Congenital rubella syndrome	Throat swab, urine, feces, spinal fluid, blood, bone marrow, conjunctival swab	CC		CC fluid	Interference, or CPE	Nt, CF, HI, IF	CC
Exanthem subitum	Blood	Monkeys	Intravenous	Blood	Experimental exanthem		
Herpes simplex	Skin lesions, brain	Mouse (newborn)	Intracerebral	Brain	Encephalitis	Nt in mice, eggs, or CC	Mouse brain, allantoic fluid
		Embryonated egg	CAM	Allantoic fluid	Pocks / Intranuclear inclusion bodies	CF	Allantoic fluid
		CC		Fluid	CPE	Nt, CF	CC

RESPIRATORY AND PAROTID

Disease	Material from patient	System for isolation	Route	Material harvested	Method of recognition	Serologic tests	Antigen / remarks
Influenza A, Influenza B, Influenza C	Throat swab, nasal washings, lung	Eggs	Amniotic and allantoic sacs	Embryonic fluids	Hemagglutinin produced	HI	Allantoic fluid
		Ferrets, mice	Intranasal	Lung	Pneumonitis	CF	
		CC		Fluid phase	CPE, hemadsorption	Nt in eggs, mice, or CC	
Parainfluenza		CC		CC fluid	Hemadsorption	Nt, CF	Allantoic fluid, mouse lung, CC
Respiratory syncytial (RS) infection		CC		CC fluid	Multinucleate giant cells with cytoplasmic inclusions	Nt, CF	CC
Common cold (rhinovirus group)	Nasopharyngeal washings, swabs	CC		CC fluid	CPE	Nt	CC

Table 29–12 (cont'd). Laboratory diagnosis of viral diseases.

(CC, cell culture. Nt, neutralization. CF, complement fixation. HI, hemagglutination inhibition. CAM, chorioallantoic membrane. ID, immunodiffusion. IF, immunofluorescence. CIE, counterimmunoelectrophoresis. RIA, radioimmunoassay. CPE, cytopathic effect.)

Disease	Human Specimens to Be Tested	Primary Isolation of Virus				Diagnostic Serologic Tests	
		CC or Animals to Be Inoculated	Route	Tissue to Be Harvested for Passage	Positive Result in Test System: Signs and Pathology	Type of Test	Source of Virus or Antigen
Mumps	Saliva, spinal fluid, urine	Monkeys	Parotid gland	Parotid gland	Parotitis	CF	Amniotic fluid
		Eggs	Amniotic and yolk sac	Amniotic fluid, yolk sac	Hemagglutinin produced	HI	Monkey parotid gland
		CC		Fluid phase	CPE, hemadsorption	Nt in CC	CC
Adenovirus group	Throat swab, pharyngeal washings, stool	CC		CC cells and fluid	CPE	CF, Nt, HI	CC
HEPATIC							
Infectious hepatitis (type A)	Blood, feces	(No satisfactory experimental system.)				Microtiter RIA	Serum, feces, liver, bile
Serum hepatitis (type B)	Blood, feces, urine					CIE, CF, ID, RIA	Serum, feces, urine
MISCELLANEOUS							
Coxsackie infection	Feces, throat swab, spinal fluid, vesicle fluid	Infant mice	Subcutaneous	Muscle	Paralysis with myositis and, with certain types, encephalitis, steatitis; pancreatitis	Nt in infant mice or CC	Mouse muscle
		CC		CC fluid	CPE	Nt, CF, HI	CC
Echovirus infection	Feces, throat swabs, spinal fluid	CC		CC fluid	CPE	Nt, CF, HI	CC
Reovirus infection	Feces, throat swabs	CC		CC fluid	CPE	Nt, CF, HI	CC
Molluscum contagiosum	Skin lesions	(No satisfactory experimental animal. Characteristic cytoplasmic inclusion bodies. Elementary bodies can be seen in the electron microscope.)					
Verrucae (warts)	Skin lesions	(No satisfactory experimental animal. Electron microscopic examination of warts shows elementary bodies.)					
Encephalomyocarditis (Col. SK-Mengo)	Blood	Mice	Intracerebral	Brain	Encephalitis	Nt in mice	Mouse brain
Epidemic keratoconjunctivitis	Conjunctivas	CC		CC cells and fluid	CPE	Nt test for adenovirus 8	CC
Foot-and-mouth disease	Skin lesions	Guinea pigs	Intracutaneous, foot pads	Foot pads	Hyperkeratosis with vesicle formation, paralysis with myositis	CF	Guinea pig foot pad
		Newborn mice		Muscle			Mouse muscle
Cytomegalic (inclusion) disease	Oral swabs, urine, various organs	CC		CC cells and fluid	CPE, inclusion bodies	Nt, CF	CC

quickly, prior exposure to infectious agents. Tests are available for mumps, herpes simplex, cat scratch fever, Western equine encephalomyelitis, and variola (or vaccinia). The skin test may lead to increase in antibodies.

Technic of Inoculation

The test for dermal hypersensitivity to virus is carried out by injecting 0.1 ml of the skin test antigen intradermally into the flexor surface of the right arm, and 0.1 ml of the control material into the same area of the left arm. The sites of injection are examined after 12–48 hours. The mean diameter of erythematous reaction and induration is measured and compared to the control.

Character of the Reaction

If the individual is hypersensitive to the skin test antigen, a mean diameter of induration and erythema varying from about 10 mm to 60 or 80 mm may be observed. Its maximum intensity is usually attained between 24 and 48 hours after injection. After 48 hours, the erythema rapidly fades.

Interpretation

In mumps, persons exhibiting dermal reactions exceeding 10 mm in mean diameter 48 hours after the inoculation of inactivated virus (positive reaction) may be regarded as resistant to mumps virus infection.

In Western equine encephalomyelitis, as in mumps, children have less dermal sensitivity than do adults.

Inoculation of skin test antigens may result in an increase in complement-fixing antibody. This must be taken into account when the CF test is employed as a diagnostic aid after a skin test.

• • •

General References

Bradstreet CMP, Pereira MS, Pollock TM: The organization of a national virological diagnostic service. Prog Med Virol 16:241, 1973.

Edwards EA & others: Visualization by immune electron microscopy of viruses associated with acute respiratory disease. J Immunol Methods 8:159, 1975.

Hollinger FB & others: Detection of hepatitis A viral antigen by radioimmunoassay. J Immunol 115:1464, 1975.

Horstmann DM: Need for monitoring vaccinated populations for immunity levels. Prog Med Virol 16:215, 1973.

Kapikian AZ & others: Visualization by immune electron microscopy of a 27-nm particle associated with acute infectious nonbacterial gastroenteritis. J Virol 10:1075, 1972.

Lennette EH: General principles underlying laboratory diagnosis of viral and rickettsial infections. Pages 1–65 in: *Diagnostic Procedures for Viral and Rickettsial Infections,* 4th ed. American Public Health Association, 1969.

Liu C: Fluorescent-antibody techniques. Pages 179–204 in: *Diagnostic Procedures for Viral and Rickettsial Infections,* 4th ed. American Public Health Association, 1969.

Melnick JL: Analytical serology of animal viruses. Pages 411–514 in: *Analytical Serology of Microorganisms.* Vol 1. Kwapinski JB (editor). Wiley, 1969.

Purcell RH & others: Radioimmunoassay for the detection of the core of the Dane particle and antibody to it. Intervirology 2:231, 1973/74.

Schmidt NJ, Lennette EH: Advances in the serodiagnosis of viral infections. Prog Med Virol 15:244, 1973.

Svehag SE: Formation and dissociation of virus-antibody complexes with special reference to the neutralization process. Prog Med Virol 10:1, 1968.

30...
Arthropod-Borne (Arbo) Viral Diseases

The **arthropod-borne viruses**, or **arboviruses**, are functionally classified as a group of infectious agents which are biologically transmitted between susceptible vertebrate hosts through the bite of a hemophagous arthropod. These viruses have the capacity to multiply in the tissues of susceptible arthropods without producing any apparent disease or damage. A vertebrate → arthropod → vertebrate cycle in nature is maintained by the vector, which develops a lifelong infection through ingestion of vertebrate blood from a viremic host.

Names of the individual viruses were originally those of the diseases produced, since recognition of the disease complex preceded the isolation of the infectious agent (yellow fever, dengue, the equine encephalitides). After that, a combination of the geographic location of the isolate with the disease produced was favored (St. Louis encephalitis, Colorado tick fever, West Nile fever, Russian spring-summer encephalitis). More recently, the convention has been to name newly isolated viruses after the geographic area where the original isolation was made (Hart Park, Kern Canyon, Cache Valley).

Although arboviruses are found on all temperate and tropical continental land masses and on some islands, they are most prevalent in the tropical rain forest areas of the earth. This is understandable in view of the favorable climatic conditions and the abundance in kind as well as in number of animal and insect species. As the arboviruses are maintained by cycles involving arthropods as well as vertebrates, the tropics offer the most favorable conditions for these complex biologic cycles.

The arboviruses consist of more than 350 viruses which are grouped according to their antigenic relationships. Each group is composed of members sharing, to varying degrees, complement-fixing, hemagglutination-inhibiting, and—less frequently—neutralizing antigens. These viruses fall into 7 major groups (10 or more members per group); 18 small groups (2–7 members per group); and many which remain ungrouped.

The arboviruses are at present being classified according to their biochemical and biophysical properties. Thus, arboviruses are included among the families **Togaviridae, Bunyaviridae, Reoviridae, Arenaviridae, Picornaviridae,** and **Rhabdoviridae** (Table 30–1).

Table 30–1. Current taxonomic status of some arboviruses.

Current Taxonomic Classification	Arbovirus Members
Togaviridae Genus *Alphavirus*	*Group A:* Aura, Chikungunya, eastern equine encephalitis, Getah, Mayaro, Middleburg, Mucambo, Ndumu, O'Nyongnyong, Pixuna, Ross River, Semliki Forest, Sindbis, Una, Venezuelan and western equine encephalitis, and Whataroa viruses
Genus *Flavivirus*	*Group B:* Bussuquara, dengue, Ilheus, Israel turkey meningoencephalitis, Japanese B encephalitis, Kunjin, Kyasanur Forest disease, Langat, louping ill, Modoc, Murray Valley encephalitis, Ntaya, Omsk hemorrhagic fever, Powassan, St. Louis encephalitis, Spondweni, tick-borne encephalitis, Uganda S, US bat salivary gland, Wesselsbron, West Nile fever, yellow fever, and Zika viruses
Bunyaviridae Genus *Bunyavirus*	Bunyamwera (18 members), Bwamba (2), C (11), California (11), Capim (6), Guama (6), Koongol (2), Patois (4), Simbu (16), and Tete (4) serogroups; 7 unassigned viruses
Possible members	Uukuniemi (7 members), Anopheles A (3), Anopheles B (2), Bakau (2), Crimean-Congo hemorrhagic fever (2), Kaisodi (3), Mapputta (3), Nairobi sheep disease (3), phlebotomus fever (20), and Turlock (3) serogroups; 8 unassigned viruses
Reoviridae Genus *Orbivirus*	African horse sickness, bluetongue, and Colorado tick fever viruses
Rhabdoviridae Genus *Vesiculovirus*	Cocal, Hart Park, Kern Canyon, and vesicular stomatitis viruses
Arenaviridae Genus *Arenavirus*	Junin, Lassa, Machupo, and Pichinde viruses
Picornaviridae Genus *Enterovirus*	Nodamura virus

All arboviruses that have been studied with regard to type of nucleic acid have been found to have an RNA genome. Most are inactivated by lipid solvents (ether or sodium deoxycholate). Exceptions to the general solvent sensitivity of arboviruses are Nodamura virus (a picornavirus) and arthropod-borne orbiviruses, including the viruses of bluetongue, African horse sickness, and Colorado tick fever, among others (see Chapter 39).

Although biochemical and biophysical classification of many arboviruses has now been made possible by advances in technic, they continue to be grouped according to their antigenic relationships for public health purposes.

(1) **Group A** (genus *Alphavirus)* and group B (genus *Flavivirus*) belong to the family **Togaviridae**, whose members have a single-stranded RNA genome with a molecular weight of $3-4 \times 10^6$. The particles are spherical and possess a lipid-containing, ether-sensitive envelope, multiply in the cytoplasm, and mature by budding. The group A viruses are significantly larger (40–80 nm) than those of group B (20–50 nm). The group A viruses are not inactivated by sulfhydryl reagents, and they also are resistant to proteases (trypsin), whereas group B viruses are sensitive to proteases. All group A viruses have been shown to multiply in arthropod vectors; not all of the group B members have been proved to have this property, but all are serologically related. The equine encephalitis viruses (western, eastern, and Venezuelan) and Sindbis and Semliki Forest viruses have received the most study; Sindbis virus (alphavirus sindbis) of Africa and India is the type species of group A. This group is responsible primarily for fevers of an undifferentiated type or encephalitis.

(2) For **group B** (genus *Flavivirus),* yellow fever virus (flavivirus febricus) is the type species. Many of the viruses can be placed in 4 antigenic subgroups: (1) Japanese B, St. Louis, and Murray Valley encephalitis viruses; West Nile fever, Ilheus, and Kunjin viruses; (2) the dengue viruses; (3) yellow fever, Uganda S, and Zika viruses; and (4) the tick-borne complex. The latter subgroup is composed of viruses capable of causing hemorrhagic fever (Omsk hemorrhagic fever, Kyasanur Forest disease viruses) or encephalitis (Russian spring-summer encephalitis, biphasic meningoencephalitis, or Powassan viruses).

(3) The **Bunyamwera supergroup** consists of 10 serogroups and includes more than 88 individual viruses. The supergroup was originally conceived to acknowledge subtle serologic cross-reactions among individual members of the serogroups. These intergroup reactions usually involve few viruses and often are detectable only by cross-complement fixation at the limits of sensitivity. All of the serogroups are indistinguishable morphologically. Hence, they have been assigned taxonomic status in the family **Bunyaviridae**, genus *Bunyavirus.*

The bunyaviruses contain a single-stranded RNA genome which is probably segmented; the molecular weight is 6.8×10^6. The virions are spherical, enveloped particles 90–100 nm in diameter. The envelope consists of a membrane 5 nm thick covered by surface projections 8–10 nm long. These surface projections are composed of 2 glycopolypeptide species which are clustered to form hollow cylindric morphologic units, 10–12 nm in diameter with a 5 nm central cavity. These units are arranged in an icosahedral surface lattice. The membrane to which the surface subunits are attached is probably a lipid bilayer. A strand-like nucleoprotein appears to be located just underneath the membrane. Bunyaviruses develop in the cytoplasm and mature by budding into intracellular (Golgi) vesicles.

All the Bunyamwera supergroup viruses multiply in arthropod vectors. They have been isolated from mosquitoes in different parts of the world, including Africa, South America, India, Malaya, Trinidad, and the USA. The most important bunyaviruses associated with disease in man and animals belong to the Bunyamwera, C, and California subgroups. Several members of the Bunyamwera subgroup cause febrile illness in man; the C subgroup causes a more acute undifferentiated febrile illness, with headache and malaise. The California subgroup causes a meningoencephalitis; 8 members of this subgroup have been isolated within the USA (see Bunyavirus Encephalitis, p 360).

(4) Another large group of arboviruses, morphologically similar but antigenically unrelated to the Bunyamwera supergroup, consists of 10 serogroups with over 56 members. They are presently regarded as "possible members" of the genus *Bunyavirus* but may be assigned to a separate taxon when more information is available. Uukuniemi virus is the prototype of this group. Several significant pathogens of man and domestic animals are included here. Of particular importance are the Crimean and Congo hemorrhagic fevers of man and Nairobi sheep disease and Rift Valley fever of sheep. Five members of the phlebotomus (sandfly) fever group (Naples, Sicilian, Punta Toro, Chagres, and Candiru) have been implicated in an undifferentiated febrile syndrome in man. *Phlebotomus papatasii* females are the vectors for most members of the sandfly fever group; however, 2 have been isolated only from mosquitoes, suggesting that this group includes both sandfly- and mosquito-borne viruses.

(5) Arboviruses now classified in the family **Reoviridae**, genus *Orbivirus,* are bluetongue, African horsesickness, and Colorado tick fever (see Chapter 39). African horse sickness spread from its enzootic area in Africa through the Eastern Mediterranean to Pakistan and India, causing in 1960 alone over 50,000 equine deaths. Its pathogenicity for man is as yet unknown.

Chenuda and several other tick-borne viruses of the Kemerovo group are similar to the orbiviruses and may be included in this genus when more information is available. Viruses of the Kemerovo group have been isolated from ticks in eastern Europe, Egypt, and Sudan, some in association with benign encephalitis in man. They may also infect horses, cattle, birds, and small mammals.

(6) Arboviruses that have been placed in the family **Arenaviridae**, genus *Arenavirus,* include Junin (Argentinian hemorrhagic fever) and Machupo (Bolivian hemorrhagic fever) viruses. Junin and Machupo are part of the Tacaribe complex of antigenically interrelated arboviruses, which also includes Amapari, Pichinde, Parana, Tamiami (isolated in the Florida Everglades), Latino, and Tacaribe (isolated from bats in Trinidad). Not all the members of the Tacaribe complex have been shown to have a mosquito vector; for some, mites have been suspected but not confirmed as vectors. Most have a rodent host, and spread to other mammals and man is unusual. Lassa fever virus, which causes a severe febrile illness with a high mortality rate in man, is also an arenavirus.

(7) Arboviruses belonging to the family **Rhabdoviridae**, genus *Vesiculovirus,* include cocal, Hart Park, Kern Canyon, and vesicular stomatitis viruses (see Chapter 33).

(8) The only arbovirus thus far included in the family **Picornaviridae** is Nodamura virus. Nodamura virus has been demonstrated to be a virulent insect virus which, contrary to widely held opinions about insect viral pathogens, can multiply in and kill mammals.

Human Infection

About 75 of the arboviruses are capable of infecting man, although only about 60% of these are known to cause overt disease. Those infecting man are all believed to be zoonotic, with man usually the accidental host who plays no important role in the maintenance or transmission cycle of the virus. Exceptions to this are urban yellow fever and dengue. Some of the natural cycles are simple and involve a nonhuman vertebrate host (mammal or bird) with a species of mosquito or tick (jungle yellow fever, the equine encephalitis viruses, and the viruses of Japanese B, St. Louis encephalitis, and Colorado tick fever). Others, however, are quite complex. For example, many cases of central European biphasic meningoencephalitis occur following ingestion of raw milk from infected goats and cows. These animals become infected by grazing in tick-infested pastures where a tick-rodent cycle is occurring.

Diseases produced by the arboviruses may be divided into 3 clinical syndromes: (1) fevers of an undifferentiated type, frequently called "dengue-like," with or without the presence of a maculopapular rash and usually relatively benign; (2) encephalitis, often with a high case fatality rate; and (3) hemorrhagic fevers, also frequently severe and fatal. These categories are somewhat arbitrary, and some arboviruses may be associated with more than one syndrome, eg, dengue.

The intensity of viral multiplication in the organism and its predominant site of localization within the tissues or organs determines the clinical syndrome. Thus, individual arboviruses can produce a minor febrile illness in some patients and encephalitis or a hemorrhagic diathesis in others. However, in an epidemic situation, one of the above syndromes will predominate, permitting a tentative differential diagnosis. A final diagnosis is based on further epidemiologic and serologic data.

The initial stage of infection by an arbovirus is asymptomatic and corresponds to the intrinsic incubation period of viral multiplication. This is followed by the abrupt onset of clinical manifestations which are closely related to viral dissemination. Malaise, headache, nausea, vomiting, and myalgia accompany fever, which is an invariable symptom and sometimes the only one. The illness may terminate at this stage, recur with or without a rash, or reveal hemorrhagic manifestations secondary to vascular abnormalities. Not infrequently, the period of viremia is asymptomatic, with the acute onset of encephalitis following localization of the virus in the CNS.

The above clinical categories are utilized in the following sections in discussing some of the most important diseases caused by the arboviruses.

TOGAVIRUS ENCEPHALITIS
(SLE, EEE, WEE)

Encephalitis may be produced by a number of neurotropic viruses. Such agents produce an infection, often in epidemic form, in which the primary clinical findings are produced by involvement of the brain and spinal cord. A number of these diseases of similar epidemiology have been grouped together as the arthropod-borne encephalitides. Although they have much in common, their geographic distribution is often quite distinct (Table 30–2). The unique geographic distribution of the arboviruses is a consequence of the ecologic distribution of the specific hosts and vectors of each virus. Thus, **western equine encephalitis (WEE)** occurs primarily in the western USA and Canada; **eastern equine encephalitis (EEE)** occurs in the eastern and southern USA; **Venezuelan equine encephalitis (VEE)** occurs in South and Central America and the southern USA; **St. Louis encephalitis (SLE)** in almost all of the USA (but its distribution in the country varies widely from one year to the next); **Japanese B encephalitis (JBE)** in the Far East (Japan, Korea, China, Malaya, India); and **Murray Valley encephalitis (MVE)** in Australia. All of the above viruses belong to the family **Togaviridae**. Arboviruses that produce California encephalitis (family **Bunyaviridae**) will be discussed in a separate section.

One of the reasons epidemics of viral encephalitis have not been recorded in the Middle East may be the prevalence of West Nile fever virus in this area. This virus, which produces a mild, self-limiting disease in man, is a member of the same genus *(Flavivirus)* as JBE, SLE, and MVE viruses and shares some antigens with them. The widespread occurrence of West Nile fever in the Middle East may result in an increase of the resistance of the population to encephalitis caused by related viruses producing more serious illness.

Partial protection against SLE may similarly exist in persons previously infected by dengue virus who possess dengue antibody.

Most arboviruses are encephalitogenic in suckling mice. Only a few produce such disease in man, when acquired by the peripheral route. Individual host susceptibility, the immune status of the patient, the development of a viral mutant, or the dosage inoculated may be important in the occasional production of encephalitis by such viruses as West Nile fever, yellow fever, or dengue.

Encephalitis (or meningoencephalitis) may also occur as a complication of a variety of other viral diseases (measles, mumps, infectious hepatitis, variola, varicella, herpes zoster, herpes simplex, and others). In some instances, a delayed hypersensitivity reaction occurs, and for this reason they have been called "post-infectious" encephalitides.

In 1973, there were 1967 cases of encephalitis, with 326 deaths, reported in the USA; of these cases, the etiology was unknown in 1450. The reported cases of arboviral encephalitis totaled 88: California encephalitis accounted for 75, EEE for 4, WEE for 4, and SLE for 5. Other viral causes or associations of reported encephalitis were as follows: mumps virus, 214 cases; varicella virus, 102 cases; measles virus, 37 cases; enteroviruses, 13 cases; herpes simplex virus, 44 cases; rubella virus, one case; and 18 cases of unspecified viral etiology. In 1974 and 1975, the pattern changed, when widespread epidemics of SLE were reported.

Properties of the Togaviruses

A. Nucleic Acid: RNA.

B. Size: The group A and B arboviruses are small, between 20 and 80 nm. Certain of the viruses have been purified and were found to contain phospholipids, fatty acid, and cholesterol in addition to nucleoprotein.

C. Reaction to Physical and Chemical Agents: New isolates are unstable at room temperature. They may be preserved by freezing at $-70°$ C, particularly in the presence of 25% rabbit serum or 4% bovine albumin. Arboviruses are inactivated by ether or by 1:1000 sodium deoxycholate. In this way new isolates may readily be distinguished from the deoxycholate-resistant enteroviruses.

D. Animal Susceptibility and Growth of Viruses: The viruses are infectious for a variety of animals, and WEE, EEE, and VEE viruses are responsible for both illness and death in horses and mules. The chief experimental animal is the mouse, which can be infected most easily by inoculation into the brain. Infant mice are especially susceptible to infection. In the susceptible vertebrate host, primary virus multiplication occurs either in myeloid and lymphoid tissues or in the vascular endothelium. Multiplication in the CNS seems to depend upon the ability of the virus to pass the blood-brain barrier and to infect nerve cells. After the

parenteral administration of small amounts of virus into chickens, doves, ducks, bats, guinea pigs, rabbits, and monkeys, a silent, inapparent infection often develops during which the virus circulates in the blood for several days. In nature this type of infection in the animal host serves as a source of virus for the insect vectors of the disease.

The viruses multiply in chick embryos when inoculated by the yolk sac or chorioallantoic routes. They readily grow in tissue cultures of chick or mouse embryo, baby hamster kidney, duck embryo, or in cultures of mammalian cell lines. In addition, *Aedes albopictus* and *A aegypti* cell lines show selective susceptibility to infection with mosquito-borne viruses, especially from group B.

All togaviruses replicate in the cytoplasm. The genome RNA, released from virus particles, functions on polyribosomes as messenger RNA to direct synthesis of a large precursor polypeptide which is cleaved to form the structural polypeptides of the virus. Genome RNA also serves as template for progeny RNA through a replicative intermediate. In these respects, their replication is similar to that of the picornaviruses. Togaviruses, however, have 2 or more structural polypeptides which undergo glycosylation and cleavage and are incorporated into the cytoplasmic membrane of the cell. The virus particle buds through the altered areas of the membrane to acquire its envelope and the glycosylated polypeptides. Only one polypeptide is found in the nucleocapsid of togaviruses, in contrast to the 4 found in picornavirus nucleocapsids.

Viral multiplication can be measured by cytopathic changes, virus-specific immunofluorescence, or the production of viral hemagglutinin as seen directly in the cell culture by the hemadsorption test. Consistent and sensitive plaque counts can be done with group A and B viruses in cultures of chick embryo, hamster BHK-21, and Vero monkey cells. Arboviruses exhibit homotypic and heterotypic interference, as well as susceptibility to interferon.

E. Antigenic Properties: Complement-fixing antigens and viral hemagglutinins may be prepared from infected brains of newborn mice (because of their low fat content). The hemagglutinins of these viruses are part of the infectious virus particle. The union between hemagglutinin and red cell is irreversible. The erythrocyte-virus complex is still infective, but it can be neutralized by the addition of antibody which results in large lattice formations.

Some of these viruses have an overlapping antigenicity which is most readily demonstrated by cross-reactions in HI tests. The overlapping is due to the presence of one or more cross-reactive antigens in addition to the strain-specific antigen. Thus immune sera prepared for one strain will contain strain-specific as well as group-specific antibodies.

A considerable degree of specificity can be obtained by adsorption of the immune serum with a heterologous virus belonging to the same group. The resulting serum, when tested for hemagglutination-inhibiting activity, reacts only with the homologous and not with the heterologous strain. Such adsorbed sera have facilitated the analysis of the complex antigenic structure of many arboviruses and the identification of newly isolated strains.

Pathogenesis & Pathology

The pathogenesis of the disease in man has not been well studied, but in certain instances the disease in experimental animals may afford a model for the human disease. Thus the equine encephalitides in horses are diphasic. In the first phase (minor illness) the virus multiplies in nonneural tissue and is present in the blood 3 days before the first signs of involvement of the CNS. In the second phase (major illness) the virus multiplies in the brain, cells are injured and destroyed, and encephalitis becomes apparent at the clinical level. The 2 phases may be distinct or may overlap. It has not been established in man whether or not there is a period of primary viral multiplication in the viscera with a secondary liberation of virus into the blood before its entry into the CNS. The viruses have been found to multiply in nonneural tissues of experimentally infected monkeys.

Certain concentrations of virus in brain tissue are necessary before the clinical disease becomes manifest. In mice the level to which the virus multiplies in the brain is influenced by genetic (a mendelian trait) as well as other factors.

The primary encephalitides are characterized by lesions in all parts of the CNS, particularly in the basal structures of the brain and in the cerebral cortex, and to a lesser degree in the spinal cord. Small hemorrhages with perivascular cuffing and meningeal infiltration—chiefly with mononuclear cells—are common. Nerve cell degeneration associated with neuronophagia occurs. Purkinje's cells of the cerebellum may be destroyed. There are also patches of encephalomalacia; acellular plaques of spongy appearance in which medullary fibers, dendrites, and axons are destroyed; and focal microglial proliferation. Thus not only the neurons but also the cells of the supporting structure of the CNS are attacked.

Although widespread neuronal degeneration is observed with all arboviruses producing encephalitis, predominant characteristics are noted. Lesions due to EEE tend to be localized in the cortex, whereas the basal nuclei are involved in WEE. Pathologic changes seen in SLE are most marked in the brain stem and midbrain. Many tick-borne encephalitides produce lesions in the anterior horn cells indistinguishable from those of poliomyelitis.

Clinical Findings

Incubation periods of the encephalitides are between 4 and 21 days. There is a sudden onset with severe headache, chills and fever, nausea and vomiting, generalized pains, and malaise. Within 24—48 hours, marked drowsiness develops and the patient may become stuporous. Nuchal rigidity is common. Mental confusion, dysarthria, tremors, convulsions, and coma develop in severe cases. Fever lasts 4—10 days. The mortality rate in most encephalitides varies, being 2—3% for WEE and 50—70% for EEE (see Table 30—2). With JBE, the mortality rate in older age groups may be as high as 80%. Sequelae may occur and include mental deterioration, personality changes, paralysis, aphasia, and cerebellar signs.

Abortive infections simulate aseptic meningitis or nonparalytic poliomyelitis. Inapparent infections are common.

In California, where both WEE and SLE are prevalent, WEE has a predilection for children and

Table 30—2. Summary of 6 major human arbovirus infections which occur in the USA.

Diseases	Exposure	Distribution	Vectors	Infection: Case Ratio (Age Incidence)	Sequelae	Mortality Rate (%)
WEE	Rural	Pacific, Mountain, West Central, Southwest	*Culex tarsalis*	50:1 (under 5) 1000:1 (over 15)	+	2—3
EEE	Rural	Atlantic, southern coastal	*Aedes sollicitans* *A vexans*	10:1 (infants) 50:1 (middle aged) 20:1 (elderly)	+	50—70
SLE	Urban-rural	Widespread	*C pipiens* *C quinquefasciatus* *C tarsalis* *C nigrapalpus*	>400:1 (young) 64:1 (elderly)	±	5—10
VEE	Rural	South and Central America, southern USA	Aedes Psorophora Culex	Unknown ratio	Unknown	0.5%
California encephalitis	Rural	North Central, Atlantic, South	(Aedes sp?)	Unknown ratio (most cases under 20)	±	Fatalities rare
Colorado tick fever	Rural	Pacific, Mountain	*Dermacentor andersoni*	Unknown ratio (all ages affected)	Rare	Fatalities rare

infants. In the same area SLE rarely occurs in infants, even though both viruses are transmitted by the same arthropod vector *(Culex tarsalis)*.

Laboratory Diagnosis

A. Recovery of Virus: The virus occurs in the blood only early in the infection, usually before the onset of symptoms. The virus is most often recovered from the brains of fatal cases following intracerebral inoculation of newborn mice.

If a transmissible agent is recovered, it should be identified by suitable serologic tests with known antisera.

B. Serology: Neutralizing and hemagglutination-inhibiting antibodies are detectable within a few days after the onset of illness. Complement-fixing antibodies appear later. The neutralizing antibody and probably the hemagglutination-inhibiting antibody endure for years, if not for life. The complement-fixing antibody is less persistent and may be lost within 2–5 years.

The HI test is the simplest diagnostic test, but it primarily identifies the group rather than the specific etiologic virus. If adult goose rather than newly hatched chick erythrocytes are used, the serum must first be adsorbed with goose erythrocytes in order to remove the nonspecific hemagglutinin found in human and other sera.

It is necessary to establish a rise in specific antibodies during infection in order to make the diagnosis. The first sample of serum should be taken as soon after the onset as possible and the second sample about 2–3 weeks later. The paired specimens must be run in the same serologic test.

The cross-reactivity that takes place within group A or B arboviruses must be considered in making the diagnosis. Thus, following a single infection by one member of the group, antibodies to other members may also appear. These group-specific antibodies are usually of lower titer than the type-specific antibody and are easy to interpret. Serologic diagnosis becomes difficult when epidemics occur in endemic areas or when the individual has been infected previously by a closely related arbovirus. Under these circumstances, a definite etiologic diagnosis may not be possible. Neutralizing, complement-fixing, and hemagglutination-inhibiting antibodies have a decreasing degree of specificity for the etiologic viral type (in the order listed).

Immunity

Immunity is believed to be permanent after a single infection. In endemic areas the population may build up immunity as a result of inapparent infections; the proportion of persons with antibodies to the local arthropod-borne virus increases with age.

Attempts at the production of artificial immunity with killed vaccines have not yielded striking results in man. Effective killed vaccines have been developed to protect horses against EEE and WEE. No effective vaccines for these diseases are at present available for man. An excellent attenuated vaccine for VEE is available for curtailing epidemics among horses and has been used experimentally in man. A vaccine for JBE is being developed.

Because of antigens common to several members within a group, the response to immunization or to infection with one of the viruses of a group may be modified by prior exposure to another member of the same group. In general, the homologous response is greater than a cross-reacting one. This mechanism may be important in conferring protection on a community against an epidemic of another related agent.

Treatment

There is no proved specific treatment. In experimental animals, hyperimmune serum is ineffective if given after the onset of disease. However, if given 1–2 days after the invasion of the virus but before the signs of encephalitis are obvious, specific hyperimmune serum can prevent a fatal outcome of the infection.

Epidemiology

In severe epidemics caused by the encephalitis viruses, the case rate is about 1:1000. In the large urban epidemic of St. Louis encephalitis that occurred in 1966 in Dallas (population 1 million), there were 545 reported cases, 145 (27%) laboratory-confirmed cases, and 15 deaths. The overall attack rate was 15 cases per 100,000, with a case fatality rate of 10%. All deaths were in persons 45 years of age or older.

SLE reappeared in 1974 associated with a major outbreak in Memphis. In 1975, widespread SLE activity occurred primarily in Illinois, Mississippi, and Texas, with several hundred cases being reported.

The epidemiology of the arthropod-borne encephalitides must account for the maintenance and dissemination of the viruses in nature in the absence of man. Most infections with the arboviruses occur in mammals or birds, with man serving as an accidental host. The virus is transmitted from animal to animal through the bite of an arthropod vector. Viruses have been isolated from mosquitoes and ticks, which serve as reservoirs of infection. In ticks, the viruses may pass from generation to generation by the transovarian route, and in such instances the tick acts as a true reservoir of the virus as well as its vector. In tropical climates, where mosquito populations are present throughout the year, arboviruses cycle continuously between mosquitoes and reservoir animals.

It is not known whether in temperate climates the virus is reintroduced each year from the outside (eg, by birds migrating from tropical areas) or whether it somehow survives the winter in the local area. A simple overwintering mechanism would be that of hibernating mosquitoes, which could reinfect birds at the time of their emergence and thus reestablish each year a simple bird-mosquito-bird cycle. Or it may be that the virus remains latent during this period in birds, mammals, and arthropods. The role of cold-blooded vertebrates (snakes, turtles, lizards, alligators, and frogs) in the ecology of certain arboviruses has not been satisfactorily explained. Garter snakes experimentally infected with western equine encephalitis virus can hibernate over the winter and circulate virus in high titers and for long periods the following spring. Normal mosquitoes can be infected by feeding on the emerged snakes and then can transmit the virus. This is a possible mechanism of overwintering of arboviruses, since the virus can be found in the blood of wild snakes. The reservoir of VEE is believed to be wild rodents; once established in an area, it therefore may be difficult to eradicate (see below).

A. Serologic Epidemiology: In highly endemic areas, almost the entire human population may become infected, and most infections are asymptomatic. This is true for Japanese B encephalitis infection in Japan. High infection-to-case ratios exist among specified age groups for many arbovirus infections (Table 30–2).

In the 1964 Houston SLE epidemic (712 reported cases), there was an inapparent infection rate of 8% in a random city survey, but in the epidemic area of the city the inapparent infection rate was 34%. The infection-to-case ratio remained about the same, however. It is obvious that the presence of infected mosquitoes is required before human infections can occur, although socioeconomic and cultural factors (air conditioning, screens, mosquito control) affect the degree of exposure of the population to these virus-carrying vectors.

In endemic areas of California, 11% of infants are born with maternal antibody to WEE and 27% have SLE maternal antibody. A direct relationship exists between the length of residence of the mother in the endemic area and the acquisition of antibody.

B. Mosquito-Borne Encephalitis: Infection of man occurs when a mosquito like *Culex tarsalis, C quinquefasciatus, C pipiens,* or *C tritaeniorhynchus* (Japan), or another arthropod bites first an infected animal and later man.

The equine encephalitides, EEE, WEE, and VEE, are transmitted by culicine mosquitoes to horses or man, from a mosquito-bird-mosquito cycle. Equines, like man, are unessential hosts for the maintenance of the virus. Human encephalitis cases occurring in conjunction with an epizootic of encephalitis in horses should alert physicians and the community to the possibility that an arbovirus epidemic may be developing. EEE and VEE in horses are severe, with up to 90% of the affected animals dying. Epizootic WEE is less frequently fatal for horses. In addition, EEE produces severe epizootics in certain domestic game birds such as pheasants, Pekin ducks, and partridges. A mosquito-bird-mosquito cycle is also observed in SLE and JBE. Swine are also an important host of JBE. Mosquitoes remain infected for life (several weeks to months). Only the female feeds on blood and can feed and transmit the virus more than once. The cells of the mosquito's midgut are the site of primary virus multiplication. This is followed by viremia and invasion of organs—chiefly salivary glands and nerve tissue, where secondary virus multiplication occurs. The arthropod remains healthy.

Infection of insectivorous bats with arboviruses

produces a viremia lasting 6–12 days without any illness or pathologic changes in the bat. While the virus concentration is high, the infected bat may infect mosquitoes which then are able to transmit the infection to chickens as well as to other bats.

In nature, mosquitoes have a close association with bats, not only in summer daytime resting places but also during the winter, in hibernation sites. Experimentally, mosquitoes were capable of transmitting virus to bats. Bats thus infected were capable of maintaining a latent virus infection, with no detectable viremia, for over 3 months at 10° C under simulated hibernation conditions. When the bats were returned to room temperature, viremia appeared after 3 days. The mosquito-bat-mosquito cycle has been suggested as a possible overwintering mechanism for some arboviruses.

C. Tick-Borne Encephalitis Complex:

1. Russian spring-summer encephalitis—This disease occurs chiefly in the early summer, particularly in man exposed to the ticks *Ixodes persulcatus* and *I ricinus* in the uncleared forest. Ticks can become infected at any stage in their metamorphosis, and virus can be transmitted transovarially. The virus persists through the winter in hibernating ticks or in vertebrates such as hedgehogs or bats. Virus is secreted in the milk of infected goats for long periods, and infection may be transmitted to those who drink unpasteurized milk. Characteristic of this disease is involvement of bulbar area or cervical cord and the development of ascending paralysis or hemiparesis.

2. Louping ill—This disease of sheep in Scotland and northern England is spread by the tick *Ixodes ricinus.* Man is occasionally infected.

3. Tick-borne encephalitis (Central European or biphasic meningoencephalitis)—This virus is antigenically related to Russian spring-summer encephalitis virus and louping ill virus. Typical cases have a biphasic course, the first phase being influenza-like and the second a meningoencephalitis with or without paralysis.

4. Kyasanur Forest disease is an Indian hemorrhagic disease caused by a virus of the Russian spring-summer encephalitis complex. In addition to man, langur (*Presbytis entellus*) and bonnet (*Macaca radiata*) monkeys are naturally infected in southern India.

5. Powassan encephalitis—This tick-borne virus is the first member of the Russian spring-summer complex to have been isolated in North America. Human infection is rare. Since 1959, when the original fatal case was reported from Canada, 6 additional cases have been confirmed. All have occurred in the northeast portion of the USA.

Each virus is limited to definite areas. It has been postulated that the viruses may have a common ancestor and have become adapted to different parts of the globe, each with its special arthropod vectors and animal reservoirs. On the other hand, a virus may be kept out of an area because the local established virus has built up an immunity in the population which, because of the overlapping serologic response, protects against a virus from another area. In this way, perhaps, the Middle East, where West Nile fever is prevalent, may be spared from the more serious Japanese B encephalitis.

Similarly, in the Caribbean area, where dengue is a common infection, antibodies against dengue virus may offer a degree of protection against yellow fever virus or SLE. Since the same mosquito vector is often involved in these diseases, it is possible that interference prevents the insect from transmitting both viruses at once.

Control

Biologic control of the natural vertebrate host is generally impractical, especially when the hosts are wild birds. The most effective method is arthropod control. Since the period of viremia in the vertebrate is of short duration (3–6 days for SLE infections of birds), any suppression of the vector for this period should break the transmission cycle. During the 1966 Dallas SLE epidemic, low-volume, high-concentration malathion mist was sprayed aerially over most of Dallas County. A striking decrease in the number and infectivity rate of the mosquito vectors occurred, demonstrating the effectiveness of the treatment.

Inactivated vaccines have not met with success. Several live attenuated encephalitis vaccines are being investigated. A live attenuated vaccine was successfully used to halt the severe epidemic of VEE in horses in Texas in 1971.

VENEZUELAN EQUINE ENCEPHALITIS

Venezuelan equine encephalitis (VEE) is a mosquito-borne viral disease which primarily produces an undifferentiated febrile illness in man and encephalitis in equine animals.

Properties of the Virus

VEE, an RNA-containing virus and a member of the group A arboviruses, is readily inactivated by ether or sodium deoxycholate. The virions are 60–75 nm in diameter and are composed of a lipoprotein envelope and a spherical core (nucleoid) with a diameter of 30–40 nm. The virus is relatively heat-labile. Animals immune to VEE show an increased resistance to EEE infection, although the converse situation is less apparent. VEE is lethal for mice, guinea pigs, hamsters, and 1-day-old chicks and is excreted in their feces, urine, and nasal secretions. The virus produces a cytopathogenic effect in baby hamster kidney cells (BHK), HeLa, duck embryo, and Vero and chick embryo fibroblast cell cultures.

Clinical Findings

Over 50% of equines infected develop CNS symptoms after an incubation period of 24–72 hours, while the remainder have an undifferentiated febrile illness. Symptoms include high fever, depression, diar-

rhea, anorexia, and weight loss. In nonfatal cases, the fever subsides and convalescence is protracted. In fatal cases, fever persists, weakness ensues, and the horse loses balance and dies within 2–4 days.

The disease in man is influenza-like in about 97% of patients who develop symptoms and consists of high fever, headache, and severe myalgia. Convalescence is often prolonged. Encephalitis occurs in approximately 3%. A mortality rate of 0.5% has been reported, usually in younger patients who develop neurologic signs. Leukopenia is common in both equines and man.

Laboratory Diagnosis

The virus may be isolated from whole blood, serum, nasopharyngeal washings, many organs, and occasionally the CSF during the acute phase of the illness. Isolations are made by intracerebral inoculation of suckling mice or in cell cultures (see above). The antibody response is similar to that found in other arbovirus diseases. Neutralizing and hemagglutination-inhibiting antibodies occur early and persist, whereas complement-fixing antibodies appear 2–3 weeks after onset but fall within 2–5 years. Serologic tests, listed in order of specificity, include Nt, CF, and HI. Cross-reactions with other members of group A are extensive using the HI test, although homologous titers are higher than the heterologous antibodies.

Epidemiology

The natural cycle for VEE involves mammals and mosquitoes. Birds and bats are susceptible. Man is only tangentially involved.

First reported in Venezuela in 1936, the disease gradually appeared in Panama and Mexico. In 1971, a severe epidemic occurred along the Texas-Mexico border which resulted in the death of several thousand horses and the occurrence of several hundred human cases. Two human cases of VEE were reported in California in 1972, but no cases in the USA have been reported in man or horses since then. In Florida, VEE is enzootic in rodents. Serologic evidence indicates that much subclinical human infection with this agent occurs in Florida, but clinical CNS disease is rare. Several subtypes of VEE exist which differ in their ability to produce disease in man and animals. It is thought that the rarity of clinical disease in Florida is due to the fact that a less virulent VEE subtype virus than exists in the southwestern USA is endemic in Florida.

Control

Because of the presence of virulent VEE in Mexican border states, immunization of all equines (including revaccination of previously vaccinated equines) with a live attenuated vaccine and local and aerial spraying of mosquitoes were begun on a routine basis in 1972. So far these measures have proved effective in limiting the spread of the disease. Strict quarantine to prevent movement of equines into areas free of the disease is also necessary. The attenuated VEE vaccine has been used experimentally in man but is not available for general use.

BUNYAVIRUS ENCEPHALITIS
(California Encephalitis)

The California complex comprises 11 closely related but antigenically distinct members. This group is part of a larger complex, the Bunyamwera supergroup, through cross-reactions in HI, CF, or Nt tests.

Properties of the California Group
The virions are spherical, 80–100 nm in diameter, and are inactivated by sodium deoxycholate and ether. Hemagglutinins are present. All members are pathogenic for suckling mice and hamsters and for a variety of cell culture preparations.

Clinical Findings & Diagnosis
The onset of California encephalitis virus infection is abrupt, typically with a severe bifrontal headache preceding a fever of 38–40° C. Vomiting, lethargy, and local or generalized convulsions may occur. Less frequently, there is only aseptic meningitis with nuchal rigidity.

Polymorphonuclear leukocytosis is frequent, with the peripheral white count above 10,000/cu mm and occasionally as high as 29,000. CSF pleocytosis, predominantly lymphocytic, is present with a range of 30–1000/cu mm. The EEG reveals generalized cerebral dysfunction with high-amplitude slow activity.

Histopathologic changes include neuronal degeneration and a patchy inflammatory response with some perivascular cuffing and edema in the cerebral cortex and meninges.

The prognosis is excellent, although convalescence may be prolonged. Fatalities are rare. Abnormal EEG patterns have occasionally persisted for 1–2 years or more, but neurologic sequelae are rare.

Serologic confirmation by HI, CF, or Nt tests is necessary in all suspected cases with appropriately spaced acute and convalescent specimens.

Epidemiology
California encephalitis virus was isolated from mosquitoes in California in 1943. It was not until 1964, however, that major outbreaks were recognized and studied.

Cases occur primarily in late July through early September in rural communities and have been most common in the upper Mississippi and Ohio River valleys, particularly in Indiana, Wisconsin, and Ohio. Scattered cases have been reported from North Carolina, Minnesota, Iowa, New York, Florida, Louisiana, Mississippi, and California. Clinical infections have occurred primarily in persons less than 21 years of age, with the majority between 4 and 14 years.

The ecologic information available suggests that these viruses are transmitted between various woodland mosquitoes and small mammals such as squirrels and rabbits. Human infection is tangential. The mechanism by which the virus is maintained during the winter months is not known. However, overwintering of Lacrosse virus, another member of the California group, in diapause eggs of the mosquito vector has been demonstrated. The virus is transmitted transovarially, and adults which develop from infected eggs can transmit the virus by bite.

WEST NILE FEVER

West Nile fever is an acute, mild, febrile disease with lymphadenopathy and rash that occurs in the Middle East, tropical or subtropical Africa, and southwest Asia.

Properties of the Virus
The virus is a group B arbovirus. It is propagated in chick embryo and tissue culture, producing plaques on cell monolayers under agar.

Clinical Findings
The virus is introduced through the bite of a Culex mosquito and produces viremia and a generalized systemic infection characterized by lymphadenopathy, sometimes with an accompanying maculopapular rash. Transitory meningeal involvement may occur during the acute stage. The virus may produce fatal encephalitis in older people, who have a delayed (and low) antibody response.

Laboratory Diagnosis
Virus can be recovered from blood taken in the acute stage of the infection. In serologic tests, the first sample should be taken early in the disease and the second 2–3 weeks later. CF, HI, and Nt tests may be used. Complement-fixing titers of 32–128 are commonly found in the convalescent specimen, remain at this level for about 3 months, and then fall slowly. Neutralizing antibodies rise somewhat more slowly, reach maximum height at about 4 months, and persist almost at the same level for over 2 years. During convalescence, heterologous complement-fixing and neutralizing antibodies develop to JBE and SLE, which are members of this same group. The heterologous response is shorter and lower than the homologous response.

Immunity
Only one antigenic type exists, and immunity is presumably permanent. Maternal antibodies are transferred from mother to offspring and disappear during the first 6 months of life.

Epidemiology
West Nile fever appears to be limited to the Middle East. However, antibodies have been found in normal adults in Africa, India, and Korea. In nonimmune populations, the attack rate is high, and abortive and inapparent infections also occur. In Cairo, over 70% of the inhabitants aged 4 years and above

have both neutralizing and complement-fixing antibodies.

This summer disease is more prevalent in rural than in urban areas. The virus has been isolated on several occasions from Culex mosquitoes during epidemics. Experimentally infected mosquitoes can transmit the virus after an extrinsic incubation period of 1–3 weeks.

Ticks may play a role as reservoir vectors of West Nile virus. Nymphs of the tick *Ornithodoros moubata* can be infected by engorging on viremic mice. The virus multiplies in the nymph and persists into the adult stage for at least 224 days. The ticks in turn can pass the virus on to chicks and mice.

Control

Mosquito abatement is a logical control measure but has not yet been proved to be effective.

YELLOW FEVER

Yellow fever (YF) is an acute, febrile, mosquito-borne illness. Severe cases are characterized by jaundice, proteinuria, and hemorrhage. YF virus is the type species of the *Flavivirus* genus of the family **Togaviridae**.

Properties of the Virus

A. Size: YF virus is about 22–38 nm in diameter.

B. Reaction to Physical and Chemical Agents: The virus may be preserved for a month in blood at 4° C, for 3 months in 50% glycerol at 0° C, and for years at −70° C. After lyophilization, it survives for years at 0° C. The virus is killed by heating at 60° C for 10 minutes and also by contact with 0.1% formalin for 48 hours at 0° C.

C. Animal Susceptibility and Growth of Virus: YF virus multiplies in a variety of animals (monkeys, mice, guinea pigs) and in mosquitoes. It is readily cultivated in the developing chick embryo and in tissue cultures made from chick or mouse embryos. All strains of the virus produce encephalitis in mice following direct inoculation into the brain. Infant mice also develop encephalitis after subcutaneous and intraperitoneal inoculations.

Strains freshly isolated from man, monkey, or mosquito are pantropic, ie, the virus invades all 3 embryonal layers. Fresh strains usually produce a severe (often fatal) infection with marked damage to the livers of monkeys after parenteral inoculation. After serial passage in the brains of monkeys or mice, such strains lose much of their viscerotropism; they cause encephalitis after intracerebral injection, but only asymptomatic infection after subcutaneous injection. Cross-immunity exists between the pantropic and neurotropic strains of the virus.

During the serial passage of a pantropic strain of YF through tissue cultures, the relatively avirulent 17D strain was recovered. This strain lost its capacity to

induce a viscerotropic or neurotropic disease in monkeys and in man and is now used as a vaccine. The virus in the vaccine may be diluted 10,000 times and still produce encephalitis and death in mice inoculated intracerebrally.

D. Antigenic Properties: Hemagglutinins and complement-fixing antigens may be prepared from infected tissues. Each antigen has 2 separable components: one is associated with the infectious particle; the other is probably a product of the action of YF virus on tissues it infects. On the basis of serologic tests, YF virus is classified as a member of the group B arboviruses.

Pathogenesis & Pathology

Our understanding of the pathogenesis of YF is based on work with the experimental infection in monkeys. The virus enters through the skin and then spreads to the local lymph nodes, where it multiplies. From the lymph nodes it enters the circulating blood and becomes localized in the liver, spleen, kidney, bone marrow, and lymph glands, where it may persist for days.

The lesions of YF are due to the localization and propagation of the virus in a particular organ. Death may result from the necrotic lesions in the liver and kidney. In severe cases, there may be almost complete destruction of the parenchymatous cells of the liver. The most frequent site of hemorrhage is the mucosa at the pyloric end of the stomach.

The distribution of the necrotic cells in the liver may be spotty but is most evident in the midzones of the lobules. The necrosis is hyaline in nature and may be restricted to the cytoplasm. These irregular hyaline masses are eosinophilic and are called Councilman bodies. Intranuclear eosinophilic inclusion bodies are also present and are of diagnostic value. During recovery, the parenchymatous cells are replaced and the liver may be completely restored.

In the kidney there is fatty degeneration of the tubular epithelium which may be secondary to the hemorrhagic diathesis. Degenerative changes also occur in the spleen, lymph nodes, and heart. Intranuclear, acidophilic inclusion bodies may be present in the nerve and glial cells of the brain. Perivascular infiltrations with mononuclear cells also occur in the brain.

Clinical Findings

The incubation period is from 3–6 days. At the onset, the patient has fever, chills, headache, and backache, followed by nausea and vomiting. A short period of remission often follows the prodrome. On about the fourth day, the period of intoxication begins with a slow pulse (90–100) relative to a high fever and moderate jaundice. In severe cases, marked proteinuria and hemorrhagic manifestations appear. The vomitus may be black owing to the presence of altered blood. Lymphopenia is present. When the disease progresses to the severe stage (black vomitus and jaundice), the mortality rate is high. On the other hand, the infection may be so mild as to go unrecognized. Regardless of severity, there are no sequelae; patients either die or recover completely.

Laboratory Diagnosis

A. Recovery of Virus: The virus may be recovered from the blood up to the fifth day of the disease. Mice inoculated intracerebrally with serum of a suspected case develop encephalitis if the virus is present. If virus is isolated, it should be identified by neutralization with specific antiserum.

Some strains of the virus act paradoxically when first isolated from patients. Undiluted serum may produce no disease in inoculated mice, whereas the same serum diluted 10 or 100 times may cause encephalitis in the inoculated mice. The explanation of this paradoxic behavior might be (1) that antibody is present in the serum in only small amounts, and that the virus may be reactivated by simple dilution, which dissociates, in part, the virus-antibody complex; or (2) that a relatively large amount of inactive virus is also present in the specimen, which interferes with the growth of the active virus unless it is diluted out. For this reason, the serum should be inoculated undiluted into one group and in various dilutions into other groups of mice.

B. Serology: Neutralizing antibodies develop early (by the fifth day) even in severe and fatal cases. In patients who survive the infection, circulating antibodies endure for life.

Complement-fixing antibodies are rarely found after mild infection or vaccination with the attenuated, live 17D strain. In severe infections they appear later than the neutralizing antibodies and disappear more rapidly.

The serologic response in YF may be of 2 types. In **primary infections** of yellow fever, specific hemagglutination-inhibiting antibodies appear first, followed rapidly by antibodies to other group B viruses. The titers of homologous hemagglutination-inhibiting antibodies are usually higher than those of heterologous antibodies. Complement-fixing antibodies rise slowly and are usually specific, as are neutralizing antibodies in primary infections especially.

In **secondary infections** where YF occurs in a patient previously infected with a group B arbovirus, hemagglutination-inhibiting and complement-fixing antibodies appear rapidly and to high titers. There is no suggestion of specificity. The highest hemagglutination-inhibiting and complement-fixing antibodies are usually heterologous. The heterologous response may be so great that accurate diagnosis by Nt test may be impossible.

Histopathologic examination of the liver in fatal cases is useful in those regions where the disease is endemic.

Immunity

Subtle antigenic differences are observed between YF strains isolated in Africa and South America. The pantropic prototype strain, Asibi, is antigenically somewhat different from the 17D vaccine strain.

An infant born of an immune mother has antibodies at birth which are gradually lost during the first 6 months of life. Reacquisition of similar antibodies is dependent upon the individual's exposure to the virus under natural conditions or by vaccination.

Epidemiology

Two major epidemiologic cycles of YF are recognized: (1) classic (or urban) epidemic YF and (2) sylvan (or jungle) YF. Urban YF involves person-to-person transmission by domestic or peridomestic Aedes mosquitoes. In the Western Hemisphere and West Africa, this species is primarily *A aegypti,* which breeds in the accumulations of water that accompany human settlement. Mosquitoes remain close to houses and become infected by biting a viremic individual. Urban YF is perpetuated in areas where there is a constant influx of susceptible persons, cases of YF, and *A aegypti.* With the use of intensive measures for mosquito abatement, urban YF has been practically eliminated in South America.

Jungle YF is primarily a disease of monkeys. In South America and Africa, it is transmitted from monkey to monkey by arboreal mosquitoes (ie, Haemagogus, Aedes) which inhabit the moist forest canopy. The infection in animals may be severe or inapparent. Persons such as woodcutters, nut-pickers, or road-builders come in contact with these mosquitoes in the forest and become infected. Jungle YF may also occur when an infected monkey visits a human habitation and is bitten by *A aegypti,* which then transmits the virus to man.

The virus multiplies in mosquitoes, which remain infectious for life. After the mosquito ingests a virus-containing blood meal, an interval of 12–14 days is required for it to become infectious. This interval is called the extrinsic incubation period.

All age groups are susceptible, but the disease in infants is milder than that in older groups. Large numbers of inapparent infections occur. The disease usually is milder in blacks. Yellow fever has never been reported in India or the Orient, even though the vector, *A aegypti,* is widely distributed there.

New outbreaks continue to occur. In Bolivia, 145 cases of jungle YF, with over 50% mortality, were reported in the first half of 1975. The disease occurred in nonimmune persons coming from distant places, usually at higher altitudes, for the rice harvests. The rice fields, with the jungle adjacent to them, are located near towns. Some cases and deaths occurred among susceptible persons who did not enter the jungle but had been working in its vicinity. The virus had established itself in this area in reservoirs close to the towns. Jungle YF rarely affects the local population, which has developed immunity by having been in contact with the virus through previous minor infections and also by frequent vaccinations. Most of the cases were in 20- to 39-year-old men, the population group most frequently sought for agricultural work, and almost all occurred in persons who had not been vaccinated. The real number of cases and deaths from jungle YF in such areas is much higher than the reports indicate, as many patients do not go to the hospital but recover or die without any report being made.

Control

Vigorous mosquito abatement programs have virtually eliminated urban YF. The last reported outbreak of YF in the USA occurred in 1905. However, with the speed of modern air travel, wherever *A aegypti* is present, the threat of a YF outbreak exists. Most countries insist upon proper mosquito control on airplanes and vaccination of all persons at least 10 days before arrival in or from an endemic zone.

An excellent attenuated, live vaccine is available in the 17D strain. Vaccine is prepared in eggs and then dispensed as a dried powder in small vials. Because it is a live virus, it must be kept cold. It is rehydrated just before use and injected subcutaneously by skin scarification or by jet injector. The vaccine contains egg proteins, and vaccinees should be questioned about allergic reactions to such proteins. A single dose produces a good antibody response in more than 95% of vaccinated persons. Persistence of antibody levels permits revaccination at intervals of 10 years, although most individuals maintain significant neutralizing titers for even longer periods. After vaccination, the virus multiplies and may be isolated from the blood before antibodies develop. With viremia, circulating interferon has been detected. It may limit the duration of viremia and may provide early resistance.

An experimental sequential immunization procedure involving 3 group B arboviruses—attenuated 17D yellow fever virus, attenuated dengue 2 virus, and attenuated Langat E5 virus—has proved successful in monkeys.

The yellow fever vaccination requirement for travelers entering the USA was eliminated in 1972.

DENGUE
(Breakbone Fever)

Dengue is a mosquito-borne infection characterized by fever, muscle and joint pain, lymphadenopathy, and rash.

Properties of the Dengue Viruses

A. Size: The diameter of these viruses is about 50 nm, with a 25 nm core.

B. Reaction to Physical and Chemical Agents: The viruses are stable for at least 5 years in the frozen state at $-70°$ C and in the lyophilized state at $5°$ C. Human blood may be infectious if kept at $5°$ C for several weeks.

C. Animal Susceptibility: Human serum containing dengue virus produces only inapparent infection in chimpanzees and monkeys. The infection is followed by the appearance of complement-fixing and neutralizing antibodies, which persist for many months.

Mice inoculated with human serum containing dengue virus rarely show signs of disease. Several strains of virus have been adapted to mice; after intracerebral inoculation, mice exhibit flaccid paralysis with the histologic lesion chiefly in the neurons. Mouse-adapted dengue virus may produce a fatal paralytic disease in monkeys, which is similar, both clinically and pathologically, to experimental poliomyelitis.

Dengue virus grows to high levels in cultures of monkey kidney (LLC-MK$_2$), hamster kidney, and HeLa cells, producing cytopathic changes which may be used for titrating virus and for measuring neutralizing antibodies. Primary isolation of dengue virus has been reported using *A albopictus* cell cultures.

D. Antigenic Properties: At least 4 distinct serotypes exist, designated types 1–4.

Complement-fixing and hemagglutinating antigens can be prepared from the brains of infected newborn mice. Although dengue and YF viruses show group relationships, this is not associated with any significant cross-immunity. Humans immunized against YF are fully susceptible to small doses of dengue virus.

Pathogenesis & Pathology

Viremia is present at the onset of fever and may persist for 3 days. The histopathologic lesion is in small blood vessels with endothelial swelling, perivascular edema, and infiltration with mononuclear cells.

Dermal or ocular inoculation with small doses of virus may produce typical attacks of dengue, mild attacks without rash, or no evidence of disease. Immunity is achieved in all 3 instances.

Clinical Findings

The onset of fever may be sudden or there may be prodromal symptoms of malaise, chills, and headache. Pains soon develop, especially in the back, joints, muscles, and eyeballs. A flushed face and injected conjunctiva are common. The temperature returns to normal after 5–6 days or may subside on about the third day and rise again about 5–8 days after onset ("saddle-back" form). A rash (maculopapular or scarlatiniform) may appear on the third or fourth day and lasts for 24–72 hours, fading without desquamation. Lymph nodes are frequently enlarged. Leukopenia with a relative lymphocytosis is a regular occurrence. Convalescence may take weeks, although complications and death are rare. Especially in young children, dengue may occur as a mild febrile illness lasting 1–3 days.

A more severe syndrome—dengue hemorrhagic fever (DHF)—may occur in individuals with heterologous dengue antibody, passively acquired (as maternal antibody) or endogenously produced. Although initial symptoms simulate normal dengue, the patient's condition abruptly worsens and is associated with hypoproteinemia, thrombocytopenia, prolonged bleeding time, or elevated prothrombin time. Dengue shock syndrome (DSS), characterized by shock and hemoconcentration, may supervene. These altered manifestations of dengue have been observed, often in epidemic form, in the Philippines, Southeast Asia, and

India—regions in which several dengue serotypes are regularly present; the mortality rate is 5—10%. In studies of the dengue diseases in Southeast Asia, DHF, with or without shock, has been found to occur more frequently when dengue type 2 is the secondary infecting virus and the patient is a female 3 years of age or older. The factors responsible for the occurrence of DSS are poorly understood but probably represent hypersensitivity reactions. It is postulated that virus-antibody complexes are formed within a few days of the second dengue infection; that the complement system is activated by these complexes; and that complement products lead to the vascular dysfunction seen in the hemorrhagic fever syndrome.

The possible role of hypersensitivity in the production of DHF indicates caution in the development of dengue virus vaccines.

Laboratory Diagnosis

Isolation of the virus is difficult. Until the use of Aedes cell cultures for primary isolation is fully evaluated, the following diagnostic tests may be done.

A. Presumptive Test: One group of mice is inoculated with fresh acute-phase serum and another group with heated serum (56° C for 30 minutes). One month later, both groups of mice are challenged with 100 LD_{50} doses of the known mouse-adapted dengue viruses. If the mice which received the fresh serum resist the challenge and the mice which received the heated serum succumb, then the serum contained dengue virus.

B. Serology: Following infection, neutralizing and hemagglutination-inhibiting antibodies appear within 7 days of onset, and complement-fixing antibodies appear 7—14 days later. Antigens representing the local serotypes present must be used in testing for antibodies.

1. Neutralizing antibodies—Homotypic antibodies have a higher titer than heterotypic antibodies in primary infections.

2. Complement-fixing antibodies—Often the heterotypic response is lower and does not persist as long as the homotypic.

3. Hemagglutination-inhibiting antibodies—Homotypic antibodies appear earlier, may be of higher titer, and may persist longer than heterotypic antibodies. Antibodies to other members of group B also appear after primary infection.

Immunity

At least 4 antigenic types of the virus exist.

Reinfection with a virus of a different serotype, 2—3 months after the primary attack, may give rise to a short, mild illness without a rash. If mosquitoes are allowed to feed on these reinfected patients, they can transmit the disease. Dengue type 1 and 2 infections are associated with the highest antibody levels. Sufficient cross-reacting antibody may be present in these situations to prevent infection with type 3 or 4.

The mouse-adapted and tissue culture-adapted strains have become attenuated and no longer produce disease in man. Persons inoculated with the attenuated virus have a solid immunity to homologous virus transmitted by infected mosquitoes or by inoculation of infectious human serum.

Persons previously vaccinated against yellow fever give a broad anamnestic antibody response to experimental immunization with attenuated dengue virus; the same is true of persons previously infected with other members of group B.

Epidemiology

The known geographic distribution of the dengue viruses today is India, the Far East, and the Hawaiian and Caribbean Islands. Dengue has occurred in the southern USA (1934) and in Australia. Most subtropical and tropical regions around the world where Aedes vectors exist are endemic areas or potential ones. For example, over 500,000 cases of dengue occurred in Colombia in 1972 following reinfestation of the Atlantic coastal areas by *A aegypti.*

Dengue virus is transmitted only by certain species of Aedes mosquitoes, particularly *A aegypti.*

The infectious cycle is as follows:

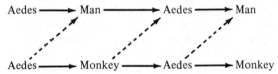

A aegypti is a domestic mosquito; *A albopictus* exists in the bush or jungle and may be responsible for maintaining the infection among monkeys (jungle dengue).

In urban communities, dengue epidemics are explosive and involve appreciable portions of the population. They often start during the rainy season, when the vector mosquito, *A aegypti,* is abundant. The mosquito is a domesticated one with a short flight range, and urban spread of dengue is frequently house-to-house. The mosquito breeds in tropical or semitropical climates in man-made water-holding receptacles around human habitation, or in tree holes or plants close to human dwellings. It apparently prefers the blood of man to that of other animals. Since *A aegypti* is also the vector of yellow fever, the outbreak of dengue (1968—1969) in the Caribbean should be viewed as a warning of even more serious epidemics. Sporadic cases and localized outbreaks continued to occur in these areas until the fall of 1975, when large numbers of cases occurred in Puerto Rico. During the next 6 months over 1300 cases were reported, the majority in the San Juan metropolitan area. About half of the reported cases could be confirmed as dengue by seroconversion. In addition, dengue type 2 virus was isolated from acute serum samples. Three cases of dengue hemorrhagic fever were also documented. The epidemic was quickly brought under control by aerial spraying with malathion to kill adult mosquitoes and by treatment of breeding sites to kill larvae.

A aegypti is the only known vector mosquito for dengue in the Western Hemisphere. The female acquires the virus by feeding upon a viremic human. Mosquitoes are infective after a period of 8–14 days (extrinsic incubation time). In man, clinical disease begins 2–15 days after an infective mosquito bite. Once infective, a mosquito probably remains so for the remainder of her life (1–3 months or more).

The virus is not passed from one generation of mosquitoes to the next. The disease is maintained constantly in the tropics, where mosquitoes are present throughout the year. Outbreaks in colder areas are terminated with the advent of cold weather.

Epidemics of dengue are usually observed when the virus is newly introduced into an area or if susceptibles move into an endemic area. If there is a year-round maintenance of the virus cycle, the disease becomes endemic, as has happened in the Caribbean area. If the infection is introduced into a temperate region where the vector disappears during the winter, the epidemic promptly comes to an end and does not reappear the next year. The endemic dengue in the Caribbean is a constant threat to the USA, where *A aegypti* mosquitoes are prevalent in the summer months.

Control

Control depends upon antimosquito measures, eg, elimination of breeding places and the use of insecticides. An experimental attenuated virus vaccine has been produced, but it has not had a large-scale field test and its broad use seems improbable until the role which hypersensitivity to dengue plays in the induction of the shock syndrome is clarified.

HEMORRHAGIC FEVER

Hemorrhagic fever has been reported from Siberia, Central Asia, Eastern and Northern Europe, Southeast Asia, and South America. It first received widespread attention in the USA during the early 1950s when American troops fighting in Korea experienced an outbreak of Korean hemorrhagic fever (KHF).

Three categories have recently been suggested for classifying the hemorrhagic fevers: (1) tick-borne, which includes some members of the Russian spring-summer encephalitis complex (Omsk hemorrhagic fever and Kyasanur Forest disease), and the Crimean-Congo hemorrhagic fever group; (2) mosquito-borne, which includes the dengue viruses (see above), Chikungunya virus, and yellow fever virus; (3) zoonotic, which includes the viruses of hemorrhagic fever with renal syndrome (KHF), Argentinian hemorrhagic fever (Junin), Bolivian hemorrhagic fever (Machupo), and Lassa fever. Marburg virus, which was associated with a 1967 outbreak of hemorrhagic fever in Germany among persons in contact with vervet monkeys from Uganda, has an unknown route of transmission. Marburg virus superficially resembles the rhabdoviruses (see Chapter 39).

Common clinical features of the epidemic hemorrhagic fevers include fever, petechiae or purpura, gastrointestinal, nasal, and uterine bleeding, hypotension, prostration, CNS signs, and thrombocytopenia. Leukopenia and proteinuria occur often.

Argentinian hemorrhagic fever was first noted near the town of Junin in 1955, when virus was isolated from patients' blood. The virus then gradually spread throughout the country.

Machupo virus was recovered from the spleen of a patient in Bolivia who died of hemorrhagic fever in 1963. The virus has been isolated from the mouse *Calomys callosus*. The systematic extermination of this field mouse has been successful in controlling the spread of the disease in Bolivia.

SANDFLY FEVER
(Pappataci Fever, Phlebotomus Fever)

Sandfly fever is a mild, insect-borne disease which occurs commonly in countries bordering the Mediterranean Sea and in Russia, Iran, Pakistan, India, Panama, Brazil, and Trinidad. The sandfly *Phlebotomus papatasii* is present in endemic areas between 20 and 45 degrees of latitude.

Properties of the Virus

The virus has a diameter of about 50 nm.

Although at least 20 separate antigenic types exist, only 5 are responsible for sandfly fever. Members of the group are antigenically distinct from other arbovirus groups, can be grown in tissue culture, and have been adapted to infant mice and hamsters, in which they produce encephalitis. They are stable to freezing and lyophilization.

Clinical Findings

In man the bite of the sandfly results in small itching papules on the skin which persist for up to 5 days. The disease begins abruptly after an incubation period of 3–6 days. For 24 hours before and 24 hours after the onset of fever, the virus is found in the blood. The clinical features consist of headache, malaise, nausea, fever, conjunctival injection, photophobia, stiffness of the neck and back, abdominal pain, and leukopenia. All patients recover. There is no specific treatment. The pathology in man is not known.

Laboratory Diagnosis

The diagnosis is made usually on clinical grounds. It may be confirmed by demonstrating a rise in antibody titer in paired serum specimens, either through Nt tests with mouse-adapted virus or HI tests utilizing a hemagglutinin associated with the virus.

Immunity

Immunity is specific for each antigenic type of virus and persists for at least 2 years.

Epidemiology

The disease is transmitted by the female sandfly, a midge only a few mm in size. In the tropics the sandfly is prevalent all year; in cooler climates only during the warm seasons. It is not definitely known how the virus remains viable during the winter. However, virus isolations have been made frequently from male sandflies, which are not bloodsuckers, suggesting that transovarial transmission may occur.

The extrinsic incubation period in the sandfly is about 1 week. The insect feeds at night; during the day, it may be found in dark places (cracks in walls, caves, houses, and tree trunks). Eggs are laid a few days after a blood meal. About 5 weeks are required for the eggs to develop into winged insects. The adult lives only a few weeks in hot weather.

In endemic areas infection and immunity occur commonly in childhood. When nonimmune adults (eg, troops) enter the area, large outbreaks can occur among the new arrivals and are occasionally mistaken for malaria.

Control

Sandflies are commonest just above the ground. Because of their small size they can pass through ordinary screens and mosquito nets. Their flight range is up to 200 yards. Prevention of disease in endemic areas rests on application of insect repellents during the night and the use of residual insecticides in and around living quarters.

COLORADO TICK FEVER
(Mountain Fever, Tick Fever)

Colorado tick fever is a mild febrile disease, without rash, which is transmitted by a tick.

Properties of the Virus

Although Colorado tick fever fulfills the functional classification of an arbovirus, its relative resistance to lipid solvents, the probable double-stranded RNA nature of its genome, and other morphologic properties suggest its inclusion in the family **Reoviridae**; its capsid architecture and acid lability would further place it in the genus *Orbivirus* (see Chapter 39).

The diameter of the virus is 80 nm with an inner capsid of 50 nm. The virus is stable to freezing and also to lyophilization. The virus is pathogenic for hamsters and mice. Upon intracerebral inoculation, mice develop paralysis. The virus multiplies in human tissue cultures and in the chick embryo. The virus is antigenically distinct from all other agents.

Pathogenesis & Pathology

The virus is transmitted through the bite of an infected tick. Virus is present in the blood during the acute stage of the illness. The pathology in man is not known.

Clinical Findings

The incubation period is 4–6 days. The disease has a sudden onset with chilly sensations and myalgia. Symptoms include headache, deep ocular pain, muscle and joint pains, lumbar backache, and nausea and vomiting. The temperature is usually diphasic. After the first bout of 2 days, the patient may feel well. Symptoms and fever then reappear and last 3–4 more days. The white count falls to 2000–3000. Except for one fatal case, no complications or deaths have been reported.

Laboratory Diagnosis

The virus may be isolated from whole blood by the intracerebral or intraperitoneal inoculation of baby hamsters or suckling mice. Viremia in man persists for at least 2 weeks.

Specific complement-fixing antigens are available from infected mouse brain. Complement-fixing and neutralizing antibodies appear during the second week of disease and persist for at least 3 years.

Immunity

Only one antigenic type is known. A single infection is believed to produce a lasting immunity.

Epidemiology

Colorado tick fever is limited to areas where the wood tick *Dermacentor andersoni* is distributed, primarily Colorado, Oregon, Utah, Idaho, Montana, and Wyoming. Patients have been in a tick-infested area 4–5 days before onset of symptoms, and in many cases ticks are found attached to their bodies. One is often unaware of the ticks' presence since their bite is painless. Cases occur chiefly in adult males, because this group is subject to greater exposure to ticks.

D andersoni collected in nature has been found to carry the virus. This tick is a true reservoir, and the virus is transmitted transovarially by the adult female. Natural infection occurs in rodents, which act as hosts for immature stages of the tick.

Control

The disease can be prevented by avoiding tick-infested areas. If this is not possible, suitable clothing is recommended (high boots, socks worn outside of trouser legs). In tick-infested areas, the body should be examined for attached ticks and these should be promptly removed. A strain adapted to chick embryo culture has had limited trials as a live vaccine.

LASSA FEVER

The first recognized cases of this disease occurred in 1969 among Americans stationed in the Nigerian village of Lassa. The causative virus is extremely virulent for persons not native to the area, with a mortality rate of 36–67% in 4 epidemics occurring in separated areas of West Africa and involving about 100 cases.

Transmission can occur by human-to-human contact, presenting a hazard to hospital personnel. Nine of 20 medical workers have died from infections. Lassa fever can involve almost all of the organ systems, although symptoms may vary in the individual patient. The disease is characterized by very high fever, mouth ulcers, skin rash with hemorrhages, pneumonia, heart and kidney damage, and severe muscle aches. Benign, febrile cases do occur. The virus can be isolated from the patient's blood and can be grown in Vero cell cultures, a continuous line from African green monkey kidney.

Lassa virus is a member of the family **Arenaviridae**. It contains RNA; the virus particles vary in size and shape (70–150 nm) and have densely spaced surface projections and dense internal granules (20–25 nm) which may be host ribosomes. The virus cross-reacts in CF tests with LCM and the Tacaribe complex, arenaviruses which also have a natural cycle of transmission in rodents.

The mode of transmission of the virus seems to involve both human-to-human contact and a non-human cycle. Spread of the disease by human-to-human contact within a hospital was originally noted. A study conducted during a 1972 epidemic in Sierra Leone demonstrated a nonhuman cycle of virus transmission. The virus was isolated from a species of African house rat, *Mastomys natalensis.* Thus, rodent control may be an effective control measure, as in the case of Bolivian hemorrhagic fever.

In early 1976 a Peace Corps volunteer returning home by plane from Africa became ill with Lassa fever after landing in Washington, DC. The diagnosis was originally confirmed by following the development of antibody by indirect immunofluorescence tests. The virus was subsequently isolated from the patient's urine. This led to the surveillance of 376 persons in 20 states who had contact with the patient. No secondary cases have been identified as of this writing.

The only therapy presently available against Lassa fever is hyperimmune serum obtained either from patients who have recovered from the disease or from naturally immune populations. Serum from recently recovered patients must be used with caution since virus may persist in the blood for several months following the acute infection.

RIFT VALLEY FEVER
(Enzootic Hepatitis)

The virus of this disease is primarily pathogenic for sheep and other domestic animals. Man is secondarily infected during the course of epizootics in domesticated animals in Africa. Infection among laboratory workers is common.

The clinical features are similar to those of dengue: acute onset, fever, prostration, pain in the extremities and joints, and gastrointestinal distress. The temperature curve is like that of dengue and yellow fever (saddle-back type). There is a marked leukopenia. The disease is short-lived, and recovery almost always is complete.

The virus has a diameter of about 30 nm. It may be propagated in a number of animals, but mice are the laboratory animals of choice. The virus can be isolated from human blood during the first 3 days of the disease. Complement-fixing, neutralizing, and hemagglutination-inhibiting antibodies develop during convalescence and persist for many years.

The disease is not contagious but is transmitted by a bloodsucking insect active at night, presumably the mosquito. Sheep can be protected if they can be screened at night.

•   •   •

General References

Arboviruses and Human Disease. Report of a WHO scientific group. WHO Technical Report Series No. 369. World Health Organization, 1967.

Bokisch VA & others: The potential pathogenic role of complement in dengue hemorrhagic shock syndrome. N Engl J Med 289:996, 1973.

Doherty RL: Arthropod-borne viruses in Australia and their relation to infection and disease. Prog Med Virol 17:136, 1974.

Ehrenkranz NJ & others: Pandemic dengue in Caribbean countries and the southern United States: Past, present and potential problems. N Engl J Med 285:1460, 1971.

Hammon WM, Sather GE: Arboviruses. Pages 227–280 in: *Diagnostic Procedures for Viral and Rickettsial Infections,* 4th ed. American Public Health Association, 1969.

Henderson BE, Coleman PH: The growing importance of the California arboviruses in the etiology of human disease. Prog Med Virol 13:404, 1971.

Horzinek MC: The structure of togaviruses. Prog Med Virol 16:109, 1973.

Luby JP, Sulkin SE, Sanford JP: The epidemiology of St. Louis encephalitis: A review. Annu Rev Med 20:329, 1969.

Monath TP: Lassa fever and Marburg virus disease. WHO Chron 28:212, 1974.

Murphy FA, Harrison AK, Whitfield SG: Bunyaviridae: Morphologic and morphogenetic similarities of Bunyamwera serologic supergroup viruses and several other arthropod-borne viruses. Intervirology 1:297, 1973.

Porterfield JS & others: Bunyaviruses and Bunyaviridae. Intervirology, vol 6, issue 1, 1976.

Reeves WC: Overwintering of arboviruses. Prog Med Virol 17:193, 1974.

Spence L, Jonkers AH, Grant LS: Arboviruses in the Caribbean islands. Prog Med Virol 10:415, 1968.

Theiler M, Downs WG: *The Arthropod-Borne Viruses of Vertebrates: An Account of the Rockefeller Foundation Virus Program, 1951–1970.* Yale Univ Press, 1973.

Von Bonsdorff CH, Pettersson F: Surface structure of Uukuniemi virus. J Virol 16:1296, 1975.

31...
Picornavirus Family
(Enterovirus & Rhinovirus Groups)

The **Picornaviridae** are small, ether-insensitive viruses with an RNA genome. Their nucleic acid is single-stranded, has a molecular weight of $2-2.8 \times 10^6$, and constitutes about 30% of the particle mass. The nucleocapsid has cubic symmetry, is naked, lacking essential lipid and carbohydrate, and ranges from 20–30 nm in diameter. Virus maturation takes place in the cytoplasm. The family includes 2 genera, *Enterovirus* and *Rhinovirus*.

Enterovirus

Enteroviruses of human origin include the following:

(1) Polioviruses types 1–3.

(2) Coxsackieviruses A–23 types and several variants.

(3) Coxsackieviruses B types 1–6.

(4) Echoviruses–31 types.

(5) Enteroviruses types 68–71. Since 1969, new enterovirus types have been assigned enterovirus type numbers rather than being subclassified as coxsackieviruses or echoviruses. The vernacular names of the previously identified enteroviruses have been retained.

The enterovirus capsid is thought to be composed of 32 morphologic subunits, possibly in the form of a rhombic triacontahedron rather than a regular icosahedron. Rhinovirus capsid architecture appears to be similar. Infective nucleic acid has been extracted from several enteroviruses and rhinoviruses.

Enteroviruses are stable at acid pH (3.0–5.0) for 1–3 hours, whereas rhinoviruses are acid-labile. Enteroviruses and some rhinoviruses are stabilized by magnesium chloride against thermal inactivation.

Enteroviruses are transient inhabitants of the human alimentary tract and may be isolated from the throat or lower intestine. Rhinoviruses, on the other hand, are isolated chiefly from the nose and throat. Among the enteroviruses which are cytopathogenic (polioviruses, echoviruses, and some coxsackieviruses), growth can be readily obtained in primary cultures of human and monkey kidney cells and certain cell lines (such as HeLa); in contrast, most rhinovirus strains can only be recovered in cells of human origin (embryonic human kidney, human diploid cell strains).

Enteroviruses grow readily in stationary cultures at 36–37° C, but the initial growth of rhinoviruses in primary fetal cell cultures is favored when cultures are rolled at 33° C. In cesium chloride, enteroviruses have a density of 1.34 gm/ml and rhinoviruses a density of 1.4 gm/ml.

Enteroviruses exist in many animals, including cattle, pigs, and mice.

Rhinovirus

Human rhinoviruses include more than 100 antigenic types. Rhinoviruses of other host species include equine rhinoviruses and foot-and-mouth disease virus and other bovine viruses.

• • •

In addition to the viruses mentioned above, certain plant and insect viruses (eg, tomato bushy stunt, turnip yellow mosaic, acute bee paralysis viruses) have properties similar to those of the picornaviruses—as do some of the RNA-containing bacteriophages.

The host range of the picornaviruses varies greatly from one type to the next, and even among strains of the same type. They may readily be induced, by laboratory manipulation, to yield variants which have host ranges and tissue tropisms different from those of certain wild strains; this has led to the development of attenuated poliovirus strains now used as vaccines.

Many picornaviruses cause diseases in man ranging from severe paralysis to aseptic meningitis, pleurodynia, myocarditis, skin rashes, and common colds. However, subclinical infection is far more common than clinically manifest disease. Different viruses may produce the same syndrome; on the other hand, the same picornavirus may cause more than a single syndrome. For these reasons, clinical disease is not a satisfactory basis of classification.

ENTEROVIRUS GROUP

POLIOMYELITIS

Poliomyelitis is an acute infectious disease which in its serious form affects the CNS. The destruction of motor neurons in the spinal cord results in flaccid paralysis. However, only a small number of infections are clinically apparent.

Properties of the Virus

A. Size: Poliovirus particles are 28 nm in diameter and have the properties of enteroviruses as listed above.

B. Reactions to Physical and Chemical Agents:

1. Ultraviolet light, drying—Poliomyelitis virus is inactivated by ultraviolet light and usually by drying. It may be preserved by freezing.

2. Reactions to heat—Poliovirus (as found in fecal material) is destroyed in aqueous suspension when heated at 50–55° C for 30 minutes, but in the presence of molar divalent cations (Mg^{++}) no loss of virus occurs. Milk, cream, and ice cream exert a protective effect; the virus is able to withstand temperatures about 5° C higher when suspended in these materials than when suspended in water. Adequate pasteurization of milk destroys the agent.

3. Chemicals—Urea inactivates poliovirus by degrading virions to procapsid substructures, while guanidine completely reduces capsid structures into soluble polypeptides. In the absence of extraneous organic matter, the virus may be inactivated by low concentrations of chlorine (0.1 ppm). However, much higher concentrations are required if the virus is to be destroyed in the feces of a virus carrier. Many common disinfectants are poor inactivating agents. The virus is destroyed only slowly by alcohol and not at all by ether or deoxycholate. This distinguishes it from the arboviruses.

C. Animal Susceptibility and Growth of Virus: Polioviruses have a very restricted host range. Most strains will infect only monkeys and chimpanzees. Infection is initiated most readily by direct inoculation into the brain or spinal cord. Chimpanzees and cynomolgus monkeys can also be infected by the oral route; in chimpanzees the infection thus produced is usually asymptomatic. The animals become intestinal carriers of the virus; they also develop a viremia that is quenched by the appearance of antibodies in the circulating blood. Unusual strains have been transmitted to mice or chick embryos.

Most strains can be grown in primary or continuous cell line cultures derived from a variety of human tissues or from monkey kidney, testis, or muscle.

D. Virus Replication: Poliovirus attaches to specific cell receptors. The presence of these receptors controls the susceptibility to virus infection. It has been shown recently that human chromosome 19 contains the genetic information for this site.

Poliovirus particle RNA serves both as its own messenger RNA and as the source of the genetic information. The RNA is infectious per se, and this infectivity requires an intact poly A sequence at the 3' end of the molecule. Polysomes held together by host messenger RNA break down early during infection and later are built up again, now held together by viral RNA. Viral protein is synthesized on the polysomes.

Although the viral genome is polycistronic, it behaves as a monocistronic messenger, ie, there is only one protein synthesis initiation site. The long primary protein structure is cleaved to yield structural and nonstructural polypeptides. One of the virus nonstructural proteins has been associated with viral polymerase activity. The cleavage of virus proteins and the assembly of the virus particle are concomitant processes in the production of mature virus. For a description of poliovirus replication, see Fig 27–8.

Guanidine in concentrations greater than 1 mM and 2-(alpha-hydroxybenzyl)-benzimidazole inhibit poliovirus multiplication in tissue culture. Guanidine acts by inhibiting the release of newly made viral RNA from the replicative complex.

E. Antigenic Properties: There are 3 antigenic types. Complement-fixing antigens are known for each. They may be prepared from tissue culture or infected CNS. Inactivation of the virus by formalin, heat, or ultraviolet light liberates a soluble complement-fixing antigen. This antigen is cross-reactive and fixes complement with heterotypic poliomyelitis antibodies. A type-specific precipitin reaction occurs when virus in sufficient concentration is used with immune animal or convalescent human sera. Two type-specific antigens are contained in poliovirus preparations and can be detected by precipitin and CF tests. They are the D or N (native) and C or H (heated) antigens. The D form can be converted to the C form by heating. The difference between the 2 is that the D form represents full particles containing RNA and the C form empty particles. Further, one polypeptide is lost during the conversion.

Pathogenesis & Pathology

The mouth is the portal of entry of the virus, and primary multiplication takes place at the sites of viral implantation in the oropharynx or intestines. The virus is regularly present in the throat and in the stools before the onset of illness. One week after onset there is little virus in the throat, but virus continues to be excreted in the stools for several weeks, even though high antibody levels are present in the blood.

The virus may be found in the blood of patients with abortive and nonparalytic poliomyelitis and in orally infected monkeys and chimpanzees in the preparalytic phase of the disease. Antibodies to the virus appear early in the natural disease and also early in the experimental disease after oral infection. They are usually present before paralysis is noted.

Viremia is also associated regularly with type 2 oral vaccination. Free virus is usually present between days 2 and 5 after vaccination, and virus is bound to antibody for an additional few days. Bound virus is detected by acid treatment, which inactivates the antibody and liberates active virus.

These findings have led to the view that the virus first multiplies in the tonsils, the lymph nodes of the neck, Peyer's patches, and the small intestine. The CNS may then be invaded by way of the circulating blood. In monkeys infected by the oral route, small amounts of antibody prevent the paralytic disease, whereas large amounts are necessary to prevent passage of the virus along nerve fibers. In man also, antibody in low titer in the form of gamma globulin may prevent paralysis if given before exposure to the virus.

Poliovirus can spread along axons of peripheral nerves to the CNS, and there it continues to progress along the fibers of the lower motor neurons to increasingly involve the spinal cord or the brain. This may occur in children after tonsillectomy. Poliovirus present in their oropharynges may enter nerve fibers exposed during tonsillectomy and spread to the brain. A similar mechanism of virus spread may be responsible for the rare instances of paralysis in a limb recently injected with an irritating material during a period of high poliovirus prevalence. Perhaps traces of virus are inadvertently introduced with the injection into peripheral nerve fibers. An alternative mechanism for the adverse effects of tonsillectomy has been suggested (see Immunity, p 371).

Poliovirus invades certain types of nerve cells, and in the process of its intracellular multiplication it may damage or completely destroy these cells. The anterior horn cells of the spinal cord are most prominently involved, but in severe cases the intermediate gray ganglia and even the posterior horn and dorsal root ganglia are often involved. Lesions are found as far forward as the hypothalamus and thalamus. In the brain, the reticular formation, the vestibular nuclei, the cerebellar vermis, and the deep cerebellar nuclei are most often affected. The cortex is virtually spared, with the exception of the motor cortex along the precentral gyrus.

Poliovirus does not multiply in muscle in vivo. Its chief site of action is in the neuron, and the changes which occur in peripheral nerves and voluntary muscles are secondary to the destruction of the nerve cell. Changes occur rapidly in nerve cells, from mild chromatolysis to neuronophagia and complete destruction. Cells which lose their function may recover completely. Inflammation occurs secondary to the attack on the nerve cells; the focal and perivascular infiltrations are chiefly lymphocytes with some polymorphonuclear cells, plasma cells, and microglia.

In addition to pathologic changes in the nervous system, there may be myocarditis, lymphatic hyperplasia, ulceration of Peyer's patches, prominence of follicles, and enlargement of lymph nodes.

Clinical Findings

When an individual susceptible to infection is exposed to the virus, one of the following responses may occur: (1) inapparent infection without symptoms, (2) mild illness, (3) aseptic meningitis, (4) paralytic poliomyelitis. As the disease progresses, one response may merge with a more severe form, often resulting in a biphasic course: a minor illness, followed first by a few days free of symptoms and then by the major, severe illness. Only about 1% of infections are recognized clinically.

The incubation period is usually between 7 and 14 days, but it may be as short as 3 days or as long as 35 days. The incubation period is defined as the time from exposure to onset of any symptoms.

A. Abortive Poliomyelitis: This is the commonest form of the disease. The patient has only the minor illness, characterized by fever, malaise, drowsiness, headache, nausea, vomiting, constipation, or sore throat in various combinations. The patient recovers in a few days. The diagnosis of abortive poliomyelitis cannot be made with assurance, even during an epidemic, except when the virus is isolated or antibody development is measured.

B. Nonparalytic Poliomyelitis (Aseptic Meningitis): In addition to the above symptoms and signs, the patient with the nonparalytic form presents stiffness and pain in the back and neck. The disease lasts 2–10 days, and recovery is rapid and complete. In a small percentage of cases, the disease advances to paralysis. Poliovirus is only one of many viruses which produce aseptic meningitis. In the absence of virologic diagnosis, poliovirus must be suspected if the disease occurs in persons associated with paralytic patients.

C. Paralytic Poliomyelitis: The major illness usually follows the minor illness described above, but it may occur without the antecedent first phase. The predominating complaint is flaccid paralysis resulting from lower motor neuron damage. However, incoordination secondary to brain stem invasion and painful spasms of nonparalyzed muscles may also occur. The amount of damage and destruction varies from case to case. Muscle involvement is usually maximal within a few days after the paralytic phase begins. The maximal recovery usually occurs within 6 months, but it may take longer.

Laboratory Diagnosis

A. Cerebrospinal Fluid: The CSF contains an increased number of leukocytes—usually 10–200/cu mm, seldom more than 500/cu mm. In the early stage of the disease, the ratio of polymorphonuclear cells to lymphocytes is high, but within a few days the ratio is reversed. The total cell count slowly subsides to normal levels. The protein content of the CSF is mildly elevated (average about 40–50 mg/100 ml), although high levels may occur and persist for several weeks after the cell count declines. The glucose content is normal.

B. Recovery of Virus: In vitro cultures of human or monkey tissues may be used.

In nonfatal cases, the virus may be recovered from throat swabs taken within a few days of the onset of illness and from rectal swabs or feces collected for longer periods. The chance of recovering the virus decreases as the disease runs its course. The virus has been found in about 80% of patients during the first 2 weeks of illness but in only 25% during the third 2-week period. No permanent carriers are known. Recovery of poliovirus from the CSF is uncommon, unlike that of the coxsackieviruses or echoviruses.

In fatal cases, the virus should be looked for in the cervical and lumbar enlargements of the spinal cord, in the medulla, and in the colon contents. Histologic examination of the spinal cord and parts of the brain should be made. If paralysis has lasted 4–5 days, it is difficult to recover the virus from the cord.

Material collected from patients should be frozen as soon as possible after collection and, if possible, kept stored in the frozen state during transit to the diagnostic laboratory.

In the laboratory, the specimens are treated with penicillin, streptomycin, and sometimes ether to destroy bacteria before inoculation of tissue cultures. If the specimen contains an agent which destroys the cells in the culture, it must be shown to be neutralized by specific antipoliomyelitis serum before the agent can be identified as poliovirus. Usually 3–6 days are required to isolate and type a strain of virus.

C. Serology: Paired serum specimens are required; the first sample must be taken as soon after the onset of illness as possible; the second, about 3–4 weeks later.

N and H complement-fixing antigens of poliovirus are described above. In the course of poliomyelitis infection, H antibodies form before N antibodies, and subsequently the level of H antibodies declines first. Early acute stage sera thus contain H antibodies only; 1–2 weeks later, both N and H antibodies are present; in late convalescent sera, only N antibodies are present. Only first infection with poliovirus produces strictly type-specific complement fixation responses. Subsequent infections with heterotypic polioviruses recall or induce antibodies, mostly against the heat-stable antigenic components shared by all 3 types of poliovirus, ie, against the poliovirus group antigen.

Neutralizing antibodies which can be measured quantitatively and rapidly by tissue culture methods also appear early and are usually already detectable at the time of hospitalization. However, if the first specimen is taken sufficiently early, a rise in titer can be demonstrated during the course of the disease. In addition to the homologous antibody which persists at high levels for years, if not for life, antibodies to other virus types may appear transiently and at low levels. Neutralizing antibody also occurs in the urine.

Type-specific viral precipitating antibodies develop in convalescence. By the microprecipitation test, only 50% of poliomyelitis patients show a 4-fold or greater rise in antibody titer (due to the early appearance and early decline of the precipitating antibody). Therefore, the microprecipitation test appears to be less useful than the CF and Nt tests.

Immunity

Immunity is permanent to the type causing the infection. There may be a low degree of heterotypic resistance induced by infection, especially between type 1 and type 2 polioviruses. This may account for the observation that second attacks of polio have most often involved types 1 and 3.

Passive immunity is transferred from mother to offspring. The maternal antibodies gradually disappear during the first 6 months of life. Passively administered antibody lasts only 3–5 weeks.

Virus neutralizing antibody forms within a few days after exposure to the virus, often before the onset of illness, and persists, apparently, for life. Its formation early in the disease implies that viral multiplication occurs in the body before the invasion of the nervous system. As the virus in the brain and spinal cord is not influenced by high titers of antibodies in the blood (which are found in the preparalytic stage of the disease), immunization is of value only if it precedes the onset of symptoms referable to the nervous system.

A decrease in resistance to poliovirus accompanies removal of tonsils and adenoids. Preexisting secretory antibody levels in the nasopharynx decrease sharply following operation (particularly in young male children) without any change in antibody levels in serum. Local antibody levels remain low or absent for as long as 7 months. In seronegative children, nasopharyngeal antibody response to poliovaccine develops significantly later and to lower titers in children previously tonsillectomized than in those with intact tonsils. Thus, surgery of this type may eliminate a valuable source of immunocompetent tissue of importance in resistance to poliovirus.

Treatment

Patients with paralysis when admitted to hospitals already have antibodies in their blood. An increase in antibody is not beneficial. Neither gamma globulin from normal adults nor convalescent serum was of value in controlled trials. Antibiotics obviously have no effect.

Epidemiology

Poliomyelitis occurs all over the world—throughout the year in the tropics and during the summer and fall in the temperate zones. Winter outbreaks have rarely been recorded. Epidemics have been rare in tropical and subtropical countries, but the virus in those areas is widely prevalent.

The disease occurs in all age groups, but children are usually more susceptible than adults because of the acquired immunity of the adult population. In isolated populations (Arctic Eskimos), poliomyelitis attacks all ages equally. In crowded primitive areas, where conditions favor the wide dissemination of virus, poliomyelitis continues to be a disease of infancy, with all children over 4 years of age already immune. In many areas of the temperate zones (USA, England, Denmark, Sweden, and Australia), the age incidence of poliomyelitis had shifted into the older age groups during recent decades. For example, in the USA, just before the development of poliovaccines, 25% of the patients were over 15 years old and most were between 5 and 15. This changing pattern of occurrence of poliomyelitis is now being seen in developing countries with rising levels of personal and community hygiene, particularly in tropical and semitropical areas. Forty-five of 71 tropical and semitropical countries reported an overall incidence of poliomyelitis in 1966 that was 3 times greater than the average annual incidence for the period 1951–1955. Large outbreaks of the disease have occurred in such areas where comprehensive and regular vaccination programs are not yet being carried out.

The case fatality rate is not easily determined because of the difficulties in diagnosing nonparalytic infections. In years of high prevalence, the case fatality rate may appear lower than in years of low prevalence because nonparalytic poliomyelitis may be diagnosed more readily at times of epidemic prevalence. The usual rate varies between 5 and 10% and is highest in the older age groups. In recent epidemics, in which a third of the cases occurred in patients over 15, two-thirds of the deaths were in this age group.

The only known reservoir of infection is man. Under conditions of poor hygiene and sanitation in warm areas, where almost all children become immune early in life, polioviruses maintain themselves in the human population by continuously infecting a small part of the population. In temperate zone countries which have high levels of hygiene, epidemics have been followed by periods of low spread of virus, until sufficient numbers of susceptible children have grown up to provide a mechanism for continuous cycles of transmission in the area. Epidemics are caused when the high degree of virus spread is accompanied by strains of high virulence. Warm weather favors the spread of virus by increasing human contacts, the susceptibility of the host, or the dissemination of virus by extrahuman sources. The virus is usually spread by human contact. Virus can be recovered from the pharynges and intestines of both patients and healthy carriers. The prevalence of infection among family associates is higher than among nonhousehold contacts. When the first case is recognized in a family, all susceptibles in the family are already infected, the result of rapid dissemination of virus.

During periods of epidemic prevalence, in both rural and urban areas, house flies *(Musca domestica)* and filth flies *(Phormia regina, Phaenicia sericata,* Sarcophaga species) may be found contaminated with poliomyelitis virus. The importance of flies in the transmission of the disease is not easily evaluated, although it is important to note that virus has been found in food naturally contaminated by flies. The virus is also present in urban sewage during periods when subclinical or clinical disease is prevalent. Although no epidemiologic evidence suggests that sewage is a source of infection, it may serve as a source of contamination of flies or of water supplies used for drinking or bathing, or through its use as fertilizer.

In temperate zones infection with poliovirus (and other enteroviruses) and the acquisition of antibodies is almost limited to the summer months. Regardless of geographic location, antibodies are acquired at an early age by those populations which live under primitive sanitary conditions, and particularly if crowding also exists. Even in the same city, there is a direct correlation between unfavorable socioeconomic status and the early development of antibodies. Neutralizing (but not complement-fixing) antibodies to each of the 3 antigenic types of poliomyelitis virus persist for several decades, even in the absence of reinfection.

Prevention & Control

Both live and killed virus vaccines are available. Formalinized vaccine (Salk) is prepared from virus grown in monkey kidney cultures. Because of the varying levels of potency of commercial vaccine, a series of at least 4 inoculations over a period of 1–2 years is recommended in the primary series. A booster immunization is necessary every 2–3 years to maintain immunity.

Until 1956, the epidemic pattern was one of wide and rather uniform attack rates over large areas irrespective of race or socioeconomic class. During the period just before inactivated poliovaccine became generally available in the USA (1951–1955), the average annual number of cases of paralytic poliomyelitis was approximately 21,000. After the widespread use of killed vaccine, several localized epidemics occurred with the cases concentrated in slum areas among unvaccinated preschool children. Some cases continued to occur even in the vaccinated; in a study of several thousand paralytic cases, 17% were in triply vaccinated children. In 1960, there were 2545 paralytic cases reported in the USA.

Oral vaccines containing live attenuated virus have been prepared, first in monkey kidney cell cultures and more recently in human diploid cell cultures. The vaccine can be stabilized by molar $MgCl_2$ so that it can be kept without losing potency for well over a year at 4° C and for at least a month at room temperature.

Because of the potential hazards (unknown viral contaminants) presented by the use of monkey kidney tissue for growth of vaccine virus, human diploid cell lines are now licensed for vaccine production. The most thoroughly studied human diploid cell line is WI-38; this cell line has been thoroughly tested and found free of microbial contamination, and can be held in the frozen state until needed for vaccine production. Safety testing with such a cell line can be far more complete than the tests that are possible within the relatively brief life span of a stock of primary cultures such as those from monkey kidney.

The live poliovaccine multiplies, infects, and thus immunizes. In the process, infectious progeny of the vaccine virus are disseminated in the community. Although the viruses, particularly type 3 and more recently type 2, mutate in the course of their multiplication in vaccinated children, only rare cases of paralytic poliomyelitis have occurred in recipients of oral poliovaccine (OPV) or their close contacts. To minimize the contact problem (ie, infecting a contact with reverted virus progeny of greater neurovirulence than the licensed vaccine), whole communities or at least entire households, including parents, should be given the vaccine at one time. Repeat vaccinations seem to be important to establish permanent immunity.

Another potential limiting factor on the use of the oral vaccine is that of interference. The alimentary tract of the child may be infected with another enterovirus at the time the vaccine is fed. This interferes with the establishment of infection and immunity and is an important problem in areas (particularly in tropical and subtropical regions) where enterovirus infections are common. Another problem in tropical areas relates to an inhibitory substance present in the alimentary tract of infants, apparently in the saliva, that prevents multiplication of the vaccine virus.

Trivalent oral poliovaccine has replaced the monovalent forms in the USA. The Committee on Infections of the American Academy of Pediatrics recommends that primary immunization of infants begin at 2 months of age simultaneously with the first DTP inoculation. The second and third doses should be given at 2-month intervals thereafter, and a fourth dose at 1½ years of age. A trivalent vaccine booster is recommended for all children entering elementary school. No further boosters are presently recommended. The primary immunization schedule for children and adolescents consists of 2 doses of trivalent vaccine at 8-week intervals followed by a third dose 6 months to a year later.

Routine immunization for adults residing in the continental USA is not felt to be necessary because of the small risk of exposure. However, adults who are at increased risk because of contact with a patient or who are anticipating travel to an endemic or epidemic area should be immunized. Pregnancy is neither an indication for nor a contraindication to required immunization. The precautions mentioned below should be noted in considering vaccination for persons known or suspected to have immunoglobulin disorders and for those preparing to undergo immunosuppressive therapy.

Hypogammaglobulinemic persons should receive special attention in evaluating cases that might be vaccine-associated. In the USA for the period 1961–1971, there were 73 poliomyelitis cases among vaccine recipients and 37 cases among contacts. Nearly 10% of these cases were shown to be in persons with immunoglobulin disorders, an incidence almost 10,000 times greater than in normal persons. Such cases in persons with immune deficiency have continued to be reported through 1974. It should be noted that poliomyelitis in such individuals develops in an atypical manner, with an incubation period generally longer than 28 days, a high rate of mortality after a long chronic illness, and unusual lesions in the CNS. In the hypogammaglobulinemic cases documented, reversion of the vaccine virus to increased neurovirulence had not occurred. All suspected cases of vaccine-induced poliomyelitis should be tested for immune globulin status. It has been recommended that only killed poliovaccine be given to persons with immunoglobulin disorders and that persons who are to be treated with immunosuppressive drugs but who lack poliovirus antibodies be immunized before therapy.

Following the introduction of live poliovirus vaccine, during 1961–1965, the annual number of paralytic cases in the USA decreased to 465. In subsequent years, the rates averaged about 40–50 cases per year,

decreasing to 18 cases in 1969. In 1970, however, 31 cases of paralytic poliomyelitis were reported, including 22 from an epidemic which occurred in Texas among unimmunized persons. In 1971, only 17 scattered cases of paralytic poliomyelitis from 12 states were reported. In 1974, only 4 cases were noted, the lowest number ever recorded. A recently recognized group of cases consists of those who developed poliomyelitis after travel to endemic areas outside the USA. Such "imported" cases usually occur in adults exposed on business or pleasure trips or in children, usually Mexican-American, living close to the border who make frequent trips to Mexico.

While the general trends established with the introduction of poliovaccines are overwhelmingly favorable, the continuing need for thorough and adequate vaccination programs cannot be overemphasized. Serologic surveys as well as surveys of vaccination status in the USA have revealed a downward trend since 1964 in the percentage of young children (1–4 years of age) who have antibody to all 3 poliovirus types and in the percentage who have been fully vaccinated. Whereas 87% of this age group had received a full course of vaccine in 1964, this percentage was only 67% in 1971. The problem of susceptibility is even more pronounced among preschool children who live in inner city and other areas where the environment is characterized by poverty and associated deficiencies of health care; only 40% of this population was fully vaccinated in 1971; in nonpoverty areas, only 68% received adequate immunization. By 1975, the figures for degree of vaccination in the different groups had not changed significantly since 1971. With the availability of effective vaccines and the success which has thus far been achieved, this lag in immunity is unfortunate and steps should be taken to rectify the situation.

Both killed and live virus vaccines induce antibodies and protect the CNS from subsequent invasion by wild virus. Low levels of antibody resulting from killed vaccine have little effect in preventing intestinal carriage of virus. However, the alimentary tract develops a far greater degree of resistance after live virus vaccine, which seems to be dependent on the extent of initial vaccine virus multiplication in the alimentary tract rather than on serum antibody level.

Gamma globulin can provide protection for a few weeks against the paralytic disease but does not prevent subclinical infection. The dose is about 0.14 ml/lb IM. Gamma globulin is effective only if given shortly before infection; it is of no value after clinical symptoms of the disease are apparent.

It is not possible to list rules for the prevention of poliomyelitis other than vaccination. Quarantine either of patients or of exposed family or intimate contacts is ineffective in controlling the spread of the disease. This is understandable in view of the large number of inapparent and therefore unrecognized infections that occur during an epidemic.

During epidemic periods (defined now as 2 or more local cases caused by the same type in any 4-week period), children with fever should be given bed rest. Undue exercise or fatigue should be avoided, especially if there is any suspicion of involvement of the nervous system. Elective nose and throat operations and dental extractions should be avoided. Children should not travel unnecessarily to or from epidemic areas. Food and human excrement should be protected from flies. Once the poliovirus type responsible for the epidemic is determined, type-specific monovalent oral poliovaccine should be administered to susceptible persons in the population.

Patients with poliomyelitis can be admitted to general hospitals provided appropriate isolation precautions are employed. All pharyngeal and bowel discharges are considered infectious and should be disposed of quickly and safely.

COXSACKIEVIRUSES

The coxsackieviruses comprise a large subgroup of the enteroviruses. They produce a variety of illnesses in human beings, including aseptic meningitis, herpangina, pleurodynia, hand-foot-mouth disease, myo- and pericarditis, and common colds. They may also have a role in some forms of diabetes (see Chapter 39). Coxsackieviruses have been divided into 2 groups, A and B, having different pathogenic potentials for the mouse. Coxsackie B viruses are the most commonly identified causative agents of viral heart disease in man.

Properties of the Viruses

A. Size: 28 nm in diameter. Density: 1.34 gm/ml.

B. Reactions to Physical and Chemical Agents: Common antiseptics, including ethanol (70%), Lysol (5%), and ether, fail to inactivate coxsackieviruses, and these viruses are also resistant to deoxycholate. Treatment with 0.1 N HCl or 0.3% formaldehyde, however, effects rapid inactivation.

C. Animal Susceptibility and Growth of Virus: Coxsackieviruses are highly infective for newborn mice. Certain strains (B1–6, A7,9,16) also grow in monkey kidney cell culture. Some group A strains grow in human amnion and human embryonic lung fibroblast cells. Chimpanzees and cynomolgus monkeys can be infected subclinically; virus appears in the blood and throat for short periods and is excreted in the feces for 2–5 weeks. Type A14 produces poliomyelitis-like lesions in adult mice and in monkeys, but in suckling mice this type produces only myositis. Type A7 strains produce paralysis and severe CNS lesions in monkeys.

Group A viruses produce widespread myositis in the skeletal muscles of newborn mice, resulting in flaccid paralysis without other observable lesions. Group B viruses can produce a myositis which is more focal in distribution than that produced by viruses of group A, but they also give rise to a necrotizing steatitis involving principally the maturing fetal fat lobules (interscapular pads, cervical and cephalic pads, etc). Encephalitis is found at times, the animals dying with

paralysis of the spastic type. Some B strains also produce pancreatitis, myocarditis, endocarditis, and hepatitis in both suckling and adult mice. The corticosteroids may enhance the susceptibility of older mice to infection of the pancreas. Normal adult mice tolerate infections with group B coxsackieviruses, but in mice subjected to sustained postweaning undernutrition (marasmus) the B3 virus produces severe disease, including persistence of infective virus in the heart, spleen, liver, and pancreas. Lymphoid tissues are markedly atrophic in marasmic animals. Transfer of lymphoid cells from normal mice immunized against the virus provides virus-infected marasmic mice with significant protection against the severe sequelae. Moreover, coxsackievirus B3 is rapidly inactivated in vitro by human lymphocyte preparations. These observations support the hypothesis that lymphocyte-mediated defense mechanisms may play an important role in normal recovery from primary viral infections.

D. Antigenic Properties: At least 29 different immunologic types of coxsackieviruses are now recognized; 23 are listed as group A and 6 as group B types. The existence of multiple distinct immunologic types is shown by (1) cross-neutralization tests in infant mice, (2) cross-complement fixation tests, (3) cross-protection tests in infant mice born of immunized mothers, and (4) cross-protection tests in chimpanzees (production of subclinical infection). Antigenic variants occur within each of the group B virus types and some of the group A types.

Several of the coxsackieviruses hemagglutinate the human type O erythrocytes, a method which can be used to differentiate these strains.

Pathogenesis & Pathology

Virus has been recovered from the blood in the early stages of infection in man and in chimpanzees. Virus is also found for a few days early in the infection in the throat and for longer periods—up to 5–6 weeks —in the stools. The distribution of virus is similar to that found in the other enteroviruses.

Group B coxsackieviruses may cause acute fatal encephalomyocarditis in infants. This appears to be a generalized systemic disease with virus replication and lesions in several organs, particularly in the CNS and heart muscle.

Clinical Findings

The incubation period of coxsackievirus infection ranges from 2–9 days. The clinical manifestations of infection with various coxsackieviruses are diverse and may present as distinct disease entities.

Infection with a coxsackievirus is suggested by the clinical manifestations of herpangina, pleurodynia, aseptic meningitis, summer minor illnesses of nonbacterial origin, or neonatal disease, particularly myocarditis. Virus is present in the CNS and heart muscle of fatal cases in the newborn. Coxsackieviruses may be responsible for myocardiopathies in adults more frequently than has been recognized.

A. Herpangina: This disease is caused by certain

group A viruses (2, 4, 5, 6, 8, 10) and is characterized by an abrupt onset of fever and sore throat. There may be anorexia, dysphagia, vomiting, and abdominal pain. The pharynx is usually hyperemic, and characteristic discrete vesicles occur on the anterior pillars of the fauces, the palate, uvula, tonsils, or tongue. The illness is self-limited and most frequent in small children.

B. Summer Minor Illnesses: Coxsackieviruses are often isolated from patients with acute febrile illnesses of short duration and without distinctive features, occurring during the summer or fall. Information is lacking on the frequency of oropharyngeal lesions in these patients, whose illnesses in other respects resemble herpangina.

C. Pleurodynia (Epidemic Myalgia, Bornholm Disease): This disease is caused by group B viruses. Fever and chest pain are almost invariably present together; they are usually abrupt in onset but are sometimes preceded by malaise, headache, and anorexia. The chest pain may be located on either side or substernally, is intensified by movement, and may last from 2 days to 2 weeks. Abdominal pain occurs in approximately half of cases, and in children this may be the chief complaint. The illness is self-limited and recovery is complete, although relapses are common.

D. Aseptic Meningitis and Mild Paresis: This syndrome is caused by all types of group B and by coxsackie A7 and A9. Fever, malaise, headache, nausea, and abdominal pain are common early symptoms. Signs of meningeal irritation with stiffness of the neck or back and vomiting may appear 1–2 days later. The disease sometimes progresses to mild muscle weakness which is often confused clinically with paralytic poliomyelitis. Patients almost always recover completely from nonpoliovirus paresis. Examination of the CSF early in the acute phase of the illness reveals an increase in the number of leukocytes up to 100/cu mm with 10–50% PMNs.

E. Neonatal Disease: Neonatal disease caused by group B coxsackieviruses may be common, with lethargy, feeding difficulty, and vomiting, with or without fever. In severe cases, myocarditis or pericarditis can occur within the first 8 days of life; it may be preceded by a brief episode of diarrhea and anorexia. Cardiac and respiratory embarrassment are indicated by tachycardia, dyspnea, cyanosis, and changes in the electrocardiogram. The clinical course may be rapidly fatal, or the patient may progress to complete recovery. The disease may sometimes be acquired transplacentally. Myocarditis has also been caused by some of the group A coxsackieviruses.

F. Colds: A number of the enteroviruses have been associated with common colds; among these are coxsackieviruses A10, A21, A24, and B3.

G. Hand, Foot, and Mouth Disease: This disease has been associated particularly with coxsackievirus A16, but A4, A5, A7, A9, and A10 have also been implicated. Virus may be recovered not only from the stool and pharyngeal secretions but also from vesicular fluid.

The syndrome is characterized by oral and pha-

ryngeal ulcerations and a vesicular rash which involves the palms and soles but may also spread to the arms and legs. Vesicles heal without crusting, which clinically differentiates them from the vesicular rashes associated with herpes- and poxvirus infections. This syndrome in rare instances has resulted in death, usually due to pneumonia.

H. Myocardiopathy: Coxsackievirus B infections are increasingly recognized as a cause of primary myocardial disease in adults as well as children. In some series, up to 39% of persons infected with coxsackievirus B5 developed cardiac abnormalities. Coxsackieviruses of group A and echoviruses have also been implicated, but to a lesser degree.

Evidence for a high degree of association of virus with disease has been obtained, usually at autopsy, by demonstration of virus localized in the myocardium, endocardium, and pericardial fluid; the presence of virus at the sites of pathologic change has been demonstrated by immunofluorescence, peroxidase-labeled antibody, or ferritin-labeled antibody. It has been estimated that about 5% of all symptomatic coxsackievirus infections induce heart disease. The virus may affect the endocardium, pericardium, myocardium, or all three. Acute myocardiopathies have been shown to be caused by coxsackieviruses A4, A14, B1–5, and others, and also by echovirus types 9 and 22 and others.

Monkeys infected with coxsackievirus B4 develop pancarditis, with a pathologic picture strikingly similar to that of rheumatic heart disease.

In experimental animals, the severity of acute viral myocardiopathy is greatly increased by vigorous exercise, hydrocortisone, alcohol consumption, pregnancy, and undernutrition and is greater in males than in females. In human illnesses, these factors may similarly increase the severity of the disease.

I. Diabetes Mellitus: Serologic studies suggest an association of diabetes of abrupt onset with past infection by coxsackievirus B4 and perhaps other members of the B group. Experimental studies support the findings in humans. Another enterovirus, encephalomyocarditis virus, induces in mice lesions in the pancreatic islets of Langerhans and an accompanying diabetes.

J. Swine Vesicular Disease: The agent of this disease is an enterovirus which antigenically is closely related to, but not identical with, coxsackievirus B5 (CB5). Furthermore, the swine virus can also infect man. Homology of 50% exists between the RNA of the British swine virus and the RNA of the prototype CB5 virus. The prototype virus was isolated in 1952. By 1975, human isolates of CB5 showed the same incomplete homology (50%) with the prototype RNA, indicating that the current strains have become modified with human passage. This variation is also noted in the drift in antigenicity of the new coxsackievirus strains from those isolated 2 decades ago. This degree of homology, about 50%, is also found between the 3 antigenic types of poliovirus.

Associated with the above RNA genomic changes are changes in the polypeptide composition of the new

CB5 isolates compared to the 1952 prototype virus. Similarly, such differences exist in the swine viruses of 1966–1971 and those of 1972–1973. In the same year, however, a swine virus from France and a human isolate of CB5 have shown virtually identical patterns. Further work is necessary to establish the pathologic and epidemiologic significance of these variations.

Laboratory Diagnosis

A. Recovery of Virus: Although the virus has been isolated from the blood early during infection, it can more readily be found in throat washings during the first few days of illness and in the stools during the first few weeks. In coxsackievirus A21 infections, the largest amount of virus is found in nasal secretions. In cases of aseptic meningitis, strains have been recovered from the CSF as well as from the alimentary tract. The procedures are similar to those employed for isolating poliomyelitis virus from clinical specimens. The specimen is inoculated into tissue cultures and also into suckling mice. In tissue culture, a cytopathic effect appears within 5–14 days. In suckling mice, signs of illness appear usually within 3–8 days with group A strains and 5–14 days with group B strains. The virus is identified by the pathologic lesions it produces and by immunologic means.

B. Serology: Neutralizing antibodies appear early during the course of the infection. The first sample of serum should be taken as soon as possible and the second about 2 weeks later, when the antibodies are already at their peak level. They persist for years.

After a coxsackievirus infection, patients may develop complement-fixing antibodies to a number of both group A and group B agents, but the neutralizing response appears to be specific for the infecting type of virus. Complement-fixing antibodies may disappear or drop to a low level within 6 months. It is impractical to perform serologic tests unless an isolate is obtained from the patient. During an epidemic, however, the prevalent pathogen can be used.

It is possible to detect and titrate serum antibody using the immunofluorescence technic. Infected coverslip cultures for use as a source of antigen may be prepared and kept frozen at −20° C for at least 1 year, making this test readily available for rapid diagnosis.

Immunity

Strains of virus studied by cross-protection tests in infant mice born of immunized mothers show the same type-specificity as that observed in Nt and CF tests. The immunity conferred by mother's milk also is type-specific.

In humans a passive transfer of neutralizing and complement-fixing antibodies from the mother to the offspring also occurs. Adults have antibodies against more types of coxsackieviruses than do children, which indicates that multiple experience with these viruses is common and increases with age.

Epidemiology

Viruses of the coxsackie group have been en-countered around the globe. Isolations have been made mainly from human feces, pharyngeal swabbings, sewage, and flies. That coxsackieviruses are widely distributed is also indicated by the detection of antibodies in serum collected from individuals in different parts of the world and by the capacity of gamma globulin prepared from pooled human serum to neutralize all of the coxsackieviruses identified and tested.

Coxsackieviruses are recovered much more frequently during the summer and early fall. Also, children develop neutralizing and complement-fixing antibodies during the summer, indicating infection by these agents during this period. Such children have much higher incidence rates for acute, febrile minor illnesses during the summer than children who fail to develop coxsackievirus antibodies.

Familial or household exposure is important in the acquisition of infections with coxsackieviruses. Once the virus is introduced into a household, all susceptible persons usually become infected, although all do not develop clinically apparent disease.

In herpangina, only about 30% of infected persons within households develop faucial lesions. Others may present a mild febrile illness without throat lesions. Virus has been found most often in patients with herpangina (85%); next most often in their neighborhood (65%) and family contacts (40%); and least often in all persons in the community (4%).

The coxsackieviruses share many properties with the echo- and polioviruses. Because of their epidemiologic similarities, enteroviruses may occur together in nature, even in the same human host or the same specimens of sewage or flies.

ECHOVIRUSES

The echoviruses (enteric *c*ytopathogenic *h*uman *o*rphan viruses) are grouped together because they infect the human enteric tract and because they can be recovered from man only by inoculation of certain tissue cultures. Over 30 serotypes are known, but not all are known to cause human illness. Aseptic meningitis, febrile illnesses with or without rash, and common colds are among the diseases caused by echoviruses.

Properties of the Viruses

A. Size: About 24–30 nm in diameter. The complement-fixing antigen (which may be part of the total virus particle) has a diameter of about 10 nm. The general properties of these viruses are similar to those of the other enteroviruses: RNA core, ether-resistant, stabilized by magnesium ions. Density: 1.34 gm/ml.

B. Growth of Virus: Monkey kidney cell culture is the method of choice for the isolation of these agents. Some also multiply in human amnion cells and cell lines such as HeLa.

Certain echoviruses agglutinate human group O

erythrocytes. The hemagglutinins are associated with the infectious virus particle. The virus and hemagglutinin may be eluted, and in the process the red cells become exhausted. The hemagglutinin is not affected by neuraminidase.

Initially, echoviruses were distinguished from coxsackieviruses by their failure to produce pathologic changes in newborn mice, but echovirus-9 can produce paralysis in newborn mice. Conversely, strains of some coxsackievirus types (especially A9) lack mouse pathogenicity and thus resemble echoviruses. This variability in biologic properties is the chief reason why new enteroviruses are no longer being subclassified as echo- or coxsackieviruses.

C. Antigenic Properties: Thirty-one different antigenic types have been identified. The different types may be separated on the basis of cross-neutralization or cross-complement fixation testing. Variants or "prime" strains exist in which the prime strain is neutralized to very low titer or not at all by the existing prototype antiserum, whereas an antiserum against the prime strain neutralizes the prototype virus as well as homologous virus.

Neutralizing antibodies are determined by measuring the dilution of serum capable of preventing the cytopathogenic effect of the virus or by plaque reduction tests. Complement-fixing antigens may be prepared from infected tissue culture fluids. Neutralizing antibodies persist much longer after infection and to higher titer than complement-fixing antibodies.

D. Animal Susceptibility: In order to be included in the echo group, prototype strains must not produce disease in suckling mice, in rabbits, or in monkeys. However, different strains can produce variants which exhibit animal pathogenicity. A number of the echoviruses have produced inapparent infections in monkeys, with mild lesions in the CNS. In the chimpanzee, no apparent illness is produced, but infection can be demonstrated by the presence and persistence of virus in the throat and in the feces and by the type-specific antibody responses.

Pathogenesis & Pathology

The pathogenesis of the alimentary infection is similar to that of the other enteroviruses. Virus may be recovered from the throat and stools; in a number of types (4, 5, 6, 9, 14, and 18) which have been associated with aseptic meningitis, the virus has been recovered from the CSF.

Clinical Findings

In order to establish etiologic association of echovirus with disease, the following criteria are used: (1) There is a much higher rate of recovery of virus from patients with the disease than from healthy individuals of the same age and socioeconomic level living in the same area at the same time. (2) Antibodies against the virus develop during the course of the disease. If the clinical syndrome can be caused by other known agents, then virologic or serologic evidence must be negative for concurrent infection with such agents. (3)

The virus is isolated in significant concentration from body fluids or tissues manifesting lesions, eg, from the CSF in cases of aseptic meningitis.

Echoviruses 4, 6, 9, 11, 14, 16, and 30 have been repeatedly associated with aseptic meningitis. Other types (including 2, 3, and 5) have been associated with aseptic meningitis only in sporadic cases. With echo-6, muscle weakness and mild paralysis have been observed. However, recovery was usually complete. A rash appears to be a common manifestation of infection with type 9 (and, less frequently, with type 4). The incidence of rash, high in young children, decreases with age. Conjunctivitis may also be present. Type 9 may occur in spinal fluid even in the absence of pleocytosis. Muscle weakness and spasm may occur and may persist for weeks. The virus has been recovered in high titer from the medulla of a fatal case.

Echo-16 can produce aseptic meningitis and also "Boston exanthem disease." Type 20 has been associated with a febrile disease involving both the respiratory and enteric tracts. Echo-28, associated with upper respiratory illness, has produced colds in volunteers and has been reclassified as rhinovirus type 1. Type 18 can produce aseptic meningitis and rash and has been associated with infantile diarrhea. Other echoviruses have also been associated with infant diarrhea. Echo-4 has been associated with vaginitis and cervicitis. For many of the echoviruses, as for many of the coxsackieviruses, no disease entities are yet known.

Laboratory Diagnosis

It is impossible in an individual case to diagnose an echovirus infection on clinical grounds. However, in the following epidemic situations, echoviruses must be considered: (1) summer outbreaks of aseptic meningitis; (2) summer epidemics, especially in young children, of a febrile illness with rash; and (3) outbreaks of diarrheal disease in young infants from whom no pathogenic enterobacteria can be recovered.

The diagnosis is dependent upon laboratory tests. The procedure of choice is isolation of virus from throat swabs, stools, rectal swabs, and, in aseptic meningitis, CSF. Echoviruses 9 and 16 have been recovered from the blood when specimens were collected very early in the disease. Serologic tests by themselves are impractical because without some clue as to the predominating virus too many enterovirus tests would be necessary. As with other enteroviruses, neutralizing and hemagglutination-inhibiting antibodies are type-specific, but heterotypic responses are common with the CF test. Nt and HI antibodies may persist for years.

If an agent is isolated in tissue culture, it is tested against different pools of antisera against enteroviruses. Determination of the type of virus present depends upon neutralization by a single serum. Infection with 2 or more enteroviruses may occur simultaneously.

Epidemiology

The epidemiology of echoviruses is similar to that of other enteroviruses. They occur in all parts of the globe. Unlike the enterobacteria, which are constantly present in the intestinal tract, the enteroviruses produce only transitory infections. They are more apt to be found in the young than in the old. In the temperate zone, infections occur chiefly in summer and autumn and are about 5 times more prevalent in children of lower income families than in those living in more favorable circumstances.

Studies of families into which enteroviruses were introduced demonstrate the ease with which these agents spread and the high frequency of infection in persons who had formed no antibodies from earlier exposures. This is true for all enteroviruses.

Wide dissemination is the rule. During a period when 149 inhabitants of a city of 740,000 were hospitalized with echo-9 disease, approximately 6%, or 45,000 persons, had a compatible illness.

Control

Avoidance of contact with patients exhibiting acute febrile illness, especially those with a rash, is advisable for very young children. Members of institutional staffs responsible for caring for infants should be tested to determine whether they are carriers of enteroviruses. This is particularly important during outbreaks of diarrheal disease among infants.

New Enterovirus Types

There are 4 new enteroviruses, types 68–71, all of which grow in monkey kidney cell cultures. Three of these are known to cause human disease (68, 70, and 71). Enteroviruses 70 and 71 were isolated in human cell cultures and subsequently adapted to monkey kidney cultures.

Enterovirus 68 was isolated from the oropharynges of children with pneumonia and bronchiolitis.

Enterovirus 70 was cultured from the conjunctivas of patients with acute hemorrhagic conjunctivitis (AHC) during epidemics in 1971 in Japan, Singapore, and Morocco. These epidemics were components of a pandemic involving tens of millions of people in Africa, Southeast Asia, Japan, India, and England during 1969–1971. The disease is most frequent in adults. Onset is sudden. AHC is an eye infection characterized by subconjunctival hemorrhage ranging from discrete petechiae to large blotches of frank hemorrhage covering the bulbar conjunctiva. Corneal involvement, in the form of epithelial keratitis, may occur but is transient. Rarely, acute lumbar radiculomyelopathy has been reported. The incubation period is about 24 hours and recovery is complete within less than 10 days. The infectious agent is highly contagious and spreads rapidly under unhygienic and crowded conditions.

Enterovirus 71, first recovered from the brain of a fatal encephalitis case, has been isolated from other sporadic cases of meningitis and encephalitis.

RHINOVIRUS GROUP

The rhinoviruses are isolated from the nose and throat, but very rarely from the feces. These viruses, as well as certain enteroviruses, influenza, parainfluenza, RS (respiratory syncytial), adenoviruses, coronaviruses, and reoviruses, cause common colds.

Properties of the Virus

A. Nucleic Acid: RNA, with a molecular weight of about 2.6×10^6, similar to that of the enteroviruses.

Size of virion: 20–30 nm in diameter.

B. Density: Rhinoviruses banded by gradient centrifugation in CsCl have a density of 1.40 gm/ml compared to enteroviruses, which have a density of 1.32–1.34. Complement-fixing activity is noted in 2 distinct bands. One peak of activity is associated with the virion at a density of 1.40 and is type-specific. The other peak, with a density of 1.30, is group-specific and may represent empty virions. This is analogous to the D and C (or N and H) antigens of poliovirus.

C. Reactions to Physical and Chemical Agents: All strains thus far studied are labile at pH 3.0–5.0 but are ether-stable. Acid lability of infectivity distinguishes rhinoviruses from other human picornaviruses. They may be stored for short periods at 4° C and indefinitely at −70° C.

D. Animal Susceptibility and Growth of Virus: These viruses have a limited host range which has made it necessary to perform all animal experiments in man or in chimpanzees. They have been propagated in cultures of human embryonic lung fibroblasts (WI-38) and in organ cultures of ferret and human tracheal epithelium. They are grown best at 33° C under slightly acidic conditions in rolled cultures. Certain of these viruses (M strains) can be isolated in, or adapted to, monkey kidney cells, while others grow readily only in cultures of human origin (H strains). However, some viruses grown only in human cell cultures have been shown by Nt test to be M strain viruses.

E. Antigenic Properties: Over 100 serotypes are known. Some cross-reactions exist (eg, types 9 and 32).

Pathogenesis & Pathology

The virus enters via the upper respiratory tract. High titers of virus in nasal secretions—which can be found as early as 2–4 days after exposure—are associated with maximal illness. Thereafter, viral titers fall, although illness persists.

Histopathologic changes are limited to the submucosa and surface epithelium. These include engorgement of blood vessels, edema, mild cellular infiltration, and desquamation of surface epithelium which is complete by the third day. Nasal secretion increases in quantity and in protein concentration.

Experiments under controlled conditions have shown that chilling, including the wearing of wet clothes, does not produce a cold nor increase susceptibility to the virus. Chilliness is an early symptom of the common cold.

Clinical Findings

The incubation period is brief, from 2–4 days, and the acute illness usually lasts for 7 days although a nonproductive cough may persist for 2–3 weeks. The average adult has 1–2 attacks each year. Usual symptoms in adults include irritation in the upper respiratory tract, nasal discharge, headache, mild cough, malaise, and a chilly sensation. There is little or no fever. There are redness and swelling of the nasal and nasopharyngeal mucosa, and the sense of smell becomes less keen. Mild hoarseness may be present. Prominent cervical adenopathy does not occur. Secondary bacterial infection may produce acute otitis media, sinusitis, bronchitis, or pneumonitis, especially in children. Type-specific antibodies appear or rise with each infection.

Immunity

Natural immunity may exist, but may be brief. Only 30–50% of volunteers can be infected with infectious material; yet the "resistant" volunteers may catch colds of the same serotype at other times. Furthermore, people in isolated areas have more severe colds and a higher incidence of infection when a cold is introduced than people in areas regularly exposed to the virus. It has also been observed that older adults experience fewer colds than young adults and children. One 3-year study of acute respiratory tract illness in college and medical students showed that the same serotype was never isolated from separate illnesses in any student who had 2 or more illnesses.

Recent work with human volunteers has shown that resistance to the common cold is independent of measurable serum antibody but perhaps is related to specific antibody in the nasal secretions. These secretory antibodies are primarily 11S IgA immunoglobulins. Secretory antibody appears to be produced locally in the mucosal lining and is not a transudate from the serum. These 11S IgA antibodies do not persist as long as those in serum, and this could explain the paradox of reinfection in a person with adequate serum antibodies. Results regarding the role of interferon in recovery are inconclusive to date.

Volunteers infected with one rhinovirus serotype resist challenge with both homologous and heterologous virus for 2–16 weeks after initial infection. Resistance to homologous challenge is complete during this period, while resistance to heterologous challenge is incomplete. This nonspecific resistance may be a factor in the control of naturally occurring colds.

Epidemiology

The disease occurs throughout the world. In the temperate zones, the attack rates are highest in early fall and winter, declining in the late spring. Members of isolated communities form highly susceptible groups.

The virus is believed to be transmitted through close contact, by large droplets. Under some circumstances, transmission of the virus by self-inoculation through hand contamination may be a more important mode of spread than that of airborne particles.

Colds in children spread more easily to others than do colds in adults. Adults in households with a child in school have twice as many colds.

In a single community, many rhinovirus serotypes cause outbreaks of disease in a single season, and different serotypes predominate during different respiratory disease seasons.

Treatment & Control

No specific treatment is available. The development of a potent rhinovirus vaccine is unlikely because of the difficulty in growing rhinoviruses to high titer in culture, the fleeting immunity, and the many serotypes causing colds. In addition, many rhinovirus serotypes are present during single respiratory disease outbreaks and may recur only rarely in the same area. Injection of purified vaccines has shown that the high levels of serum antibody are frequently not associated with similar elevation of local secretory antibody, which may be the most significant factor in disease prevention.

FOOT-AND-MOUTH DISEASE
(Rhinovirus of Cattle)

This highly infectious disease of cattle, sheep, pigs, and goats is rare in the USA but endemic in Mexico and Canada. It may be transmitted to man by contact or ingestion. In man the disease is characterized by fever, salivation, and vesiculation of the mucous membranes of the oropharynx and of the skin of the palms, soles, fingers, and toes.

The disease in animals is highly contagious in the early stages of infection when viremia is present and when vesicles in the mouth and on the feet rupture and liberate large amounts of virus. Excreted material remains infectious for long periods. The mortality rate in animals is usually low but occasionally, with strains of high virulence, reaches 70%. Infected animals become poor producers of milk and meat. Many cattle serve as foci for infections up to 8 months.

The infective particle contains RNA and has a diameter of 23 ± 2 nm; a noninfective 12S particle which is associated with it has a diameter of 7–8 nm. Both particles can function as complement-fixing antigens. The virus is acid-labile (at pH 3.0) and has a density of 1.43 gm/ml. The virus survives freezing and is not affected by drying at ordinary temperatures.

Immunity is adequate but of short duration. Passive antibody is transferred in the colostrum. At least 7 antigenic types are known with at least 53 subtypes.

A variety of animals are susceptible to infection. The typical disease can be reproduced by inoculating the virus into the pads of the foot. The reaction in infant mice inoculated with the virus of foot-and-mouth disease is similar to their reaction to inoculation with coxsackieviruses: paralysis results as a consequence of myositis. The virus grows readily in tissue culture of cattle tongue or hamster BHK-21 cells. Formalin-treated vaccines have been prepared from virus grown in such tissue cultures. However, such vaccines do not produce a long-lasting immunity, and frequent booster inoculations are necessary. Vaccines inactivated with acetylethyleneimine and containing an oil adjuvant may be more efficient. Attenuated virus vaccines have been used with reported success.

The methods of control of the disease are dictated by its high degree of contagiousness and the resistance of the virus to inactivation. When foci of infection occur in the USA, all exposed animals are slaughtered and their carcasses destroyed. Strict quarantine is established, and the area is not presumed to be safe until susceptible animals fail to develop symptoms within 30 days. Another method is to quarantine the herd and vaccinate all unaffected animals. Other countries have successfully employed systematic vaccination schedules. Some nations (eg, USA and Australia) forbid the importation of potentially infective materials such as fresh meat, and the disease has been eliminated in these areas. Even so, migrating birds may play a role in carrying the virus from one country to another, as from France and Holland to England.

•   •   •

General References

Boucher DW, Notkins AL: Virus-induced diabetes mellitus. 1. Hyperglycemia and hypoinsulinemia in mice infected with encephalomyocarditis virus. J Exp Med 137:1226, 1973.

Craighead JE: The role of viruses in the pathogenesis of pancreatic disease and diabetes mellitus. Prog Med Virol 19:161, 1975.

Hamory BH & others: Human responses to two decavalent rhinovirus vaccines. J Infect Dis 132:623, 1975.

Hamre D: Rhinoviruses. Monogr Virol, vol 1, 1968.

Harris TJR, Brown F: Correlation of polypeptide composition with antigenic variation in the swine vesicular disease and coxsackie B$_5$ viruses. Nature 258:758, 1975.

Hierholzer JC, Hilliard KA, Esposito JJ: Serosurvey for "acute hemorrhagic conjunctivitis" virus (enterovirus 70) antibodies in the southeastern United States, with review of the literature and some epidemiologic implications. Am J Epidemiol 102:533, 1975.

Lerner AM, Wilson FM: Virus myocardiopathy. Prog Med Virol 15:63, 1973.

Lundquist RE, Ehrenfeld E, Maizel JV Jr: Isolation of a viral polypeptide associated with poliovirus RNA polymerase. Proc Natl Acad Sci USA 71:4773, 1974.

Melnick JL, Wenner HA: Enteroviruses. Pages 529–602 in: *Diagnostic Procedures for Viral and Rickettsial Infections,* 4th ed. American Public Health Association, 1969.

Melnick JL & others: Picornaviridae. Intervirology 4:303, 1974.

Miller DA & others: Human chromosome 19 carries a poliovirus receptor gene. Cell 1:167, 1974.

Mirkovic RR & others: Enterovirus type 70: The etiologic agent of pandemic acute hemorrhagic conjunctivitis. Bull WHO 49:341, 1973.

Ogra PL, Karzon DT: Formation and function of poliovirus antibody in different tissues. Prog Med Virol 13:156, 1971.

Rossen RD, Kasel JA, Couch RB: The secretory immune system: Its relation to respiratory viral infection. Prog Med Virol 13:194, 1971.

Schmidt NJ, Magoffin RL, Lennette EH: Association of group B coxsackieviruses with cases of pericarditis, myocarditis, or pleurodynia by demonstration of immunoglobulin M antibody. Infect Immun 8:341, 1973.

Spector DM, Baltimore D: The molecular biology of poliovirus. Sci Am 232:25, May 1975.

Taber LH & others: Rapid diagnosis of enterovirus meningitis by immunofluorescent staining of CSF leukocytes. Intervirology 1:127, 1973.

Wyatt HV: Poliomyelitis in hypogammaglobulinemics. J Infect Dis 128:802, 1973.

32...
Hepatitis Viruses

Acute viral hepatitis remains a major worldwide public health problem. Epidemiologic and laboratory investigations indicate that at least 2 specific viruses are involved in this disease. These agents have been designated (1) viral hepatitis type A—infectious hepatitis (IH), short incubation hepatitis (MS-1), or epidemic jaundice—and (2) viral hepatitis type B—serum hepatitis (SH), long incubation hepatitis (MS-2), or homologous serum jaundice. Both agents produce acute inflammation of the liver, resulting in a clinical illness characterized by fever, gastrointestinal symptoms such as nausea and vomiting, and jaundice. Identical histopathologic lesions are observed in the liver.

Recently, a previously unrecognized form of transfusion-associated hepatitis has been observed that is neither type A nor type B, nor is it related to other viruses occasionally implicated in hepatitis, eg, cytomegaloviruses, Epstein-Barr virus. The clinical features are similar to those of type B hepatitis.

The earlier epidemiologic separation of type A and type B hepatitis into "infectious hepatitis" and "serum hepatitis" based on their patterns of transmission has been challenged. Hepatitis A virus (HAV), transmitted primarily by the fecal-oral route, may be transmitted occasionally by the parenteral route. Correspondingly, the virus for type B hepatitis (HBV) produces sporadic infections principally after parenteral inoculation of virus-infected blood or blood products, although recent studies have demonstrated that transmission by a nonpercutaneous route can occur.

Appreciation of the existence of these lesser known modes of transmission is important when attempting to correlate presently established clinical classifications of viral hepatitis with the presence or absence of hepatitis B-associated antigen. This antigen was originally detected in 1963 in the serum of an apparently healthy Australian aborigine by reacting the serum in immunodiffusion tests with serum from a multiply transfused hemophiliac, but its association with viral hepatitis was not recognized until 1967. This was a major breakthrough in hepatitis research, and the relationship of HBAg to viral hepatitis type B is now well established.

The incidence of this unique antigen in acute hepatitis associated with transfusions or drug abuse has been reported to be 50–75%. In chronic active hepatitis, the prevalence rate has varied but is around 30%

in most series. It is uncommon in alcoholic cirrhosis. A high prevalence of the hepatitis B-associated antigen has been observed in cases of primary liver cancer in some areas of the world, although an etiologic relationship to hepatoma has yet to be established. The antigen is not present in sera from well-documented cases of common-source epidemics of viral hepatitis A or in sera from volunteers who have received the MS-1 strain of type A hepatitis.

The Committee on Viral Hepatitis, National Academy of Sciences, has recommended a standard nomenclature for the hepatitis viruses, antigens, and antibodies:

HAV	Hepatitis A virus
HBV	Hepatitis B virus
HB_sAg	Hepatitis B antigen, which exists as a separate small 22 nm particle and which is also present on the surface of the large 42 nm Dane particle (see below).
HB_cAg	Hepatitis B core antigen present within the Dane particle
Anti-HB_s	Antibody to HB_sAg. This replaces the previously used term HBAb.
Anti-HB_c	Antibody to HB_cAg

Various designations that have been used previously for HB_sAg include (1) Australia or Au antigen; (2) serum hepatitis or SH antigen; (3) Au/SH antigen; (4) hepatitis antigen or HA; and (5) hepatitis-associated antigen or HAA. The new terminology is more appropriate, since "Australia" implies an unusual association with that country, HA and HAA are nonspecific with respect to the type of hepatitis, and SH indicates only a parenteral mode of spread.

General Properties of the Viruses

A. Hepatitis Type A: Purified hepatitis A virus has a buoyant density in CsCl of 1.32–1.35 gm/ml, with a minor peak banding around 1.4 gm/ml. The virus is stable to heat (60° C for 1 hour), ether, and acid but is inactivated by heating at 100° C for 5 minutes, by ultraviolet light (1 minute at 1.1 watts), and by 1:4000 formalin (3 days at 37° C). It withstands freezing for periods of many years. The resistance of viral hepatitis A to disinfection procedures emphasizes the need for extra precautions in dealing with hepatitis patients and their products.

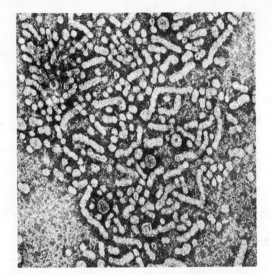

Figure 32–1. Unfractionated HB$_S$Ag-positive human plasma diluted 1:10. Filaments, 22 nm spherical particles, and Dane particles are shown (77,000 ✕).

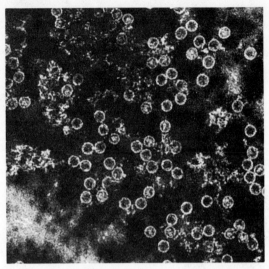

Figure 32–2. HB$_C$Ag purified from infected liver nuclei (122,400 ✕). The diameter of the core particles is 26 nm. (Fields, Dreesman, and Cabral.)

The virus most closely resembles the enteroviruses. Electron microscopic examination of infected marmoset liver reveals intracytoplasmic localization of virus particles. The nucleic acid type has not been conclusively determined.

Hepatitis A virus initially was identified in stool and liver preparations by employing immune electron microscopy as the detection system (Fig 29–3). The addition of specific hepatitis A antisera from convalescent patients to fecal specimens obtained from patients early in the incubation period of their illness prior to the onset of jaundice permitted concentration and visibility of virus particles by the formation of antigen-antibody aggregates. The virus particle is small (approximately 27 nm in diameter), does not appear to be enveloped, and exhibits cubic symmetry. Recently, more sensitive serologic assays such as the microtiter solid-phase immunoradiometric assay and immune adherence have made it possible to detect hepatitis A antigen in stools, liver homogenates, and bile and to measure specific antibody in serum.

B. Hepatitis Type B: HB$_S$Ag is closely associated with hepatitis B infections. Electron microscopy of HB$_S$Ag-reactive serum has revealed 3 morphologic forms (Fig 32–1). The most numerous are spherical particles measuring 22 nm in diameter (Fig 27–24). These small particles appear to be made up exclusively of HB$_S$Ag—as do tubular or filamentous forms, which have the same diameter but may be over 200 nm long. Larger, 42 nm spherical particles, often referred to as Dane particles, are less frequently observed. These particles are more complex. The outer surface or envelope contains HB$_S$Ag and surrounds a 27 nm inner core which contains HB$_C$Ag (Figs 32–2 and 32–3). Overproduction of the surface component apparently results in the 22 nm particles. DNA polymerase activi-

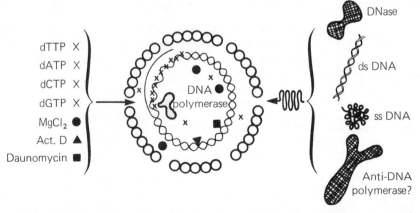

Figure 32–3. A model of the core antigen derived from Dane particles containing DNA polymerase and double-stranded DNA. (From Robinson. Reproduced from *Developments in Biological Standardization*, vol 30, 1974. © S. Karger AG, Basel.)

ty and an endogenous DNA template were found to be associated with the inner core of the Dane particle. The DNA template has been shown to consist of double-stranded DNA with a molecular weight of approximately 1.6×10^6. These observations suggest that the Dane particle is the virus of hepatitis B.

The density of the 22 nm spherical particles is between 1.2 and 1.22 gm/ml in CsCl and between 1.16 and 1.18 gm/ml in sucrose. The Dane particles have a density of 1.24 gm/ml in CsCl, while the inner core particles band lower in the gradient at a density between 1.31 and 1.34 gm/ml.

The stability of HB_SAg does not always coincide with that of the infectious agent. However, both are stable at $-20°$ C for more than 20 years, to repeated freezing and thawing, and to plasma fractionation procedures. For example, Cohn ethanol fractionation of HB_SAg-positive serum concentrates HB_SAg in subfraction III (thrombin), with reduced concentrations found in fraction I (fibrinogen, factor VIII). Low amounts or none are detected in fraction V (albumin), whereas no detectable HB_SAg is ever found in fraction II (normal immunoglobulin). Heat inactivation of albumin (60° C, 10 hours) apparently modifies or inactivates HBV since infectivity has not been associated with the administration of HB_SAg-containing lots. However, immunogenicity is retained. The stability of HBV where noted in the above fractions has resulted in numerous warnings against the indiscriminate use of blood products in therapy.

The virus is stable at 37° C for 60 minutes but not at temperatures above 60° C. At 100° C for 10 minutes, HBV infectivity is lost but HB_S antigenicity is retained. Similarly, HB_SAg is stable at pH 2.4 for up to 6 hours, but HBV infectivity is lost. Sodium hypochlorite, 0.5% (eg, 1:10 Clorox), destroys antigenicity within 3 minutes at low protein concentrations, but undiluted serum specimens require higher concentrations (5%). HB_SAg is not destroyed by ultraviolet irradiation of plasma or other blood products, and viral infectivity may also resist such treatment.

HBV regularly produces a subclinical infection in chimpanzees. Rhesus monkeys may also be infected, but the results have been erratic.

Pathology

Microscopically, there is spotty parenchymal cell degeneration with necrosis of hepatocytes, particularly in the central lobular area, a diffuse lobular inflammatory reaction, and disruption of liver cell cords. These parenchymal changes are accompanied by reticuloendothelial (Kupffer) cell hyperplasia, periportal infiltration by mononuclear cells, and cell degeneration. Localized areas of necrosis with ballooning or acidophilic bodies are frequently observed. Later in the course of the disease, there is an accumulation of macrophages containing lipofuscin near degenerating hepatocytes. Disruption of bile canaliculi or blockage of biliary excretion may occur following liver cell enlargement or necrosis. Preservation of the reticulum framework allows hepatocyte regeneration so that the highly ordered architecture of the liver lobule can be ultimately regained. The damaged hepatic tissue is usually restored in 8–12 weeks.

In 5–15% of patients, the initial lesion consists of submassive necrosis with impaired regeneration leading to bridging collapse. The occurrence of this lesion in patients over age 40 frequently presages a precarious clinical course leading to fibrosis, cirrhosis, and death.

Persistent (unresolved) viral hepatitis, a mild benign disease which may follow acute hepatitis B in 10–12% of adult patients, is characterized by sporadically abnormal transaminase values and hepatomegaly. Histologically, the lobular architecture is preserved with portal inflammation, swollen and pale hepatocytes (cobblestone arrangement), and slight to absent fibrosis. This lesion is frequently observed in asymptomatic carriers, does not progress toward cirrhosis, and has a favorable prognosis.

Chronic active (aggressive) hepatitis features a spectrum of histologic changes from inflammation and necrosis to collapse of the normal reticulum framework with bridging between the portal triads or central veins. HB_SAg is observed in 10–50% of these patients. The prognosis is guarded, with progression to macronodular cirrhosis frequently occurring.

Occasionally, during acute viral hepatitis, more extensive damage may occur which prevents orderly liver cell regeneration. Such fulminant or massive hepatocellular necrosis is seen in 1–3% of jaundiced patients with hepatitis B but is rare in hepatitis A ($<$ 0.1%).

In hepatitis B patients, electron microscopic studies have revealed 27 nm particles in liver cell nuclei which are morphologically similar to the inner core of the Dane particles. Correspondingly, immunofluorescence studies indicate that during HBV infection HB_CAg is found primarily in the nucleus, whereas HB_SAg is localized in the cytoplasm. HB_SAg and HB_CAg are rarely found in the same cell, and there appears to be an inverse relationship between the severity of the lesion and the abundance of HB_SAg. Hepatocytes with a ground-glass appearance are laden with cytoplasmic HB_SAg and are often found in biopsy specimens from patients with persistent viral hepatitis. Nuclear HB_CAg predominates in patients whose immune system is compromised. Histochemical technics utilizing orcein, aldehyde-fuchsin, or peroxidase-antiperoxidase on paraffin-embedded tissue now can detect HB_SAg in hepatocytes with the same level of sensitivity and specificity as that observed with frozen tissue.

Clinical Findings (Table 32–1)

In individual cases it is not possible to make a reliable clinical distinction between hepatitis A and hepatitis B or the more recently described non-A, non-B transfusion-associated hepatitis agent (hepatitis C virus). Other viral diseases which may present as hepatitis are infectious mononucleosis, yellow fever, cytomegalovirus infection, herpes simplex, rubella, and some enterovirus infections. Hepatitis may occasion-

Table 32—1. Epidemiologic and clinical features of human hepatitis virus infections.

	Viral Hepatitis Type A	Viral Hepatitis Type B
Incubation period	15—45 days (avg, 25—30)	50—180 days (avg, 60—90)
Principal age distribution	15—29 years*	15—29 years†
Seasonal incidence	Throughout the year but tends to peak in autumn	Throughout the year
Route of infection	Predominantly fecal-oral	Predominantly parenteral
Occurrence of virus/antigen		
Blood	2 weeks before to ≤ 1 week after jaundice	Months to years
Stool	2 weeks before to 2 weeks after jaundice	Infrequently present
Urine, semen	?	Infrequently present
Saliva	?	Frequently present
Clinical and laboratory features		
Fever > 38° C (100.4° F)	Common	Less common
Duration of transaminase elevation	1—3 weeks	1—6+ months
Immunoglobulins (IgM levels)	Elevated	Usually normal
HB$_S$Ag (Au antigen)	Not present	Present
Immunity		
Homologous	Yes	Yes
Heterologous	No	No
Duration	Probably lifetime	Probably lifetime
Gamma globulin prophylaxis	Regularly prevents jaundice	Prevents jaundice only if gamma globulin is of sufficient potency against hepatitis B virus

*Nonicteric hepatitis A is common in children.
†Primarily drug-related; transfusion-associated cases are primarily age 30 or older.

ally occur as a complication of leptospirosis, syphilis, tuberculosis, toxoplasmosis, and amebiasis, all of which are susceptible to specific drug therapy. Other important differential diagnoses include biliary obstruction, primary biliary cirrhosis, Wilson's disease, drug toxicity, and drug hypersensitivity reactions.

In viral hepatitis, the onset of jaundice is often preceded by gastrointestinal symptoms such as nausea, vomiting, severe anorexia, and fever which may mimic influenza. Jaundice may appear within a few days of the prodromal period, but anicteric hepatitis is more common.

Extrahepatic manifestations of viral hepatitis (primarily type B) include (1) a transient serum sickness-like prodrome consisting of urticaria, rash, and non-migratory polyarthralgia or arthritis occurring 1—6 weeks prior to the onset of hepatitis in 15—20% of patients; (2) polyarteritis nodosa; and (3) glomerulonephritis. Circulating immune complexes have been suggested as the cause of these syndromes.

Complete recovery occurs in most hepatitis A cases and in over 85% of the type B hepatitis cases. Hepatitis A is more severe in adults than in children, in whom it often goes unnoticed. Approximately 3% of patients with acute icteric type B hepatitis ultimately develop chronic active hepatitis. Case fatality rates appear to vary with age and may reflect underlying conditions rather than any increased pathogenicity of the specific etiologic agent. For the epidemiologic years 1973—1974, the case fatality rate for hepatitis B among persons age 29 years or younger was 0.5—0.6%; for the age group 30 years and over, it was 2%. The rates are highest for transfusion-associated cases (2.7%). Fulminant hepatitis is lethal in 75—80% of

cases and is highly correlated with age. Twenty to thirty percent of survivors develop chronic active hepatitis.

The potential courses of acute viral hepatitis have been discussed in the section on pathology. Uncomplicated viral hepatitis rarely continues for more than 10 weeks without improvement. Relapses occur in 5—20% of cases and are manifested by abnormalities in liver function with or without the recurrence of clinical symptoms. A posthepatitis syndrome may occur, especially in postmenopausal women. It is characterized by repeated episodes of anorexia, irritability, lethargy, weakness, headaches, and right upper quadrant pain. This syndrome is due to interference with normal estrogen metabolism in the liver and can be successfully treated with estrogens and progesterone in women.

As shown in Table 32—1, virus persists in the blood and stools of patients with viral hepatitis A for variable times. Transmissibility appears to be minimal 2 weeks after jaundice. HB$_S$Ag (and presumably the virus) may persist in the blood of a healthy person for years after infection and such blood consequently represents a continual potential source of infection. HB$_S$Ag has been detected in nasopharyngeal washings (saliva), semen, feces, and urine of some patients with hepatitis B.

Laboratory Features

Liver biopsy permits a tissue diagnosis of hepatitis. Tests for abnormal liver function, such as serum alanine aminotransferase (SGPT) and bilirubin, supplement the clinical, pathologic, and epidemiologic findings. Transaminase values in acute hepatitis range between 500 and 2000 units and are almost never below 100 units. SGPT values are usually higher than SGOT. A sharp rise in the SGPT with a short duration (3–19 days) is more indicative of viral hepatitis A, whereas a gradual rise with prolongation (35–200 days) appears to characterize viral hepatitis B infections.

Leukopenia is typical in the preicteric phase and may be followed by a relative lymphocytosis. Large atypical lymphocytes such as are found in infectious mononucleosis may occasionally be seen.

Further evidence of liver dysfunction and host response is reflected in a decreased serum albumin and increased serum globulin. Elevation of gamma globulin and serum transaminase is frequently used to gauge chronicity and activity of liver disease. In many patients with hepatitis A, an abnormally high level of IgM is found which appears 3–4 days after the SGPT begins to rise. Hepatitis B patients have normal to slightly elevated IgM levels.

Numerous tests are available for the measurement of HB_sAg and anti-HB_s (Table 32–2 and Chapter 29). Agarose gel diffusion is the simplest procedure, but it is also the least sensitive and requires 24–72 hours for completion. Its major advantage is that a positive precipitin line can be confirmed as HB_sAg by demonstrating a line of identity with a reference HB_sAg. A rapid technic widely used by blood banks and diagnostic laboratories until recently is counterelectrophoresis (CEP). Complement fixation is slightly more sensitive

than CEP, but the test is more complicated to perform. The most sensitive and specific method for detecting HB_sAg or anti-HB_s is the radioimmunoassay (RIA). This test and the red cell agglutination (RCA) technic, which employs HB_s antibody-coated cells in a microtiter system, have replaced CEP as the methods of choice for detecting HB_sAg. The passive hemagglutination (PHA) technic, which uses HB_s antigen-coated cells, is an excellent and rapid method for detecting anti-HB_s, rivaling RIA in sensitivity.

The particles containing HB_sAg are antigenically complex. Each contains a group-specific antigen, *a*, in addition to 2 pairs of mutually exclusive subdeterminants, *d/y* and *w/r*. Thus, 4 phenotypes of HB_sAg have been observed: *adw*, *ayw*, *adr*, and *ayr*. In the USA, *adw* is the predominant subtype among asymptomatic carriers, whereas *ayw* has frequently been observed in dialysis-associated outbreaks and among parenteral drug abusers. These virus-specific markers are useful in epidemiologic investigations since secondary cases have the same subtype as the index case. The evidence indicates that these antigenic determinants are the phenotypic expression of HBV genotypes and are not determined by host factors.

The clinical and serologic course of events that occurs following exposure to HBV is depicted in Fig 32–4. DNA polymerase activity, which is probably representative of the viremic stage of hepatitis B, occurs early in the incubation period, coinciding with the first appearance of HB_sAg. The latter is usually detectable 3–6 weeks in advance of clinical and biochemical evidence of hepatitis and persists throughout the clinical course of the disease but typically disappears by the sixth month after exposure. Occasionally, HB_sAg persists in patients who develop chronic active hepatitis. In patients destined to become carriers, the initial illness may be mild or inapparent, manifested only by an elevated transaminase determination.

Anti-HB_c is frequently detected at the onset of clinical illness approximately 3–6 weeks after HB_sAg reactivity appears. Because this antibody is directed against the internal component of the hepatitis B virion, its appearance in the serum is indicative of viral replication. In the typical case of acute type B hepa-

Table 32–2. Methods used to detect HB_sAg and anti-HB_s and their relative sensitivities.

Method	HB_sAg	Anti-HB_s	Time to Complete Test
Agarose gel diffusion	1	1	24–72 hours
Counterelectrophoresis	5	10	1 hour
Complement fixation	10	1	18 hours
Passive hemagglutination (HB_sAg-coated cells)	Not applicable	4000	3–6 hours
Red cell agglutination (anti-HB_s-coated cells)	250	Not applicable	3 hours
Radioimmunoassay	1000	4000	3–120 hours

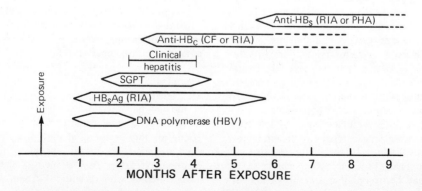

Figure 32–4. Clinical and serologic events occurring after exposure to hepatitis B virus.

titis, the anti-HB$_c$ titer falls after recovery. In contrast, high titers of anti-HB$_c$ persist in the sera of all chronic HB$_s$Ag carriers. Antibody to HB$_s$Ag is first detected at a variable period after the disappearance of HB$_s$Ag. It is present in low concentrations usually detectable only by the most sensitive methods.

Recently, a new antigen-antibody system has emerged—the anti-*e*/*e* antigen. Data have accumulated that suggest an association between *e* antigen and infectivity.

A virus-like particle has been detected by immune electron microscopy in fecal extracts of hepatitis A patients (Fig 29–3). The antigen appears early in the disease and usually disappears within 3 weeks following the onset of jaundice. Morphologically, the particles are 27 nm in diameter, do not have an envelope, and show cubic symmetry.

Using a micro solid-phase immunoradiometric assay, type A hepatitis-associated antigen has been detected in liver, stool, bile, and blood of naturally infected humans and experimentally infected chimpanzees. The detection of significant levels of hepatitis A antigen in the blood of infected chimpanzees supports previous epidemiologic evidence of viremia during the acute stage of the disease. Peak titers of hepatitis A antigen are detected in the stool about 6–11 days prior to the first detectable liver enzyme abnormalities.

Attempts to isolate HAV or HBV in a cell or organ culture system have generally not been successful. Chimpanzees and some species of marmosets have been found to be susceptible to human viral hepatitis type A. HAV infections among imported chimpanzees are well known as an important cause of hepatitis in animal caretakers.

Successful transmission of HBV to chimpanzees has been achieved. The infection resulted in serologic, biochemical, and histologic evidence of type B hepatitis. Immunofluorescence and electron microscopy revealed HB$_s$Ag in the cytoplasm and virus-like particles with HB$_c$Ag in the nuclei of hepatocytes. Serial passage has been successful. No evidence for hepatitis B transmission from chimpanzee to man has been reported.

Virus-Host Immune Reactions

Currently there is serologic evidence for 2 hepatitis viruses—type A (short incubation hepatitis virus) and type B (long incubation hepatitis virus). A single infection with either confers homologous but not heterologous protection against reinfection. Infection with HBV of a specific subtype, eg, HB$_s$Ag/*adw*, appears to confer immunity to other HB$_s$Ag subtypes, probably because of their common group *a* specificity.

Most cases of hepatitis type A presumably occur without jaundice during childhood, and by late adulthood there is a widespread resistance to reinfection. However, recent serologic studies in this country indicate that the incidence of infection among certain populations may be declining as a result of improvements in sanitation commensurate with a rise in the standard of living. It has been estimated that as many

as 50–75% of young middle to upper income adults in the USA may be susceptible to type A hepatitis, and people who live in poorer circumstances or crowded institutions (eg, the armed forces) are at increased risk.

The immunopathogenetic mechanisms that result in viral persistence and hepatocellular injury in type B hepatitis remain to be elucidated. An imbalance between suppressive and cytopathic immune responses of the host has been hypothesized to account for the various pathologic manifestations of this disease. It is postulated that antibody-dependent, complement-mediated cytolysis or cellular effector mechanisms are responsible for the hepatic injury observed, whereas noncytopathic synthesis of viral components, surface expression of viral antigens or liver-specific neoantigens, and shedding of virus are primarily modulated by the humoral immune response.

Various host responses, immunologic and genetic, have been proposed to account for the higher frequency of HB$_s$Ag persistence observed in infants or children compared to adults and in certain disease states, eg, Down's syndrome, leukemia (acute and chronic lymphocytic), leprosy, thalassemia, and chronic renal insufficiency. Patients with Down's syndrome are particularly prone to persistent antigenemia (but low antibody frequency) and inapparent infections, and they show a significantly greater prevalence of these disorders than is found in other mentally retarded patients. This does not imply that these patients have an increased susceptibility to HBV. On the contrary, among other equally exposed patients who are residents within the same institution, the total serologic evidence of HBV infection is similar except that the antigen carrier rate is low whereas the antibody prevalence is high. An immunologic difference in the host response to the virus is apparently responsible for this serologic dichotomy.

Persistent antigenemia and mild or subclinical infections are more frequently observed in individuals who have been infected with low doses of virus. Correspondingly, a direct relationship between virus dose and time of appearance of HB$_s$Ag or an abnormal SGPT value has been reported, ie, the incubation period becomes longer as the dose of virus diminishes.

The frequency of the chronic HB$_s$Ag carrier state following acute icteric type B hepatitis is not known but is probably under 10%. More than half of these patients continue to exhibit biochemical and histologic evidence of chronic liver disease, ie, chronic persistent or chronic active hepatitis.

Treatment

Treatment of the patient with hepatitis is directed at allowing hepatocellular damage to resolve and repair itself under optimal conditions. In previously healthy young military recruits, ad libitum ward privileges or strenuous exercise did not appear to alter the acute course of hepatitis A. Therapeutic administration of corticosteroids with or without azathioprine has been successful in inducing remissions and prolonging survival in patients with progressive chronic active hepatitis. These drugs are not recommended for use in cases of acute viral hepatitis and do not alter the clinical course of severe or fulminant hepatitis. Patients should be advised to avoid hepatotoxins such as alcohol during convalescence.

Epidemiology

The incidence of reported cases of acute hepatitis in the USA increased from 52,583 in 1969 to 67,810 in 1971 (an incidence of 33.5 cases per 100,000 population), then decreased 12% by 1973 to 28.2 cases per 100,000 population. Seventy percent of the reported cases were categorized as hepatitis A (non-B). These numbers greatly understate the actual incidence, since only 10–20% of the cases seen by physicians are reported and because many persons contract hepatitis in mild form and do not seek treatment.

In the past decade, hepatitis B, which is associated with drug abuse as well as transfusions, increased in incidence at twice the rate of hepatitis A but showed a 2% decrease in 1972.

As shown in Table 32–1, there are marked differences in the epidemiologic features of hepatitis A and hepatitis B infections.

A. Viral Hepatitis Type A (Short Incubation Hepatitis): Outbreaks of type A hepatitis are common in families and institutions, summer camps, and especially among troops. The most likely mode of transmission under these conditions is by the fecal-oral route through close personal contact. Intestinal carriers are either relatively few or epidemiologically unimportant. The clinical disease is most often manifest in children and young adults. The ratio of anicteric to icteric cases in adults is about 1:1; in children, it may be as high as 12:1.

Sudden, explosive epidemics of type A hepatitis usually result from fecal contamination of a single source (eg, drinking water, food, milk, or nonhuman primates). HAV may infrequently be transmitted by the use of contaminated needles and syringes or through the administration of blood. Under these conditions, the shorter incubation period may be of diagnostic significance.

The largest waterborne epidemic, due to contamination with raw sewage, occurred in New Delhi in 1955–1956, resulting in an estimated 1100 cases among 250,000 people in a single week. Food-borne outbreaks such as the one which in 1974 paralyzed the hospital services of an eastern USA city emphasize the potential danger of these common-source outbreaks. The consumption of raw oysters or improperly steamed clams obtained from water polluted with sewage has also resulted in several outbreaks of hepatitis.

Other recently identified sources of potential infection are nonhuman primates. Since 1961 there have been over 35 outbreaks in which primates, usually chimpanzees, have infected humans in close personal contact with them. The disease in humans is usually mild and indistinguishable from viral hepatitis type A; subclinical cases occur frequently. Most of the primates responsible were recent arrivals in the USA, less than 3 months having elapsed from their entry to the time of appearance of the index case. These animals probably acquire the infection after arrival and transmit the virus to their caretakers. A persistent carrier state is unlikely since the number of new cases diminishes with residence.

B. Viral Hepatitis Type B (Long Incubation Hepatitis): The virus of type B hepatitis is also worldwide in distribution. There is no seasonal trend and no particular predilection for any age group, although there are definite high-risk groups such as parenteral drug abusers, institutionalized patients, health care personnel, individuals who have recently received blood transfusions, hemodialysis patients and staff, high promiscuity populations, and newborn infants born to mothers with type B hepatitis. The incidence of hepatitis B among recipients of blood transfusions is 0.3–3%. Since mandatory screening of blood donors for HB$_s$Ag was instituted and commercial donors are being replaced with all-volunteer donor sources, the number of icteric cases of transfusion-associated hepatitis has been substantially reduced. At this writing, 80–90% of the hepatitis cases observed in 1976 in blood recipients are unrelated serologically to hepatitis A or B viruses, to Epstein-Barr virus, or to cytomegalovirus. It is apparent that transfusion-associated hepatitis and type B hepatitis are by no means equivalent and that another etiologic agent (hepatitis C?) must be considered.

Cases of hepatitis B appear sporadically and are often associated with the parenteral inoculation of infective human blood (or its products), usually obtained from an apparently healthy carrier. Thousands of cases have occurred following parenteral administration of human serum, plasma, whole blood or blood products, or vaccines that contained human serum. Many others have been infected by improperly sterilized syringes, needles or lancets, or even by tattooing. The estimated ratio of anicteric to icteric infections is reported to be as high as 100:1.

A nonpercutaneous mode of transmission—suspected from a number of earlier field studies and from family clusters of hepatitis B cases—has been experimentally documented in human volunteers by oral administration of undiluted infectious plasma. This mechanism for the spread of hepatitis B is obviously more common than previously appreciated, particularly among sexual partners of symptomatic or asymptomatic carriers of HB$_s$Ag and among residents of crowded institutions. Detection of HB$_s$Ag in saliva, nasopharyngeal washings, semen, menstrual fluid, and vaginal secretions adds support to the concept that hepatitis B can be transmitted by nonpercutaneous routes. In most instances, HB$_s$Ag concentration in the blood is greater than that found in the secretions or excretions. It is quite possible that contamination of these sources by blood or plasma may account for their infectiousness. Within families, sharing razors or the inadvertent use of another person's toothbrush can result in hepatitis B infection. There is some evidence that the risk of contracting hepatitis B within a family constellation is less if the liver biopsy of a chronic HB_sAg carrier is normal than if it reveals evidence of hepatitis.

Transmission of hepatitis B through vaginal intercourse has not been adequately documented. However, a strong association exists between serologic evidence of type B hepatitis and certain patterns of sexual behavior such as promiscuity, intimate contact with multiple sex partners (increased exposure), and homosexuality of long duration. The exact mode of transmission has not been ascertained.

Health care personnel (surgeons and other physicians, dentists, nurses, laboratory technicians, and blood bank personnel) have a higher incidence of hepatitis and prevalence of detectable HB_sAg or anti-HB_s (or both) than those who have no occupational exposure to patients or blood products. The risk that these apparently healthy HB_sAg carriers (especially medical and dental surgeons) represent to the patients under their care remains to be determined but is probably small.

Hepatitis B infections are common among patients and staff of hemodialysis units. Family contacts are also at increased risk. As many as 50–75% of the renal dialysis patients who contract hepatitis B reportedly become chronic carriers of HB_sAg compared with 2% of the staff group, emphasizing the immunologic differences in host response.

Data are accumulating that indicate that the presence of e antigen in a person's serum may be a useful marker for infectivity; in contrast, the lack of infectivity appears to correlate best with the presence of anti-e.

Persons who have received a transfusion, especially from a paid donor, have a higher incidence of hepatitis and HB_s antigenemia than nontransfused persons. This has led to the recommendation that anyone who has received a transfusion should not be allowed to serve as a blood donor. However, as commercial sources of blood donors are eliminated and newer, more sensitive methods for detecting HB_sAg (RIA, RCA) are employed, this recommendation is becoming less important.

The incubation period of hepatitis B is 50–180 days, with a mean between 60–90 days. It appears to vary with the dose of HBV administered and the route of administration, being prolonged in patients infected by a nonpercutaneous route.

Gamma globulin and albumin are blood products which appear free from the risk of hepatitis B. Their method of preparation includes cold ethanol fractionation. In addition, albumin is heated to 60° C for 10 hours.

Prevention & Control

The ultimate aim in the prevention and control of hepatitis is the development of a safe and effective vaccine. Such a vaccine for hepatitis B is on the horizon. Preliminary observations in an institution where hepatitis has always been endemic demonstrated that the infectivity of hepatitis B virus was destroyed or modified by heating for 1 minute at 98° C, but its HB_s antigenicity remained intact. Four susceptible children received 2 inoculations with the inactivated serum and were subsequently exposed to HBV. The inactivated virus produced anti-HB_s in 3 of the 4 children, and all 4 revealed significant protection against the challenge HB virus. Another 10 children received only one inoculation before exposure. Five of the 10 were protected from hepatitis B infection and the other 5 developed unusually mild infection after the exposure to infectious virus, suggesting that one inoculation at least modifies the severity of the illness.

More recently, a viral vaccine has been prepared by purifying HB_sAg associated with the 22 nm particles from healthy HB_sAg-positive carriers. Fortunately, protection is conferred by antibody to the a antigen, an antigen which is common to all subtypes. Preparations containing intact 22 nm particles as well as polypeptides derived from 22 nm particles are presently being tested in chimpanzees as possible vaccines for hepatitis B. Efficacy studies in chimpanzees immunized with the intact 22 nm particles have revealed no serologic or biochemical evidence of type B hepatitis following challenge with live virus.

Since a source of large amounts of HAV has not been found, the development of a vaccine for hepatitis A awaits new findings, such as a tissue culture system in which to grow the agent.

Until such time that vaccines are available, prevention and control of hepatitis must be directed toward interrupting the chain of transmission and toward the use of passive immunization.

A. Viral Hepatitis Type A: The appearance of hepatitis in camps or institutions is often an indication of poor sanitation and poor personal hygiene. Control measures are directed toward the prevention of fecal contamination of food, water, or other sources by the individual. Reasonable hygiene—such as hand washing after bowel movements or before meals, the use of disposable plates and eating utensils, and the use of 0.5% sodium hypochlorite (1:10 dilution of Clorox) as a disinfectant—is essential in preventing the spread of HAV during the acute phase of the illness and for several weeks thereafter. All needles, syringes, blood-counting pipets, and lancets which have come in contact with the blood of hepatitis patients should be sterilized by heating. Infectivity studies indicate that the risk of transmitting hepatitis A is greatest from 2 weeks before to 2 weeks after the onset of jaundice. Transmission by the aerosol route appears relatively unimportant. (See General Properties of Viruses.)

Immune serum globulin (ISG) is prepared from large pools of normal adult plasma and confers passive protection in 80–90% of those exposed when given within 1–2 weeks after exposure to hepatitis A. Its prophylactic value decreases with time, and its administration more than 6 weeks after exposure or after the onset of clinical symptoms is not indicated.

ISG may not prevent infection from occurring if there is continued exposure to the virus, but it does exert a moderating influence on the illness so that clinical symptoms and jaundice do not usually develop. This often results in long-lasting natural immunity superimposed on the passive immune state. An intramuscular dose of approximately 0.01–0.02 ml/lb (0.02–0.04 ml/kg) is specifically recommended for household contacts of cases or for persons exposed to a common source of infection. Routine administration is not indicated for pupil or teacher contacts—unless a school- or classroom-centered outbreak has occurred—nor for office, factory, or hospital contacts. For the interruption of epidemics in institutions or for prophylaxis of persons at high risk (missionaries, Peace Corps volunteers, military personnel, persons working with newly imported chimpanzees, or travelers to endemic areas), prophylactic ISG is recommended every 4–6 months at a dose of approximately 0.02–0.05 ml/lb (0.05–0.11 ml/kg).

Recommendations for ISG prophylaxis against hepatitis A have recently been revised by the Public Health Service Advisory Committee on Immunization Practices and are shown in Table 32–3.

B. Viral Hepatitis Type B: Persons who have had hepatitis should not be used as blood donors. However, even persons without a history of hepatitis and with normal liver function tests may be carriers of the virus. The duration of the carrier state is not known. Sensitive methods for detecting HB$_s$Ag in blood donors are now being employed by all blood banks to avoid administering HB$_s$Ag-positive blood. Nevertheless, cases of posttransfusion hepatitis B continue to occur although at a reduced frequency. Since the incidence of posttransfusion hepatitis (both B and non-B) is higher among recipients of commercial (paid donor) blood or blood from first-time donors, the establishment of an all-volunteer population who donate periodically would be an important measure for eliminating transfusion-associated hepatitis.

In transfused patients, the risk of contracting overt hepatitis appears to be reduced in recipients of **frozen** washed red blood cells. Removal of plasma and using the washing procedure rather than the freezing process appear to reduce the concentration of HB$_s$Ag and of virus sufficiently to prevent occurrence of clinical disease. Administration of donor blood containing anti-HB$_s$ has not been associated with an increased incidence of hepatitis B following transfusion. Correspondingly, anti-HB$_s$ in the sera of recipients prior to transfusion appears to offer protection against hepatitis B infections.

The resistance of HBV to physical and chemical agents makes it difficult to treat human blood and its products to render them safe for human inoculation. Infectivity of plasma or other materials may be reduced or even eliminated by boiling or by using a combination of ultraviolet irradiation, heat, and 0.35% betapropiolactone, but none of these treatments have proved to be particularly acceptable. Application of a 0.5% sodium hypochlorite solution (final concentration) appears to destroy HB$_s$Ag activity (and presumably the infectious virion) when used for disinfecting material having a low concentration of protein. Stronger concentrations (5%) are required in the presence of whole sera. Autoclaving and the use of ethylene oxide gas are both acceptable methods for disinfecting metal objects, instruments, or heat-sensitive equipment. Another useful germicide is 2% activated glutaraldehyde.

Since as little as 0.0001 ml of plasma can transmit the disease, a single carrier of hepatitis B virus might "infect" a large batch of pooled plasma. It has been recommended, therefore, that pooled plasma should not be used. If pools must be used, they should be made from no more than 5 donors and each unit tested for HB$_s$Ag by one of the more sensitive methods (eg, RIA) prior to pooling. Plasma should be used only in cases of emergency, because of the possibility of transmitting hepatitis B to a patient who is already ill.

The use of disposable needles and syringes is recommended to reduce the possibility of viral contamination. Cases have also been traced to tattooing. Dentists must autoclave, gas, or chemically disinfect their instruments between patient use.

Studies on passive immunization using specific hepatitis B immune globulin have been encouraging. A special immune globulin from plasma containing anti-HB$_s$ with a titer 50,000 times greater than the standard commercial ISG was prepared and administered to 10 susceptible children 4 hours after they had been exposed to infectious serum (MS-2). Six subjects failed to develop HB$_s$ antigenemia or biochemical evidence of hepatitis, for a 60% level of protection. In contrast, 13 of 15 children who received normal ISG under the same conditions and all 11 control children who received the same dose of virus but without ISG became infected (HB$_s$Ag-positive).

In 2 clinical trials completed in 1975, the protective activity of 3 preparations of immune globulin containing varying levels of antibody to HB$_s$Ag was compared. Subjects included hospital personnel accidentally exposed to hepatitis B and newly admitted patients or recently hired employees of renal dialysis units. The results suggest that anti-HB$_s$-rich preparations of ISG confer significant levels of protection against hepatitis B infection for periods of 6–8 months. However, this temporary protection by antibody-rich gamma globulins may impede the subsequent development of natu-

Table 32–3. Guidelines for ISG prophylaxis against hepatitis A.

Person's Weight (lb)	ISG Dose (ml)	
	Routine	High Risk* (Prolonged Exposure)
< 50	0.5	1.0
50–100	1.0	2.5
> 100	2.0	5.0

*Within limits, larger doses of ISG provide longer-lasting but not necessarily more protection. Therefore, more ISG is prescribed in high-risk situations where continuous exposure is anticipated (institutional contacts, travelers to foreign countries).

ral, long-lasting immunity resulting from one or more exposures to HB virus (passive-active immunity), a condition less likely to occur when smaller concentrations of anti-HB$_S$ are administered.

Evidence of passive-active immunity also was more frequently observed among newly admitted institutionalized patients who received standard ISG containing a low concentration of anti-HB$_S$ when compared to those treated with an anti-HB$_S$-rich preparation of ISG. It is noteworthy that both preparations successfully prevented the development of a chronic carrier state. Similarly, administration of specific hepatitis B ISG to spouses of patients with acute type B hepatitis has been shown to be effective in preventing not only symptomatic type B hepatitis but the infection itself.

Prevention of transfusion-associated hepatitis by the administration of standard ISG has not been consistently demonstrated in carefully conducted trials. Therefore, its routine administration to recipients of blood transfusions is not recommended.

Proper donor selection and the development of a central registry for identification of carriers can lower the incidence of transfusion-associated hepatitis. In addition, blood or its products should be used only when necessary, since the risk of hepatitis appears to increase with the number of units administered. Hepatitis B virus may be transmitted to personnel in blood transfusion laboratories, but there is no evidence for the transmission of infection from members of the staff to blood or blood products.

Despite a low degree of contagiousness, physicians should become aware that a nonparenteral (oral) mode of transmission can occur in viral hepatitis type B, especially among close personal contacts and in closed populations (institutions).

The following information on control and prevention of type B hepatitis has been acquired from clinical and epidemiologic studies and is based on recommendations made by the Center for Disease Control and the Committee on Viral Hepatitis of the National Academy of Sciences.

(1) A confirmed positive test for HB$_S$Ag is indicative of acute or chronic viral hepatitis type B or of the healthy carrier state. Such tests should be performed on at least 2 separate blood samples from the individual to avoid possible errors in handling or identification and should include a test for specificity.

(2) The presence of HB$_S$Ag in the blood of a patient with acute viral hepatitis type B is usually transient. HB$_S$ antigenemia that lasts more than 4 months after the onset of illness should be regarded as persistent antigenemia and specifies those persons likely to become chronic carriers of the antigen.

(3) The chronic carrier of HB$_S$Ag may or may not have demonstrable evidence of related liver disease.

(4) Testing for HB$_S$Ag by the most sensitive methods should be required for all blood donors. HB$_S$Ag carriers should be prohibited from donating blood.

(5) Although the infectiousness of hepatitis patients positive for HB$_S$Ag diminishes when the antigen

is no longer demonstrable in the blood, such people currently are not accepted as blood donors.

(6) With respect to risk of transmission to others, there is no indication at this time that routine HB$_S$Ag testing of any specific professional or occupational group should be required. There may be circumstances, such as in dialysis centers or other areas of possible high risk, when it might be prudent to institute regular antigen and antibody testing for various members of the staff but, as a general rule, *routine* testing of professional or occupational groups should not be required on a regular basis.

(7) Standard human immune serum globulin (ISG) is of no demonstrable value in the treatment of HB$_S$Ag carriers.

(8) Further studies regarding the use of ISG with high titers of anti-HB$_S$ among contacts of hepatitis B patients or carriers are needed to establish efficacy, standardize titer and change requirements, and determine guidelines for use.

(9) All confirmed cases of type B hepatitis should be promptly reported to the local or state health department. This permits more accurate hepatitis surveillance and identifies epidemiologic trends.

(10) Persons identified in the course of diagnostic studies, blood donor testing, or seroepidemiologic investigations as transient or persistent carriers of HB$_S$Ag should be so informed and educated regarding the mechanisms of HBV spread so that they might reduce transmission to others. The presence of liver disease should be excluded in these individuals.

(11) Patients with acute type B hepatitis generally need not be isolated so long as blood and instrument precautions are stringently observed, both in the general patient care areas and in the laboratories. Staff should wear gloves or other protective clothing when in contact with blood or blood-contaminated objects from these patients. Both staff and patients should practice good personal hygiene, especially handwashing.

(12) Because spouses and intimate contacts of persons with acute type B hepatitis are at greater risk of acquiring clinical type B hepatitis than those exposed to healthy carriers, they need to be warned about practices which might increase the risk of infection or transmission.

(13) There is no justification for removing HB$_S$Ag-positive carriers from patient contact in the absence of evidence of disease transmission. The use of gloves and possibly masks should reduce the potential for HBV transmission. If transmission from antigen-positive health personnel to patients is clearly demonstrated, more restrictive measures should be considered, such as limiting patient contact to nonsurgical and nondental procedures.

(14) There is no evidence that asymptomatic HB$_S$Ag-positive food handlers pose a health risk to the general public.

(15) Women who acquire type B hepatitis while pregnant can transmit the disease to their infants. The risk of transmission is increased during the third tri-

mester and during the postpartum period. Infants who become HB$_S$Ag-positive generally do so within 1–2 months, but testing should continue at monthly intervals for at least 6 months. Most develop persistent antigenemia.

(16) The mechanisms which result in HBV dissemination are not well understood but may relate to viral replication reflected by hepatocellular injury, positive tests for DNA polymerase, and the presence of *e* antigen. Until more information is acquired, particularly with regard to the communicability of infection from the healthy carrier, only routine precautions such as those which apply to percutaneous routes of potential transmission should be initiated.

●   ●   ●

General References

Aach RD & others: Risk of transfusing blood containing antibody to hepatitis-B surface antigen. Lancet 2:190, 1974.

Almeida JD, Rubenstein D, Stott EJ: New antigen-antibody system in Australia-antigen-positive hepatitis. Lancet 2:1225, 1971.

Blumberg BS & others: The discovery of Australia antigen and its relation to viral hepatitis. Perspec Virol 7:223, 1971.

Committee on Viral Hepatitis, US National Academy of Sciences-National Research Council: The public health implications of hepatitis B antigen in human blood: A revised statement. Morbid Mortal Wkly Rep 23:125, 1974.

Feinstone SM, Kapikian AZ, Purcell RH: Hepatitis A: Detection by immune electron microscopy of a viruslike antigen associated with acute illness. Science 182:1026, 1973.

Gregory PB & others: Steroid therapy in severe viral hepatitis. N Engl J Med 294:681, 1976.

Hilleman MR & others: Development and utilization of complement-fixation and immune adherence tests for human hepatitis A virus and antibody. Am J Med Sci 270:93, 1975.

Hollinger FB: Hepatitis viruses. Pages 819–833 in: *Manual of Clinical Microbiology*. American Society for Microbiology, 1974.

Hollinger FB & others: Detection of hepatitis A viral antigen by radioimmunoassay. J Immunol 115:1464, 1975.

Kaplan PM & others: DNA polymerase associated with human hepatitis B antigen. J Virol 12:995, 1973.

Krugman S, Giles JP: Viral hepatitis, type B (MS-2 strain): Further observations on natural history and prevention. N Engl J Med 288:755, 1973.

Melnick JL, Dreesman GR, Hollinger FB: Approaching the control of viral hepatitis type B. J Infect Dis 133:210, 1976.

Melnick JL, Hollinger FB: Hepatitis virology. Pages 345–365 in: *Progress in Liver Diseases.* Vol 4. Popper H, Schaffner F (editors). Grune & Stratton, 1972.

Prince AM & others: Antibody against serum-hepatitis antigen: Prevalence and potential use as immune serum globulin in prevention of serum-hepatitis infections. N Engl J Med 285:933, 1971.

Proceedings of a Symposium on Viral Hepatitis (sponsored by the National Academy of Sciences). Am J Med Sci 270:3–413, 1975. [Entire issue.]

Provost PJ & others: Biophysical and biochemical properties of CR326 human hepatitis A virus. Am J Med Sci 270:87, 1975.

Robinson WS, Clayton DA, Greenman RL: DNA of a human hepatitis B virus candidate. J Virol 14:384, 1974.

Szmuness W, Harley EJ, Prince AM: Intrafamilial spread of asymptomatic hepatitis B. Am J Med Sci 270:293, 1975.

Szmuness W & others: On the role of sexual behavior in the spread of hepatitis B infection. Ann Intern Med 83:489, 1975.

Vyas GN, Perkins HA, Schmid R (editors): *Hepatitis and Blood Transfusion.* Grune & Stratton, 1972.

World Health Organization Technical Report Series No. 570: *Viral Hepatitis.* Report of a WHO Scientific Group, 1975.

33...
Rabies & Other Viral Diseases of the Nervous System; Slow Viruses

RABIES

Rabies is an acute infection of the CNS which is almost always fatal. The virus is usually transmitted to man from the bite of a rabid animal.

Properties of the Virus

A. Size and Morphology: Rabies virus has been assigned to the **Rhabdoviridae** family on the basis of morphologic and biochemical properties which it has in common with vesicular stomatitis virus of cattle and a number of animal, plant, and insect viruses. Some members of the family multiply in arthropods as well as in vertebrates.

The rhabdoviruses are characterized by rod-shaped particles which vary in length from 60–400 nm and in width from 60–85 nm. Animal rhabdoviruses tend to be bullet-shaped in appearance. The particles are surrounded by a membranous envelope with protruding spikes 10 nm long. Inside the envelope is a ribonucleocapsid which in electron micrographs appears to be striated. The rhabdoviruses are characterized by a genome of single-stranded RNA of molecular weight $3-5 \times 10^6$ which by itself is not infectious and does not serve as messenger. Virions contain an RNA-dependent RNA polymerase as a structural component.

Rabies virus is a typical bullet-shaped rhabdovirus with a cylinder diameter of about 70 nm and a length of about 175 nm. The virion buoyant density in CsCl is 1.2 gm/ml.

Some antigenic relationships exist among rabies virus, Lagos bat virus, and 3 rhabdoviruses isolated from shrews, midges, and mosquitoes. This group is antigenically distinct from other rhabdoviruses.

B. Reaction to Physical and Chemical Agents: Rabies virus survives storage at 4° C for weeks; it can survive subzero temperatures for much longer periods, but only in the absence of CO_2. On dry ice, therefore, it must be stored in glass-sealed ampules. In glycerol it may be kept alive for weeks at room temperature. After desiccation from the frozen state, rabies virus is stable for years at 4° C. The virus deteriorates in dilute suspension in the absence of protein.

The rabies virus is killed rapidly by ultraviolet irradiation or sunlight. Thermal inactivation occurs in 1 hour at 50° C and in 5 minutes at 60° C. Lyophilized virus resists temperatures of 55° C for 24 hours.

The virus is rapidly inactivated by strong acids and alkali and by bichloride of mercury. Viral infectivity is destroyed by lipid solvents (0.1% sodium deoxycholate or ether) and by trypsin.

C. Animal Susceptibility and Growth of Virus: Rabies virus has a wide host range. All warm-blooded animals, including man, are susceptible. The virus is widely distributed in infected animals, having been detected (in order of decreasing frequency) in the nervous system, saliva, urine, lymph, milk, and blood. Recovery from infection is rare except in certain bats, where the virus has become peculiarly adapted to the salivary glands. Vampire bats may transmit the virus for months without themselves ever showing any signs of disease. Latent rabies virus has been reactivated in a laboratory animal by injection of corticotropin 5 months after infection.

When freshly isolated in the laboratory, the strains are referred to as street virus. Such strains show long and variable incubation periods (usually 21–60 days in dogs) and regularly produce intracytoplasmic inclusion bodies. The inoculated animals may exhibit long periods of excitement and viciousness. The virus may invade the salivary glands as well as the CNS.

Serial brain-to-brain passage in rabbits yields a "fixed" virus which no longer multiplies in extraneural tissues. This fixed virus multiplies rapidly, and the incubation period is shortened to 4–6 days. At this stage, inclusion bodies are found only with difficulty.

The virus may be propagated in chick embryos, baby hamster kidney cells, and human diploid cell cultures. It cannot be passaged in the latter cultures by transfer of tissue culture fluid but only by transfer of infected cells to uninfected human diploid cultures.

One strain (Flury), after serial passage in chick embryos, has been modified so that it fails to produce disease in animals injected extraneurally. This attenuated virus is used for vaccination of animals.

D. Antigenic Properties: Separation of the virus particle components is making possible a study of their antigenic properties. It has recently been shown that the purified spikes from rabies virus particles are responsible for the elicitation of neutralizing antibody in animals. As discussed below, vaccination against rabies is hazardous at present. The use of a subunit vaccine made from the purified virus particle spikes should eliminate this hazard in the near future. Similarly, antiserum prepared against the purified nucleocapsid has proved useful in conjunction with fluorescent marker antibodies as a diagnostic tool.

Pathogenesis & Pathology

Rabies virus multiplies in the muscle or connective tissue and is propagated through the endoneurium of the Schwann cells or associated tissue spaces of the sensory nerves to the CNS. It multiplies there and may then spread through peripheral nerves to the salivary glands and other tissues. Rabies virus has not been isolated from the blood of infected persons.

It has been suggested that the incubation period depends on the distance the virus has to move from its point of entry to the brain. Support for this view lies in the higher attack rate and shorter incubation period in persons suffering from wounds about the face. In experimental infection of animals, however, there is no relationship between incubation period and site of inoculation. The higher attack rates and shorter incubation periods associated with face wounds may be due to the more severe lacerations and the greater degree of penetration of infecting virus. Even after direct introduction of the virus into the brains of animals, the incubation period is sometimes 12 weeks. The long incubation periods in rabies may result from a transitory failure of the virus to multiply.

There are a general hyperemia and pronounced nerve cell destruction in the cerebral and cerebellar cortices, midbrain, basal ganglia, pons, and especially in the medulla. Demyelinization occurs in the white matter, and degeneration of axons and myelin sheaths is common. In the spinal cord, the posterior horns are most severely involved. If the bite has occurred on an arm or leg, the corresponding posterior horn shows extensive destruction (neuronophagia and cellular infiltrations), which may extend into the dorsal root ganglia of the same area of the spinal cord. Cellular infiltrations are usually mononuclear in character and are often perivascular and perineural. They are minimal if the patient dies after a short disease but are more extensive when the disease is prolonged.

Rabies virus produces a specific cytoplasmic inclusion, the Negri body, in infected nerve cells. The demonstration of such inclusions is pathognomonic of rabies but may not be observed in all cases. The inclusions are eosinophilic, sharply demarcated, and more or less spherical, measuring 2–10 μm in diameter. Several may be found in the cytoplasm of large neurons. They occur throughout the brain and spinal cord but are most frequently found in Ammon's horn of the hippocampal formation. Negri bodies have been found to contain rabies virus antigens.

Paralysis and death due to allergic encephalomyelitis may follow a course of killed or attenuated rabies vaccine made from infected CNS tissue or (much more rarely) from duck embryo tissue. Therefore, histopathologic examination of the brain and spinal cord in fatal paralytic cases must reveal specific inclusion (Negri) bodies before rabies can definitely be established as the cause of death. Serologic tests are useless here, since antibodies would have been formed either in the course of the disease or by the vaccination procedure.

The virus multiplies outside the CNS. When found in the salivary glands, it is accompanied by cellular interstitial infiltrations and by necrosis of the acinar cells of mucus-secreting tissue. The adrenal medulla, the acinar epithelium of the pancreas, and the renal tubules may also show acute degeneration.

Clinical Findings

The usual incubation period in dogs ranges from 3–8 weeks, but it may be as short as 10 days. Clinically, the disease in dogs is divided into 3 phases: prodromal, excitative, and paralytic. The prodromal phase is characterized by fever, sluggish corneal reflexes, and a sudden change in the temperament of the animal; docile animals may become snappy and irritable, whereas aggressive animals may become more affectionate. The excitative phase lasts 3–7 days, during which the dog shows symptoms of irritability, restlessness, nervousness, and exaggerated response to sudden light and sound stimuli. At this stage the animal is most dangerous because of its tendency to bite. The animal has difficulty in swallowing, suffers from convulsive seizures, and enters finally into a paralytic stage characterized by paralysis of the whole body followed by coma and death. Sometimes the animal goes into the paralytic stage without passing through the excitative stage.

The incubation period in man varies from 2–16 weeks or more, but in a significant proportion of cases it is only 2–3 weeks. It is usually shorter in children than in adults. The clinical spectrum can be divided into 4 phases: a short prodromal phase, a sensory phase, a period of excitement, and a paralytic or depressive phase. The prodrome, lasting 2–4 days, begins with malaise and may be accompanied by any of the following: anorexia, headache, nausea and vomiting, sore throat, and fever. Usually there is an abnormal sensation around the site of infection. The patient may show increasing nervousness and apprehension. General sympathetic overactivity is observed, including lacrimation, pupillary dilatation, and increased salivation and perspiration. The act of swallowing precipitates a spasm of the throat muscles; a patient may allow saliva to drool from his mouth simply to avoid swallowing and the associated painful spasms. (Because of the patient's apparent fear of water, the disease has been known as hydrophobia since ancient days.) This phase is followed by convulsive seizures and death, usually 3–5 days following onset. If the patient survives this acute excitement phase, he becomes listless, stuporous, and finally comatose. Progressive paralytic symptoms may intervene before death but are not common. A form of Landry's ascending paralysis was the predominant clinical feature in cases of rabies transmitted by vampire bats in Trinidad and Latin America.

Since the disease may be transmitted through a

minor wound from an apparently healthy dog, a history of exposure is not always obtainable.

Hysteria may simulate certain features of rabies, particularly in persons who have been near a rabid animal or have been bitten by a nonrabid one.

Laboratory Diagnosis

A. Histopathology of Animals: The diagnosis of rabies has long been based on the finding of cytoplasmic inclusions (Negri bodies) in the nerve cells of a naturally infected patient or animal or in the brains of animals inoculated in the laboratory. Impression preparations of brain tissue (Ammon's horn) are often used in the microscopic examination for Negri bodies. If Negri bodies cannot be found in the brain of an animal suspected of having rabies, a suspension of the brain or submaxillary salivary gland should be passed to other animals (mice, rabbits, hamsters).

Currently, tissues infected with rabies virus are identified by means of the direct fluorescent antibody (FA) technic, which is the method of choice as regards speed and accuracy of identification. (See Chapter 28.)

Specific labeled antirabies hamster serum is superior to horse serum for detecting rabies virus antigen in infected tissues.

Even after an apparently healthy dog or cat bites a person, it should be isolated and watched by a veterinarian for the next 10 days. If the animal remains healthy, the person has presumably not been exposed to the virus. Any illness in the animal should be reported immediately to the local health department. If signs suggestive of rabies develop, the animal should be killed and the head removed and shipped under refrigeration to a qualified laboratory designated by the local or state health department, where the brain should be examined for Negri bodies by immunofluorescence or histologic criteria. Negri bodies occur in cytoplasm and have a distinct internal structure with basophilic granules in an acidophilic matrix.

Early signs of rabies in wild or stray animals cannot be interpreted reliably; therefore, any such animal that bites or scratches a person should be killed at once (without unnecessary damage to the head) and the brain examined as above.

If examination of the animal's brain by FA technic is negative for rabies, the bitten person need not be treated unless the bite or scratch is from a bat. In the case of bat exposure, examination of an infected animal's brain material may not reveal the presence of rabies virus, and antirabies treatment probably should not await results of tests of the animal (see Treatment). Almost half of infected bats have no detectable inclusion (Negri) bodies, and many harbor the virus only in their salivary glands or brown fat.

B. Recovery of Virus: The virus can be isolated from the patient's saliva, inoculated into mice (intracerebrally) or hamsters (intramuscularly). Brain tissue should be collected from fatal cases and inoculated in a similar fashion. Next to the nervous tissue, the submaxillary glands are the best source of virus. Inoculated mice usually develop flaccid paralysis of the legs

and then die. Their brains should be examined for Negri bodies by immunofluorescence. If Negri bodies cannot be found, the isolated virus should be identified by its neutralization by specific antiserum.

C. Serology: In the past, with a single exception, patients with rabies have not recovered, and serologic tests were of little value. Antibodies may develop in an unvaccinated person during the course of the disease. Antibodies may also develop after vaccination. Antirabies antibodies can be detected by neutralization, complement fixation, or immunofluorescence.

Immunity & Vaccines

Only one antigenic type of rabies virus is known. All infections have been held to be fatal; however, in 1970 a single recovered case was documented. Preexposure or postexposure prophylaxis must provide, therefore, effective levels of antibodies to prevent the multiplication and spread of rabies virus. Duck embryo vaccine (DEV) is the only currently licensed rabies virus vaccine available for human use in the USA. DEV is prepared in embryonated duck eggs infected with the Pasteur rabbit brain fixed virus and is then inactivated with propiolactone. Major complications associated with DEV are uncommon. Systemic symptoms such as fever, malaise, or myalgia occur in about 33% of vaccine recipients. Acute anaphylactic reactions and posttreatment paralysis have been reported occasionally.

Nerve tissue vaccine (NTV) is no longer used in the USA. NTV is a rabbit brain tissue preparation infected with a fixed virus and inactivated by phenol and incubation at 37° C (Semple type) or ultraviolet irradiation. Vaccines prepared from nerve tissue (Semple vaccine) are dangerous because the foreign brain material may sensitize the person being vaccinated and produce an allergic encephalitis and paralysis. Allergic encephalitis is the result of a delayed hypersensitivity reaction. The foreign brain material in the vaccine acts as an antigen to stimulate cellular reactivity toward brain antigens in the vaccinated individual. Such reactions occurring in the nervous system give rise to inflammation and degeneration. This response occurs in about one out of every 500–10,000 persons vaccinated and is more likely to occur in persons previously vaccinated against rabies. In certain instances, the risk of allergic encephalitis or paralysis from the vaccine may be greater than the risk of contracting rabies. Death has occurred in a ratio of 1:35,000 persons treated.

Canines are presently immunized with an attenuated rabies virus adapted to chick embryos (Flury strain). Its failure to multiply in man and the low viral titers obtained (small antigenic mass) make this vaccine unsuitable for postexposure prophylaxis in man. The low-egg-passage (LEP) vaccine has been used successfully for mass immunization of dogs. This strain remains pathogenic for cattle, cats, and puppies. Several rabies vaccines prepared in cell culture (porcine, canine, and hamster kidney) have been licensed in recent years for use in various domestic animals.

Recent comparative tests in dogs, documenting the efficacy of the newer vaccines and the LEP-Flury vaccine, showed that good protection against challenge by street rabies virus was conferred by the modified live vaccines tested but not by an inactivated vaccine prepared in hamster kidney, even when administered with adjuvant.

Even though only 1–3 cases in humans are reported each year in the USA, some 35,000 persons receive postexposure prophylaxis annually. This represents over 500,000 doses of vaccine.

Experimental attenuated live or inactivated virus vaccines have been developed by propagating the virus in WI-38 human diploid and other cells. One such vaccine using inactivated virus has been shown in small studies to produce antibody in 100% of volunteers. Antibody levels after 3 injections given over a 1-week period were similar to the levels produced after 14 injections of DEV and seemed much longer-lasting. It is hoped that new potent and nonallergenic vaccines will become available.

Treatment (Tables 33–1 and 33–2)

Despite the rarity of clinical human rabies in the USA at present, an estimated 1 million persons annually are bitten by animals; about 35,000 receive postexposure rabies prophylaxis with duck embryo vaccine (DEV), and 3000 are given antirabies serum as well. Immediate and thorough local treatment of all bite wounds and scratches is of vital importance (see below and Table 33–1). The perplexing problem of whether or not to immunize persons who may have been exposed to rabies by contacts with animals suspected of being infectious must be resolved immediately by the physician; the longer treatment is postponed, the less likely it is to be effective. All available methods of postexposure prophylaxis carry some risk of serious reactions.

Although major complications related to DEV are rare, minor adverse reactions are common. The efficacy of vaccine alone as a postexposure prophylactic agent has been questioned, and a combination of antirabies serum and vaccine has therefore been recommended for persons bitten by rabid or probably rabid animals (see below and Table 33–2). One antirabies serum at present commercially available is prepared in a heterologous species, horses, and has been reported

Table 33–1. Checklist of treatments for animal bites.

1. Immediate copious flushing of wound with soap and water.
2. Thorough wound cleansing under medical supervision.
3. If antirabies serum is indicated, infiltration of part of dose into wound.
4. Tetanus prophylaxis and antibacterial treatment when required.
5. No sutures or wound closure advised.

Table 33–2. Guide for postexposure antirabies prophylaxis.*

The following recommendations, for USA exposures, are only a guide. They should be used in conjunction with knowledge of the animal species involved, circumstances of the bite or other exposure, vaccination status of the animal, presence of rabies in the region, and current recommendations of US Public Health Service to local or state health departments.

Animal and Its Condition		Treatment†	
	Condition at Time	Kind of Exposure	
Species	of Attack	Bite‡	Nonbite§
Wild			
Skunk			
Fox			
Raccoon	Regard as rabid	S + V¹	S + V¹
Bat			
Domestic			
Dog or	Healthy	None²	None²
cat	Escaped (unknown)	S + V	V³
	Rabid	S + V¹	S + V¹
Other	Consider individually (see Treatment section of this chapter).		

*Recommendations of the Public Health Service Advisory Committee on Immunization Practices, 1972.

†V = rabies vaccine; S = antirabies serum.

‡Bite = Any penetration of skin by teeth.

§Nonbite = Scratches, abrasions, open wounds.

¹Discontinue vaccine if fluorescent antibody (FA) tests of animal killed at time of attack are negative.

²Begin S + V at first sign of rabies in biting dog or cat during holding period (10 days).

³Fourteen doses of duck embryo vaccine.

to cause serum sickness in up to 46% of recipients; therefore, it should be used *only* when indicated. An antirabies serum prepared from human rabies immune globulin has been developed and is available in limited quantities. It is very expensive. The recommended dose is 20 IU/kg. In one study, 46% of patients receiving a higher dose—ie, 40 IU/kg—had levels of neutralizing antibody of less than 1:5 seventy days after receiving, in addition, a 16-dose course of DEV. The current recommendation for use of human antirabies serum includes, in addition, a 23-dose course of DEV.

Every exposure to possible rabies infection must be individually evaluated in consultation with local or state health department officers. In the USA, the following factors should be considered before specific antirabies treatment is begun (Table 33–2): **(1) Species of biting animal:** Carnivorous animals (particularly skunks, foxes, coyotes, raccoons, dogs, and cats) and bats are more likely to be infective, whereas bites from rabbits, squirrels, chipmunks, rats, and mice and from adequately vaccinated domestic animals seldom require specific antirabies prophylaxis. **(2) Circumstances of biting incident:** An unprovoked attack is more likely to mean that the animal is rabid; bites during attempts to feed or handle an apparently healthy animal can generally be considered provoked. (3) **Type of exposure**: Since transmission is by inoculation of infectious saliva through the skin, the nature and extent of exposure must be considered (Table 33–2). (4) **Vaccination status of the animal**: A properly immunized animal has only a minimal chance of developing rabies and transmitting the virus. (5) **Presence of rabies in the region**: Adequate laboratory and field records may indicate that there is no rabies infection present in a particular domestic species within a region.

Since rabies virus is assumed to multiply in the muscle or connective tissue and to become fixed to nerve tissue soon after exposure, and since the interval between exposure and onset of symptoms is frequently less than 21 days, the importance of early, adequate local wound therapy supplemented by antiserum and vaccine is emphasized. All bites inflicted by animals which may be rabid should immediately be scrubbed and flushed thoroughly and repeatedly with 20% soap in water, 1% quaternary ammonium compound, or 43–70% ethanol. In emergencies, alcoholic beverages of 86 proof or greater can be used. Such cleaning of the wound is a very important preventive measure. If hyperimmune antirabies serum is indicated (Table 33–2), some should be infiltrated around the wound. Tetanus prophylaxis and other antibacterial measures may also be required.

Postexposure prophylactic measures include active and passive immunization. For active immunization, DEV is preferable because of its lower rate of CNS reactions. If vaccine alone is indicated, 14 daily injections are given. When serum is used together with vaccine, 23 doses of the vaccine are recommended. The primary series is given either as 21 daily doses or as 14 doses in the first 7 days (twice daily or one double dose daily), and then 7 daily doses. Two booster doses, one 10 days and the second 20 days or more after completion of the primary course, are necessary to assure lasting protection.

Hyperimmune serum has proved effective in preventing rabies, and its use in combination with vaccine is considered the best postexposure prophylaxis. Hyperimmune serum is recommended for **all bites** by animals **in which rabies cannot be excluded** and for nont e exposure to animals proved or suspected to be rabid (Table 33–2). Up to 50% of the antiserum should be used to infiltrate the wound and the rest administered intramuscularly. The schedule indicated in the above paragraph counteracts the suppression of immune response frequently associated with passive-active immunization procedures. Because horse serum has induced serum sickness in up to 46% of persons receiving it, it should be used *only* when indicated (Table 33–2). Human rabies immune globulin circumvents the risk of serum sickness, is as effective as animal sera, and does not provoke allergic reactions.

The usefulness of hyperimmune rabies antiserum, in addition to its local virus-neutralizing capability, is its ability to markedly prolong the incubation period. This provides a longer period of time for development of vaccine-stimulated antibody, which can then appear before the passively administered antibody disappears.

If clinical rabies develops, intensive supportive treatment should be given; prolonged survival is possible, and a recovery has been reported.

Epidemiology

Most human cases are caused by the bite of an infected animal. Man is an accidental host and is not a reservoir of infection. Infection from man to man is very rare. Rabies in man occurs commonly in some areas of the world, particularly in Iran, India, the Philippines, North Africa, and Thailand. About 1000 cases annually are reported to the World Health Organization, and about 1 million people throughout the world are given postexposure immunization against rabies each year. In the USA since 1963, only 1–3 cases of human rabies have been reported annually. However, rabies in animals occurs each year throughout Asia, Africa, Europe, and the Americas.

The increase in wildlife rabies, especially in skunks, has resulted in an increased risk of human exposure from wild animal contacts. Since 1950, there have been 24 human rabies cases in the USA resulting from the bites of rabid wildlife: 9 from skunks, 7 from foxes, 6 from bats, and one from a bobcat. The risk of rabies from wild animals is not limited to exposures incurred in the field. Wild animals trapped and sold as pets have on several occasions been responsible for human exposures.

In most countries, dogs remain the chief source of human exposure requiring prophylaxis; cats are the second most common overall source, with other sources being cattle, jackals, raccoons, and rodents. In South America, in the vicinity of Trinidad, rabies is transmitted by the vampire bat. This animal usually feeds on cattle and may cause large epizootics among them. However, it may also bite man. The infection is also present in fruit-eating bats, which serve as a reservoir of virus for the vampires.

In the USA since 1959, the number of cases of rabies in wild animals has exceeded those in domestic animals; skunks, foxes, bats, and raccoons are the major wildlife reservoirs. In 1974, there were 3123 reported cases of rabies. Seventy percent (2208 cases) were in wild animals, including 1157 skunks, 512 bats, 298 foxes, and 188 raccoons. Rabid skunks were reported in 27 states. In various areas of the world the predominant rabid species may be dogs, foxes, cattle, or bats.

Rabies is present in colonial and noncolonial frugivorous and insectivorous bats in the USA and Canada. Although no rabid bats were detected in the USA before 1953, bat rabies must have been present much earlier. Since the initial discovery, bat rabies has been reported from every one of the 48 contiguous states, accounting for a significant portion of animal rabies; in 1972, the bat was the only animal species found rabid in 17 of the 45 states which reported rabid bats. Bats are able to transmit the disease to quadrupeds, to human beings, and to other bats. Rabies-infected insectivorous bats are known to inhabit caves also inhabited by vampire bats. Transmission from one bat species to the other may account for the infection of Mexican free-tailed bats, since the latter may winter in Mexico—within the range of the vampire bat.

The virus carrier rate may be high in bats: 1% or more of apparently healthy bats may carry virus, as do 9% of those with abnormal signs. Virus may be found either in the brain or in the salivary glands, or both.

Bats are important because of the great number of healthy carriers in bat populations which maintain ever-shifting foci of rabies infection, providing a constant source of infection for wildlife, domestic animals, and man, and offering a means of persistence of the virus in nature. In addition, aerosol transmission of rabies can occur in caves inhabited by bats.

Control

In cities, rabies is best controlled by destroying stray dogs and by compulsory vaccination of all others. During outbreaks and for at least 6 months after each case, all dogs should be muzzled. Imported dogs should be quarantined for 6 months. Canine quarantine in England is now 1 year.

Apparently healthy pet dogs or cats that have bitten human beings should be isolated for 10 days. If rabies is suspected after that period, the animal should be humanely killed for diagnosis. A stray or wild animal which has bitten a person should be killed at once for diagnosis (see Laboratory Diagnosis; Treatment).

In view of the prevalence of rabies in wild animals, physicians must be alert to the possibility of rabies in any unprovoked attack, particularly by a skunk, fox, or bat. Bat rabies presents special problems because almost 50% of rabies-infected bats have no inclusion (Negri) bodies, and many harbor the virus only in their salivary glands or brown fat. Antirabies treatment is indicated for all persons or animals bitten by bats.

Preexposure prophylaxis with duck embryo vaccine (DEV) is recommended for persons subjected to a high risk, eg, veterinarians, animal caretakers, mailmen, field personnel, and certain laboratory workers. Preexposure immunization is also recommended for spelunkers (bat rabies and the possibility of aerosol infection in caves) and for individuals, especially children, who are going to live in areas where rabies is enzootic (eg, military personnel, Peace Corps volunteers).

The schedule for immunization is either 2 doses 1 month apart followed by a third dose in 6 months, or 3 weekly injections with a fourth dose 3 months later. The first schedule produces neutralizing antibody in 80–90% of vaccinees by 1 month after the third dose; the second, useful for more rapid immunization, elicits antibody response in about 80% of vaccinees. Antibody development should be confirmed by a serum neutralization test 3–4 weeks after the last injection (tests can be arranged by state health department laboratories), and if no antibody is detected, booster doses should be given until a response is demonstrated.

If the high-risk situation continues, a booster injection should be given every 2–3 years.

When an immunized person with previously demonstrated rabies antibody is bitten by a rabid animal, it is suggested that he receive 5 daily doses of vaccine plus a booster dose 20 days later. Antirabies serum is not necessary in this case and, in fact, might inhibit a rapid anamnestic response. For nonbite exposures, an immunized person with antibody needs only a single dose of vaccine. However, if it is not known whether an exposed person ever had antibody, the complete postexposure antirabies treatment should be given.

In areas where vampire bats or foxes transmit rabies, prophylactic vaccination of cattle should be carried out.

ASEPTIC MENINGITIS

This disease is characterized by acute onset, fever, headache, and stiff neck. There is pleocytosis of the spinal fluid consisting largely of mononuclear cells. The fluid is bacteria-free, with a normal glucose content and often a slightly elevated protein content.

Etiology

Aseptic meningitis may be caused by a variety of agents: (1) primarily neurotropic viruses (poliomyelitis, lymphocytic choriomeningitis, and arthropod-borne encephalitis viruses); (2) viruses not primarily neurotropic (enteroviruses, mumps, herpes simplex, herpes zoster, infectious mononucleosis, infectious hepatitis, varicella, and measles); (3) spirochetes (*Treponema pallidum* and leptospirae); (4) bacteria, as in silent brain abscess and inadequately treated bacterial meningitis; and (5) mycoplasmas or chlamydiae.

Diagnosis

The diagnosis of aseptic viral meningitis is made by exclusion of bacterial causes of the symptom complex. Specific etiologic causes of aseptic meningitis can usually be determined only by isolation of the agent or the demonstration of a rise in specific antibodies. However, epidemiologic features have diagnostic value. (See discussions of specific agents.)

Laboratory Findings

The peripheral white count is usually normal, but in lymphocytic choriomeningitis eosinophilia may appear a few days after onset. There is pleocytosis of the CSF; polymorphonuclear cells often predominate during the first 24 hours, but a shift to lymphocytes usually occurs thereafter. In mumps and poliomyelitis, the usual range is 50–300 cells, but more may be found. In herpes simplex and leptospiral meningitis, up to 300 cells is usual. In lymphocytic choriomeningitis there may be 500–3000 cells or more. Protein levels of the spinal fluid are often elevated.

LYMPHOCYTIC CHORIOMENINGITIS

Lymphocytic choriomeningitis (LCM) is an acute disease characterized usually by the aseptic meningitis syndrome or by a mild systemic influenza-like illness but occasionally by a severe encephalomyelitis or a fatal systemic disease. The incubation period is usually 18–21 days but may be as short as 1–3 days. The mild systemic form, which is rarely recognized clinically, is characterized by fever, malaise, generalized muscle aches and pains, low backache, weakness, and, in some patients, respiratory symptoms, including sore throat and cough. The temperature returns to normal after 3–14 days, and the patient is well by that time.

LCM virus is 50–150 nm in size. It is identical morphologically—and cross-reacts serologically—with arboviruses of the Tacaribe complex (eg, Junin and Machupo viruses of South American hemorrhagic fevers and Lassa fever virus). These RNA-containing, enveloped viruses belong to the arenavirus family (see Chapters 27 and 30).

Diagnosis

Specific diagnosis can be made by the isolation of virus from spinal fluid or blood during the acute phase and by serologic tests demonstrating a rise in antibody titer between acute and convalescent serum specimens. Complement-fixing antibodies rise to diagnostic levels in 3–4 weeks, fall gradually in ensuing weeks, and reach normal levels after several months. Neutralizing antibodies appear later and reach diagnostic levels 7–8 weeks after onset; they persist for as long as 4–5 years.

Laboratory Findings

In the prodromal period (or mild systemic form), leukopenia with relative lymphocytosis is frequently present. In patients with the meningitic form, occasional leukocytosis up to 20,000 with an increase mainly in polymorphonuclear leukocytes is seen. CSF pleocytosis is higher than in most other forms of aseptic meningitis, ranging between 100 and several thousand cells; about half of patients have counts greater than 600. The cells are predominantly lymphocytes. The average protein content is about 100 mg/100 ml. Abnormal CSF findings persist for several weeks.

Epidemiology & Control

The disease is endemic in mice and other animals (dogs, monkeys, guinea pigs) and is occasionally transmitted to man. One large epidemic in the USA was caused by infected pet hamsters. There is no evidence of person-to-person spread.

Infected gray house mice, probably the most common source of human infection, excrete the virus in urine and feces. The virus may be harbored by mice throughout their lives, and females transmit it to their offspring, which in turn become healthy carriers. Mice inoculated as adults develop a rapidly fatal generalized infection. In contrast, congenitally or neonatally in-

fected mice do not become acutely ill, but 10–12 months later many develop a fatal debilitating disease involving the CNS. The animals exhibit chronic glomerulonephritis and hypergammaglobulinemia; the glomerular lesions are due to deposition of antigen-antibody complexes, and the infection in mice is considered an immune complex disease (see Slow Virus Diseases, below, and Persistent Viral Infections & Immune Complex Diseases, Chapter 27).

The mode of transmission to man is not known, but contaminated dust and food are probably vehicles. *Trichinella spiralis* can be infected experimentally, and it has been suggested that this parasite may serve as a means of conveying the virus from one animal to another and perhaps to man through an intermediate host such as the pig.

Mice should be eliminated from the home.

ENCEPHALITIS LETHARGICA
(Von Economo's Disease)

Several thousand cases of this acute type of encephalitis occurred during the winter seasons between 1915 and 1926. Epidemics did not occur after that time, and the disease has not been seen in recent years. A virus is presumed to have been the cause. The pathologic findings were similar to those produced by the neurotropic viruses. Onset was gradual, with malaise, headache, fever, and aching of joints and muscles; this was followed by signs suggesting mesencephalic involvement. Somnolence and stupor were common. The case fatality rate was about 40%. Neurologic sequelae (eg, paralysis agitans) are common in survivors.

EPIDEMIC NEUROMYASTHENIA
(Benign Myalgic Encephalomyelitis)

A number of outbreaks of epidemic neuromyasthenia have been reported in Europe and the USA. No etiologic agent has been isolated, although viruses are believed to play a role. The main features of the disease are fatigue, headache, intense muscle pain, slight and transient paresis, mental disturbances, and objective evidence of diffuse involvement of the CNS. The illness is sometimes confused with poliomyelitis. Young and middle-aged adults are principally afflicted. Sporadic cases have also been reported.

MENGO FEVER
(Columbia-SK Infection, Encephalomyocarditis Virus Infection)

This virus has been recovered in eastern USA and in Uganda. It appears to infect man only rarely, producing a mild febrile illness (3-day fever with spinal fluid lymphocytosis). Only one case has been proved by virus isolation. The patient had fever, headache, nuchal rigidity, photophobia, vomiting, and short periods of delirium. The virus was isolated from the blood on the first and second days of illness, and antibodies appeared during convalescence. A few instances have been recorded in which sera from individuals suffering from CNS diseases neutralized the virus.

The virus is pathogenic for many animals, including mice, guinea pigs, monkeys, and chick embryos. It has been isolated in nature from the cotton rat, mongoose, rhesus monkey, baboon, chimpanzee, and Taeniorhynchus mosquitoes. Neutralizing antibodies are present in wild rats collected in certain areas of the USA and Uganda, but they are rarely found in man. The virus can cause lesions in the CNS and in skeletal and cardiac muscle. An outbreak of fatal myocarditis caused by this virus has been observed in pigs.

The agent belongs to the picornavirus family. It has a diameter of about 25 nm and contains 30% RNA. It is a satisfactory antigen in the CF test and also agglutinates sheep erythrocytes. Antibodies can be measured by Nt, CF, and HI methods.

SLOW VIRUS DISEASES: CHRONIC VIRAL DISEASES OF THE CNS & OTHER PROGRESSIVE DEGENERATIVE DISORDERS

Since 1965, three neurologic diseases of man have been shown to be caused by chronic, persistent, slow virus infections: kuru, Creutzfeldt-Jakob disease, and subacute sclerosing panencephalitis (SSPE). Viral etiology has been reported or strongly suspected in a number of other chronic CNS diseases, including multiple sclerosis, which afflicts about 100,000 people in the USA alone.

Some animal viruses are capable of producing chronic infections of the CNS which may be manifest as progressive degenerative disorders, and these animal infections have served as useful models for approaches to similar degenerative disorders of man. These diseases include visna of sheep in Iceland, scrapie of sheep in Britain, and transmissible mink encephalopathy. The progressive neurologic diseases produced by these viruses may have incubation periods of up to 5 years before the clinical manifestations of the infections become evident.

Visna and **progressive pneumonia (maedi)** viruses are closely related agents which cause slow infections in sheep. Because of the remarkable similarities between these viruses and the RNA tumor viruses, they have been grouped together in the family **Retroviridae**. The visna and progressive pneumonia viruses constitute a subfamily **Lentivirinae**. The similarities include the following: virion assembly and maturation by a bud-

ding process, virion size (70–100 nm), the presence of virion-associated RNA-directed DNA polymerase (reverse transcriptase), 4S and 70S RNA, and a similar polypeptide profile (see Chapter 40). In addition, purified visna and progressive pneumonia viruses contain projections or "spikes" on their outer membrane, and negatively stained particles resemble those of Rous sarcoma virus. Internal strand-like structures, similar to those described for the avian, murine, and feline C-type viruses, also have been noted.

Visna virus infects all of the organs of the body of the infected sheep; however, pathologic changes are confined primarily to the brain, lungs, and reticuloendothelial system. There is a long incubation period, and virus can be recovered from the animal as long as 4 years after inoculation. Infected animals develop antibodies to the virus; these can be detected in the CSF as well as the serum of sick animals.

Spongiform Encephalopathies of Man & Animals

Four degenerative CNS diseases—kuru and **Creutzfeldt-Jakob disease** of man, **scrapie** of sheep, and **transmissible encephalopathy** of mink—have similar pathologic features, but their agents have been very difficult to study because they have not yet been shown to induce either circulating antibody or a cellular immune response. Thus, it has been suggested that they may be related, but this cannot be confirmed because proof of interrelationships depends chiefly upon antigen-antibody reactions. Another puzzling aspect of these agents is their "invisibility" to repeated attempts at observation by electron microscopy, despite the fact that estimates of their size, based upon their retention by filters having pores of known dimensions, show them to be large enough to be detected by electron microscopy. Another characteristic not usually associated with typical viruses is their high degree of resistance to inactivation by heat, formalin, nucleases, and ultraviolet irradiation; however, infectivity is destroyed by phenol or ether. It has been suggested that these may represent an entirely new class of agents different from true viruses, possibly containing a very small nucleic acid in the same size range as "viroids" (see Chapter 27).

Scrapie, which behaves as a recessive genetic trait in sheep, shows marked differences in genetic susceptibility of different breeds. Susceptibility to experimentally transmitted scrapie has been found to range from zero to over 80% in sheep, whereas goats are almost 100% susceptible. The transmission of scrapie to mice, in which the incubation period is greatly reduced, has facilitated study of the disease. Scrapie has also been transmitted to a laboratory monkey; this ability to infect primates suggests that greater precautions may be needed to avoid human use of scrapie-infected meat since the agent resists cooking temperatures.

Current knowledge of scrapie is based on studies of the disease in mice. The length of incubation is influenced by the dose of virus and the mouse genotype; it can be as short as 100 days or may be longer than the lifespan of the mouse. There is an almost clockwork precision in the development of the experimental disease. Under defined conditions of infection, the incubation time can be measured with a standard error of only 1–2% of the mean, which is somewhat difficult to reconcile with the random behavior of other neurotropic viruses. There is little doubt that the long incubation period is due to the slow rate of multiplication in brain, possibly because of a limited number of replication sites.

The unusual stability of the scrapie agent (see above) may be related to its intimate association with cell membranes. The smallest membrane fragments with infectivity have a diameter < 50 nm, and there is some indication that the scrapie-specific portion may be much smaller. The infectious scrapie agent may consist of a small specific nucleic acid with a coat derived entirely from the host cell. Its molecular weight, from ionizing radiation data, may be only 150,000, the size of viroid RNA.

Recently, virus-like particles 14 nm in diameter have been isolated from mouse brain infected with the scrapie agent. It is not yet known whether these particles are indeed the scrapie agent. They may represent a virus which is latently present in the brain and activated by scrapie infection but which plays no role in the disease. However, it is interesting that the 14 nm size corresponds to the theoretical smallest size for a spherical virus.

Transmissible mink encephalopathy (TME) is caused by a virus which induces clinical disease and neurologic lesions in the gray matter of the brain similar to those of scrapie. The virus is about 35 nm in size and has a long incubation period in mink that are naturally infected—presumably by the oral route. Some believe that TME represents a strain of sheep scrapie acquired by mink fed infected sheep meat.

The 2 **human spongiform encephalopathies** of demonstrated viral cause involve lesions markedly similar to those of scrapie and mink encephalopathy. These are **Creutzfeldt-Jakob (C-J) disease** (subacute presenile dementia) and **kuru**, an unusual degenerative disease of the CNS found among certain tribes of New Guinea. Brain material from patients afflicted with **kuru** or C-J disease can produce similar diseases when injected into chimpanzees, and the passage of diseased chimpanzee brain into healthy animals transfers the diseases to other chimpanzees. The incubation period of the diseases in chimpanzees is measured in months or years. Both diseases have been transmitted to numerous other species of nonhuman primates (monkeys, gibbons). Efforts to transmit C-J disease or kuru to small laboratory animals, in which a shorter incubation period might speed studies of the agent and the disease, have not generally succeeded as yet. An instance strongly suggesting human-to-human transmission of C-J disease by corneal transplant has been documented; the patient developed the disease 18 months after trans-

Table 33—3. Slow virus infections.

Disease	Virus	Host(s)	Incubation Period	Nature of Disease
Diseases of man				
Kuru	< 220 nm (probably < 100 nm)	Man (chimpanzees, monkeys)	Months to years	Spongiform encephalopathy
Creutzfeldt-Jakob (C-J) disease	?	Man (chimpanzees, monkeys)	Months to years	Spongiform encephalopathy
Subacute sclerosing panencephalitis (SSPE)	Measles variant	Man	2–20 years	Chronic sclerosing panencephalitis
Progressive multifocal leukoencephalopathy (PML)	Papovavirus	Man	?	CNS demyelination
Diseases of animals				
Scrapie	< 50 nm, perhaps 14 nm	Sheep (goats, mice)	Months to years	Spongiform encephalopathy
Transmissible mink encephalopathy (TME)	35 nm	Mink (other animals)	Months	Spongiform encephalopathy
Visna	70–100 nm (oncornavirus-like)	Sheep	Months to years	CNS demyelination
Aleutian disease of mink	25 nm	Mink	Months	Immune complex disease
Lymphocytic choriomeningitis (LCM)	50–150 nm	Mice (man occasionally infected)	Months (in mice)	Immune complex disease (in congenitally or neonatally infected mice)

plant and subsequently died. Portions of the brain were taken at autopsy and preserved in 10% formol saline (4% formaldehyde) for 7 months. A brain suspension was then injected into a chimpanzee, which developed symptoms of C-J disease 17 months later.

The failure of 10% formol saline, routinely used in pathologic studies, to destroy the infectivity of the virus of C-J disease supports the need for caution in handling these tissues. Similar studies are in progress with chimpanzees inoculated with formalin-fixed kuru-infected brain tissue. The effects of formaldehyde on scrapie virus, another of the prototype subacute spongiform virus encephalopathies, are pertinent. Fixation of infected mouse brain in 10% formol saline for 10 days at ambient temperature reduced the infectivity titer by only 1.4 logs ($10^{8 \cdot 1} - 10^{6 \cdot 7}$ mouse LD_{50} per milliliter). The high resistance of scrapie—and now C-J virus—in whole tissue and in suspension to inactivation by formaldehyde bears watching.

Kuru occurs only in the Fore tribe and the neighboring tribes of the eastern highlands of New Guinea. The disease consists of relentless progressive cerebellar ataxia, tremors, dysarthria, and emotional lability without significant dementia. It occurs more frequently in women than in men, which coincides with the customs surrounding cannibalism. The remains of dead relatives were handled and eaten primarily by women and children. Since cannibalism has been outlawed, the incidence of the disease has decreased, and it is now felt that this was the primary mode of transmission of the agent.

Creutzfeldt-Jakob disease, a rare sporadic disorder that has been observed in a wide variety of geographic locations, is characterized by neuropathologic lesions similar to the spongiform degeneration observed in kuru, but it is clinically and pathologically distinguishable from kuru both in man and in chimpanzees. C-J disease is characterized by severe progressive dementia, myoclonic fasciculations, ataxia, and somnolence.

For the 4 recognized spongiform viral encephalopathies (kuru, C-J disease, scrapie, and mink encephalopathy), the basic lesion at the cellular level is the same: intracytoplasmic vacuolation in the axonal and dendritic processes of neurons, with coalescence of the vacuoles to form a ballooning and destruction of the cells. In each disease there is little or no perivascular infiltration with mononuclear cells and no meningeal involvement, primary demyelination, or CSF pleocytosis and no consistent changes in sedimentation rate, clinical chemistry values, or febrile reactions at any stage of disease. It has been suggested that the causative agents may be closely related; in any case, until further characterization of the agents has been accomplished, they might conveniently be considered together. Recent studies of scrapie and TME in hamsters have shown that these diseases are almost indistinguishable histologically, biochemically, or biologically when compared in a common experimental host. Other spongiform encephalopathies and progressive dementias (**Alper's disease, Pick's disease, Alzheimer's disease**) are suspected of having a viral cause also. Some strains of the scrapie agent can produce cerebral amyloid deposits in mice which are broadly similar to the amyloid plaques seen in aged human beings and in Alzheimer's disease and Down's syndrome.

Other CNS Degenerative Disorders

Subacute sclerosing panencephalitis (SSPE), a rare but fatal disease characterized by inflammatory cell infiltration, gliosis, and demyelination of the CNS, is associated with helical structures morphologically and antigenically similar to the internal components of measles virus. A virus closely resembling measles virus has been isolated from infected brain tissue by co-cultivation of the living tissue with normal human cells, which are highly susceptible to the virus. The virus is not localized exclusively in brain tissues, for isolations have been made from lymph nodes as well (see Chapter 35). Elevated serum CSF levels of measles antibody strongly suggest that the patient has SSPE. Similar helical structures suggestive of an incomplete paramyxovirus have been observed in muscle biopsies in chronic polymyositis.

A progressive panencephalitis has recently been reported in patients with congenital **rubella.** The neurologic illness developed in the second decade and consisted of spasticity, ataxia, seizures, and progressive decline in intellectual ability.

Papovaviruses have been isolated from brain tissue of patients with **progressive multifocal leukoencephalopathy (PML),** a rare CNS complication found in patients suffering from chronic leukemia, Hodgkin's disease, lymphosarcoma, or carcinomatosis, or in others receiving immunosuppressants. The virus most often isolated, the JC subtype, is distinct antigenically and biologically from known papovaviruses but cross-reacts with SV40 to a small extent. The JC isolate induces brain tumors in hamsters that resemble glioblastomas and medullablastomas but without demyelination. A second variant, the SV40-PML subtype, is similar to SV40 both antigenically and in biologic properties. In hamsters it produces tumors and a tumor-antibody response indistinguishable from those induced by SV40 itself. Another papovavirus, the BK subtype, was recovered from the urine of a patient on immunosuppressive therapy but has not been associated with any disease.

Serologic tests have established an antigenic relationship between BK virus and SV40 for both the structural and T antigens, and biochemical studies show that BK virus polypeptides are similar in molecular weight to those of SV40. BK virus can also transform hamster cells in culture. (See Papovavirus section in Chapter 40.)

On the basis of seroepidemiologic studies of antibody occurrence in the population, human infections with these agents are common despite the rarity of the neurologic disease. Clinical remission attributed to administration of cytarabine has been reported in one patient in whom PML was confirmed by histologic study of brain biopsy. Immune electron microscopy and hemagglutination inhibition showed that the patient had high antibody levels against JC virus. In spite of the association of the papovavirus with PML, its etiologic role remains to be established.

Chronic virus infections may be associated with other progressive degenerative diseases of the CNS of man. Russian virologists have reported isolation of a virus responsible for "amyotrophic lateral sclerosis" (ALS) which has been passed to monkeys. The experimental disease had an incubation period of 5 years, and the histopathologic changes produced were similar to those of the natural disease of human beings. However, attempts to confirm these findings have not yet succeeded. The magnitude of the problem of ALS can be better appreciated when one considers that the incidence (new cases per year) and death rate approach those of multiple sclerosis, although the prevalence (living cases at any one time) is much lower since most ALS patients survive for only a few years.

Viral etiology has been suggested for **Guillain-Barré syndrome** on the basis of isolation of echoviruses from the CSF of some patients who had concurrent antibody rises against the same echovirus serotype. More recent evidence has also implicated herpesviruses in this syndrome.

Many investigators consider **multiple sclerosis (MS)** to be the result of a hypersensitivity phenomenon associated with a disturbance in the immune mechanism. However, recent epidemiologic, immunologic, and clinicopathologic findings suggest a possible viral association, with a virus either as a direct cause or as a provoking factor in development of an autoimmune response. Evidence is mounting that, if a virus is involved, the agent may be a member of the paramyxovirus family—the family to which measles virus also belongs.

In the chronic diseases mentioned above (progressive multifocal leukoencephalopathy, subacute sclerosing panencephalitis, multiple sclerosis), as well as in systemic lupus erythematosus and sarcoidosis, viral antibodies are often present at levels higher than in matched controls. What is not yet known is whether the high levels (1) occur before the chronic disease, indicating a viral etiology; (2) occur at the same time the chronic disease becomes manifest, as a result of a common defect in immunity; or (3) occur after the chronic disease is visible, as a result of a decrease in cell-mediated immunity brought on by the disease.

New clues to the cause of persistent infections have been reported recently. DNA transcripts of an RNA virus (measles) were observed to be integrated into the DNA of chronically infected cell cultures. Similarly, DNA sequences homologous to the RNA genome of measles virus were reported to be present in systemic lupus erythematosus tissue.

In other chronically infected cell systems (induced by arboviruses and by respiratory syncytial virus), infectious virus was also found to be integrated into the cellular DNA. In transfection experiments, DNA preparations from the chronically infected cells could be introduced into susceptible cells to yield infectious virus.

Immune Complex Diseases

In a number of the human progressive degenerative disorders of suspected viral cause, the immunologic response of the host to the virus may be responsible for the pathologic changes and for the clinical illness (see Chapter 27, sections on Persistent Viral Infections & Immune Complex Diseases). Two diseases of animals which serve as models in exploring this type of pathogenesis are lymphocytic choriomeningitis (LCM) in mice (see this chapter, section on LCM) and Aleutian disease (AD) of mink. In both diseases, the virus appears to persist in the chronically infected animal in a form, thought to be within a virus-antibody complex, in which the antibody is unable to neutralize and eliminate the virus. Deposition of these antigen-antibody complexes throughout a relatively long period of infection is believed to produce the basic lesions of the disease. Similar pathologic changes have been observed in human multiple myeloma and in certain human connective tissue disorders of unknown cause.

Aleutian disease of mink is a chronic viral infection which appears to be species-specific except for the closely related ferret. All genetic types of mink can be infected, but those of the Aleutian genotype die 100—150 days after infection, whereas non-Aleutian mink may live for a year or more. The basic lesion is systemic proliferation of plasma cells, with marked hypergammaglobulinemia involving overproduction of IgG. Although the virus replicates rapidly in animals after infection—just as in an acute type of viral infection—and antibody is produced, the infection persists until eventually the mink develops glomerulonephritis, which leads to renal failure and death. The virus may be found throughout the course of the animal's life, in serum, organs, and urine. The size of the agent is about 25 nm. Virus appears to circulate as infectious virus-antibody complexes in which the antibody is unable to neutralize the virus. The persistence of the virus might be explained by the virus-antibody complex entering the macrophages, in which antibody would be digested, allowing the virus to replicate. Such a mechanism would render the serum antibody response ineffective in quenching the infection. The circulating virus-antibody complexes produce glomerular changes which result in renal failure and death of the mink, and the disease is considered an immune complex disease.

•   •   •

General References

Bauer WR, Turel AP, Johnson KP: Progressive multifocal leuko-encephalopathy and cytarabine. JAMA 226:174, 1973.

Cho HJ, Greig AS: Isolation of 14-nm virus-like particles from mouse brain infected with scrapie agent. Nature 257:685, 1975.

Corey L, Hattwick MAW: Treatment of persons exposed to rabies. JAMA 232:272, 1975.

Emmons RW & others: A case of human rabies with prolonged survival. Intervirology 1:60, 1973.

Fuccillo DA, Kurent JE, Sever JL: Slow virus diseases. Annu Rev Microbiol 28:231, 1974.

Gajdusek DC: Slow virus infection and activation of latent infections in aging. Adv Gerontol Res 4:201, 1972.

Hotchin J & others: Persistent and slow virus infections. Prog Med Virol 18:1, 1974.

Jabbour JT & others: Epidemiology of subacute sclerosing pan-encephalitis (SSPE): A report of the SSPE Registry. JAMA 220:959, 1972.

Lampert PW, Gajdusek DC, Gibbs CJ: Subacute spongiform virus encephalopathies: Scrapie, kuru and Creutzfeldt-Jakob disease. A review. Am J Pathol 68:626, 1972.

Matsumoto S: Rabies virus. Adv Virus Res 16:257, 1971.

Melnick JL, Richardson LS: Slow viruses. Pages 2968–2974 in: *Pathology of the Nervous System.* Vol 3. Minckler J (editor). McGraw-Hill, 1972.

Naryan O & others: Etiology of progressive multifocal leukoen-cephalopathy: Identification of papovavirus. N Engl J Med 289:1278, 1973.

Oldstone MBA: Virus neutralization and virus-induced immune complex disease: Virus-antibody union resulting in immu-noprotection or immunologic injury—two sides of the same coin. Prog Med Virol 19:84, 1975.

Porter DD: A quantitative view of the slow virus landscape. Prog Med Virol 13:339, 1971.

Rubin RH, Sikes RK, Gregg MB: Human rabies immune globu-lin: Clinical trials and effects on serum anti-γ-globulins. JAMA 224:871, 1973.

Rubin RH & others: Adverse reactions to duck embryo rabies vaccine. Ann Intern Med 78:643, 1973.

Weiner LP, Johnson RT, Herndon RM: Viral infections and demyelinating diseases. N Engl J Med 288:1103, 1973.

Wiktor TJ, Plotkin SA, Grella DW: Human cell culture rabies vaccine. JAMA 224:1170, 1973.

Wiktor TJ & others: Antigenic properties of rabies virus com-ponents. J Immunol 110:269, 1973.

Zhdanov VM: Integration of viral genomes. Nature 256:471, 1975.

34...
Orthomyxovirus (Influenza) & Coronavirus Families

ORTHOMYXOVIRUS FAMILY

The name **myxovirus**—virus with an affinity for mucins—was originally proposed for the first members of the group, the influenza viruses, now classified as the **Orthomyxoviridae**. These viruses are pleomorphic in shape and contain RNA in a helical nucleocapsid surrounded by an ether-sensitive envelope. Other viruses, including mumps, measles, respiratory syncytial, and parainfluenza viruses, possess certain characteristics in common with the influenza viruses but differ in other important respects and have been placed in a separate family, **Paramyxoviridae**. The diameter of the inner ribonucleoprotein (RNP) helix is 9 nm for the **Orthomyxoviridae** and 18 nm for the **Paramyxoviridae** (see Chapter 35).

The orthomyxoviruses have an additional distinguishing feature. Their RNA genome is single-stranded and segmented, composed of 6 distinct and separate pieces with a total molecular weight of $2-4 \times 10^6$. Paramyxoviruses have a genome which is a single molecule of single-stranded RNA with a molecular weight of $3-5 \times 10^6$.

All orthomyxoviruses recognized to date are considered influenza viruses and can be classed as type A, B, or C on the basis of their RNP antigen, which does not cross-react between types. Until 1972, the classification of influenza viruses was based upon assignment of type according to the RNP antigen and subtype according to the hemagglutinin antigen (eg, A2). However, another antigen, the neuraminidase, undergoes antigenic variation independently of the hemagglutinin variations. Furthermore, both the hemagglutinin and neuraminidase antigens of influenza A viruses of human origin may be closely related to certain strains from nonhuman hosts. To permit uniform and adequate description of influenza viruses, the notation for influenza A viruses now includes the **strain designation** and a **description of the hemagglutinin and neuraminidase antigens**. The following are examples of the designation of a given isolate under the new system:

A/Hong Kong/1/68(H3N2)
A/turkey/Wisconsin/1/66(Hav5N2)
A/swine/Taiwan/1/70(H3N2)

The descriptions above indicate that the influenza virus isolated from turkeys in Wisconsin in 1966 contains neuraminidase antigenically related to that of the human Hong Kong/68 isolate and also contains an unrelated hemagglutinin. However, the virus isolated from swine in Taiwan in 1970 contains both hemagglutinin and neuraminidase antigens related to those of the human Hong Kong/68 isolate.

INFLUENZA

Influenza is an acute respiratory tract infection which usually occurs in epidemics. Three immunologic types of influenza virus are known: A, B, and C. Antigenic changes appear to be continually taking place within the A group of influenza viruses and to a lesser degree in the B group, while influenza C appears to be antigenically stable. In addition to human types, influenza A strains are known for pigs, horses, ducks, and chickens (fowl plague). Some of the animal isolates possess antigenic properties similar to the virus strains circulating in the human population.

Influenza virus type C differs in a number of respects from the type A and type B viruses; for example, its receptor-destroying enzyme does not appear to be a neuraminidase, and its virion structure is not fully understood. In the classification officially approved by the International Committee on Taxonomy of Viruses in 1975, types A and B were established as a genus, *Influenzavirus,* within the family **Orthomyxoviridae**, but type C was accorded only "probable genus" status. Most of the studies on which the following descriptions are based were conducted chiefly with influenza virus type A.

Properties of the Virus

A. Size of Virus and Its Components: Influenza virus consists of pleomorphic, approximately spherical particles having an external diameter of about 110 nm and an inner electron-dense core of 70 nm.

The surface of the virus particles is covered with 2 types of projections or spikes approximately 10 nm long possessing either the hemagglutinin or the neuraminidase activity of the virus. A model of the influenza virion has been recently proposed to indicate the function and the location of the various protein structural components (Fig 34–1).

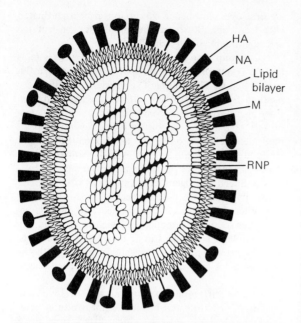

Figure 34–1. A model of the influenza virion. The innermost component is the helical ribonucleoprotein (RNP), which is 9 nm in diameter. It is as yet unknown whether the RNP is one long molecule or is divided into pieces like the virus RNA. The nucleocapsid is further organized by the coiling of the whole RNP strand into a double helix 50–60 nm in diameter. The protein component of this structure has a molecular weight of 60,000 and is associated with the group-specific CF antigen. A protein (M) shell surrounds the nucleoprotein and forms the inner part of the virus envelope. It is composed of a small protein (molecular weight 26,000) and constitutes about 40% of the virus protein. About 20% of the virus particle is composed of lipid, apparently derived from the host cell. The lipid is formed into a bilayer structure. The hemagglutinin (HA) spike is responsible for the agglutination of erythrocytes by this virus. It is composed of 2 molecules of a glycoprotein (molecular weight 75,000) which may or may not be cleaved to form 2 disulfide-linked glycopeptides of molecular weight 27,000 and 53,000. The smaller of these is present at the end of the molecule which is attached to the lipid. The neuraminidase (NA) spike is responsible for the receptor-destroying activity of the virus; this activity results in elution of the virus from host cells or erythrocytes. The role of its activity in virus replication is unknown. It is composed of 4 polypeptide molecules with a molecular weight of about 60,000. The arrangement of these molecules is still a matter of debate. Both the HA and the NA spikes have been purified, and a study of the purified protein has helped to explain antigenic changes of the virus. (From Compans & Choppin.)

Nucleic acid of the influenza virus is not a single molecule, and 6 distinct and separable components have been resolved. The summed molecular weights of these RNA pieces total 2–4 million per virion. The base composition of viral RNA is rich in uridine and does not vary significantly from strain to strain but differs from RNA of the host cell. Most of the polynucleotides that comprise the RNA of the virion terminate with a uridine residue at the 3' end.

Because of a divided genome, viruses of this group

exhibit several biologic phenomena such as high recombination frequency, multiplicity reactivation, and ability to synthesize hemagglutinin and neuraminidase after chemical inactivation of viral infectivity.

The viral RNAs are not known to be infectious, but some evidence suggests that the viral ribonucleoprotein is infectious. This structure contains the virion-associated RNA-dependent RNA polymerase as well as the genome. Evidently, all messenger RNA is complementary to the virion RNA. In this respect, orthomyxoviruses are similar to paramyxoviruses, rhabdoviruses, and reoviruses.

B. Reactions to Physical and Chemical Agents: Influenza virus is relatively stable and may be stored at 4° C for a week and at 0° C for longer periods. The virus is less stable at −20° C than at +4° C. The infectivity is best preserved at −70° C or by lyophilization of the crude virus suspensions. Infectivity is destroyed by heating at 56° C for a few minutes. However, the infectivity of the virus can be stabilized by 1 M $MgSO_4$ to such a degree that heating at 50° C for 30 minutes has hardly any deleterious effect. Infectivity is destroyed by treatment with ether, formaldehyde, phenol, and other protein denaturants. The hemagglutinin and the complement-fixing antigens are more stable to physical and chemical agents than the mature infective virus. Ultraviolet irradiation destroys the infectivity, toxicity, hemagglutinating activity, neuraminidase activity, and CF antigen, in that order.

Infectivity is destroyed at pH 3.0, and both infectivity and hemagglutination are more stable at alkaline pH than at acid pH.

C. Animal Susceptibility and Growth of Virus: Human strains of the virus can infect a number of different animals; ferrets are more susceptible than other species. Serial passage in mice increases its virulence for this animal, producing extensive pulmonary consolidation and death. The developing chick embryo readily supports the growth of virus, but for most strains even a high level of infection fails to produce grossly detectable lesions.

From the A/WS influenza virus, mutants were derived which grow readily in the mouse brain and induce fatal encephalitis in these animals.

Wild influenza viruses do not grow well in tissue cultures. In most instances, only an abortive growth cycle occurs, ie, viral subunits are synthesized but no new infectious progeny, or very little, is formed. From virtually all influenza strains it is possible to select mutants which will grow well and induce cytopathic effects and plaques (under agar overlay) in rhesus monkey kidney cells or calf kidney cells. Several passages are usually necessary before such viruses are isolated. Striking exceptions are the fowl plague virus and the neurotropic mutant of WS virus (NWS), which grow well in tissue cultures of divergent origin. It has also been shown that this property can be transferred from these viruses to other influenza viruses by means of genetic recombination.

Because of the poor growth of many strains in monkey cells, initial isolation is best accomplished by the use of both amniotic inoculation of embryonated chicken eggs and inoculation of monkey cell cultures. The process of infection begins by adsorption of the virus onto its receptor sites (neuraminic acid-containing glycoproteins). The HA protein is the virus component involved in this reaction. The other spike protein, neuraminidase, can destroy the site. The interaction of these 2 activities is complex and is not completely understood. The virus particle is taken into the cell, where it is disrupted, causing a decrease or "eclipse" in detectable virus shortly after infection.

Intracellular synthesis of the viral RNA and protein then occurs. Synthesis of viral RNA in the nucleus starts between 1 and 2 hours after infection and reaches a maximum level at 3 hours. The RNA pieces appear to replicate independently.

All virus proteins are synthesized in the cytoplasm, although the nucleus appears to be involved in the processing of some virus proteins, especially the nucleoprotein. All the virus envelope proteins appear to be associated with membranes soon after their synthesis. Apparently, virus particles are formed by binding of the spike proteins (HA and NA) to portions of the cell membrane, whereupon the M protein associates closely with this part of the membrane. RNP then binds specifically to these altered areas, and budding of the virus particle occurs. Neuraminidase may be important in the release of the completed virus.

The kinetics of virus replication vary widely with the host cell and the virus strain. In the most efficient systems, virus production reaches a plateau 8–12 hours after infection.

In most influenza virus systems, noninfectious particles capable of hemagglutination are produced (von Magnus phenomenon). These particles, called "incomplete," increase in number upon serial, high-multiplicity passage of the virus. The incomplete particles are smaller and more pleomorphic than standard virus, and, furthermore, they interfere with replication of standard virus. They are now known as defective interfering or DI particles. The defect apparently resides in the virus RNA, since the largest virus RNA piece is missing from DI particles.

The multiplication of influenza virus is inhibited by amantadine (see Treatment), dactinomycin, p-fluorophenylalanine, and mitomycin C.

D. Biologic Properties:

1. **Hemagglutination**—All strains of influenza virus agglutinate erythrocytes from chickens, guinea pigs, and humans, and—unlike paramyxoviruses—agglutinate erythrocytes from many other species as well. Agglutination of red blood cells occurs when the hemagglutinin interacts with a specific receptor on the red blood cell membrane. This receptor is a glycoprotein (3×10^4 molecular weight) which is composed of amino acids, hexose, hexosamine, and sialic acid. This glycoprotein serves both as the receptor site for the hemagglutinin and as the substrate for the viral neuraminidase. Cleavage of the glycoprotein by the enzyme dissociates the virion from the red cell, resulting in spontaneous elution. After elution, the cell receptors

are destroyed and hence can no longer be agglutinated with fresh virus; however, the eluted virus can reattach and agglutinate additional cells.

2. **Group antigen**—All influenza A virus strains share a common antigen, distinct from those of influenza B and C. This soluble (S) antigen is found in the medium from infected cell cultures and has been identified as a tyrosine-rich component of the ribonucleoprotein of the virus. In soluble form, the antigen has a molecular weight of 5.3×10^4 and is identified by CF. Antibody to this nucleoprotein antigen does not induce resistance to the virus in man or animals.

3. **Specific antigens**—The infectious virus particles induce in animals the development of virus-neutralizing and other antibodies, and the inoculated animals become resistant to infection. Influenza virus administered in large amounts is toxic for laboratory animals. The effect is apparently associated directly with the virus particles and can be prevented by specific antibody.

The specific viral (V) antigen is the envelope component of the virus and includes hemagglutinin, neuraminidase, and CF antigen, which differs from the S antigen.

The hemagglutinin is the principal specific envelope antigen, and differences in this antigen among strains of virus can be shown by HI tests. Antibody to the HA neutralizes virus and appears to be the chief protective mechanism.

The specific antigenicity of the neuraminidase has been demonstrated by inhibition of the enzymatic activity, by immunodiffusion, and by a neuraminidase-specific HI test.

Neuraminidase is antigenically distinct from the hemagglutinin and is governed by a separate gene locus; hence, it can vary independently of the hemagglutinin. The antigens of the hemagglutinin and the neuraminidase of the virus are the basis for classifying new strains. Antibody against the neuraminidase does not neutralize the virus, but it modifies the infection, probably by its effect on the release of virus from the cells. The antibody against the neuraminidase occurs in sera of humans who experience infection. The presence of antineuraminidase antibody results in marked protection.

4. **Filamentous forms**—In addition to the spherical particles, elongated forms possessing the same surface projections have been observed. The filamentous forms also agglutinate red cells and elute from them. They may represent a stage in virus multiplication, and probably some of the spheres arise by segmentation of the long forms. In its early passages in chick embryos, the virus is usually in filamentous form, but with serial passage it takes on the spherical appearance described above. Whether the virus is spherical or filamentous in the human host is not known.

5. **Genetic recombination**—Genetic recombination of influenza strains occurs with high frequency, which provides the basis for interspecies transfer of influenza virus from animals to man. This may be due to the existence of viral RNA in several physical units which

replicate independently and are then assembled into infectious virions. Genetic dimorphism is exhibited in other characteristics such as virulence, antigen variation, inhibitor susceptibility, particle morphology, and the neuraminidase to hemagglutinin ratio.

Pathogenesis & Pathology

The virus enters the respiratory tract in airborne droplets. Viremia has been reported rarely. Virus is present in the nasopharynx from 1–2 days before to 1–2 days after onset of symptoms. The virus enzyme, neuraminidase, lowers the viscosity of the mucous film in the respiratory tract, laying bare the cellular surface receptors and promoting the spread of virus-containing fluid to lower portions of the tract. Even when neutralizing antibodies are in the blood they may not protect against infection. Antibodies must be present in sufficient concentration at the site of action of the virus ie, at the superficial cells of the respiratory tract. This can be achieved only if the antibody level in the blood is high or if antibody is secreted locally.

Inflammation of the upper respiratory tract is the usual extent of pathology. Pneumonia is rare but may be fatal. In such cases, the lungs show interstitial inflammation, with necrosis of bronchiolar and alveolar epithelium. The virus causes necrosis of the ciliated and goblet cells of the tracheal and bronchial mucosa but does not affect the basal layer of epithelium. The pneumonia is often associated with secondary bacterial invaders: staphylococci, pneumococci, streptococci, and *Haemophilus influenzae.*

Clinical Findings

The incubation period is only 1 or 2 days. Chills, malaise, fever, muscular aches, prostration, and respiratory symptoms may occur. The fever persists for about 3 days; complications are not common, but pneumonia and, rarely, CNS involvement with encephalomyelitis, polyneuritis, or Guillain-Barré syndrome do occur. Myocarditis and pericarditis have also been described. Recently, cases of Reye's syndrome (encephalopathy and fatty liver) have been reported following influenza B. The syndrome has also been seen following other viral diseases such as chickenpox. The mechanism by which the virus might induce this syndrome is not known. Illness due to influenza C virus was much milder than that due to influenza A or B viruses and has not been seen recently.

When influenza appears in epidemic form, the clinical findings are consistent enough so that the disease can be diagnosed in most cases on this basis alone; sporadic cases are almost impossible to diagnose solely on clinical grounds. Mild as well as asymptomatic infections occur. The severity of the pandemic of 1918–1919 has been attributed to the fact that bacterial pneumonia often developed.

The pandemic of 1957–1958 was clinically a mild disease. However, during the early winter of 1957–1958, in 100 cities of the USA, deaths were 40,000 above expectancy. Of the associated pneumonias, the largest number were pneumococcal. However, the vast majority of pneumonia-associated deaths were in the small (10%) staphylococcal group. Two to 3 months after the first wave of infections, a second wave of 20,000 influenza and pneumonia deaths occurred. In most of the fatal cases, typical influenza symptoms preceded the pneumonia; from a number of the cases studied, influenza virus was obtained from the lung tissue at autopsy.

The lethal impact of an influenza epidemic is reflected in the excess deaths due to cardiovascular and renal diseases as well as those due to pneumonia and influenza. Pregnant women and older persons suffering from chronic diseases have a higher risk of death. In young children, influenza A2 (Asian type) has been associated with croup.

Laboratory Diagnosis

Influenza can be readily diagnosed by laboratory procedures. For antibody determinations, the first serum should be taken less than 5 days after onset and the second about 10–14 days later.

For rapid detection of influenza virus in clinical specimens, positive smears from nasal swabs and washings may be demonstrated by specific staining with fluorescein-labeled antibody.

A. Recovery of Virus: Throat washings or garglings are obtained within 3 days after onset and should be tested at once or stored frozen. Penicillin and streptomycin are added to limit bacterial contamination, and embryonated eggs are inoculated by the amniotic route. Amniotic and allantoic fluids are harvested 2–4 days later and tested for hemagglutinins by the addition of 1% suspensions of chicken and guinea pig erythrocytes. If results are negative, passage is made to fresh embryos. If hemagglutinins are not detected after 2 such passages, the result is negative.

If a strain of virus is isolated—as demonstrated by the presence of hemagglutinins—it is titrated in the presence of type-specific influenza sera to determine its type. The new virus belongs to the same type as the serum which inhibits its hemagglutinating power.

Primate cell cultures (human or monkey) are susceptible to certain human strains of influenza virus. Rapid diagnosis can be made by growing the virus from the clinical specimen in cell culture and then staining the cultured cells with fluorescent influenza antibody 24 hours later, when infected cells are rich in antigen even though they may appear normal.

The phenomenon of hemadsorption is utilized for the early detection of virus growth in cell cultures. Guinea pig red cells or human O cells are added to the cultures 24–48 hours after the clinical specimens have been inoculated and are viewed under the low power lens. Positive hemadsorption shows red blood cells firmly attached to the cell culture sheets as rosettes or chains. Cultures which are negative at 24 hours can be reincubated for several more days with the red blood cell suspensions and examined periodically. The cytopathogenic effects of the influenza viruses are often minimal and difficult to detect in tissue cultures, and the production of hemagglutinin may be too low to permit its detection in the culture fluid. Hemadsorption provides a more sensitive testing procedure.

B. Typing of New Isolates: A double immunodiffusion (DID) test has been described recently for typing influenza virus isolates. In contrast to the conventional CF test for the internal nucleoprotein antigens of influenza, DID requires no special equipment or expensive reagents and may be easily performed in laboratories with a minimum of resources. The allantoic fluid content of a single infected embryonated egg may be used for the DID test. In addition, type-specific nucleoprotein or matrix protein antisera are needed.

The procedure is as follows. The isolates to be typed are inoculated into embryonated chicken eggs, incubated for 2–3 days at 35° C, and then chilled overnight at 4° C. Uninoculated eggs are included for the preparation of negative control antigens. Virus from the infected allantoic fluid is precipitated with mild acid, centrifuged, and resuspended. The DID test can be performed on commercially available agar plates. Reference antisera are placed in the outer wells, and the plates are allowed to stand at room temperature for 15–20 minutes. The virus harvest, after disruption by detergent, is added to the center well. The plates are incubated overnight in a moist atmosphere, and precipitin lines are read the following morning.

Matrix protein antiserum appears to be slightly more sensitive than nucleoprotein antiserum for typing influenza virus isolates, presumably because of the greater amount of matrix protein antigen in the virion.

The DID test is also applicable to identification of isolates from primary rhesus monkey kidney cell cultures. Culture fluids are treated in the same manner as for allantoic fluid harvests. The test is reasonably sensitive for primary cell cultures, but the low virus titers often associated with early virus passages may limit its use. A subpassage in embryonated eggs may sometimes be required for identification of cell culture isolates.

C. Serology: Paired sera can be used to detect rises in hemagglutination-inhibiting, complement-fixing, or virus-neutralizing antibodies. Of these, the hemagglutination-inhibiting antibody is most frequently employed. Normal sera often contain nonspecific mucoprotein inhibitors which must first be destroyed by treatment with RDE (receptor-destroying enzyme of *Vibrio cholerae* cultures), trypsin, carbon dioxide, or periodate. Because normal persons usually have influenza antibodies, a 4-fold or greater increase in titer is necessary to indicate influenza infection. Peak levels of antibodies are present 2 weeks after onset, persist for about 4 weeks, and then gradually fall during the course of a year to preinfection levels. When using the strain-specific CF test (with V antigen), the peak antibody levels are found in the fourth week.

Within one type of influenza virus, strains may differ markedly in antigenicity. It is best to use recently isolated strains.

Complement-fixing antigens are of 2 types. One is the soluble substance (S antigen), which is antigenically type-specific but fails to show antigenic differences between strains of one type. The other is associated with the virus particle (V antigen) and is highly specific for different strains within each type. It is of special advantage for demonstrating antibody rise when the first serum specimen was not taken early after the onset of the disease.

Immunity

Three immunologically unrelated types of influenza virus are known and are referred to as influenza A, B, and C. In addition, the swine, equine, and avian influenza viruses are antigenically related to the human influenza A virus. Influenza C virus exists as a single and stable antigenic type, in contrast to the variations known among the influenza A and B viruses.

At least 18 different antigenic components have been determined in type A strains of influenza virus by quantitative adsorption methods. More undoubtedly exist. Strains share their antigenic components, but in varying proportions. For example, the 1947 strains known as A′ or A1 possess major antigens in common with 1946–1950 strains and minor antigens in common with 1934 and 1953 strains. A strain generally shares its major antigens with strains prevalent within a few years of its isolation and its minor antigens with strains prevalent several years before or after its isolation. The wide sharing of antigenic components in some of the new isolates indicates that the antigenic components of strains prevalent several years ago have not completely disappeared even though the most common antigens are of the most recent A2 (Asian) set.

Two possible mechanisms for the antigenic variation of influenza virus have been suggested:

(1) All the possible configurations may be present in a pool of antigens which exist throughout the globe; from these, highly infectious strains arise and initiate epidemics. High antibody levels to recent strains in the human population will inhibit strains with major antigens which were dominant in recently prevalent strains and will select strains of different antigenic composition.

Serial passage of virus in mice vaccinated with the homologous strain yields a virus with an apparent rearrangement of antigens or the appearance of new antigens. The passage virus multiplies more readily in mice vaccinated with the parent virus, and it evokes an antibody which reacts well with the passage virus but only poorly with the parent strain. The change in antigenic character evolves slowly on passage; a change of great magnitude involving almost all the antigenic components of the virus does not occur quickly.

(2) Antigenically different strains may be selected by means of genetic recombination induced by environmental factors such as passage in a partially immune host. When critical concentrations of 2 strains of influenza virus are simultaneously injected into mice or eggs, a new strain sharing the properties of each parent

strain may be recovered; this has been attributed to genetic recombination. However, another interpretation of these findings is that the 2 "parent" strains may mutually interfere, thus preventing the multiplication of the characteristic major particles from each strain, and allowing the minority particles of each strain to be selected for replication. This might result in the recovery of strains with antigens capable of reacting with one or both of the "parent" strains but featuring still other heretofore unrecognized components.

Antibodies are important in immunity against influenza, but they must be present at the site of virus invasion. Work with experimental animal models has shown that resistance to initiation of infection is related to antibody against the hemagglutinin portion of the virus. Decreased extent of viral invasion and decreased ability to transmit virus to contacts are related to antibody directed against the neuraminidase of the virus.

Virus-neutralizing antibody occurs earlier in nasal secretions and rises to high titers sooner among those already possessing high concentrations of IgA in their nasal washings prior to the infection. Even though infected with influenza virus, such individuals remain well. In contrast, those with low nasal wash IgA levels prior to infection are highly susceptible not only to infection but also to clinical illness. Before antibodies can be detected in the respiratory secretions, they must exist in high concentration in the serum.

Treatment

In the past there was no specific treatment for influenza. Amantadine hydrochloride (see p 127) is an antiviral drug for systemic administration licensed in the USA for use in the prevention of influenza A2. The drug acts by blocking the penetration of influenza A2 into cells, thereby preventing viral replication and cell destruction. It is not intended to be used in the treatment of the established disease or influenzal or respiratory diseases other than influenza A2.

When doses in excess of 200 mg/day are given, CNS manifestations such as nervousness, insomnia, dizziness, and ataxia may occur, particularly in elderly patients.

Epidemiology

Influenza occurs in successive waves of infection, with peak incidences during the winter. Influenza A infections may vary from a few isolated cases to extensive outbreaks which within a few weeks involve 10% or more of the population, with rates of 50–75% in children of school age. The period between epidemic waves of influenza A is 2–3 years. It is believed that only type A viruses cause pandemics. Extensive pandemics have occurred; during the pandemic of 1918–1919, over 20 million people died following influenza infection, mostly from secondary bacterial pneumonia. Influenza B does not spread through a community as quickly as influenza A. Its interepidemic period varies from 3–6 years.

About 80 million cases occurred during the 1957–1958 pandemic of Asian influenza (A2). The illnesses were generally mild, but the estimated number of pneumonia-influenza deaths in the USA was 60,000 above normal during the pandemic. Older age groups have the lowest incidence of influenza but the highest case fatality rate—especially among those who suffer from chronic debilitating diseases.

Asian strain influenza virus was disseminated extensively around the world within 3 months after the disease spread from the mainland of China to Hong Kong (spring of 1957). The seeding of virus in Europe and in the USA during the summer months prepared for the epidemic disease which occurred in the fall season. The pandemic occurred in a period of 6 months. Increased human mobility was responsible for the rapid spread. Many outbreaks in the early stages of the pandemic could be directly traced to passengers and crews of air and surface vessels which had recently arrived from epidemic regions.

The next cycle of epidemic influenza, in 1962, was caused by influenza B. At that time, over 12,000 excess deaths occurred, primarily among the elderly. In 1963, an epidemic of A2 influenza occurred with 34,000 excess deaths, mainly among the elderly.

In the summer of 1968, an outbreak of influenza was reported from Hong Kong which then spread rapidly around the world. In the USA there were an estimated 30 million cases with nearly 20,000 deaths. This epidemic was due to a new antigenic variant. Although the isolates were still classified as influenza A2, they exhibited a greater dissimilarity from earlier A2 strains than had been previously observed.

Toward the end of September 1971, increases in the incidence of influenza due to virus A2 were observed in Bulgaria, Hungary, and Romania. From these foci the disease spread west and north, and by mid-January 1972 large outbreaks were being reported from most countries in western Europe and Scandinavia. European and Asian parts of the USSR were also affected. The disease was generally mild, although deaths from respiratory disease exceeded the expected number. In the southern hemisphere, outbreaks were reported from South Africa in May 1972 and from Argentina in June. A considerable increase in incidence was reported from New Zealand in July and from Australia later in the year. A new variant of A2 (A/England/42/72) was isolated during the epidemic season in England. Until April 1972, this variant was very rarely isolated except in southern India, but since then it has spread throughout the world.

In 1975 a new variant, A/Victoria, was isolated in Australia. Currently, the A/Victoria strains are the more commonly reported isolates worldwide, but 2 other antigenically distinct strains of influenza A continue to be found: A/England and A/Tokyo. Although sporadic isolation of the Japan and England strains in the United States may occur, the A/Victoria strains predominated in early 1976.

In the USA early in 1976, a new type A virus began appearing; this virus was obtained from 5 patients (one of whom died) in Fort Dix, New Jersey, at the same time as numerous Victoria-like isolates were also being obtained from other patients. All 5 isolates were identified as being similar to swine influenza A as regards both the hemagglutinin and the neuraminidase antigens (Hsw1N1). In a platoon with confirmed cases, 34% developed antibodies to the swine-related virus, whereas rates were as low as 6% in platoons without confirmed cases. If the swine isolates represent a radically new strain beginning to spread through the human population, they could foreshadow a large and very serious pandemic, for few persons under age 50 years have antibodies to swine influenza A virus. The 1918–1919 influenza virus which caused the worldwide pandemic shared antigens with swine influenza virus, but since the pandemic strain disappeared in the late 1920s there has been little evidence of human infection with strains having the swine antigens except in some individuals in frequent contact with swine. To assist in detecting any spread of the new swine-related virus, the Center for Disease Control, USPHS, has provided state and WHO collaborating laboratories with instructions and reagents for viral isolation and serologic testing appropriate for recognition of the swine virus antigens.

The main reason for the periodic occurrence of epidemic influenza is the accumulation of a sufficient number of susceptibles in a population which harbors the virus in a few subclinical or minor infections throughout the year. Epidemics may be started when the virus mutates to a new antigenic type which has survival advantages and to which antibodies in the population are low. Antibodies against the pandemic Asian strain were very rare prior to 1957 except in persons who were alive during 1889.

In early life the range of the influenza antibody spectrum is narrow, but it becomes progressively broader in later years. The antibodies (and immunity) acquired from the initial infections of childhood are of limited range and reflect the dominant antigens of the prevailing strains. Later exposures to viruses of related but differing antigenic composition result in an antibody spectrum broadening toward a larger number of the common antigens of influenza viruses. Exposures later in life to antigenically related strains result in a progressive reinforcement of the primary antibody. The highest antibody levels in a particular age group therefore reflect the dominant antigens of the virus responsible for the childhood infections of the group. Thus, a serologic recapitulation of past infection with influenza viruses of different antigenic makeup can be obtained by studying the age distribution of influenza antibodies in normal populations.

Antibodies against swine influenza (perhaps related to the pandemic influenza strain of 1918) have not been found in persons born after 1923. However, as indicated above, isolations early in 1976 have suggested a return of the 1918 pandemic strain. Persons born during 1923–1933 had their first influenza experience with a type A virus closely related to the 1933 WS strain. Those born between 1934 and 1943 do not possess swine or WS antibodies but have antibodies against another type A virus, PR-8.

Another antigenic change occurred among the A viruses in 1946. Strains occurring between 1946 and 1957 have been called A1 strains because, although related to the older viruses, they had a major difference in antigenic constitution. The influenza antibodies in persons born between 1946 and 1957 are chiefly against the A1 strains.

Most of the world's population probably have been immunized with the A1 strains, because almost all sera contain detectable titers of A1 antibody. However, during the 10-year period of A1 prevalence there were many modifications of antigenic structure even within the A1 group of viruses. With the widespread appearance of the type A2 Asian strain in 1957, the A1 set of viruses has been largely replaced, just as the PR-8 set of viruses disappeared when the A1 set began its period of prevalence in 1947.

Type A2 virus seems to be related to previous influenza viruses, in that sera in 1957 from people who were 70 years of age or older often contained antibody against A2 isolates. Furthermore, anti-A2 antibody increases were found in sera from this age group after injections of type A vaccine which did not contain the A2 virus (anamnestic response). This suggests that viruses prevalent during the 1889 pandemic contained antigens shared with the 1957 Asian strains.

Studies have been made on sera of isolated Pacific islanders whose only exposure to influenza occurred during the 1918 pandemic. Neutralizing antibody titers were greatest to the human A strains (PR-8 and BH), which were isolated in 1934 and 1935; they were significantly lower to swine influenza virus (isolated in 1931) and absent to human type A viruses isolated in 1940–1946 and to the later human types of A1 and A2. The study in the Pacific islanders shows that the viruses circulating 17 years later were still antigenically related to the virus causing the disaster of 1918.

Influenza B type appears to be changing antigenically since almost all strains of type B influenza virus isolated in 1965–1966 were closely related to B/Singapore/3/64, which differed significantly from the formerly prevalent variant represented by B/Maryland/1/59. In 1972, a new variant was isolated in Hong Kong (B/HK/5/72) and spread to Japan and Australia. Strains with antigens intermediate between earlier B strains and the new Asian strain then appeared in Europe. Since only 1% of the population of the USA possessed antibodies for the new B strain, vaccine was produced against it.

Control

The subcutaneous inoculation of influenza virus, inactivated by formalin or ultraviolet irradiation, induces in man a relatively transient increase in resistance to infection with the same or closely related strains, which may reduce the incidence of the disease by 75%. Influenza vaccine is one of the less satisfactory immunizing agents. It offers only a short duration of protection, the possibility of sensitization or severe allergic reactions in persons hypersensitive to eggs (the vaccine viruses are grown in chick embryos), and the possibility of toxic reactions to the high concentration of virus material administered parenterally. The greatest difficulty is the uncertainty of protection because of the changing antigenicity of the circulating influenza strains. While the vaccines composed of current influenza strains can protect against minor antigenic drift occurring from season to season, existing vaccines become virtually useless against the major antigenic shifts that occur every 10–15 years.

It is possible that the number of antigens might be finite even though they vary in proportions from one influenza strain to the next. If several strains of differing but broad antigenic composition are included in the vaccine, effective control against influenza might still become possible. Such a vaccine should yield an antigenic mass in which all known influenza antigens are adequately represented. On the other hand, the possibility of antigenic drift among these agents might be almost limitless and the outlook for effective control dubious.

A. Past Control Measures: Influenza vaccines of 3 decades ago yielded encouraging results until the appearance, in 1947, of the A1 strains against which the then-current vaccine was ineffective. Since that time, the production of influenza vaccines has been handicapped by the recurrent need, each time a major antigenic shift appears in wild virus, to select new strains of appropriate antigenic nature. In a race against time, new wild strain isolates with the new antigenic character have to be adapted by passage in eggs until, through selection in mass culturing, a variant emerges that is able to produce the high yield of virus in eggs that is required for large-scale vaccine production. In the months required before the vaccine can become available, the new virus strain can sweep through the population.

B. Present Control Measures: Vaccination is currently recommended in the USA only for persons not allergic to eggs or egg products who have chronic debilitating conditions and are known to be at increased risk of mortality from influenza (in general, persons of any age with chronic cardiovascular-renal, bronchopulmonary, or metabolic disorders; and all persons over 65 years of age). For these groups, annual immunization is recommended. Purified vaccines containing less nonviral protein are now available and recommended. With purified influenza vaccine, only one dose is needed to accomplish basic immunization.

If a major epidemic is forecast, appropriately altered vaccine should be administered, as soon as available, to the high-risk groups and their families and also to selected employment groups which provide essential community services.

Vaccines made from subviral antigens are also available. For their preparation, the intact virion is disrupted by treatment with ether or sodium deoxycholate and the nucleic acid is selectively removed by precipitation, leaving the virus proteins. Such purified noninfectious viral antigens do not produce fever or other symptoms even in sensitive preschool children. Another possible advantage of this type of vaccine is that the virus disruption may expose antigenic components hidden in the intact virion; consequently, the antibody response may be broader than after administration of vaccines prepared from the intact virion.

Vaccination should be performed as soon as practicable after September 1 and completed by mid-November. Since a 2-week delay in antibody development may be expected, it is important that immunization be carried out before epidemics occur in the area.

The Bureau of Biologics, Food and Drug Administration, reviews influenza vaccine formulations regularly and recommends reformulation with contemporary antigens when indicated. Bivalent influenza vaccine for the 1975–1976 period should contain at least 1200 chick cell agglutinating (CCA) units of antigen in the following proportions: 350 CCA units of a type A strain comparable to the prototype A/Port Chalmers/1/73 (H3N2), 350 CCA units of a type A strain comparable to the prototype A/Scotland/840/74 (H3N2), and 500 CCA units of a type B strain, B/Hong Kong/5/72.

C. Future Control Measures: Efforts toward improvement of influenza vaccines have progressed in several directions, and the results already are seen in the diminished toxicity of current vaccines and the availability of highly purified vaccines and of vaccines prepared from subviral antigens. The experimental use of vaccines emulsified in mineral oil adjuvants and injected intramuscularly has given higher and more lasting antibody responses. Intranasal administration of killed virus vaccines or of live attenuated vaccines has had variable results.

Present research in influenza vaccines is directed at 3 factors: (1) protection from clinical illness, (2) prevention of epidemics, and (3) production of long-lasting immunity so that yearly immunization would not be necessary. Several new types of influenza vaccines are now being tested in an attempt to fulfill these goals. One is a neuraminidase-specific vaccine which induces antibody only to the neuraminidase antigen of the virus. Antibody to neuraminidase reduces both the amount of virus which replicates in the respiratory tract and the ability to transmit virus to contacts. It significantly reduces clinical symptoms when a vaccinee is exposed to live influenza virus but allows subclinical infection as demonstrated by the production of hemagglutinin antibody. It is postulated that the resulting immunity would be longer-lasting than that achieved with the presently licensed vaccines, but studies to substantiate this claim have not been completed.

An attenuated live virus vaccine has been developed and used widely in the USSR. Attenuated strains have been prepared by serial transfer of influenza strains through embryonated eggs. They are antigenically identical with the virulent ones, but when administered intranasally in high concentrations they do not produce local or general symptoms in adults and produce only mild symptoms in children. However, they multiply in the upper respiratory tract and produce immunity. These and other live influenza virus vaccines present difficulties in obtaining sufficient attenuation of the desired strain without losing immunogenic potency, and there is the same problem of antigenic shifting that is seen with the parenterally administered vaccines.

Two new approaches to influenza vaccines deserve mention.

1. Recombinant vaccines—Influenza viruses are known to recombine genetically, forming stable "hybrids" having characteristics from each parent strain. Experimental vaccines now have been produced by co-cultivation of strains having the properties desired (antigens of new wild variant combined with ability to grow to high yields in eggs) and by selection of the recombinant progeny in which these properties are obtained. The first "man-made" hybrid virus for human immunization, recombinant X-31, has been used in vaccine production in Denmark, Romania, the United Kingdom, and—on a limited basis—in the USA. This recombinant was obtained by co-cultivating a strain of the Hong Kong subtype of A2 with a high-yielding standard laboratory strain, A0/PR8/34. The progeny, which included both high- and low-yield viruses of A0 and A2 antigenicity, were then passaged in the presence of A0 antibodies to eliminate the strains having A0 antigens, and the resulting strains (now including only those with Hong Kong [A2] antigens) were passaged at high dilutions to allow the high-yield progeny strains to "outgrow" the low-yield strains. The resulting virus X-31 is indistinguishable from its Hong Kong virus parent in its hemagglutinin and neuraminidase antigens by a number of serologic tests, and yet yields high amounts of virus far exceeding those obtained with its (early-passage) Hong Kong subtype parent.

The X-31 experimental vaccine has been tested, in parallel with a standard A2 vaccine, in volunteers who were subsequently challenged with live virus of a current wild strain and in military populations exposed to natural infections. From the serologic responses and also from the protection conferred against the wild strain, the recombinant vaccine is judged to be as effective as the standard vaccine.

Once a new wild variant is recognized, deliberate "tailoring" in the laboratory can greatly shorten the process of preparing vaccines for defense against the new variant. It may be possible to develop a "library" of recombinant strains of all known antigenic compositions, to be at hand immediately whenever future genetic shifts appear in the wild virus population. Recombination technics could also be utilized to select strains for adaptation to temperature sensitivity (see below).

2. Temperature-sensitive mutants—In efforts to overcome the problems encountered with previous live virus vaccines, temperature-sensitive (ts) mutants are being investigated. Selection of ts mutants unable to replicate at temperatures of the lung parenchyma (37° C) but replicating well at the lower temperatures of the nasopharyngeal mucosa (32–34° C) may permit adequate immunizing replication of a vaccine virus without severe symptoms or pulmonary pathology. The ts property has been associated with loss of virulence. Once a desired ts defect is established, recombination should permit this property to be combined with the desired antigenicity needed to combat new wild virus strains when they appear.

CORONAVIRUS FAMILY

The **Coronaviridae**, although resembling orthomyxoviruses in some respects, are a separate family that includes the human "IBV-like" viruses, avian *infectious bronchitis virus* (IBV), *mouse hepatitis virus* (MHV), transmissible gastroenteritis virus of swine, and others. The human strains have been associated with acute upper respiratory illnesses in adults.

Properties of the Viruses

The most marked characteristic which distinguishes these viruses from the orthomyxoviruses is 20 nm long, club-shaped or petal-shaped projections, instead of spikes, which are widely spaced on the outer surface of the viral envelope. The fringe of projections resembles the solar corona. The diameter of the enveloped particle is usually between 80 and 160 nm, and the particle contains a helical nucleocapsid 7–9 nm in diameter. The virus genome contains a single piece of RNA, with a molecular weight of 9 million, corresponding to 60–70S. This large RNA is of the same size as oncornavirus RNA. After heating, the large RNA dissociates into 35S and 4S pieces in a manner similar to that of the oncornavirus genome. The coronavirus nucleocapsids develop in the cytoplasm and mature by budding into cytoplasmic vesicles. Viral antigen has been detected exclusively in the cytoplasm of infected cells. The particles have a buoyant density of about 1.16 gm/ml. They contain essential lipid (they are sensitive to ether and chloroform) and are also acid-labile.

Growth of Virus

The human coronaviruses are extremely fastidious in their growth requirements, making routine isolation difficult. Some strains can be cultured only in human embryonic tracheal and nasal organ cultures. Others require human embryonic intestine or kidney cell cultures. Occasional strains have been adapted to suckling mouse brain. Optimal temperatures for growth are 33–35° C; significantly lower yields are produced at 37° C.

Antigenic Properties

The human prototype strain is 229E. Other human isolates grown in tissue culture show a strong antigenic relationship to this strain, but only a limited relationship to the human coronaviruses isolated in organ cultures, or to the mouse coronavirus, MHV. Several of the organ-culture-grown human strains are more broadly reactive and appear to have strong antigenic relationship to MHV. Avian IBV appears to have no antigenic relationships to the human or murine agents.

The agar gel diffusion technic has revealed at least 3 separate antigens for IBV. A complement-fixing antigen is present, but a hemagglutinin has been detected only with the avian IBV and several human isolates (OC38–43).

Clinical Features & Laboratory Diagnosis

The human coronaviruses produce "colds," usually afebrile, in adults. If virus can be isolated, diagnosis should be confirmed by demonstrating a significant rise in complement-fixing or neutralizing antibody titer to the agent in acute and convalescent serologic specimens.

In the absence of virus isolation, serologic diagnosis can be made on the basis of significantly increased antibody titers. The CF test is a more sensitive index of human coronavirus infections than is virus isolation with the tissue culture or organ systems in use at present. A technic has been developed for serodiagnosis of infections with strain 229E, which does not hemagglutinate; this test utilizes the capacity of postinfection sera to agglutinate red cells coated with coronavirus antigen. The test is type-specific and as sensitive as the Nt test and has advantages of being rapid and convenient.

Epidemiology

As indicated in the foregoing, the coronaviruses do not appear to be an important cause of acute respiratory illness in children, but serologic evidence indicates that they may be a major cause of respiratory illness in adults during some winter months when the incidence of colds is high but the isolation of rhinoviruses or other respiratory viruses is low. A recent study has shown that these viruses are a common cause of virus-induced exacerbations in patients with chronic bronchitis.

Recent evidence suggests that the apparent infrequency of coronavirus infections in children may be a result of the type of test used: initial infections with strain 229E are accompanied by only a transient complement-fixing antibody response, whereas in reinfections (which would be more commonly seen in adults) the CF response is enhanced and the neutralizing antibody response is diminished. Therefore, the Nt test should be the procedure of choice for infants and young children and the CF test more sensitive for older children and adults.

●　　●　　●

General References

Bradburne AF, Tyrrell DAJ: Coronaviruses of man. Prog Med Virol 13:373, 1971.

Compans RW, Choppin PW: Reproduction of myxoviruses. Pages 179–252 in: *Comprehensive Virology*. Vol 4. Fraenkel-Conrat H, Wagner RR (editors). Plenum Press, 1975.

Couch RB & others: Induction of partial immunity to influenza by a neuraminidase-specific vaccine. J Infect Dis 129:411, 1974.

Dourmashkin RR, Tyrrell DAJ: Electron microscopic observations on the entry of influenza virus into susceptible cells. J Gen Virol 24:129, 1974.

Dowdle WR & others: Natural history of influenza type A in the United States, 1957–1972. Prog Med Virol 17:91, 1974.

Dowdle WR & others: A simple double immunodiffusion test for typing influenza viruses. Bull WHO 51:213, 1974.

Hamre D, Beem M: Virologic studies of acute respiratory disease in young adults. 5. Coronavirus 229E infections during six years of surveillance. Am J Epidemiol 96:94, 1972.

Influenza in animals. Bull WHO 47:439, 1972.

International conference on Hong Kong influenza. Bull WHO 41:335, 1969.

Jackson GG, Muldoon RL: Viruses causing common respiratory infections in man. 5. Influenza A (Asian). J Infect Dis 131:308, 1975.

Kilbourne ED & others: Correlated studies of a recombinant influenza virus vaccine. 1. Derivation and characterization of virus and vaccine. Schulman JL & others: 2. Definition of antigenicity in experimental animals. Couch RB & others: 3. Protection against experimental influenza in man. Leibovitz A & others: 4. Protection against naturally occurring influenza in military trainees. J Infect Dis 124:449, 1971.

Kingsbury DW: Replication and functions of myxovirus ribonucleic acids. Prog Med Virol 12:49, 1970.

Laver WG, Downie JC, Webster RG: Studies on antigenic variation in influenza virus: Evidence for multiple antigenic determinants on hemagglutinin subunits of A/Hong Kong/68 (H3N2) virus and the A/England/72 strains. Virology 59:230, 1974.

Rossen RD & others: The secretory immune system: Its relation to respiratory viral infection. Prog Med Virol 13:194, 1971.

Schulman JL: Effects of immunity on transmission of influenza: Experimental studies. Prog Med Virol 12:128, 1970.

Tyrrell DAJ & others: Coronaviridae. Intervirology 5:76, 1975.

Webster RG, Laver WG: Antigenic variation in influenza virus: Biology and chemistry. Prog Med Virol 13:271, 1971.

35...
Paramyxovirus Family & Rubella Virus

The **Paramyxoviridae** are a large family including 3 genera: *Paramyxovirus* (mumps, parainfluenza types 1–5, and Newcastle disease), *Morbillivirus* (measles, canine distemper, and bovine rinderpest), and *Pneumovirus* (respiratory syncytial). Rubella virus, based on its biochemical and biophysical properties, is classified in the *Rubivirus* genus of the **Togaviridae** family but is discussed in this chapter because of its epidemiologic and clinical similarities to the paramyxoviruses. A wide variety of diseases are caused by the various members of the paramyxovirus family, including respiratory illnesses, measles, mumps, and acute and chronic neurologic diseases.

Properties of the Paramyxoviridae

A. Structure of the Virion: The virus particle consists of a pleomorphic membrane-containing, ether-sensitive envelope covered with spikes enclosing a helical ribonucleoprotein nucleocapsid, 18 nm in diameter by 1 μm in length. The RNA, which constitutes 5% of the nucleocapsid weight, consists of a single molecule of $5–6 \times 10^6$ molecular weight. The larger size of the nucleocapsid and the unsegmented nature of the RNA genome clearly differentiate the paramyxoviruses from the orthomyxoviruses. The major morphologic and functional characteristics of the virus particle are shown in Fig 35–1.

B. Biologic Properties:

1. Hemagglutinin and neuraminidase—Most members of the family have been shown to adsorb to mucoprotein receptors on erythrocytes and host cells. The property is manifested by the larger virus particle spike glycoprotein (HN). In some members of the group this protein has a second property, acting as a receptor-destroying enzyme or neuraminidase. For this reason, hemagglutination tests are performed at 4° C, where the hemagglutinin is active and the neuraminidase is not.

2. Hemolysin—Most members have the ability to lyse erythrocytes, a property distinct from the hemagglutinin. This property requires either intact virus particles or pieces of the virus membrane (which can be partially reassembled from separated virus protein and lipid). The smaller virus glycoprotein is thought to be especially important in this reaction.

3. Cell fusion—Another biologic property of paramyxoviruses is the ability to cause cell fusion, which

was first recognized in the 19th century as giant cell formation in human infection. This ability to fuse cells is now used for the creation of cell hybrids, an important tool in somatic cell genetics.

4. Persistent infection—Most members of the family have the ability to cause a persistent noncytocidal infection of cultured cells. The clinical importance of this property is emphasized by the disease subacute sclerosing panencephalitis (SSPE), a fatal neurologic disease of humans caused by persistent infection with measles virus.

C. Replication: The RNA genome of viruses of this group is not infectious and does not function as

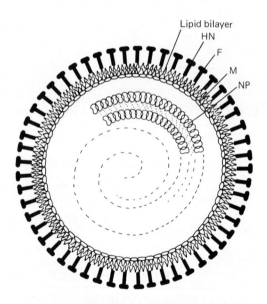

Figure 35–1. The components of paramyxoviruses. HN: Larger virus glycoprotein, responsible both for hemagglutination and receptor-destroying activities of the virus particle. F: Smaller virus glycoprotein, involved in cell fusion by these viruses and probably in the entry of the virus into the cell. Lipid bilayer: The lipid is cell-derived but probably altered in composition from that of the normal cell. M: Nonglycosylated membrane protein. The HN, F, M, and lipid bilayer can be disrupted, destroying hemolytic activity, and then reassembled, without the nucleocapsid, whereupon hemolytic activity is restored. NP: Ribonucleoprotein, the major complement-fixing antigen. (From Choppin and Compans, 1974.)

messenger RNA. Instead, the viral genome is transcribed into shorter RNA molecules which serve as messenger and are complementary to the genome. Their replication thus closely resembles that of the rhabdoviruses. Like orthomyxoviruses and rhabdoviruses, the paramyxoviruses possess an RNA-dependent RNA polymerase which is a structural component of the virion and produces the initial messenger RNA.

MUMPS
(Epidemic Parotitis)

Mumps is an acute contagious disease characterized by a nonsuppurative enlargement of one or both of the parotid glands, although other organs may also be involved.

Properties of the Virus

A. Morphology and Biochemical Properties: The mumps virus particle has the typical paramyxovirus morphology. Typical also are the biologic properties of hemagglutination, neuraminidase, and hemolysin. The property of hemagglutination can be inhibited by specific antisera to mumps virus, and this inhibition can be used to measure antibody responses. Similarly, the nucleocapsid of the virus particle forms the major component of the "S" (soluble) complement-fixing antigen.

B. Reactions to Physical and Chemical Agents: The hemagglutinin, the hemolysin, and the infectivity of the virus are destroyed by heating at 56° C for 20 minutes. The skin test antigen and the complement-fixing antigen are more heat stable, withstanding 65° C and 80° C respectively for 30 minutes.

The attenuated vaccine virus is stable for 1 year in the lyophilized state; when reconstituted, it is stable for 8 hours at 40° C.

C. Animal Susceptibility and Growth of Virus: In monkeys, mumps can produce a disease which is very much like that in human beings. Parotitis is produced by introducing the virus into Stensen's duct or directly into the gland by injection. The swollen gland is a good source of virus or of skin-testing antigen. By the use of fluorescent antibody, the virus has been located in the cytoplasm of acinar cells.

The virus also grows readily in embryonated eggs, especially in the amniotic sac. Passage of mumps virus in such embryos so modifies the virus that its pathogenicity for man and monkeys is greatly decreased. This method of attenuation was used to prepare the live virus vaccine. The virus has also been grown in cell culture, in which it may produce large multinucleated giant cells (syncytia) and a hemagglutinin.

D. Skin Test: A skin test antigen for determining hypersensitivity to mumps virus is available. A positive test is considered to be erythema and induration greater than 15 mm 24–48 hours after injection. Recent studies have seriously questioned the value of the skin test in predicting immune status, since both false-positives and false-negatives occur with considerable frequency.

Pathogenesis & Pathology

Two theories exist regarding the pathogenesis of mumps. (1) The virus travels from the mouth by way of Stensen's duct to the parotid gland where it undergoes primary multiplication. This is followed by a generalized viremia and localization in testes, ovaries, pancreas, thyroid, or brain. (2) Primary replication occurs in the superficial epithelium of the respiratory tract. This is followed by a generalized viremia and simultaneous localization in the salivary glands and other organs.

Little tissue damage is associated with uncomplicated mumps. The ducts of the parotid glands show desquamation of the epithelium, and polymorphonuclear cells are present in the lumens. There are interstitial edema and lymphocytic infiltration. With severe orchitis, the testis is congested and punctate hemorrhage as well as degeneration of the epithelium of the seminiferous tubules is observed. CNS pathology may vary from perivascular edema to inflammatory reaction, glial reaction, hemorrhage, or demyelination.

Clinical Features

The incubation period ranges from 12–35 days but most commonly is 18–21 days. A prodromal period of malaise and anorexia is followed by rapid enlargement of one or both parotid glands as well as other salivary glands. Swelling may be confined to one parotid gland, or one gland may enlarge several days before the other. The gland enlargement is associated with pain, especially when tasting acid substances. The salivary adenitis is commonly accompanied by low-grade fever and lasts for approximately a week.

The testes and ovaries may be affected, especially after puberty. Twenty percent of males over 13 years of age who are infected with mumps virus develop orchitis, which is often unilateral and does not usually lead to sterility. Because of the lack of elasticity of the tunica albuginea, which does not allow the inflamed testis to swell, atrophy of the testis may follow secondary to pressure necrosis. Secondary sterility does not occur in women because the ovary, which has no such limiting membrane, can swell when inflamed.

Mumps accounts for 10–15% of aseptic meningitis observed in the USA and is more common among males than females. Meningoencephalitis usually occurs 5–7 days after the inflammation of the salivary glands; however, the CNS complication may occur simultaneously or in the absence of parotitis and is usually self-limiting. The CSF usually contains lymphocytes (10–2000/cu mm). Pleocytosis may persist for weeks, even after the patient appears to have recovered.

Rare complications of mumps include (1) a self-limiting polyarthritis which resolves without residual deformity; (2) pancreatitis associated with transient hyperglycemia, glycosuria, and steatorrhea (it has been suggested that diabetes mellitus may occasionally follow); (3) nephritis; (4) thyroiditis; and (5) unilateral nerve deafness (hearing loss is complete and permanent). Mumps has been implicated as a possible etiologic agent in the production of aqueductal stenosis and hydrocephalus in children. Injection of mumps virus into suckling hamsters has produced similar lesions.

Laboratory Diagnosis

Laboratory studies are usually not required to establish the diagnosis of typical cases. However, mumps can sometimes be confused with enlargement of the parotids due to suppuration, foreign bodies in the salivary ducts, tumors, etc. In cases without parotitis, particularly in aseptic meningitis, the laboratory can be particularly helpful in establishing the diagnosis.

A. Recovery of Virus: Isolation of virus from patients should be attempted with saliva, CSF, or urine collected within 4 or 5 days after the onset of illness. Urine is a useful source of virus late in the infection. The saliva should be taken near the orifices of Stensen's ducts. After treatment with antibiotics, the specimen is inoculated into cultures of monkey kidney cells. Virus present in inoculated cultures may be detected in 5–6 days by adsorption of chicken or guinea pig cells by the infected cells. A 0.4% suspension of red blood cells is added to cell cultures, and hemadsorption is detected after incubation at room temperature for 3–5 minutes or at 4° C for 20–30 minutes. Direct inhibition of the hemadsorption with specific antiserum to mumps virus identifies the isolate. An alternative—but less sensitive—method of isolation is to incubate the specimen into the amniotic cavities of 8-day-old chick embryos. Viral hemagglutination can be detected in the amniotic fluid of the infected embryos within 5 days, and the hemagglutination can be inhibited with specific antibody.

Mumps and its complications, particularly meningoencephalitis, constitute an important disease problem, and more rapid diagnostic methods would be a welcome advance. A recent study has shown that immunofluorescence technics can be used for the early detection of mumps virus isolated in cell cultures or adsorbed directly from clinical specimens onto guinea pig erythrocytes. A specific diagnosis can be made in a few hours to 2–3 days, in contrast to about 6 days by the standard hemadsorption or hemagglutination methods.

B. Serology: Antibody rise may be detected by testing matched acute and convalescent sera, the first sample being taken as soon after the onset of illness as possible, the second about 2–3 weeks later. The CF test is best for specificity and accuracy, although HI may be used. A 4-fold or greater rise in antibody titer is evidence of mumps infection.

A CF test on a single serum sample obtained soon after onset of illness may serve for a presumptive diagnosis if both soluble (S) and viral (V) antibodies are measured. S antibodies develop early, within a few days after onset, and sometimes reach a high titer before V antibodies can be detected. In early convalescence, both S and V antibodies are present at a high level. Subsequently, S antibodies disappear more rapidly, leaving V antibodies as a long-term marker of previous infection. After several years, even V antibodies may be hardly detectable or present at low levels (1:4 serum dilution). The intradermal injection of ultraviolet- or heat-inactivated virus stimulates the reappearance of V antibodies in high titer. Neutralizing antibodies, which also appear during convalescence, can be determined in eggs but are more easily determined in cell culture using the degree of inhibition of viral cytopathogenicity as a measure of antibodies.

C. Skin Test Antigen: Delayed type hypersensitivity may be noted about 3–4 weeks after onset. The skin test is less reliable than serologic tests to establish evidence of past infection.

Immunity

Immunity is permanent after a single infection. Only one antigenic type exists. Passive immunity is transferred from mother to offspring; thus it is rare to see mumps in infants under 6 months of age.

The noninfective skin test antigen, available commercially, may induce antibody formation or increase titers which have fallen to low levels.

Treatment

Gamma globulin is of no value for decreasing the incidence of orchitis, even when given immediately after parotitis is first noted.

Epidemiology

Mumps occurs throughout the world endemically throughout the year. Epidemics are facilitated where crowding favors the dissemination of the virus. The disease reaches its highest incidence in children 5–15 years of age, but epidemics in army camps are not uncommon. The peak incidence occurs in winter and spring. Although morbidity rates are high, mortality is negligible, even when the nervous system is involved.

The only known reservoir of infection is man. It is believed to be transmitted by direct contact, airborne droplets, or fomites contaminated with saliva and, perhaps, urine. The period of communicability is from about 4 days before to about a week after the onset of symptoms. More intimate contact is necessary for the transmission of mumps than for measles or varicella.

About 30–40% of infections with mumps virus are inapparent. Individuals with subclinical mumps acquire immunity. During the course of inapparent infection, they can serve as sources of infection for others.

Antibodies to mumps virus are transferred across the placenta and are gradually lost during the first year of life. In urban areas, antibodies are then acquired gradually, so that the 15-year-old group has about the same prevalence of persons with antibodies as the adult group. Antibodies are acquired at the same rate by persons living under favorable or unfavorable socioeconomic conditions.

Control

Mumps is usually a mild childhood disease and immunization for prevention does not carry the same urgency as the more serious preventable diseases, ie, polio, diphtheria, and tetanus. However, a live attenuated virus vaccine is available, and its use is recommended for children over 1 year of age and for adolescents and adults who have not had mumps parotitis. A single dose of the vaccine given subcutaneously produces detectable antibodies in 95% of vaccinees. The long-term duration of immunity induced by the vaccine is not known, but 5-year observations indicate continuing protection against natural infection.

Combination live virus vaccines (measles-mumps-rubella, measles-rubella, and rubella-mumps) have been licensed. A combined measles-mumps-rubella vaccine administered to children who were initially without antibody produced antibodies to each of the viruses in about 95%.

PARAINFLUENZA VIRUS INFECTIONS

The parainfluenza viruses are members of the paramyxovirus genus, having morphologic and biologic properties which are typical of the genus. They grow well in primary monkey or human epithelial cell culture but poorly or not at all in the embryonated egg. They produce a minimal cytopathic effect in primary cell culture but are recognized by the hemadsorption method. The parainfluenza viruses are relatively unstable, and activity falls off even at freezing temperatures. Laboratory diagnosis may be made by the HI, CF, and Nt tests.

Parainfluenza 1

Included here are **Sendai virus**, also known as the **hemagglutinating virus of Japan (HVJ)**, and **hemadsorption virus type 2 (HA-2)**. Sendai virus has been reported to be the etiologic agent of pneumonia in pigs and pneumonitis of newborn infants, but the endemicity of the virus in laboratory mice in which the isolations were made makes it difficult to evaluate the role of the virus as a cause of human illness. However, Sendai virus is important both in somatic cell genetics, where it is used to produce cell fusion, and as a model for studying paramyxovirus replication. Clinically, the most important member of this group appears to be the widespread HA-2 virus. Although it is not cytopathogenic for monkey kidney cell cultures, it is detected in such cultures by the hemadsorption test, ie, the clumping of guinea pig erythrocytes on the surfaces of the infected cells in the culture. It appears to be one of the main agents producing croup in children, but it can also cause coryza, pharyngitis, bronchitis, bronchiolitis, pneumonia, and undifferentiated upper respiratory illness. In adults it produces respiratory symptoms like those of the common cold, with reinfection occurring in persons with antibodies from earlier infections.

Immunization with inactivated parainfluenza type 1 vaccine stimulates antibody appearance in the blood but not in nasal secretions. Recipients of such a vaccine remain susceptible to reinfection. In contrast, natural infection stimulates antibody appearance in the nasal secretions and concomitant resistance to reinfection.

Parainfluenza 2

This group includes the **croup-associated (CA) virus**, also known as the acute laryngotracheobronchitis virus of children. The virus grows in human cells (HeLa, lung, amnion) and monkey kidney, in which syncytial masses are produced with loss of cell boundaries. The virus agglutinates chick and, to a lesser degree, human O erythrocytes. Adsorption and hemagglutination occur at 4° C, and elution of virus takes place rapidly at 37° C. However, the cells reagglutinate when returned to 4° C.

Antigenically, type 2 is unrelated to other myxoviruses except mumps. Mumps patients develop type 2 antibodies.

Parainfluenza virus 2 occurs spontaneously in 30% of lots of monkey kidney cells grown in culture.

Parainfluenza 3

The viruses in this group are also known as **hemadsorption virus type 1 (HA-1)**. They are detected in monkey kidney cultures by the hemadsorption technic. Serial passage in culture may lead to cytopathic changes. Multinucleated giant cell plaques are produced under agar in certain continuous human cell lines.

The virus has been isolated from children with mild respiratory illnesses as well as from children suffering from croup, bronchiolitis, or pneumonitis. Strains of type 3 virus have been isolated from nasal secretions of cattle ill with a respiratory syndrome known as "shipping fever." At least 70% of market cattle bled at slaughter have parainfluenza 3 antibodies.

After infection with parainfluenza 1 or 2, complement-fixation titers rise not only to the infecting type but also to type 3, because of shared antigens.

Parainfluenza 4

The M-25 strain is the parainfluenza 4 prototype. It does not produce any cytopathic effects, does not grow in embryonated eggs, and can be recognized only by the hemadsorption technic. As far as is known, this virus causes no human illness.

Parainfluenza 5

No known human pathogens are included in this group, but it does include SV5, a simian virus which has been widely studied as a representative member of the paramyxovirus group.

Clinical Features & Control

Children in the first year of life with primary infections caused by parainfluenza virus type 1, 2, or 3 may have serious illness ranging from laryngotracheitis and croup (particularly type 2) to bronchitis, bronchiolitis, and pneumonitis (particularly type 3). Virtually all infants have maternal antibodies to parainfluenza viruses in serum, yet such antibodies do not prevent infection or disease. Reinfection of older children and adults also occurs in the presence of antibodies arising from an earlier infection. However, such reinfections usually present as nonfebrile upper respiratory infections ("colds"), whereas primary parainfluenza infections in the first year of life are responsible for up to 20% of acute nonbacterial respiratory diseases requiring hospitalization.

The incubation for type 1 is 5–6 days; that for type 3 is 2–3 days. Most children have acquired antibodies to all 3 types before age 10.

Inactivated parainfluenza vaccines injected subcutaneously induce antibodies but no resistance to infection. Similar vaccines given as aerosols induce antibodies in the respiratory tract (secretory IgA) as well as in serum and may be protective. Live vaccines to be given in the first few weeks of life are being investigated.

NEWCASTLE DISEASE CONJUNCTIVITIS

Newcastle disease virus is a typical member of the paramyxovirus genus that is primarily pathogenic for fowl. It produces pneumoencephalitis in young chickens and "influenza" in older birds. In man it may produce an inflammation of the conjunctiva. Recovery is complete in 10–14 days. The infection in man is an occupational disease, limited to laboratory workers and to poultry workers handling infected birds. The virus is widely studied in laboratories both as an important animal pathogen and as a laboratory model of virus infection.

The virus grows readily in the embryonated egg, in chick embryo cell culture, or HeLa cells, and produces hemagglutination.

Human erythrocytes treated with the virus are agglutinated by specific serum against Newcastle virus and also by sera from certain patients with infectious mononucleosis and hepatitis. After contracting mumps, many persons develop antibodies which not only react with mumps virus but also cross-react with Newcastle disease virus.

Newcastle antibodies can be measured by the HI, CF, and Nt tests using chick embryos or tissue cultures. Normal human sera possess a heat-labile, nonspecific inhibitor which can be destroyed by heating at 56° C for 30 minutes.

MEASLES
(Rubeola)

Measles is an acute, highly infectious disease characterized by a maculopapular rash which often becomes confluent and blotchy.

Properties of the Virus

A. Morphology and Biologic Properties: Although measles virus has the typical paramyxovirus morphology, it, along with the animal viruses canine distemper and bovine rinderpest, forms a distinct genus, *Morbillivirus.* These 3 viruses share extensive antigenic similarities and all apparently lack neuraminidase activity. Measles virus can agglutinate erythrocytes of baboons and monkeys, but apparently by interaction with a different cell receptor from that used by orthomyxovirus. With measles virus, higher titers are obtained in the HA test at 37° C than at 4° C and, since the virus does not elute from the erythrocytes at the higher temperature, 37° C is used for these tests. Measles virus also causes hemolysis, and, as is true in the case of other paramyxoviruses, this activity can be separated from the hemagglutinin.

B. Reactions to Physical and Chemical Agents: The virus is destroyed by heating at 56° C for 60 minutes, by 1:4000 formaldehyde after 4 days at 37° C, or after ultraviolet irradiation. Measles virus is destroyed by sonic oscillation at exposures which do not diminish the infectivity of poliovirus or the echoviruses. It remains infective when stored at subzero temperatures or when lyophilized. Measles virus, like other myxoviruses, can be stabilized by molar $MgSO_4$ so that it resists heating at 50° C for 1 hour.

C. Animal Susceptibility and Growth of Virus: The experimental disease has been produced in monkeys. They develop fever, catarrh, Koplik's spots, and a discrete papular rash. The virus has been grown in chick embryos, cell cultures of human, monkey, and dog kidney tissue, and in human continuous cell lines. In cell cultures, multinucleate syncytial giant cells form by fusion of mononucleated ones, and other cells become spindle-shaped in the course of their degeneration. Nuclear changes consist of margination of the chromatin and its replacement centrally with an acidophilic inclusion body. Measles virus is relatively unstable after it is released from cells. During the culture of the virus, the intracellular virus titer is 10 or more times the extracellular.

Pathogenesis & Pathology

The virus enters the respiratory tract, becomes implanted, and multiplies there. By the time the prodromal catarrhal period and the rash appear, the virus is present in the blood, throughout the respiratory tract, and in nasopharyngeal, tracheobronchial, and conjunctival secretions. It persists in the blood and nasopharyngeal secretions for 2 days after the appearance of the rash. Transplacental transmission of the virus appears to result in congenital measles.

Koplik's spots consist of vesicles in the mouth formed by focal exudations of serum and endothelial cells, which are followed by focal necrosis. In the skin the superficial capillaries of the corium are first involved, and it is here the rash makes its appearance. The appearance and spread of exudate in the epidermis are followed first by vacuolation and necrosis of epithelial cells and then by vesicle formation. Generalized lymphoid tissue hyperplasia occurs. Multinucleate giant cells are found in lymph nodes, tonsils, adenoids, spleen, and appendix; giant cells with viral antigen have also been found in skin lesions and Koplik's spots. In the rare cases of encephalomyelitis, the histopathologic findings include diffuse petechial hemorrhage, lymphocytic infiltration, and, later, patchy demyelination in the brain and spinal cord.

Defective measles virus genomes (nucleoprotein helical structures lacking the envelope of the mature virion) have been identified within the inclusion bodies found in brain nerve cells in **subacute sclerosing panencephalitis (SSPE)**. The viral antigen can be detected by means of immunofluorescence. The virus has been isolated from biopsy specimens of brain and from lymph nodes of patients with SSPE by co-cultivation of lymph node cells and HeLa cells. The virus was identified by hemagglutination inhibition, immunofluorescence, and neutralization tests. The presence of a latent intracellular measles virus in lymph node cells suggests a tolerant infection with defective cellular immunity. This defect in immunity (congenital or measles-induced) may permit viremia to persist, with measles-carrying lymphocytes moving into the CNS to initiate SSPE.

Clinical Findings

The incubation period is about 10 days to onset of fever and 14 days to appearance of rash. When passive immunization has been attempted too late to prevent infection, the incubation period may be as long as 21 days. The prodromal period is characterized by fever, sneezing, coughing, running nose, redness of eyes, Koplik's spots (enanthems of the buccal mucosa), and lymphopenia. The fever and cough persist until the rash appears and then subside within 1–2 days. The rash spreads over the entire body within 2–4 days, becoming brownish in 5–10 days. Symptoms are most marked when the rash is at its peak but subside rapidly thereafter.

In measles, the respiratory tract becomes more susceptible to invasion by bacteria, especially hemolytic streptococci; bronchitis, pneumonia, and otitis may follow. Bacterial complications require antibiotics.

Encephalomyelitis occurs in about 1:1000 cases. There appears to be no correlation between the severity of the measles and the appearance of neurologic complications. The cause of measles encephalitis is unknown. It has been suggested that early CNS involvement is caused by direct viral invasion of the brain. Later appearance of CNS symptoms is associated with demyelination and may be an immunopathologic reaction. Symptoms referable to the brain usually appear a few days after the appearance of the rash, often after it has faded. There is a second bout of fever, and the patient may be drowsy or have convulsions. There is pleocytosis of the CSF. Survivors may show permanent mental disorders (psychosis or personality change) or physical disabilities, particularly seizure disorders. The mortality rate in encephalitis associated with measles is about 10–30%, and many survivors (40%) show sequelae.

Measles virus appears to be responsible for subacute sclerosing panencephalitis (SSPE; Dawson's inclusion body encephalitis), a fatal degenerative brain disorder. The disease manifests itself in children and young adults by progressive mental deterioration, myoclonic jerks, and an abnormal EEG with periodic high-voltage complexes. The disease develops a number of years after the initial measles infection.

Laboratory Diagnosis

Measles is usually easily diagnosed on clinical grounds. About 5% of cases lack Koplik's spots and are difficult to differentiate clinically from infection with rubella virus, certain enteroviruses, and adenoviruses.

A. Recovery of Virus: In cell culture, measles virus can be isolated from the blood and nasopharynx of a patient from 2–3 days before the onset of symptoms to 1 day after the appearance of rash. Human amnion or kidney cell cultures are best suited for isolation of virus.

B. Serology: Specific neutralizing, hemagglutination-inhibiting, and complement-fixing antibodies develop early, with maximal titers near the time of onset of rash. Years after the clinical disease, antibodies may still be found, for there is only a gradual decline in antibody titer with age.

In view of the fact that measles and canine distemper share an antigen, measles patients develop antibodies which react with canine distemper virus. Similarly, dogs, after infection with distemper virus, develop antibodies which fix complement with measles antigen. Rinderpest virus is also related to measles. All 3 agents appear in the urine, and for the animal diseases lesions occur in the bladder and kidney.

Immunity

There appears to be only one antigenic type of measles virus, as one attack generally confers lifelong immunity. Repeated attacks are rarely observed except in persons with immune disorders. Most so-called second attacks represent errors in diagnosis of the initial or the present illness.

Epidemiology

Measles is endemic throughout the world. In general, epidemics recur regularly; the interepidemic interval is about 2–3 years. The state of immunity of the population is the determining factor. The disease flares up when there is an accumulation of susceptible children. Older people are resistant from previous exposures. By the age of 20 years, over 80% have had an attack of the disease. The severity of an epidemic is a function of the number of susceptibles. Only about 1% of susceptibles fail to contract measles on their first close contact with a patient.

The pattern of antibody development in a community coincides with the age-specific attack rate. Antibodies are acquired more rapidly in large families, but there is no relationship with socioeconomic factors.

When the disease is introduced into isolated communities where it has not been endemic, all age groups develop clinical measles. A classic example of this was the introduction of measles into the Faroe Islands in 1846; only old people over 60 years of age, who had been alive during the last epidemic, escaped the disease. In such places, where the disease strikes rarely, its consequences are often disastrous and the mortality rate may be as high as 25%.

The highest incidence of measles is in the late winter and spring. Infection is contracted by inhalation of droplets expelled in sneezing or coughing. Measles is spread chiefly by children during the catarrhal prodromal period; they are infectious from 1–2 days prior to the onset of symptoms until a few days after the rash has appeared.

Control

Live attenuated measles virus vaccine can effectively prevent measles and represents the most effective control measure. Prior to the introduction of the vaccine, over 500,000 cases of measles occurred annually in the USA. Following mass immunization in 1966–1967, the number of cases decreased to 67,000 and 22,000 annually in the next 2 years. The lack of immunization of children from certain segments of the population resulted in 75,000 cases in 1971; however, with renewed emphasis on immunization, the number of cases declined again to 32,000 in 1972. In many areas of the USA, measles continues to occur in sporadic epidemics among nonimmunized children. In such epidemics, the attack rate for immunized and nonimmunized children is approximately 2% and 34%, respectively.

An estimated $1.3 billion was saved through vaccination programs in the first 10 years since live measles virus vaccine was licensed in 1963. The $3 per dose cost of some 58.5 million doses of vaccine distributed between 1963 and 1972 averted almost 24 million cases, saved 2400 lives, and prevented about 7900 cases of mental retardation. In addition, there were savings of 78 million school days, over 12 million physician visits, and 1.3 million hospital days.

Less attenuated vaccine virus may produce fever and a modified skin rash in a fair number of vaccinees; this reaction can be prevented by the simultaneous administration of gamma globulin (0.01 ml/lb body weight) **at a separate site from the vaccine**. The further attenuated vaccine viruses do not produce symptoms and do not require the use of gamma globulin. The different vaccine viruses appear to be equally effective in producing immunity. Infection with wild measles virus does occur in some vaccinees, and mild cases of measles with vesicular lesions as well as a morbilliform rash have been reported.

Measles antibodies cross the placenta and protect the infant during the first 6 months of life. In some, maternal antibody may persist for almost a year. Vaccination with the live virus fails to take during this period, and immunization is not recommended during the first year of life. Vaccination is also not recommended in persons with febrile illnesses, allergies to eggs or other products used in the production of the vaccine, and in persons with congenital or acquired immune defects.

Killed measles vaccine should not be used, as certain vaccinees become sensitized and develop local reactions when revaccinated with live attenuated virus or a severe illness upon contracting natural measles.

Measles may also be prevented or modified by administering antibody early in the incubation period. Human gamma globulin contains antibody titers of 200–1000 against 100 $TCID_{50}$ of virus. With small doses, the disease can be made mild and immunity ensues. With a large dose of gamma globulin, the disease can be prevented; however, the person remains susceptible to infection at a later date. Antibodies given later than 6 days after exposure are not likely to influence the course of the disease.

RESPIRATORY SYNCYTIAL (RS) VIRUS

This agent is an extremely labile paramyxovirus which produces a characteristic syncytial effect (pseudo giant cell) in serially propagated human cell cultures. It is the single most important agent causing infantile bronchiolitis and pneumonia.

Although similar to the other paramyxoviruses in appearance, this agent is sufficiently different to be classified in a separate genus, *Pneumovirus,* along with pneumonia virus of mice. The particle is slightly smaller than that of the paramyxoviruses, as is the nucleocapsid (80–120 nm and 11–15 nm, respectively). The virus has not been shown to be capable of hemagglutination, although it does possess the typical surface projections.

RS virus, which contains an RNA genome, can form DNA intermediates which are perpetuated in actively dividing human cells and which can be recovered in a form directly infectious for susceptible cells. In this transfection property it behaves like the **Retroviridae**, which include the oncornaviruses. Recently, other RNA viruses have also been reported to use this mechanism in order to persist for extended periods in eukaryotic cells.

A soluble complement-fixing antigen can be separated from the virus particle by sedimenting the latter in the high-speed centrifuge. The virus is so labile that 90% of infectivity is lost by a single cycle of slow freezing and thawing. However, the virus is stable when it is rapidly frozen and stored at −70° C.

RS virus has not been grown in eggs. It is not pathogenic for any of the laboratory rodents. It occurs spontaneously in chimpanzees and has been associated with coryza in these primates.

RS virus is recovered significantly more often from infants and children with respiratory illness than from controls free of such disease. In young infants (first 6 months of life) with bronchiolitis or pneumonia, the RS virus recovery rates were 39% and 23%, respectively, as against zero among hundreds of control infants without respiratory disease. Infection in older infants and children resulted in milder upper respiratory tract disease than that which occurred in the first half year of life.

Only 20% of infants under 6 months develop a complement-fixing antibody rise, and only 45% develop neutralizing antibody during convalescence.

RS virus spreads extensively in the childhood population every year during the winter months.

RS virus infection in adult volunteers showed that reinfection occurs readily even though all the volunteers had moderate to high levels of neutralizing antibody prior to challenge. This antibody may have been responsible for the mild nature of the observed cold-like illnesses. Serum neutralizing antibody is not very effective in providing resistance to severe lower respiratory tract disease of early life. Thus, bronchiolitis and pneumonia due to RS virus are common in infants in the first 3–4 months of life even though maternally transmitted antibody is present at significantly high levels.

The clinical disease in young infants may actually be the result of an antigen-antibody reaction that results when the infecting virus meets maternally transmitted antibody. For this reason, RS vaccines that produce antibodies in the serum but not in the nasal secretions may do more harm than good. Efforts to develop an attenuated vaccine that infects subclinically and induces nasal antibody are encouraging, but no commercial vaccine is as yet available.

· · ·

RUBELLA
(German Measles)

Rubella is an acute febrile illness characterized by a rash and posterior auricular and suboccipital lymphadenopathy which affects children and young adults. Infection in early pregnancy may result in serious abnormalities of the fetus.

Properties of the Virus

The virus is an RNA-containing, ether-sensitive virus about 60 nm in diameter. It contains a 30 nm internal nucleocapsid with a double membrane and forms by budding from the endoplasmic reticulum into intracytoplasmic vesicles and at the marginal cell membrane. Projections of the virion, 6 nm long, possess hemagglutinin which agglutinates red blood cells of day-old chicks, adult geese, or pigeons; there is no spontaneous elution, and hemagglutination is not affected by treating the erythrocytes with receptor-destroying enzyme. The virus is relatively labile but can be stored at −70° C.

On the basis of physical and chemical characteristics—the possession of RNA which sediments at 40S; 3 major virus particle proteins (2 glycoproteins and an internal core protein)—rubella virus belongs to the *Rubivirus* genus of the **Togaviridae** family.

Rubella virus can be propagated in cell culture. In some cultures, the virus produces detectable cytopathologic changes. These cells include human amnion cells, human thyroid cells, serially passaged lines of rabbit cornea (SIRC) and rabbit kidney (RK-13) cells, and a line of monkey kidney (VERO) cells. In other cell cultures, rubella virus replicates without causing a cytopathic effect; however, interference is induced which protects the cells against the cytopathic effect of other viruses. Thus, a standard method of isolating rubella virus consists of inoculating green monkey kidney cells with the specimen and, after 7–10 days of incubation, challenging the cultures with echovirus 11. If echovirus cytopathic effect develops, the specimen is considered negative for rubella virus; conversely, the absence of echovirus cytopathic effect implies the presence of rubella virus in the original specimen.

A newly recognized acute-phase precipitating antigen, *rho,* has been found in the blood of patients with rubella infection and in fluids from rubella virus-infected cell cultures.

1. POSTNATAL RUBELLA

Pathogenesis

Infection occurs through the mucosa of the upper respiratory tract. The virus probably replicates primarily in the cervical lymph nodes. After a period of 7 days, viremia develops which lasts until the appearance of antibody on about day 12–14. The development of antibody coincides with the appearance of the rash, suggesting an immunologic basis for the rash. During the viremic period, virus can be isolated from the urine and feces; after the rash appears, the virus remains detectable only in the nasopharynx.

Clinical Features

Rubella is usually heralded by the acute onset of malaise, low-grade fever, and a morbilliform rash appearing on the same day. Less often, systemic symptoms may precede the rash by 1 or 2 days, or the rash and lymphadenopathy may occur without systemic symptoms. The rash, which starts on the face and extends over the trunk and extremities, rarely lasts more than 3 days. Posterior auricular and suboccipital lymphadenopathy are consistent physical findings. Transient arthralgia and arthritis are commonly seen in adult females. Rare complications include thrombocytopenia and encephalitis.

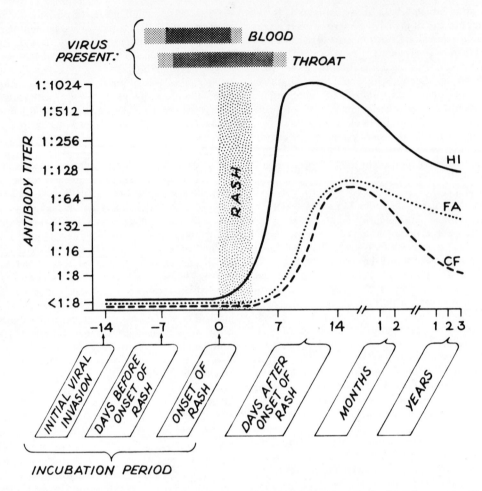

Figure 35—2. Virus and antibody dynamics in rubella. HI = hemagglutination-inhibiting antibody; FA = fluorescent antibody; CF= complement-fixing antibody.

Unless an epidemic occurs, the disease is extremely difficult to diagnose clinically since the rash caused by other viral agents such as the enteroviruses may appear similar. However, the viruses display characteristic seasonal variations, with rubella having a peak occurrence in the spring and enterovirus infections in the summer and fall.

Immunity

Rubella antibodies appear in the serum of patients as the rash fades, and the titer of antibody rises rapidly over the next 1–3 weeks. A sizable portion of the initial antibody consists of IgM which can usually be detected for 2–8 weeks following the illness. Although serologic diagnosis can best be accomplished by analysis of acute and convalescent sera, a single sample obtained 2 weeks after the rash may provide presumptive evidence of rubella by demonstrating rubella virus antibodies in the IgM fraction. However, when using very sensitive methods for detecting rubella-specific IgM, this antibody has been found to persist for 10 months after the acute infection.

One attack of the disease confers lifelong immunity, as only one antigenic type of the virus exists. A history of rubella is not a reliable index of immunity. This can best be determined by assaying the serum for antibody. The presence of antibody at a 1:8 dilution implies immunity. Immune mothers transfer antibodies to their offspring, who are then protected for 4–6 months.

Treatment

There is no specific treatment unless the patient is pregnant. Rubella-like illness in the first trimester of pregnancy should be substantiated by isolation of the virus from the throat or by demonstrating a 4-fold rise in antibody titer to the virus by means of the HI, CF, or Nt test. Laboratory-proved rubella in the first 10 weeks of pregnancy is almost uniformly associated with fetal infection. Therapeutic abortion is strongly recommended in laboratory-proved cases to avoid the birth of malformed infants.

Gamma globulin has been used by some for pregnant women exposed to rubella during the first trimester. However, gamma globulin does not inhibit viremia, and it is the virus in the blood that infects the fetus. There is no convincing evidence that gamma globulin offers any benefit to the patient or the fetus.

2. CONGENITAL RUBELLA SYNDROME

Pathogenesis

Rubella infection during pregnancy may result in infection of the placenta and fetus. A limited number of cells of the fetus become infected. Although the virus does not destroy the cells, the growth rate and ultimate doubling potential of the cells are altered, which results in fewer than normal numbers of cells at birth. The earlier in pregnancy that infection occurs, the greater the chance of extensive involvement with the birth of an infant afflicted by severe anomalies. Infection in the first month of pregnancy results in abnormalities in about 80% of cases, while detectable defects are found in about 15% of infants acquiring the disease during the third month of gestation. The intrauterine infection is associated with chronic persistence of the virus which may last for 12–18 months after birth.

Clinical Findings

Infants with congenital rubella syndrome may have one or more abnormalities which include defects of the heart and great vessels (patent ductus arteriosus, pulmonary artery stenosis, pulmonary valvular stenosis, ventricular septal defect, and atrial septal defect), eye defects (cataracts, glaucoma, and chorioretinitis), and neurosensory deafness. Infants may also display intrauterine growth retardation, failure to thrive, hepatosplenomegaly, thrombocytopenia with purpura, anemia, osteitis, and an encephalitic syndrome leading to mild to severe cerebral palsy. The infants often have increased susceptibility to infection, and evaluation of their immunoglobulins may reveal abnormalities, most commonly elevated IgM with low levels of IgG and IgA.

There is a 20% mortality rate among congenitally virus-infected infants symptomatic at birth. Some virus-infected infants appearing normal at birth may manifest abnormalities at a later date. Severely affected infants may require institutionalization. Those less severely affected are able to function satisfactorily as adults.

Recently, a syndrome of progressive panencephalitis has been described in teenage children with congenital rubella. These children had been functioning well prior to the onset of the neurologic symptoms.

Immunity

While maternal antibody in the form of IgG is transferred to the infant with congenital rubella, the infant also produces antibodies to the virus and, as found with other intrauterine infections (syphilis, toxoplasmosis, and cytomegalovirus), the antibody is IgM. Nonaffected infants lose maternal antibody.

Epidemiology

The virus has been recovered from the nasopharynx, throat, blood, and urine. The infection is spread by respiratory pathways (droplets).

Infants continue to be infectious, with virus found in the throat and CSF, for up to 18 months after birth. The persistence of virus in the CSF may in part explain the CNS disease observed in many infants. Virus has been recovered from almost all of the body tissues tested postmortem and from antemortem specimens of throat swabs, urine, CSF, feces, peripheral blood, bone marrow, conjunctival sac fluid, middle ear fluid, and lens material.

Congenitally infected infants who appear normal but who shed virus are capable of transmitting rubella to susceptible contacts such as nurses and physicians caring for the infants. This represents a serious hazard to women in the first trimester of pregnancy, who should avoid contact with these babies.

Rubella without rash (rubella sine eruptione) may occur. This is of importance because it is now known that inapparent rubella infection (with viremia) acquired during pregnancy has the same deleterious effect on the fetus as rubella with the typical rash.

3. CONTROL OF RUBELLA

In the 20th century, major epidemics of rubella have cycled at intervals of 6–9 years. After each epidemic, cases declined for the next 5 years, then increased to epidemic levels 6–9 years after the last major outbreak. Since the 1964 epidemic, when more than 20,000 infants were born with the severe manifestations of congenital rubella, the number of cases of rubella steadily decreased through 1974. It is disturbing to note an increase in the numbers of cases in 1975.

In the USA, the control of rubella is being achieved by routine vaccination of children 1–12 years of age and selected immunization of adolescents and women of childbearing age. From 1966 until 1969, when a live attenuated virus vaccine was licensed, about 50,000 cases were being reported annually. Since 1969, the number of cases has declined steadily to an all-time low of 12,000 cases in 1974; the number then increased to 16,000 in 1975.

Since the introduction of vaccine, scattered outbreaks have been reported, chiefly among nonvaccinated adolescents in high school and college who were too old to have received vaccine in the routine immunization program for children under 12 years of age.

In accordance with the recommendations of the USPHS, many states now vaccinate school children against rubella.

In postpubertal females, the vaccine produces self-limited arthralgia and arthritis in about one-third of the vaccinees. Since rubella virus vaccine appears to cross the placenta and infect the fetus, the vaccine should not be given to a postpubertal female unless she has been proved not to be pregnant, has been demonstrated serologically to be susceptible, understands that it is imperative not to become pregnant for at least 3 months after vaccination, and is adequately warned of the complications of arthralgia.

In children, the vaccine may also produce mild febrile episodes with arthralgia, often several months after vaccination, but without any permanent residual effects.

Vaccinated children are not infectious and do not transmit the virus to contacts at home, even to mothers who are susceptible and pregnant. In contrast, nonimmunized children can bring home wild virus and spread it to all susceptible family contacts.

Persons with abnormal immune functions or those who are sensitive to chicken or duck proteins or to neomycin should not receive the vaccine.

Opinions have been expressed that vaccination of children cannot prevent future infection of pregnant women exposed to wild virus. Therefore, vaccination limited to prepubertal girls and women in the immediate postpartum period has been proposed. It would seem wise for all pregnant women to undergo a serum antibody test for rubella and, if found to be susceptible, receive a vaccination immediately after delivery. Conception in the 6–8 weeks after delivery is rare, so the risk of harming a fetus would be minimal.

Reports have differed concerning the persistence of vaccine-induced immunity, the risk of subclinical reinfection of vaccinees upon subsequent exposure to wild virus, and the consequent danger of unrecognized transmission of the virus to pregnant women. Persons who produce *high* antibody levels after vaccination have maintained satisfactory levels for at least 5 years. However, among the vaccinated children whose original antibody levels were *low,* as many as 25% had lost all detectable antibodies 5 years later. They presumably are once again susceptible to rubella and, once infected, may infect their contacts. For proper control of the disease, vaccinated populations should be under continuing surveillance both for antibody levels and for the occurrence of rubella cases, so that proper control measures can be taken to fill in any gaps in immunity.

● ● ●

General References

Brunnell PA & others: Ineffectiveness of isolation of patients as a method of preventing the spread of mumps: Failure of the mumps skin-test antigen to predict immune status. N Engl J Med 279:1357, 1968.

Center for Disease Control: Rubella virus vaccine: Recommendation of the Public Health Service Advisory Committee on Immunization Practices. Ann Intern Med 75:757, 1971.

Chanock RM: Parainfluenza viruses. Pages 434–456 in: *Diagnostic Procedures for Viral and Rickettsial Infections,* 4th ed. American Public Health Association, 1969.

Choppin PW, Compans RW: Reproduction of paramyxoviruses. Pages 95–178 in: *Comprehensive Virology.* Vol 4. Fraenkel-Conrat H, Wagner RR (editors). Plenum Press, 1975.

Harris RW, Isacson P, Karzon DT: Vaccine-induced hypersensitivity: Reactions to live measles and mumps vaccines in prior recipients of inactivated measles vaccine. J Pediatr 74:552, 1969.

Henle W: Mumps virus. Pages 457–482 in: *Diagnostic Procedures for Viral and Rickettsial Infections,* 4th ed. American Public Health Association, 1969.

Jabbour JT & others: Epidemiology of subacute sclerosing panencephalitis (SSPE): A report of the SSPE registry. JAMA 220:959, 1972.

Katz SL, Enders JF: Measles virus. Pages 504–528 in: *Diagnostic Procedures for Viral and Rickettsial Infections,* 4th ed. American Public Health Association, 1969.

Kim HW & others: Epidemiology of respiratory syncytial virus infection in Washington, DC. 1. Importance of the virus in different respiratory tract disease syndromes and temporal distribution of infection. Am J Epidemiol 98:216, 1973.

Kingsbury DW: The molecular biology of paramyxoviruses. Med Microbiol Immunol (Berl) 160:73, 1974.

Lennette DA, Emmons RW, Lennette EH: Rapid diagnosis of mumps virus infections by immunofluorescence methods. J Clin Microbiol 2:81, 1975.

Linnemann CC Jr: Measles vaccine: Immunity, reinfection and revaccination. Am J Epidemiol 97:365, 1973.

Parkman PD, Meyer HM Jr: Prospects for a rubella virus vaccine. Prog Med Virol 11:80, 1969.

Pattison JR, Dane DS, Mace JE: Persistence of specific IgM after natural infection with rubella virus. Lancet 1:185, 1975.

Rawls WE: Congenital rubella: The significance of virus persistence. Prog Med Virol 10:238, 1968.

Townsend JJ & others: Progressive rubella panencephalitis: Late onset after congenital rubella. N Engl J Med 292:990, 1975.

Waterson AP: Measles. Proc R Soc Med 67:1109, 1974.

Weinstein L: Rubella immunization. N Engl J Med 288:100, 1973.

36 ...
Poxvirus Family

The **Poxviridae** are a large family that includes 6 genera. The genera have been established on the basis of the members having antigens in common—in addition to the nucleoprotein (NP) antigen common to all poxviruses—and their being able to recombine genetically.

Except for the genus *Orthopoxvirus*, members of each genus also have a common host range. The orthopoxviruses (vaccinia, variola, alastrim, cowpox, ectromelia, rabbitpox, and monkeypox) also vary in virulence and pathogenicity for experimental animals. They are ether-resistant and agglutinate chicken red cells. The genus *Avipoxvirus* (natural hosts: birds) is also ether-resistant; included in the genus are the viruses of fowlpox, pigeonpox, turkeypox, canarypox, quailpox, and lovebirdpox. Ungulates are the natural hosts of the genus *Capripoxvirus*. Its members (sheeppox, goatpox) are ether-sensitive and probably do not possess hemagglutinating properties. The genus *Leporipoxvirus* contains the poxviruses of rodents (fibroma and myxoma). These are also ether-sensitive; transmission by arthropods may occur. Viruses of the genus *Parapoxvirus* differ morphologically—the virion is smaller and is ovoid or cylindric, and the external coat is thicker. Its members do not multiply in embryonated eggs or common experimental animals. They are ether-sensitive and do not possess hemagglutinating properties. Natural hosts are also ungulates (orf virus of sheep, ulcerative dermatosis of sheep, bovine papular stomatitis, milker's nodule). Viruses of the genus *Entomopoxvirus* are limited to arthropods and probably do not multiply in vertebrates.

SMALLPOX & RELATED VIRAL INFECTIONS OF MAN

VARIOLA MAJOR
(Classical Smallpox, Asiatic Smallpox),
VARIOLA MINOR (Alastrim),
VACCINIA

Smallpox (variola major) is an acute infectious disease characterized by severe systemic involvement and a single crop of skin lesions which proceeds through macular, papular, vesicular, and pustular stages over a period of 5–10 days. A mild form (variola minor) also occurs. Vaccinia is a related poxvirus, attenuated for man, and has long been in use as (the first) live virus vaccine. Monkeypox can infect both monkeys and humans, producing symptoms resembling those of smallpox. Yaba virus, a simian poxvirus, induces benign tumors in monkeys and can produce similar lesions in man.

The viruses of variola major and minor are indistinguishable from each other serologically and are differentiated only in minor ways from the viruses of vaccinia and cowpox. All of these related viruses may be distinguished by the maximum temperature at which they will grow in eggs. The origin of the vaccinia virus is unknown. It may have stemmed from cowpox or it may have originated from variola virus.

Properties of the Virus

A. Size and Nucleic Acid: The DNA genome has a very large molecular weight, 160×10^6, sufficient to code for several hundred proteins.

The members of the pox family are about 230×300 nm. The virus particles are brick-shaped when visualized in dried films in the electron microscope but ellipsoid when seen in ultrathin sections of infected cells. A poxvirus consists of an outer lipoprotein membrane, or envelope, which surrounds the proteinaceous lateral bodies, and a core with a thick membrane, enclosing the double-stranded DNA genome (Figs 27–30 and 27–31).

Highly purified vaccinia virus has a chemical composition resembling that of a bacterium. It contains protein, DNA, phospholipid, neutral fat, and carbohydrate. A DNA-dependent RNA polymerase and several other enzymes have been isolated from the cores of purified virions.

B. Reactions to Physical and Chemical Agents: Both variola and vaccinia withstand drying for months. In the moist state, the virus is destroyed at 60° C for 10 minutes, but in the dry state it can resist 100° C for 5–10 minutes. Acids (pH 3.0) destroy the virus within an hour. Alcohol in 50% concentration or potassium permanganate in 0.01% concentration destroys the virus within 1 hour at room temperature.

C. Animal Susceptibility and Growth of Virus: The host range of variola virus is restricted to man and monkeys. Unlike vaccinia virus, it cannot be propagated in rabbits or mice. However, it grows readily on the chorioallantoic membrane of the 10- to 12-day-old chick embryo. It produces characteristic small, white lesions differing from the large vaccinia lesions, which have central depressions due to necrosis. Vaccinia virus grows readily in cultures of chick embryo or primate cells, producing necrosis of the cells.

D. Antigenic Properties: Antigenic relationships among poxviruses are determined with the use of extracts of infected cells. Up to 20 antigens capable of forming precipitin lines with antiviral antiserum can be detected. Viruses of the vaccinia-variola group are very similar antigenically and differ by not more than one antigen by this technic. Viruses of the myxoma-fibroma group are not neutralized by antiserum to the vaccinia-variola group, and no major antigens in the respective cell extracts cross-react. However, the inner core of all poxviruses contains a common antigen within a complex of the viral DNA, and about half the virus protein, which can be released from the core by alkaline digestion.

In addition to structural antigens, poxviruses produce soluble antigens and hemagglutinins. Vaccinia virus contains a heat-labile (L) antigen which is destroyed at 60° C and a heat-stable (S) antigen which withstands treatment at 100° C. Both antigens may be present in soluble form in infected tissue. They appear to be different antigenic components of a complex LS antigen, an elongated protein with a molecular weight of about 240,000. In addition, the virus contains deoxynucleoprotein, which is also antigenic. Adsorption of immune sera with LS or NP antigens fails to remove neutralizing antibody. Upon the LS antigens depend the serologic tests for smallpox diagnosis. LS antigens from variola and from vaccinia virus are antigenically similar, using either convalescent sera from smallpox patients or rabbit antivaccinia serum.

A third antigen has been isolated with a molecular weight of 100,000–200,000 which, unlike the other antigens studied, is capable of combining with virus-neutralizing antibody and when injected into animals confers some resistance to infection.

The hemagglutinin of vaccinia, variola, or infectious ectromelia (mousepox) is not an integral part of the virion and can be obtained free from the much larger virus particles. The hemagglutination reaction with chicken red cells can be inhibited by vaccinia immune serum, convalescent smallpox serum, or ectromelia immune serum. The hemagglutinin is a lipoprotein complex, associated with a particle 65 nm in diameter. It is heat-stable; it is distinct from the LS antigens but does not exhibit receptor-destroying (neuraminidase) activity.

It should be noted that all the vaccinia virus antigens studied are complexes of several polypeptides and have not been related to single, well-defined polypeptides as is the case, for example, with influenza virus hemagglutinin.

Poxvirus Multiplication

A. Virus Penetration and Uncoating: The intra-cellular uncoating of the virion is basically a 2-stage process. Virus particles establish contact with the cell surface and are then engulfed in phagocytic vacuoles of the cell. Inside the cell, a phagolysozome vacuole develops which initiates first stage uncoating, probably by means of hydrolytic enzymes in the vacuoles. Under control of the cell, this step results in degradation of the outer membrane and lateral bodies, releasing the nucleoprotein core into the cytoplasm. The second uncoating step involves degradation of the nucleoprotein core, liberating DNA and rendering it sensitive to deoxyribonuclease.

For second stage uncoating to occur there is a requirement for both RNA and protein synthesis, which implies information transfer from DNA to RNA. When protein synthesis is inhibited either at the transcription stage (dactinomycin) or at the translational stage (fluorophenylalanine or puromycin), the breakdown of the virus occurs normally but it is not followed by liberation of naked DNA.

A poxvirus carries within its core 2 important enzymes, RNA polymerase and poly(A) polymerase. RNA polymerase mediates the synthesis of poxvirus messenger RNA (mRNA) and can function while the DNA is encased in the core. This mRNA is transcribed within the virus core and is then released into the cytoplasm where it codes for the synthesis of proteins which direct the release of virus DNA from the core, allowing further expression of the viral genome. Poly(A) polymerase is capable of adding adenylate residues from ATP to the 3′ ends of polynucleotides.

Poxviruses inactivated by heat can be reactivated either by viable poxviruses or by poxviruses inactivated by nitrogen mustards (which inactivate the DNA moiety). The reactivation is due to the stimulation of the uncoating protein. Heat-inactivated virus cannot cause second stage uncoating because of the heat lability of the DNA-dependent RNA polymerase. The significance of poxvirus reactivation lies in the fact that it embraces the whole of the poxvirus group and that any poxvirus can reactivate any other poxvirus, suggesting that all members of the poxvirus group carry the RNA polymerase in their cores.

B. Intracellular Sequence of Multiplication: The initial stage of virus multiplication is the transcription of virus DNA within the core. About 14% of the genome is transcribed at this stage. The resulting polypeptides include the virus-specific thymidine kinase and the proteins responsible for second stage uncoating (see above). During this period, the synthesis of host macromolecules is efficiently inhibited, possibly by a structural component of the virus.

After the release of the viral DNA (second stage uncoating), additional early mRNA is transcribed which codes for additional enzymes and some early structural components of the virus. Most of the structural components made early are found to be part of the virus core. By 4 hours after infection, viral DNA replication utilizing the early enzymes occurs within discrete areas of the cytoplasm. These areas have been called virus factories (or inclusion bodies) and can be located by cytochemical and immunofluorescent technics (see Fig 27–28).

After the synthesis of viral progeny DNA has begun, the synthesis of the early virus proteins is inhibited and late viral mRNA and protein are made. These proteins include most of the virus structural proteins and the enzymes found within the virus particle. DNA replication then ceases.

The assembly of the virus particle from the manufactured components is a complex process. Many of the polypeptides which become part of the virus particle are modified by the addition of sugars (glycosylation) or phosphorus (phosphorylation) or by proteolytic cleavage. Poxviruses are unique in that de novo formation of virus membranes occurs (see Figs 27–30 and 27–31).

Morphogenesis of the virus particle has been studied with the electron microscope. The principal stages are as follows: (1) In the earliest form, the developmental bodies appear as hollow spheres surrounded by virus membranes and embedded either in a very dense cytoplasmic mass constituting an inclusion (or virus factory) or in a less dense matrix near the nucleus in cells without typical inclusion bodies. (2) The spheres become filled with a homogeneous material of low electron density. (3) A small, dense granule appears in each developmental body and grows at the expense of the low-density material. (4) Following growth of the granule, particles are found having the dimensions of mature viruses and having complex internal structures resembling bars or dumbbells. (5) Mature virions are made up of a DNA-containing central body encased by double membranes, surrounded by protein, and all enclosed within 2 outer membranes.

The immature forms appear 4–5 hours after infection, followed within 2 hours by the mature infective virus. The infection spreads gradually in the cell for the next 16 hours. Thus, thin sections observed in the electron microscope 24 hours after infection show that the virus is being manufactured throughout the cytoplasm. Ten thousand virus particles per cell are produced.

Release of the virus may be by 2 methods— budding or lysis—and some particles may gain a cell-related envelope, since intracellular and extracellular rabbitpox virus particles differ antigenically.

C. Virus Induced Enzymes: Infection of a cell by vaccinia virus leads to the synthesis of several enzymes that are under the control of the virus genome. The enzymes that have been described thus far are DNA polymerase, RNA polymerase, poly(A) polymerase, 2 different DNases, 2 different nucleotide phosphohydrolases, thymidine kinase, and protein kinase.

Of these, thymidine kinase has been studied in detail and mutants have been isolated that do not induce the formation of this enzyme even though virus multiplication proceeds at normal rates. Thymidine kinase activity first increases about 2 hours after infection and rises to 10 times the normal level by 10 hours after infection. The increase is completely inhibited under conditions inhibiting the synthesis of protein.

The time course for synthesis of thymidine kinase and DNA polymerase indicates that the genetic code for thymidine kinase can be expressed before the breakdown of viral cores, whereas DNA polymerase can be synthesized only after the uncoating of the viral DNA. The DNA polymerases from vaccinia-infected cells and uninfected cells differ significantly with regard to ion exchange chromatographic properties, primer response, pH optimum, heat inactivation, and inhibition by vaccinia antiserum.

Seven of the above enzymes have been demonstrated to be associated with purified vaccinia virus particles. These are RNA polymerase, poly(A) polymerase, an acid DNase-exonuclease, a neutral DNase-endonuclease, 2 nucleotide phosphohydrolases, and the protein kinase.

D. Virus Inhibitors: Cells infected with vaccinia virus and treated with bromodeoxyuridine (BUDR) produce viral antigen in the cytoplasm and yield particles that have incorporated BUDR in their nucleic acid in place of thymidine. Such particles are malformed and noninfectious.

The assembly of vaccinia virus envelope and virus particles is blocked in cells treated with rifampin. The primary action of rifampin on vaccinia development occurs during envelope formation. In addition, rifampin prevents the formation of a core polypeptide of the vaccinia virion. Rifampin appears to inhibit the cleavage of a larger molecular weight polypeptide which is the precursor of the core polypeptide.

Pathogenesis & Pathology of Smallpox

The portal of entry of variola virus is through the mucous membranes of the upper respiratory tract. During the incubation period, the virus may propagate in lymphoid and other tissues. Inasmuch as there are no open lesions on the mucosal surface during incubation, the patient is not infectious during this period. After the entry of the virus, the following are believed to take place: (1) primary multiplication in the lymphoid tissue draining the site of entry; (2) transient viremia and infection of reticuloendothelial cells throughout the body; (3) a secondary phase of multiplication in these cells, leading to (4) a secondary, more intense viremia; and (5) the clinical disease.

The skin lesion follows the localization of virus in the epidermis from the bloodstream. The virus can be isolated from the blood in the early phases of the disease but not after the second day of fever (except in fatal cases). The clinical improvement which follows with the development of the skin eruption is held to be the result of the rapid appearance of antibodies. The pustulation of the skin lesions may give rise to a secondary fever; this is believed to be the result of the absorption of the products of cell necrosis rather than of a secondary bacterial infection.

Neither in mild nor in severe cases are bacteria found in the blood during the early viremic (preeruptive febrile) phase. In severe cases, bacteria may be found in the blood about the eighth to twelfth days of disease during the pustular phase. Skin pustules may become contaminated, usually with staphylococci, sometimes leading to a number of bacterial complications (osteomyelitis, septic joints).

Early in the course of the illness (preeruptive phase), the disease is hardly infective. On the first or second day of disease, saliva is negative for virus, but by the sixth to ninth days it is usually positive. At this time lesions in the mouth tend to ulcerate and discharge virus into the oral cavity. Thus early in the disease infectious virus has its source in the lesions in the mouth and upper respiratory tract. Later, pustules break down and discharge virus in the environment of the smallpox patient.

Histopathologic examination of the skin shows that proliferation of the prickle-cell layer occurs early and that these proliferated cells contain large numbers of cytoplasmic inclusions. There is infiltration of mononuclear cells, particularly around the vessels in the corium. Epithelial cells of the malpighian layer become swollen through distention of cytoplasm and undergo "ballooning degeneration." The vacuoles in the cytoplasm enlarge and distend the cell membrane. This finally breaks down, and the coalescence with neighboring, similarly affected cells results in the formation of vesicles. As the disease progresses, the vesicles enlarge and then become filled with white cells and tissue debris. In variola minor, the basilar layer is little involved, whereas in variola major and vaccinia all the layers are involved and there is actual necrosis of the corium. Thus scarring is seen after variola major and vaccinia but not after variola minor.

The cytoplasmic inclusions (Guarnieri bodies) are sometimes round or oval, homogeneous, and acidophilic, but often the inclusion body has a granular appearance with an irregular outline.

Clinical Findings

A. Variola Major (Smallpox): The incubation period is about 12 days. The onset may be gradual or sudden. One to 5 days of fever and malaise precede the appearance of the exanthems, which are papular for 1–4 days, vesicular for 1–4 days, and pustular for 2–6 days, forming crusts which fall off 2–4 weeks after the first sign of the lesion and leave pink scars which fade slowly. In each area affected, the lesions are generally found in the same stage of development. The temperature falls within 24 hours after the rash appears.

The nature and extent of the rash are functions of the severity of the disease. Vaccinated contacts may develop a febrile illness called **variola sine eruptione**. They have all the symptoms of the preeruptive stage of smallpox, but the disease progresses no further. In severe cases, the rash is hemorrhagic. The case mortality rate varies from 5% (discrete rash) to over 40% (confluent rash).

B. Variola Minor (Alastrim): The symptoms during the prodromal period are similar to those of variola major but not so severe. The distribution and course of the eruption are also similar, but the lesions are less profuse. The disease is like that of mild variola major in vaccinated persons. Mortality is under 1%.

Modified or mild smallpox may occur when the infecting virus is of low virulence, as in variola minor, or when the patient has some immunity, as in variola major in vaccinated individuals. In modified smallpox of either type, lesions are smaller and more superficial and develop more rapidly than in severe smallpox. The real difference between them lies in the disease transmitted to contacts: variola minor invariably gives rise to a mild disease in the contacts, whereas modified variola major often gives rise to severe smallpox.

Laboratory Diagnosis

The tests which should be used at various stages of smallpox are shown in Table 36–1. They are especially important in previously vaccinated persons, in whom the clinical course may be atypical. They depend upon direct microscopic examination of material from skin lesions, recovery of virus from the patient, identification of viral antigen from the lesion, and demonstration of antibody in the blood. The direct examination of clinical material in the electron microscope can also be used for rapid identification of virus particles and can readily differentiate smallpox from chickenpox.

The virus is sometimes found in the blood in moderately severe cases during the first day or so of illness, and regularly in the severe, fulminating, hemorrhagic case. The virus is found regularly in the skin of all cases, and typical histopathologic findings are present in the skin of fatal cases.

A. Smears: In a high percentage of cases, carefully prepared and properly stained smears from lesions of the papular and vesicular stages give a positive result within 30 minutes after the sample is submitted. Smears on grease-free slides are made with material from papules or from the bases of vesicles by first removing the superficial epidermis and then scraping the lesion gently with the point of a knife or a needle. The smears are washed with distilled water and ether, fixed with alcohol, and stained as follows: a mixture of equal parts of 1% gentian violet and 2% sodium bicarbonate is filtered onto the slide and allowed to react for 5 minutes with steaming. If elementary bodies are seen in large numbers, a presumptive diagnosis of smallpox can be made.

B. Virus Culture: The detection of virus on the chorioallantoic membrane of the 12- to 14-day-old chick embryo is the most reliable laboratory test. It is the easiest way of distinguishing cases of smallpox from generalized vaccinia which may occur in vaccinated persons during an epidemic period, for the lesions produced by these viruses on the membrane differ markedly. The use of the chick embryo is more reliable than the corneal inoculation of the rabbit (Paul's test), which may be followed by a specific keratitis. The lesion becomes apparent in 2–3 days. Its specificity should be confirmed by histologic examination of the membranes and by hemagglutination inhibition and neutralization with antivaccinia serum on passage of the virus into other eggs.

Susceptible cultures may be prepared from hu-

Table 36—1. Laboratory tests in diagnosis of smallpox. (After Downie.)

Stage of Illness	Material to Be Examined	Microscopic Examination of Smears From Skin Lesions	Culture on Chick Embryo Chorioallantois or in Cell Culture	Detection of Antigen by Agar Gel Diffusion or Complement Fixation	Detection of Antibody
Preeruptive illness	Blood		May be positive	May be positive	Usually negative
Macular and papular	Smears (on slides) from skin lesions	Usually positive	Usually positive	May be positive	
	Blood				Usually negative
Vesicular	Vesicle fluid and smears (on slides) from base of vesicles	Usually positive	Usually positive	Usually positive	
	Blood				Usually negative
Pustular	Pustule fluid	May be positive	Usually positive	Usually positive	
	Blood				May be positive
Crusting	Crusts	Usually negative	Usually positive	Usually positive	
	Blood				Usually positive
Later	Blood				Usually positive
Time required for completion of test		1 hour	1—3 days	3—24 hours	3—24 hours

man embryonic tissue, monkey kidney, or continuous cell lines. Three days are usually required for cytopathic changes to become evident, but virus may be detected 1–2 days earlier by hemadsorption with added chick cells, by development of typical cytoplasmic inclusions in stained coverslip preparations from the culture, or by immunofluorescence.

C. Antigen Detection: Antigen can be detected readily by immunodiffusion or by CF test if sufficient material is collected from the skin lesion.

D. Antibody Determination: After the first week, neutralizing, complement-fixing, and hemagglutination-inhibiting antibodies may be detected. Antibody tests are of little value in recently vaccinated persons. However, as the complement-fixing antibody is transient and is rarely found more than 12 months after vaccination, its detection is of diagnostic value in patients with variola sine eruptione who have been vaccinated over a year previously. Only certain chickens provide suitable erythrocytes for the HI test.

Differential Diagnosis

Variola major and variola minor may be distinguished on epidemiologic grounds and by laboratory tests in chick embryos. Variola minor fails to produce pocks at incubator temperatures above 38° C, whereas pocks are readily produced at elevated temperatures by variola major virus, which is also more lethal for the embryos. Unusual cases of smallpox may be confused with varicella, pustular acne, meningococcemia, blood dyscrasias, drug rashes, and other illnesses associated with a skin eruption, but none of these illnesses yield materials which give positive laboratory tests for variola virus or its antibody (Table 36–1).

Vaccinia virus, cowpox virus, monkeypox virus, and herpesvirus can be distinguished from smallpox virus by the morphologic pattern of the pocks produced on the chorioallantois. Vaccinia virus pocks are large, with necrotic centers, while cowpox and monkeypox virus pocks are hemorrhagic. Herpesvirus pocks are smaller than those of variola virus.

Vaccinia, unlike variola, can be passed serially in rabbits by skin-to-skin passage.

Immunity

Children are born with maternal antibodies, but these are lost within a few months after birth. At that time artificial immunity can be produced by vaccination (see Control, below). In countries where vaccine is used, unless an emergency exists, it is better to postpone vaccination until the second year of life. Vaccination in infancy may be responsible for attenuation of the disease in later life. Immunity is demonstrable 8 or 9 days following vaccination, reaches its maximum within 2 or 3 weeks, and is maintained at an appreciable level for a few years. In endemic areas and in heavily exposed persons, vaccination should be repeated at yearly intervals.

In those who recover from smallpox, active immunity persists for years.

Passively transferred antibody can protect unvaccinated persons from smallpox. However, antibodies alone are not sufficient for recovery from primary poxvirus infection. In the human host, neutralizing antibodies develop within a few days after onset of smallpox but do not prevent progression of lesions, and patients often die in the pustular stage with high antibody levels. There is strong evidence that cell-mediated immunity may be as important as circulating antibody. Patients with hypogammaglobulinemia generally react normally to vaccinations and develop immunity despite the apparent absence of antibody. Immunity is accompanied by well-developed delayed cutaneous hypersensitivity to vaccinia. Patients who have defects in both cellular immune response and antibody response develop a progressive, usually fatal disease upon vaccination.

It is difficult to determine the relative importance of cellular versus humoral immunity to poxviruses. The macrophage migration inhibition test has been used to measure delayed hypersensitivity to virus infections in vitro. If macrophages and lymphocytes pelleted in capillary tubes are placed in culture chambers, the macrophages migrate out of the tubes over the glass surface. If antigen is placed in the culture chamber, macrophages fail to migrate from the tubes. Inhibition of migration of the macrophages is due to a factor produced by the sensitized lymphocytes upon contact with the antigen. Studies with fibroma virus, a poxvirus that produces benign tumors in rabbits, indicate that there is a good correlation between the onset of delayed hypersensitivity to fibroma infection and inhibition of migration (Fig 36–1). Tumor regression does not occur until several days after a positive skin test and a positive migration inhibition test are observed. Increase in tumor size after onset of delayed hyper-

sensitivity is not due to spread of the infection but to a local immune reaction due to infiltration of inflammatory cells into the lesion. Animals bearing tumors become resistant to reinfection on the fifth day after the primary infection, which correlates with development of delayed hypersensitivity.

In addition to a delayed hypersensitivity reaction which could suppress virus synthesis and spread at the site of infection (pathogenesis of the vaccinia skin lesion), production of interferon, which would block virus synthesis, is a possible defense mechanism. This is supported by the observations that irradiated animals, without detectable antibody or delayed hypersensitivity, recovered from vaccinia infection as rapidly as untreated control animals.

It is probable that active immunity is promoted through a combination of humoral and cellular responses.

Treatment

Vaccinia immune globulin (VIG) is available for immediate shipment anywhere in the USA. VIG is prepared from blood provided by revaccinated servicemen. Indications for use of VIG are accidental inoculation of vaccine in the eye, eczema vaccinatum, and prevention or lessening of the severity of the disease in contacts of smallpox cases. VIG should be given as soon as possible after exposure. After clinical smallpox

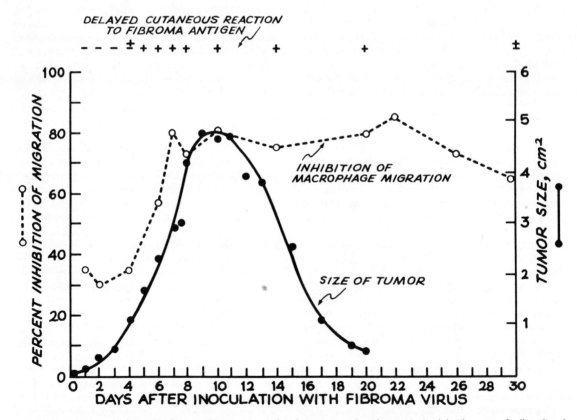

Figure 36–1. Temporal relationship between fibroma virus-induced tumor growth and regression and development of cell-mediated immune response as measured in vivo by skin testing and in vitro by macrophage migration inhibition. (From Tompkins and Rawls.)

is evident, VIG is of no value, since by that time in the course of the disease the patient has already made high titers of his own neutralizing antibodies.

Antibiotics have no effect in the early stages of smallpox but may be of value in treating secondary bacterial infection in the pustular stage.

Several compounds with activity against herpesviruses, ie, vidarabine and cytarabine (cytosine arabinoside) (see Chapter 27), have been used in an attempt to treat patients with variola major. In studies with vidarabine, no difference was found between the study group and the control group. Patients treated with cytosine arabinoside had an increase in mortality rate over patients treated with a placebo.

Methisazone (Marboran) is effective as prophylaxis but does not appear to be useful in treatment of established disease (see Chapter 27).

Epidemiology

Although smallpox is contagious, recent epidemiologic evaluations indicate that it is considerably less so than measles or influenza. Transmission can often be traced to direct contact between cases. Indirect contact may also occur, as in the infection of laundry workers through infected bedclothes. The virus can survive for months; outbreaks in England have been initiated by cotton imported from Egypt.

Patients may be infectious during the incubation period. Virus has been isolated from throat swabs taken from family contacts of patients with smallpox. Variola virus was isolated from 34 of 328 family contacts examined 4–8 days after the onset of illness in a family member. Only 4 of these contacts developed clinical smallpox; this occurred 5–7 days after the swabs were collected.

Lesions of the throat occur earlier than lesions of the skin. Early erosion of the lesions on the mucous membranes leads to heavy contamination of the oral, nasal, and bronchial secretions. Skin lesions become infective later.

In the absence of vaccination, all human beings are susceptible to smallpox. The disease occurs at all seasons of the year but is less prevalent in summer.

The epidemiologic features of smallpox make the virus amenable to total eradication: there is no known nonhuman reservoir, and chronic, asymptomatic carriage of the virus does not occur. Since virus in the environment of the patient derives from lesions in the mouth and throat (and later the skin), patients with infection sufficiently severe to transmit the disease are likely to be so ill that they quickly reach the attention of medical authorities. And the close contact now considered requisite for effective spread of the disease generally makes for ready identification of a patient's contacts so that specific control measures can be instituted to interrupt the cycle of transmission.

With the introduction of a heat-stable lyophilized vaccine that retains its viability under field conditions in tropical areas, vaccination has become widespread and effective in reducing the incidence of smallpox. Since 1967, a worldwide Smallpox Eradication Program sponsored by the WHO has been pursued with remarkable success. Approximately 131,000 cases were reported in 1967, but only 31,318 cases in 1970; the number of countries reporting one or more cases declined from 42 in 1967 to 23 in 1970. In 1973, when over 100,000 cases were reported, Bangladesh, India, and Pakistan accounted for more than 95% of the world's total of cases, each country recording that year its highest reported incidence of smallpox since at least 1967. The situation in Ethiopia is in notable contrast. In 1971, Ethiopia recorded 26,329 cases, virtually half the world's total of cases. In 1973, only 4000 cases were recorded despite far more complete reporting than was possible in 1971, the first year of its eradication program. In Brazil, where cases during 1967–1970 numbered in the thousands, only 19 cases were reported in 1971. No cases have been reported in South America since 1971.

As of August 1975, 18,000 cases of smallpox had been reported, a decrease of 90% as compared to the same period during 1974. Disease was present in only 3 countries (Somalia by importation; endemic in Bangladesh and Ethiopia). This figure represents a 100% decline in India, which for the first time in history has not had a reported case for several months, and a 50% decrease in Ethiopia. Bangladesh accounted for 80% of the cases in 1975 but has been free of cases since October of that year. The global program of smallpox eradication has reached the point that progress is now monitored in terms of the number of "infected villages" in each area. A village is considered infected until 6 weeks have elapsed since onset of rash of the last case and until a special search is made to confirm that no further cases have occurred.

In the USA, no cases have been reported since 1949. In Europe, 51 importations of the disease have been documented since 1950. During 1951–1960, an average of 26 cases resulted from each of 23 such incidents. However, 18 importations in 1961–1965 and 10 in 1966–1970 were more readily controlled and gave rise to fewer indigenous cases. More than half of the infections in these outbreaks were acquired in a hospital (through contact with either patients or hospital staff members).

Individual cases of smallpox were imported into Japan from Bangladesh and into England from India in 1973. There was no secondary spread. A laboratory accident in London in 1973 caused 4 cases of smallpox, including 2 deaths.

Although explosive outbreaks of smallpox may occur in endemic areas as a result of war and similar dislocations, the probability of exportation of smallpox from countries in which it is endemic is limited not only by the decline in incidence of the disease but also by a change in its socioeconomic distribution. In virtually all endemic nations, its distribution is becoming like that of poliomyelitis and diphtheria in the USA—a vestigial disease of isolated rural villages and urban slums, whose inhabitants would be unlikely to travel abroad or to have much contact with foreign visitors.

Control (Vaccination)

The introduction of living vaccinia virus into the skin dates from Jenner's work, published in 1798. Variolation, the introduction into the skin of variola virus obtained from mild cases of smallpox, had been used before this time for centuries by the Chinese. Vaccinia virus for vaccination is prepared from vesicular lesions ("lymph") produced in the skin of calves or sheep. (Recent experiments suggest that equally good virus for vaccination may be prepared in cell cultures of bovine embryos. Cell culture virus, like virus grown in chick embryos, can be harvested under bacteriologically sterile conditions.) The final product contains 40% glycerol and 0.4% phenol in order to destroy bacteria and keep the vaccine from freezing at its storage temperature of $-10°$ C. Commercial calf lymph vaccine of good potency should contain about 4×10^{10} virus particles per ml, which can be measured by electron microscopic counting methods. This should be the equivalent of about 10^8 infectious units per ml. WHO standards require that smallpox vaccines have a potency of not less than 10^8 pock-forming units per ml.

Vaccine as issued to physicians can be stored for several weeks in the ordinary refrigerator without significant loss in potency. Once removed to room temperature, it should be used within a few days. Deterioration of vaccine is a problem in tropical countries, where it is often necessary to send vaccinators on long journeys from the base laboratory. For tropical countries, dried vaccinia virus is recommended. Stable lyophilized vaccinia virus has been prepared from the chorioallantoic membranes of hens' eggs. The availability of a jet injection instrument permits the rapid, effective administration of vaccine where large numbers of persons can gather at a single location.

A. Time of Vaccination: In 1971, the USPHS recommended discontinuance of routine nonselective vaccination in the USA. However, vaccination of persons at special risk will be continued (see below). Primary vaccination has usually been carried out in infants between 4 and 6 months of age. However, eczema vaccinatum, unduly severe takes, progressive vaccinia, and other complications are all more commonly seen under the age of 1 year. Therefore, when necessary, vaccinating between 1 and 2 years of age is preferable to vaccinating in the first year of life. Infants suffering from skin diseases or those with siblings who have skin diseases should not be vaccinated because the vaccinia virus may localize in the lesions of the vaccinated child or of the contact (eczema vaccinatum).

Revaccination has been done at regular intervals (before entering school and again at the age of 16 or so) or in the face of possible exposure to smallpox. In the few countries where smallpox is endemic, revaccination is recommended at yearly intervals. If vaccine is to be used in nonepidemic areas, revaccination should be considered at regular 3-year intervals since resistance to infection falls off sharply 3 years after vaccination. All resistance to infection is felt to be gone 20 years following vaccination.

Smallpox may occur in spite of successful vaccination. Early allergic responses may be mistaken for immune reactions. To afford real protection, vaccination must be successfully performed before exposure. When vaccination immediately follows exposure, it is much less protective.

B. Technic: The methods used are multiple pressure, multiple puncture, or jet injection, but in all technics inoculation should be intradermal, never subcutaneous. The skin on the arm over the lower part of the posterior border of the deltoid muscle is used. It is prepared by swabbing with acetone or ether or by washing with soap and water. After the area is dry, a drop of the vaccine is placed on the skin and the side of the needle is then pressed firmly through the drop of vaccine into the superficial layers of the skin. For primary vaccination, 10 pressures are adequate; for revaccination, 30 pressures should be made. The point of the needle should not draw blood. With the jet injection instrument, specially prepared vaccine should be used. After the vaccination has been completed, excess vaccine should be removed from the skin with dry, sterile gauze. No dressing should be applied.

C. Reactions and Interpretations:

1. Primary take—In the fully susceptible person, no reaction is seen until the third or fourth day, at which time a papule appears that is surrounded by a narrow areola of hyperemia. The papule increases in size until vesiculation appears (on the fifth or sixth day). The vesicle reaches its maximum size by the ninth day and then becomes pustular, usually with some tenderness of the axillary nodes. Desiccation follows and is complete in about 2 weeks, leaving a depressed pink scar which ultimately turns white. The reading of the result is usually made on the seventh day. If this reaction is not observed, vaccination should be repeated with vaccine from another lot until a successful result is obtained.

2. Revaccination—

a. A successful revaccination (major reaction) is one which on examination 1 week (6–8 days) later shows a vesicular or pustular lesion or an area of definite palpable induration or congestion surrounding a central lesion, which may be a scab or an ulcer. Only this reaction indicates with certainty that virus multiplication has taken place.

b. Equivocal reactions may represent immunity but may also represent merely allergic reactions to a vaccine that has become inactivated. When an equivocal reaction occurs, the revaccination should be repeated using a new lot of vaccine. A second reading should be made after 6–8 days, and vaccination should again be repeated if the result is still equivocal. This should be done at a different site.

D. Complications of Vaccination:

1. Bacterial infection of the vaccination site—This is rare and can be attributed to faulty technic of vaccination or to subsequent infection of the vaccinial lesion. Tetanus is reported to occur only when the vaccinated area has been covered by a dressing.

2. Generalized vaccinia—This is manifested by the

which are larger than the virus itself. The virus appears to form within this larger sphere.

The virus is cytopathic for human and monkey cell cultures but has not yet been serially transferred in culture. Virus particles in extracts from lesions of molluscum contagiosum interfere with the growth of heterologous viruses in cultures of mouse embryo cells. This interference action can be used to study biologic properties of the virus.

• • •

General References

Armstrong JA, Metz DH, Young MR: The mode of entry of vaccinia virus into L cells. J Gen Virol 21:533, 1973.

Baxby D: Identification and interrelationships of the variola/vaccinia subgroup of poxviruses. Prog Med Virol 19:215, 1975.

Boulter EA, Appleyard G: Differences between extracellular and intracellular forms of poxvirus and their implications. Prog Med Virol 16:86, 1973.

Downie AW, Kempe CH: Poxviruses. Pages 281–320 in: *Diagnostic Procedures for Viral and Rickettsial Infections,* 4th ed. American Public Health Association, 1969.

Dumbell KR: Laboratory aids to the control of smallpox in countries where the disease is not endemic. Prog Med Virol 10:388, 1968.

Foege WH, Eddins DL: Mass vaccination programs in developing countries. Prog Med Virol 15:205, 1973.

Lane JM, Millar JD, Neff JM: Smallpox and smallpox vaccination policy. Annu Rev Med 22:251, 1971.

Moss B: Reproduction of poxviruses. Pages 405–474 in: *Comprehensive Virology.* Vol 3. Fraenkel-Conrat H, Wagner RR (editors). Plenum Press, 1975.

37 . . .
Adenovirus Family

The **Adenoviridae** consist of 2 genera—*Mastadeno-virus* and *Aviadenovirus*—with over 80 species or anti-genic types recognized. There are at least 33 human adenoviruses; some cause acute respiratory diseases and others cause pharyngitis. Some adenoviruses also cause certain external diseases of the eye. Certain adeno-viruses serve as models of cancer viruses because they produce tumors in hamsters. Adenoviruses occur in many animal species: avian, bovine, canine (infectious canine hepatitis virus), murine, porcine, simian, and others.

Properties of the Virus

A. Nucleic Acid: Double-stranded DNA. The DNA content of adenoviruses ranges from 11.6–13.5%. Molecular weight of the DNA is $20–25 \times 10^6$. Base ratio determinations revealed 3 distinct groups of adenoviruses: those with a low guanine + cytosine (G + C) content (48–49%); those with an intermediate G + C content (50–53%); and those with a high G + C content (56–60%). The strongly oncogenic adenovirus types 12, 18, and 31 are the only members of the group with low G + C, while certain adenoviruses in the intermediate group (types 3, 7, 14, 16, 21) are mildly oncogenic. This grouping has been confirmed by cross-hybridization of nucleic acid isolated from virions of each group. It is possible to isolate the DNA in an infectious form.

B. Size: The infective virus particles, 70–90 nm in diameter, are icosahedrons with shells (capsids) com-posed of 252 subunits (capsomeres). No outer enve-lope is known. Three major soluble antigens are sepa-rable from the infectious particle by differential cen-trifugation. These antigens—a group-specific antigen common to all adenovirus types, a type-specific anti-gen unique for each type, and a toxin-like material which also possesses group specificity— represent virus structural protein subunits produced in large excess of the amount utilized for synthesis of infectious virus.

C. Reactions to Physical and Chemical Agents: These viruses are ether-resistant but are heat-labile, being destroyed at 56° C for 30 minutes. They are relatively stable to pH 5.0–9.0 and to temperatures between 4 and 50° C. The viruses are usually stored frozen. They can be lyophilized without loss of activity.

D. Animal Susceptibility and Transformation of Cells: The virus does not commonly produce disease in laboratory animals but can produce fatal infections in newborn hamsters (type 5), tumors in newborn ham-sters (types 3, 7, 12, 14, 16, 18, 21, 31), and broncho-pneumonic lesions in young colostrum-deprived pigs. Although virus cannot be recovered from adenovirus-induced hamster tumors, a new antigen induced by the virus can be detected by complement fixation or immunofluorescence. This antigen, called tumor or T antigen because of its association with tumor or trans-formed cells, can also be detected in the cytolytic cycle of the virus. Hamster cells can be transformed in vitro by the oncogenic human adenoviruses. These cells contain the adenovirus tumor antigen, do not contain infectious virus, and will produce tumors when inocu-lated into adult hamsters. Adenovirus messenger RNA (mRNA) can be detected in the cytoplasm and nucleus of both transformed and tumor cells. Recent reports indicate that only a small part (<10%) of the adeno-virus genome is present in many transformed cells. This may explain the inability to recover infectious virus from such cells. Hybridization studies have indicated that when different types of adenovirus cause trans-formation, the sequences of viral mRNA found in the transformed cell are also different.

With simian adenovirus 7 (SA7), the intact genome as well as the heavy and light halves of the viral DNA are capable of inducing tumors when in-jected into newborn hamsters.

Extensive studies have failed to demonstrate adenovirus DNA or viral-specific mRNA in human tumors.

E. Replication of Virus: Adenoviruses are cyto-pathic for human cell cultures, particularly primary kidney and continuous epithelial cells. Growth of virus in tissue culture is associated with a stimulation of acid production (increased glycolysis) in the early stages of infection. The viruses grow and cause changes in hu-man epithelial cells more rapidly than in fibroblasts. The cytopathic effect usually consists of marked rounding and aggregation of affected cells into grape-like clusters.

Monolayer cultures infected with adenoviruses take up neutral red just like healthy living cells. The infected cells do not lyse even though they round up and leave the glass surface on which they have been grown.

In HeLa cells infected with adenoviruses, rounded intranuclear inclusions, which progress from eosinophilic and Feulgen-negative to basophilic and Feulgen-positive, are prominent. With types 3, 4, and 7, the amount of DNA increases in the nuclei of infected cells. The virus particles develop in the nucleus and frequently exhibit crystalline arrangement. The crystals are strongly Feulgen-positive, indicating that the virus particles themselves contain DNA. A large percentage of cells infected with type 5 virus also contain crystals, but these crystals are not composed of viral particles. The crystals often exceed 30 μm in length and are readily visible in the light microscope. They are composed of protein and are devoid of nucleic acid. The crystalline protein has not been identified.

The tumor antigen (see ¶ D above) is induced early during the replicative cycle of the virus, prior to the synthesis of viral DNA and viral capsid proteins (see Fig 27–9). Adenovirus-specific proteins are synthesized in the cytoplasm of infected cells and then move rapidly into the nucleus where viral maturation occurs. In the adenovirus growth cycle in human epithelial cells, new virus particles can be detected about 16–20 hours after inoculation and continue to be formed at a uniform rate for the next 24 hours. About 7000 virus particles are produced per infected cell, and most of them remain intracellular. Particles having a density of 1.34 are highly infectious (1 particle in 5 is infectious), whereas those having densities of less than 1.30 are noninfectious since they lack the DNA core. Crude infected cell lysates show huge quantities of capsomeres, sometimes partially assembled into viral components.

Recently, additional proteins have been identified in adenovirus-infected cells. Two such proteins have been isolated by their ability to bind to DNA. Studies with temperature-sensitive mutants have shown that these are virus-coded and essential for virus replication.

In cells derived from other species, the human adenoviruses undergo an abortive replicative cycle. Adenovirus tumor antigen, mRNA, and DNA are all synthesized, but no capsid proteins or infectious progeny are produced.

F. Antigenic Properties: At least 31 antigenic types have been isolated from man, and a number of additional types have been isolated from other animals. At present, numerous distinct serotypes are known for simian, bovine, canine, murine, and avian species. They

Table 37–1. Comparative data on adenovirus type 2 morphologic and antigenic subunits and protein components.

Appearance	Name	Number Per Virion	Molecular Weight	Antigen	Specificity	Protein Components
Virion	DNA		23,000,000			
Virion	Protein		150,000,000			
O	Hexon	240	210,000 400,000 320,000 360,000	A	Group	II
(hexons)	Hexons	20	3,600,000			II, VIII, IX
O—	Penton	12	280,000 1,100,000			III, IV
O	Penton base	12	210,000	B	Subgroup	III
—o	Fiber	12	70,000	C	Type	IV
Core	DNA	1	23,000,000	P		
Core	Protein		29,000,000			V, VI, VII
	Protein		13,000			VIII, IX
	Protein		7,500			X

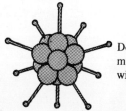

Dodecon: Hemagglutinin made up of 12 pentons with their fibers.

are specific by cross-neutralization tests, but complement fixation tests reveal cross-reactions among the types. A common antigen shared by all mammalian strains differs from the corresponding antigen of avian strains. Virus preparations treated with heat or formalin to kill their infectivity still contain complement-fixing antigen.

Adenoviruses contain 4 complement-fixing antigens—A, B, C, and P—whose characteristics are described in Table 37–1. The hexon antigens form the majority of the capsomeres of the adenocapsid (240) and are 8 nm in diameter. The penton antigens are made up of the penton base capsomeres and the fiber protruding from them. The pentons are found at the 12 vertices of the capsid and are also 8 nm in diameter. Associated with the penton base antigen is a toxin-like activity which causes tissue culture cells to detach from the surface on which they are growing. Attached to each penton base is a fiber antigen. For adenovirus type 5, the fiber antigen consists of a rod (2 X 20 nm) with a 4 nm knob at the distal end. However, the dimensions of the fiber antigen vary with the adenovirus type. The P antigen of adenoviruses is an internal antigen, which is released upon virus disruption and is very unstable. The hemagglutinating activity of adenovirus is associated with the penton and fiber antigens. Excess pentons produced in cells infected with some types of adenovirus (3, 4, 7, 9, 11, 15) form dodecahedral aggregates of 12 pentons (dodecons) which have hemagglutinating activity.

An endonuclease activity, which seems to attack specific sites of viral DNA rich in GC base pairs, is associated with purified virions.

Polyacrylamide gel electrophoresis of purified adenovirus and adenovirus subunits after disruption by detergent (sodium dodecyl sulfate) and urea has revealed 12 virus-specific polypeptides, 3 of which are associated with the DNA-containing viral core. The hexon capsomere is composed of 3–6 molecules of a single type (component II) which comprises about 50% of the total virion. Groups of these hexon capsomeres ("groups of nine") are associated with 2 additional minor polypeptides (components VIII and IX). The penton base is composed of a single type of peptide (component III), as is the fiber antigen (component IV) also. The internal core released by treatment of the virion with 5 M urea contains the viral DNA in association with one arginine-rich polypeptide (component VII) and 2 other polypeptides (components V and VI), which together account for 20% of the total virion. In addition, there is a very small polypeptide (component X) whose role and location in the virion remain unknown and which may be resolved into additional polypeptides (Fig 37–1). There is some evidence that some of the smaller virion polypeptides are derived by proteolytic cleavage from larger molecules.

A hemagglutinin has been used to separate the human viruses into 3 subgroups. Group A (types 3, 7, 11, 14, 16, 20, 21, 25, 28) agglutinates rhesus but not rat erythrocytes; group B (8, 9, 10, 13, 15, 17, 19, 22, 23, 24, 26, 27, 29, 30) agglutinates rat cells but not (or hardly) rhesus cells; group C (1, 2, 4, 5, 6) fails to agglutinate rhesus cells and only partially agglutinates rat cells. Types 12, 18, and 31 do not usually agglutinate, but some strains partially agglutinate rat cells. The hemagglutination inhibition test is being used for type-specific identification.

Some cross-reactions have been noted, particularly between types 3 and 7; 7, 11, and 14; 10 and 19; 15 and 28; 14 and 16; and 12, 18, and 31.

G. Adenovirus-SV40 "Hybrids": Certain adenoviruses grown in monkey kidney cell cultures were

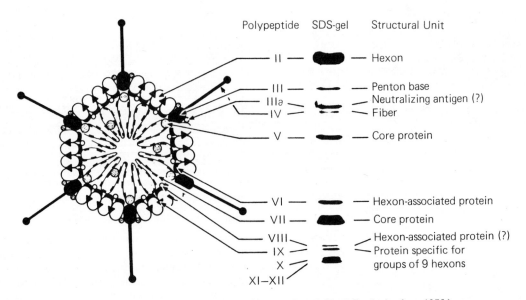

Figure 37–1. A topographical model of adenovirus type 2. (From Everitt & others, 1975.)

found to be contaminated with papovavirus SV40. After removal of all infectious SV40 by passage in the presence of specific SV40 antiserum, the viruses still contained certain genetic markers of SV40 (eg, tumor-inducing capacity or induction of SV40-specific antigens). Although the hybrid virus populations can be completely neutralized by type-specific adenovirus antiserum, they still contain SV40 genetic material, which appears to be covalently linked to the adenovirus. (See Chapter 40 for further discussion.)

Two types of adenovirus-SV40 hybrids have been detected. PARA-adenovirus consists of 2 particles—a nonhybrid adenovirion and the defective adenovirus-SV40 genome encased in an adenovirus capsid (PARA). PARA can be transcapsidated from one adenovirus serotype to another. The second type of hybrid, the Ad2+ND viruses, consists of a series of nondefective adenovirus 2 isolates carrying different amounts (5–44%) of the SV40 genome. These hybrid viruses have been useful in the genetic analysis of SV40.

H. Adenosatellite Virus: During the course of biophysical studies on adenoviruses, 20 nm particles were found in several adenovirus preparations; they have subsequently been classified in the parvovirus family. These particles contain single-stranded DNA and a protein coat with icosahedral symmetry. The single-stranded DNA has been shown to be present within the satellite virion as either plus or minus complementary strands in separate particles. Upon extraction, the minus and plus strands unite to form a double-stranded helix. The molecular weight of the DNA in the virion is $1.4–1.8 \times 10^6$; the nucleic acid constitutes 19% of the infectious particle. The G + C content is 61%. The agent has been named adenosatellite virus or adeno-associated virus. Three major structural proteins have been demonstrated for adenosatellite virus, which appears to be defective and unable to replicate in the absence of adenoviruses. Four antigenic types of satellite viruses are recognized; they are antigenically unrelated to adenoviruses. Types 1–3 naturally infect man; type 4 infects monkeys. They are not known to be pathogenic, although an association with adenovirus type 3 conjunctivitis has been suggested.

Herpesvirus may act as a partial helper for satellite virus replication. In cells co-infected with herpesvirus, infectious satellite DNA and capsid protein are made but not assembled into satellite virions. Some herpesvirus-transformed cell lines are also capable of acting as partial helper for adenosatellite virus.

When satellite virus infects cells in the absence of helper virus, it penetrates into the nucleus, where it is uncoated, although no satellite RNA synthesis occurs. Satellite virus may induce a latent infection in the absence of helper virus. Cellular DNA from such latently infected cell lines contains 3–5 satellite genome equivalents per cell but no detectable satellite antigen or virus. However, the satellite virus can be promptly and efficiently rescued by addition of helper virus.

Pathogenesis & Pathology

At least 5 adenovirus types have been demon-strated in the tissues of adenoids and tonsils removed at surgery by growing epithelium from such tissue for prolonged periods in culture. The viruses could not be isolated from nasopharyngeal swabs or from suspensions of adenoids and tonsils of the same persons by inoculation of such material into susceptible cell cultures. In most patients who yielded these viruses, the homotypic serum antibody titers were high. It is likely that these antibodies were gradually washed from the outgrowing cells during several weeks of biweekly changes of tissue culture fluid.

Viruses of this group were found in cultured adenoidal or tonsillar tissues of 57% of children.

Clinical Findings

The acute illness, sometimes called febrile catarrh, is characterized by fever, pharyngitis, and cough, often with conjunctivitis, rhinitis, otitis, laryngitis, tracheo-bronchitis, or pneumonitis, accompanied by constitutional symptoms. Adenovirus diseases include syndromes designated as undifferentiated acute respiratory disease, pharyngoconjunctival fever, nonstreptococcal exudative pharyngitis, and primary atypical pneumonia, occasionally with pleural effusion, not associated with the development of cold agglutinins.

Pharyngoconjunctival fever may be caused by several adenovirus types. It is characterized by fever, conjunctivitis, pharyngitis, malaise, and cervical lymphadenopathy. The conjunctival features of the disease are readily reproduced when any adenovirus is swabbed onto the eyes of volunteers. However, under natural conditions, only types 3 and 7 regularly cause outbreaks in which conjunctivitis is a predominant symptom. Types 1, 2, 5, and 6 have produced sporadic cases of conjunctivitis. However, even when large numbers of the latter infections are occurring, conjunctivitis is an infrequent finding.

Type 8 is the cause of epidemic keratoconjunctivitis (shipyard eye). The disease is characterized by an acute conjunctivitis, with enlarged, tender preauricular nodes, followed by keratitis which leaves round, subepithelial opacities in the cornea for up to 2 years. Type 8 infections have been characterized by their lack of associated systemic symptoms except in infants. Intussusception of infancy has been reported to be caused by adenoviruses 1, 2, 3, and 5, which readily spread by the enteric route.

Types 11 and 21 have been reported as the cause of acute hemorrhagic cystitis in children. Virus commonly occurs in the urine of such patients.

A new adenovirus, type 34, has been associated with afebrile illness in a renal transplant patient and may have been latent in the transplanted kidney.

Laboratory Diagnosis

A. Recovery of Virus: The viruses are isolated by inoculation of tissue cultures of human cells in which characteristic cytopathic changes are produced. The viruses have been recovered from throat swabs, conjunctival swabs, rectal swabs, stools of patients with acute pharyngitis and conjunctivitis, and urine of patients with acute hemorrhagic cystitis. Virus isolations from the eye are obtained almost exclusively from those with conjunctivitis.

B. Serology: In almost all cases, the neutralizing antibody responses of infected persons show a 4-fold or greater rise against the type recovered from the patient, and in general no response, or much lesser response, to other types. Neutralizing antibodies are measured in human cell cultures using the cytopathic end-point in tube cultures, or by the color test in panel cups or tubes under oil. The latter test depends upon the phenomenon that growth of adenovirus in HeLa cell cultures is accompanied by an excess production of acid over that of the uninfected control cultures, and that this viral lowering of pH can be prevented by immune serum. The pH is measured by incorporating phenol red into the medium and observing the color changes after 3 days of incubation. Serum and cell control cultures reach a pH of 7.4; virus activity is indicated by a pH of 7.0; and neutralization is presumed to have occurred where the pH is 0.2 unit above that of the virus control.

Infection of human beings with any adenovirus type stimulates a rise in complement-fixing antibodies to adenovirus antigens of all types. The CF test, using the common antigen, is of considerable value as an easily applied method for detecting infection by a member of the group. Complement-fixing antibody levels often go from negative to titers of 128.

A highly sensitive and reproducible radioimmunoassay has been developed to measure serum antibody to type 5 fiber antigen. In response to vaccination with the fiber subunit, volunteers exhibited a 54-fold increase in antifiber antibody in the radioimmunoassay.

Immunity

Studies in human volunteers revealed that type-specific neutralizing antibodies protect against the disease, but the protection is not absolute. It was possible to infect 27% of persons with evidence of previous infection with the same type as that given. Infections with the viruses were frequently induced without the production of overt illness.

The occurrence of neutralizing antibodies against one or more types in different age groups shows that antibodies may be present in over 50% of infants 6–11 months of age. In one study, a substantial increase in antibodies occurred in children 2 years of age, but very little additional increase occurred in children 3–5 years old. Marked increases were observed in the 6–15 and 16–34 age groups, in which the majority of persons had antibodies to 3 or more types. Normal healthy adults were found to have antibodies to at least 4–5 types of 6 tested.

The neutralizing antibodies to types 1 and 2 are especially prevalent in younger age groups, positive reactions occurring in 56% and 72%, respectively, of persons 6–15 years of age. Antibodies against types 3 and 4 were less prevalent in young adulthood than those for types 1 and 2. Neutralizing antibodies probably persist for life.

Infants are usually born without complement-fixing antibodies but develop these by 6 months of age. Older individuals with neutralizing antibodies to 4 or more strains frequently give completely negative complement fixation reactions. The complement-fixing antibodies may decline but may persist for varying periods (up to 7 years). The variation in persistence may be due to a number of factors such as repeated exposure to adenoviruses or the presence of the virus in a latent form. In studies of military recruits, it was shown that the incidence of infection (especially due to types 3 and 4) was not influenced by the presence of group complement-fixing antibodies.

Epidemiology

Man is commonly infected with adenoviruses, the virus being readily spread from person to person. In civilian populations, only 2–4% of acute respiratory diseases are caused by adenoviruses, but in military groups the incidence of respiratory disease caused by these viruses is high.

Type 3 has been recovered commonly from patients with acute pharyngitis and conjunctivitis, a 5-day illness that occurs endemically in the general population as well as in sharp outbreaks. The virus is found in stools and throat cultures in the acute phase of the illness. The concentration of virus may reach 10 million infectious doses per gram of stool. Some patients continue to excrete virus in the feces for at least 2 months. The virus has also been isolated from sewage during epidemic prevalence.

Type 1, 2, and 5 infections occur chiefly during the first years of life and are associated with illnesses characterized by fever and pharyngitis. These are the types most frequently obtained from the adenoids and tonsils.

Respiratory disease due to types 3, 4, 7, 14, and 21 occurs commonly and widely among military recruits. Adenovirus disease causes great disability when large numbers of men are being inducted into the armed forces; consequently, its greatest impact is during periods of mobilization. During a 1-year study, 10% of the 58,000 recruits given basic training were hospitalized for a respiratory illness caused by an adenovirus. During the winter, the incidence of respiratory disease in recruits was about 20 per thousand per week, and adenovirus accounted for 72% of all the respiratory disease. During the summer, the incidence fell to 2 per thousand and only 12% of these illnesses were caused by adenovirus. In contrast, adenovirus disease is not a problem in seasoned troops, the rates in recruits being 33 times higher. In recruit infections, 25% had a severe disease requiring hospitalization while in another 25% the disease was sufficiently mild to permit treatment at the dispensary. The remainder suffered either a very mild or an inapparent infection.

In children, type 7 has been associated with acute respiratory illnesses (high fever and involvement of nose, throat, conjunctiva, cervical lymph nodes, and lungs) and also with gastroenteritis, and type 21 has been associated with bronchitis, bronchial pneumonia, and acute hemorrhagic cystitis. A large number of adenovirus types have been isolated in a small percentage of infants with diarrhea in different parts of the world, but their etiologic relationship to the disease has not been established.

The conjunctivitis caused by certain adenoviruses and the evident association of types 3 and 7 cases with swimming pools suggest a relation with swimming pool conjunctivitis. The systemic clinical findings, duration and character of the ocular findings, and absence of inclusions in conjunctival smears distinguish these illnesses from inclusion conjunctivitis caused by chlamydiae.

Epidemic keratoconjunctivitis was unknown in the USA until 1941, when it spread from Australia via the Hawaiian Islands to California and the Pacific Coast. There it spread rapidly through the shipyards and other industries, thence to the East Coast, and finally to the Midwest. In the USA the incidence of neutralizing antibody to type 8 adenovirus in the general population has been about 1%, whereas in Japan it has been over 30%. In the USA, types 3, 6, and 7 are commonly involved in conjunctivitis. In Japan, type 8 spreads via the respiratory route in children.

At least 13 antigenic types were isolated in a study of conjunctival specimens in Saudi Arabia, with most of the strains being isolated during the summer from children under 2 years.

Canine hepatitis virus is an adenovirus. Therefore, human beings infected with adenoviruses develop complement-fixing antibodies against canine hepatitis virus.

Prevention & Control

A trivalent vaccine was prepared by growing type 3, 4, and 7 viruses in monkey kidney cultures and then inactivating the viruses with formalin.

Since certain vaccine strains have been found to be contaminated genetically with the papovavirus SV40 tumor determinants, and since most strains of "clean" adenoviruses do not grow well in monkey kidney cells, vaccine made from contaminated strains was withdrawn from use in the USA in 1964. New vaccines are under study. One is made from purified hexons and thus circumvents the problem of contaminated genetic material. A second is made in human diploid cells using noncontaminated live virus and is given orally in a coated capsule to liberate the virus into the intestine. By this route, the live vaccine produces a subclinical infection which confers a high degree of immunity against wild strains. It does not spread from the vaccinated person to his contacts.

Live virus vaccines against type 4 and type 7 have been developed and used in military populations. When both are administered simultaneously, vaccinees respond with neutralizing antibodies against both virus types.

Rigid asepsis during eye examination is essential in the control of epidemic keratoconjunctivitis.

• • •

General References

Everitt E, Lutter L, Philipson L: Structural proteins of adenoviruses. 12. Location and neighbor relationship among proteins of adenovirion type 2 as revealed by enzymatic iodination, immunoprecipitation and chemical cross-linking. Virology 67:197, 1975.

Everitt E & others: Structural proteins of adenoviruses. 10. Isolation and topography of low molecular weight antigens from the virion of adenovirus type 2. Virology 52:130, 1973.

Fujinaga K, Green M: Mechanism of viral carcinogenesis by DNA mammalian viruses. 5. Properties of purified viral-specific RNA from human adenovirus-induced tumor cells. J Mol Biol 31:63, 1968.

Jackson GG, Muldoon RL: Viruses causing respiratory infection in man. 4. Reoviruses and adenoviruses. J Infect Dis 128:811, 1973.

Kelly TJ Jr & others: Structural studies on two adenovirus 2-SV40 hybrids containing the entire SV40 genome. Cold Spring Harbor Symp Quant Biol 39:409, 1975.

Maizel JV Jr, White DO, Scharff MD: The polypeptides of adenovirus: Soluble proteins, cores, top components and the structure of the virion. Virology 36:126, 1968.

Neurath AR, Rubin BA: *Viral Structural Components as Immunogens of Prophylactic Value.* Vol 4 in: *Monographs in Virology.* Melnick JL (editor). Karger, 1971.

Philipson L, Lindberg U: Reproduction of adenoviruses. Pages 143–227 in: *Comprehensive Virology.* Vol 3. Fraenkel-Conrat H, Wagner RR (editors). Plenum Press, 1974.

Rapp F, Melnick JL: Papovavirus SV40, adenovirus and their hybrids: Transformation, complementation, and transcapsidation. Prog Med Virol 8:349, 1966.

Rose HM: Adenoviruses. Pages 205–226 in: *Diagnostic Procedures for Viral and Rickettsial Infections,* 4th ed. American Public Health Association, 1969.

Rubin BA, Tint H: The development and use of vaccines based on studies of virus substructures. Prog Med Virol 21:144, 1975.

Schmidt NJ, Lennette EH, King CJ: Neutralizing, hemagglutination-inhibiting and group complement-fixing antibody responses in human adenovirus infections. J Immunol 97:64, 1966.

Schmidt OW, Cooney MK, Foy HM: Adeno-associated virus in adenovirus type 3 conjunctivitis. Infect Immun 11:1362, 1975.

Top FH & others: Immunization with live types 7 and 4 adenovirus vaccines. 2. Antibody response and protective effect against acute respiratory disease due to adenovirus type 7. J Infect Dis 124:155, 1971.

38 . . .
Herpesvirus Family

At least 25 viruses have been placed in the family **Herpesviridae**. They all contain a core of double-stranded DNA surrounded by a protein coat that in turn is enclosed in an envelope. The coat exhibits icosahedral symmetry. The enveloped form is 100–150 nm in diameter; the "naked" virion is 100 nm in diameter and contains 162 capsomeres.

The molecular weight of the DNA of herpesviruses varies from $50–135 \times 10^6$ and constitutes less than 10% of the particle weight. The guanine + cytosine content also varies, the range being 44–74%. The family is very heterogeneous, and establishment of genera is difficult because of a lack of information about most members of the family.

Herpes simplex virus types 1 and 2, varicella-zoster virus, EB virus, and cytomegalovirus infect man. Types 1 and 2 viruses are readily found extracellularly in the fluid phase of tissue cultures, but the other members of the group are more firmly associated with the cell. Although varicella and zoster strains have been grown in a number of tissue cultures, they have not yet been obtained free in the fluid phase (except when grown in cells from human thyroid). The EB herpesvirus appears to replicate only in a restricted number of lymphoid cell cultures, including those from humans and some primates.

Herpesviruses that infect lower animals are B virus of Old World monkeys, herpesviruses saimiri, aotus, and ateles, marmoset herpesvirus of New World monkeys, pseudorabies virus of pigs, virus III of rabbits, infectious bovine rhinotracheitis virus, equine rhinopneumonitis (equine abortion) virus, canine herpesvirus, infectious laryngotracheitis virus of fowls, and cytomegalovirus of monkeys, guinea pigs, mice, and other animal species. Herpesviruses are also known for birds, fish, fungi, and oysters.

Herpesviruses have been linked with malignant diseases in man and lower animals: herpes simplex viruses types 1 and 2 with labial and cervical carcinomas, respectively, of man; the EB virus with Burkitt's lymphoma of African children and with nasopharyngeal carcinoma; the Lucké virus with renal adenocarcinomas of the frog; Marek's disease virus with a lymphoma of chickens; the Hinze virus with a lymphoma of rabbits; and a number of New World primate herpesviruses with reticulum cell sarcomas and lymphomas in these animals.

HERPES SIMPLEX
(Herpes Febrilis, Herpes Labialis, Herpetic Gingivostomatitis, Eczema Herpeticum, Herpes Genitalis)

Infection with herpes simplex virus (herpesvirus hominis) may take several clinical forms. The infection is most often inapparent. The usual clinical manifestation is a vesicular eruption of the skin or mucous membranes. Infection is sometimes seen as severe keratitis, which may lead to blindness. The virus may also cause other severe illnesses such as meningoencephalitis and a systemic illness of the newborn, both of which are often fatal.

Properties of the Virus

A. Nucleic Acid: DNA. Molecular weight of DNA, $85–100 \times 10^6$. For type 1, the buoyant density in CsCl is 1.725 gm/ml and the guanine + cytosine content is 66–68%; for type 2, the buoyant density is 1.727 gm/ml and the guanine + cytosine content is 70%. Types 1 and 2 show 50% sequence homology.

B. Size: The virus consists of a DNA-containing core embedded in a protein capsid surrounded by an outer membrane. Electron microscopic studies of preparations of purified capsids suggest that the core contains the viral DNA spooled around a cylindric mass within the capsid. Fig 38–1 shows this arrangement. The core is surrounded by the 100 nm icosahedral capsid, made up of 162 morphologic subunits (capsomeres arranged with 5:3:2 axial symmetry). Each hexameric capsomere appears to be 12.5 nm long and 8.5 nm in diameter with a central hole of 4 nm. Between the capsid and the envelope is a layer called the tegument, the size of which varies considerably among the herpesviruses. The envelope frequently shows periodic projections from its surface and is probably derived from the inner nuclear membrane of the infected cell. The envelope, which contains lipid, carbohydrate, and protein, is rapidly removed by ether treatment.

The structural proteins of herpes simplex virus have been characterized on polyacrylamide gel electrophoresis. As many as 30 polypeptides have been found in the enveloped virion.

C. Reactions to Physical and Chemical Agents:

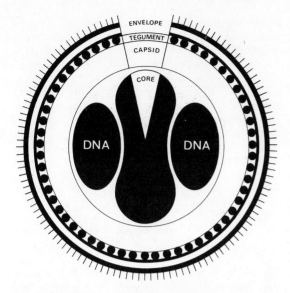

Figure 38–1. Thin section of HSV-1 herpesvirion and its architectural components. See text for details. (After Roizman & Furlong, 1974.)

Suspensions of infected tissue may be stored in the frozen state. Long considered as exceedingly thermolabile, herpesvirus can be stabilized by 1 M Na$_2$SO$_4$ so that it withstands heating at 50° C, but the virus is not protected by 1 M MgSO$_4$ or 2 M NaCl. Herpesvirus is extremely thermosensitive at isotonic concentrations of any salt but becomes stable as the virus is diluted with distilled water. In the dry state, herpes simplex virus may withstand temperatures as high as 90° C. It is destroyed by ether, 1% phenol, 0.5% formaldehyde, and by photodynamically active dyes (proflavine, neutral red) in the presence of light.

D. Animal Susceptibility and Growth of Virus: The virus has a wide host range and can infect rabbits, guinea pigs, mice, hamsters, rats, and the chorioallantois of the embryonated egg.

In rabbits, herpesvirus produces a typical vesicular eruption in the skin of the inoculated area. Generalized disease and meningoencephalitis develop in some cases. Corneal inoculation results in dendritic keratitis and keratoconjunctivitis. With some strains, the corneal involvement is regularly followed by encephalitis. Whether or not encephalitis has been manifest, the virus may remain latent in the brains of survivors, and anaphylactic shock can precipitate an acute relapse of encephalomyelitis. In rabbits, herpetic keratitis may be followed by healing, but infective herpesvirus may be recovered from the eye intermittently.

The chorioallantoic membrane of embryonated chick eggs is particularly susceptible to infection. The lesions are raised white plaques, and their number is directly proportionate to the concentration of infectious virus particles. The plaques produced by herpesvirus type 2 are larger and morphologically distinct from the tiny plaques produced by type 1 virus. The virus grows readily and produces plaques in almost any

commonly used cell culture. Infected cells contain typical inclusions; inclusion body formation is followed by necrosis of cells (cytopathic effect).

In Chinese hamster cells, which contain only 22 chromosomes, the virus causes breaks in region 7 of chromosome No. 1 and in region 3 of the X chromosome. The Y chromosome is unaffected.

E. Virus Replication: The virus enters the cell either by fusion with the cell membrane or by pinocytosis. It is then uncoated, and the DNA becomes associated with the nucleus. Soon after infection, normal cellular DNA and protein synthesis virtually stop as virus replication begins. The virus induces a number of enzymes, some of which it probably codes for, including thymidine kinase and DNA polymerase. Thymidine kinases produced by different herpesviruses are serologically different from each other and different from the enzyme in uninfected cells. Recently, the drug phosphonoacetic acid has been shown to specifically inhibit herpesvirus replication by inhibiting viral DNA polymerase. This drug may have potential as a chemotherapeutic agent.

The synthesis of up to 50 virus-specific polypeptides (of which about 30 end up as structural proteins of the virus) can be visualized by polyacrylamide gel electrophoresis of infected cell extracts. Virus proteins are synthesized in the cytoplasm and are selectively transported to the nucleus, where assembly into nucleocapsids occurs. Maturation occurs by budding of nucleocapsids through the altered inner nuclear membrane. Enveloped virus particles are then released from the cell through tubular structures that are associated with virus infection and which are continuous with the outside of the cell or from vacuoles which release their contents at the cell surface (Fig 27–6).

F. Defective Interfering Herpesvirions: Serial passage of undiluted herpes simplex virus type 1 and type 2 results in cyclic production of infectious and defective virions. Defective virions interfere with the replication of standard virus and stimulate overproduction of a large molecular weight (175,000) polypeptide which may have a regulatory function. Defective virions contain a new species of DNA with a CsCl buoyant density of 1.732 gm/ml. The biologic role of the defective virions is not known, but they may play a role in latency and in cancer.

G. Helper Function: Herpesvirus is able to provide a partial helper function for the propagation of the defective adenovirus-associated satellite virus. Coinfection with herpesvirus allows the satellite virus to develop to the stage of producing infectious viral DNA and viral protein. However, for satellite virus assembly to take place, simultaneous adenovirus replication is required. (See Chapter 37.)

H. Antigenic Properties: Associated with the growth of the virus is the production of numerous (7–12) precipitating antigens. These antigens represent individual structural and nonstructural viral proteins. Some of these antigens are common to both types 1 and 2 and some are specific for one type.

I. Differentiation of Types 1 and 2: Herpes simplex virus types 1 and 2, although they cross-react serologically, may be distinguished by a number of tests: (1) The use of type-specific antiserum prepared by adsorption of the viral antiserum with heterotypically infected cells or by inoculation of rabbits with individual type-specific proteins. (2) The greater temperature sensitivity of type 2 infectivity. (3) Preferential growth in different cell species. Chick embryo cells are more resistant to type 1 than type 2. Thus, type 2 virus forms large pocks when inoculated into the chorioallantoic membrane of embryonated hens' eggs, while type 1 forms small pocks. Type 2 virus replicates well in chick embryo fibroblast cells, while type 1 replicates poorly. (4) Type 2 virus is more neurovirulent in laboratory animals than type 1. (5) Type 2 is more resistant to IUDR or cytarabine in primary cell cultures.

J. Oncogenic Properties: After inactivation of their lytic capabilities (by ultraviolet irradiation), herpesviruses types 1 and 2 can cause transformation of cultured hamster cells which may induce tumors when inoculated into newborn hamsters. Viral genetic information can be demonstrated in the tumor cells.

Pathogenesis & Pathology

The lesion in the skin involves proliferation, ballooning degeneration, and intranuclear acidophilic inclusions. In fatal cases of herpes encephalitis, there are meningitis, perivascular infiltration, and nerve cell destruction, especially in the cortex. Intranuclear inclusions are found in glial cells and, less frequently, in nerve cells. Neonatal generalized herpes infection is characterized by multiple areas of focal necrosis with a mononuclear reaction and formation of intranuclear inclusion bodies in all organs (particularly the liver), often with extensive destruction of the adrenals. Survivors may sustain permanent damage.

The fully formed inclusion is typical of the Cowdry type A inclusion body. During the early stages of its formation, it is rich in DNA (Feulgen-positive, stains blue with hematoxylin and eosin) and virtually fills the nucleus, compressing the chromatin to the nuclear margin. When it has completely developed, the inclusion loses its DNA (Feulgen-negative, stains pink with hematoxylin and eosin) and is separated by a halo from the chromatin at the nuclear margin. Viral antigen is present in the inclusion only in the early stages of infection; the fully developed intranuclear inclusion is devoid of virus.

Clinical Findings

Herpesvirus may cause various clinical entities, and the infections may be primary or recurrent. Primary infections which occur in persons without antibodies often result in the virus assuming a latent state in the host. Latent infections persist in persons with antibodies, and recurrent infections are common (eg, recurrent herpes labialis). The primary infection in most individuals is clinically inapparent and thus not recognized. However, antibody production invariably accompanies the infection. The recurrent attacks often

follow nonspecific stimuli such as exposure to excess sunlight, fever accompanying certain infections, menstruation, or emotional stresses.

A. Herpesvirus Type 1: The clinical entities attributable to herpesvirus type 1 include the following:

1. Acute herpetic gingivostomatitis (aphthous stomatitis, Vincent's stomatitis)—This is the most common clinical entity caused by primary infections with type 1 herpesvirus. It occurs most frequently in small children (1–3 years of age). The manifestations of the disease include extensive vesiculo-ulcerative lesions of the mucous membranes of the oral cavity, fever, irritability, and local lymphadenopathy. The incubation period is short (about 3–5 days), and the illness is self-limiting, with a duration of 1–2 weeks.

2. Eczema herpeticum (Kaposi's varicelliform eruption)—This is a primary infection, usually with herpesvirus type 1, in a person with chronic eczema. In this illness, there may be extensive vesiculation of the skin over much of the body and high fever. In rare instances, the illness may be fatal.

3. Keratoconjunctivitis—The initial infection with herpesvirus may be in the eye, producing severe keratoconjunctivitis. Recurrent lesions of the eye may also occur. Herpetic keratitis is suggested by typical dendritic corneal ulcers or by vesicles which appear on the eyelids. In either primary or recurrent keratitis, there may be progressive involvement of the deeper layers of the cornea (corneal stroma) with permanent opacification and blindness.

4. Meningoencephalitis—A severe form of encephalitis may be produced by herpesvirus type 1. In adults, the neurologic manifestations may suggest localization of the brain lesions in the temporoparietal area of the cerebral cortex. Electroencephalographic and arteriographic studies frequently confirm the presence of local brain changes. Pleocytosis (chiefly of lymphocytes) is present in the CSF; however, definite diagnosis during the illness can usually be made only by isolation of the virus (or by demonstrating viral antigens by immunofluorescence) in brain tissue obtained by biopsy or at postmortem. The disease carries a high mortality rate, and those who survive often have residual neurologic defects.

5. Herpes labialis (cold sores, herpes febrilis)— This is the most common disease produced by type 1. Clusters of localized vesicles occur, usually at the mucocutaneous junction of the lips. The vesicle ruptures, leaving a painful ulcer which heals without scarring. The lesions may recur, repeatedly and at various intervals of time, in the same location of the lip. The permanent site of latent herpes simplex virus is thought to be the trigeminal ganglion.

B. Herpesvirus Type 2: The clinical entities associated with herpesvirus type 2 include the following:

1. Genital herpes (herpes progenitalis)—Genital herpes is characterized by vesiculo-ulcerative lesions of the penis of the male or the cervix, vagina, and perineum of the female. The lesions are more severe among persons without antibodies to either type of herpesvirus, and in some there may be fever, malaise, and inguinal lymphadenopathy. In women with herpesvirus antibodies, only the cervix or vagina may be involved, and the disease may therefore be asymptomatic. Recurrence of the lesions is common.

2. **Neonatal herpes**–Herpesvirus type 2 may be transmitted to the newborn during birth by contact with herpetic lesions in the birth canal. Premature infants are more often affected than full-term ones. The spectrum of illness produced in the newborn appears to vary from mild to severe generalized disease with a fatal outcome. Severely affected infants who survive may have permanent brain damage. To avoid infection, delivery by cesarean section and vigorous gamma globulin therapy of babies born of mothers with antepartum genital herpes have been used. To be effective, cesarean section must be performed before rupture of the membranes, since infection has been reported in infants delivered by section after 2–3 hours of ruptured membranes. Gamma globulin has not definitely been proved effective.

Transplacental infection of the fetus with types 1 and 2 herpes simplex virus has been postulated to account for some congenital malformations.

C. Miscellaneous: Localized lesions of the skin caused by type 1 or 2 may occur in abrasions which become contaminated with the virus (traumatic herpes). These lesions are most often seen on the fingers of dentists and hospital personnel (herpetic whitlow) and on the bodies of wrestlers.

Primary and recurrent herpes can occur in the nose (acute herpetic rhinitis).

Mild aseptic meningitis has been attributed to the virus, and recurrent episodes of meningeal irritation have been observed.

Epidemiologic evidence has demonstrated that in most geographic areas patients with cervical cancer have a high frequency of type 2 antibodies. However, it is uncertain whether the virus plays an etiologic role. (See Chapter 40.)

Laboratory Diagnosis

A. Recovery of Virus: The virus may be isolated from tissues exhibiting herpetic lesions (skin, cornea, or brain). It may also be found in the throat, saliva, and stools. In the primary infection, it may be present for up to 2–3 weeks in the throat and in the stools. Because it may be isolated at times from the throats of apparently healthy carriers, the isolation of herpesvirus is not in itself sufficient evidence to indicate that this virus is the etiologic agent of the disease under investigation.

Inoculation of tissue cultures, or of the chorioallantois of the chick embryo (12 days old), is used for virus isolation. The appearance of a typical cytopathic effect and intranuclear inclusion bodies in cell cultures or of typical pocks (or plaques) on the membrane suggests the presence of herpesvirus. Identification of the agent as herpesvirus is established by neutralization of the virus by specific herpes antiserum. With tissue culture–the method of choice–a provisional diagnosis can be made 24 hours after receipt of the specimen.

B. Serology: Antibodies may be measured quantitatively by neutralization tests on the chorioallantois of the chick embryo (pock-counting method), in mice, or in cell cultures. The early stage of the primary immune response is characterized by the appearance of neutralizing antibody detectable only in the presence of fresh complement. This antibody is of short duration and is replaced by neutralizing antibody that can function independently of complement.

Since the success of treatment of herpes simplex virus encephalitis is determined by early diagnosis, a rapid means of diagnosis is obviously desirable. Recent data have demonstrated that passive hemagglutinating antibodies in the CSF are a better indicator of the presence of infectious virus than are circulating antibody titers in serum. In the passive hemagglutination test, herpesvirus is fixed to tanned red blood cells. When serum or CSF contains herpesvirus antibodies, the sheep cells agglutinate. Unlike nearly all other tests, results are obtainable within hours and the test is 3–20 times more sensitive than the conventional neutralizing antibody test.

A soluble complement-fixing antigen of considerably smaller size than the virus can be prepared from infected chorioallantoic membranes or from tissue culture. The soluble antigen of herpesvirus may be used to detect dermal hypersensitivity in previously infected persons. There is a good correlation between dermal hypersensitivity and the presence of serum antibodies.

As early as the fourth or fifth day after a primary infection, neutralizing and complement-fixing antibodies appear. They reach their peak in about 2–3 weeks. They may be retained for life, perhaps as the result of repeated stimulation by recurrent infections with the virus. An increase in antibody titer is essential for establishing a diagnosis. The presence of antibody in a single sample of serum is of little value, for the majority of adults have antibodies in their blood at all times.

Following a primary infection with type 1 or type 2 virus, neutralizing antibody titers to both viral types can be increased about 4- to 8-fold if complement is added to the virus-antibody mixture. No difference occurs in the degree to which complement enhances homotypic and heterotypic antibody.

After a primary type 1 infection, the IgM neutralizing antibody response is type-specific, but after a primary type 2 infection the IgM which develops neutralizes both type 1 and type 2 virus. After a recurrent type 1 infection, patients continue to possess IgG antibodies to type 1 and type 2 but do not develop IgM antibodies to either type. In patients with prior type 1 infection who are then superinfected with type 2 virus, the antibody response elicited may be higher to type 1 than to type 2.

About 30% of patients with herpes simplex infections show heterologous increases in preexisting complement-fixing antibody titers to varicella-zoster virus. The heterologous reactions occur most often in patients currently infected with herpes simplex who have recently experienced a varicella-zoster infection. Infection with varicella-zoster virus is followed less frequently by an increase in herpes simplex antibody.

Immunity

Children are usually born with passively transferred maternal antibodies. This antibody is lost during the first 6 months of life, and the period of greatest susceptibility to primary herpes infection occurs between 6 months and 2 years. Type 1 antibodies begin to appear in the population in early childhood; by the time of adolescence, they are present in most persons. Antibodies to type 2 (genital herpesvirus) are not acquired in the general population until the age of adolescence and sexual activity.

After recovery from a primary infection (inapparent, mild, or severe), the virus is often carried in a latent state, in the presence of antibodies. Antibodies appear after the primary infection but may fall in titer after a few months.

Treatment

Idoxuridine (5-iodo-2'-deoxyuridine, IUDR) and cytarabine (cytosine arabinoside, Ara-C) have varying effectiveness against herpes simplex keratitis when given early in the course of the disease. The drug is instilled locally, 1–2 drops in each eye every 1–2 hours day and night. These agents inhibit replication of virus in vitro and in vivo, but drug-resistant variants appear. Treatment of acute herpetic epithelial keratitis with IUDR may result in prompt suppression of clinical manifestations. About three-fourths of patients treated with IUDR are asymptomatic within 1 week after onset, whereas about half of patients treated with curettage and cauterization of the cornea are asymptomatic in the same period. However, the virus is not eradicated by treatment, and the rate of relapse appears to be similar in IUDR-treated and -untreated individuals. IUDR apparently acts by suppressing but not eradicating virus production. Some strains of virus, particularly those of type 2, are not affected by the drug. IUDR has no effect on systemic disease, is toxic, and should not be used for this purpose. Ara-C has also been disappointing as a systemic drug in viral infections.

Adenine arabinoside (vidarabine, Ara-A), a new antiviral compound active against members of the herpesvirus family and much less toxic, is currently being investigated. Preliminary reports are very encouraging. (See Chapter 27.)

Herpesviruses are sensitive to photoinactivation when sensitized with substances such as neutral red and proflavine. Proper application of these agents to active type 1 and type 2 skin lesions followed by exposure to light has been reported to reduce the duration of the lesion and the rate of recurrence.

Epidemiology & Control

The epidemiology of type 1 and type 2 herpesvirus differs. Herpesvirus type 1 is probably more constantly present in man than any other virus. Primary infection occurs early in life when maternal antibodies

decline, often taking the form of a vesicular stomatitis. Even though antibodies develop, the virus is not eliminated from the body; a carrier state is established which lasts throughout life and is punctuated by transient attacks of herpes. If primary infection is avoided in childhood, it may not occur in later life; this is because adults may be less susceptible to primary herpetic infection (perhaps as a result of their thicker, more resistant epithelium), and also because the likelihood of picking up infection in the home may not be so great for adults as for children (less exposure to salivary contamination).

The highest incidence of type 1 virus carriage in the oropharynx of healthy persons occurs among children 6 months to 3 years of age. The virus is found less often in children 4–14 years of age, and rarely in persons 15 years of age and older or in infants under 6 months of age. A corollary of this is that 70–90% of adults have type 1 antibodies.

Type 1 virus is transmitted more readily in families of lower socioeconomic groups; the most obvious explanation is their more crowded living conditions and their lower hygienic standards. The virus is spread by direct contact (saliva or stools) or indirectly from utensils contaminated with the saliva of a virus carrier. The source of infection for children is usually a parent who has had a recurrence of a herpetic lesion a few days before the onset.

Type 2 virus is spread venereally. Infection begins after puberty. The occurrence of type 2 virus or antibody in the adult population depends on socioeconomic factors affecting exposure to venereally transmitted agents.

No specific control measures are recommended. However, patients with eczema should be protected from sources of infection.

Although clinically severe complications can result from primary or recurrent herpesvirus infection, little effort has been made to develop an effective vaccine. One reason for this has been the observation that herpes recurs in the presence of circulating antibody. However, a vaccine to prevent primary infection would also be expected to control recurrent herpes.

VARICELLA-ZOSTER VIRUS

VARICELLA
(Chickenpox)
ZOSTER
(Herpes Zoster, Shingles, Zona)

Varicella (chickenpox) is a mild, highly infectious disease, chiefly of children, which is characterized by a vesicular eruption of the skin and mucous membranes. However, in immunocompromised children the disease may be severe. The etiologic agent is a virus which is morphologically and antigenically similar to the virus of zoster.

Zoster (shingles) is a sporadic, incapacitating disease of adults (rare in children) which is characterized by an inflammatory reaction of the posterior nerve roots and ganglia, accompanied by crops of vesicles (like those of varicella) over the skin supplied by the affected sensory nerves.

Both diseases are caused by the same virus. Varicella is the acute disease which follows after primary contact with the virus, whereas zoster is the response of the partially immune host to a reactivation of varicella virus present in latent form in the body.

Properties of the Virus

Varicella-zoster virus is morphologically identical to herpes simplex virus. The virus propagates in cultures of human embryonic tissue and produces typical intranuclear inclusion bodies. Supernatant fluids from such infected cultures contain a complement-fixing antigen but no infective virus. Fluids harvested from infected thyroid cells have yielded infectious virus. The virus has not been propagated in laboratory animals. A similar agent can be obtained from vesicular fluid of zoster patients and from the CSF in cases of zoster manifesting a lymphocytic pleocytosis.

Inoculation of vesicle fluid of zoster into children produces vesicles at the site of inoculation in about 10 days. This may be followed by generalized skin lesions precisely like those of varicella. Generalized varicella may occur in such inoculated children without local vesicle formation. Contacts of such children develop typical varicella after a 2-week incubation period. Children who have recovered from zoster virus-induced infection are resistant to varicella, and those who have had varicella are no longer susceptible to primary zoster virus.

Antibody to varicella-zoster virus can be measured by CF, gel precipitation, neutralization, or indirect immunofluorescence to virus-induced membrane antigens. Varicella-zoster virus has been shown to be antigenically related to "varicella" type viruses of monkeys and to share at least one common antigen with herpes simplex virus.

The virus has a colchicine-like effect on human cells. Arrest in metaphase, overcontracted chromosomes, chromosome breaks, and formation of micronuclei are often seen.

Pathogenesis & Pathology

A. Varicella: The route of infection is probably the mucosa of the upper respiratory tract. The virus probably circulates in the blood and localizes in the skin. Swelling of epithelial cells, ballooning degeneration, and the accumulation of tissue fluids result in vesicle formation. In nuclei of infected cells, particularly in the early stages, eosinophilic inclusion bodies are found.

B. Zoster: In addition to skin lesions—histopathologically identical to those of varicella—there is an inflammatory reaction of the dorsal nerve roots and ganglia. Often only a single ganglion may be involved. As a rule, the distribution of lesions in the skin corresponds closely to the areas of innervation from an individual root ganglion. There is cellular infiltration, necrosis of nerve cells, and inflammation of the ganglion sheath. Destruction of the sensory nerve fibers from the corium has been demonstrated, with degeneration of the corresponding fibers of the spinal cord.

In some cases varicella virus seems to be neurotropic and to enter and remain within nerve cells for long periods. Years later, various insults (eg, pressure on a nerve) may cause a flare-up of the virus along posterior root fibers, whereupon zoster vesicles appear. Thus, varicella-zoster and herpes simplex viruses are similar in their ability to induce latent infections with clinical recurrence of disease in man.

Clinical Findings

A. Varicella: The incubation period is usually 14–21 days. Malaise and fever are the earliest symptoms, soon followed by the rash, first on the trunk and then on the face, the limbs, and the buccal and pharyngeal mucosa. Successive fresh vesicles appear in crops during the next 3–4 days, so that all stages of papules, vesicles, and crusts may be seen at one time. The eruption is found together with the fever and is proportionate to its severity. Complications are rare, although encephalitis does at times occur about 5–10 days after the rash. The mortality rate is much less than 1% in uncomplicated cases. In neonatal varicella (contracted from the mother just before or just after birth), the mortality rate may be as high as 20%. In varicella encephalitis, the mortality rate is about 10%, and another 10% are left with permanent injury to the CNS. Primary varicella pneumonia is rare in children but may occur in about 20–30% of adult cases. Fatalities have been reported. About 10% of cases of Reye's syndrome are associated with chickenpox.

Although varicella is rare in women of childbearing age, congenital defects have been reported in infants born following maternal varicella during the first trimester of pregnancy.

Children with immune deficiency disease or those receiving immunosuppressant or cytotoxic drugs as therapy for leukemia or other malignancies are at high risk of development of very severe and often fatal illness. This may be due to the leukemia itself or to the drugs used in its treatment, which may inhibit the immune response.

Chromosome breaks have been observed in leukocytes from children with chickenpox.

B. Zoster: The incubation period is unknown. The disease starts with malaise and fever which are soon followed by severe pain in the area of skin or mucosa supplied by one or more groups of sensory nerves. The inflammatory reaction, typically found in the dorsal nerve roots and ganglia, occasionally spreads to the anterior horn cells, resulting in a paralysis which is usually temporary. Within a few days after onset, a crop of vesicles appears over the skin supplied by the affected nerves. The eruption is usually unilateral; the trunk, head, and neck are most commonly involved. Lymphocytic pleocytosis in the CSF may be present.

In patients with localized zoster and no underlying disease, vesicle interferon levels peak early during infection (by the sixth day), whereas patients with disseminated infection peak later. In both types of patients, peak interferon levels are followed by clinical improvement within 48 hours. Vesicles pustulate and crust, and dissemination is halted.

Zoster tends to disseminate when there is an underlying disease, especially if the patient is on immunosuppressive drugs. The suppressed immune system may not be able to produce sufficient interferon to halt the infection.

Laboratory Diagnosis

Vesicle fluid contains both antibody and a complement-fixing antigen. The demonstration of cytopathogenicity of varicella and of zoster viruses in tissue culture and the detection of a soluble complement-fixing antigen in the culture fluids now form the basis of serologic tests. A precipitation test in agar gel indicates the identity of varicella and zoster antigens, and the test has been used to follow the development of precipitating antibodies in patients. Antibodies in human serum can also be demonstrated using the immunofluorescence technic. The sera are reacted with infected tissue cultures, and the antigen-antibody complex is then exposed to antihuman globulin labeled with fluorescein isothiocyanate.

In varicella (primary infection), specific antibody appears both in IgM and in IgG. In zoster (secondary infection), specific antibody is present only in IgG.

Laboratory tests are of value in differential diagnosis. Failure to obtain positive complement fixation with vesicle fluid or crust suspension when mixed with vaccinial antiserum and failure to grow and produce lesions on the chorioallantoic membrane of the chick embryo suggest varicella rather than smallpox.

A rapid method for differentiating between vesicular lesions caused by herpesviruses (lesions due to herpes simplex or varicella-zoster viruses) and those caused by poxviruses (smallpox or generalized vaccinia) is to examine vesicle fluid for the presence of typical herpes- or poxvirus particles by negative staining in the electron microscope.

Herpes simplex can be readily differentiated from zoster by isolating a virus which infects chick embryos, rabbits, and mice.

Immunity

Varicella and zoster viruses are identical agents, the 2 diseases being the result of differing host responses. Previous infection with varicella leaves the patient with enduring immunity to varicella. However, zoster may occur in persons who have contracted varicella at an earlier date. This is probably a reactivation of a varicella virus infection which has been latent for many years.

Individuals with a recent history of varicella or zoster infection respond to infection with herpes simplex virus with a concomitant complement-fixing antibody rise to herpes simplex and varicella-zoster viruses.

Treatment

Gamma globulin of high specific antibody titer prepared from pooled plasma of patients convalescing from herpes zoster (zoster immune globulin, ZIG) can be used to prevent or modify the development of the illness in immunocompromised children who have been exposed to varicella. Standard immune serum globulin is without value because of the low titer of varicella antibodies.

ZIG is available, through physicians, from the Center for Disease Control in Atlanta. The requirements for release of ZIG for treatment include (1) a history of susceptibility to varicella, (2) close exposure to active varicella within the preceding 72 hours, and (3) presence of high-risk disease or predisposing condition (leukemia or lymphoma, immunodeficiency syndrome, or treatment with immunosuppressive medication). Adults are not eligible for ZIG prophylaxis.

Idoxuridine and cytarabine inhibit replication of the viruses in vitro. Massive doses of cytarabine intravenously for 2 days have been claimed to stop further dissemination of the lesions within 48 hours. However, treatment can prolong the course of recovery in patients with immunologic dysfunction by further depressing host responses.

Adenine arabinoside (vidarabine, Ara-A) has been effective in adults with severe varicella pneumonia, immunocompromised children with varicella, and adults with disseminated zoster. (See Chapter 27.)

Epidemiology

Zoster occurs sporadically, chiefly in adults and without seasonal prevalence. In contrast, varicella is one of the common epidemic diseases of childhood (peak incidence is in children 2–6 years of age), although adult cases do occur. It is more common in winter and spring than in summer. Varicella became a nationally notifiable disease in 1972, and a total of 140,627 cases were reported in the USA that year.

Varicella readily spreads, presumably by droplets as well as by contact with skin. Contact infection is rare in zoster, perhaps because the virus is absent in the upper respiratory tract.

Zoster, whether in children or adults, can be the source of varicella in children and can initiate large epidemics.

Control

None is available for the general population.

Since varicella may spread rapidly among patients in hospital wards, particular attention should be paid to exposed children with immunologic dysfunctions (eg, children with leukemia or other malignancies, children with hereditary immune deficiencies, or those receiving corticosteroids, antimetabolites, or cytotoxic drugs). Varicella in such children poses the threat of pneumonia, encephalitis, or death. ZIG may be used to modify the disease in such children who have been exposed to varicella.

A live attenuated varicella vaccine has been developed in Japan and tested in hospitalized children who had been exposed to varicella. The vaccine was shown to be safe and effective in preventing spread of the disease. However, additional field studies are needed.

. . .

CYTOMEGALOVIRUS
(Cytomegalic Inclusion Disease, Salivary Gland Virus Disease)

Cytomegalic inclusion disease is a generalized infection of infants caused by intrauterine or early postnatal infection with the cytomegaloviruses. The disease causes severe congenital anomalies in about 10,000 infants in the USA per year. Cytomegalovirus can be found in the cervix of up to 10% of healthy women. Cytomegalic inclusion disease is characterized by large basophilic (or sometimes eosinophilic) intranuclear inclusions and small cytoplasmic inclusions which occur in the salivary glands, lungs, liver, pancreas, kidneys, endocrine glands, and, occasionally, in the brain. Most fatalities occur in children under 2 years of age. Inapparent infection is common during childhood and adolescence. Severe cytomegalovirus infections are frequently found in adults receiving immunosuppressive therapy.

Properties of the Virus
A. General Properties: Morphologically, cytomegalovirus is indistinguishable from herpes simplex or varicella-zoster virus. The virus contains DNA. The molecular weight of the DNA is $80-90 \times 10^6$, with a density of 1.716 gm/ml in CsCl and a guanine + cytosine content of 58%.

In infected human fibroblasts, virus particles are assembled in the nucleus. The envelope of the virus is derived from the inner nuclear membrane. The growth cycle of the virus is slower, and infectious virus is more cell-associated than herpes simplex virus.

B. Reaction to Physical and Chemical Agents: Cytomegalovirus loses its infectivity when heated at $56°$ C for 30 minutes, when exposed to 20% ether for 2 hours, or when kept at pH below 5.0. It is relatively stable when stored at $-90°$ C in the presence of 35% sorbitol.

In the presence of isotonic saline solutions containing bicarbonate, the virus is (paradoxically) inactivated at a faster rate at $4°$ C than at $37°$ C. The virus is more stable when suspended in distilled water.

C. Animal Susceptibility: All attempts to infect animals with human cytomegalovirus have failed. A number of animal cytomegaloviruses exist, all of them species-specific. Histopathologic studies indicate that a similar infection occurs in rats, hamsters, moles, rabbits, and monkeys. The virus isolated from monkeys propagates in cultures of monkey as well as human cells.

Human cytomegalovirus replication in vitro is limited to human fibroblasts. Such limited host specificity in vitro is of interest since the virus is often isolated from epithelioid cells of the host. Nonpermissive human epithelioid cells, however, can be made permissive for cytomegalovirus by prior treatment of cells with IUDR.

Pathogenesis & Pathology
In infants, cytomegalic inclusion disease is congenitally acquired, probably as a result of primary infection of the mother during pregnancy. The virus can be isolated from the urine of the mother at the time of birth of the infected baby, and typical cytomegalic cells, $25-40$ μm in size, can be found in the placental chorionic villi of the infected neonate.

Foci of cytomegalic cells are found in fatal cases in the epithelial tissues of the liver, lungs, kidneys, gastrointestinal tract, parotid gland, pancreas, thymus, thyroid, adrenals, and other regions. The cells can be found also in the urine sediment, gastric washings, or adenoid tissue of healthy children. The route of infection in older infants, children, and adults is not known.

The incidence of typical inclusions within salivary glands of 10–33% of routine autopsies in children, and the isolation of the virus from urine and from tissue cultures of adenoids of healthy children, strongly suggest subclinical infections at a relatively young age. The virus may persist in the salivary glands and other organs for long periods in a latent state or as a chronic infection.

Inclusions are rarely found in adult salivary glands, and virus is not recovered from the mouths of adults. Disseminated inclusions in adults occur in association with other severe diseases.

Clinical Findings
Congenital infection may result in death of the fetus in utero or may produce the clinical syndrome of cytomegalic inclusion disease with signs of prematurity, jaundice with hepatosplenomegaly, thrombocytopenic purpura, pneumonitis, and CNS damage (microcephaly, periventricular calcification, chorioretinitis, optic atrophy, and mental or motor retardation). Congenital cytomegalic inclusion disease was once believed to result in death, but infants with the disease may survive initial infection and live for many years.

It has been estimated that one of every 1000 infants (in the USA this means more than 3000 per year) is seriously retarded as a result of congenital infection with cytomegalovirus.

Inapparent intrauterine infection can occur and perhaps occurs frequently. These infections have been discovered while doing large-scale studies of newborn infants. Elevated IgM specific for cytomegalovirus or isolation of the virus from the urine has been reported in as many as 1% of apparently normal newborns. Such infections have been implicated as possible causes of mental retardation and hearing loss.

Many women who have been infected naturally with cytomegalovirus at some time prior to pregnancy begin to excrete the virus from the cervix during the last trimester of pregnancy. At the time of delivery, infants pass through the infected birth canal and become infected, although they possess high titers of maternal antibody acquired transplacentally. These infants begin to excrete the virus in their urine at about 8–12 weeks of age. They continue to excrete the virus for several years but apparently do not exhibit any clinical symptoms.

Acquired infection with cytomegalovirus is common and usually inapparent. In children, acquired infection may result in hepatitis, interstitial pneumonitis, or acquired hemolytic anemia.

Cytomegalovirus has recently been associated with an infectious mononucleosis-like disease without heterophil antibodies. "Cytomegalovirus mononucleosis" occurs either spontaneously or after transfusions of fresh blood during major surgical interventions ("postperfusion syndrome"). The incubation period is about 30–40 days. Rise of cytomegalovirus antibody and cytomegaloviruria are common features of the disease. Cytomegalovirus has been isolated from the peripheral blood leukocytes of such patients. Hence, it is presumed that the postperfusion syndrome is caused by cytomegalovirus harbored in the leukocytes of the blood donors.

Patients with malignancies or immunologic defects or those undergoing immunosuppressive therapy for organ transplantation may develop cytomegalovirus pneumonitis or hepatitis and occasionally generalized disease. The infection rate may be as high as 80%. An important source of the virus, particularly in seropositive patients (those with viral antibodies), is the recipient himself. In patients requiring immunosuppressive therapy, a latent infection may be reactivated when host susceptibility to infection is increased by this therapy. In seronegative patients without evidence of previous cytomegaloviral infection, the virus may be transmitted exogenously. In one study, seronegative transplant patients who received kidneys from seronegative donors became infected at a lower rate (30%) than those who received kidneys from seropositive donors (83%). Thus, the kidneys themselves may be the source of virus.

Laboratory Diagnosis

A. Recovery of Virus: The virus can be recovered from mouth swabs, urine, liver, adenoids, kidneys, and peripheral blood leukocytes by inoculation of human fibroblastic cell cultures but not human epithelial cultures. In cultures, 1–2 weeks are usually needed for cytologic changes consisting of small foci of swollen, rounded, translucent cells with large intranuclear inclusion bodies, margination of chromatin, and sharply defined nuclear membranes. The cytoplasm may contain small basophilic bodies. Cell degeneration progresses slowly, and the virus concentration is much higher within the cell than in the fluid. Prolonged serial propagation is needed before the virus reaches high titers.

B. Serology: Antibodies may be measured by neutralization tests in tissue culture. A soluble complement-fixing antigen of considerably smaller size than the virus can be prepared from infected human embryonic fibroblast cultures. In contrast to the infectious virus, the complement-fixing antigen is less stable at 37° C than at 4° C. Antibodies in human sera can also be demonstrated using the immunofluorescence technic.

An antigenic heterogeneity exists, so that the human viruses form an antigenic spectrum rather than falling into distinct serotype groups.

Immunity

Complement-fixing and neutralizing antibodies have been found in a high proportion of human sera. In young children possessing complement-fixing antibodies, virus may be detected in the mouth and in the urine for many months. Reinfection is suggested by an antibody rise, superimposed on the preexisting antibody level, which may occur at the time of virus isolation.

Virus may occur in the urine of children even though serum-neutralizing antibody has been present for as long as 2 years. This suggests that the virus may propagate in the urinary tract rather than being passively excreted from the bloodstream. Virus is not present in young children who have not yet acquired complement-fixing antibody.

Intrauterine infection may occur and produces a serious disease in the newborn. Infants infected during fetal life may be born with antibody which continues to rise after birth in the presence of persistent virus excretion. (This is similar to the situation in congenital rubella infection.)

Most infants infected with cytomegalovirus in the perinatal period are asymptomatic, and continuing infection occurs in the presence of high antibody titers.

Treatment

There is no specific treatment. Administration of immune gamma globulin has been suggested for generalized infections accompanying debilitating diseases but has not been shown to be effective.

Epidemiology & Control

Except for the congenital infection, the mechanism of virus transmission in the population remains unknown. Widespread infection with cytomegaloviruses occurs, as indicated by the increase in the rate of antibody appearance with age. This reaches 80% in individuals over 35 years of age. The rate of virus excretion among institutionalized children is 10 times that in children of comparable age in the population at large, suggesting virus transmission by close contact.

A live cytomegalovirus "vaccine" has been developed in England and has had some preliminary clinical trials. Since cytomegalovirus, like other herpesviruses, causes latent persistent infection, considerably more information about the epidemiology of the disease and the natural history of the virus in the body is needed before large-scale use of such a "vaccine" would appear to be justified, particularly since there is little evidence that the so-called attenuated vaccine differs from the wild virus.

Specific control measures are not available. Isolation of newborns with generalized cytomegalic inclusion disease from other neonates is advisable.

EB HERPESVIRUS
(Infectious Mononucleosis, Burkitt's Lymphoma, Nasopharyngeal Carcinoma)*

The presence of EB (Epstein-Barr) virus, an antigenically distinct member of the herpesvirus family, was initially detected by means of electron microscopy in a small proportion of cells in continuous lymphoblastoid cell lines derived from Burkitt's lymphoma, a tumor indigenous for children (mostly boys), in central Africa. EB virus has also been detected in cell lines derived from nasopharyngeal carcinomas or peripheral blood leukocytes of patients with infectious mononucleosis as well as from normal individuals. EB virus is apparently the etiologic agent of infectious mononucleosis and has been associated with Burkitt's lymphoma and nasopharyngeal carcinoma.

There is some evidence to link primary EB virus infections with acute neurologic diseases, including Guillain-Barré syndrome, Bell's palsy, meningoencephalitis, and transverse myelitis.

Properties of the Virus
A. Morphology and Size: EB virus is indistinguishable in size and structure from the other human herpesviruses.

In CsCl density gradients, EB viral DNA has a buoyant density of 1.722 gm/ml. The guanine + cytosine content is 58%.

B. Virus Growth: Attempts to infect human adult and cord blood lymphocytes and marmoset lymphocytes in vitro with EB virus have resulted in the establishment of continuous cell lines suggesting that these cells have been transformed by the virus. Furthermore, both owl monkeys and marmosets inoculated with cell-free EB virus developed fatal malignant lymphomas. Lymphoblastoid cells from these animals can be continuously cultured and give positive immunofluorescence reactions with EB virus-specific antisera.

It is not yet clear whether EB virus is a passenger virus or whether it is the agent responsible for continuous proliferation of peripheral blood leukocytes in culture. Only leukocytes that contain the EB viral genome appear to have the capacity to replicate in

*The oncogenic features of EB herpesvirus are discussed as such in Chapter 40.

vitro. Cell transformation has been obtained when human leukocytes, free of EB antibody, were inoculated with cell-free EB virus preparations. However, it remains to be seen whether EB virus is essential for establishment of continuous lymphoblastoid cell lines, for lines have been described which lack EB virus particles and immunofluorescent antigen.

C. Antigenic Properties: EB virus is distinct from all of the other human herpesviruses.

Immunity
The most widely used serologic procedure for EB virus infection is the indirect immunofluorescence test with acetone-fixed smears of cultured Burkitt's lymphoma cells. The cells containing the EB virus are those which exhibit fluorescence after treatment with fluorescent antibody. In another type of serologic test, semipurified virus particles extracted from the cells have been used as complement-fixing antigen. The immunofluorescence test is more sensitive for detecting low levels of antibody than the CF test with viral antigen. Detectable levels of both types of antibody seem to persist for many years.

Other antigens can be demonstrated in the lymphoblastoid cells, some of which are most probably virus-induced but nonstructural antigens. Among these are the soluble antigens demonstrable by CF and precipitation tests in cell extracts of different lymphoblastoid cell lines, and the antigens demonstrable by immunofluorescence on the surface of viable cells obtained from fresh or cultured Burkitt's tumors as well as from other lymphoblastoid cell lines. Antibodies to these antigens can be detected only in sera that have antibody to EB viral antigens (see above) but not in those that lack it. This indicates that the antigens are induced by EB virus.

Epidemiology
Seroepidemiologic studies using the immunofluorescence technic and CF reaction indicate that infection with EB virus is common in different parts of the world and that it occurs early in life. In some areas, including urban USA, about 50% of children 1 year old, 80–90% of children over age 4, and 90% of adults have antibody to EB virus. The mechanism of virus transmission is unknown.

Antibody to EB virus is also present in nonhuman primates, and it is probable that some of these animals were infected in nature. EB virus has also been detected in lymphoblastoid lines derived from peripheral leukocytes of normal chimpanzees and baboons.

EB Virus & Human Disease
The great majority of EB virus infections are clinically inapparent. On the basis of studies dealing with the level of EB antibody in various populations, the virus has been associated with lymphoproliferative disorders such as infectious mononucleosis, Burkitt's lymphoma, and postnasal carcinoma.

The strongest association at present is that between EB virus and infectious mononucleosis (glandular fever). This is a disease of children and young adults characterized by fever and enlarged lymph nodes and spleen. The total white blood count may range from 10,000–80,000/cu mm, while polymorphonuclear leukocytes may drop to low levels (about 2000/cu mm). Monocytes and large lymphocytes are increased and show morphologic abnormalities. Bone marrow cells or peripheral blood leukocytes from patients with infectious mononucleosis, grown in culture, develop into permanent lymphoblastoid cell cultures. Circulating atypical mononuclear cells in such patients are capable of active DNA synthesis and mitotic activity.

During the course of infection, 50–80% of patients develop heterophil antibodies. These antibodies are of diagnostic importance and are measured by their ability to agglutinate sheep erythrocytes. The test can be made more specific by adsorbing nonspecific substances with guinea pig kidney and with boiled beef erythrocytes. The heterophil antibody in normal human serum is adsorbed by the guinea pig kidney, whereas the antibody of infectious mononucleosis is adsorbed only by the boiled beef erythrocytes.

Epidemics of infectious mononucleosis are common in institutions where young people live. It has not been clearly demonstrated, even with human volunteers, that this disease can be transmitted artificially, and its infectious nature is not well documented.

Patients with infectious mononucleosis develop antibodies against EB virus as measured by immunofluorescence with virus-bearing cells. Antibodies appear early in the acute disease, rise to peak levels within a few weeks, and remain high during convalescence. Unlike the short-lived heterophil antibodies, those against EB virus persist for years.

Thus, on the premise that the seroconversion observed is a consequence of primary exposure, EB virus has been implicated as the etiologic agent of infectious mononucleosis. However, in some of the cases studied, pre-illness sera have revealed low levels of EB antibodies. An IgM immune response (characteristic of primary infections) to EB virus occurs during the early stages of disease. It is possible that the antigenic stimulus may result from the excessive growth of lymphoid cells which already harbor the virus or which are susceptible to the virus present in a few cells in occult form.

The role that EB virus may play in Burkitt's lymphoma (a tumor of the jaw in African children and young adults) and postnasal carcinoma (a nasopharyngeal tumor extremely common in males of Chinese origin) is less well established. The association with EB virus is based primarily on the finding that the incidence of antibody is more frequent and the antibody titers are higher among patients with Burkitt's lymphoma and postnasal carcinoma than in healthy matched controls or individuals suffering from other types of malignancies. The significance of these associations is questionable at present in view of similar serologic findings in patients with sarcoidosis, lupus erythematosus, and lepromatous leprosy. On the other hand, the viral genome has been detected in Burkitt's lymphoma and nasopharyngeal carcinoma cells but not in control cells using a molecular hybridization technic. Studies of the EB virus-New World monkey system should help to elucidate the relationship between EB virus and human disease.

SMON HERPESVIRUS

A virus has been reported from human cases of subacute myelo-optic neuropathy (SMON). The virus contains DNA, is ether-sensitive, and morphologically resembles a herpesvirus. The virus is neutralized by antiserum to avian infectious laryngotracheitis virus, another member of the herpesvirus family.

SMON is characterized by a polyneuritis causing disturbances of gait, numbness of the extremities, and muscular weakness. The disease has been widespread in Japan, with over 10,000 cases reported in the past decade. A controversy exists about whether the disease is caused by the reported virus or by the drug iodochlorhydroxyquin, commonly used in Japan and elsewhere for traveler's diarrhea. The drug was banned in Japan after 1970, and since then virtually no cases have been reported.

B VIRUS
(Herpesvirus of Old World Monkeys)

B virus infection of man is an acute, usually fatal, ascending myelitis and encephalitis. Cases have followed (1) the bites of apparently normal monkeys, which were healthy carriers of the virus; or (2) contact with materials (tissue culture fluids) derived from monkeys. Human cases are rare but are increasing as the number of persons handling monkeys and preparing vaccines from kidney cultures increases. Herpes B virus is most commonly found in rhesus, cynomolgus, and bonnet macaque monkeys.

The size of the virus is about 110 nm. It may be preserved in 50% glycerol at 4° C or may be stored at −20° C or below, or in the lyophilized state.

Because B virus infection occurs naturally in rhesus and cercopithecus monkeys, it has been named herpesvirus simiae. It is related to herpes simplex and pseudorabies viruses. The virus is transmissible to monkeys, rabbits, guinea pigs, and newborn mice. The virus grows in the chick embryo, producing pocks on the chorioallantoic membrane. Experimentally infected animals exhibit intranuclear inclusions and multinucleated giant cells. The same cytologic lesion is produced in cultures of rabbit, monkey, or human cells.

The virus enters through the skin and localizes at the site of the monkey bite, producing vesicles and then necrosis of the area. From the site of the skin lesion, the virus enters the CNS by way of the peripheral nerves. The picture is predominantly that of a meningoencephalomyelitis; there is also focal necrosis of the lymph glands, spleen, and adrenals.

About 3 days after exposure, the patient develops vesiculopustular lesions at the site followed by regional lymphangitis and adenitis. About 7 days later, motor and sensory abnormalities occur; this is followed by acute ascending paralysis, involvement of the respiratory center, and death.

Virus can be recovered from the brain, spinal cord, and spleen of fatal cases. Suspensions of these tissues are inoculated into rabbit kidney cell cultures or intradermally into rabbits; a necrotic lesion of the skin occurs, and the rabbit develops myelitis. The agent is established as B virus by the histopathologic findings (intranuclear inclusion bodies) and by serologic identification. Herpes antiserum neutralizes B virus hardly at all, whereas B virus antiserum neutralizes both herpes simplex and B viruses equally well.

There is no specific treatment once the clinical disease is manifest. However, gamma globulin (if known to contain B virus antibodies) is recommended in large doses as a preventive measure immediately after the patient is bitten by the monkey. Infiltration of the wound with B virus antiserum has been suggested.

An experimental killed B virus vaccine has induced antibody responses in a number of human recipients, but its protective value has not yet been proved.

B virus infection occurs in monkeys as a latent infection much as herpes simplex occurs in man. The virus has been recovered from monkey saliva, brain, spinal cord, and from many lots of monkey kidney culture (the starting material for preparing poliomyelitis and other vaccines for human use).

A total of 24 cases of monkey B virus infection have been reported throughout the world, half from the USA. Of the 24 patients, 23 had encephalitis and 18 died. Of the 18 cases for which information is available, 14 had received a bite or scratch wound, one had a history of a puncture with a contaminated needle, one had been cut on 2 occasions by glass from monkey tissue cell culture, and 2 had no reported prior injury.

MARMOSET HERPESVIRUS
(Herpesvirus of New World Monkeys)

Several herpesviruses have been isolated from New World monkeys, including herpesviruses T, saimiri, ateles, saguinus, and aotus. These viruses are interesting in that they appear to have a natural monkey host in which they are present with little apparent effect but produce serious disease when they infect monkeys of another genus. Thus, they resemble herpes simplex virus in man. Some of these viruses are antigenically related to herpes simplex, and some appear to be distinct.

Two of these viruses—herpesviruses saimiri and ateles—have been shown to produce malignant disease in other primates. They thus form useful model systems for viral oncologists. Experiments have demonstrated that monkeys can be protected from the malignant effect of these viruses by vaccination with live attenuated or killed virus.

●　●　●

General References

Aronson MD & others: Vidarabine therapy for severe herpesvirus infections. JAMA 235:1339, 1976.

Asano Y & others: Application of a live attenuated varicella vaccine to hospitalized children and its protective effect on spread of varicella infection. Biken J (Osaka) 18:35, 1975.

Barahona H, Melendez LV, Melnick JL: A compendium of herpesviruses isolated from non-human primates. Intervirology 3:175, 1974.

Baringer JR: Herpes simplex virus infection of nervous tissue in animals and man. Prog Med Virol 20:1, 1975.

Benyesh-Melnick M: Human cytomegaloviruses. Pages 762–772 in: *Manual of Clinical Microbiology*, 2nd ed. American Society for Microbiology, 1974.

Gershon AA, Steinberg S, Brunell PA: Zoster immune globulin: A further assessment. N Engl J Med 290:243, 1974.

Herpesvirus and cervical cancer: Symposium sponsored by the American Cancer Society. Cancer Res 33:1345, 1973.

Inoue YK: An avian-related new herpesvirus infection in man: Subacute myelo-optico-neuropathy (SMON). Prog Med Virol 21:35, 1975.

Joncas JH: Clinical significance of the EB herpesvirus infection in man. Prog Med Virol 14:200, 1972.

Kaplan AS: *The Herpesviruses.* Academic Press, 1974.

Miller G: Epstein-Barr herpesvirus and infectious mononucleosis. Prog Med Virol 20:84, 1975.

Nahmias AJ, Roizman B: Infection with herpes-simplex viruses 1 and 2. N Engl J Med 289:719, 1973.

Pagano JS: Infections with cytomegalovirus in bone marrow transplantation: Report of a workshop. J Infect Dis 132:114, 1975.

Plummer G: Cytomegaloviruses of man and animals. Prog Med Virol 15:92, 1973.

Roizman B, Furlong D: The replication of herpesviruses. Pages 229–403 in: *Comprehensive Virology.* Vol 3. Fraenkel-Conrat H, Wagner RR (editors). Plenum Press, 1974.

Schaffer PA: Temperature-sensitive mutants of herpesviruses. Pages 51–100 in: *Current Topics in Microbiology and Immunology.* Vol 70. Springer, 1975.

Schmidt NJ, Forghani B, Lennette EH: Type specificity of complement-requiring and immunoglobulin M neutralizing antibody in initial herpes simplex virus infections of humans. Infect Immun 12:728, 1975.

Schmidt NJ, Lennette EH: Neutralizing antibody responses to varicella-zoster virus. Infect Immun 12:606, 1975.

Weller TH: The cytomegaloviruses: Ubiquitous agents with protean clinical manifestations. (2 parts.) N Engl J Med 285:203, 267, 1971.

39...
Reoviruses, Orbiviruses, & Other Viral Infections of Man

REOVIRIDAE

The reoviruses of man were the first viruses shown to possess a genome of double-stranded RNA. A number of other viruses have since been found to have this unusual characteristic, and they have been grouped together in the family **Reoviridae**. The Reoviridae contain double-stranded RNA in several segments (usually 10–12), exhibit icosahedral symmetry, lack an envelope, and are resistant to lipid solvents; they mature in the cytoplasm as unenveloped particles with an electron-dense core. Virus development occurs in association with a cytoplasmic granular matrix and is accompanied by formation of regularly substructured filaments and tubules.

Reoviridae fall into 2 distinct genera on the basis of antigenicity, acid lability, and capsid architecture: (1) genus *Reovirus* with a particle size of 75–80 nm and a capsid with a double layer of capsomeres having 92 morphologic subunits in the outer layer; and (2) genus *Orbivirus,* which includes the ether-resistant arboviruses (bluetongue and African horsesickness viruses, Colorado tick fever virus [see Chapter 30], and others).

REOVIRUSES

The reoviruses are a group of **respiratory** and **enteric orphan** viruses once classified as echovirus type 10. Reoviruses are thought to cause only mild respiratory and gastrointestinal illnesses.

Properties of the Viruses

A. Size of Virus and Its Components: Reovirus particles are about 75–80 nm in diameter and are ether-resistant. They are morphologically similar to the wound tumor virus which produces tumors in plant stems and leaves that have been subjected to trauma. Reoviruses are unusual in that they possess 2 distinct capsid shells, each composed of capsomeres. The virus particle within the inner shell is called the core. Although capsomeres can be seen clearly on both shells, their spatial interrelationships are uncertain. Spikes are seen on the core particle as if arranged in an icosahedral pattern. The structural proteins of the virion consist of 9 polypeptides of 3 size classes.

About 15% of the virus particle weight is RNA, which includes the double-stranded RNA genome and numerous molecules of small pieces of single-stranded RNA. The unique feature of the reovirus genome is that it exists as a collection of 10 discrete and unique segments, ranging in molecular weight from $0.5-3 \times 10^6$, for a total of about 15×10^6. Each of these 10 segments maintains a 3' terminus in the intact virion, and each is linked to a different site on the core surface.

The double-stranded reovirus RNA is characterized by its melting in a narrow temperature range, having only slight reactivity with formaldehyde, showing resistance to hydrolysis by pancreatic ribonuclease, and exhibiting a general appearance and stiffness similar to that of double-stranded DNA on electron microscopic examination.

The small, single-stranded RNA oligonucleotides can account for a variable amount (up to 20%) of the total RNA content, or about 3000 molecules per virion. Each oligonucleotide contains 2–20 bases; about half of the bases are adenine. The significance of the small RNA pieces is unknown, but they may represent internal transcripts produced by the RNA-dependent RNA polymerase which is a component of the reovirus core.

B. Reactions to Physical and Chemical Agents: Reoviruses are unusually stable to heat; heating at 56° C for 30 minutes does not completely destroy reovirus infectivity as it does that of most other viruses. Furthermore, at 37° C, a period of 30–42 days is required to completely destroy infectivity. At 4° C, infectivity is detectable for months. Reoviruses are also unusually stable to pH and are not inactivated at a pH as low as 3.5. Reoviruses are relatively resistant to many chemicals, including 2% Lysol, 3% formalin, and 1% hydrogen peroxide for 1 hour at room temperature. However, they are inactivated by 70% ethanol.

A unique property of reoviruses is that they are activated in the presence of high concentrations of magnesium ions (0.5 M $MgCl_2$) so that their infectivity titer is increased by heating at 37–55° C, yielding a particle-to-infectivity ratio of almost 1:1 (vs 15:1

before heating). This treatment has no effect on the titer of the viral hemagglutinin. On the other hand, exposing the virus to temperatures between $-20°$ C and $-40°$ C in the presence of 0.5 M $MgCl_2$ almost completely destroys the infectivity of the virus and also inactivates its hemagglutinin.

Increase in infectivity can also be obtained by treating the virus with the proteolytic enzymes chymotrypsin and pancreatin. This treatment results in removal of the outer layer of capsomeres.

C. Antigenic Properties: Three distinct but related types of reovirus are demonstrable by Nt and HI tests. All 3 types share a common complement-fixing antigen. Reoviruses contain a hemagglutinin for human O erythrocytes. The human red cell receptors for the reovirus hemagglutinin are not affected by the receptor-destroying enzyme of *Vibrio cholerae* but are destroyed by 1:1000 potassium periodate.

D. Growth of Virus: Reovirus has a prolonged growth cycle and a tendency to accumulate within the cell. Host macromolecular synthesis is not depressed by the virus until late in infection. After adsorption within the cytoplasm of reovirus-infected cells, the outer shell of the virus is removed and a core-associated RNA transcriptase transcribes mRNA molecules from one strand of the genome RNA still contained in the core. The 10 functional mRNA molecules correspond in size to the 10 genome segments. Furthermore, these 10 mRNA pieces are translated both in vivo and in vitro into 10 polypeptide products, the primary gene products of reoviruses. Further cleavage of these proteins produces a total of 16 virus polypeptides in infected cells. Seven primary gene products are found in the virus particle along with 2 cleavage products. The remaining 3 primary gene products and 4 cleavage products may have catalytic or regulatory functions.

Reovirus protein synthesis occurs in the cytoplasm localized within intracytoplasmic structures (spindles and centrioles) which are involved in cell mitosis. Abolition of spindle tubules by colchicine does not affect total virus production but only alters the site of progeny virus formation.

Messenger RNA-like molecules are used to synthesize progeny double-stranded RNA. A virus-induced RNA-dependent RNA polymerase, the replicase, which is associated with newly synthesized subviral particles, is responsible for this conversion. The manner in which these particles mature into virus particles is unknown.

A number of temperature-sensitive mutants have been isolated. Mutants of one group synthesize double-stranded RNA, single-stranded RNA, and viral polypeptides, even under nonpermissive conditions. Mutants of this group are defective in uncoating, as well as in morphopoiesis, and the defect probably resides in one of the outer capsid shell polypeptides. Another group carries a mutation in a nonstructural polypeptide which functions very early in a catalytic or regulatory capacity, so that viral RNA synthesis is severely limited. Recombination of mutants is often highly efficient, presumably because it proceeds not by breakage and re-formation of covalent bonds but by reassortment of sets of genome RNA segments.

Reoviruses produce a distinctive cytopathic effect in monkey kidney cultures, in which cells separate from the sheet. At this stage, the nuclei are intact but the cytoplasm contains inclusion bodies in which the virus particles are found. The viruses also grow in kidney cultures of other species. The viruses grow in newborn mice, some producing signs of overt disease, with lesions of the nerve cells, myocardium, and liver. Inoculated monkeys develop lesions in the ependymal lining of the ventricles and choroid plexus. A strain isolated from a chimpanzee with rhinitis produced the common cold syndrome when passed by nasal instillation into other chimpanzees. The virus also multiplies in chick embryos.

Inoculation of pregnant mice with reovirus may lead to a prolonged virus infection of the developing fetus and embryopathy. Some offspring develop severe illness (interstitial pneumonia, renal tubular necrosis) soon after birth. Some congenitally infected mice later develop growth retardation and eye signs. Finally, some offspring develop no apparent illness but have a prolonged tolerant infection with immune paralysis.

Wound tumor virus not only multiplies in plant cells but also replicates in the nervous system and other organs of its insect vector, the leafhopper.

Epidemiology

The reoviruses have been found in man, chimpanzees, monkeys, mice, and cattle. Antibodies are also present in other species.

All 3 types have been recovered from healthy children. In addition, type 1 virus has been recovered from young children during an outbreak of minor febrile illness occurring in winter. Type 2 virus has been recovered from children with diarrhea or steatorrheic enteritis and from chimpanzees with epidemic rhinitis. Type 3 has been recovered from children with a febrile upper respiratory disease or with diarrhea and from naturally infected cattle. A number of strains have been recovered from patients in Africa with Burkitt's lymphoma.

Human volunteer studies have failed to demonstrate a clear cause and effect relationship of reoviruses to human illness. In inoculated volunteers, reovirus is recovered far more readily from feces than from the nose or throat. Almost all volunteers infected with reovirus type 1 developed heterotypic hemagglutination inhibition antibodies to types 2 and 3, while those infected with reovirus type 3 developed only homotypic antibody.

ORBIVIRUSES

Most orbiviruses multiply in and are transmitted by insects. Many orbivirus isolations have been from insects, with relatively few from vertebrates, although antibodies to these viruses are widely distributed in the latter. None of these viruses cause serious clinical disease in man but may cause mild fevers (see Colorado Tick Fever in Chapter 30). Serious animal pathogens include bluetongue virus of sheep and African horse-sickness virus.

Within the orbivirus genus, there are at least 16 serologic subgroups. Their virions range from 60–80 nm in diameter. They possess very characteristic, large capsomeres with the appearance of rings, a feature reflected in their name (Latin *orbis* ring). These viruses also may have a double shell, but in most of them the outer layer is diffuse, with little discernible substructure, and easily dissociated.

The orbiviruses have not been as extensively studied as the reoviruses, but the available data indicate that their replicative cycle is similar. They are more sensitive to low pH (3.0 for 3 hours at 4° C) than are the reoviruses.

Recent evidence suggests that an orbi-like virus is the etiologic agent of acute nonbacterial gastroenteritis of children. The virus has been found by electron microscopy in duodenal mucosa of children with the disease and has been identified by immune electron microscopy in stool samples. A 4-fold or greater increase in antibody by CF and by immune electron microscopy has been found in numerous patients in several outbreaks throughout the world. The agent is related serologically to animal orbivirus pathogens (epizootic diarrhea of infant mice virus and the Nebraska calf diarrhea virus).

quency of detection has averaged 70%. During the peak of the winter outbreak, the virus has been observed in specimens from 80–90% of infants and young children hospitalized with diarrhea.

Isolation in cell culture has not been achieved, but the virus does replicate in fetal intestinal organ cultures. Antibody to the virus can be assayed by indirect immunofluorescence. This technic appears to be more sensitive than CF for serodiagnosis.

The disease can be induced by the 70 nm virus in experimental animals; newborn piglets, calves, and rhesus monkeys develop diarrheal illness when given a human stool filtrate containing the virus. The viral shedding patterns in infected gnotobiotic piglets were consistent with those observed for infants with diarrhea. In gnotobiotic piglets, the maximal amount of virus in feces was present shortly before or at the onset of diarrhea. Their intestines provide an excellent source of antigen for assay of antibody by indirect immunofluorescence (IF).

Serologic surveys (IF and CF) for prevalence of antibody to the virus indicate that infection is widespread in the USA. Over 60% of infants are infected by the end of the first year, and few children escape infection by their fourth year.

The human virus has been shown to be related antigenically to Nebraska calf diarrhea virus, the virus of epizootic diarrhea of infant mice, the SA11 virus of monkeys, and the O virus (isolated from compost and presumably of sheep origin). Three of the viruses of this closely related group cause gastroenteritis in the natural host.

.   .   .

GASTROENTERITIS VIRUS TYPE B

The syndrome of nonbacterial endemic infantile gastroenteritis differs from the epidemic form in a number of characteristics. The attack rate is very low among family contacts. The illness is clinically more severe and is of longer duration. It is one of the commonest causes of childhood illness throughout the world and a leading cause of death in underdeveloped countries.

The major pathogen of nonbacterial infantile diarrhea is a 70 nm virus which morphologically resembles the **Reoviridae** and has been variously designated as duovirus, rotavirus, or reovirus-like agent. It is antigenically different from the known reoviruses and orbiviruses and has not been classified definitely.

Electron microscopy has shown virus particles in duodenal mucosa obtained by biopsy in sick infants, and immune electron microscopy has confirmed this finding in their stool filtrates.

The 70 nm virus has recently been associated with infantile diarrhea throughout the world. The particle has been detected in approximately 40% of infants with diarrhea. However, during the winter months, when infection appears to be most common, the fre-

GASTROENTERITIS VIRUS TYPE A

Epidemic nonbacterial gastroenteritis is characterized by (1) the absence of bacterial pathogens; (2) a clinical course of gastroenteritis with rapid onset and recovery and relatively mild systemic signs; and (3) an epidemiologic pattern of a highly communicable disease which spreads rapidly with no particular predilection in terms of age or geography. Although various terms have been used in reports of different outbreaks (eg, epidemic viral gastroenteritis, viral diarrhea, winter vomiting disease, epidemic diarrhea and vomiting) in which a particular clinical feature predominated, recent studies of outbreaks and of the illness transmitted to volunteers suggest that the clinically distinct syndromes described may be different manifestations of infection by the same agent.

Viral particles have been demonstrated by use of immune electron microscopy (IEM) in stool specimens from patients with gastroenteritis. In one outbreak in Norwalk, Ohio, a virus was detected in stool specimens obtained during acute illness. The virus had a diameter of about 27 nm and a buoyant density of 1.38–1.41 gm/ml.

All attempts to isolate the "Norwalk" agent in tissue culture have failed. However, volunteer experiments have clearly shown that the appearance of the virus coincides with the clinical illness. Antibody develops during the illness and is protective against reinfection with that agent.

Particles resembling the Norwalk agent in size and buoyant density were also visualized by IEM in stool filtrates derived from 2 of 6 other outbreaks of transmissible nonbacterial gastroenteritis. These 2 viruses were present in a lower concentration in stool than the Norwalk agent and were detectable by IEM only after stool filtrates were concentrated. The 2 viruses were distinct antigenically. However, one of the viruses shared antigenic determinants with the Norwalk agent. Thus, there appear to be at least 2 serotypes among the 27 nm gastroenteritis viruses.

On the basis of natural spread of the disease and of observations in volunteers, viral gastroenteritis type A has an incubation period of 16–48 hours. Onset is rapid, and the clinical course lasts 24–48 hours; symptoms include combinations of diarrhea, nausea, vomiting, low-grade fever, abdominal cramps, headache, and malaise. No sequelae have been reported. At present no specific laboratory test is generally available; the diagnosis depends upon negative findings for bacterial or other viral pathogens and upon the clinical and epidemiologic characteristics of the disease.

Treatment is symptomatic. Because of the infectious nature of the stools, care should be taken in their disposal.

CROHN'S DISEASE, ULCERATIVE COLITIS, & OTHER CHRONIC DISEASES OF THE GASTROINTESTINAL TRACT

Crohn's disease (regional ileitis) in particular—but other chronic gastrointestinal diseases also—has long been suspected of being due to a transmissible agent. Animal experiments have shown that granulomas can be induced in the footpads of mice inoculated with tissue homogenates from patients with Crohn's disease. Tissue homogenates have also produced the disease in rabbits.

Recently, a small (< 50 nm), RNA-containing, ether- and acid-stable virus has been isolated from patients with Crohn's disease, ulcerative colitis, and several other chronic gastrointestinal diseases. The virus is stable after heating for 1 hour at 50° C. It has been isolated from human diploid fibroblast (WI-38) cell cultures, from surgical resections and biopsy material obtained from all parts of the gastrointestinal tract except the duodenum, and from regional lymph nodes and gallbladder tissue. It can be adapted to grow in rhesus monkey kidney and human intestinal tissue cultures. The etiologic significance of this finding has yet to be proved, but the finding strengthens the argument that viruses may play an important role in these diseases.

WARTS
(Verrucae, Human Papovavirus)

Human wart virus (human papilloma virus) belongs biologically to the papovavirus group (*pa*pilloma, *po*lyoma, *va*cuolating viruses). Papillomaviruses include viruses of rabbits, cattle, and man; polyomaviruses include polyoma viruses of mice, vacuolating viruses of rabbits and monkeys (SV40), and a virus associated with progressive multifocal leukoencephalopathy (PML) of man. These viruses produce tumors in their natural host or in another species (see Chapter 40). They are ether-resistant DNA viruses, 43–53 nm in diameter, and contain 72 capsomeres in their outer shell.

Human wart virus has not been grown in tissue culture or laboratory animals. Therefore, information is based only upon observations of infections in man.

Common skin warts (verrucae) can be spread by autoinoculation, through scratching; or by direct or indirect contact. A filtrable agent recovered from warts has reproduced warts in volunteers. Crystalline virus particles with a diameter of about 53 nm can be obtained from those warts which have intranuclear inclusions in their rete cells. Thin sections of such papillomas have revealed crystalline masses within the nucleus. Warts without intranuclear inclusions have not revealed the virus particles. By electron microscopic counting procedures, warts contain their highest concentration of virus particles when they are about 6 months old; 6–12 months is also the period of peak antibody titers in the patient.

The nuclei of normal skin cells are uniform in size, and the DNA content shows little variation from cell to cell. In contrast, wart-infected skin exhibits large and variable nuclear sizes, and also much higher and more variable DNA values which cannot be explained by increased polyploidy or by increased cell division. Eosinophilic intranuclear inclusions occur with greater frequency in plantar warts (43%) than in common verruca vulgaris (4%).

Patients carrying warts possess specific 19S (IgM) antibodies directed against this human papovavirus. However, the titers as measured by complement fixation are low and difficult to detect regularly. Antibodies as measured by immunodiffusion can be detected more frequently. Recent data have shown that if the complement fixation titer is not measurable and the immunodiffusion titer is relatively high (1:8 or more), the immunoglobulin type is IgM. With the complement-fixing technic, only wart IgG (7S) antibodies can be measured, whereas with immunodiffusion both IgM and IgG antibodies can be measured. The prognosis for healing can be based on the type of antibody detected: if antibodies are measurable by immunodiffusion (either IgM or IgG or both) but in low concentrations at the time of therapy, or if they are of IgM type only, although of high titer, healing occurs with no greater frequency than in cases where antibodies are not measurable. The highest probability for the cure of warts is in those patients having measurable complement-fixing antibodies (ie, IgG antibodies in relatively high titers). Specific antibody has been detected also in some people with no history of warts.

Patients with transplanted kidneys and receiving immunosuppressive drugs experience an increased incidence of active infections with certain viruses (eg, herpes simplex and cytomegaloviruses) which are characterized by latent infections, presumably because the immunosuppression permits such latent infections to erupt into clinical manifestations. This increased incidence is also observed with warts. Another virus, morphologically a papovavirus but antigenically distinct from human wart virus, has recently been isolated from the urine of an immunosuppressed renal transplant recipient.

There is good evidence of antigenic identity between viruses from hand warts and from plantar warts. There is preliminary evidence that a similar (but not identical) virus also causes genital warts (condyloma acuminatum). Some evidence also suggests that virus from maternal genital warts may perinatally infect infants, who subsequently develop laryngeal papillomas. Although laryngeal papillomas are not a common disease, those affected—usually children—are often seriously debilitated by the obstructive nature of the lesions, which recur and often require repeated surgical removal.

Papovaviruses have also been associated with progressive multifocal leukoencephalopathy (PML). Large numbers of virus particles can be seen under the electron microscope in infected brain cells, and a number of isolates of a distinct human papovavirus resembling SV40—but not identical with it—have been made in cell cultures (see Slow Virus Diseases in Chapter 33). (For further discussion of papovaviruses, see Chapter 40.)

EXANTHEM SUBITUM
(Roseola Infantum)

Exanthem subitum is a mild, nonfatal disease occurring almost exclusively in infants between 6 months and 3 years of age. At times it is confused with rubella. The causative agent is found in the serum and throat washings during the febrile period. The febrile disease but without rash can be transmitted to monkeys with serum which has been passed through bacteria-tight filters.

The incubation period is about 10–14 days. The onset is abrupt; the temperature may rise to 40–41° C and last 5 days. There is usually lymphadenopathy. Seizures are frequent. The rubelliform rash characteristically follows the disappearance of fever by a few hours and affects most of the body but not the face. Leukopenia is present with a relative lymphocytosis. All patients recover promptly without any specific therapy.

The disease increases in the spring and fall and may occur in mild epidemics. As a rule, only single cases occur in families.

FIFTH DISEASE
(Erythema Infectiosum)

A viral cause has been postulated for this disease. In one epidemic, 10% of the cases were associated with evidence of rubella infection; however, in most cases no causative agent could be identified. The disease is moderately contagious and occurs mainly in children. There are no prodromal symptoms. Fever, if present, is low-grade. The diagnosis is based on the appearance of a rash, which occurs in 3 stages. It begins with marked erythema of the cheeks, which gives a "slapped cheek" appearance. An erythematous maculopapular rash then spreads over the trunk and extremities. The rash fades with central clearing, giving a lacy appearance. It may be pruritic. Complications are rare. No treatment is necessary.

MARBURG (GREEN MONKEY) VIRUS DISEASE

Marburg virus disease is an acute febrile infection first recognized in 1967 during an epidemic among laboratory workers exposed to the infected tissues of imported African green monkeys *(Cercopithecus aethiops)* in Germany and Yugoslavia. Person-to-person nosocomial transmission occurred from the hospitalized primary cases to medical attendants. No further epidemics or sporadic cases have appeared among persons exposed to nonhuman primates in America or Europe. Nevertheless, serologic surveys have indicated that the virus is present in East Africa (Uganda and Kenya) and causes infections in monkeys and man. Two cases occurred in 1975 among tourists traveling through Africa.

Marburg virus has been isolated in guinea pigs and various cell culture systems. The virus particle seems to contain lipid and RNA and has an elongated cylindric or filamentous shape when viewed with the electron microscope. Although this appearance and the cytoplasmic inclusions observed in infected cells by light microscopy superficially resemble those of rabies and related viruses, the basic morphologic structure of Marburg virus is distinctive, and it shares no antigenic properties with rhabdoviruses or with any other known viruses. Marburg virus is not currently classified in any virus group.

Monkeys of various species, including *C aethiops,* have been experimentally inoculated with Marburg virus. These animals developed a uniformly fatal infection which pathologically resembled the disease in man.

Marburg virus disease is an acute infectious disease which presents with fever, malaise, headache, myalgia, and gastrointestinal symptoms of vomiting and diarrhea. Clinical jaundice is not seen, but chemical evidence of liver damage appears during the second week of illness. Proteinuria and renal failure occur in the severely ill. The mortality rate is about 30% in hospitalized patients. Complications include bacterial pneumonia, orchitis, and acute psychosis. Convalescence is prolonged, with lethargy, fatigue, and loss of hair continuing for 3—4 weeks. Complement-fixing antibodies are present in the serum by the second or third week of illness.

Treatment is symptomatic. Careful attention must be paid to electrolyte balance, acid-base balance, and renal function. Severe hemorrhage may occur. Transfusion of convalescent plasma may be of help. Extreme care should be taken to prevent exposure of medical personnel to blood, saliva, and urine from the patient. Infectious virus can persist for up to 3 months in semen.

CAT SCRATCH FEVER
(Benign Lymphoreticulosis)

Cat scratch fever is characterized by malaise, fever, and regional lymphadenitis. A cat scratch, cat bite, or merely contact with cats generally occurs a few days before onset. The primary reaction may be a cutaneous or vesicular lesion at the site of the scratch, followed by inflammation, and frequently suppuration, of the regional lymph nodes. Lymphadenitis may persist for 1—3 weeks or longer. An ocular manifestation takes the form of the oculoglandular symptom complex, similar to that which may occur in nocardiosis, tularemia, and tuberculosis.

Heat-inactivated suspensions of infected lymph nodes or heat-inactivated pus from a bubo serve as skin-test antigens. They yield a tuberculin type of erythematous reaction about 24 hours after inoculation into convalescents.

The agent may belong to the chlamydiae. Stained sections of infected lymph nodes in some cases were reported to contain elementary bodies similar in appearance to those of psittacosis. Furthermore, convalescent sera from patients with cat scratch fever some-times fix complement in the presence of the psittacosis-LGV group antigen.

The disease is frequently not diagnosed, being confused with other infections of the lymph nodes. It occurs throughout the world. All age groups are susceptible, but cases usually occur in children and young adults. In addition to transmission by contact with cats, cases have followed insect bites, laceration while cutting meat, and pricks from thorns or splinters. Cats are believed to be merely mechanical transmitters of the infection. They do not become ill.

The tetracycline antibiotics may shorten the course of the disease and prevent suppuration. However, even without treatment, recovery is complete within a few months.

DIABETES MELLITUS

As early as 1899, viruses were suspected as one of the causes of diabetes mellitus in man, and there have been numerous reports showing a temporal relationship between onset of several different virus infections and the development of diabetes. Mumps virus has been a popular candidate, but such a relationship could be a chance one in view of the high incidence of mumps infection and the disease. Interest has been stimulated recently by retrospective serologic studies showing that newly diagnosed patients with abrupt-onset diabetes had significantly higher titers or greater prevalence of neutralizing antibodies against coxsackieviruses B1, B4, or B5 than did nondiabetic controls. Furthermore, a variant of encephalomyocarditis virus of mice—a member of the picornavirus family to which coxsackieviruses belong—can produce in laboratory mice a disease resembling diabetes; development of the disease depends also upon the strain and sex of the mice. Although these findings provide only circumstantial evidence, they strengthen the case for viral infection as a possible factor in some forms of diabetes. It seems clear, however, that if a virus is incriminated, it will be in complex interaction with genetic and metabolic features of the host rather than a simple phenomenon of direct viral causation.

• • •

General References

Aronson MD & others: Isolation and characterization of a viral agent from intestinal tissue of patients with Crohn's disease and other intestinal disorders. Prog Med Virol 21:165, 1975.

Bishop RF & others: Virus particles in epithelial cells of duodenal mucosa from children with acute non-bacterial gastroenteritis. Lancet 2:1281, 1973.

Blacklow NR & others: Acute infectious nonbacterial gastroenteritis: Etiology and pathogenesis. (An NIH Conference.) Ann Intern Med 76:993, 1972.

Craighead JE: The role of viruses in the pathogenesis of pancreatic disease and diabetes mellitus. Prog Med Virol 19:161, 1975.

Davidson GP & others: Importance of a new virus in acute sporadic enteritis in children. Lancet 1:242, 1975.

Joklik WK: Reproduction of Reoviridae. Pages 231–334 in: *Comprehensive Virology*. Vol 2. Fraenkel-Conrat H, Wagner RR (editors). Plenum Press, 1974.

Kapikian AZ & others: Reoviruslike agent in stools: Association with infantile diarrhea and development of serologic tests. Science 185:1049, 1974.

Kapikian AZ & others: Visualization by immune electron microscopy of a 27-nm particle associated with acute infectious nonbacterial gastroenteritis. J Virol 10:1075, 1972.

Murphy FA & others: Physicochemical and morphological relationships of some arthropod-borne viruses to bluetongue virus: A new taxonomic group. Electron microscopic studies. J Gen Virol 13:273, 1971.

Newman JFE & others: Characterization of a rotavirus. Nature 258:631, 1975.

Pyrhönen S, Penttinen K: Wart-virus antibodies and the prognosis of wart disease. Lancet 2:1330, 1972.

Rosen L: Reoviruses. Pages 735–739 in: *Manual of Clinical Microbiology*, 2nd ed. American Society for Microbiology, 1974.

Wood HA: Viruses with double-stranded RNA genomes. J Gen Virol 20:61, 1973.

Wyatt RG & others: Comparison of three agents of acute infectious nonbacterial gastroenteritis by cross-challenge in volunteers. J Infect Dis 129:709, 1974.

Wyatt RG & others: In vitro cultivation in human fetal intestinal organ culture of a reovirus-like agent associated with nonbacterial gastroenteritis in infants and children. J Infect Dis 130:523, 1974.

40...
Oncogenic Viruses

Although a viral origin for cancer has not been demonstrated in man, it would be illogical to suppose that the human species is unique in the animal world in escaping virus-induced malignant tumors. There are several reasons for believing that proof of viral etiology of at least some types of human cancer will be forthcoming: (1) the well-established viral etiology of benign warts and of molluscum contagiosum of man; (2) the many clinical, pathologic, and epidemiologic similarities between other human tumors and those of lower animals which have been shown to be caused by viruses; (3) the unquestionable role of numerous ordinary animal viruses, including human adenoviruses, in producing experimental cancer in animals; and (4) the biophysical, biochemical, and antigenic similarities between animal tumor viruses and viruses of man. Thus it is hoped that continuing research into the mechanism of viral oncogenesis with known tumorigenic animal viruses will provide models for the investigation of the possible viral etiology of cancer in man.

Although the first known malignancy of viral origin, avian leukemia, was discovered early in this century, the field of viral oncology has only recently received wide attention. Intensified research has led to the discovery of the viral etiology of many common tumors in lower animals. Recent contributions have been made largely because of technologic advances in tissue culture methods, the use of newborn animals of defined genetic constitution for assay, and the application of modern biophysical, biochemical, and immunologic methods.

The tumor-inducing viruses can be classified into 2 main groups with differing physical, chemical, and biologic properties: those which contain RNA as their genetic material (oncornaviruses = oncogenic RNA viruses) and those which contain DNA.

This review is concerned with in vivo and in vitro carcinogenesis by representative members of the 2 groups of viruses, for they serve as models in the quest for knowledge of viral carcinogenesis in man.

GENERAL PROPERTIES OF TUMOR VIRUSES

Ample evidence obtained by research on transformation of single cells in vitro indicates that cancer originates as a single cell phenomenon. Once altered, the cell possesses new abnormal properties which are genetically transmitted to daughter cells. These genetic changes may be expressed as measurable morphologic, metabolic, and antigenic alterations. In the animal, the outcome of these phenomena may be one of 2 kinds: either the altered cells invade surrounding tissue and metastasize to distant organs and tissues, resulting in host death; or the host may retain its homeostasis through humoral or cellular immune control mechanisms. Thus, a tumor may be defined as a permanently or temporarily uncontrolled growth of cells. It may be generalized or metastatic, culminating in the death of the animal (malignant tumor), or may remain localized and eventually regress (benign tumor).

How tumor viruses render cells malignant and how they differ in this respect from ordinary cytocidal viruses are questions which have not yet been fully answered, but the application of quantitative methods to the study of virus-cell interactions in tissue culture and for the detection of virus-induced macromolecules integrated into the genome of cells they have rendered malignant has brought some understanding of the mode of action of tumor viruses.

Virus infection of a cell has been described as the penetration of one genetic system into the sphere of action of another. Infection of a cell by a cytocidal virus results exclusively in cell death, but infection by a tumor virus leads to a synchronous virus-cell coexistence resulting in profound change in the properties of the infected cells. This phenomenon, called **cell transformation**, has been best studied in vitro.

Transformation may be recognized by an increase in the rate of cellular metabolism and multiplication and by a change in the appearance of the cells or of their arrangement in culture, usually as a result of lack of contact inhibition. When a virus induces transformation, small foci of cells resembling microtumors often appear in the culture. Statistical considerations show that a focus is produced by a single virus particle; the number of foci is thus a measure of the transforming titer of the virus. The most reliable test of true oncogenic transformation of an in vitro system is the ability of transformed cells to produce a tumor when injected into the proper animal host. This is not always possible, however, and one must then use as criteria of transformation heritable changes in cell phenotype. The most prominent of these changes are loss of contact inhibition, changes in cell adhesion, altered morphology to a rounded cell shape, increase in growth rate, increased cell motility, and acquisition of new antigens. These and other changes in virus-transformed cells—growth under soft agar, increased glycolysis, decrease in serum requirement for growth and for glycolysis, increased agglutinability of cells by lecithins, etc—appear to be related to functional changes in cell membranes during the process of transformation.

Although the biochemical basis for these func-

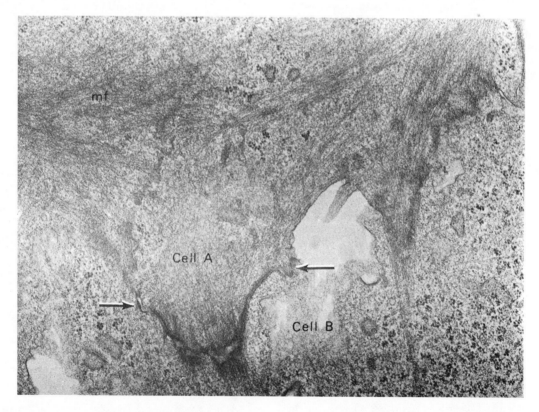

Figure 40–1. Normal rat kidney cells with numerous microfilaments (mf) at intercellular adherens junctions (arrows) between cell A and cell B (32,500 ×). (Altenburg & Steiner.)

tional membrane changes is not well understood, recent evidence suggests that altered synthesis of the carbohydrate-containing lipids and proteins of the cell surface may be involved. These alterations include incomplete elongation of the heterosaccharide moiety of glycolipids and loss of a large molecular weight glycoprotein from the cell surface. Another manifestation of the cell surface changes that accompany virus transformation is the loss of microfilaments (Fig 40—1) and the acquisition of numerous finger-like projections (microvilli) that extend from the cell surface (Fig 40—2).

Even though the DNA and RNA tumor viruses differ profoundly in their mode of replication, recent findings that oncornavirus genes, like those of the DNA tumor viruses, become integrated into host cell chromosomal DNA (see below) suggest a possible common mechanism of oncogenesis by the 2 groups of viruses.

RNA-CONTAINING TUMOR VIRUSES
(Oncornaviruses)

The oncornaviruses listed in Table 40—1 are similar to each other in structure, chemical composition, reaction to chemical and physical agents, and mode of growth. Based on certain morphologic, antigenic, and enzymatic differences, they have been divided into A, B, and C (and possibly D) types of viruses. It has been proposed recently that the oncornaviruses be classified as a separate subfamily (**Oncovirinae**) within a larger family of viruses named **Retroviridae** (see Chapter 27), since all its members possess an antigenically specific reverse transcriptase (see below).

Oncornaviruses are widespread in nature and are known to cause natural tumors in the host of origin. With the exception of the murine mammary tumor virus and some more recently recognized viruses, the oncornaviruses fall into species-specific groups of agents inducing either leukemias or sarcomas; hence the term leukemia-sarcoma complex for these agents.

Oncornaviruses have been recognized which are endogenous in the natural hosts without producing disease but capable of replicating in tissue culture; according to their host range in culture, they fall into 3 classes: (1) ecotropic (capable of growth in cells of the natural host), (2) xenotropic (capable of growth only in cells of a different species), and (3) amphotropic (capable of growth in both autologous and heterologous cells).

Those viruses which have been well studied can be divided into 6 groups on the basis of antigenic make-up, host range, and type of malignancy.

(1) The avian leukemia-sarcoma complex: A group of antigenically related avian agents which are found to cause mainly leukemias (eg, avian leukemia

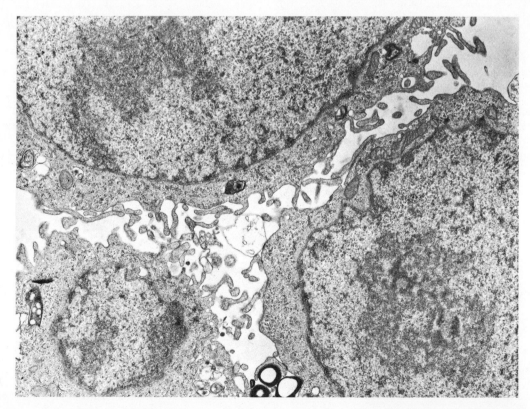

Figure 40—2. Rat kidney cells transformed by murine sarcoma-murine leukemia virus complex (14,100 ×). The cells are held together loosely by intertwining microvilli. Cytoplasmic microfilaments are very sparse. (Altenburg & Steiner.)

Table 40–1. Some properties of RNA-containing tumor viruses (oncornaviruses).

Virus*	Abbreviations Used	Host of Origin	Natural Tumors (Host of Origin)	Experimental Host Range In Vivo Tumor	In Vitro Cell Transformation	Size (nm)	Morphology (Particle Type)	Site of Virus Maturation	Persistence of Infectious Virus in Tumor
Avian complex									
Leukemia	ALV†	Chicken	Yes	Chicken, turkey	Chicken‡		C		
Sarcoma (Rous)	RSV			Avian, rodent, monkey	Avian, rodent, bovine, monkey, man				
Murine complex									
Leukemia	MuLV	Mouse	Yes	Mouse, rat, hamster	Mouse§		C		
Sarcoma	MSV		No	Mouse, rat, hamster	Mouse, rat, hamster				
Murine mammary tumor								Budding at cell membrane	Yes
(Bittner)	MTV	Mouse	Yes	Mouse		70–100	B		
Feline complex									
Leukemia	FeLV	Cat	Yes	Cat			C		
Sarcoma	FeSV			Cat, dog, rabbit, monkey	Cat, dog, monkey, man				
Other									
Viper		Viper	Yes				C		
Hamster, leukemia?	HaLV	Hamster					C		
Rat, leukemia?	RaLV	Rat					C		
Bovine, lymphoma		Cow	Yes				C		
Primate									
Woolly monkey, sarcoma	SSV-1	Monkey	Yes	Monkey	Monkey		C		
Gibbon, leukemia	GALV	Ape	Yes				C		
Monkey, mammary carcinoma (Mason-Pfizer)	M-MPV	Monkey			Monkey		D		

*A series of endogenous C type viruses exist that are not oncogenic but replicate in tissue culture; the murine, feline (RD-114), and primate (baboon) viruses are xenotropic (see text).

†The term RAV has been used for ALV strains associated with the defective Bryan strain of RSV (BH-RSV).

‡Attained with avian myeloblastosis virus only.

§Attained with the Abelson strain of MuLV only.

Table 40–2. Examples of classification of avian oncornaviruses.

Antigenic Subgroup	Representative Viruses* Leukemia Strains	Rous Sarcoma Strains	Ability of Viruses Within Antigenic Subgroups to Grow In: Genetically Defined Chick Embryo Cells C/O	C/A	C/B	C/AB	C/BC	C/E	Japanese Quail Cells
A	RAV-1 AMV-1 RIF-1	SR-RSV-A MH-RSV PR-RSV-A	+†	0	+	0	+	+	+
B	RAV-2 AMV-2 RIF-2	SR-RSV-B HA-RSV	+	+	0	0	0	+	0
C	RAV-7 RAV-49	PR-RSV-C‡ B77‡	+	+	+	+	0	+	±
D	RAV-50	SR-RSV-D‡ CZ-RSV-D‡	+	+	±	±	±	+	0
E	RAV-0 RAV-60 ILV	None	+	+	0	0	0	0	+

*Abbreviations: RSV = Rous sarcoma virus; RAV = Rous-associated virus; AMV = avian myeloblastosis virus; RIF (resistance-inducing factor) = field strains of avian leukemia viruses that interfere with the focus-forming capacity of RSV; ILV = induced leukemia viruses; SR = Schmidt-Ruppin strain; MH = Mill Hill strain; PR = Prague strain; HA = Harris strain; B77 = Bratislava 77 strain of RSV; CZ = Carr-Zilber strain.

†+ = Cells fully susceptible; ± = intermediate cell susceptibility; 0 = cells resistant.

‡Strains of RSV capable of inducing tumors in rodents and of transforming rodent cells.

viruses [ALV]) or mainly sarcomas (eg, Rous sarcoma viruses [RSV]). They have been classified into 7 major groups (A–G) based on their envelope antigenicity. This classification, based on antigenic cross-reactions in neutralization and immunofluorescence tests with antisera prepared in chickens, is in agreement with a classification based on virus host range and virus interference in embryonic cells of genetically defined chickens and of other avian species (Table 40–2). A dominant cell gene governs the susceptibility of chicken cells (C/O, C/A, C/B, etc) to avian oncornaviruses in subgroups A–D; in susceptible cells, viruses within one antigenic subgroup interfere with each other but not with viruses of the other antigenic subgroups (Table 40–2). Susceptibility of cells to the endogenous viruses in subgroup E (Table 40–2) is controlled by 2 independently segregating autosomal genes; one codes for the receptor sites and is dominant for susceptibility, and the other has an epistatic inhibitory effect on the expression of susceptibility. The more recently identified subgroups F and G contain endogenous leukemia-like viruses of pheasants with a host range distinct from that of the agents in groups A–E.

A new group of avian C type viruses, the avian reticuloendotheliosis viruses (REV), has been described. REV contain a 60–70S RNA but are antigenically distinct from the avian leukemia-sarcoma group of viruses and lack the p30 antigen (see below). Furthermore, there is no antigenic cross-reactivity between the reverse transcriptase (see below) of REV and the avian leukemia-sarcoma viruses nor homology between their RNAs.

(2) The murine leukemia-sarcoma complex: Many different strains of murine leukemia virus (MuLV) have been associated with a variety of leukemias in mice. Four of these have been most prominently used for classification purposes; they bear the name of the investigator first reporting the strain—Gross (G-MuLV), Friend (F-MuLV), Moloney (M-MuLV), and Rauscher (R-MuLV). On the basis of type-specific antigens, found both on the virion surface and on the surface of infected cells, the existing MuLV strains have been divided into 2 main antigenic groups, one carrying the protein coat antigens of the Friend-Moloney-Rauscher (FMR) viruses and the other the antigens of the Gross (G) virus. This classification has been supported by virus neutralization, complement fixation, immunofluorescence, and cytotoxic tests. A new grouping of these agents into N-tropic, B-tropic, and NB-tropic viruses has been suggested based on virus host range in genetically defined mouse embryo cells. The first group contains agents capable of replicating mainly in cells derived from NIH/Swiss (N) mice; the second group of viruses replicates mainly in cells derived from BALB/c (B) mice; and the third group, composed of laboratory strains only, replicates equally well in both types of cells. Unlike the avian oncornavirus system, this grouping is not in accord with the above antigenic classification since viruses of the G group can be either N- or B-tropic and viruses of both FMR and G groups

have been found to be NB-tropic. Furthermore, unlike the avian oncornavirus system, a dominant cell gene governs resistance to MuLV rather than susceptibility.

Recent evidence indicates that all strains of mice studied to date contain xenotropic C type viruses, which can replicate in cells of other species (human, rat) but not in murine cells. They possess the p30 antigen and reverse transcriptase characteristic (see below) of established MuLV strains but differ from them in envelope antigenicity.

The complex also includes the antigenically related murine sarcoma viruses (MSV) capable of inducing sarcomas. Five different strains of MSV have been recognized to date: H-MSV (Harvey), FJB-MSV (Finkel, Biskis, and Jinkins), M-MSV (Moloney), Ki-MSV (Kirsten), and GZ-MSV (Gazdar). All 5 strains exist as mixtures of MSV and MuLV and bear the antigenicity of the associated MuLV.

(3) Murine mammary tumor virus (MTV): (Also known as milk factor or Bittner virus.) A B type virus, antigenically distinct from the above murine oncornaviruses, transmitted through the milk and responsible for mammary carcinomas in certain strains of mice. Other strains of MTV have been recognized that are transmitted also through the egg and sperm. The different strains of MTV share protein coat antigens and fall into one major antigenic group.

(4) The feline leukemia-sarcoma complex: A group of antigenically related feline leukemia viruses (FeLV), which cause leukemias in the cat, and feline sarcoma viruses (FeSV), which cause sarcomas in the cat as well as in other species such as dogs, rabbits, and monkeys. These agents have been divided into 3 subgroups (A–C) on the basis of protein coat antigenicity and of host range and virus interference patterns in tissue culture.

Recent evidence indicates the existence of nontumorigenic endogenous viruses (such as RD-114) in domestic cats that are distinct from the above FeLV and FeSV strains and are xenotropic in that they replicate in different mammalian cells but not in feline cells.

(5) The hamster leukemia-sarcoma complex: A group of agents morphologically similar to but antigenically distinct from the murine oncornaviruses. The hamster leukemia viruses (HaLV) appear to be indigenous to the hamster and have been best characterized in tissue culture as nontransforming agents present in stocks of hamster-specific sarcoma viruses (HaSV). The latter have been derived from MSV-induced sarcomas in hamsters and are oncogenic in hamsters but not in mice. They are considered to consist of the MSV genome in the envelope of the helper HaLV—hence the altered host range and protein coat antigenicity. It remains to be seen whether or not more than one serotype of HaLV exists.

(6) Primate oncornaviruses: Three oncornaviruses, antigenically distinct from other simian agents and from oncornaviruses of other species, have been isolated from spontaneous tumors of primates: 2 antigenically related C type agents, from a woolly monkey fibrosarcoma (woolly monkey sarcoma virus or simian sarcoma virus type 1 [SSV-1]) and from gibbon apes with lymphosarcoma or myelogenous leukemia (gibbon ape leukemia virus [GALV]), and an antigenically distinct, apparently D type agent (the monkey Mason-Pfizer virus [M-MPV]) from a rhesus monkey mammary tumor. SSV-1 is tumorigenic for newborn marmosets; both SSV-1 and M-MPV can transform primate cells in vitro, whereas the gibbon virus induces myelogenous leukemia in recipient gibbons but is a nontransforming agent. Like sarcoma viruses of other species, SSV-1 is associated with a nonleukemogenic and nontransforming C type virus termed simian sarcoma-associated virus (SSAV).

Several oncornaviruses have been isolated from normal baboon cells by co-cultivation with permissive host cell lines. The baboon viruses are infectious for cells from various mammalian species but have not replicated in baboon cell lines, ie, they are xenotropic. These viruses, for which no tumorigenicity has been demonstrated, are distinct from the gibbon and woolly monkey viruses but are closely related to endogenous feline viruses (RD-114).

(7) Other: C type oncornavirions have been detected in viper, rat, guinea pig, and bovine malignancies as well as in placentas of normal baboons, rhesus monkeys, and human beings. Of these, the viper and rat agents have been isolated and characterized in culture as nontransforming viruses; akin to the HaLV, the rat virus (termed rat leukemia virus [RaLV]) serves as a helper virus for the replication of defective MSV in rat cells.

There have been reports of C type particles associated with various malignancies of man and of B type particles associated with human breast cancer. Two C type viruses, ESP-1 and RD-114, initially thought to be of human origin, have been subsequently identified as a strain of MuLV and a recently recognized endogenous feline C type virus, respectively. As of this writing, all human oncornavirus isolates that have been reported seem on further analysis to have been laboratory contaminants.

Properties of the Viruses*

A. Morphology and Size: Electron microscopic studies of infected cells reveal budding virus particles at the cellular membrane and mature particles in intracellular spaces (Fig 40-3). The particles range in size

*For general properties of viruses, see Chapter 27.

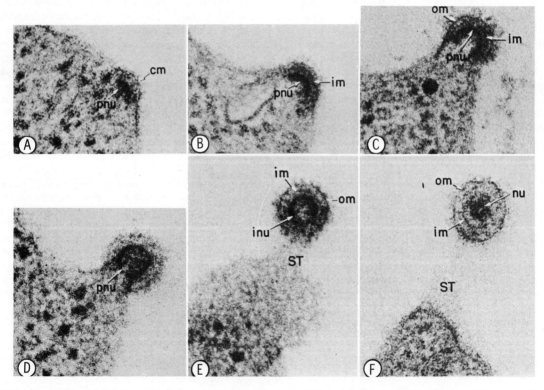

Figure 40—3. Virus budding at cell membrane of different leukemic myeloblasts either from circulating blood or tissue culture after various periods in vitro (X 215,000). Micrographs show different stages in increased size of dense prenucleoid (pnu), first beneath cell membrane (cm) in (A) and subsequent involvement of cell membrane in (B) and (C). Structures suggestive of outer (om) and inner particle membranes (im) are in buds in (B) and (C). A later stage of the bud is shown in (D). (E) shows typical "immature" avian tumor virus particle before nucleoid (inu) condensation. (F) shows dense nucleoid (nu) characteristic of "free" particles. The surface of buds and particles peripheral to outer membrane is irregular and indistinct. ST = stalk. (Courtesy of De Thé G, Becker C, Beard JW: J Natl Cancer Inst 32:201, 1964.)

from 100–120 nm. The mature particle consists of an RNA- and protein-containing, electron-dense nucleoid (55 nm in diameter) which can be either central (in C type particles) or eccentric (in B type particles). The nucleoid is separated from a glycoprotein- and lipid-containing outer membrane (envelope) by an electron-lucent area (halo). The envelope is derived from the cellular membrane during the process of budding, which is the characteristic mode of release for all oncornaviruses. The nucleoid of immature (A type) particles is electron-transparent because of the absence of nucleic acid. Biologic activity has been associated only with mature particles. The particles associated with biologic activity of the primate virus M-MPV (see Table 40–1) appear to be morphologically distinct and are presently classified as D type particles.

Particles extracted from affected organs, from the plasma of viremic animals, or from cells infected in vitro and stained with phosphotungstic acid (negative staining) reveal similarities with myxoviruses. Like myxoviruses, the envelope of MTV (and possibly avian myeloblastosis virus [AMV]) has surface projections about 10 nm long. Treatment of oncornavirus particles with Tween 80-ether results in disruption of the envelope and release of the nucleoids, which have a higher buoyant density (1.22–1.27 gm/ml) than that of the intact virion (1.16–1.18 gm/ml). Upon negative staining, the nucleoids reveal filamentous nucleoprotein strands (3–4 nm in diameter), often contained within peripheral tightly coiled helical structures (7–9 nm in diameter). The peripheral helical structure (nucleocapsid) has been assumed to form, during virus maturation, a supercoiled hollow sphere which is unstable and which in the mature virion uncoils to fill the nucleoid with the nucleoprotein strands (Fig 40–4). The nucleoprotein strands appear to represent the soluble group-specific (gs) antigen characteristic for each group of oncornaviruses (see below), which is also released from the virus particles after Tween 80-ether treatment.

B. Chemical Composition: Oncornavirions consist of approximately 60–70% protein, 30–40% lipids, 1–2.5% RNA, 2% carbohydrates (primarily glycoproteins), and a small amount of double-stranded 7S DNA, presumably of cell origin. The RNA isolated from purified virions is single-stranded and consists of a major 60–70S (molecular weight $1–2 \times 10^7$) viral component, and variable amounts of single-stranded molecules of cell origin: 4–10S transfer (t) RNA, 28S and 18S ribosomal RNA, and a 7S RNA of undetermined nature. The fast-sedimenting 60–70S viral RNA appears to be an aggregated structure that can be dissociated by agents capable of breaking hydrogen bonds (heat, dimethyl sulfoxide) into 3–4 major 30–40S (molecular weight $3–4 \times 10^6$) subunits and smaller subunits, the most prominent of which is a 4S RNA with the properties of tRNA. Each of the 30–40S subunits contains covalently linked adenylic acid-rich sequences, a property similar to that of cell messenger RNA. Within the avian oncornaviruses, polyacrylamide gel electrophoretic studies have revealed 2 functionally different classes of 30–40S subunit, a larger (class "a") subunit characteristic of transforming sarcoma viruses (RSV), and a smaller (class "b") subunit characteristic of transformation-defective (but not replication-defective) mutants of RSV and of the avian leukemia viruses (ALV). The larger sarcoma RNA subunits appear to contain all the nucleotide sequences present in the smaller leukemia RNA subunits as well as additional sequences, presumably those required for transformation. One hypothesis that has been well received is that the 60–70S RNA of the avian sarcoma viruses constitutes a polyploid genome of 3–4 genetically identical class "a" subunits and that nontransforming viruses (class "b" subunits) arise through a process of a single deletion of the sequences required for transformation. A similar relationship has not been found between the 30–40S RNA subunits of the mammalian sarcoma-leukemia viruses. Further genetic studies may answer the question of whether the 60–70S viral RNA genome of oncornaviruses is polyploid (nonsegmented), with each 30–40S subunit representing the entire viral genome, or haploid (segmented), with each 30–40S subunit containing different genetic information. Since recombination between avian oncornaviruses occurs readily, the answer may be soon forthcoming.

Purified oncornaviruses of all species have been shown to contain a DNA polymerase that can transcribe in vitro viral RNA to DNA (RNA-dependent DNA polymerase, also known as reverse transcriptase)

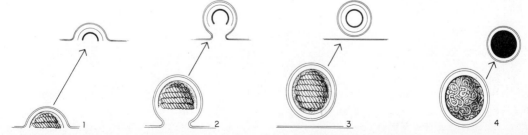

Figure 40–4. Schematic diagram of the morphologic development of a budding C type virus particle to a mature extracellular form. The nucleocapsid helix starts forming a shell immediately below the site of viral budding (stage 1), which in thin section will appear as a crescent-like structure. Ultimately, a hollow sphere is formed (stage 3) which in section appears as 2 concentric closed rings. At this stage, the virus is budded-off from the cell membrane and the hollow, spherical nucleoid undergoes a rapid structural transition to yield a condensed nucleoid (stage 4). (Courtesy of Sarkar NH, Nowinski RC, Moore DH: J Virol 8:564, 1971.)

Table 40–3. Antigens of oncornaviruses.

Antigens	Location	Chemical Properties of Major Antigens	Specificity	Detection — Most Common Methods	Detection — Reagents
Type (sub-group)-specific	(a) Virion envelope (b) Virus-infected cells	Glycoproteins (MW 45,000–70,000), ether-sensitive	Cross-reaction between strains within a subgroup;* lack of cross-reaction outside a subgroup, within a species, or between species	Neutralization, complement fixation,† immunofluorescence, immunodiffusion	(a) Sera of animals bearing virus-producing tumors (b) Antisera against intact virions
Group-specific	(a) Virion core (b) Virus-infected cells (c) Virus-free tumor (transformed) cells (d) Certain normal cells	Basic polypeptides (MW 10,000–30,000), ether-resistant	**gs-1**, species-specific‡ **gs-3**, interspecies-specific; shared by mammalian C type viruses	Complement fixation, immunofluorescence, immunodiffusion, radioimmunoassay	(a) Sera of animals bearing virus-free tumors (b) Antisera to disrupted virions (c) Monospecific antisera to purified polypeptides

*Number of subgroups for respective C type viruses: avian (7), murine (2), feline (3).

†COFAL test for ALV; COMUL test for MuLV; COCAL test for FeLV.

‡See Table 40–4 for further details on specificity of gs-1 and gs-3 cross-reactivities; both reactivities reside in a major basic polypeptide, molecular weight 30,000 (named p30); recent evidence indicates that the p30 polypeptide possesses also a type-specific determinant.

and can subsequently synthesize double-stranded DNA molecules after the single-stranded DNA molecules have been liberated from the resulting RNA-DNA hybrid by another enzyme activity (RNase H). Three other enzymes—DNA ligase, DNA endonuclease, and DNA exonuclease—apparently involved in integration of viral DNA into cell DNA, are also present in oncornavirions.

These findings lend support to the assumption that oncornavirus RNA replicates in vivo through a DNA intermediate (see below). The reverse transcriptase of oncornaviruses has been purified and shown to be a viral core protein with a molecular weight of about 60,000, separable from the gs antigens of oncornavirions (see below). It appears, however, to have the same species and interspecies antigenic reactivities as those described for the gs antigens (see below and Tables 40–3 and 40–4) and has proved to be a useful diagnostic tool for the identification of oncornaviruses of different species as well as for differentiating between the oncornaviral enzyme and cell DNA polymerases.

Table 40–4. Examples of cross-reactions between group-specific antigens of oncornaviruses.

Viruses*	Species-Specific (gs-1) C Type: Avian	Murine	Feline	Rat	Hamster	Primate	Viper	B Type Murine	D Type Primate	Interspecies-Specific (gs-3) C Type: Avian	Murine	Feline†	Rat	Hamster	Primate†	Viper	B Type Murine	D Type Primate
C type																		
Avian	+	–	–	–	–	–	–	–	–	–	–	–	–	–	–	–	–	–
Murine	–	+	–	–	–	–	–	–	–	–	+	+	+	+	+	–	–	–
Feline	–	–	+	–	–	–	–	–	–	–	+	+	+	+	+	–	–	–
Rat	–	–	–	+	–	–	–	–	–	–	+	+	+	+	+	–	–	–
Hamster	–	–	–	–	+	–	–	–	–	–	+	+	+	+	+	–	–	–
Primate	–	–	–	–	–	+	–	–	–	–	+	+	+	+	+	–	–	–
Viper	–	–	–	–	–	–	+	–	–	–	–	–	–	–	–	–	–	–
B type																		
Murine	–	–	–	–	–	–	–	+	–	–	–	–	–	–	–	–	–	–
D type																		
Primate	–	–	–	–	–	–	–	–	+	–	–	–	–	–	–	–	–	–

*See Table 40–1 for further details on viruses in each group.

†In addition to the data presented here and pertaining to the leukemia-sarcoma complexes of viruses, the p30 proteins of endogenous xenotropic C type viruses of feline (RD-114) and primate (baboon) origin have been shown to share a set of cross-reactive gs-3 determinants not detected in any of the leukemia-sarcoma complexes of viruses.

It was originally thought that reverse transcriptase activity was unique for oncornaviruses. However, other RNA viruses free of demonstrable oncogenicity but inducing latent infections in their host of origin also possess the enzyme. This is true for 2 antigenically related viruses inducing "slow" infections of sheep—visna virus and progressive pleuropneumonia virus (PPV)—and for syncytium-forming ("foamy") viruses of primate, bovine, and feline origin. These agents are classified in the same taxonomic order as the oncornaviruses (see above, family **Retroviridae**), since in addition to the presence of reverse transcriptase, they share other biologic and biophysical properties.

Visna virus and PPV have been shown to transform mouse cells in vitro, and their RNA genome was found to be a 60–70S molecule with the same physicochemical properties as those of oncornavirions. The syncytium-forming viruses have not been shown to transform cells but they have revealed a resistance to inactivation by ultraviolet light and an inhibition of replication by actinomycin D and by thymidine analogues similar to that of oncornaviruses. Since these agents do not appear to be oncogenic, it seems that both the presence of reverse transcriptase within virions and their presumed replication through a DNA intermediate are phenomena with broader implications as far as pathogenesis is concerned.

Other enzymes (RNA ribonuclease, nucleotide kinase, protein kinase, etc) may also be associated with purified oncornavirus preparations; however, as shown earlier for the enzyme adenosine triphosphatase (ATPase) associated with AMV, some of them may turn out to be cell enzymes incorporated within the viral envelope during the process of maturation.

C. Reactions to Chemical and Physical Agents: Being enclosed in a lipid-containing envelope, the RNA tumor viruses are sensitive to ether. They are readily inactivated by heating ($56° C$ for 30 minutes), by mild acid treatment (pH 4.5), and by formalin at 1:4000. The RNA tumor viruses can be preserved at $70° C$ or lower temperatures.

D. Antigenic Properties: (See Tables 40–3 and 40–4.) Two types of antigens are found in oncornaviruses: (1) Type-specific or subgroup-specific antigens associated with the viral envelope and characteristic of individual strains, or groups of strains, within oncornaviruses of each species. They are detectable in neutralization, complement fixation, immunodiffusion, and immunofluorescence tests with sera of animals carrying virus-producing tumors or with antisera prepared against intact virions. The envelope antigens of the avian and murine C type viruses contain at least 2 glycoprotein components with molecular weights of 70,000 and 45,000. There is no cross-reaction between the envelope antigens of the avian and mammalian oncornaviruses or between oncornaviruses of different mammalian species. Furthermore, there is no cross-reaction between the C type and B type viruses within the murine system and the C type and D type viruses within the primate system. (2) Group-specific (gs) antigens associated with internal polypeptides of the virion

core. They are detectable by complement fixation, immunodiffusion, and immunofluorescence tests and by radioimmunoassay using sera of animals of heterologous species that bear virus-induced (but usually virus-free) tumors, antisera prepared against Tween 80-ether disrupted virions, or monospecific antisera to individual polypeptides.

Several internal polypeptides carry gs antigenic reactivity, the major gs antigen (p30) being a basic polypeptide with a molecular weight of approximately 30,000. This major gs antigen, termed gs-1 antigen, is shared by and is species-specific for the C type viruses within a host species (avian, feline, hamster, murine, primate, rat, viper); the same is true for different strains of the B type murine MTV. No cross-reactions have been observed between the gs-1 antigen of the avian oncornaviruses and that of the mammalian oncornaviruses. Furthermore, there is no cross-reaction between the gs-1 antigen of the C type and the B type murine viruses or the C type and D type primate viruses. The gs antigens of the mammalian C type viruses carry, in addition to the species-specific determinant (gs-1 antigen), an interspecies antigenic determinant also termed gs-3 antigen or "gs-interspec." Both the gs-1 species-specific reactivity and the gs-3 interspecies reactivity have been found to reside in the p30 polypeptide. This interspecies (gs-3) antigen is shared by all the mammalian C type viruses; the avian oncornaviruses and the B and D type mammalian oncornaviruses are free of such interspecies antigenic reactivity. Recent evidence indicates that in addition to gs-1 and gs-3 reactivities, the p30 polypeptide carries a virus type-specific reactivity (like the envelope antigen).

Tumor Induction With Oncornaviruses
    A. Avian Leukemia-Sarcoma Complex:
    1. Avian leukemia viruses (ALV)—Leukemic diseases are common in chickens, and the leukemia-inducing viruses are widely spread in normal as well as in diseased chicken populations. The main types of viral leukemias encountered are lymphoid, myeloid, and erythroid. They derive their names from the characteristic primitive cells (lymphoblast, myeloblast, erythroblast) found in large quantities in the blood of the diseased animal, and from this terminology the names of the viruses have evolved: avian lymphomatosis virus, myeloblastosis virus, and erythroblastosis virus.

Infectious virus and physical particles of the virus may be found in high concentration in tumor cells, peripheral blood, and other organs of the affected animals, a phenomenon not encountered with the DNA tumor viruses. Myeloblasts or erythroblasts taken from diseased birds and grown in tissue culture continue to release virus, which in turn can induce the malignancy on inoculation into chickens.

Malignancy can be induced in newborn or adult animals by inoculation with cell-free virus derived from diseased animals or from leukemic cells grown in culture. Serial transplantation can also be made with leukemic cells; the resulting malignancy is eventually composed of cells of the recipient host, which suggests that it is virus-induced.

Almost all flocks of chickens are infected with various strains of ALV, especially lymphomatosis virus. The virus is transmitted horizontally through the saliva and feces, producing an infection in the adult animal characterized by transitory viremia and enduring antibodies. Relatively few adult birds develop clinical disease. Vertical transmission has been demonstrated from the viremic hen but not from the viremic rooster, ie, nongenetic vertical transmission, to be distinguished from genetic vertical transmission in which oncornavirus information is transmitted through the germ line in the form of a DNA provirus (see below). It results in congenitally infected viremic chickens, tolerant to the virus, free of antibodies, and permanent shedders of the virus. The incidence of leukemia in congenitally infected animals is much higher than in animals infected by contact.

2. Rous sarcoma viruses (RSV)—Rous sarcoma virus has undergone countless passages experimentally since it was first isolated in 1911, and it probably now differs from the naturally occurring virus. Several strains of RSV exist which differ in their oncogenicity, antigenic structure, and host range. The most common laboratory strains are listed in Table 40–2.

RSV causes sarcoma in birds of all ages and in chick embryos; unlike lymphomatosis virus, however, it is not naturally transmitted. RSV also induces tumors in ducks, turkeys, pigeons, and other birds; certain virus variants (Schmidt-Ruppin and other strains) also induce tumors when inoculated into newborn rats, Syrian and Chinese hamsters, rabbits, mice, guinea pigs, and even monkeys. The presence of infectious virus and of physical particles of the virus is a common finding in avian but not in mammalian tumors.

B. Murine Leukemia-Sarcoma Complex:

1. Murine leukemia viruses (MuLV)—To date, numerous leukemogenic murine viruses have been isolated. The types of leukemia vary. For example, in mice of certain lines the Graffi virus causes mainly myeloid forms of leukemia, whereas in others lymphatic leukemia occurs in a high percentage of cases. In certain experiments Gross virus causes almost all known types of leukemic disease: lymphatic, stem cell, myeloid, and monocytic leukemia, erythroblastosis, chloroleukemia, lymphosarcoma, and reticulum cell sarcoma. Most leukemia viruses have proved pathogenic in rats; the Moloney virus has proved to be pathogenic in hamsters as well.

Newborn animals are most susceptible to the effect of leukemogenic viruses, but the disease can also be produced in young and adult animals. Genetic factors play an important role in the susceptibility of mice to the virus, the nature of the disease caused, and the transmission of the virus. Thymectomy reduces the attack rate of lymphatic leukemia but not that of the myeloid forms. Thymectomy has no effect on the multiplication of the viruses in other organs. In infected animals, large amounts of infectious virus and

virus particles occur in the blood and in tumor tissue. Some MuLV strains can be transmitted through milk, the ovum, and the sperm.

The murine leukemia viruses are also widespread in nature. In certain "high-leukemia" strains (AKR), the Gross virus is the cause of the natural disease; infectious virus is genetically transmitted from mother to offspring, and the congenitally infected animals are tolerant to the virus. Certain "low-leukemia" strains of mice (C57BL) harbor genetically transmitted MuLV information; irradiation or x-ray treatment results in the production of lymphoid leukemia, yielding infectious virus which is capable of inducing infection in other hosts and has been named radiation-induced leukemia virus (RadLV).

2. Murine sarcoma virus (MSV)—Different strains of MSV have been recognized that bear the antigenicity of the MuLV with which they exist in consort. Unlike MuLV, the MSV virions cause sarcomas in newborn mice, rats, and hamsters. After passage in rats and hamsters, some MSV strains have acquired the protein coat of the endogenous RaLV and HaLV, respectively. Passage of some strains in rat cells has resulted in the acquisition of rat nucleic acid sequences by the RNA of the MSV genome.

C. Murine Mammary Tumor Virus (MTV): Tumorigenesis by different strains of MTV is a result of a complex interaction between the virus, the genetic constitution of the host, and hormonal factors. The most common strain, the Bittner agent, is found naturally in certain "high mammary cancer" strains of inbred mice in which mammary adenocarcinomas develop early in life, with large amounts of infectious virus and B type particles in the tumor, milk, blood, and other tissues. In such animals, Bittner virus is transmitted from mother to offspring through the milk.

The virus induces adenocarcinomas of the mammary gland only, and only in mice of susceptible lines. The latent period is 6–12 months. Newborn and suckling mice are susceptible to the virus if it is administered by the oral, subcutaneous, or intraperitoneal route. Adult animals are considerably more resistant, but this resistance can be overcome by administering massive doses of virus. Animals that do not develop tumors remain infected subclinically and transmit the virus to their progeny. The main pathway of spread of the virus is through the milk.

More recent work with different, highly inbred strains of mice indicates that the distribution of MTV is ubiquitous, and virus strains have been described which are transmitted through the ovum as well as the sperm, apparently in the form of an integrated DNA provirus (genetic vertical transmission). Electron microscopic, immunologic, and biologic investigations have revealed the presence of MTV in various "low mammary cancer" strains of mice. In some strains the virus is detected in an overt form; in others, after irradiation or treatment with carcinogens.

Hybridization studies indicate that tissues of both "low" and "high" mammary cancer strains of mice contain MTV DNA sequences and varying amounts of MTV RNA; a high degree of correlation appears to exist between the concentration of intracellular viral RNA and mammary tumor incidence, suggesting that during genetic vertical transmission oncogenesis is regulated at the level of DNA–RNA transcription. Mendelian analysis indicates that genetic transmission of viral information and resistance to superinfection by MTV are controlled by the same or similar genes.

D. Feline Leukemia-Sarcoma Complex: Several isolates of feline leukemia virus (FeLV) and feline sarcoma virus (FeSV) have been derived to date from cats with leukemia and fibrosarcoma, respectively. When inoculated into newborn kittens, FeLV induces transmissible leukemia and FeSV induces transmissible fibrosarcoma. The virus is found in the tumor cells, bone marrow cells, and blood of the infected animals. FeSV causes sarcomas also in dogs, rabbits, and monkeys.

E. Other Oncornaviruses: Woolly monkey sarcoma virus (SSV-1) induces sarcomas in newborn marmosets and the gibbon ape leukemia virus (GALV) induces leukemias in gibbons. Some of the other oncornaviruses listed in Table 40–1 have been associated with malignancies of the host of origin but have not yet been shown to induce tumors in any host. As indicated above, hamster leukemia virus (HaLV) and rat leukemia virus (RaLV) are nontumorigenic endogenous C type viruses of their hosts. The recently discovered endogenous C type viruses of the domestic cat (RD-114) and of baboons also appear to be nontumorigenic.

Oncornavirus Replication & Cell Transformation

A characteristic property of RNA tumor viruses is that they are not cytocidal for the cells in which they replicate. Like other viruses, oncornaviruses pass through an eclipse phase. The infected cell then produces new infectious virus, continues to multiply, and may or may not undergo malignant transformation depending upon the virus or the cell used. Infectious virus and virus particles are readily detected in most of the tumor cells or cells transformed in vitro. As shown by electron microscopic and tissue culture studies, the viruses mature at the cellular membrane; they are continuously released from the cell by budding from the cellular membrane (Fig 40–3).

Early studies with oncornaviruses had shown that inhibitors of DNA synthesis could prevent virus replication and cell transformation if applied during the first 8–12 hours after infection but not thereafter. Low doses of actinomycin D (which blocks DNA-directed RNA synthesis) were inhibitory throughout the replicative cycle. These findings indicated that transient DNA synthesis and DNA transcription are required for replication and transformation and led to the assumption that oncornaviruses may replicate through a DNA intermediate. According to the "provirus" theory proposed by Temin, the entering viral RNA is transcribed to DNA early after infection. The RNA-DNA hybrid is then further transcribed to a double-stranded DNA which, during cell division, integrates into the host cell DNA. The newly integrated virus-specific DNA (provirus) serves both as a permanent template for the transcription of progeny viral RNA molecules and as a heritable gene for transformation.

The discovery of the enzyme transcriptase, present in purified virions and capable of transcribing viral RNA to DNA in an in vitro reaction system, has strengthened the assumption that oncornaviruses replicate through a DNA intermediate. The role of the viral DNA polymerase during virus replication has not yet been completely determined. Such an activity is suggested by the existence of noninfectious variants of RSV and MSV that are deficient in the enzyme and by the finding that certain mutants of RSV with a temperature-sensitive defect for initiation of replication also contain a temperature-sensitive enzyme. The most convincing evidence to date stems from the isolation of infectious DNA (complementary to viral RNA) from mammalian fibroblasts that had been transformed by RSV (including a temperature-sensitive mutant) but were virus-free; transfer of the isolated DNA into chick embryo fibroblasts resulted in cell transformation and the production of infectious RSV biologically and antigenically identical to the original RSV strain used to transform the cells from which the DNA was derived.

The availability of virus-specific single-stranded and double-stranded DNA products, synthesized enzymatically in vitro, has opened new avenues for observation of the mode of replication of oncornaviral RNA in infected and transformed cells. Single-stranded DNA synthesized in vitro by the reverse transcriptase of RSV appears to be entirely complementary to the viral RNA. The viral DNA products, as well as the 70S viral RNA, have been used as radioactive hybridizing probes to detect virus-specific DNA and RNA species within infected or transformed cells. The same probes can be used to detect the synthesis of intracellular viral nucleic acid species during the early stages of infection and transformation. The results obtained to date are beginning to substantiate the proviral scheme of oncornavirus replication. Work evolving with both RSV and MuLV indicates the following:

(1) Between 3–6 hours after infection, double-stranded viral DNA (provirus) is synthesized and found as a free molecule (molecular weight about 3×10^6) in the cell cytoplasm, indicating that reverse transcription occurs in the cytoplasm (for RSV this has also been demonstrated to occur in enucleated cells). Preliminary evidence with MuLV suggests that this process is preceded by the formation of viral RNA-DNA hybrid molecules.

(2) Between 6–10 hours after infection, the newly synthesized provirus can be detected in a free form (predominantly as a closed circular duplex with a native molecular weight of 6×10^6) in the cell nucleus.

(3) After 10 hours, the provirus begins to be detected in a covalently integrated form within the cell chromosome, and by 24 hours postinfection most of

the provirus is found in an integrated state—presumably as a linear part of the chromosome.

(4) After it is integrated into the cell chromosome, the viral DNA becomes a template for the synthesis of viral genome RNA and of viral messenger (m) RNA—the former being detected first in the nucleus and at a later stage in the cytoplasm. The mRNA is found associated with polysomes and has nucleotide sequences identical to those of the viral genome RNA (plus strand).

(5) Whereas in productive infection with oncornaviruses mRNA goes on to be translated into viral proteins, cells which have integrated the viral genome (detected as chromosomal proviral DNA by hybridization) but do not produce viral progeny appear to exhibit varying degrees of transcriptional control; some may reveal appreciable amounts of RNA and proteins (gs antigens), whereas others fail to show detectable RNA but can be induced to produce infectious virions after chemical treatment (see below).

Unlike transformation with DNA tumor viruses, transformation by oncornaviruses occurs with high efficiency, especially in the presence of polyanions such as diethylaminoethyl-dextran. The exact mechanism by which oncornaviruses transform susceptible cells is not clear as yet, and the number of viral genes required for virus replication and for transformation is not known. As indicated above, studies with nontransforming mutants of RSV suggest that the replicating and cell-transforming capacities reside in different subunits of the viral genome. Work now unfolding with temperature-sensitive mutants of RSV that fail to transform cells but can replicate at the nonpermissive temperature is beginning to elucidate the viral functions required for the maintenance of the transformed state; cells transformed with a particular mutant at the permissive temperature lose their transformed phenotype within a few hours after a shift to the nonpermissive temperature; conversely, cells that have lost their transformed phenotype at the nonpermissive temperature regain it after a shift to the permissive temperature. These results suggest that the continuous presence of a functional viral gene product is necessary for maintenance of the transformed state. Furthermore, since with these mutants viral replication is unperturbed at the nonpermissive temperature, the gene product necessary for cell transformation is evidently not required for virus replication. Mutants of RSV that are temperature-sensitive for both virus replication and cell transformation have been described with similar results; as indicated above, 2 such mutants have been shown to possess a temperature-sensitive reverse transcriptase. Further work with such mutants as well as with mutants of RSV and MSV that can transform cells but cannot replicate is now being done in an attempt to determine which viral genes are required for virus replication, for initiation of cell transformation, and for the maintenance of the transformed state.

A. Avian Leukemia-Sarcoma Complex:

1. **Avian leukemia viruses (ALV)**—Most strains of ALV multiply in cultures of chick embryo fibroblasts without causing any cytopathic change or cell transformation. Virus replication in such cells can be detected by means of an immunofluorescence focus assay with type-specific chicken antisera, by the production of virus-specific gs antigen and reverse transcriptase, or by failure of the cells to transform when exposed to RSV, a phenomenon termed **interference**. The interfering property of the leukemia viruses is utilized to measure their activity in tissue culture in an RIF (resistance-inducing factor) test. Cells chronically infected with leukemia viruses can be propagated in serial passage, yielding large quantities of virus capable of inducing neoplasia in vivo or of inducing interference with RSV in vitro.

Morphologic transformation of susceptible mesenchymal target cells into myeloblast-like cells has been achieved only with the avian myeloblastosis virus (AMV). The transformed cells multiply exponentially and produce new virus which in turn is capable of producing neoplasia in vivo or transformation in vitro. This in vitro transforming ability of AMV is used as a means of quantitatively assaying the virus.

2. **Rous sarcoma virus (RSV)**—Unlike the leukemia viruses, with which they share many physical and antigenic properties, Rous sarcoma viruses are unique among tumor viruses in the speed and high frequency with which they induce malignant transformation of the infected cell. Infection of chick embryo cells with RSV results in foci of transformed cells, the morphology of which varies for the virus strain used. Virus activity is measured as the number of focus-forming units (FFU) per unit volume. In vitro, transformed chick or duck cells usually continue to release virus; both transformed cells and virus released from them can induce tumors in vivo.

The Schmidt-Ruppin (SR-RSV), Carr-Zilber (CZ-RSV), Prague (PR-RSV), and B77 strains of RSV (Table 40–2), which have been shown to induce tumors in mammals (including macaque and marmoset monkeys), can induce transformation in chick embryo cells as well as in mouse, rat, or hamster embryo fibroblast cells. The transformed chick embryo cells continue to produce infectious virus. Infectious virus cannot be demonstrated in cell-free extracts from the transformed rodent cells by conventional methods. However, these cells usually contain the integrated provirus, the gs antigen characteristic for the avian oncornaviruses and, in some instances, virus particles as well. Infectious RSV can be rescued from viable nonpermissive transformed cells either by their implantation into chickens or by their co-cultivation in vitro with susceptible chick embryo cells, usually in the presence of ultraviolet-inactivated Sendai virus, which facilitates the formation of heterokaryons. Transformation of human embryo, bovine embryo, and monkey cells has been reported with some of the Rous sarcoma viruses.

Some important features of RSV-cell interaction have come to light from work with the "defective" Bryan high-titer strain of RSV (BH-RSV): (1) Cell transformation is a function of the RSV genome; and

(2) antigenicity, host range, and sensitivity to specific interference by ALV strains are governed by the protein coat in which the RSV genome is encapsidated. It was found that stocks of BH-RSV contain a 10-fold excess of a nontransforming ALV—hence the term Rous-associated virus or RAV for the ALV in such preparations. When selective pressures were applied to obtain infection with the RSV component alone, it turned out that pure RSV can induce cell transformation but cannot reproduce new, infectious virus (Fig 40–5)—hence the term "defective."

Cells transformed by RSV alone fail to produce infectious virus or protein coat antigen, and such cells are called nonproducers (NP cells). However, NP cells, capable of multiplying for many generations, contain the group-specific antigen of avian oncornaviruses and the RSV genome. Superinfection of continuously propagated NP cells with a nontransforming RAV "helper" virus results, through phenotypic mixing, in the production of infectious RSV which possesses the antigenicity of the RAV helper virus but is capable of transforming new cells in vitro and of inducing sar-

comas in vivo (Fig 40–5). Different, antigenically distinct RAV strains such as RAV-1, RAV-2, RAV-0, etc have been used and the resulting infectious pseudotypes—RSV (RAV-1), RSV (RAV-2), RSV (RAV-0), etc—have been shown to possess the antigenicity, host range, and interference properties of the corresponding helper RAV virus. However, such alteration in the viral envelope does not cause a heritable stable change in the RSV genome.

These observations indicate that BH-RSV is unable to code for its own viral envelope and requires a helper virus to perform this function. In addition to infectious strains of ALV, this helper function is provided by the endogenous viruses in antigenic subgroup E (see Table 40–2), which are present in certain avian cells and are released spontaneously (RAV-0) or can be activated either by superinfection with RSV or RLV or by chemical treatment (see below). Furthermore, these findings indicate that a sarcoma genome could enter a wide range of otherwise nonpermissive cells provided it is encoded in an envelope to which the cells have receptors for permissive penetration. Indeed, recent

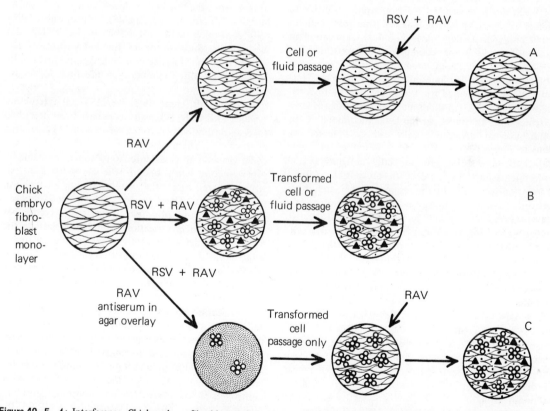

Figure 40–5. *A:* Interference. Chick embryo fibroblasts infected with RAV never transform, continue to produce infectious virus (black dots), and are resistant to superinfection with the (RSV + RAV) "high titer" Bryan strain of RSV. *B:* Transformation. Chick embryo fibroblasts infected with the (RSV + RAV) "high titer" Bryan strain of RSV undergo transformation (foci of rounded cells). The transformed cells release both RSV (black triangles) and RAV (black dots). Transformation of new cultures can be achieved by either passage of intact transformed cells or virus-containing tissue culture fluid. *C:* Selection of NP cells. Limiting dilution of the (RSV + RAV) "high titer" Bryan strain plated on chick embryo fibroblasts under an agar overlay containing RAV antiserum forms foci of transformed NP (free of infectious virus) cells. Transformation of new cultures can be achieved only by passage of intact NP cells. NP cells superinfected with a "helper" RAV release both infectious RSV and infectious RAV.

studies have demonstrated that phenotypic mixing occurs between oncornaviruses (both avian and murine) and vesicular stomatitis virus (VSV), an unrelated RNA-containing enveloped rhabdovirus with a very wide host range in tissue culture. An RSV(VSV) pseudotype which can be neutralized only by antiserum to VSV acquires the wide host range of VSV. On the other hand, pseudotypes of a VSV genome and an ALV protein coat VSV(ALV) are neutralized by the antiserum specific for the antigenic type of ALV used and acquire the restricted host range specific for the corresponding type (see Table 40–2). Since, as indicated above, phenotypic mixing does occur with resident endogenous oncornaviral genomes, these latter studies with VSV may indeed open avenues for the search for oncornaviral genes in human tumor cells (see below).

B. Murine Leukemia-Sarcoma Complex:

1. Murine leukemia viruses (MuLV)–Laboratory strains of the FMR group can be propagated in vitro in mouse embryo fibroblasts of unrestricted genotype. On the other hand, the Gross virus and naturally occurring leukemia viruses have been found to replicate only in cells of certain strains of mice. With the exception of the recently recognized Abelson strain of MuLV (a defective strain of MuLV that can transform cells in vitro and induces leukemias in mice), replication in susceptible cells is not accompanied by overt morphologic changes, and the infected cells continue to release infectious MuLV for indefinite periods of time. However, the virus released from such chronically infected cells is about one ten-thousandth as infectious as virus circulating in the blood of the leukemic animal. Virus replication in susceptible cells can be detected by several indirect tests: the assays described in Table 40–3 for measuring group-specific antigen; a viral interference test that detects the prevention of focus formation with MSV by the resident MuLV; and, more recently, a test measuring the development of reverse transcriptase activity in infected cells. A quantitative plaque assay for MuLV has been developed. Rat cells (XC cells) which had been transformed by the Prague strain of Rous sarcoma virus (but are virus-free) can fuse with MuLV-infected mouse cells to form giant cells which are detected as visible plaques. In addition, a rapid quantitative tissue culture assay for MuLV has been described that makes use of a transformed, sarcoma virus-positive, leukemia virus-negative (S^+L^-) line of BALB/3T3 mouse cells that contains the MSV genome but is free of detectable infectious virus; upon addition of exogenous MuLV, typical MSV foci appear proportionate to the concentration of MuLV used for superinfection.

2. Murine sarcoma virus (MSV)–Infection of mouse, rat, hamster, or human embryo cells with MSV results in foci of transformed cells, and virus activity can be measured in focus-forming units (FFU) per unit volume. Some similarity exists between the various strains of MSV and the defective Bryan strain of RSV (BH-RSV). Similar to BH-RSV, MSV preparations contain an excess of nontransforming MuLV, and

phenotypic mixing between MSV and MuLV results in the formation of infectious MSV (MuLV) pseudotypes. Also similar to the BH-RSV system, (1) the host range and antigenicity of the MSV pseudotypes are governed by the helper MuLV used, and (2) MSV by itself can induce transformation of mouse cells but requires helper MuLV for replication of infectious particles.

Pseudotypes can be formed through phenotypic mixing between defective MSV genomes and other nontransforming mammalian C type viruses. As indicated earlier, infection of hamsters in vivo or hamster cells in vitro (that contain the nontransforming HaLV) results in transformed cells that release MSV (HaLV) pseudotype capable of infecting hamster but not mouse cells. Similarly, MSV infection of rat cells that carry the endogenous RaLV results in transformed cells releasing MSV (RaLV) pseudotype; in the case of the Kirsten and Harvey strains of MSV (Ki-MSV; H-MSV), which were originally derived by inoculation of Ki-MuLV and H-MuLV into rats, it appears that recombination also occurs between the MSV genomes and the endogenous rat C type virus since they contain sequences of both MuLV and RaLV in their nucleic acid. Feline leukemia virus (FeLV) has been used as a helper for the defective MSV, with a resulting MSV(FeLV) pseudotype capable of transforming feline cells and other cells susceptible to FeLV but not mouse cells. Substitution of the FeLV protein coat with that of the Moloney murine leukemia virus results in an MSV (M-MuLV) pseudotype infectious for mouse cells.

Several different defective MSV-cell interaction systems (NP cells, S^+L^- cells, etc) have been described to date dealing with varying degrees of MSV genome expression in the absence of release of infectious sarcoma virus; in all cases, infectious MSV is rescuable by superinfection with one of the above-listed helper viruses as well as by the woolly monkey and gibbon oncornaviruses. These genetic interactions between RNA tumor viruses of unrelated species deserve further study, for such investigations may indeed lead to the discovery of defective viral genomes in human tumor cells; recent evidence indicates that continuous passage of MSV or MuLV in human cells results in the production of altered virions that replicate better in human than in murine cells.

C. Murine Mammary Tumor Virus: In vitro propagation of these agents by conventional tissue culture methods has not been successful. However, cell lines have been derived from mammary tumors, propagated in continuous culture, and found to contain intracellular proviral DNA. Virus production was found to be controlled at the DNA-RNA transcriptional level—the higher the concentration of intracellular viral RNA, the higher the yield of intact MTV. It has also been found that the addition of a synthetic glucocorticoid, dexamethasone, to such cultures results in increased transcription and a 10- to 100-fold increase in MTV yield. These systems offer new possibilities to study the mechanism of MTV replication and of MTV-hormone interaction at a cellular level.

D. Feline Oncornaviruses: The leukemia virus (FeLV) undergoes vegetative replication in feline, canine, monkey, and human cells. The infected cells remain morphologically unaltered and continue to release infectious virus, leukemogenic for the newborn kitten. The sarcoma virus (FeSV) has been found to transform in vitro cell cultures of feline, canine, monkey, and human origin.

Similar to the avian and murine systems, cells infected with FeLV are resistant to transformation by FeSV or MSV (FeLV) pseudotypes. This interference test is being used as a quantitative in vitro assay for the detection and classification of FeLV strains.

Virus-Induced Tumor-Specific Transplantable Antigens (TSTA)

One of the principal characteristics of carcinogenesis by the oncornaviruses is the continuous release of infectious virus from most of the in vivo or in vitro transformed cells. This property has made the assessment of new virus-induced but nonvirion antigens in these cells more difficult than in the case of cells transformed by DNA-containing viruses since the latter cells are usually free of infectious virions (see below).

However, work with virus-induced leukemias in highly inbred strains of mice indicates that the leukemic cells possess new antigens specific for the virus strain inducing the leukemia. These experiments are based on the principles of graft rejection among unrelated mice. Thus, mice of one genetically defined strain accept autologous and syngeneic grafts. However, they reject allogeneic grafts and develop immunity against transplantation antigens in the allogeneic graft. Animals that have rejected allogeneic grafts still accept subsequent syngeneic grafts which lack the foreign transplantation antigens.

Transplantation immunity has been demonstrated in several of the virus-induced murine leukemias. Tumors induced in various strains of mice by one of the leukemia viruses share a common antigen, presumably under the genetic direction of the virus. Highly inbred mice inoculated with allogeneic Moloney virus-induced leukemic cells (homografts) develop immunity to the normal transplantation antigens and consequently reject these cells. At the same time, however, immunity also develops to the tumor-specific antigen as shown by the resistance of these mice to a subsequent challenge with syngeneic Moloney virus-induced leukemic cells (isograft).

Nonimmunized mice accept such isografts. The same type of immunity can be induced by subthreshold doses of viable syngeneic cells (isografts) or by large doses of irradiated syngeneic cells which do not grow in the recipient host. This finding strengthens the assumption that the tumor cells not only contain infectious virus but also acquire new virus-induced antigens.

Transplantation antigens in virus-induced leukemia cells can also be measured by in vitro tests which employ autologous or syngeneic cells and sera of tumor-bearing animals or sera of animals immunized by one of the methods mentioned above.

By means of this system, the presence of reacting antigens has been demonstrated in murine leukemia cells induced by several of the murine leukemia viruses. The tests most commonly utilized are the indirect immunofluorescence test and the cytotoxic test. In the immunofluorescence test, the surface of the reacting cells stains in the presence of the specific antiserum. In the cytotoxic test, antibody directed against cellular antigens reacts with the cell possessing these antigens in the presence of complement. The antibody-cell reaction results in cell death which can be measured in vivo by the failure of the antibody-treated cells to grow when inoculated into a syngeneic host. The reaction can also be measured in vitro. Thus, one can count the dead cells when stained with dyes like trypan blue, or one can measure the release of ^{51}Cr from damaged cells that have been prelabeled with ^{51}Cr. As with the in vivo transplantation immunity, the in vitro reactions are specific for all the leukemias induced by the same virus. Cross-reacting antigens exist in leukemia cells induced by the Friend, Moloney, or Rauscher (FMR group) viruses. However, the reactions are mono-specific for leukemias induced by the Gross or Graffi virus.

Transplantation antigens cross-reacting with those induced in leukemic cells by the FMR leukemia viruses have also been found in mouse sarcomas induced by murine sarcoma virus (MSV). This cross-reaction is due to the fact that all preparations of infectious MSV contain murine leukemia virus with the antigenicity of the FMR group. Preimmunization of mice with irradiated virus-induced syngeneic sarcoma cells results in transplantation resistance to challenge with unirradiated sarcoma cells or syngeneic leukemia cells induced by the viruses of the FMR group. The reverse is also true.

The transplantation antigen in MSV-induced sarcoma cells can also be detected in vitro by a colony inhibition test. This test measures the ability of either serum (in the presence of complement) or lymph node cells from animals in which the tumors have regressed (immune animals) to inhibit in vitro the plating efficiency of MSV-induced sarcoma cells. Lymph node cells of mice with progressively growing MSV-induced sarcomas (nonimmune animals) can also inhibit in vitro the colony formation of their own tumor cells, indicating an effective cellular immunity in such animals. However, tumor-bearing animals have circulating serum factors (blocking serum factor) that appear to coat and thus protect the tumor cells from destruction by immune lymph node cells in the colony inhibition test. The blocking serum factors may be circulating antigen-antibody complexes. It is thus possible that these same serum factors play a similar tumor-protecting role in vivo in animals with progressive tumors. With the use of the colony inhibition test, transplantation antigen has been demonstrated for MTV-induced mammary carcinomas in mice.

Transplantation type antigen similar to that described for the murine leukemias has also been demonstrated for some mouse sarcomas induced by the Schmidt-Ruppin strain of RSV (SR-RSV). Inbred mice immunized with allogeneic sarcoma cells induced by SR-RSV or with irradiated syngeneic cells induced by the same virus develop transplantation resistance to challenge with syngeneic cells. Immunization with the virus alone, free of cells, does not confer this type of resistance.

Because of the recent availability of mutants of RSV and MSV that are temperature-sensitive for transformation, a more precise delineation of virus-induced transplantation type antigens at a cellular level is now possible.

Inheritance of Oncornavirus Genes

The finding that oncornaviruses become integrated as a DNA provirus into the chromosomes of cells they infect has stimulated studies dealing with the modes of transmission of these viruses in nature. As discussed earlier, transmission of fully infectious virus is either horizontal or congenital (nongenetic vertical transmission)—both types entailing infection of somatic cells of an animal and resulting in overt malignancy with continuous virus production.

It has long been assumed, however, that oncornavirus genes can enter the germ cells of animals and, once established, continue to be transmitted through an indefinite number of generations with no detriment to the animal. Earlier studies with inbred animals had indicated that most are of the "low cancer" type and are virtually free of oncornavirus-associated malignancies. Subsequent findings with inbred "virus-free" avian and murine species showed that tumors induced in such animals by means of irradiation or treatment with carcinogens or tumors occurring in old age contained oncornavirus information, such as virus-specific DNA sequences detectable by hybridization and virus-specific gs antigens. In addition, the same information was found in virtually all embryonic tissues of "virus-free" chickens or mice. It was thus assumed that such cells contained heritable viral genes and that the gs antigen represented an expression of such genes.

Indeed, further genetic studies with inbred strains of chickens and of mice indicated that gs antigen expression is controlled by a single dominant autosomal host cell gene that is inherited in a simple mendelian manner. Furthermore, chick embryo cells have been found to contain a chick-cell-associated helper factor (chf) that is regarded as the precursor of the endogenous RAV-0 (see p 473). This factor is also heritable in nature and appears to be genetically linked to the same gene controlling gs antigen expression; thus, chick embryo cells appear to contain at least 2 heritable virus markers.

The most direct evidence for the presence of heritable viral genes in normal avian or murine cells has come from activation experiments in tissue culture. Exposure of normal chick cells derived from leukemia virus-free embryos (whether containing gs antigen and chf or not) to ionizing radiation, chemical carcinogens, 5'-bromodeoxyuridine (BUDR), or 5-iododeoxyuridine (IUDR) resulted in the production of an RNA virus with all the tissue culture characteristics of an avian leukemia virus. Similarly, exposure of virus-free mouse embryo cells to IUDR, BUDR, or cyclohexamide resulted in the production of an RNA virus with the tissue culture characteristics of a murine leukemia virus; genetic breeding experiments indicate that in mice activation of complete virus depends upon 3 or possibly 4 independent chromosomal loci, 2 of which appear to be located in the endogenous viral genome. These experiments led to the conclusion that normal murine and avian cells have the complete genetic potential for specifying a leukemia C type RNA virus. Furthermore, as indicated earlier, dexamethasone has been found to induce infectious MTV (B type virus) from "virus-free" cultured mammary tumor cells.

Following these initial observations, evidence has accumulated over the past several years that inherited endogenous oncornavirus genes exist as an integral part of the chromosomes of normal cells of many different species: mouse, chicken, rat, hamster, pig, cat, and primate. Such cells have been found to contain DNA sequences homologous to the oncornaviruses of the corresponding species; and furthermore, these sequences are common for all strains tested to date within a species. It is presumed that these oncornavirus genomes have become fixed in the germ line of the various species early during evolution and have been transmitted as cellular genes through ensuing generations. Under usual circumstances the expression of the inherited viral genes is under tight cellular control, and viral RNA or gs antigens may or may not be detected in tissues or cultured cells. However, in most instances, cells of all the above species can be induced to produce complete infectious virions by the chemical treatments mentioned above and in some instances by superinfection with exogenous oncornaviruses or by co-cultivation with cells of heterologous species. It is of interest that many of the endogenous oncornaviruses induced to date are xenotropic and do not replicate in cells of the species of origin but only in cells of heterologous species. Many of the newly isolated endogenous oncornaviruses of various species have been studied by the laboratory procedures developed for those viruses known to induce malignancies after exogenous infection. Those isolated from different strains of a species have been shown to be alike in regard to host range, nucleic acid sequences, and antigenic properties of proteins and polymerase; they appear to differ from the known oncogenic viruses within a species in terms of host range and certain antigenic properties.

The discovery of the ubiquitousness of endogenous oncornaviruses has led to elegant studies suggesting that their viral genomes have become fixed in the germ line of various animals prior to speciation. For example, the endogenous viruses of Old World primates (baboon, rhesus monkey, green monkey, and others) have been found to possess a class of viral DNA sequences (that characteristic for the baboon endogenous virus) which is not found in either New World monkeys (woolly monkey, owl monkey, and others), apes (gibbon, gorilla, man, and others), or other species. Similarly, the endogenous virus of the domestic cat (RD-114) is different from the known feline leukemia virus (FeLV), which is transmitted horizontally. It remains uncertain at present whether indeed these endogenous viruses have evolved within the germ line or represent a result of exogenous infection that had occurred millions of years ago prior to speciation. The finding that the baboon endogenous virus and the RD-114 endogenous virus of the domestic cat (but not the other feline oncornaviruses) share common DNA sequences and antigens suggests that the virus of the Old World primate (baboon) had infected these cats and had become fixed in their germ cell line after they had evolved away from most other feline species. Even though these types of studies open new and exciting avenues for further study of evolutionary fixation of oncornaviral genes, the significance of inherited oncornaviral genes in the process of natural oncogenesis remains unclear. Indeed, most of the rescued endogenous viruses have not yet been found to transform cells in vitro or to be oncogenic in vivo, even though recent reports suggest that at least some possess oncogenic activity and, in one case, transforming capacity.

These developments tend to reinforce the oncogene hypothesis of Huebner and Todaro, which states that the entire genome of oncornaviruses (the virogene) is an intrinsic part of the heritable genetic material of vertebrate cells. According to the hypothesis, the oncogene is the segment of the virogene that codes for the production of "transforming protein(s)" responsible for tumorigenesis; the remaining segments code for the production of gs antigens, envelope antigens, and enzymes involved in virus replication. The degree of expression of different components of the viral genome is controlled by host cell regulatory genes and by environmental factors such as physical and chemical carcinogens. The hypothesis thus invokes the integration of the oncornaviral genome into cell DNA (provirus) and the existence of repressors, coded for by regulatory genes in normal cells, that control the expression of the endogenous virus information. There is no experimental evidence to support the existence of either a repressor or a transforming protein, and the evidence is still tenuous that the induced C type viruses are oncogenic either in vivo or in vitro.

There appears to be little difference between the oncogene hypothesis and the provirus hypothesis of Temin inasmuch as they both invoke integration of viral genetic material into cell DNA even though the former deals with the concept of endogenous viral information and the latter with exogenous information. Temin's recent protovirus hypothesis, which attempts to explain the common features of carcinogenesis and cell differentiation, states that regions of cell DNA serve as templates for the synthesis of RNA which, through the reverse transcriptase, serve as templates for new DNA synthesis; the new DNA then becomes integrated into the DNA of the original or adjacent cells of the organism, resulting in gene amplification and modification of the original information. Since the theory assumes that this modification takes place only in somatic cells but not in germ cells, it also assumes that an occasional somatic cell on a random basis could contain all the information for a C type virus. The high frequency with which induction of C type viruses from somatic cells occurs would tend to argue against the protovirus theory as an attempt to explain the heritable nature of oncornavirus information.

It remains for future experimentation to validate or reject the 2 hypotheses described above as they pertain to carcinogenesis. However, if heritable oncornavirus information is as ubiquitous as it appears to be, then the mechanism by which an exogenous oncornavirus renders a cell malignant remains to be elucidated.

DNA-CONTAINING TUMOR VIRUSES
(Papovaviruses & Adenoviruses; Oncogenic Herpesviruses)

Papovaviruses & Adenoviruses

Of the DNA-containing tumor viruses listed in Table 40–5, the papovaviruses and adenoviruses serve as the best understood models of virus-induced but virus-free solid tumors. Viruses in these 2 groups share many properties such as cubic symmetry, naked virions, lack of essential lipids, resistance to ether and mild acid (pH 3.0), and multiplication in the cell nucleus (Tables 27–1 and 40–5). They differ, however, in size, in number of capsomeres, and in antigenic structure.

Papovaviruses

The name papova is derived from the first 2 letters of the names of the oncogenic viruses included in this group: *pa*pilloma viruses of man, rabbit, cow, and dog; *po*lyoma virus of mouse; and *va*cuolating (SV40) virus of monkeys. Recently, several human papovaviruses have been identified which are serologically related to but not identical with SV40 virus and which possess oncogenic potential. Two of these, JC virus and SV40-PML virus, were isolated from brains of patients with progressive multifocal leukodystrophy (PML); the JC virus causes transmissible virus-yielding gliomas in newborn hamsters. The third agent, BK virus, isolated from immunosuppressed renal allograft recipients, causes malignant transformation of hamster cells in vitro and also induces tumors in hamsters. Serologic surveys show that infections with JC and BK viruses are common in humans. The capsid antigens of JC and BK viruses are unique, but the tumor antigen induced by each cross-reacts antigenically with that induced by SV40.

A. Morphology and Nucleic Acid: Papovavirus particles exhibit icosahedral symmetry, have a naked capsid composed of 72 capsomeres, and have diameters of 45–55 nm. They contain double-stranded DNA with a molecular weight of 3×10^6 for polyoma and SV40 viruses and 5×10^6 for the papilloma viruses. Infectious DNA has been isolated from all 3 viruses.

Table 40–5. Some properties of DNA-containing tumor viruses.

Virus	Host of Origin	Natural Tumors (Host of Origin)	Experimental Host Range		Size (nm)	Structure	Site of Virus Maturation	Persistence of Infectious Virus in Tumor
			In Vivo Tumors	In Vitro Cell Transformation				
Papovaviruses								
Papilloma:								
Human	Man	Yes	Man		45–55	Icosahedral symmetry	Nucleus	Yes
Rabbit	Rabbit	Yes	Rabbit					
Bovine	Cow	Yes	Cow	Bovine				
Canine	Dog	Yes	Dog					
Polyoma	Mouse	No	Mouse, hamster, other rodents	Mouse, hamster, rat				No
SV40	Monkey	No	Hamster	Hamster, mouse, monkey, man				
Adenoviruses								
Human types 3, 7, 11, 12, 14, 16, 18, 21, 31	Man	No	Hamster, rat, mouse	Hamster, rat, man	70–90	Icosahedral symmetry	Nucleus	No
Simian (some)	Monkey	No						
Bovine type 3	Cow	No						
Avian (CELO)	Chicken	No						
Herpesviruses								
Human:								
Type 2	Man		Hamster	Hamster	100	Icosahedral symmetry	Nucleus	No
EB virus	Man		Monkey	Man, monkey				
Monkey (Melendez, lymphoma)	Monkey	No	Monkey					
Avian (Marek, neuro-lymphoma)	Chicken	Yes	Chicken					
Frog (Lucké, carcinoma)	Frog	Yes	Frog					
Rabbit (Hinze, lymphoma)	Rabbit	No	Rabbit					
Poxviruses								
Molluscum contagiosum	Man	Yes	Man		230 X 300	Complex symmetry	Cytoplasm	Yes
Yaba	Monkey	Yes	Monkey					
Fibroma-myxoma	Rabbit, squirrel, deer	Yes	Rabbit, squirrel, deer					

DNA extracted from all 3 viruses has been shown to exist as circular molecules. Upon analytical ultracentrifugation, the DNA sediments into 2 components with sedimentation constants of 20S and 16S (polyoma, SV40) or 28S and 21S (papilloma). The heavier component has a twisted circular form that may convert to the lighter (circular or linear) component when single-strand breaks are introduced. Both of these DNA components are known to be infectious, to transform cells in vitro, and to produce tumors in vivo. In addition, a linear component with a sedimentation coefficient of 14S that represents random fragments of host cell DNA is incorporated into some papovavirus capsids (rather than viral DNA), and such particles are termed pseudovirions—a situation akin to the phenomenon of generalized transduction in the bacterial system (see Chapter 4). Hybridization studies also indicate the occurrence of covalent linkage of cell DNA segments into the circular DNA of papovaviruses during replication in cells infected at high multiplicity—similar to the situation with specialized transducing phage (see Chapter 4). Furthermore, under specialized experimental conditions, a DNA segment containing functional lambda phage genes has been incorporated into the circular DNA of SV40. These findings open avenues for study of possible transducing events in eukaryotic cells whereby functionally defined segments of genetic information can be transmitted from cell to cell.

There is evidence for some similarity between the DNA of the oncogenic papovaviruses and mammalian cell DNA: (1) The guanine + cytosine (G + C) content of the DNA of these viruses varies between 41–49%, which is very similar to mammalian host cell DNA (40–42% G + C). (2) Hybridization of viral DNA with cell DNA reveals that there is some complementarity of base sequences between viral DNA and host cell DNA. (3) Analysis of nearest neighbor base sequences reveals that the doublet pattern of the viral DNA closely resembles that of the host cell DNA with a rarity of the G + C doublet.

The SV40 genome: The use of bacterial restriction enzymes, endonucleases which make double-stranded breaks at specific sites in DNA, has permitted the application of physical mapping technics to analyses of the SV40 genome. These technics have allowed rapid elucidation of the molecular biology of SV40 since physical mapping of a viral genome can be accomplished much faster than classical genetic analyses which require years for completion. A large battery of restriction endonucleases has been screened for the cleavage patterns generated with SV40 DNA. It will soon be possible to obtain small, specific, defined regions of the viral genome.

The use of restriction enzymes has facilitated the following types of studies, among others: (1) determination of the initiation site for viral DNA replication, (2) establishment of the temporal order of synthesis of regions of the SV40 genome, (3) determination of the direction of transcription along the circular SV40 genome and the strand from which the stable species of mRNAs are derived, (4) study of the transcription of virus-specific sequences in transformed cells, and (5) location of temperature-sensitive lesions (present in ts mutants) on the viral genome. A summary of the current status of the SV40 map is shown in Fig 40-6.

The ability to recognize and identify specific regions of the viral genome has also permitted the description of a variety of types of variant molecules, most of which are defective for replication. When SV40 is serially passaged in permissive cells at high multiplicity of infection, virus particles with defective genomes accumulate. Some of these SV40 variants contain cellular DNA sequences covalently linked to viral DNA (substituted molecules). Distinctive deletions (loss) of viral DNA may occur at many different sites in the genome; duplicated segments of viral DNA may also be present. Repeated high multiplicity passage may give rise to viruses with grossly altered genomes which consist predominantly of cellular DNA but which retain a small portion of SV40 DNA. It is striking that the initiation site for viral DNA replication is preserved in every variant molecule analyzed. It appears that a genome length 70–100% the length of parental SV40 DNA is necessary for the molecule to be encapsidated. Examples of 2 such aberrant SV40 molecules are diagrammed in Fig 40-6.

Similar studies have been performed with other members of the papovavirus group (polyoma- and papillomavirus) and are now being extended to the adenovirus and herpesvirus molecules. Obviously, the cleavage patterns in the latter 2 systems are more complex since the genomes are larger. However, the region required for transforming activity by the human adenoviruses has already been localized to the left-hand 7% of the viral DNA molecule on the basis of fragment analysis.

B. Reaction to Chemical and Physical Agents: Papovaviruses are resistant to heating (50° C for 1 hour), ether, and acid treatment (pH 3.0). SV40 and polyoma viruses can be inactivated at 50° C in the presence of high concentrations of $MgCl_2$; this has been used to eliminate SV40 virus from stocks of oral poliovaccine since the infectivity of poliovirus is stabilized under these conditions. Papovaviruses can be stored at −20° C for long periods with no loss of infectivity. Infectivity of the viruses is decreased by 1:4000 formalin solution, but they are not inactivated as

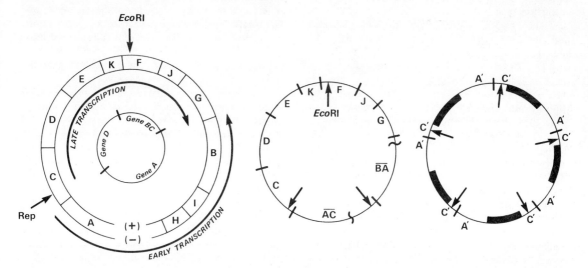

Figure 40-6. On the left is a map of the wild-type SV40 genome. The letters A–K indicate the fragments generated by *Hin*d restriction enzyme. The single cleavage site recognized by *Eco*RI restriction enzyme is shown in fragment F. The unique initiation site for viral DNA synthesis is indicated by the "Rep" arrow in fragment C. The regions transcribed for early and late message are shown; the arrows indicate the direction of transcription. The tentative locations of the 3 recognized SV40 genes (A, BC, and D) are shown on the inner circle. On the right are 2 examples (there could be many others) of defective SV40 genomes. The first, ev-1117, was cloned from a third high-multiplicity passage stock by complementation with a late temperature-sensitive mutant. The molecule is 83% of the length of SV40 DNA and has a deletion in the early region of the genome (between fragments A and B) plus a duplication of a DNA segment (AC). The other example, ev-1101, was cloned from a 13th passage stock using wild-type helper virus. It retains only a small part of the SV40 genome (portions of A and C fragments containing the origin of viral DNA replication, shown by small arrows) linked to cellular DNA (heavy lines); these segments are repeated in tandem fashion 5 times in the molecule. (After Brockman and Nathans.)

readily as poliovirus and adenovirus. Consequently, live SV40 has been recovered from several lots of killed poliovirus and killed adenovirus vaccines.

C. Antigenic Properties: Each of the papovaviruses is antigenically distinct. The viruses induce the production of specific neutralizing and complement-fixing antibodies. Polyoma, JC, and BK viruses hemagglutinate red blood cells.

Adenoviruses

Adenoviruses comprise a large group of agents that occur widely in humans, monkeys, cattle, dogs, swine, mice, and chickens. Over 30 antigenic types exist for the human species alone; of these, types 3, 7, 11, 12, 14, 16, 18, 21, 31, and perhaps others cause tumors in newborn animals, particularly hamsters. All of these viruses were isolated from human beings, and serologic surveys show that infection is common with most of these types.

Several simian adenoviruses, bovine adenovirus type 3, and avian adenovirus are tumorigenic when inoculated into newborn hamsters.

The oncogenic adenoviruses are similar in structure to other adenoviruses and have naked capsids 70–90 nm in diameter, with 252 capsomeres arranged in icosahedral symmetry. They contain double-stranded linear DNA with a molecular weight of 2.3×10^7. The DNA of a highly oncogenic simian adenovirus (SA7) appears to be infectious in tissue culture as well as tumorigenic for newborn hamsters; it appears that infectious DNA can also be isolated from human adenovirus type 1.

The oncogenic human adenoviruses may be classified into 2 subgroups: highly oncogenic (types 12, 18, and 31) and weakly oncogenic (types 3, 7, 11, 14, 16, and 21). Those in the highly oncogenic subgroup are the only adenoviruses with a low G + C content in their DNA (48–49%, a value similar to that of the papovaviruses and cellular DNA). The weakly oncogenic types have an intermediate G + C content of 50–53%. A third subgroup of adenoviruses (types 1, 2, 5, and 6) that are nononcogenic but transform rat embryo cells in vitro has a high G + C content (55–61%). A further relationship between members within each of the 3 subgroups stems from DNA-DNA or DNA-messenger RNA (mRNA) homology studies. Maximal DNA-DNA or DNA-mRNA hybridization is attained only between viruses within a subgroup with negligible intersubgroup hybridization. (The highly oncogenic simian adenovirus SA7 has a high G + C content, similar in value to the nononcogenic human adenoviruses).

Tumor Induction With Papovaviruses & Adenoviruses

A. Papilloma Viruses: Papilloma viruses are the only members of the papovavirus group known to cause natural tumors in their hosts of origin. They cause warts or papillomas in human beings, rabbits, cows, and dogs. The ecology of these viruses is not known, but they are found in large quantities in papillomas. Although the human wart virus was the first virus transmitted experimentally from host to host, only the rabbit papilloma virus has been studied extensively for its tumor-inducing properties. In the wild cottontail rabbit (the natural host), the virus causes large benign skin papillomas which, on rare occasions, become malignant carcinomas. When inoculated into the domestic rabbit, the virus also produces benign skin papillomas which may either regress or develop into malignant carcinomas. Tumors can be induced in both rabbit species with the DNA isolated from the virus. Infectious virus can be readily recovered from the papillomas of cottontail rabbits but not from their carcinomas; virus cannot be isolated from either papillomas or carcinomas of domestic rabbits. However, infectious DNA has been isolated from such tumors. Transplantation of carcinoma cells results in carcinomas in the new host.

B. Polyoma Virus: Latent infection with polyoma virus is widespread among laboratory and wild mice. Young mice are infected naturally in the first few weeks by contamination with urine and saliva of adults. Intrauterine infection is not known to occur. Not a single natural tumor of mice, the host of origin, has been uncovered. However, the virus is highly tumorigenic when inoculated into newborn mice or hamsters, which develop tumors within a few weeks of inoculation of large doses of virus. Newborn rats, rabbits, guinea pigs, and ferrets are also susceptible. Infectious DNA isolated from the virus is tumorigenic. The commonest tumors are spindle cell sarcomas, but epithelial tumors also occur in mice. The tumors appear in a number of sites—hence the name polyoma. The tumors are usually free of infectious virus or virus particles. As few as 10 tumor cells transplanted into a susceptible adult animal result in new tumors which can be further transplanted. Tumor cells can be serially grown in vitro and retain malignancy.

C. SV40 Virus: Simian vacuolating virus, or SV40, is commonly found in uninoculated cultures of rhesus and cynomolgus monkey kidney cells in which the virus apparently grows without causing a cytopathic effect. Introduction of fluids from such cultures into renal cell cultures derived from the African green or grivet monkey *(Cercopithecus aethiops sabaeus)* is followed by prominent cytoplasmic vacuolization—hence the name vacuolating virus. Isolation of the virus was quickly followed by demonstration of its oncogenic potential when introduced into newborn hamsters. It is not known, however, whether tumors develop in monkeys as a result of natural infection. Millions of people have been exposed to this virus as a contaminant of viral vaccines, both live and inactivated. After ingestion of live poliovaccine, many children continued to excrete SV40 for as long as 5 weeks. SV40 virus (as well as its infectious DNA) causes sarcomas at the site of inoculation in newborn hamsters. The tumors are usually free of infectious virus and virus particles. Tumor cells can be serially passed in adult hamsters and cause the same type of tumors as those induced by the virus itself. Both primary and transplanted tumors can be serially propagated in tissue culture and retain malignancy. SV40 has recently been shown to induce lymphomas in weanling hamsters.

D. Adenoviruses: Adenovirus types 12, 18, and 31 cause undifferentiated sarcomas at the site of inoculation—and less commonly at other sites—in newborn hamsters, rats, and mice. Adenovirus type 7 causes tumors in 25% of inoculated newborn hamsters, but the latent period is longer than with other types, and the tumors are usually malignant lymphomas or lymphosarcomas. With adenoviruses 3, 11, 14, 16, and 21, the latent period before the appearance of sarcomas in newborn hamsters is even longer than that for type 7. Adenoviral tumors contain no infectious virus. Tumors can be maintained in serial passage by means of transplantation of tumor cells into adult animals of the appropriate species; tumor cells may also be grown serially in tissue culture and retain malignancy.

Cell Transformation With Papovaviruses & Adenoviruses

Unlike oncornaviruses, which can cause productive infection in permissive cells without killing them, the DNA tumor viruses can either cause productive infection and kill the cell in the process of making more virus or can transform the cell without subsequent virus production. One or the other may predominate, depending upon the cell and not the virus: productive infection in permissive cells and transformation in nonpermissive cells. However, the 2 states are not always mutually exclusive, since productive infection can take place in a small percentage of nonpermissive cells; conversely, under conditions preventing virus replication, transformation of permissive cells can be achieved.

The papilloma viruses cannot be readily propagated in culture. The adenoviruses, which induce cytocidal infection in a variety of cells, can transform hamster, rat, and human cells in vitro but with limited success. The polyoma and SV40 viruses, however, have a marked cell-transforming potential.

Infection of permissive mouse embryo cells with polyoma virus is mainly cytocidal, but infection of nonpermissive hamster embryo cells with the same virus results mainly in cell transformation. Similarly, SV40 almost always undergoes cytocidal multiplication in permissive green monkey kidney cells, but infection of nonpermissive hamster, mouse, or human fibroblast cells frequently results in cell transformation. Hamster or mouse cells transformed in tissue culture by either polyoma or SV40 viruses can produce tumors when inoculated into the appropriate host— sometimes when as few as 10–100 cells are used as inoculum.

The time required for transformation of cells by DNA tumor viruses may differ widely for different viruses and different cells. Polyoma virus usually causes transformation soon after it penetrates the cell, so that the susceptible cells exposed to polyoma virus promptly produce clones made up entirely of newly transformed cells. With SV40 and adenovirus, obvious trans-

formation may not take place for weeks because only a tiny fraction of the cell population seems responsive to the transforming ability of the virus added to the culture. Even with polyoma virus, however, a large amount of virus is required to induce transformation. Since the dose response of cell transformation by polyoma virus is linear—a reflection of a one-hit curve—a single effective particle is sufficient to cause transformation. It should be noted that with many viruses one infectious unit is equivalent to more than one virus particle (in some cases up to 10,000). With polyoma virus, 40–100 virus particles are equivalent to one infectious (replicating) unit. For transformation of hamster fibroblasts—the most sensitive system known— one transforming unit is equivalent to 1 million particles. Presumably, only one of these million particles is effective in the transformation process, just as only one of the 40 particles is effective in initiating cytocidal infection.

The initial events during productive (cytocidal) and nonproductive (transforming) infection with DNA tumor viruses are common: synthesis of DNA, mRNA, and early antigens (see below); stimulation of cell DNA synthesis; and the apparent integration of viral DNA into cell chromosome DNA. However, there appears to be a further choice of pathways leading either to replication of complete virions or to cellular transformation. Fewer viral genes seem to be involved in transformation than in viral replication: (1) With polyoma virus, only about 50% of the viral DNA responsible for cytocidal infection is involved in the transformation process. The cytocidal effectiveness of the virus is inactivated (by ultraviolet light, x-ray, and other agents) at a rate twice that of its transforming ability. (2) Cells transformed by either papovaviruses or adenoviruses do not contain the viral capsid antigen or infectious viral nucleic acid. (3) Cells can be transformed by a defective mutant of SV40 virus which is unable to direct the synthesis of capsid protein. (4) Work with temperature-sensitive (ts) mutants of SV40 has identified one viral gene, the A gene, as being involved in transformation. The A gene product is required both for initiation and for maintenance of the transformed state. Cells transformed by tsA mutants lose a variety of properties characteristic of transformed cells when shifted up to the nonpermissive temperature, and they acquire growth properties typical of normal cells. When the cells are shifted back down to permissive conditions, the transformed phenotype is reacquired. tsA is an early SV40 gene the product of which is required for initiation of viral DNA synthesis. It is probable that the gene A protein is actually T antigen (see below). The function of the A protein in the transformed cells remains to be elucidated.

Cells transformed in vitro by papovavirus or adenovirus—or cells of tumors induced in vivo by these viruses—may release infectious virus for a short time, whereupon virus-free transformed cells and tumors emerge. However, the virus-free transformed cells contain a limited number of viral DNA molecules (usually between 1 and 10) detectable by hybridization with viral RNA synthesized in vitro from a viral DNA template. Although the entire viral genome appears to be present in most SV40-transformed cells, only a fragment (representing about 14%) of the adenovirus genome tends to be retained in transformed cells. In vitro transformation assays with restriction enzyme fragments of viral DNA have localized the transforming activity in the left-hand end 7% of the adeno-5 DNA molecule.

Fractionation and alkali denaturation studies indicate that the viral DNA present in papovavirus-transformed cells is covalently bound to chromosomal cell DNA, apparently as a provirus, akin to the prophage of lysogenic bacterial cells (see Chapters 4 and 9). There is increasing evidence that papovaviral DNA integrates into cell DNA during transformation. "DNA transfer" or "transfection" experiments with SV40-transformed cells suggest that, as in lysogenic bacterial cells, the entire SV40 genome is integrated. Introduction into permissive monkey kidney cells of chromosomal DNA from SV40-transformed cells that are incapable of yielding infectious virus by any means (see below) results in the production of infectious viral DNA within 6 hours.

Additional evidence for the presence of integrated viral genes stems from transcriptional studies. Cells transformed by adenoviruses as well as by papovaviruses (polyoma and SV40) contain in their cytoplasm a small but highly specific fraction of viral mRNA. This mRNA can be detected by its ability to hybridize with viral DNA. The mRNA is specific for the virus that had originally induced the transformation since it is not found in normal cells nor in cells transformed by a different virus.

Studies with SV40-transformed cells have shown that, in addition to the cytoplasmic virus-specific mRNA (molecular weight $< 1.5 \times 10^6$), these cells contain a much larger (molecular weight $> 4 \times 10^6$) nuclear RNA which is made up of covalently linked SV40 and host cell nucleotide sequences; unlike the cytoplasmic mRNA, the high molecular weight nuclear RNA is capable of hybridizing with both SV40 DNA and DNA from the nuclei of untransformed cells. This finding supports the concept that the DNA of the transforming virus is integrated into the host cell chromosome and suggests that the larger nuclear RNA may be a precursor of smaller virus-specific mRNA.

Additional evidence for the presence of an integrated viral genome or at least a portion of it in papovavirus- or adenovirus-transformed or tumor cells comes from the discovery in such cells of new nonviral cellular antigens specified by the virus inducing the transformation (see below). This permits recognition of the specificity of viral transformation.

In some instances, the situation resembles that of the Rous sarcoma virus genome in mammalian cells, and infectious virus can be rescued from virus-free transformed cells; thus, in hamster or mouse cells transformed by SV40, infectious virus may be produced when the virus-free transformed cells are grown with virus-susceptible cells under conditions favoring

fusion of the 2 types of cells. (Ultraviolet-inactivated Sendai virus is usually used as the fusing agent.) The currently accepted sequence of events, which results in the rescue of infectious SV40 from transformed cells following fusion with susceptible cells, is shown schematically in Fig 40–7. Infectious SV40 can be rescued from some transformed cells that fail to yield virus in cell fusion experiments. This is achieved by introducing large quantities of chromosomal DNA from the transformed cells into permissive green monkey kidney cells (transfection technic).

Papovavirus- & Adenovirus-Induced Antigens in Transformed or Tumor Cells

Cells transformed by papovaviruses and adenoviruses are free from virion structural antigens but contain several virus-induced antigens that are specific for the transforming virus and are distinct from the antigens induced by a heterologous virus. Their presence in tumor or transformed cells indicates that at least some of the virus-specific mRNA species in such cells (see above) are translated into recognizable proteins.

A. Tumor-Specific Transplantation Antigens (TSTA): As shown in Fig 40–8, TSTA can be detected by measuring the resistance of virus-immunized animals to challenge with neoplastic cells. Adult animals immunized with active virus are resistant to challenge of large doses (10^5-10^6) of virus-free transformed or tumor cells, whereas nonimmune animals develop tumors when inoculated with as few as 10–100 cells.

This type of immunity is unrelated to circulating viral antibodies but is specifically associated with an antigen at the cell surface. It is presumed that this immunity occurs because the active virus induces this new antigen in some cells of the adult animal, and the new antigen in turn elicits a cellular immune response resulting in subsequent rejection of transformed cells carrying the same antigen.

Virus-specific TSTA can also be demonstrated in virus-free transformed cells by their ability to block viral carcinogenesis. Thus, tumors fail to develop in hamsters inoculated at birth with oncogenic virus if either x-ray treated (to prevent cell replication) oncogenic transformed cells or viable nononcogenic transformed cells (derived from a different species, such as man) are injected during the latent period.

The TSTA of SV40 and polyoma viruses has been also detected during productive replication in permissive cells. It appears to be an early antigen in that its synthesis is not prevented by inhibitors of DNA synthesis.

Another antigen has been reported for SV40-transformed hamster cells. A cell surface (S) antigen which can be detected in immunofluorescence colony inhibition and cytotoxicity tests with sera of SV40-immunized hamsters that have resisted challenge with virus-free transformed cells. A cell surface (S) antigen can also be detected in polyoma virus-transformed cells reacted with sera of mice that had rejected allogeneic polyoma virus-induced (but virus-free) tumor cells.

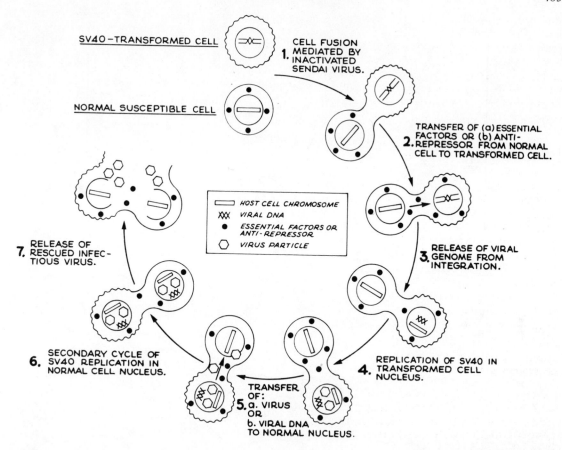

Figure 40—7. Rescue of infectious SV40 virus from transformed cells following fusion with susceptible cells. (After Butel, Tevethia, and Melnick.)

This S antigen may be related to TSTA; however, transplantable SV40-transformed hamster cells containing S antigen but lacking TSTA have been described.

Cells transformed by SV40 contain fetal antigen on their surface; normal pregnant hamsters contain antibodies (detectable by immunofluorescence) to the surface of SV40-transformed cells. This antigen may represent a host protein coded for by a region of the cell genome that had been derepressed by the SV40 genome during the process of transformation. It remains to be seen, however, whether this fetal antigen is related to the TSTA.

A transplantation type immunity exists also in the rabbit papilloma system. Rabbits bearing transplanted virus-free carcinomas fail to produce papillomas when injected with virus. Virus-induced papillomas regress much more rapidly in animals preimmunized with virus-free papilloma tissue than in nonimmunized animals. In addition, rabbits whose primary virus-induced papillomas have regressed fail to develop tumors when inoculated with infectious nucleic acid, whereas rabbits bearing persistent primary virus-induced papillomas or carcinomas respond to such nucleic acid inocula with new tumors as readily as previously uninfected control rabbits.

The colony inhibition test has been used to detect TSTA in virus-induced papilloma or carcinoma cells with results identical to those described for the MSV system.

B. Tumor or T Antigen: Tumor (T) antigen appears in the nucleus of tumor cells or cells transformed in vitro (Fig 40—8). It can be measured by immunofluorescence or CF tests employing antibodies which develop in sera of animals bearing large primary or transplanted tumors. This antigen has been demonstrated for polyoma, SV40, and adenoviruses. (Adenovirus T antigen can be detected not only in the nucleus but also in the cytoplasm.)

The T antigens are unrelated to viral capsid (V) antigens but are specific for the inducing virus and are the same in cells of different species transformed by the same virus.

T antigens immunologically identical with those found in in vitro transformed cells or tumor cells are also synthesized by papovaviruses and adenoviruses (including nontumorigenic strains) during productive infection in permissive cells. T antigen is formed in the nucleus early during the replicative cycle prior to the synthesis of viral DNA and viral capsid protein. Formation of the T antigen is not inhibited by drugs which

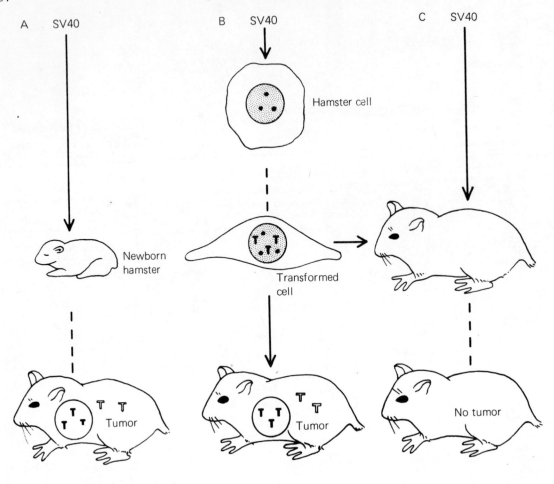

T   Tumor antigen

T   Antibody specific to tumor antigen

Figure 40–8. Tumor (T) antigen. *A:* Newborn hamsters inoculated with SV40 often develop tumors. *B:* Similarly, hamster cells grown in culture and transformed by SV40—meaning that they were given permanent heritable changes—can induce tumors when transplanted to young adult hamsters. The tumor cells as well as the transformed cells contain the T antigen and the tumor-bearing animal develops antibodies to the T antigen. *C:* Transplantation immunity. A hamster into which transformed cells are transplanted after the adult animal has been inoculated with SV40 virus resists the tumor-causing effect of transformed cells. The virus acts as a vaccine, inducing in certain of the animal's cells a new antigen ("transplantation antigen"); this in turn elicits an immune response, and the animal eliminates the cells bearing the new antigen. The animal also rejects cells that have been transformed in vitro which evidently carry the same "transplantation antigen." (From: *The Footprints of Tumor Viruses,* by Fred Rapp & Joseph L. Melnick. Copyright © 1966 by Scientific American, Inc. All rights reserved.)

prevent DNA synthesis. However, its induction is inhibited by drugs which prevent synthesis of DNA-dependent RNA or protein synthesis or by interferon treatment of the cells prior to infection. The biologic function of the virus-induced T antigens remains unknown, although evidence is mounting in the SV40 system that the T antigen is actually the gene A protein involved both in initiation of viral DNA synthesis and in maintenance of the transformed phenotype.

Another SV40 antigen, designated the U antigen, has been described. Although similar in many respects to T antigen, which is heat-labile, the U antigen is heat-stable. The relationship of U antigen to T antigen

and to other SV40-specific antigens remains unclear at this time.

Incorporation of SV40 Into Adenoviruses

In resistant cells derived from monkey kidney, virtually all human adenoviruses are "defective"; they induce the production of T but not of V antigen. If SV40 virus is added to the system, infectious adenovirus is formed abundantly. It appears that the SV40 complementation function affects some posttranscriptional event in the adenovirus replicative cycle.

A virus population was obtained from a preparation of adenovirus type 7 that had been grown in the presence of SV40; it has the ability to replicate in monkey kidney cells and to induce synthesis of both SV40 and adenovirus T antigens; it does not induce SV40 V antigen but induces adeno-7 V antigen. Tumors induced by this population in hamsters bear the T antigen and TSTA of both SV40 and adeno-7.

This population was found to be comprised of 2 types of particles, one being the adenovirus type 7 and the other a stable SV40-adenovirus "hybrid" containing SV40 genetic material encased in an adenovirus type 7 protein coat. The adenovirus particle can readily multiply in human kidney cells but not in monkey kidney cells. The hybrid particle has been named PARA (particle aiding the replication of adenovirus). PARA has properties normally associated with SV40: it induces the synthesis of SV40 tumor and transplantation antigens (the adenovirion does not), and it aids the replication of adenovirus in monkey kidney cell cultures (Fig 40–9). The genome of PARA appears to consist of defective adenovirus type 7 DNA, representing about 85% of an adenovirus genome, covalently linked to a portion (about 50%) of an SV40 genome.

PARA is defective. By itself, PARA cannot replicate in monkey kidney cells; it requires a helper adenovirus which provides the protein coat. It has also been found that the adenovirus type 7 coat of PARA in the PARA-adenovirus type 7 population can be exchanged for the specific protein coat of unrelated adenovirus types (such as types 1, 2, 3, 5, 6, 12, 16, etc) by a process termed transcapsidation (Fig 40–9). Like the original PARA-adenovirus type 7 population, all PARA-adenovirus serotypes induce the SV40 T antigen and the SV40 transplantation antigen. Transfer of the SV40 determinant of PARA into the protein coats of nononcogenic adenoviruses has resulted in the acquisition of oncogenic properties by these viruses. Thus, PARA-adenovirus types 1, 2, 5, and 6 readily induce tumors in newborn hamsters, whereas the parental serotypes do not.

A series of nondefective hybrids is also known which consists of complete adenovirus type 2 genome linked to varying amounts of SV40 DNA and encased in adenovirus type 2 capsid. These hybrids are proving useful in the elucidation of the function expressed by the SV40 genome. Through the use of physical mapping technics, the precise amount of SV40 information has been determined for each hybrid. Through comparison of the SV40 antigens (T, U, TSTA) expressed in cells infected by each of the hybrids, a map has been constructed for SV40 genes that code for the different antigens.

Oncogenic Herpesvirus

Herpesviruses of lower animals are the most recent group of DNA-containing viruses shown to possess oncogenic capacity (see Table 40–5). They possess the biophysical and biochemical properties of other members of the herpesvirus group (see Chapter 38).

A. Simian Herpesviruses: Two oncogenic herpesviruses of monkeys have been recognized that are antigenically distinct from each other and from other herpesviruses. Herpesvirus saimiri (HVS), also named Melendez after its discoverer, and herpesvirus ateles (HAV) have been isolated from kidney cultures of squirrel and spider monkeys, respectively. Both agents cause a latent inapparent infection in the host of origin, and a high proportion of the animals possess antiviral antibodies; infection apparently occurs early in life, and the infected animals are virus carriers for life. However, both agents are highly oncogenic for other primates. HVS induces the development of malignant lymphomas in marmosets, owl, and spider monkeys and reticuloproliferative diseases in Cebus and African green monkeys. The virus is especially pathogenic for cottontop marmosets, causing death from lymphoma within 48 days after inoculation. HVA also induces malignant lymphomas in cottontop marmosets and other monkeys. In tissue culture, both agents are capable of replication in a variety of cells with the production of infectious virus and viral antigens. Malignant cells derived from inoculated animals or lymphocytes derived from virus carriers within the natural host are free of infectious virus or antigens; however, within 1–3 days after their cultivation in culture, both antigens and infectious virus are produced.

B. Marek's Disease Virus (MDV): MDV is the causative agent of a highly contagious and apparently malignant lymphoproliferative disease of chickens with a predilection for nerve tissue (Marek's disease). Several different strains of MDV with slight differences in antigenicity, virulence, and tissue tropism have been recognized. The severity of the disease is influenced by both the virus strain and the genetic constitution of the host. In vivo, the virus undergoes an abortive cycle of replication in most tissues of the infected chicken, and the disease can be transmitted by passage of intact lymphoid cells that contain the virus genome but not infectious virus. On the other hand, infectious virus is produced by the epithelial cells of the feather follicle, and such cell-free virus produces the disease when inoculated into susceptible chickens; this virus is stable and remains in infectious form for a long time (over 10 weeks) in contaminated litters and droppings, thus accounting for the high contagiousness and spread of the disease. The lymphoproliferative disease can be prevented by vaccination with an attenuated strain of MDV or with an antigenically related herpesvirus of turkeys that is nonpathogenic for chickens; the vaccine does not prevent infection with the wild virus, but such infections are not followed by tumor formation. This development lends assurance that MDV is the etiologic agent of the disease.

C. Lucké's Herpesvirus (LHV) of Frogs: A renal adenocarcinoma (Lucké tumor) occurs very frequently in a population of wild frogs, *Rana pipiens,* and LHV has been implicated as the etiologic agent. The virus appears to be temperature-sensitive in its expression: tumor cells of tumor-bearing frogs in hibernation or maintained in the laboratory at low temperature reveal virion-containing inclusion bodies, whereas those of frogs captured in the spring or summer or maintained

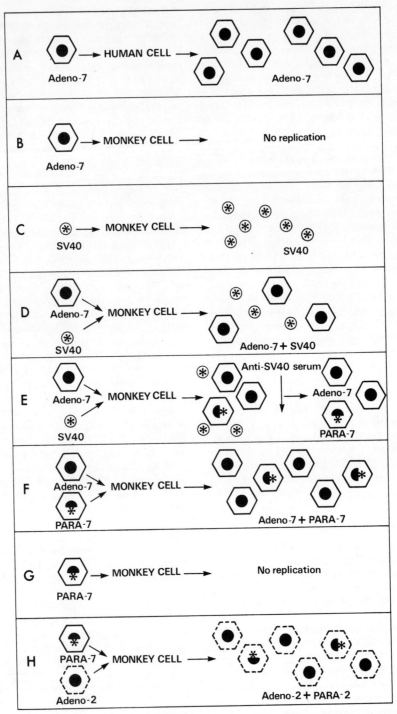

Figure 40–9. Mutual dependence between adeno particles and PARA in "hybrid" populations. The synthesis of SV40 tumor antigen by a "hybrid" requires the multiplication of both adeno particles and PARA. Adenovirus multiplies in human (A) but not in monkey kidney cells (B). SV40 replicates in monkey cells (C), where it also acts as a helper for adenovirus (D). In the product of D, some adenovirus particles exist which contain defective SV40 DNA in their genome. As shown in E, such particles with the hybrid genome induce the formation of SV40 T antigen in the course of infection. Treating the product of the infected cells with anti-SV40 serum binds the SV40 particles, leaving a mixture of pure adenovirus-7 particles and particles containing the combined adeno-SV40 DNA (E). The latter are called PARA because the particles aid in the replication of adenovirus in monkey cells (F). PARA particles are unable to replicate alone in monkey cells (G), but when a cell is infected with both pure adenovirus (type 2) and PARA of another antigenic adenovirus (type 7), transcapsidation occurs and the PARA genome now acquires the coat of the helper adenovirus. This results in an SV40-adenovirus type 2 "hybrid" population containing both pure adeno-2 and PARA-2 particles (H).

in the laboratory at higher temperature do not. The virus cannot be propagated in tissue culture, but cell-free extracts of virus-containing tumors can induce Lucké tumors in developing frog embryos. Other viruses, including herpesviruses unrelated to LHV, have been isolated in tissue culture from Lucké tumors; however, they have thus far failed to induce tumors in developing frog embryos. It would thus appear most likely that LHV is the causative agent of the tumor, especially if further evidence is obtained that the above-mentioned viruses are indeed free of oncogenic potential.

D. Herpesvirus of Rabbit Lymphoma (Hinze): A herpesvirus (herpesvirus sylvilagus) indigenous to wild cottontail rabbits has been recently recognized as a distinct member of the herpesvirus group. When inoculated into weanling cottontail rabbits (but not domestic rabbits), the virus induces generalized hyperplasia of lymphoid elements and in some instances malignant lymphomas as well. The in vivo virus-lymphoid cell relationship remains to be elucidated; however, leukocytes from infected rabbits have been shown to produce detectable virus after cultivation in culture. In tissue culture the virus can be propagated equally well in cells of both cottontail and domestic rabbits.

VIRUSES & HUMAN CANCER

Recent progress in understanding viral carcinogenesis in animals has offered new approaches in the quest for viral causes of at least some human cancers. Based on the new knowledge of animal tumor-virus model systems, 3 main avenues are being extensively explored:

(1) Studies Following the Models of Tumorigenesis in Animals by Oncornaviruses

As described earlier, oncornaviruses appear to be ubiquitous in nature and have been associated with leukemias and sarcomas in many animal species. Following these models, many attempts have been made to determine whether overt infectious oncornavirus-like agents are associated with leukemias or solid tumors of man. All such studies have yielded negative results.

Early studies on human leukemias and human solid tumors revealed some similarities to animal malignancies induced by oncornaviruses. Particles similar to C type oncornaviruses were detected by electron microscopy in cells or plasma of patients with leukemia and in solid tumors of man such as Hodgkin's lymphoma, lymphosarcomas, and sarcomas. Similar particles have been reported in some cell lines derived from human malignancies by electron microscopy or by labeling the cells with radioactive uridine and measuring the release of particles with a density in sucrose gradients of 1.16–1.18 gm/ml. Particles similar to C

type viruses have also been detected in normal human placental tissue—akin to the findings with placental tissues of subhuman primates. A number of reports have claimed the isolation of oncornavirus from leukemic cells grown in culture. However, it seems that these "isolates" are laboratory contaminants since further analysis has shown that they are antigenically related to previously known animal oncornaviruses.

Particles resembling the murine mammary tumor virus (B type particles) have been detected in human mammary cancer and in the milk of Parsi women (a population in India with a very high incidence of mammary cancer) and of American women with a family history of mammary cancer. However, later studies have questioned the validity of the morphologic observations. Even though the infectious nature of these particles remains questionable, evidence suggests that they contain high molecular weight RNA (70S) and reverse transcriptase enzyme activity characteristic of oncornaviruses. This work has been aided by the development of a method for simultaneous detection of the enzyme activity and the high molecular weight RNA of known oncornavirions. Preliminary data suggest a relationship between the human particles and murine mammary tumor virus (MTV). Sera of women with mammary cancer were reported to neutralize the activity of MTV, and rabbit antisera to purified MTV were reported to precipitate a soluble antigen in sera of women with mammary cancer. Furthermore, the DNA synthesized in vitro by the enzyme of MTV (using MTV RNA as a template) was found to hybridize with polysomal RNA obtained from human mammary adenocarcinomas. No such hybridization was observed with RNA derived from other human malignancies or normal tissues, and the DNA product of the reverse transcriptases of the Rauscher strain of murine leukemia virus (R-MuLV) or of avian myeloblastosis virus also failed to hybridize with the RNA from the human mammary adenocarcinoma. It was also reported that the RNA in extracts from human mammary adenocarcinomas is a 70S component encapsidated together with RNA-directed DNA polymerase in a particle with the density characteristic of oncornavirions. The DNA synthesized in vitro by the human 70S RNA-enzyme complex hybridized specifically with the RNA of MTV.

Using the same procedures, the same group reporting the above data found the presence of RNA complementary to the RNA of R-MuLV (but not to that of MTV) in other human malignancies unrelated to breast cancer. DNA obtained from R-MuLV by the use of reverse transcription in vitro was found to hybridize with RNA obtained from cells of various leukemias, lymphomas (including Burkitt's lymphoma), and sarcomas. RNA in cells from various human leukemias has been reported to be a 70S RNA complexed with reverse transcriptase. The DNA synthesized from this complex has been observed to hybridize specifically with the RNA of R-MuLV but not with the RNA of MTV or of avian myeloblastosis virus; it also appears that this DNA contains sequences common to those present in leukemic but not normal leukocytes. These results appear to be corroborated by a report on the presence of reverse transcriptase in cells of patients with acute lymphoblastic leukemia; further work is needed to characterize the enzyme found in leukemic cells since the possibility that it may be a cellular enzyme has not been ruled out. However, a later study suggests that cells of patients with myelogenous leukemia possess an oncornaviral-type reverse transcriptase that is distinguishable from other cell DNA polymerases and serologically related to the reverse transcriptase of primate oncornaviruses and, to a lesser extent, to that of R-MuLV.

As indicated earlier, the role of reverse transcriptase of the known animal oncornaviruses in viral carcinogenesis is not clear at present. The above findings with human malignancies tend to suggest the presence of virus-related information. However, they should be treated with caution inasmuch as other workers, using DNA-DNA (rather than DNA-RNA) hybridization procedures, have failed to corroborate the findings—although both procedures are equally sensitive in the oncornaviral model systems. Further experiments are needed in which different strains of oncornaviruses are used as a probe to ascertain the ultimate significance of virus-related RNA and enzymes in human malignancies. However, the methodology now at hand is leading to a further search for enzymatic evidence of possible human oncornaviruses in human malignancies.

(2) Studies Following the Models of Tumorigenesis in Animals by DNA Tumor Viruses

In view of the finding that, with few exceptions, solid tumors induced in experimental animals by papovaviruses and adenoviruses are free of infectious virus or of infectious nucleic acid, it is not surprising that all attempts to isolate viruses from a variety of solid human tumors have met with complete failure.

Following the findings on the presence of virus-specific mRNA in DNA virus-induced (but virus-free) tumors, a search in human tumor tissues for mRNA hybridizable with the DNA of the known oncogenic virus was attempted. Special attention was given to the adenoviruses since they are oncogenic in experimental animals and are widespread in man. However, the results to date have failed to indicate that any of the human tumors examined contain adenovirus-specific mRNA.

Earlier studies had demonstrated the presence of papovavirus-like particles in the brains of patients with progressive multifocal leukoencephalopathy (PML), a rare demyelineating disease of man usually occurring as a complication of a previous malignancy of the reticuloendothelial system or of immunosuppressive therapy. As indicated earlier (see p 477), 2 human papovaviruses—SV40-PML virus and JC virus—have been isolated from brains of patients with PML, and another human papovavirus, BK, has been isolated from immunosuppressed renal allograft recipients free of PML. The 3 agents are antigenically distinct from each other but share common antigens with the simian papovavirus SV40. Evidence is accumulating that all 3 viruses are oncogenic for hamsters and can transform hamster cells in vitro; the same patterns of virus-tumor cell or virus-transformed cell interactions, characteristic of SV40, are observed with the human agents—production of T antigen and TSTA, rescue of infectious virus through fusion with susceptible cells, etc. The significance of these viruses to human malignancies remains to be determined. Seroepidemiologic surveys indicate that infections with JC and BK virus are very common in man (with about 70% of adults having antibodies). The human papovavirus infections do not appear to be related to exposure to the simian SV40 virus, either through contact with rhesus monkeys (the natural host for SV40) or through vaccination with potentially SV40-containing poliovirus vaccines.

(3) Immunologic Studies

The knowledge of virus-induced T antigens in tumors (or in transformed cells) and of T antibodies in the tumor-bearing animals has led to similar immunologic studies in cancer of man. Tests of the sera of cancer patients for the presence of complement-fixing or immunofluorescence antibodies to the T antigens of SV40 or adenovirus have yielded negative results.

Carcinomas of the gastrointestinal tract have been found to contain an antigen which is absent from normal adult gut cells but present in embryonal gut cells. This antigen has been named carcinoembryonic antigen (CEA), and it is believed that its appearance in gastrointestinal carcinomas is due to genetic derepression. The antigen can be isolated and purified from the tumor or embryonic tissue and can be detected by means of several different tests with antisera to it prepared in goats or rabbits. Patients with gastrointestinal carcinomas have circulating CEA that is presumably released from the tumor cells. The exact nature of this antigen and the antibody response monitored in the cancer patient remain to be determined. Tumor cells from different patients with Hodgkin's disease may contain a common antigen detectable with antisera prepared in heterologous animals.

The knowledge that transplantation type antigens in virus-induced tumors can be detected by an in vitro colony inhibition test has been recently applied to the elucidation of similar antigens in some human tumors. Lymphocytes from children bearing neuroblastomas have been found to inhibit the plating efficiency of their tumor cells grown in culture. Lymphocytes of their mothers but not from unrelated controls had the same inhibitory effect. Evidence is lacking that the antigens being measured in the neuroblastoma cells are indeed virus-induced.

Transplantation type antigens have been detected in various other human tumors using the colony inhibition test with the patient's lymphocytes and cells from the autologous tumor. It appears that tumors of certain histologic types in different patients share transplantation type antigens. However, further well-controlled studies are needed before it can be concluded that such tumors possess common antigens. It also appears that cells from patients with leukemia possess antigens to which autologous humoral and cell-mediated immune reactions develop. Evidence is accumulating that—similar to the animal model systems described above—patients with advanced cancer have circulating serum factors that can block the in vitro reaction of autologous lymphocytes in the colony inhibition test. Further studies in this direction may lead to an understanding of the mechanisms involved in tumor progression or regression in vivo.

Herpesviruses & Human Malignancies

Herpes simplex virus type 2: In recent years a great deal of attention has been focused on herpesviruses of man as potential oncogenic agents. Herpes simplex virus type 2 is venereally transmitted in man (see Chapter 38). Seroepidemiologic studies reveal a high degree of association between infection with this virus and invasive carcinoma of the cervix. The prevalence of herpes type 2 antibody in women with the disease was found to be much higher than that of matched controls. In many but not all studies, women with cervical dysplasia and carcinoma in situ (considered by some to be premalignant lesions leading to invasive carcinoma) had an increased prevalence of herpes type 2 antibody. Follow-up of such patients as well as prospective seroepidemiologic surveys of different populations may shed further light on whether the association found is covariable or etiologic.

A higher incidence of antibodies to nonstructural antigens induced by herpesvirus has also been observed among patients with cervical cancer (as compared to normal individuals or patients with breast cancer). In addition, the presence of herpesvirus DNA and mRNA has been reported in a cervical cancer biopsy. These findings, together with the capacity of herpesvirus to transform hamster embryo fibroblasts into tumorigenic cells, lend support to the oncogenic potential of this agent in man.

EB herpesvirus (EBV): A high degree of association exists between the EB (Epstein-Barr) virus, a widespread herpesvirus of man, and 2 human malignancies: Burkitt's lymphoma, a tumor with a predilection for the jaw and peculiar to children in Central Africa; and postnasal (nasopharyngeal) carcinoma, found with higher frequency in Chinese male populations in Southeast Asia than in other populations. The virus was detected initially by electron microscopy and subsequently by immunofluorescence in cultured Burkitt's lymphoma cells (but not in the original tumor) that maintain their lymphoid character upon continuous in vitro propagation. The high incidence and high titers of EB antibody (detectable by immunofluorescence, complement fixation, and gel diffusion tests) in patients with Burkitt's lymphoma and postnasal carcinoma led to the assumption that the association may be etiologic.

However, subsequent seroepidemiologic surveys showed that infection with EBV in normal populations

is widespread not only in Africa and Asia but also all over the world. Furthermore, EBV has an extreme predilection for cells of lymphoid origin, particularly for human B lymphocytes which have specific EBV receptors. The virus occurs regularly in cell lines derived not only from Burkitt's lymphoma and postnasal carcinoma but also from peripheral blood leukocytes of patients with infectious mononucleosis and other disease entities, as well as from normal individuals.

Normal lymphocytes have a limited life span in vitro but can be transformed into continuous cell lines by EBV. Such permanent lines have a diploid (or nearly diploid) karyotype, carry several copies of the viral genome in each cell, and express EBV nuclear antigen. Regardless of whether or not mature virus is produced, all cells that carry EBV DNA express the EBV nuclear antigen. Similar lines that spontaneously contain EBV DNA and nuclear antigen can be established from lymphocytes in peripheral blood or in lymph nodes of persons with EBV antibodies but not from lymphocytes of seronegative persons.

The question remains whether EBV is etiologically related to lymphoma and postnasal carcinoma or whether it represents a passenger virus present in the lymphoid cells of the tumor. Indeed, other viruses, eg, herpes simplex virus and reovirus, have been isolated from Burkitt's lymphomas. The passenger concept assumes that lymphoma cells appearing in EBV-carrying persons—and for EBV-unrelated reasons—pick up the virus. As the cells multiply, the amount of virus is increased and antibody production occurs, similar to the situation with normal lymphocytes. However, the non-Burkitt lymphomas that are common in the USA and most other areas of the world arise in EBV antibody-positive persons who do not pick up the virus even though their EBV-negative lymphoma cells can be infected and transformed with EBV in vitro. The EBV-sensitive lymphoma cells that appear in seropositive American patients are protected from horizontal spread of the virus in vivo by neutralizing antibodies. This supports the view that EBV-positive Burkitt lymphomas in African children originate from cells carrying the EBV genome. It has been suggested that EBV can transform oncogenically only those cells with a special competence, such as a genetic deficiency in some regulatory mechanism. Such cells might be those with the chromosome-14 translocation which has recently been found to be characteristic of malignant Burkitt's lymphoma.

In DNA-DNA hybridization studies, small quantities of EBV DNA have been detected in virus-free biopsy specimens of Burkitt's lymphoma and postnasal carcinoma; these findings are similar to those obtained with cell lines derived from the same tumors. Each cell carries multiple copies of the viral genome; part is in free circular, covalently closed form and another part is integrated with the cell genome. However, such studies still do not answer the question whether the partial viral genome detected is the cause of the malignancy or results from a secondary infection of the tumor cells by the virus.

Cells explanted from Burkitt tumors grow into continuous lines (called lymphoma lines) more easily than cells derived from peripheral blood of persons with infectious mononucleosis or persons who are otherwise antibody-positive. Lymphoma lines, furthermore, differ from lymphoblastoid lines derived in vitro from nonlymphomatous persons. In contrast to the uniform character of the lymphoma lines, lymphoblastoid lines are heterogeneous in morphologic, functional, and growth properties. Perhaps the development of lymphoma involves the appearance in vivo of a particular neoplastic cell type not present in the normal lymphocyte population transformed by EBV. As mentioned, a specific chromosome-14 translocation is present in Burkitt's lymphoma biopsies and established lines but not in EBV lymphoblastoid lines of nonlymphoma origin, and this chromosome translocation might well be the indicator of the EBV-converted cancer cell.

Support for an oncogenic role of EBV comes from studies in the marmoset, a South American monkey. Marmoset lymphocytes (akin to human lymphocytes) can be transformed in tissue culture by cell-free EBV, resulting in continuous virus-positive lines. Cells of such a marmoset lymphoid line (infected with EBV derived from a lymphoid line of a patient with infectious mononucleosis) as well as cell-free virus derived from the cells were found to induce malignant lymphomas in cottontop marmosets. Also, human lymphocytes transformed by EBV (either in vitro or in vivo) can grow as malignant tumors when transplanted into immunologically deficient xenogenic hosts (nude mice).

In regard to **nasopharyngeal carcinoma**, the EBV genome is regularly present in the tumor regardless of geographic occurrence. However, in these tumors the viral genome and the expressed nuclear antigen are not carried by the T lymphocytes which infiltrate the tumor but by the actual carcinoma cells. Since the tumors occur more frequently in certain ethnic groups, particularly in Chinese, the genetic makeup of the host cell may determine whether an oncogenic transformation may take place. Thus, the situation in principle would be similar to that discussed for Burkitt's lymphoma even though the susceptible cell type, and therefore the resulting tumor, would be different.

Hepatitis B Virus & Hepatoma

Patients with primary carcinoma of the liver have a high prevalence of hepatitis B surface antigen (HB_sAg). For example, in Senegal, the frequency of antigen detection was 61% in hepatoma versus 11% in matched controls; in Taiwan, 80% versus 15%; in Japan, 37% versus 3%; and in Spain, 35% versus 1%. Three interpretations have been offered for this association of hepatitis B virus infection and liver cancer.

(1) Hepatitis B virus infects patients with liver cancer or with cirrhosis (a precursor condition), who have a high susceptibility to infection and the development of the chronic carrier state. However, in areas of high hepatoma prevalence, hepatitis B carrier infections occur most frequently in childhood, and it seems that the virus carrier state occurs before the tumor and not after.

(2) The HB_sAg carrier state is a cause of cirrhosis, and the hepatoma arises from regenerative nodules by mechanisms in which the hepatitis virus is not involved. This view is supported by finding an increase of hepatoma among alcoholic cirrhosis patients, but many cases (perhaps the majority) of hepatoma associated with HB_sAg develop in persons without cirrhosis.

(3) Hepatitis B virus is an oncogenic virus transforming the liver cells it invades. Other cocarcinogenic influences might be necessary for the induction of the cancer; these might be genetic, hormonal, immunologic, or environmental. If hepatitis virus is an essential oncogenic factor, then elimination of hepatitis B infection by vaccination should also reduce the occurrence of hepatoma. Such vaccines are now under development. Since the virus has not yet been grown in culture, the source of vaccine is plasma of HB_sAg carriers. The vaccines under consideration are either whole HB_sAg or its immunizing glycopolypeptide subunits.

•   •   •

General References

American Cancer Society: Symposium on herpesvirus and cervical cancer. Cancer Res 33:1345, 1973.

Anderson Hospital and Tumor Institute Symposium: *Cellular Membranes and Tumor Cell Behavior.* Williams & Wilkins, 1975.

Benyesh-Melnick M, Butel J: Oncogenic viruses. Pages 403–485 in: *The Molecular Biology of Cancer.* Busch H (editor). Academic Press, 1974.

Biggs PM, De-Thé G, Payne LN (editors): *Oncogenesis and Herpesviruses II.* International Agency for Research on Cancer (Lyon), 1975.

Butel JS, Tevethia SS, Melnick JL: Oncogenicity and cell transformation by papovavirus SV40: The role of the viral genome. Adv Cancer Res 15:1, 1972.

Cold Spring Harbor Symposium on Quantitative Biology: Vol 39: *Tumor Viruses.* Cold Spring Harbor, New York, 1975.

Dulbecco R: Cell transformation by viruses and the role of viruses in cancer. J Gen Microbiol 79:7, 1973.

Epstein MS, Achong BG: The EB virus. Annu Rev Microbiol 27:413, 1973.

Green M: Oncogenic viruses. Annu Rev Biochem 39:701, 1970.

Gross L: *Oncogenic Viruses.* Pergamon Press, 1970.

Habel K: Antigens of virus-induced tumors. Adv Immunol 10:229, 1969.

Hakomori SI: Structure and organization of cell surface glycolipids: Dependency on cell growth and malignant transformation. Biochim Biophys Acta 417:55, 1975.

Hampar B & others: Activation of an endogenous mouse type C virus by ultraviolet-irradiated herpes simplex virus types 1 and 2. Proc Natl Acad Sci USA 73:646, 1976.

Hill M, Hillova J: RNA and DNA forms of the genetic material of C-type viruses and the integrated state of the DNA form in the cellular chromosome. Biochim Biophys Acta 355:7, 1974.

Huebner RJ & others: Suppression of murine type-C RNA virogenes by type-specific oncornavirus vaccines: Prospects for prevention of cancer. Proc Natl Acad Sci USA 73:620, 1976.

Klein G: The Epstein-Barr virus and neoplasia. N Engl J Med 293:1353, 1975.

Melnick JL, Adam E, Rawls WE: The causative role of herpesvirus type 2 in cervical cancer. Cancer 34:1375, 1974.

Nathans D: Restriction endonucleases in the analysis and restructuring of DNA molecules. Annu Rev Biochem 44:273, 1975.

Prince AM & others: A case/control study of the association between primary liver cancer and hepatitis B infection in Senegal. Int J Cancer 16:376, 1975.

Rapp F, Melnick JL: Papovavirus SV40, adenovirus and their hybrids: Transformation, complementation, and transcapsidation. Prog Med Virol 8:394, 1967.

Rowe WP: Genetic factors in the natural history of murine leukemia virus infection. Cancer Res 33:3061, 1973.

Temin HM, Baltimore D: RNA-directed DNA synthesis and RNA tumor viruses. Adv Virus Res 17:129, 1972.

Todaro GJ, Huebner RJ: The viral oncogene hypothesis: New evidence. Proc Natl Acad Sci USA 69:1009, 1972.

Tooze J: *The Molecular Biology of Tumor Viruses.* Cold Spring Harbor Laboratory, 1973.

Vigier P: RNA oncogenic viruses: Structure, replication and oncogenicity. Prog Med Virol 12:240, 1970.

Virus Cancer Program, National Cancer Institute Symposium: Immunological control of virus-associated tumors in man: Prospects and problems. Cancer Res 36:559, 1976.

Appendix:
Medical Parasitology

Although all of the medically significant micro-organisms considered in this *Review* are parasitic in their human hosts, the biomedical discipline of **parasitology** has traditionally been concerned only with the parasitic protozoa, helminths, and arthropods. This chapter offers no more than a brief survey of the protozoan and helminthic parasites of medical importance, with particular attention to those forms whose identification depends upon microscopic study. The chapter is designed as a first point of reference; the text is supplemented by tabular materials and by several pages of illustrations. The following texts are recommended for detailed reference.

Medical Parasitology
Brown HW: *Basic Clinical Parasitology,* 4th ed. Appleton-Century-Crofts, 1975.

Faust EC, Beaver PC, Jung RC: *Animal Agents and Vectors of Human Disease,* 4th ed. Lea & Febiger, 1975.

Faust EC, Russell PF, Jung RC: *Craig & Faust's Clinical Parasitology,* 8th ed. Lea & Febiger, 1970.

Clinical Aspects
Goldsmith RS: Infectious diseases: Metazoal. Chap 26, pp 863–882, in: *Current Medical Diagnosis & Treatment 1976.* Krupp M, Chatton MJ (editors). Lange, 1976.

Goldsmith RS: Infectious diseases: Protozoal. Chap 25, pp 850–862, in: *Current Medical Diagnosis & Treatment 1976.* Krupp M, Chatton MJ (editors). Lange, 1976.

Heyneman D: Medical parasitology. Chap 18, pp 346–395, in: *Physician's Handbook,* 18th ed. Krupp M & others (editors). Lange, 1976.

Hunter GW III, Frye WW, Swartzwelder JC: *A Manual of Tropical Medicine,* 5th ed. Saunders, 1976.

Knight R & others: Progress report: Intestinal parasites. Gut 14:145, 1973.

Maegraith BG: *Exotic Diseases in Practice: The Clinical and Public Health Significance of the Changing Geo-graphical Patterns of Diseases With Particular Reference to the Importation of Exotic Infections Into Europe and North America.* Heineman, 1965.

Maegraith BG: *Adams & Maegraith: Clinical Tropical Diseases,* 5th ed. Blackwell, 1971.

Wilcocks C, Manson-Bahr PEC: *Manson's Tropical Diseases,* 17th ed. Williams & Wilkins, 1972.

Woodruff, AW (editor): *Medicine in the Tropics.* Livingstone, 1974.

Medical Entomology
James MT, Harwood RF: *Herms's Medical Entomology,* 6th ed. Macmillan, 1969.

CLASSIFICATION

The parasites of man in the phylum Protozoa may be classified in 4 groups designated, by various authors, as subdivisions and classes (see Chapter 1) or as classes and subphyla:

(1) **Mastigophora** or flagellates, with one or more whip-like flagella and, in some cases, an undulating membrane (eg, trypanosomes). These include intestinal and genitourinary flagellates *(Giardia, Trichomonas, Retortamonas [Embadomonas], Enteromonas, Chilomastix)* and blood and tissue flagellates *(Leishmania, Trypanosoma).*

(2) **Sarcodina,** typically ameboid, are represented in man by species of *Entamoeba, Endolimax, Iodamoeba,* and *Dientamoeba.*

(3) **Sporozoa** undergo a complex life cycle, often involving 2 different hosts (eg, arthropod and vertebrate). Hemogregarines, piroplasms (eg, tick-borne *Babesia,* which causes serious infections of livestock and pets), and Microsporidia (eg, *Nosema,* which infects insects and other invertebrates) are not dealt with here. The Coccidia, a subclass of essentially intestinal Sporozoa (family Eimeriidae), and the hemosporidians, including the malaria parasites (*Plasmodium,* family Plasmodiidae) are represented in man. *Sarcocystis,* infecting many animals and sometimes man, and *Toxoplasma,* a very common human parasite, have recently been shown also to be coccidians. *Toxoplasma* seems to be basically a parasite of cats, from which hosts *Isospora*-like infective cysts (oocysts) are passed in the

By Donald Heyneman, PhD—Professor, G.W. Hooper Foundation and Department of International Health, University of California School of Medicine (San Francisco); and Frederick L. Dunn, MD, PhD—Professor, G.W. Hooper Foundation and Department of International Health, University of California School of Medicine (San Francisco). The illustrations on pp 513–523 are by P.H. Vercammen-Grandjean, DSc.

feces. *Sarcocystis* is closely related, being considered identical to *Isospora* by some specialists, though this is still a matter of considerable research interest and uncertainty.

4. **Ciliophora** or **Ciliata,** complex protozoa bearing cilia characteristically distributed in highly organized rows or patches, with 2 kinds of nuclei in each individual. *Balantidium coli,* an intestinal ciliate of man and pigs, is the only human parasite representative of this group.

The parasitic worms or helminths of man belong to 2 phyla:

(1) **Platyhelminthes** (flatworms), which lack a true body cavity (celom) and are characteristically flat in dorsoventral section. All medically important species belong to the classes **Cestoda** (tapeworms) and **Trematoda** (flukes). The tapeworms or cestodes are hermaphroditic, band-like, segmented, and have no digestive tract. The flukes or trematodes are typically leaf-shaped and hermaphroditic, but the schistosomes *(Schistosoma* species) are more elongated and have separate sexes. The important tissue and intestinal cestodes of man belong to the following genera: *Diphyllobothrium, Spirometra, Taenia, Echinococcus, Hymenolepis,* and *Dipylidium.* Medically important trematode genera, in addition to *Schistosoma,* include *Paragonimus, Clonorchis, Opisthorchis, Fasciolopsis, Heterophyes, Metagonimus,* and *Fasciola.*

(2) **Nemathelminthes** (roundworms), which are represented in man by many parasitic species in the class Nematoda. All are worm-like, unsegmented, round in body section, with a well-developed digestive system, and separate sexes. Many families of roundworms have parasitic species that infect man.

These are tabulated in Table 4 together with the other parasitic helminths. An essential procedure in diagnosis of many helminthic infections is microscopic recognition of ova or larvae in feces, urine, blood, or tissues. Illustrations of diagnostically important stages can be found on pp 517–523; certain important characteristics of the microfilariae, embryonic filariid worms, are also presented in tabular fashion (see Table 5).

GIARDIA LAMBLIA

Giardia lamblia is a flagellated protozoon found in the duodenum and jejunum of man, the cause of flagellate diarrhea or giardiasis.

Morphology & Identification

A. Typical Organisms: The trophozoite of *G lamblia* is a heart-shaped, bilaterally symmetric organism, 10–18 μm in length. There are 4 pairs of flagella, 2 nuclei with prominent central karyosomes, 2 axostyles, and a single or double parabasal body. A large concave sucking disk in the swollen anterior portion occupies much of the ventral surface. The swaying or dancing motion of *Giardia* trophozoites in fresh preparations is unmistakable. In an unfavorable environment the parasite encysts. These cysts, 10–14 μm in length, are ellipsoid, thick-walled, and contain 2–4 nuclei, usually at one end, and various structures of the trophozoite.

B. Culture: This organism has not been cultivated for prolonged periods on artificial media—a testament to its parasitologic specialization.

Pathogenesis & Clinical Findings

Giardia lamblia is usually weakly pathogenic or nonpathogenic for man. Cysts may be found in large numbers in the stools of entirely asymptomatic persons. In some persons, however, large numbers of parasites attached to the bowel wall may cause irritation and low-grade inflammation of the duodenal or jejunal mucosa, with consequent acute or chronic diarrhea and steatorrhea. The stools may be watery, semisolid, greasy, bulky, and foul-smelling at various times during the course of the infection. Malaise, weakness, weight loss, abdominal cramps, distention, and flatulence may occur. Some of these symptoms may be due to interference with fat absorption as well as to mechanical irritation of the bowel. The bile ducts and gallbladder may also be invaded, causing a mild catarrhal cholangitis and cholecystitis. Children are more liable to clinical giardiasis than adults. Symptoms may continue for long periods and may prove intractable or extremely difficult to eliminate.

Diagnostic Laboratory Tests

Diagnosis depends upon finding the distinctive cysts in formed stools, or cysts and trophozoites in liquid stools. Concentration methods may be necessary to detect asymptomatic infections, but the parasite is usually abundant in the stool when gastrointestinal symptoms are present. Examination of the duodenal contents may be necessary to establish the diagnosis when the symptoms relate only to the biliary system.

Treatment

Administration of quinacrine hydrochloride (Atabrine) will cure about 90% of *G lamblia* infections. Metronidazole (Flagyl) is an alternative. The course of treatment may be repeated if necessary. Only symptomatic patients require treatment.

Epidemiology

G lamblia is cosmopolitan and common, especially in young children. Man is infected by ingestion of fecally contaminated water or food containing *Giardia* cysts. Epidemic outbreaks have been reported at ski resorts and other areas in the USA where overloading of sewage facilities or contamination of the water supply has resulted in sudden outbreaks of giardiasis. Numerous reports have been made of giardiasis among American tourists returning from Leningrad, presumably from contaminated hotel water supplies.

TRICHOMONAS

The trichomonads are flagellate protozoa with 3–5 anterior flagella, an axostyle, and an undulating membrane. Of the 3 species infecting man only *Trichomonas vaginalis* is pathogenic, causing trichomoniasis.

Morphology & Identification

A. Typical Organisms: *Trichomonas vaginalis* is pear-shaped, with a short undulating membrane extending to mid-body, and 4 anterior flagella. It normally measures 15–20 μm in length, but may reach 30 μm. The organism moves with a characteristic wobbling and rotating motion. The nonpathogenic trichomonads, *T hominis* and *T tenax,* cannot readily be distinguished from *T vaginalis* when alive. When fixed and stained, *T tenax* measures 6–10 μm in length; in other respects it is identical with *T vaginalis. T hominis* measures 8–12 μm and bears 5 anterior flagella and a long undulating membrane extending the full length of its body. The parabasal body is small or absent. For all practical purposes, trichomonads found in the mouth are *T tenax;* in the intestine, *T hominis;* and in the genitourinary tract (both sexes), *T vaginalis.*

B. Culture: *T vaginalis* may be cultivated in a variety of solid and fluid cell-free media, in tissue cultures, and in the chick embryo. *T tenax* and *T hominis* will grow particularly well in sheep serum in saline; media used for culturing the intestinal amebas are also satisfactory. *T vaginalis* requires more complex media for optimal growth. CPLM (cysteine-peptone-liver-maltose) medium is one of the most satisfactory. Simplified trypticase serum is usually used for semen cultures.

C. Growth Requirements: *T vaginalis* grows well under anaerobic conditions, somewhat less well aerobically. The pH optimum is 5.5–6.0; the temperature optimum is 35–37° C. The following substances appear to be essential for optimal growth: cysteine, a fermentable carbohydrate, 20% animal serum, 0.1% agar, and a heat-labile factor destroyed by autoclaving.

Pathogenesis, Pathology, & Clinical Findings

T hominis and *T tenax* are generally considered to be harmless commensals. *T vaginalis* is capable of causing low-grade inflammation, particularly when the infection is heavy. The organisms have a toxic action on tissue culture cells and will produce extensive lesions in germ-free animals. The intensity of infection, the pH of vaginal and other secretions, the physiologic status of the vaginal and other genitourinary tract surfaces, and the accompanying bacterial flora are among the factors affecting pathogenicity. The organisms cannot survive at normal vaginal acidity of pH 3.8–4.4; nor can they survive at the nearly neutral vaginal pH found in young girls and elderly women.

In the female the infection is normally limited to the vulva, vagina, and cervix; it does not usually extend to the uterus. The mucosal surfaces may be tender, inflamed, eroded, and covered with a frothy yellow or cream-colored discharge. In the male the prostate, seminal vesicles, and urethra may be infected. Signs and symptoms in the female, in addition to profuse vaginal discharge, include local tenderness, vulval pruritus, and burning. About 10% of infected males have a thin, white urethral discharge.

Diagnostic Laboratory Tests

A. Specimens and Microscopic Examination: Vaginal or urethral secretions or discharge should be examined microscopically in a drop of saline or Trichomonas Diluent for characteristic motile trichomonads. Dried smears may be stained with hematoxylin or one of the Romanowsky stains for later study.

B. Culture: Culture of vaginal or urethral discharge, of prostatic secretion, or of a semen specimen may reveal organisms when direct examination is negative.

Immunity

Infection confers no apparent immunity. Little is known about the immune responses to trichomonads.

Treatment

Successful treatment of vaginal infection requires the destruction of the trichomonads, for which topical and systemic metronidazole (Flagyl) is the recommended drug; topical treatment for the restoration of normal vaginal epithelium and acidity; and measures to ensure that reinfection will not occur. The patient's sexual partner should be examined and treated simultaneously if necessary. Postmenopausal patients may require treatment with estrogens to improve the condition of the vaginal epithelium. For vaginal infections treated with metronidazole, topical treatment with Floraquin (a mixture containing diiodohydroxyquinoline, dextrose, lactose, and boric acid) or furazolidonenifuroxime (Tricofuron) is usually effective. Prostatic infection can be cured with certainty only by systemic treatment with metronidazole.

Epidemiology & Control

T vaginalis is a common cosmopolitan parasite of both males and females. Infection rates vary greatly but may be quite high in some populations—often 40% or higher—particularly where the quality of female hygiene is poor. Coitus is the common mode of transmission, but contaminated towels, douche equipment, examination instruments, and other objects may be responsible for some new infections. Infants may be infected at birth. Most infections, in both sexes, are asymptomatic or cause inconsequential symptoms. Control of *T vaginalis* infections always requires detection and treatment of the infected male sexual partner at the same time that the infected female is treated; mechanical protection (condom) should be used during intercourse until the infection is eradicated in both partners.

T hominis is also cosmopolitan and common, particularly in the tropics. Transmission is by the fecal-oral route.

T tenax, apparently transmitted directly from

mouth to mouth, is found throughout the world. The prevalence in some populations reaches 10–20%.

OTHER INTESTINAL FLAGELLATES

Retortamonas intestinalis, Chilomastix mesnili, and *Enteromonas hominis* are nonpathogenic intestinal parasites of man which must be distinguished in the laboratory from the pathogenic amebas and flagellates.

Retortamonas intestinalis

This cosmopolitan but rare parasite lives as a commensal in the human intestine. The trophozoite is small, ovoid, and 4–9 μm long, with a single nucleus, a cytostome, and 2 flagella, one anterior and one emerging from the cytostome. The oval or pear-shaped cyst, 4–7 μm long, has a single nucleus, sometimes dumbbell-shaped, with fibrils along the margins of the cytostome. The organism can be cultivated in media suitable for the trichomonads. Laboratory diagnosis depends upon detection of the cysts or trophozoites in stool specimens. Transmission presumably takes place by ingestion of the cysts.

Enteromonas hominis

Human infections with this very small intestinal flagellate have been reported in many parts of the world. Although it is generally rare, high infection rates have been recorded in some populations. The oval trophozoite is 4–10 μm long, uninucleate, and bears 4 flagella (3 anterior, one posterior). There is no cytostome. The cyst is oval, 6–8 μm long, with 1–4 nuclei. When quadrinucleate, the nuclei are arranged in pairs at the poles. Cultivation is easy on ordinary flagellate media. Laboratory diagnosis and transmission are as for *Retortamonas intestinalis.*

Chilomastix mesnili

This parasite, which can be confused with *Trichomonas* in the laboratory, is more common than *R intestinalis* and *E hominis.* It is found throughout the world. Some workers consider it to be mildly pathogenic, but there is little evidence to support this. The trophozoite is pear-shaped, 6–24 μm long, with anterior flagella, a large cytostome bearing a fourth flagellum, and a large single anterior nucleus. The spiral motion of the trophozoite is unlike that of *Trichomonas.* The distinctive cyst is lemon-shaped, uninucleate, 7–10 μm long, with conspicuous fibrils forming the margins of the cytostome. Cultivation, laboratory diagnosis, and transmission are as for the 2 flagellates discussed above.

THE HEMOFLAGELLATES

The hemoflagellates of man include the genera *Trypanosoma* and *Leishmania.* There are 2 distinct types of human trypanosomes: (1) African, causing sleeping sickness and transmitted by tsetse flies *(Glossina): Trypanosoma rhodesiense* and *T gambiense;* and (2) American, causing Chagas' disease and transmitted by cone-nosed bugs (*Triatoma,* etc): *T (Schizotrypanum) cruzi.* (Another species, *T rangeli* of South America, infects man without causing disease.) The genus *Leishmania,* usually divided into 3 species infecting man (though this matter is still unresolved), causes cutaneous (Oriental sore), mucocutaneous (espundia), and visceral (kala-azar) leishmaniasis. All forms of these infections are transmitted by sandflies (*Phlebotomus* in the Old World, *Lutzomyia* in the New World).

The genus *Trypanosoma* appears in the blood as trypomastigotes, with elongated bodies supporting a lateral undulating membrane and a flagellum that borders the free edge of the membrane and emerges at the anterior end as a whip-like extension (see p 516). The kinetoplast, present in all forms found in man, is a darkly staining body containing DNA, lying immediately adjacent to the tiny node (blepharoplast) from which the flagellum arises. Other developmental forms among the hemoflagellates include (1) a leishmanial rounded intracellular stage, the amastigote (see below and p 516); (2) a flagellated extracellular stage, the promastigote (formerly called leptomonad), a lanceolate form without an undulating membrane, with a kinetoplast at the anterior end; and (3) an epimastigote (formerly called crithidia), a more elongated extracellular stage with a short undulating membrane and a kinetoplast placed more posteriorly but still anterior to the nucleus.

In *Leishmania* life cycles, only the amastigote and promastigote are found, the latter being restricted to the insect vector. In *T cruzi,* all 3 may occur in man, and trypomastigote and epimastigote in the vector. In African trypanosomes, the latter 2 flagellated stages also occur in the tsetse fly vector, but only the trypomastigote has been observed in man—though recent research suggests that intracellular amastigotes occur in experimental mice and may be present in man as well.

1. LEISHMANIA

The genus *Leishmania,* widely distributed in nature, includes 3 morphologically indistinguishable pathogenic agents of man: *L donovani* (causing visceral leishmaniasis), *L tropica* (cutaneous leishmaniasis), and *L braziliensis* (mucocutaneous leishmaniasis). *L braziliensis* has been recently divided into 2 species groups, *L braziliensis* and *L mexicana,* each of which may prove to consist of a number of species. Similarly, *L tropica* and *L donovani* have each been divided by some workers into 2 or more species and several subspecies.

Morphology & Identification

A. Typical Organism: Only the first stage, the

nonflagellated amastigote—formerly called Leishman-Donovan (LD) bodies (see p 515)—occurs in the mammalian host. The sandfly transmits the infective promastigotes by bite. The promastigotes rapidly change to amastigotes after phagocytosis by macrophages, then multiply, filling the cytoplasm of the macrophages. The infected cells burst, the released parasites are again phagocytosed, and the process is repeated, producing a cutaneous lesion or visceral infection, depending upon the species of parasite. The amastigotes are oval, $2-6 \times 1-3$ μm, with a laterally placed oval vesicular nucleus and a distinct dark-staining kinetoplast, usually rod-like.

B. Culture and Growth Characteristics: In NNN or Tobie's medium, only the promastigotes are found. *L donovani* usually grows slowly, the promastigotes forming tangled clumps in the fluid. *L tropica* grows more quickly, promastigotes forming small rosettes in the fluid and giving it a fine granular appearance with a distinct surface film, while *L braziliensis* may produce a wax-like surface. In tissue cultures, intracellular amastigotes may be obtained in addition to the extracellular promastigotes.

C. Variations: Strain differences in virulence, tissue tropism or predilection, biologic, epidemiologic, and pharmacodynamic characteristics have been observed with all 3 species. Consequently, overlap and considerable variability in pathology and clinical pictures occur.

Pathogenesis, Pathology, & Clinical Findings

L donovani, the causative organism of kala-azar, spreads from the site of inoculation to multiply in reticuloendothelial cells, especially macrophages in spleen, liver, lymph nodes, and bone marrow. This is accompanied by vascularity and marked hyperplasia, especially of the spleen. Progressive emaciation is usually accompanied by remarkably little prostration in spite of growing weakness. There is irregular fever, sometimes hectic. Untreated infections are usually fatal.

L tropica causes a dermal lesion at the site of inoculation by the sandfly: cutaneous leishmaniasis, Oriental sore, Delhi boil, etc. Mucous membranes are rarely involved. The dermal layers are first affected, with cellular infiltration and proliferation of amastigotes intracellularly and spreading extracellularly, until the infection penetrates the epidermis and causes ulceration. Satellite lesions may be found, rarely massively proliferated. These are tuberculoid, sometimes with few or no parasites, and are regarded as anergic manifestations which may be unresponsive to treatment.

L braziliensis causes mucocutaneous or nasopharyngeal (naso-oral) leishmaniasis. It is known by many local names, the most familiar of which is espundia. The pathologic findings are the same as those of *L tropica* infections, but the initial lesions are more superficial and tend to metastasize to mucous surfaces where they may form polypoid growths and long-lasting, fungating, destructive lesions. This is the characteristic clinical picture of espundia, most commonly

found in the Amazon basin. At high altitudes in Peru, the clinical features (uta) tend to resemble those of Oriental sore. In Mexico the ears are frequently involved (chiclero ulcer), usually with an indolent infection without ulceration and few parasites. The latter agent is considered a distinct species, *L mexicana.* (The taxonomy of the New World species is in a state of flux, as previously noted.)

Diagnostic Laboratory Tests

A. Specimens: Lymph node aspirates, scrapings, and biopsies are important in the cutaneous forms; lymph node aspirates, blood, and spleen or liver puncture are important in kala-azar. Purulent discharges are of no value for diagnosis, although nasal scrapings may be useful.

B. Microscopic Examination: Giemsa-stained smears and sections may show amastigotes, especially in material from kala-azar and the edges of Oriental sores.

C. Culture: NNN medium is the medium of choice. Blood culture is satisfactory only for *L donovani* and then often fails to detect infection; lymph node aspirates are suitable for all forms; and tissue aspirates, biopsy material, scrapings, or small biopsies from the edges of ulcers are useful for the cutaneous forms (and often for kala-azar also). A blood-agar culture, Tobie's medium, is also popular. However, only promastigotes can be cultivated in the absence of living cells.

D. Serology: The formol-gel (aldehyde) test of Napier is a nonspecific test that depends on an elevated serum globulin in kala-azar: 1 drop of commercial formalin in 1 ml of serum forms an opalescent gel. The IHA (indirect hemagglutination antibody test) or the IFA (indirect fluorescent antibody test) may be useful but lacks sufficient sensitivity and may cross-react with *T cruzi.* A skin test is epidemiologically important in indicating past exposure to any of the leishmanias (Montenegro test).

Immunity

Recovery confers a solid and permanent immunity, although it usually is species-specific and may be strain-specific as well. Natural resistance varies greatly among individuals, between different ages and sexes, and among various species of mammals. Vaccination significantly reduces the incidence of Oriental sore, especially if the more florid "wet" type is the vaccine source.

Treatment

Single lesions may be cleaned, curetted, treated with antibiotics if secondarily infected, and then covered and left to heal. Pentavalent antimony sodium gluconate (Pentostam, Solustibosan) is the drug of choice for all forms. Pentamidine isethionate (Lomidine) is useful for kala-azar resistant to this drug. Cycloguanil pamoate has been recommended for espundia, which is frequently quite unresponsive to treatment.

Epidemiology, Prevention, & Control

Kala-azar is found focally in most tropical and subtropical countries. Its local distribution is related to the prevalence of specific sandfly vectors. In the Mediterranean littoral and in middle Asia and South America, domestic and wild canids are reservoirs, and in the Sudan various wild carnivores and rodents are reservoirs of endemic kala-azar. Control is aimed at destroying breeding places and dogs and protecting people from sandfly bites. Oriental sore is essentially Asiatic, also occurring in the Mediterranean region and North Africa. The "wet" type is rural, and burrowing rodents are the main reservoir; the dry type is urban, and man is presumably the only reservoir. For *L braziliensis* there are a number of wild but apparently no domestic animal reservoirs. Sandfly vectors are involved in all forms.

2. TRYPANOSOMA

Hemoflagellates of the genus *Trypanosoma* occur in the blood of mammals as mature elongated trypomastigotes. Other stages of the life cycle occur in mammalian tissues in *T cruzi,* but in all species a multiplying epimastigote stage as well as infective trypomastigotes (metacyclic trypanosomes) occur in the alternative host, an insect vector. Trypanosomes cause trypanosomiasis (sleeping sickness, Chagas' disease, and asymptomatic trypanosomiasis) in man. The parent form in Africa is *T brucei* (causing nagana in livestock and game animals, with antelopes as a natural reservoir); the 2 human forms, *T rhodesiense* and *T gambiense,* are now regarded by some as subspecies of *T brucei.* The 3 forms are indistinguishable morphologically but differ ecologically and epidemiologically.

Morphology & Identification

A. Typical Organisms: African *T gambiense* and *T rhodesiense* both vary in size and shape of the body and length of the flagellum (12–42 μm, usually 15–30 μm) but are essentially indistinguishable. "Slender forms" 25–30 μm long usually predominate over "stumpy forms" with short flagella. The latter form is infective to the insect host and possesses a full battery of enzymes for energy metabolism. The elongated form requires host metabolic assistance and is specialized for rapid multiplication in the vertebrate bloodstream. The same forms are seen in blood as in lymph node aspirates. Somewhat stumpy forms with posterior (as opposed to central) nuclei occur rather more frequently in *T rhodesiense* than in *T gambiense.* The blood forms of the American *T cruzi* are present during the early acute stage and at intervals thereafter in smaller numbers. They are typical trypomastigotes, varying about a mean of 20 μm, frequently curved in a C-shape when fixed and stained. The tissue forms most common in heart muscle, liver, and brain develop from agglomerations of amastigotes that have multiplied to form an intracellular colony after invasion of the host cell or phagocytosis of the parasite. *T rangeli* of South America infects man without causing disease and must therefore be carefully distinguished from the pathogenic species.

B. Culture: *T cruzi* and *T rangeli* are readily cultivated (3–6 weeks) in fluid or diphasic media. The various developing forms may also be recognized in clean triatomids (reduviids) which have fed on patients (xenodiagnosis), in which case the 2 species can be distinguished by the fact that *T cruzi* is confined to the hindgut whereas *T rangeli* is usually present in the salivary glands also.

C. Growth Requirements: *T cruzi* requires at least hemin, ascorbic acid, and certain unidentified but dialyzable substances present in serum. The African forms require at least these for development, but neither these nor other known substances suffice to support development to the infective trypanosomal stage. The blood of some apparently uninfected persons inhibits growth of the African species.

D. Variation: The African blood forms are polymorphic, as noted above. The blood trypanosomes of *T cruzi* are monomorphic, but the tissue forms essentially repeat all developmental stages seen in the reduviid vector. Variations in virulence are well recognized: *T rhodesiense* is usually regarded as a virulent zoonotic form and *T gambiense* as a more chronic, though still usually fatal form. Both may be morphologically stable or periodically mutating to produce waves of distinct serotypes in the human host (marked by alternation between slender and stumpy trypomastigote populations). *T gambiense* is of lower virulence to laboratory animals than *T rhodesiense,* but by passage it can be made to rival the latter in virulence. Strains of *T cruzi* of low virulence to laboratory animals and apparently also to man are known, mostly from the southern USA and northern Mexico.

Pathogenesis, Pathology, & Clinical Findings

Infective trypanosomes of *T gambiense* and *T rhodesiense* are introduced through the bite of the tsetse fly and multiply at the site of inoculation to cause variable induration and swelling (the primary lesion), which may progress to form a trypanosomal chancre, spreading to lymph nodes, bloodstream, and, in terminal stages, to the CNS, where it produces the typical sleeping sickness syndrome: lassitude, inability to eat, tissue wasting, unconsciousness, and death. Infective forms of *T cruzi* pass to humans by inoculation of infected bug feces into the conjunctiva or a break in the skin, *not* by the bite of the bug (which is the mode of entry of the nonpathogenic *T rangeli*). At the site of inoculation they progress from the amastigote to the promastigote and epimastigote stages and multiply to cause variable induration and swelling; they may form a chagoma. Chagas' disease is common in infants, who show such dramatic acute responses that it is sometimes described as if it were a purely pediatric disorder. Particularly in children, unilateral swelling of the eyelids (Romaña's sign) is frequent and characteristic at onset. The primary lesion is accompanied by fever, acute regional lymphadenitis, and dissemination to blood and tissues. The parasites can usually be detected within 1–2 weeks as trypomastigotes in the blood. Subsequent developments depend upon the organs and tissues affected and on the nature of multiplication and release of toxins. The African forms multiply extracellularly as trypomastigotes in the blood as well as in the tissues. *T cruzi* multiplies mostly within reticuloendothelial cells, going through a cycle starting with large agglomerations of amastigotes. In both African and American forms, multiplication in the tissues is punctuated by phases of parasitemia with later destruction by the host of the blood forms, accompanied by characteristic bouts of intermittent fever gradually decreasing in intensity. Parasitemia is more commonly found in *T rhodesiense* and is intermittent and scant with *T cruzi.*

The release of toxins explains much of the systemic as well as local or tissue reactions (eg, blood vessels and lymph sinuses in African forms; reaction around infected reticuloendothelial and other cells in the American form). The organs most seriously affected are the CNS and heart muscle. Interstitial myocarditis is extreme in Chagas' disease and is the most common serious element in the clinical picture. It is least evident in the chronic gambian infection. CNS involvement is most characteristic of African trypanosomiasis except that untreated rhodesian infection often leads to death before brain damage occurs. *T rhodesiense,* a highly virulent organism, appears in the CSF in about 1 month and *T gambiense* in several months, but both are present in small numbers. *T gambiense* infection is chronic and in about a year leads to progressive diffuse meningoencephalitis. The more rapidly fatal *T rhodesiense* produces the same condition of somnolence and coma only during the final weeks of a terminal infection. Other organs affected are the liver and spleen, especially with chronic *T cruzi* infection, which produces a vigorous reticuloendothelial system response, often simulating kala-azar (splenomegaly, hepatomegaly, bone marrow hyperplasia and engorgement).

Invasion of nerve plexuses in the alimentary tract walls leads to megaesophagus and megacolon, especially in the Brazilian strain of Chagas' disease. All 3 trypanosomes are transmissible through the placenta, and congenital infections are reported in hyperendemic areas.

Diagnostic Laboratory Tests

A. Specimens: Blood (thick and thin films, for culture, and for serology), preferably collected when the temperature rises; CSF, lymph node aspirate, and sometimes marrow primary lesion aspirates or splenic puncture are valuable for diagnostic tests. Uninfected triatomid bugs are required if xenodiagnosis of *T cruzi* is intended. The latter test can only be done during the early weeks of infection, the period of parasitemia.

B. Microscopic Examination: Fresh blood (or aspirated tissue in saline) is kept warm and examined immediately for the actively motile trypanosomes. Thick films may be stained by Field's rapid method or with Giemsa's stain. Thin films stained with Giemsa's stain are necessary for confirmation. Centrifugation may be necessary. Tissue smears must be stained for identification of the pretrypanosomal stages. Centrifuged CSF should be similarly examined; there is seldom more than one trypanosome per ml. The most reliable tests are blood examinations for *T rhodesiense;* gland puncture for *T gambiense;* and CSF examination for *T rhodesiense* and advanced *T gambiense.*

C. Culture: Any or all of the specimens required for microscopic examination may be inoculated into media such as Tobie's, Wenyon's semisolid, NNN, or Senekji's medium for attempted culture of *T cruzi* or *T rangeli.* The organisms are grown at 22–24° C and subcultured every 1–2 weeks, centrifuged material being examined microscopically for trypanosomes. However, trypanosomes are usually very scanty in the blood in Chagas' disease except perhaps in the early acute phase. Culture of the African forms is unsatisfactory.

D. Animal Inoculation: *T cruzi* and *T rangeli* may be detected by inoculating blood intraperitoneally into a number of mice (when available, pups and kittens are animals of first choice). *T rhodesiense* is often detectable (and *T gambiense* with some effort) by this procedure in mice. Trypanosomes appear in the blood in a few days after successful inoculation.

E. Serology: A positive indirect IHA, IFA, or CF (Machado's) test provides confirmatory support in *T cruzi* infection. African forms cause IFA reactions, but these are of limited diagnostic value.

F. Xenodiagnosis: This is the method of choice in suspected Chagas' disease if other examinations are negative, especially during the early phase of disease onset. About 6 clean laboratory-reared triatomid bugs are fed on the patient, and their droppings examined in 7–10 days for the various developmental forms. Defe-

Table 1. Differentiation of *T cruzi* and *T rangeli.*

	T cruzi	*T rangeli*
Blood forms		
Size	20 µm	Over 30 µm
Shape	Often C-shaped in fixed preparations	Rarely C-shaped
Posterior kinetoplast	Terminals relatively large	Distinctly subterminal, small
Developmental stages in tissues	Amastigote to epimastigote	Not found (only trypomastigotes)
Triatomid bugs		
In salivary gland or proboscis (or both)	Always absent	Usually present
In hindgut or feces	Present	Present

cation follows shortly after a fresh meal, or it may be forced by gently probing the anus and then squeezing the bug's abdomen—*taking care that the anus is in contact with a drop of saline or serum to prevent accidental self-infection by a sudden spray from the anus. Laboratory infection with T cruzi is a distinct hazard because of the lack of suitable chemotherapy and poor prognosis.* Xenodiagnosis is impracticable for the African forms.

G. Differential Diagnosis: *T rhodesiense* and *T gambiense* are morphologically identical but may be distinguished by their geographic distribution, vector species, and their behavior in man (since they cause different clinical pictures and are distributed differently in tissues and blood). In rats, *T rhodesiense* is usually more virulent. The differentiation of *T cruzi* from *T rangeli (T ariarii, T guatemalense)* is practicable and important since *T rangeli* is innocuous. The points of differentiation are shown in Table 1.

Immunity

Man apparently shows some individual variation in natural resistance to all 3 pathogenic trypanosomes. Strain-specific complement-fixing and protecting antibodies can be detected in the plasma, and these presumably lead to the disappearance of blood forms. The tissue forms are apparently less accessible, and it is significant that each relapse of African trypanosomiasis is apparently due to a strain serologically distinct from the preceding one. Apart from such relapses, Africans free from symptoms may be found to have trypanosomes in the blood.

Treatment

There is no effective drug treatment for American trypanosomiasis, although Bayer-2502 (Lampit) may temporarily relieve some patients with trypomastigotes still present in the blood. African trypanosomiasis is treated principally with suramin sodium (Germanin) or pentamidine isethionate (Lomidine), the former preferably for gambiense and the latter for rhodesiense. Late disease with CNS involvement requires melarsoprol (Mel B), as well as suramin or tryparsamide in the presence of parasitemia and active infection of lymph nodes.

Epidemiology, Prevention, & Control

African trypanosomiasis is restricted to recognized tsetse fly belts. Broadly, *T gambiense,* transmitted mostly by the streamside tsetse *Glossina palpalis,* extends from west to central Africa and produces a relatively chronic infection with progressive CNS involvement. *T rhodesiense,* transmitted mostly by the woodland-savannah *G morsitans,* is more restricted, being confined to the south and east of Lake Tanganyika, and therefore causes a smaller number of cases; but it is more virulent. Bushbuck and other antelopes may serve as reservoirs of *T rhodesiense,* whereas man himself is the principal reservoir of *T gambiense.* Control depends upon searching for and then isolating and treating patients with the disease; controlling

movement of people in and out of fly belts; using insecticides in vehicles; and instituting fly control principally with insecticides and by altering habitats. Contact with reservoir animals is difficult to control.

Chemoprophylaxis, eg, with suramin sodium, is difficult but may be considered.

American trypanosomiasis (Chagas' disease) is important only in certain parts of Central and South America, although infection of animals with virulent or mild strains extends much more widely, eg, into the southern USA, and a few autochthonous human cases have been recently reported in Texas. Certain triatomid bugs become as domiciliated as bedbugs, and infection may be brought in by rats, opossums, or armadillos—which may themselves become domiciliated and then spread the infection to domestic animals. Since no effective treatment is known, it is particularly important to control the vectors with residual insecticides and habitat destruction and to avoid contact with animal reservoirs. Chagas' disease occurs only among people in poor economic circumstances. An estimated 8,000,000 persons harbor the parasite, and many of these have an impaired heart and a resulting sharply reduced life expectancy.

ENTAMOEBA HISTOLYTICA

Entamoeba histolytica is a parasite commonly found in the large intestine of man, certain higher primates, and some domiciliated and commensal animals. Most cases are asymptomatic except in humans or animals living under stress or unnatural conditions (eg, in zoo-held primates).

Morphology & Identification

A. Typical Organisms: Three stages are encountered: the active ameba, the inactive cyst, and the intermediate precyst. The ameboid trophozoite is the only form present in tissues and is also found in fluid feces during amebic dysentery. Its size is $15-30~\mu m$. The cytoplasm is granular and may contain red cells (pathognomonic) but ordinarily no bacteria. Iron-hematoxylin staining shows the nuclear membrane to be lined by fine, regular granules of chromatin, forming a distinct, even network around the periphery; the karyosome is central, small, and deeply staining. Movement of trophozoites in fresh material is relatively brisk and usually unidirectional. Pseudopodia are finger-like and broad, reactions that are absent at lower temperatures or with precystic amebas.

Cysts are present only in the lumen of the colon and in fluid and formed feces. Subspherical cysts of actively pathogenic amebas range from $10-20~\mu m$, but smaller cysts (of debatable significance but now generally accepted as cysts of a nonpathogenic form, *E hartmanni*) range down to $3.5~\mu m$. These small forms (average below $10~\mu m$) are regarded as a distinct species *(E hartmanni)* or a distinct subspecies *(E histolytica* var *hartmanni).* The cyst wall, $0.5~\mu m$ thick, is hyaline. The initial uninucleate cyst may contain a glycogen vacuole and distinctly staining chromatoidal bodies or bars with characteristic rounded ends (in contrast to splinter chromatoidals in developing cysts of *E coli*). Nuclear division within the cyst produces the final quadrinucleate cyst, during which time the chromatoid bodies and glycogen vacuoles disappear. Diagnosis in most cases rests on the characteristics of the cyst since trophozoites usually appear only in diarrheic feces in active cases (see p 513) and survive for only a few hours. Stools may contain cysts with 1–4 nuclei depending on their degree of maturation. (See the Keys on pp 501–502.)

B. Culture: Trophozoites are readily studied in cultures; both en- and excystation can be controlled.

C. Growth Requirements: Growth is most vigorous in various rich complex media under partial anaerobiosis at 37° C and pH 7.0—with a mixed flora or at least a single coexisting species. Growth in tissue culture is also best under partial anaerobiosis.

D. Variation: Variations in cyst size are due to nutritional differences, possible host effects, and occurrence of the small nonpathogenic form, *E histolytica* var *hartmanni* (or *E hartmanni*). Possible change in behavior between a generally noninvasive commensal form and invasive phases of the same population is generally considered unlikely.

Pathogenesis, Pathology, & Clinical Findings

Multiplication among trophozoites occurs by binary fission. Young trophozoites (amebulae) emerge from ingested cysts after their activation in the stomach and duodenum. Four amebulae (one for each cyst nucleus) leave the cyst, and each divides once to form 8 small trophozoites. These pass to the cecum and produce a population of lumen-dwelling trophozoites. Disease results (in about 10% of the infections) when the trophozoites invade the intestinal epithelium. The greatest concentration of amebas is at the sites of maximum fecal stasis, ie, the cecum and lower ascending colon, sigmoid colon, and rectum. Mucosal invasion by amebas with the aid of proteolytic enzymes leads to discrete, tiny, flask-shaped cavities containing cell debris, mucus, and the organisms. Among asymptomatic cyst passers the trophozoites exist in the intestinal lumen without being invasive. Active invasion is stimulated or induced by bacteria, host condition, genetic characteristics of the parasite strain, or other factors and leads to lateral invasion of small cavities, undermining their edges and producing ulcers, which eventually may coalesce. This is accompanied by diarrhea or dysentery. Trophozoites are often carried out with mucus and a few red cells in the fluid feces. In the absence of gross inflammation, destruction and regeneration proceed simultaneously unless secondary infection supervenes. These processes may lead to appendicitis, perforation, hemorrhage, and occasionally stricture, amebic granuloma (ameboma), self-healing, or pseudopolyposis. Because the bowel wall is friable, surgery is contraindicated in the active stage.

Extraintestinal infection is assumed to be metastatic, since it rarely occurs by direct extension from the bowel. By far the most common form is amebic hepatitis or liver abscess (4% or more of clinical infections, with much variation in different populations), which is assumed to be due to microemboli, including trophozoites carried through the portal circulation. Abscess often develops without being clinically evident. It is assumed that hepatic microembolism (with trophozoites) is a common accompaniment of bowel lesions but that these diffuse focal lesions rarely progress. The slight hepatic enlargement and tenderness (and the chronically impaired liver function) encountered in acute, subacute, and chronic intestinal infection may be nonspecific. A true amebic abscess is progressive, nonsuppurative (but occasionally secondarily infected), and destructive without compression and formation of a wall. The contents are necrotic and typically sterile, active amebas being confined to the walls. A characteristic "anchovy paste" is produced in the abscess and is seen on surgical drainage. More than half of patients with amebic liver abscess give no history of intestinal infection; and only one-eighth of them pass cysts in their stools. Amebic abscesses also occur rarely elsewhere (eg, lung, brain, spleen, or draining through the body wall). Any organ or tissue in contact with active trophozoites may become a site of invasion and abscess.

Diagnostic Laboratory Tests

A. Specimens: Fluid feces, fresh and warm for immediate examination for trophozoites, or preserved in PVA (polyvinyl alcohol) or MIF (Merthiolate-iodine-formaldehyde) fixatives for mailing to a diagnostic laboratory (in a double mailing tube, the inner one of metal); formed feces for cysts; fluid feces after saline purge—or high enema after saline purge—for cysts and trophozoites. Scrapings and biopsies may be obtained through a sigmoidoscope. Liver abscess aspirates should be collected in a series of approximately 20 ml samples for detection of trophozoites and all discarded but the last. Blood is required for serologic tests and cell counts.

B. Microscopic Examination: If possible, always examine fresh warm feces for trophozoites. Otherwise, stain smears with trichrome or iron-hematoxylin stain. The stools in amebic dysentery can usually be distinguished from those in bacillary dysentery by the fact that the former contain much fecal debris; small amounts of blood with strings of nontenacious mucus and red cells often degenerated and clumped; few polymorphonuclear cells or macrophages, though these are not degenerated as in bacillary dysentery; scattered Charcot-Leyden crystals; and trophozoites. Although considerable experience is required to distinguish *E histolytica* from commensal amebas (see below and pp 513 and 514), it is necessary to do so because misdiagnosis often leads to unnecessary treatment or overtreatment.

Differentiation of *E histolytica* (H) and *E coli* (C), the most common other intestinal ameba, can be made in stained smears as follows:

1. **Trophozoites**—The cytoplasm in H is glassy, with almost no inclusions except perhaps red cells and vacuoles (spherical when present). The cytoplasm in C is granular, with many bacterial and other inclusions and ellipsoidal vacuoles. Ectoplasm usually is clearly demarcated in H but not in C. The nucleus of H has a very small central endosome and fine regular chromatin granules lining the periphery (sometimes in a crescentic distribution); the nucleus of C has a larger, eccentric endosome, and the peripheral chromatin is more coarsely beaded and less evenly distributed around the nuclear membrane; the nucleus at times appears to rest in a clear vacuole. Moribund trophozoites and precysts of H and C are generally indistinguishable.

2. **Cysts**—Glycogen vacuoles disappear during successive divisions. Nuclei resemble those of the trophozoites. Occasional cysts of H and C may have 8 and 16 nuclei, respectively. Cysts of H in many preparations contain many uninucleate early cysts; these are rarely seen with C. Binucleate developing cysts of C often show the nuclei pushed against the cell wall by the large central glycogen vacuole. Chromatoidal bodies in early cysts of H are blunt-ended bars; those of C are splinter-like, do not have blunt, rounded ends, and often occur in clusters. *E coli* is present in 15–20% of normal individuals.

C. Culture: Diagnostic cultures are made in a layer of fluid overlying a solid nutrient base, partial anaerobiosis being produced by appropriate incubation or by use of thioglycollate. Dobell's diphasic and Cleveland-Collier media are most often used for diagnosis, and media such as Balamuth's for investigation.

D. Serology: The CF test is not always satisfactory because a good and highly specific antigen is not available. The indirect hemagglutination test is now used routinely and is of value when stool examinations are negative, as in extraintestinal amebiasis. Commercial preparations are available employing the latex agglutination technic (Serameba); Ouchterlony double diffusion (ParaTek); and counterelectrophoresis (Amoebogen). Positive responses to several tests are of value in supporting a tentative diagnosis in doubtful cases of extraintestinal amebiasis.

Treatment

Metronidazole (Flagyl) was considered the drug of choice but is now suspected of causing serious side-effects. However, the risk of giving metronidazole may be worth taking in a seriously ill patient with intestinal amebiasis or liver abscess. Dehydroemetine or emetine is still useful for severe hepatic abscess when rapid drug action is required. Metronidazole has been reported to be less effective for cyst passers, for which oxytetracycline plus a direct-acting amebicide may still be preferred. Among such drugs are diiodohydroxyquin, chiniofon, carbarsone, acetarsol, diloxanide furoate, and paromomycin. Diloxanide furoate is the drug of choice for nondysenteric intestinal amebiasis, although this drug is not available for clinical use in the USA. Diiodohydroxyquin at higher than prescribed doses or with prolonged use may produce optic neuritis. Cardiac toxicity from emetine must be carefully considered and monitored; alcohol with metronidazole is contraindicated.

Epidemiology, Prevention, & Control

Cysts are usually ingested through contaminated water. In the tropics, contaminated vegetables and food are also important cyst sources; flies have been incriminated in areas of fecal pollution. Asymptomatic cyst passers are the main source of contamination and may be responsible for severe epidemic outbreaks where sewage leaks in the water supply or breakdown of sanitary discipline occurs (as in mental, geriatric, or children's institutions). A high-carbohydrate, low-protein diet favors the development of amebic dysentery both in experimental animals and in known human cases. Control measures consist of improving environmental and food sanitation. Treatment of carriers is controversial, although it is agreed that these people should be barred from food handling. No fully satisfactory and safe drug is yet available for chemoprophylaxis.

OTHER INTESTINAL AMEBAS

Entamoeba histolytica must be distinguished from 4 other amebas which are also intestinal parasites of man: (1) *E coli* (see also above), which is very common; (2) *Dientamoeba fragilis,* the only intestinal ameba other than *E histolytica* that has been suspected of causing diarrhea and dyspepsia, but in the manner of *Giardia* and not by invasion; (3) *Iodamoeba bütschlii;* and (4) *Endolimax nana.* These amebas and their cysts are illustrated on pp 513 and 514. To facilitate detection, cysts should be concentrated by the zinc sulfate flotation technic. Unstained, trichrome- or iron-hematoxylin-stained, and iodine-stained preparations should be searched systematically. Mixed infections may occur. PVA fixation is especially valuable for preservation of trophozoites; MIF is of particular usefulness for population surveys. The presence of nonpathogenic amebas is strongly indicative of poor sanitation or of accidental fecal contamination—both warnings of possible exposure to pathogenic *E histolytica.*

Key for Identification of Amebic Trophozoites

Examine fresh warm feces; or, if this is impracticable, feces that have been promptly preserved while still fresh and warm. Include exudate and flecks of mucus in the specimen.

(1) If all trophozoites have one nucleus, see paragraph (2), below.

If more than half of trophozoites have 2 nuclei, the organism is:

Dientamoeba fragilis—a small (mostly 5—15 μm) rounded ameba with nuclei containing a large chromatin mass in a clear space; no peripheral chromatin and no cysts. *D fragilis* prevalence is sometimes high in institutional populations. Often overlooked.

(2) If nucleus has peripheral granules, see paragraph (3), below.

If the nucleus has no peripheral granules, a subspherical endosome larger than the radius of the nucleus, and is surrounded by large light granules, the organism is:

Iodamoeba bütschlii—an ameba with a characteristic cyst (see below). Its prevalence is usually very low.

(3) If the peripheral granules of the nucleus are regularly arranged and the endosome is small, see paragraph (4), below.

If the peripheral granules are scattered and scarce and the endosome is irregular and much larger than the radius of the nucleus, the organism is:

Endolimax nana—a small organism often present in 15—20% of a population.

(4) If the cytoplasm is not coarsely granular, nuclei are always invisible in saline preparations, trophozoites move steadily and in one direction by streaming into blunt pseudopods, and some contain erythrocytes undergoing digestion but not bacteria; or if in an iron-hematoxylin-stained preparation the nuclear membrane is delicate and lined with a single layer of fine chromatin granules and the karyosome is minute and central, the organism is either:

Entamoeba histolytica—The pathogenic trophozoites are present only in dysenteric or diarrheal fluid feces, and are usually large (20—60 μm). (Do not confuse with macrophages containing erythrocytes; these may also contain bacteria, and they do not progress in one direction with single blunt pseudopods.) Verify identification by examining a series of stool specimens and searching for identifiable cysts. Pathogenic trophozoites are most often found in flecks of mucoid exudate.

or: *Entamoeba hartmanni (E histolytica* var *hartmanni,* or small race *E histolytica* of some authors)—nonpathogenic and present in fluid or formed feces, always small (8—15 μm). See Cysts, below.

If present in fluid, semiformed, or formed feces, the cytoplasm is coarsely granular, nuclei are sometimes visible in saline preparation, trophozoites do not move progressively but protrude pseudopods in several directions simultaneously, the cytoplasm contains bacteria but not erythrocytes; if in iron-hematoxylin preparations the nuclear membrane is distinct and lined with large and irregular chromatin granules; or if larger than 15 μm, the organism is:

Entamoeba coli—a normal commensal that may be almost impossible to differentiate from *E histolytica* in a fluid stool, except in the cystic state (see below).

Key for Identification of Amebic Cysts

No cysts are known for *Dientamoeba fragilis.*

(1) If mature cysts have 4 nuclei, see paragraph (2), below.

If mature cysts are often irregularly shaped, have 1—2 large nuclei with a large eccentric karyosome and an adjoining cluster of granules and a large iodine-staining vacuole, the organism is:

Iodamoeba bütschlii.

If mature cysts have 8 nuclei, the organism is:

Entamoeba coli.

(2) If quadrinucleate cysts are oval or ellipsoid and the nuclei have distinct large chromatin masses, the organism is:

Endolimax nana.

If the cysts are spherical and the nuclei have regular peripheral chromatin granules and a small karyosome, the organism is:

Entamoeba histolytica or *E hartmanni* (mean diameters respectively above and below 10 μm).

Table 2. Time factors of the various plasmodia in relation to cycles.

	Length of Sexual Cycle (in mosquito at 27° C)	Prepatent Period* (in man) (Pre-erythrocytic Cycle)	Length of Asexual Cycle (in man)
P vivax (tertian or vivax malaria)	8–9 days	8 days	48 hours
P malariae (quartan or malariae malaria)	15–20 days	15–16 days	72 hours
P falciparum (malignant tertian or falciparum malaria)	9–10 days	5–7 days	36–48 hours
P ovale (ovale malaria)	14 days	9 days	48 hours

*Pre-erythrocytic period only. Full incubation period before clinical malaria usually includes prepatent period (which ends 48 hours after infection of the erythrocytes) plus 2 or 3 erythrocytic schizogonic cycles and may extend over a much longer time.

THE PLASMODIA

The sporozoan protozoa of the genus *Plasmodium* are pigment-producing ameboid intracellular parasites of vertebrates with one habitat in red cells and another in cells of other tissues. Transmission to humans is by the bloodsucking bite of females of various species of mosquitoes of the genus *Anopheles*.

Morphology & Identification

A. Typical Organisms: There are at least 5 species of plasmodia that may infect man: *P vivax, P ovale, P malariae, P falciparum,* and *P knowlesi*. Natural transmission of *P knowlesi* to man has only recently been demonstrated in Malaysia. In addition, at least 2 species of nonhuman primate plasmodia, *P cynomolgi* and *P brasilianum,* are transmissible to man experimentally and probably also in nature. The morphology and certain other characteristics of the 4 principal species that infect man are summarized in Table 3. (See also illustrations on p 516.) *P cynomolgi* is similar to *P vivax* in morphology and in erythrocytic cycle length. *P knowlesi,* morphologically distinct from the other species, is also unique in having a 24-hour erythrocytic schizogonic cycle.

B. Culture: Human malaria parasites have been cultivated with limited success in fluid media containing serum, erythrocytes, inorganic salts, and various growth factors and amino acids. Such media will sup-

Table 3. Some characteristic features of the malaria parasites of man (Romanowsky-stained preparations).

	P vivax (Benign Tertian Malaria)	*P malariae* (Quartan Malaria)	*P falciparum* (Malignant Tertian Malaria)	*P ovale* (Ovale Malaria)
Parasitized red cells	Enlarged, pale. Fine stippling (Schüffner's dots). Primarily invades reticulocytes, young red cells.	Not enlarged. No stippling (except with special stains). Primarily invades older red cells.	Not enlarged. Coarse stippling (Maurer's clefts). Invades all red cells regardless of age.	Enlarged, pale. Schüffner's dots conspicuous. Cells often oval, fimbriated, or crenated.
Level of usual maximum parasitemia	Up to 30,000/cu mm of blood.	Less than 10,000/cu mm.	May reach 500,000/cu mm.	Less than 10,000/cu mm.
Ring stage trophozoites	Large rings (1/3–1/2 red cell diameter). Usually one chromatin granule; accolé forms rare; ring delicate.	Large rings (1/3 red cell diameter). Usually one chromatin granule; ring compact.	Small rings (1/5 red cell diameter). Often 2 granules; frequent accolé forms; multiple infections common; ring delicate.	Large rings (1/3 red cell diameter). Usually one chromatin granule; ring dense.
Pigment in developing trophozoites	Fine; light brown; scattered fine particles.	Coarse; dark brown; scattered clumps; abundant.	Coarse; black; few clumps.	Coarse; dark yellow-brown; scattered coarse particles.
Older trophozoites	Very pleomorphic.	Occasional band forms.	Compact and rounded. Very rare in peripheral blood.	Compact and rounded.
Mature schizonts (segmenters)	More than 12 merozoites (14–24).	Less than 12 large merozoites (6–12). Often rosette.	Usually more than 12 merozoites (8–32). Very rare in peripheral blood.	Less than 12 large merozoites (6–12). Often rosette.
Gametocytes	Round or oval.	Round or oval.	Crescentic.	Round or oval.
Distribution	All forms in peripheral blood.	All forms in peripheral blood.	Only rings and crescents (gametocytes) in peripheral blood.	All forms in peripheral blood.

port the malaria parasites through a few cycles of schizogony. Cultivation of certain other species has been more successful; the avian plasmodia, in particular, can be grown in tissue cultures as well as in chick or duck embryos. Studies in culture have provided much fundamental biologic information about these protozoa.

C. Growth Characteristics and Requirements: In host red cells the parasites convert hemoglobin to globin and hematin, which becomes the characteristic malarial pigment. Globin is split by proteolytic enzymes and digested. Oxygen, dextrose, lactose, and erythrocytic protein are also utilized. Growth requirements, in addition to carbohydrates, proteins, and fats, include methionine, riboflavin, ascorbic acid, pantothenic acid, and para-aminobenzoic acid.

D. Variation: Variations of strains exist within each of the 4 typical human species. Variations have been detected in morphology, pathogenicity, resistance to drug therapy, infectivity for mosquitoes, and other characteristics. Complete immunity is usually strain-specific.

Pathogenesis, Pathology, & Clinical Findings

Human infection results from the bite of an infected female *Anopheles* mosquito, in which the sexual or sporogonic cycle of development takes place (production of infective sporozoites). The first stage of development in man takes place in parenchymal cells of the liver (the pre-erythrocytic cycle). At the end of this cycle, parasites (merozoites) leave their ruptured parasitized cells, enter the bloodstream, and invade erythrocytes. Other merozoites may continue in the liver or in the exoerythrocytic cycle of asexual schizogony. Parasites in the red cells multiply in a species-characteristic fashion, leaving their host cells synchronously. This is the erythrocytic cycle of asexual schizogony, with successive broods of merozoites appearing at 48-hour intervals *(P vivax, P ovale,* and *P falciparum)* or every 72 hours *(P malariae).* The incubation period includes the pre-erythrocytic cycle and at least one or 2 erythrocytic cycles. For *P vivax* and *P falciparum,* this period is usually 10–15 days, but it may be much longer (in some cases even months). The incubation period of *P malariae* averages about 28 days. *P falciparum* multiplication is confined to the red cells after the first liver cycle. Without treatment, falciparum infection will terminate spontaneously in less than 2–3 years (usually 6–8 months) unless it ends fatally in a shorter period. The other 3 species continue to multiply in liver cells long after the initial bloodstream invasion, or, it is now thought, there may be a *delayed* multiplication in the liver. The exoerythrocytic cycles coexist with erythrocytic cycles and may persist after the parasites have apparently disappeared from the peripheral blood. Resurgence of an erythrocytic infection (relapse) occurs when merozoites from the liver are not phagocytosed in the bloodstream and succeed in reestablishing a red cell infection (clinical malaria). *P vivax* and *P ovale* infections may persist without treatment for as long as 5 years. *P*

malariae infections lasting 40 years have been reported, though these are thought to be *recrudescences* of a cryptic infection rather than a true relapse from a liver infection.

During the erythrocytic cycles, certain merozoites become differentiated as male and female gametocytes. Thus, the sexual cycle begins in the vertebrate host. For completion of this cycle and its continuation into the sporogonic phase, the gametocytes must be taken up and ingested by bloodsucking female *Anopheles* as outlined in Fig 1.

P vivax, P malariae, and *P ovale* parasitemias are relatively low-grade, primarily because the parasites favor either young or old red cells but not both; *P falciparum* invades red cells of all ages, and the parasitemia may be very high. *P falciparum* also causes the parasitized red cells to agglutinate and adhere to capillary walls, with resulting obstruction, thrombosis, and local ischemia. *P falciparum* infections are therefore frequently more serious than the others, with a much higher rate of severe or fatal complications (cerebral malaria, malarial hyperpyrexia, gastrointestinal disorders, algid malaria, blackwater fever).

P malariae has also been implicated in a nephrotic syndrome in children—"quartan nephrosis"—with a peak incidence at about age 5. It is characterized by generalized edema, oliguria, massive proteinuria, and hypoproteinemia. Tubular degeneration is visible in renal biopsy specimens. Glomerular lesions include basement membrane thickening and sometimes fibrosis. An antigen-antibody complex to quartan malaria or an autoimmune response to the sensitized kidney may be responsible for the patchy, membranous glomerulonephrosis, progressive sclerosis, and secondary tubular changes. According to Maegraith, it is a degenerative, not an inflammatory, condition and is therefore a nephrosis and not a nephritis. The prognosis is good with early diagnosis, poor in advanced disease. The response to antimalarials given before irreversible renal changes occur is usually good.

Periodic paroxysms of malaria are closely related to events in the bloodstream. An initial chill, lasting from 15 minutes to 1 hour, begins as a generation of parasites rupture their host red cells and escape into the blood. Nausea, vomiting, and headache are common at this time. The succeeding febrile stage, lasting several hours, is characterized by a spiking fever, sometimes reaching 105° F or more. During this stage, the parasites presumably invade new red cells. The third or sweating stage concludes the episode. The fever subsides, and the patient falls asleep and later awakes feeling relatively well. In the early stages of infection, the cycles are frequently asynchronous and the fever patterns irregular; later, the paroxysms may recur at regular 48- or 72-hour intervals. As the disease progresses, splenomegaly and, to a lesser extent, hepatomegaly appear. A normocytic anemia also develops, particularly in *P falciparum* infections.

Diagnostic Laboratory Tests
A. Specimens and Microscopic Examination: The

EXOGENOUS PHASE IN MOSQUITO
SEXUAL CYCLE (SPOROGONY)

ENDOGENOUS PHASE IN MAN
ASEXUAL CYCLE (SCHIZOGONY)

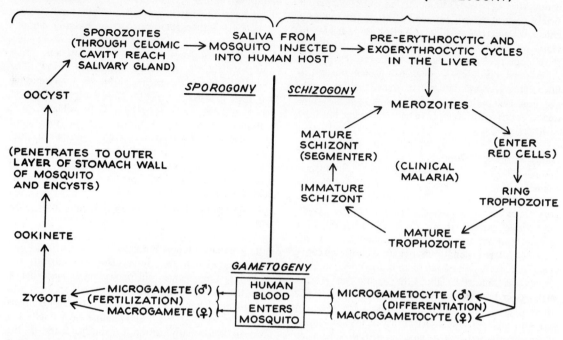

Figure 1. Life cycle of the malaria parasites. Continuous cycling or delayed multiplication in the liver may cause periodic relapse over several years (2–3 years in *P ovale,* 6–8 years in *P vivax*), and a low-level blood infection may have a long-delayed resurgence of multiplication (recrudescence) in *P malariae.* However, relapse does not occur with *P falciparum,* though a long prepatent period may occur (perhaps drug-suppressed), resulting in initial symptoms appearing up to 6 months or more after exposure.

thick blood film stained with one of the Romanowsky stains (usually Giemsa's) is the mainstay of malaria diagnosis. This preparation concentrates the parasites and permits detection even of light infections. Examination of thin blood films, also stained with Giemsa's stain, is necessary as a second step for parasite species differentiation.

B. Other Laboratory Findings: Normocytic anemia of variable severity, with poikilocytosis and anisocytosis, may be detected. During the paroxysms there may be transient leukocytosis; subsequently, leukopenia develops with a relative increase in large mononuclear cells. Hepatic function tests may give abnormal results during attacks, but liver function reverts to normal with treatment or spontaneous recovery. The presence of protein and casts in the urine of children with *P malariae* is suggestive of quartan nephrosis. In severe *P falciparum* infections, renal damage may cause oliguria and the appearance of casts, protein, and red cells in the urine.

Immunity

The mechanisms of immunity in malaria have been the cause of considerable study but are still not clearly understood. An acquired strain-specific complete immunity has been observed which appears to depend upon the presence of parasites in the bloodstream of the host. This so-called **premunition** or con-

comitant immunity is soon lost after the parasites disappear from the blood. Exoerythrocytic forms in the liver cannot alone support premunition, and they elicit no host inflammatory response. Hence, superinfection of the liver by homologous strains can continue to occur. Premunition is heavily dependent upon the reticuloendothelial system, which becomes extremely active in patent malaria infections (ie, infection with detectable blood forms). In addition to acquired strain-specific immunity, natural genetically determined partial immunity to malaria occurs in some populations, notably in Africa, where such hemoglobinopathies as sickle cell anemia, glucose-6-phosphate dehydrogenase deficiency, and other hereditary blood dyscrasias appear to provide considerable protection against lethal levels of *P falciparum* infection (though low-level infection is widespread in these populations).

Treatment & Prevention

Chloroquine (Aralen) is the drug of choice for treatment of all forms of malaria during the acute attack. This drug will terminate *P falciparum* infections, in which there are no exoerythrocytic forms. Primaquine, which disposes of the exoerythrocytic tissue forms, must be used in conjunction with chloroquine to achieve complete cure of other forms of malaria. There is no satisfactory alternative to primaquine for eradication of tissue forms, but other compounds, eg, amodiaquine (Camoquin), quinine, and proguanil (Paludrine), are available for treatment of acute attacks. Drug-resistant strains of *P falciparum* should be treated with quinine (intravenously in severe cases), with pyrimethamine and either sulfadiazine or dapsone, or with sulformethoxine plus pyrimethamine.

Suppressive prophylaxis can be achieved with chloroquine diphosphate or amodiaquine except in chloroquine-resistant falciparum areas, such as southeast Asia and parts of South America, where various combinations of quinine and sulfonamides must be relied on.

Epidemiology & Control

Malaria today is generally limited to the tropics and subtropics; in years past, transmission occurred in many temperate regions. Temperate zone malaria is usually unstable and relatively easy to control or eradicate; tropical malaria is often more stable, difficult to control, and far more difficult to eradicate. In the tropics, malaria generally disappears at altitudes above 6000 feet. *P vivax* and *P falciparum,* the most common species, are found throughout the malaria belt. *P malariae* is also broadly distributed but considerably less common. *P ovale* is rare except in West Africa, where it seems to replace *P vivax.* All forms of malaria can be artificially transmitted by blood transfusion from an infected donor, but natural infection (other than transplacental transmission) takes place only through the bite of an infected female *Anopheles* mosquito.

Malaria control depends upon elimination of mosquito breeding places, personal protection against mosquitoes (screens, netting, repellents), suppressive drug therapy for exposed persons, and adequate treatment of cases and carriers. Eradication, a highly complex field, requires elimination of contact between *Anopheles* mosquitoes and man for a sufficient length of time to permit elimination, by treatment and spontaneous cure, of all cases in an area. At the end of this period a state of anophelinism-without-malaria will theoretically have been achieved. The results of massive efforts in highly endemic tropical areas have thus far been disappointing. Many costly eradication projects that have been under way for the past 20 years are being replaced with control programs specifically geared to the mosquito vector ecology and the disease epidemiology of each area.

ISOSPORA

Isospora belli and *Isospora hominis* are intestinal sporozoan protozoa of man, the causes of a disease known as coccidiosis or isosporosis. Numerous species of intestinal sporozoa or coccidia, some of them important pathogens, occur in other animals.

Morphology & Identification

A. Typical Organisms: Although all life cycle stages are known for many species of coccidia, only the elongated ovoid oocysts are known for *I belli* and *I hominis.* The life cycles of these parasites in man have never been adequately studied, but intestinal biopsies of patients with chronic isosporiasis recently demonstrated asexual schizogonic and sexual phases. In addition, important new information is available from studies with *Sarcocystis* (see *S lindemanni,* below). The oocyst of *I hominis* measures about $16 \times 10 \mu m$; that of *I belli* is larger, $25-33 \times 12-16 \mu m$. The oocyst may contain a single sporoblast, 2 sporoblasts, or 2 sporocysts, each with 4 sporozoites. In fresh stool specimens, *I belli* oocysts are often monosporoblastic; *I hominis* oocysts are more often disporoblastic or even disporocystic. In addition, the *I belli* oocyst wall is often asymmetric, whereas that of *I hominis* is smoothly ovoid or spherical.

B. Culture: These parasites have not been cultivated.

Pathogenesis & Clinical Findings

The isospora that infects humans inhabits the small intestine, where schizogony takes place below the intestinal epithelial cells. The oocysts are shed into the intestinal lumen and pass out in the stools. Signs and symptoms of coccidiosis are apparently due to the invasion and multiplication of the parasites in the intestinal mucosa. Infections may be silent or symptomatic. About 1 week after ingestion of viable cysts, a low-grade fever, lassitude, and malaise may appear, followed soon by mild diarrhea and vague abdominal pain. The infection has been thought to be self-limited after 1–2 weeks, but a recent review describes cases with diarrhea, weight loss, and fever lasting from 6 weeks to 6 months. Symptomatic coccidiosis is more common in children than in adults. Chronic infections previously recorded were in poorly nourished populations living under unsanitary conditions where continued reinfection was possible.

Diagnostic Laboratory Tests

Diagnosis rests upon detection of the immature oocysts of *I belli* or the mature oocysts and sporocysts of *I hominis* in fresh stool specimens. Stool concentration technics are usually necessary.

Immunity

Apparently no immunity is conferred by infection. The many species of coccidia are notably host-specific.

Treatment

Treatment of mild cases consists of bed rest and a bland diet for a few days. No specific treatment has been described for the more severe and chronic conditions.

Epidemiology

Human coccidiosis is usually sporadic and most common in the tropics and subtropics, although high prevalence rates have been described for Rumania, Holland, and Chile. It is moderately endemic in parts of South Africa, several South American countries, and islands of the Southwest Pacific. More than 800 cases have so far been reported in the Western Hemisphere, including more than 40 from the USA (California and the southeastern states). The infection is easily overlooked on routine stool examination for parasites and is probably more common than the records indicate. New infections result from ingestion of viable cysts.

SARCOCYSTIS LINDEMANNI

Sarcocystis lindemanni of man, along with other species of *Sarcocystis,* is a protozoon that has recently been shown to be a coccidian. These parasites, some species of which are pathogenic, are found in the muscles of many kinds of vertebrate animals. Human volunteers fed raw beef and pork with *Sarcocystis* cysts later passed *Isospora*-like oocysts in their stools. Similar results have been obtained with dogs and cats. No tissue phase of *Isospora* has yet been found, though recent experimental evidence in laboratory animals suggests that *Sarcocystis* may be the tissue stage of *Isospora* in man. This controversial subject is currently a matter of intensive research interest.

Morphology & Identification

In the muscles the parasites develop in elongated cysts, known as sarcocysts or "Miescher's tubes," measuring from less than 1 mm to several cm in length. The sarcocyst is partitioned by septa into chambers containing many uninucleate crescentic spores or "Rainey's corpuscles." The mature corpuscle, properly called a **cystozoite,** is a trophozoite comparable to the merozoite of *Plasmodium* that develops into a gametocyte. It is $10-15$ μm in length, pointed at one end, rounded at the other, with an oval vacuole near the pointed end. The cystozoites, when set free by rupture of the cyst, are motile; they have occasionally been found in blood films from mammalian hosts. *S lindemanni* of man is morphologically indistinguishable from species found in other animals.

Pathogenesis & Clinical Findings

Heavy sarcocystis infections may be fatal in some species of animals (eg, mice, sheep, swine). Extracts of the parasite contain a toxin, sarcocystin, which is probably responsible for the pathogenic effects. This toxin is fatal when injected into rabbits. About 15 cases of human infection have been reported, mostly at autopsy following death due to other causes; however, inapparent infections are probably common. It is not clear that the parasite is pathogenic for man. Fleeting subcutaneous swellings, eosinophilia, and heart failure have, however, been attributed to *S lindemanni.* Sarcocysts have been found in man in the heart, larynx, and tongue as well as in the skeletal muscles of the extremities.

Diagnostic Laboratory Tests

Since the infection ordinarily causes no symptoms or signs in man, it is usually detected only at autopsy. A reliable CF test has been developed for detection of suspected infections. Other tests should be developed now that *Isospora*-like sporocysts and oocysts have been found in the feces of volunteers fed *Sarcocystis* cysts. The feces of humans, cats, and dogs who have an experimental *Sarcocystis* infection generally demonstrate sporocysts separated from the thin-walled oocysts (rather than the intact oocysts seen in other coccidial infections).

Treatment

There is no known effective treatment.

Epidemiology

Sarcocystis shows little host specificity; cross-infections between various hosts can easily be produced. Since most *Sarcocystis* species are morphologically identical, it is likely that many of the described species (including *S lindemanni*) are not valid. Man is probably infected by ingestion of raw or poorly cooked infected lamb, beef, or other meats. *Sarcocystis* infections are particularly common in sheep, cattle, and horses. There appears to be a 2-host cycle, with sarcocysts being formed in the muscles of *herbivores* (including man) and oocysts in the intestine of *predators* such as cats and dogs (and man). Humans appear to be able to develop both the asexual form of the parasite (sarcocysts in muscles) and the sexual form (oocysts in the intestine). Herbivores are infected by eating grass contaminated with oocysts or sporocysts, while predators are infected when they eat infected herbivore tissues.

TOXOPLASMA GONDII

Toxoplasma gondii is a coccidian protozoon of worldwide distribution that infects a wide range of animals and birds but does not appear to cause disease in them. The normal final hosts are the cat and other members of the family Felidae. The organism in man produces either neonatal or postnatal toxoplasmosis. The former is usually of great severity and the latter generally much less so. The great majority of human infections are asymptomatic.

Morphology & Identification

A. Typical Organisms: The organisms consist of boat-shaped, thin-walled cells, $4-7 \times 2-4$ μm within tissue cells and somewhat larger (up to 10×4 μm) outside them. They stain lightly with Giemsa's stain; fixed cells often appear crescentic. Packed intracellular aggregates may be seen (cf p 515). True cysts are found in the brain or certain other tissues. These cysts contain many thousands of spore-like trophozoites capable of initiating a new infection in the animal ingesting the cyst-bearing tissues.

B. Culture: *T gondii* may be cultured only in the presence of living cells, in tissue culture or eggs. Typical intracellular and extracellular organisms may be seen.

C. Growth Requirements: Optimal growth is at about 37–39° C in living cells.

D. Variations: There is considerable strain variation in infectivity and virulence, possibly related to the degree of adaptation to a particular host. Variations in microscopic appearance are negligible.

Pathogenesis, Pathology, & Clinical Findings

The trophozoite directly destroys cells and has a predilection for parenchymal cells and those of the reticuloendothelial system. Man is relatively resistant, but a low-grade lymph node infection resembling infectious mononucleosis may occur. Congenital infection leads to stillbirths, chorioretinitis, intracerebral calcifications, psychomotor disturbances, and hydrocephaly or microcephaly. In these cases, the mother was infected during pregnancy. A major cause of blindness and other congenital defects is prenatal toxoplasmosis. Infection during the first trimester generally results in stillbirth or major CNS anomalies.

Diagnostic Laboratory Tests

A. Specimens: Blood, bone marrow, CSF, and exudates for direct inspection; lymph node biopsy material; tonsillar and striated muscle biopsies; and ventricular fluid (in neonatal infections) may be required.

B. Microscopic Examination: Smears and sections stained with Giemsa's stain may show the organism. The densely packed cysts ("pseudocysts"), chiefly in the brain or other parts of the CNS, suggest chronic infection. Identification must be confirmed by isolation in animals.

C. Animal Inoculation: This is essential for definitive diagnosis. A variety of specimens are inoculated intraperitoneally into groups of mice that have been dye-tested to make certain that they are free from infection. If no deaths occur, the mice are observed for about 6 weeks, and tail or heart blood is then tested for specific antibody. The diagnosis is confirmed by demonstration of cysts in the brains of the inoculated mice.

D. Serology: The Sabin-Feldman dye test is valuable for diagnosis and surveys. It depends upon the appearance in 2–3 weeks of antibodies that will render the membrane of laboratory-cultured living *T gondii* permeable to alkaline methylene blue, so that organisms are unstained in the presence of positive serum. A CF test may be positive (1:8 titer) as early as 1 month after infection, but it is valueless in many chronic infections. The IFA and IHA tests are routinely used for diagnostic purposes. Frenkel's intracutaneous test is of limited clinical value but is useful for epidemiologic surveys.

Immunity

There are great variations in strains and hosts, and a degree of acquired immunity (or premunition in some cases) may develop. Antibodies in mothers, as detected in either blood or milk, tend to fall within a few months.

Treatment

Acute infections can be treated with a combination of pyrimethamine and trisulfapyrimidines. Spiramycin has been used in Europe and apparently is superior to the other drugs; it will be available soon in the USA.

Epidemiology, Prevention, & Control

Transplacental infection of the fetus has long been recognized as a mode of transmission. Domestic cats have recently been incriminated in the transmission of the parasite to man. The infective stage is an *Isospora*-like oocyst found only in the cat and other felids. Rodents also appear to play a role in transmission since they harbor cysts in their tissues that are transmissible to cats. New control recommendations are being devised in the light of many new epidemiologic findings. Measures leading to minimization of human contact with cat feces are clearly important in control, particularly for pregnant women with negative serologic tests. Further work on the similar life histories and relationships of *Toxoplasma, Sarcocystis,* and *Isospora* will lead to greater epidemiologic understanding and improved control.

BALANTIDIUM COLI

Balantidium coli, the cause of balantidiasis or balantidial dysentery, is the largest intestinal protozoon of man. Morphologically similar ciliate parasites are found in swine and lower primates.

Morphology & Identification

A. Typical Organisms: The trophozoite is a large, ciliated, oval organism, 60 × 45 μm in average dimensions (occasionally almost twice as large). Its motion is characteristic, a combination of steady, boring progression and rotation around the long axis. The cell wall is lined with spiral rows of cilia which also extend into the deep and conspicuous anterior cytostome. The cytoplasm surrounds 2 contractile vacuoles, food particles and vacuoles, and 2 nuclei—a large, kidney-shaped macronucleus and a much smaller, spherical micronucleus. When the organism encysts, it secretes a spherical or oval double-layered wall. The macronucleus, contractile vacuoles, and portions of the ciliated cell wall may be visible in the cyst, which ranges from 45–65 μm in diameter.

B. Culture: These organisms may be cultivated in a variety of simple media, including those used for cultivation of intestinal amebas.

Pathogenesis, Pathology, & Clinical Findings

When cysts are ingested by the new host, the cyst

walls dissolve and the released trophozoites descend to the colon, where they feed on bacteria and fecal debris, multiply, and form cysts that pass out in the feces. It seems apparent that most infections are harmless. However, rarely, the trophozoites will invade the mucosa and submucosa of the large bowel and terminal ileum. As they multiply, abscesses and irregular ulcerations with overhanging lips are formed. The number of lesions formed depends upon the intensity of infection and the degree of individual host susceptibility. Chronic recurrent diarrhea, alternating with constipation, is the commonest clinical manifestation, but attacks of severe dysentery with bloody mucoid stools, tenesmus, and colic may occur intermittently in light as well as heavy infections. Extreme cases may mimic severe intestinal amebiasis. Fatal cases have occasionally been reported.

Diagnostic Laboratory Tests

The diagnosis of balantidial infection, whether symptomatic or not, depends upon laboratory detection of trophozoites in liquid stools or, more rarely, of cysts in formed stools. There are no other constant and distinctive laboratory findings. Sigmoidoscopy may be useful for obtaining material directly from ulcerations for examination. Culturing is rarely necessary for diagnosis.

Immunity

Man appears to have a high natural resistance to balantidial infection. Factors underlying individual susceptibility are not known.

Treatment

A course of oxytetracycline may be followed by diiodohydroxyquin if necessary.

Epidemiology

B coli is found in man throughout the world, particularly in the tropics, but it is a rare infection. Only a few hundred cases have been recorded. Infection results from ingestion of viable cysts previously passed in the stools by humans and possibly by swine. Although it has been generally accepted that pigs are important sources of human infections, some epidemiologic evidence suggests that this may not be so.

PNEUMOCYSTIS CARINII

Pneumocystis carinii, now thought to be a fungus related to the yeasts, formerly was placed with the sporozoans and is included here for completeness, though it very likely is properly placed elsewhere. It appears to be widely distributed among animals in nature—including rats, mice, and dogs—but usually without causing disease in them. The organism may cause an interstitial plasma cell pneumonitis in man, particularly in infants, old people, and patients receiving immunosuppressive therapy.

Morphology & Identification

A. Typical Organisms: The most characteristic stage is a rosette of 8 pear-shaped "sporozoites," each 1–2 μm, in a "cyst" 7–10 μm in diameter. Earlier stages consist of 1–4 nuclei in a mucoid sphere, respectively staining red and blue within a red-violet membrane when heavily stained with Giemsa's stain. Organisms are seen in large numbers packed in foamy material and among many plasma cells and eosinophils in the pulmonary alveoli and bronchioles of fatal cases. Some organisms may be within histiocytes. Pulmonary infections with pneumonitis have been reported in rats.

B. Culture: Not reported. Attempts to culture the organism in the lungs of cortisone-treated rats or mice should be made.

Pathogenesis, Pathology, & Clinical Findings

Most infections in man are probably inapparent. Excessive multiplication leading to blocking of the alveolar respiratory surface appears to occur, especially in premature or marasmic infants but also in those whose resistance has been lowered, ie, children and adults receiving corticosteroids, cytotoxic drugs, or antibiotics over extended periods, or those suffering from agammaglobulinemia. An interstitial plasma cell pneumonitis develops (detectable in x-rays), with alveoli filled with organisms and foamy material.

Diagnostic Laboratory Tests

The organism is usually discovered after autopsy, but lung puncture biopsy has been reported to be successful. Staining is difficult. Heavy Giemsa staining should be used simultaneously with Böhmer's hematoxylin (30 minutes, without differentiation) and periodic acid-Schiff stain for mucopolysaccharides.

Treatment

Pentamidine isethionate and pyrimethamine are the drugs with most promise.

Epidemiology, Prevention, & Control

The mode of infection is unknown, but cysts, presumably inhaled, may be derived from domestic rodents or pets or from carrier adults.

HELMINTHS: OVA IN FECES & MICROFILARIAE IN BLOOD & TISSUES

Ova (pp 518 and 523) may be detected in feces (or urine, with *Schistosoma haematobium* and sometimes *S japonicum*), preferably after concentration by zinc sulfate centrifugal sedimentation or formalin-triton-NE-ether technics (especially for operculated and schistosome eggs). Eggs of *Enterobius* may be collected directly from the anal margins with cellulose tape on the end of a spatula.

Microfilariae (see Table 5 and p 517) are the embryonic or prelarval stages of filariid worms in humans.

Table 4. Diseases due to helminths.

C = cestode (tapeworm)   N = nematode (roundworm)   T = trematode (fluke)

Disease and Parasite	Location in Host	Mode of Transmission	Geographic Distribution	Treatment of Choice
Angiostrongyliasis; eosinophilic meningoencephalitis *Angiostrongylus cantonensis* (larval) (N), rat lungworm	Larvae in meninges	Eating raw shrimps, prawns; raw garden slugs; aquatic and land snails; infested lettuce	Local in Pacific, especially southwest	Thiabendazole (experimental)
Ascariasis *Ascaris lumbricoides* (N), common roundworm	Small intestine; larvae through lungs	Eating viable eggs from feces-contaminated soil or food	Worldwide, very common	Mebendazole, L-tetramisole, pyrantel pamoate, piperazine citrate
Capillariasis *Capillaria philippinensis*	Small intestine	Undercooked marine fish	Philippines	Mebendazole
Clonorchiasis *Clonorchis sinensis* (T), Chinese liver fluke	Liver	Uncooked freshwater fish	China, Korea, Indochina, Japan, Taiwan	Chloroquine, bithionol, hexachloroparaxylol (China). (Treatment unsatisfactory.)
Cysticercosis (bladder worm) *Taenia solium* (larval) (C)	Subcutaneous; eye, meninges, brain, etc	Ingestion of eggs or regurgitation of gravid proglottid from lower GI tract	Worldwide	Surgical excision
Dipetalonemiasis *Dipetalonema perstans* (N) *(Acanthocheilonema perstans)* (nonpathogenic?)	Peritoneal and other cavities; microfilariae in blood	Bite of gnat *Culicoides*	Equatorial Africa; N coast of S America, Argentina, Panama, Trinidad	Not treated
Dracontiasis *Dracunculus medinensis* (N), Guinea worm	Subcutaneous; usually leg, foot	Drinking water with *Cyclops*	Africa, Arabia to Pakistan; locally elsewhere in Asia	Mechanical or surgical extraction; thiabendazole, niridazole
Echinococcosis, hydatidosis *Echinococcus granulosus,* (larval) *E multilocularis* (larval) (C), hydatid worm	Liver; lung, brain	Contact with dogs, foxes, other canids; eggs from feces	Worldwide but local; sheep-raising areas	Surgical aspiration and excision
Enterobiasis *Enterobius vermicularis* (N), pinworm	Cecum, colon	Anal-oral; self-contamination and internal reinfection	Worldwide	Pyrantel pamoate, piperazine, pyrvinium pamoate
Fascioliasis *Fasciola hepatica* (T), sheep liver fluke	Liver	Watercress, aquatic vegetation	Worldwide, especially sheep-raising areas	Emetine or dehydroemetine (subcutaneous); bithionol, chloroquine
Fasciolopsiasis *Fasciolopsis buski* (T), giant intestinal fluke	Small intestine	Aquatic vegetation	E and SE Asia	Hexylresorcinol crystoids, bithionol, stilbazium iodide
Filariasis *Wuchereria bancrofti,* *Brugia malayi* (N), human filarial worms	Lymph nodes; microfilariae in blood	Bite of mosquitoes; several species	Tropical and subtropical, very local but widespread	Diethylcarbamazine
Filariasis, occult *Dirofilaria* species (N), heartworm	Lungs (larvae)	Infected mosquitoes?	India, SE Asia	Diethylcarbamazine or not treated
Gnathostomiasis *Gnathostoma spinigerum* (N), rat stomach worm	Subcutaneous, migratory	Uncooked fish	E and SE Asia	Surgical excision, diethylcarbamazine
Heterophyiasis *Heterophyes heterophyes* (T), intestinal fish fluke of man	Small intestine	Uncooked fish (mullet)	China, Korea, Japan, Taiwan; Israel; Egypt	Tetrachlorethylene, hexylresorcinol crystoids
Hookworms *Ancylostoma duodenale,* *Necator americanus* (N)	Small intestine: larvae through lungs	Through skin, infected soil; from drinking contaminated water *(Ancylostoma)*	Worldwide tropics and North America *(Necator);* temperate zones *(Ancylostoma)*	Bephenium, L-tetramisole, pyrantel pamoate, bitoscanate, mebendazole

Table 4 (cont'd). Diseases due to helminths.

Disease and Parasite	Location in Host	Mode of Transmission	Geographic Distribution	Treatment of Choice
Larva migrans: Cutaneous, creeping eruption *Ancylostoma braziliense* and other domestic animal hook- worms (N)	Subcutaneous, migrat- ing larvae	Contact with soil con- taminated by dog or cat feces	Worldwide	Thiabendazole
Visceral *Toxocara* species, cat and dog roundworms (N)	Liver, lung, eye, brain, other viscera; migrat- ing larvae	Ingesting soil contami- nated by dog or cat feces	Worldwide	Thiabendazole, corti- costeroids
Loiasis *Loa loa* (N)	Subcutaneous, migra- tory; eye. Micro- filariae in blood	Bite of deer flies, *Chrysops*	Equatorial Africa	Surgical removal, diethylcarbamazine, or not treated
Mansonelliasis *Mansonella ozzardi* (N) (nonpathogenic) Manson's filaria	Body cavities; micro- filariae in blood	Bite of gnat *Culi- coides*	Argentina, N coast of S America; Caribbean islands; Panama, Yucatan	Not treated
Metagonimiasis *Metagonimus yokogawai* (T), intestinal fish fluke of man	Small intestine	Uncooked fish	As for *Heterophyes* plus USSR, Balkans, Spain	Tetrachlorethylene, hexylresorcinol crystoids
Onchocerciasis *Onchocerca volvulus* (N), nodular or blinding worm	Subcutaneous; micro- filariae in skin, eyes	Bite of black fly *Simulium*	Equatorial Africa; C and S America	Surgery, diethylcarbamazine
Opisthorchiasis *Opisthorchis felineus,* *O viverrini* (T), Asian liver flukes	Liver	Uncooked fish	E Europe, USSR; Thailand	Chloroquine (treat- ment unsatisfactory)
Paragonimiasis *Paragonimus westermani* (T), lung fluke	Lung	Raw crabs	E and S Asia; N Cen- tral Africa; S America; animals in N America	Bithionol, chloro- quine
Schistosomiasis *Schistosoma haematobium* (T), schistosomes or bilharzia worms, blood flukes; vesicular blood fluke	Venous vessels of uri- nary bladder, large intestine; liver		Africa, widely; Mada- gascar; Arabia to Lebanon	Niridazole, antimony sodium dimercapto- succinate, stibophen, hycanthone
S japonicum (T), Japanese blood fluke	Venous vessels of small intestine; liver	Cercariae (larvae) penetrate skin in snail- infested water	China, Philippines; Japan; potentially Taiwan	Potassium antimony tartrate (tartar emet- ic), sodium antimony tartrate
S mansoni (T), Manson's blood fluke	Venous vessels of colon, rectum; liver		Africa to Near East; parts of S America, Caribbean tropics and subtropics	Stibophen, antimony sodium dimercapto- succinate, hycan- thone, niridazole, tar- tar emetic
Sparganosis *Spirometra mansoni* (larval) (C), pseudophyllidean larva or sparga- num from frogs, snakes, some birds and mammals (adult worms in felids or canids)	Intraorbital wound if used as poultice	Native poultices such as infected raw frog flesh	Orient, occasionally other countries, in- cluding N and S America	Surgical removal
Strongyloidiasis *Strongyloides stercoralis* (N), threadworm	Duodenum, jejunum; larvae through skin, lungs	Through skin and (rarely) by internal reinfection	Worldwide	Thiabendazole, pyr- vinium pamoate
Tapeworm disease (see also Cysticer- cosis, Echinococcosis, Spargano- sis); taeniasis *Diphyllobothrium latum* (C), broad fish tapeworm	Small intestine	Uncooked freshwater fish	Alaska, E Canada, Great Lakes area, NW Florida, parts of S America; N Europe, E Mediterranean, Asiatic USSR, Japan; Australia	Quinacrine, niclosa- mide

Table 4 (cont'd). Diseases due to helminths.

Disease and Parasite	Location in Host	Mode of Transmission	Geographic Distribution	Treatment of Choice
Dipylidium caninum (C), dog tapeworm	Small intestine	Ingestion of crushed fleas, lice from pets	Worldwide	Quinacrine, niclosamide
Hymenolepis diminuta (C), rat tapeworm	Small intestine	Indirectly from rats, mice via infected insects	Worldwide	Quinacrine, niclosamide
H nana (C), dwarf tapeworm	Small intestine	Anal-oral transfer of eggs or ingestion of infected insects; internal reinfection	Worldwide	Niclosamide
Taenia saginata (C), beef tapeworm	Small intestine	Uncooked beef	Worldwide	Niclosamide, quinacrine, paromomycin
T solium (C), pork tapeworm (see also Cysticercosis)	Small intestine	Uncooked pork	Worldwide	Quinacrine, niclosamide, paromomycin
Trichinosis *Trichinella spiralis* (N), trichina worm	Larvae in striated muscle	Uncooked pork	Worldwide	Thiabendazole, corticosteroids
Trichostrongyliasis *Trichostrongylus* species (N)	Small intestine	Ingestion of infective third stage from feces-contaminated food or soil; contact with herbivore feces	E Europe, USSR, Iran	Bephenium, pyrantel pamoate, thiabendazole
Trichuriasis *Trichuris trichiura* (N), whipworm	Cecum; colon	Ingestion of eggs from feces-contaminated soil	Worldwide	Mebendazole, hexylresorcinol enema, thiabendazole

Table 5. Microfilariae.

Filariid	Disease	Distribution	Vectors	Microfilariae		
				Sheath	Tail Nuclei	Periodicity*
Wuchereria bancrofti	Bancroftian and Malayan filariasis: lymphangitis, hydrocele, elephantiasis	Worldwide 41° N to 28° S	Culicidae (mosquitos)	+	Not to tip	Nocturnal or nonperiodic
Brugia malayi		Oriental region to Japan	Culicidae (mosquitos)	+	Two distinct	Nocturnal or subperiodic
Loa loa	Loiasis; Calabar swellings; conjunctival worms	Western and Central Africa	*Chrysops*, deer fly, mango fly	+	Extend to tip	Diurnal
Onchocerca volvulus	Onchocerciasis: skin nodules, blindness, dermatitis	Africa, Central and South America	*Simulium*, buffalo gnat, black fly	−	Not to tip	Nonperiodic in skin fluids.
Dipetalonema (or *Acanthocheilonema*) *perstans*	Dipetalonemiasis or acanthocheilonemiasis (minor disturbances)	Africa and South America	*Culicoides*, biting midge	−	Extend to tip	Nocturnal or diurnal or nonperiodic
Dipetalonema streptocerca	Usually nonpathogenic	Western and Central Africa	*Culicoides*	−	Extend to tip	In skin only
Mansonella ozzardi	Ozzard's mansonelliasis (benign), occasionally hydrocele	Central and South America	*Culicoides*	−	Not to tip	Nonperiodic

*Microfilariae are found in peripheral blood (in blood smear) only at night (nocturnal periodicity), largely at night or during crepuscular hours (subperiodicity), largely during daylight hours (diurnal periodicity), or without clear distinction (nonperiodic). Periodicity appears to be correlated with the bloodsucking habits of the chief vector insect in the particular area of transmission of the filaria.

PROTOZOA IN FECES (× 2000)

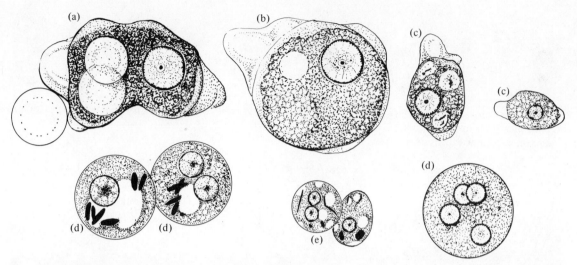

Entamoeba histolytica. (a) and (b) Trophozoite (vegetative form) with ingested red cells in (a); (c) *E hartmanni* trophozoite showing food vacuoles, not red cells; (d) cysts with 1, 2, and 4 nuclei and chromatoid bodies; (e) *E hartmanni* binucleate cyst (left), uninucleated precyst (right).

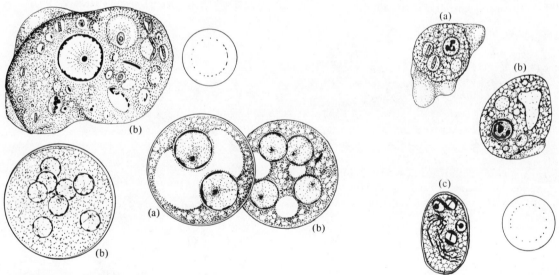

Entamoeba coli. (a) Trophozoite with vacuoles and inclusions; (b) cysts with 2, 4, and 8 nuclei, the latter being mature.

Endolimax nana. (a) Trophozoite; (b) precystic form; (c) binucleate cyst.

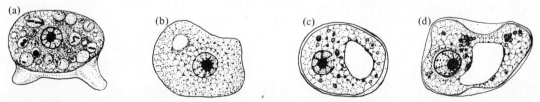

Iodamoeba bütschlii. (a) Trophozoite; (b) precystic form; (c) and (d) cysts showing large glycogen vacuole (unstained in iron-hematoxylin preparation). Note variable shape of cysts.

[Simple double circles represent the size of red cells.]

PROTOZOA IN FECES (× 2000)*

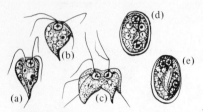

Enteromonas hominis. (a, b, c) Trophozoites; (c) dividing form; (d)
and (e) quadrinucleate cysts.

Retortamonas intestinalis. (a) and
(b) Trophozoites; (c) cyst.

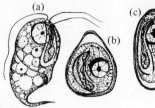

Chilomastix mesnili. (a) Trophozoite; (b) and (c) cysts.

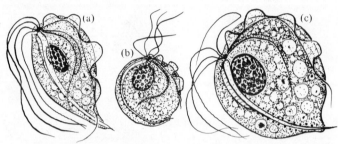

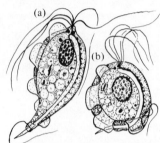

*Trichomonas vaginalis.** (a) Normal trophozoite; (b)
round form after division; (c) common form seen in
stained preparation. **Cysts not found.**

Trichomonas hominis. (a) Normal and
(b) round forms of trophozoites,
probably a staining artifact.

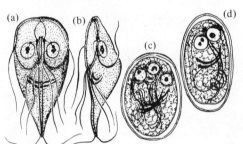

Giardia intestinalis. (a) "Face" and (b) "profile"
of vegetative forms; (c) and (d) cysts (binucleate [d] and quadrinucleate stages).

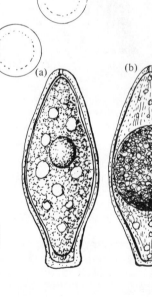

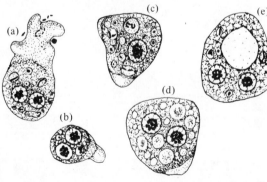

Dientamoeba fragilis. Trophozoites (cysts not found):
(a) active, (b) small, (c) mononuclear, (d) and (e)
resting.

Isospora hominis. (a) Degenerate oocyst; (b) unsegmented oocyst; (c) oocyst segmented into 2 sporoblasts after passage into feces. Mature oocyst with
sporoblasts developed into sporocysts, each containing 4 sporozoites not shown.

[Simple double circles represent the size of red cells.]

**Trichomonas vaginalis* is found in vaginal and prostatic secretions.

PROTOZOA IN FECES (× 2000)

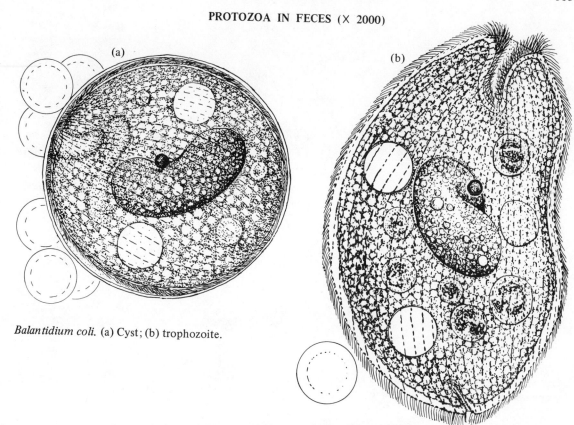

(a)

(b)

Balantidium coli. (a) Cyst; (b) trophozoite.

PROTOZOA IN BLOOD AND TISSUES (× 2000)

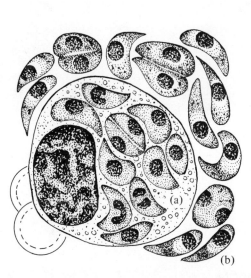

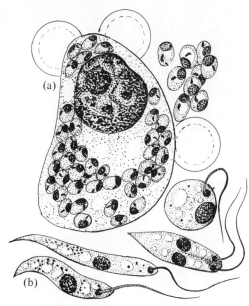

Toxoplasma gondii. (a) Trophozoites in large mononuclear cells; (b) free in blood. Not found within red cells, but parasitize many other cell types, particularly reticuloendothelial. Cyst not shown.

Leishmania donovani. (a) Large reticuloendothelial cell of spleen with amastigotes. (b) Promastigotes as seen in sandfly gut or in culture.

[Simple double circles represent the size of red cells.]

PROTOZOA IN BLOOD (× 1700)

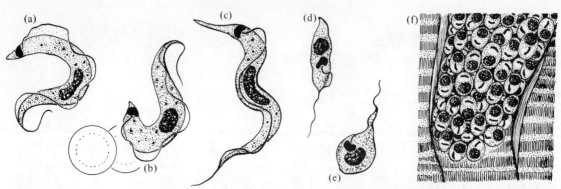

Trypanosoma cruzi. (a, b, c) Trypomastigotes in blood; (d) and (e) epimastigote (with short anterior undulating membrane); (f) amastigote colony in heart muscle cell.

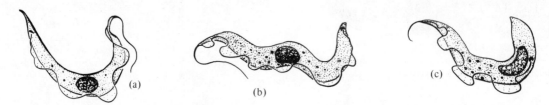

Trypanosoma gambiense (or *T rhodesiense,* indistinguishable in practice). (a, b) Trypomastigotes in blood; (c) epimastigote (intermediate type; kinetoplast not yet anterior to nucleus); found in tsetse fly, Glossina sp.

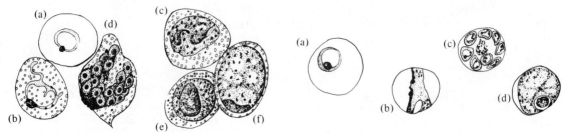

Plasmodium vivax. (a) Young signet ring trophozoite; (b) ameboid trophozoite; (c) mature trophozoite; (d) mature schizont, showing a distorted host cell; (e) microgametocyte; (f) macrogametocyte with compact nucleus. Note Schüffner's dots and enlarged host cells.

Plasmodium malariae. (a) Developing ring form of trophozoite; (b) band form of trophozoite (note absence of granules); (c) mature schizont in "rosette" with 8 merozoites; (d) mature gametocyte.

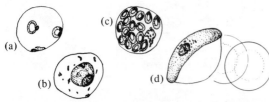

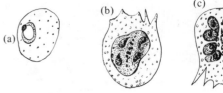

Plasmodium falciparum. (a) Ring stage, or young trophozoites (triple infection); (b) mature trophozoite showing clumped pigment in cytoplasm and Maurer's clefts in erythrocyte; (c) mature schizont; (d) mature gametocyte; (b) and (c) stages rarely seen in peripheral blood. Gametocytes in blood are diagnostic.

Plasmodium ovale. (a) Young signet ring trophozoite and Schüffner's dots; (b) ameboid trophozoite developing in fimbriated erythrocyte; (c) mature schizont showing 8 merozoites.

[Simple double circles represent the size of red cells.]

MICROFILARIAE (× 600)
(in blood or tissue fluids)

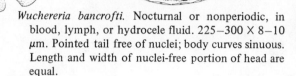

Wuchereria bancrofti. Nocturnal or nonperiodic, in blood, lymph, or hydrocele fluid. 225–300 × 8–10 μm. Pointed tail free of nuclei; body curves sinuous. Length and width of nuclei-free portion of head are equal.

Loa loa. Diurnal periodicity, in blood. 250–300 × 6–9 μm. Nuclei extend to tip of tail.

Brugia malayi. Nocturnal or subperiodic, in blood, lymph, or lymphocele fluid. 160–260 × 5–6 μm. Two nuclei in tip of tail; body curves angular or kinky; nuclei-free portion of head longer that it is wide.

Onchocerca volvulus. Nonperiodic, in skin and connective tissue lymphatics (rare in blood). 300–500 × 5–9 μm. Unsheathed; no nuclei in tip of tail.

Dipetalonema perstans. Nonperiodic, in blood. 200 × 4 μm. Unsheathed; nuclei to tip of blunt-ended tail.

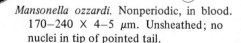

Mansonella ozzardi. Nonperiodic, in blood. 170–240 × 4–5 μm. Unsheathed; no nuclei in tip of pointed tail.

Dipetalonema streptocerca. Nonperiodic. 180 × 2–3 μm. Unsheathed; found in skin only, not in blood. Nuclei to tip of blunt-ended tail.

[Simple double circles represent the size of red cells.]

OVA OF TREMATODES (× 400)
(as seen in feces)

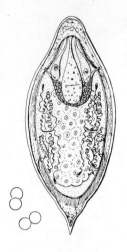

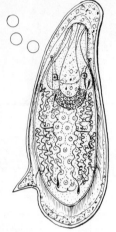

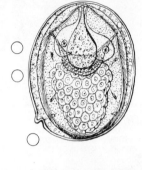

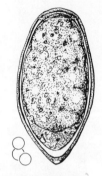

Schistosoma japonicum. Embryonated ovum with small lateral spine, often not visible.

Paragonimus westermani. Unembryonated operculated ovum.

Schistosoma haematobium. Terminally spined embryonated ovum (containing miracidium).

Schistosoma mansoni. Laterally spined embryonated ovum (containing miracidium).

Clonorchis sinensis. Small operculated and embryonated ovum.

Heterophyes heterophyes (a) or *Metagonimus yokogawai* (b). Minute embryonated operculated ova.

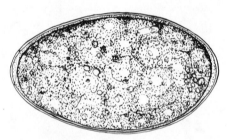

Fasciola hepatica or *Fasciolopsis buski.* Unembryonated operculated ovum.

OVA OF NEMATODES (× 400)

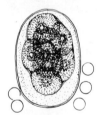

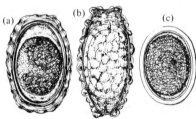

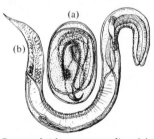

Ancylostoma duodenale or *Necator americanus.* Note shape, thin shell, 4–8 cell stage.

Ascaris lumbricoides. (a) Fertilized unembryonated ovum; (b) unfertilized ovum; (c) fertilized decorticated ovum.

Strongyloides stercoralis. (a) Embryonated ovum (rare in feces); (b) rhabditiform larva (usually seen in feces).

Trichostrongylus orientalis. Unembryonated ovum. (Rare in man except in specific areas, eg, Iran).

Trichuris trichiura. Unembryonated double-plug ovum.

Enterobius vermicularis. Embryonated ovum. Note flattening on one side, thin shell. Deposited on perianal skin.

[Simple circles represent the size of red cells.]

ADULT TREMATODES
(in intestine or tissues)

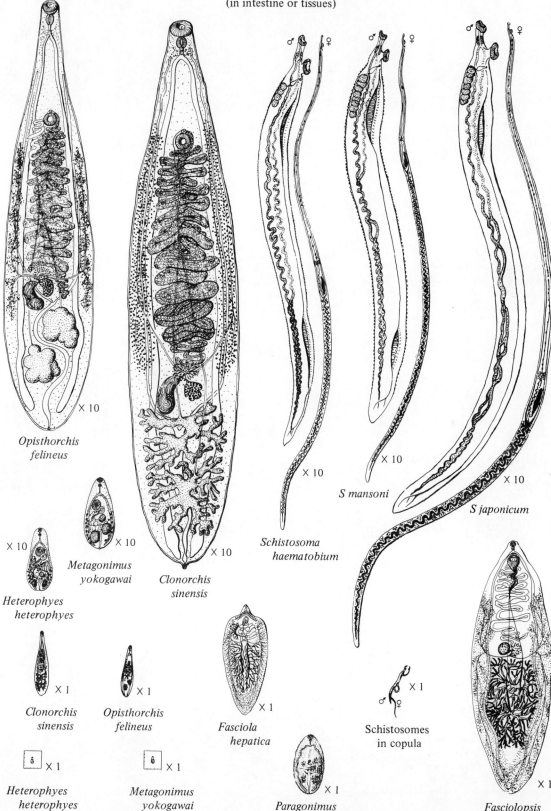

Opisthorchis
felineus

× 10

Metagonimus
yokogawai

× 10

Heterophyes
heterophyes

× 10

Clonorchis
sinensis

× 10

Schistosoma
haematobium

× 10

S mansoni

× 10

S japonicum

× 10

Clonorchis
sinensis

× 1

Opisthorchis
felineus

× 1

Fasciola
hepatica

× 1

Schistosomes
in copula

× 1

Fasciolopsis
buski

× 1

Heterophyes
heterophyes

× 1

Metagonimus
yokogawai

× 1

Paragonimus
westermani

× 1

INTESTINAL AND TISSUE NEMATODES

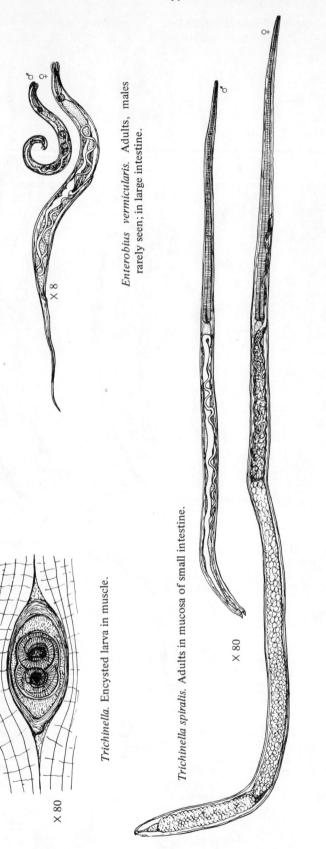

×80

Trichinella. Encysted larva in muscle.

×8

Enterobius vermicularis. Adults, males rarely seen; in large intestine.

×80

Trichinella spiralis. Adults in mucosa of small intestine.

×80

Strongyloides stercoralis. (a) Parasitic female, lateral view, in human intestine; (b) free-living female in soil; (c) free-living male in soil; (d) rhabditiform larva passed in feces or in free-living cycle in soil; (e) filariform or infective larva in soil, ready to penetrate human skin.

INTESTINAL NEMATODES

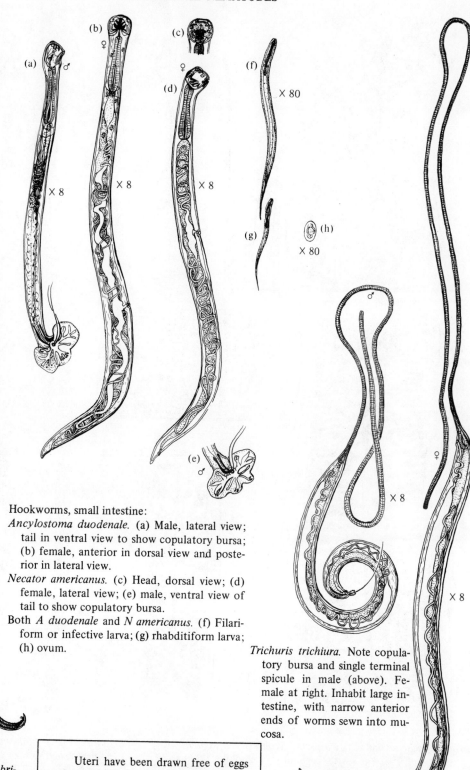

Hookworms, small intestine:

Ancylostoma duodenale. (a) Male, lateral view; tail in ventral view to show copulatory bursa; (b) female, anterior in dorsal view and posterior in lateral view.

Necator americanus. (c) Head, dorsal view; (d) female, lateral view; (e) male, ventral view of tail to show copulatory bursa.

Both *A duodenale* and *N americanus.* (f) Filariform or infective larva; (g) rhabditiform larva; (h) ovum.

Ascaris lumbricoides. Male at right. Lumen of small intestine.

Uteri have been drawn free of eggs and testes of spermatozoa for simplicity. Actual specimens often appear to be solid masses of eggs or spermatozoa.

Trichuris trichiura. Note copulatory bursa and single terminal spicule in male (above). Female at right. Inhabit large intestine, with narrow anterior ends of worms sewn into mucosa.

CESTODES (TAPEWORMS)

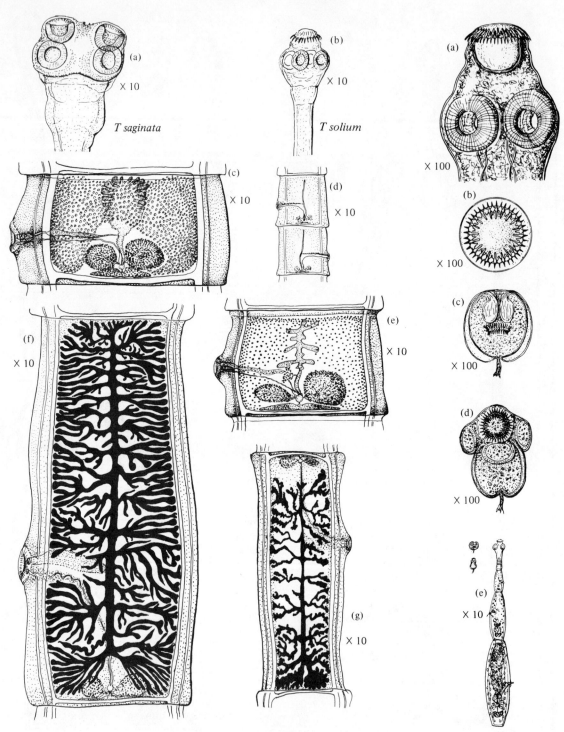

Taenia saginata and *T solium*. (a) Scolex of *T saginata;* (b) scolex of *T solium* with beginning of strobila; (c) mature proglottid of *T saginata;* (d) immature proglottids of *T solium;* (e) mature proglottid of *T solium;* (f) gravid proglottid of *T saginata* with much more numerous uterine ramifications than in *T solium* (see at right); (g) gravid proglottid of *T solium.*

Echinococcus granulosus. (a) Scolex of adult; (b) end view of rostellum, showing arrangement of 2 hook rows; (c) larva from hydatid fluid, invaginated; (d) same, evaginated; (e) entire adult worm and larval scoleces (left).

CESTODES

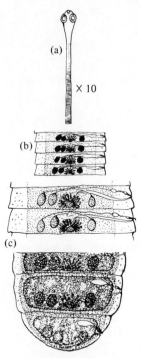

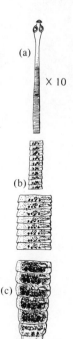

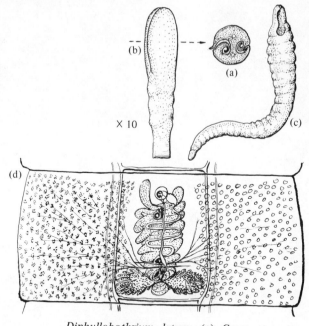

Diphyllobothrium latum. (a) Cross-section through scolex; (b) scolex and beginning of the strobila; (c) plerocercoid larva (in fish muscles); (d) developing proglottid.

Hymenolepis diminuta. (a) Unarmed scolex and beginning of strobila; (b) some genitally mature proglottids; (c) gravid proglottids.

Hymenolepis nana. (a) Armed scolex and beginning of strobila; (b) some genitally mature proglottids; (c) gravid proglottids.

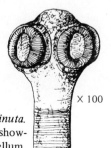

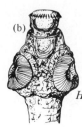

Hymenolepis diminuta. Scolex and neck, showing unarmed rostellum.

Hymenolepis nana. (a) Scolex with hooked rostellum retracted; (b) same with rostellum everted.

OVA OF CESTODES (× 400)

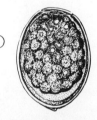

Hymenolepis diminuta

Hymenolepis nana

Taenia saginata, T solium, or *Echinococcus*

Diphyllobothrium latum

[Simple circles represent the size of red cells.]

Index